University of Massachusetts, Amherst

Voyaging Through Precalculus

With contributions
from Brian Emond

Excerpts Taken From:

Intermediate Algebra, Third Edition
by Elayn Martin-Gay

Precalculus, Third Edition
by Robert F. Blitzer

Precalculus, Instructor's Edition
by Robert F. Blitzer

 PEARSON
Custom
Publishing

 PEARSON
Prentice
Hall

Excerpts taken from:

Intermediate Algebra, Third Edition
by Elayn Martin-Gay
Copyright © 2007, 2003, 1999 by Prentice-Hall, Inc.
A Pearson Education Company
Upper Saddle River, New Jersey 07458

Precalculus, Third Edition
by Robert F. Blitzer
Copyright © 2007, 2004, 2001 by Prentice-Hall, Inc.

Precalculus, Instructor's Edition
by Robert F. Blitzer
Copyright © 2007, 2004, 2001 by Prentice-Hall, Inc.

PEARSON CUSTOM PUBLISHING
501 Boylston Street, Suite 900, Boston, MA 02116
A Pearson Education Company

A Message from the Precalculus Course Chair

Welcome to your Precalculus course! Some of you have been very successful in math courses in the past, and some of you not so successful. Some of you have come to the University of Massachusetts as recent high school graduates, and some of you have been out of school for some time. But no matter what your history has been in previous math classes, I am confident that you will do very well in this class if you develop good study habits, and follow the recommendations I have listed below.

You will notice that this custom text is from two different books. This allows us to provide you with the best possible preparation for Calculus for both business and science, at the lowest possible price.

There is a companion online student support system that comes free with this text and provides you with tutorial resources 24 hours a day, seven days a week. Although there is no substitution for one-on-one help with your professor or teaching assistants, the system MyMathLab® provides you with step-by-step problem-solving assistance, video instruction, and your personalized study plan that identifies where you need additional instruction.

But all of this support is of no value if you do not develop proper habits of mind. The following are some suggestions that can help you be successful.

- **Attend all classes.** Come on time, and don't leave early, or you may miss something important.

- **Take "good" notes.** Don't write down everything that is said or shown. Just "annotations" and diagrams that will help you remember how to complete the task, and still be able to listen and see what you are being taught. If you don't understand, ask for clarification during class so you don't get left behind.

- **Actively participate in class.** Take a chance! Give answers and ask questions. You've heard before that if you have a question, chances are that there are a number of your classmates that have the same question. By asking questions, you help your professor assess if she/he is getting the concept across.

- **Start your homework as soon as possible.** Don't wait until the night (or hours) before class. Do it while the information is still fresh in your mind.

- **Stay organized.** Keep a Precalculus folder where you can put notes, past exams and quizzes, class syllabus, Help Center schedule and any course information. Don't forget to put your name on the cover with your professor's name, office and phone number. DO NOT put any of your personal information on it in case it gets lost. The finder can contact your professor.

- **Speak the language.** Use proper math terms when asking questions or discussing concepts. It will help with your understanding, and that of others.

- **Make friends in class.** If you know the class community, you will feel more like a part of the class. Exchange contact information with one or two classmates. This way if you missed class you can get the notes, and have someone with whom you can study.

- **Learn how to use the MyMathLab(r) software.** There are learning aids available to you that will make your life easier if you know how to use them. If you have questions on it's use, call the student support line at **1-800-677-6337**

Finally, **forget about any problems you have had with mathematics in the past.** Remember, you would not have been accepted at the University of Massachusetts if you couldn't do this work. With all of the support systems we have put in place, if you are a conscientious student, you will be successful in this class. As it has been said...today is the first day of the rest of your life! Enjoy your Precalculus experience!

Brian D. Emond
Precalculus Course Coordinator
Dept. of Mathematics and Statistics
University of Massachusetts, Amherst

Precalculus Course Policies

MyMathLab®: MyMathLab is an online homework and course study system. It contains an online version of your textbook with links to multimedia resources, such as video clips of lessons and step-by-step solutions of problems. There is also a personalized study plan automatically generated from your previous work that links you to unlimited tutorial exercises for further study, so you can practice until you have mastered the skills. **You are required to register and begin your assignments immediately.** To register, go to www.coursecompass.com and click in the "Students Register" bar, then follow the instructions. You will need your professor's course number, which is **different** from the Spire schedule number). Your professor will assume you have registered your class through MyMathLab (MML) no later than the beginning of the second class. If you have any problems with MML, call the student help line at 1-800-677-6337

Calculators: It is recommended that you purchase a graphing calculator, such as the TI-82 or 83. Refer to the calculator user's guide for instruction on the use of the graphing calculator. Your instructor will not be providing instruction on calculator use, however you need to develop calculator competency.

Computers: MyMathLab requires that you have a PC computer available for your use with a **Windows XP or Windows 2000 operating system, with Internet Explorer 6.0 or 7.0.** If you do not have your own, OIT has a number of places on campus where students have access to windows systems. You should look in the OIT web page: http://www.oit.umass.edu/. There is also a pricy converter for Mac's available so that they may run Window's applications. MyMathLab expects to have the Mac version up and running in January 2008.

Homework: The only way to master Precalculus is to practice. Therefore, homework is required when assigned, and due at the start of class. No late work accepted. All assignments will be assigned through MyMathLab. The time window of the assignment opens at the end of each class, and is due for submission anytime from then up to the start of the next class. The window for that assignment will then close. There generally is no extra credit work, except for your online study plan, so **DO YOUR HOMEWORK!**

Quizzes: Weekly quizzes will also be assigned online through MyMathLab. Check each week for the day and time each quiz window is opened and closed.

Attendance: "Students are expected to attend all regularly scheduled classes at the University for which they are registered." (*Undergraduate Rights and Responsibilities*). In order to receive the benefit of my instruction, you need to be in class. Absences are excused for University approved reasons only, such as religious holidays, illness and off-campus trips

Free Tutoring: There will be free tutoring in the **PRECALCULUS HELP CENTER.** The Tutors are Undergraduate Teaching Assistants working with the Precalculus courses. The schedule will be announced at the beginning of the semester. Be sure to sign in and out to receive credit for being there.

Leaving class early: Leaving class early is disruptive to the rest of the class, and constitutes an absence. If for some reason you need to leave class early some given day, please let your professor know at the beginning of class and you will not be charged with an absence.

Special Accommodations: If you have a documented learning disability that specifies extended test time, the law mandates that **you must approach your professor.** Although she/he may have your education accommodation forms, we don't know all of you by name or remember who has an individualized accommodation plan. You need to renew your accommodation plan with Disability Services every semester.

Accommodations can include extended test time, class notes, and other learning aids. Go to Disability Services in Whitmore 231for more information.

Cell Phones / Electronic listening devices / Ear phones: The use of cell phones and other electronic devices in class is prohibited. Phones going off in class are disruptive. **Shut them off before entering class.** (If there is some special reason you need to be available to answer your phone, tell me at the start of the class, and set your phone to vibrate rather than ring). You can't hear me or your classmates if you are wearing earphones, so remove them at the start of class. Violations will result in your expulsion from that day's class.

Academic honesty: Cheating will not be tolerated and violators will be prosecuted through the Ombud's Office. This includes, but is not limited to, having someone else do your online homework and quizzes, and turning in false attendance sheets. Penalties can be failure of the course, academic probation, suspension and even expulsion.

Contents

4 Systems of Equations and Inequalities   223

Taken from: *Intermediate Algebra*, Third Edition, by Elayn Martin-Gay
Precalculus, Third Edition, by Robert Blitzer

5 Polynomials and Polynomial Functions   287

Taken from: *Intermediate Algebra*, Third Edition, by Elayn Martin-Gay

6 Rational Expressions   363

Taken from: *Intermediate Algebra*, Third Edition, by Elayn Martin-Gay

1

Real Numbers and Algebraic Expressions

Taken from:
Intermediate Algebra, Third Edition, by Elayn Martin-Gay

1.1 TIPS FOR SUCCESS IN MATHEMATICS

Before reading this section, remember that your instructor is your best source of information. Please see your instructor for any additional help or information.

Objective **A** Getting Ready for This Course

Now that you have decided to take this course, remember that a *positive attitude* will make all the difference in the world. Your belief that you can succeed is just as important as your commitment to this course. Make sure that you are ready for this course by having the time and positive attitude that it takes to succeed.

Next, make sure that you have scheduled your math course at a time that will give you the best chance for success. For example, if you are also working, you may want to check with your employer to make sure that your work hours will not conflict with your course schedule.

On the day of your first class period, double-check your schedule and allow yourself extra time to arrive on time in case of traffic problems or difficulty locating your classroom. Make sure that you bring at least your textbook, paper, and a writing instrument. Are you required to have a lab manual, graph paper, calculator, or some other supply besides this text? If so, also bring this material with you.

Objective **B** General Tips for Success

Below are some general tips that will increase your chance for success in a mathematics class. Many of these tips will also help you in other courses you may be taking.

Exchange names and phone numbers or e-mail addresses with at least one other person in class. This contact person can be a great help if you miss an assignment or want to discuss math concepts or exercises that you find difficult.

Choose to attend all class periods. If possible, sit near the front of the classroom. This way, you will see and hear the presentation better. It may also be easier for you to participate in classroom activities.

Do your homework. You've probably heard the phrase "practice makes perfect" in relation to music and sports. It also applies to mathematics. You will find that the more time you spend solving mathematics exercises, the easier the process becomes. Be sure to schedule enough time to complete your assignments before the next class period.

Check your work. Review the steps you made while working a problem. Learn to check your answers in the original problems. You may also compare your answers with the answers to selected exercises section in the back of the book. If you have made a mistake, try to figure out what went wrong. Then correct your mistake. If you can't find what went wrong, don't erase your work or throw it away. Bring your work to your instructor, a tutor in a math lab, or a classmate. It is easier for someone to find where you had trouble if they look at your original work.

Learn from your mistakes. Everyone, even your instructor, makes mistakes. Use your errors to learn and to become a better math student. The key is finding and understanding your errors. Was your mistake a careless one, or did you make it because you can't read your own math writing? If so, try to work more slowly or write more neatly and make a conscious effort to carefully check your work. Did you make a mistake because you don't understand a concept? If so, take the time to review the concept or ask questions to better understand it.

Know how to get help if you need it. It's all right to ask for help. In fact, it's a good idea to ask for help whenever there is something that you don't understand. Make sure you know when your instructor has office hours and how to find his or her office. Find out whether math tutoring services are available on your campus. Check on the hours, location, and requirements of the tutoring service. Know whether software is available and how to access this resource.

Organize your class materials, including homework assignments, graded quizzes and tests, and notes from your class or lab. All of these items will make valuable references throughout your course and when studying for upcoming tests and the final exam. Make sure that you can locate these materials when you need them.

Read your textbook before class. Reading a mathematics textbook is unlike reading a novel or a newspaper. Your pace will be much slower. It is helpful to have paper and a pencil with you when you read. Try to work out examples on your own as you encounter them in your text. You should also write down any questions that you want to ask in class. When you read a mathematics textbook, sometimes some of the information in a section will be unclear. But after you hear a lecture or watch a videotape on that section, you will understand it much more easily than if you had not read your text beforehand.

Don't be afraid to ask questions. You are not the only person in class with questions. Other students are normally grateful that someone has spoken up.

Hand in assignments on time. This way you can be sure that you will not lose points for being late. Show every step of a problem and be neat and organized. Also be sure that you understand which problems are assigned for homework. If allowed, you can always double-check the assignment with another student in your class.

Objective C Using This Text

There are many helpful resources that are available to you in this text. It is important that you become familiar with and use these resources. They should increase your chances for success in this course.

- *Practice Problems.* Each example in every section has a parallel Practice Problem. As you read a section, try each Practice Problem after you've finished the corresponding example. This "learn-by-doing" approach will help you grasp ideas before you move on to other concepts.

- *Chapter Test Prep Video CD.* The book contains a CD. This CD contains all of the Chapter Test exercises worked out by the author. This supplement is very helpful before a classroom chapter test.

- *Lecture Video CDs.* Exercises marked with a ⊚ are fully worked out by the author on video CDs. Check with your instructor for the availability of these video CDs.

- *Symbols at the beginning of an exercise set.* If you need help with a particular section, the symbols listed at the beginning of each exercise set will remind you of the numerous supplements available.

- *Objectives.* The main section of exercises in each exercise set is referenced by an objective, such as **A** or **B**, and also an example(s). There is also often a section of exercises entitled "Mixed Practice," which is referenced by two or more objectives or sections. These are mixed exercises written to prepare you for your next exam. Use all of this referencing if you have trouble completing an assignment from the exercise set.

- *Icons (Symbols.)* Make sure that you understand the meaning of the icons that are beside many exercises. ⊚ tells you that the corresponding exercise may be viewed on the video segment that corresponds to that section. ✎ tells you that this exercise is a writing exercise in which you should answer in complete sentences. △ tells you that the exercise involves geometry.

- *Integrated Reviews.* Found in the middle of each chapter, these reviews offer you a chance to practice—in one place—the many concepts that you have learned separately over several sections.

- *End of Chapter Opportunities.* There are many opportunities at the end of each chapter to help you understand the concepts of the chapter.

  Chapter Highlights contain chapter summaries and examples.

  Chapter Reviews contain review problems. The first part is organized section by section and the second part contains a set of mixed exercises.

  Chapter Tests are sample tests to help you prepare for an exam. The Chapter Test Prep Video CD, found in this text, contains all the Chapter Test exercises worked by the author.

  Cumulative Reviews are reviews consisting of material from the beginning of the book to the end of that particular chapter.

- *Study Skill Builders.* This feature is found at the end of many exercise sets. In order to increase your chance of success in this course, please read and answer the questions in these Study Skill Builders.

- *The Bigger Picture.* This feature contains the directions for building an outline to be used throughout the course. The purpose of this outline is to help you make the transition from thinking "section by section" to thinking about how the mathematics in this course is part of a bigger picture.

See the Preface at the beginning of this text for a more thorough explanation of the features of this text.

Objective D Getting Help

If you have trouble completing assignments or understanding the mathematics, get help as soon as you need it! This tip is presented as an objective on its own because it is so important. In mathematics, usually the material presented in one section builds on your understanding of the previous section. This means that if you don't understand the concepts covered during a class period, there is a good chance that you will not understand the concepts covered during the next class period. If this happens to you, get help as soon as you can.

Where can you get help? Many suggestions have been made in this section on where to get help, and now it is up to you to do it. Try your instructor, a tutoring center, or a math lab, or you may want to form a study group with fellow classmates. If you do decide to see your instructor or go to a tutoring center, make sure that you have a neat notebook and are ready with your questions.

Objective E Preparing for and Taking an Exam

Make sure that you allow yourself plenty of time to prepare for a test. If you think that you are a little "math anxious," it may be that you are not preparing for a test in a way that will ensure success. The way that you prepare for a test in mathematics is important. To prepare for a test:

1. Review your previous homework assignments.
2. Review any notes from class and section-level quizzes you have taken. (If this is a final exam, also review chapter tests you have taken.)
3. Review concepts and definitions by reading the Highlights at the end of each chapter.
4. Practice working out exercises by completing the Chapter Review found at the end of each chapter. (If this is a final exam, go through a Cumulative Review. There is one found at the end of each chapter except Chapter 1. Choose the review found at the end of the latest chapter that you have covered in your course.) *Don't stop here!*
5. It is important that you place yourself in conditions similar to test conditions to find out how you will perform. In other words, as soon as you feel that you know the material, get a few blank sheets of paper and take a sample test. There is a Chapter Test available at the end of each chapter, or you can work selected

problems from the Chapter Review. Your instructor may also provide you with a review sheet. During this sample test, do not use your notes or your textbook. Then check your sample test. If you are not satisfied with the results, study the areas that you are weak in and try again.

6. On the day of the test, allow yourself plenty of time to arrive at where you will be taking your exam.

When taking your test:

1. Read the directions on the test carefully.

2. Read each problem carefully as you take the test. Make sure that you answer the question asked.

3. Watch your time and pace yourself so that you can attempt each problem on your test.

4. If you have time, check your work and answers.

5. Do not turn your test in early. If you have extra time, spend it double-checking your work.

Objective **F** Managing Your Time

As a college student, you know the demands that classes, homework, work, and family place on your time. Some days you probably wonder how you'll ever get everything done. One key to managing your time is developing a schedule. Here are some hints for making a schedule:

1. Make a list of all of your weekly commitments for the term. Include classes, work, regular meetings, extracurricular activities, etc. You may also find it helpful to list such things as laundry, regular workouts, grocery shopping, etc.

2. Next, estimate the time needed for each item on the list. Also make a note of how often you will need to do each item. Don't forget to include time estimates for the reading, studying, and homework you do outside of your classes. You may want to ask your instructor for help estimating the time needed.

3. In the exercise set that follows, you are asked to block out a typical week on the schedule grid given. Start with items with fixed time slots like classes and work.

4. Next, include the items on your list with flexible time slots. Think carefully about how best to schedule items such as study time.

5. Don't fill up every time slot on the schedule. Remember that you need to allow time for eating, sleeping, and relaxing! You should also allow a little extra time in case some items take longer than planned.

6. If you find that your weekly schedule is too full for you to handle, you may need to make some changes in your workload, classload, or in other areas of your life. You may want to talk to your advisor, manager or supervisor at work, or someone in your college's academic counseling center for help with such decisions.

1.1 EXERCISE SET

FOR EXTRA HELP

Student Solutions Manual

PH Math/Tutor Center

CD/Video for Review

Math XL
MathXL®

MyMathLab
MyMathLab

1. What is your instructor's name?

2. What are your instructor's office location and office hours?

3. What is the best way to contact your instructor?

4. Do you have the name and contact information of at least one other student in class?

5. Will your instructor allow you to use a calculator in this class?

6. Is tutorial software available to you? If so, what type and where?

7. Is there a tutoring service available on campus? If so, what are its hours? What services are available?

8. Have you attempted this course before? If so, write down ways that you might improve your chances of success during this second attempt.

9. List some steps that you can take if you begin having trouble understanding the material or completing an assignment.

10. How many hours of studying does your instructor advise for each hour of instruction?

11. What does the ✎ in this text mean?

12. What does the ◉ in this text mean?

13. What does the △ in this text mean?

14. Search the minor columns in your text. What are Practice Problems?

15. When might be the best time to work a Practice Problem?

16. Where are the answers to Practice Problems?

17. What answers are contained in this text and where are they?

18. What solutions are contained in this text and where are they?

19. What and where are Integrated Reviews?

20. What video CD is contained in this book, where is it, and what material is on it?

21. Chapter Highlights are found at the end of each chapter. Find the Chapter 1 Highlights and explain how you might use it and how it might be helpful.

22. Chapter Reviews are found at the end of each chapter. Find the Chapter 1 Review and explain how you might use it and how it might be useful.

23. Chapter Tests are found at the end of each chapter. Find the Chapter 1 Test and explain how you might use it and how it might be helpful when preparing for an exam on Chapter 1. Include how the Chapter Test Prep Video in the book may help.

24. Read or reread objective **F** and fill out the schedule grid below.

	Monday	Tuesday	Wednesday	Thursday	Friday	Saturday	Sunday
7:00 a.m.							
8:00 a.m.							
9:00 a.m.							
10:00 a.m.							
11:00 a.m.							
12:00 p.m.							
1:00 p.m.							
2:00 p.m.							
3:00 p.m.							
4:00 p.m.							
5:00 p.m.							
6:00 p.m.							
7:00 p.m.							
8:00 p.m.							
9:00 p.m.							

1.2 ALGEBRAIC EXPRESSIONS AND SETS OF NUMBERS

Objectives

A Identify Natural Numbers, Whole Numbers, Integers, Rational, and Irrational Real Numbers.

B Write Phrases as Algebraic Expressions.

Recall that letters that represent numbers are called **variables.** An **algebraic expression** is formed by numbers and variables connected by the operations of addition, subtraction, multiplication, division, raising to powers, or taking roots. For example,

$$2x, \qquad \frac{x+5}{6}, \qquad \sqrt{y} - 1.6, \qquad \text{and} \qquad z^3$$

are algebraic expressions or, more simply, expressions. (Recall that the expression $2x$ means $2 \cdot x$.)

Algebraic expressions occur often during problem solving. For example, the B747-400 aircraft costs $8443 per hour to operate. The algebraic expression $8443t$ gives the total cost to operate the aircraft for t hours. (*Source: The World Almanac, 2005*)

To find the cost to operate the aircraft for 5.2 hours, for example, we replace the variable t with 5.2 and perform the indicated operation. This process is called **evaluating an expression,** and the result is called the **value** of the expression for the given replacement value.

In our example, when $t = 5.2$ hours,

$$8443t = 8443(5.2) = 43,903.6$$

Thus, it costs $43,903.60 to operate the B747-400 aircraft for 5.2 hours.

When evaluating an expression to solve a problem, we often need to think about the kind of number that is appropriate for the solution. For example, if we are asked to determine the maximum number of parking spaces for a parking lot to be constructed, an answer of $98\frac{1}{10}$ is not appropriate because $\frac{1}{10}$ of a parking space is not realistic.

We practice writing algebraic expressions in Objective B and evaluating algebraic expressions in Section 1.5.

Objective A Identifying Common Sets of Numbers

Let's review some common sets of numbers and their graphs on a **number line.** To construct a number line, we draw a line and label a point 0 with which we associate the number 0. This point is called the **origin.** If we choose a point to the right of 0 and label it 1, the distance from 0 to 1 is called the **unit distance** and can be used to locate more points. The **positive numbers** lie to the right of the origin, and the **negative numbers** lie to the left of the origin. The number 0 is neither positive nor negative.

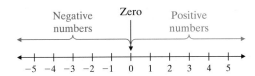

✔**Concept Check**   Use the definitions of positive numbers, negative numbers, and zero to describe the meaning of *nonnegative numbers*.

A number is **graphed** on a number line by shading the point on the number line that corresponds to the number. Some common sets of numbers and their graphs are shown next.

Identifying Numbers

Natural numbers: $\{1, 2, 3, \dots\}$

Whole numbers: $\{0, 1, 2, 3, \dots\}$

Integers: $\{\dots, -3, -2, -1, 0, 1, 2, 3, \dots\}$

Each listing of three dots, …, is called an **ellipsis** and means to continue in the same pattern.

A **set** is a collection of objects. The objects of a set are called its **members or elements.** When the elements of a set are listed, such as those displayed in the box, the set is written in **roster** form. A set can also be written in **set builder notation,** which describes the members of the set but does not list them. The following set is written in set builder notation.

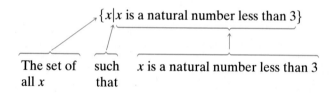

$\{x \mid x \text{ is a natural number less than 3}\}$

The set of all x — such that — x is a natural number less than 3

This same set written in roster form is $\{1, 2\}$.

A set that contains *no* elements is called the **empty set** or **null set,** symbolized by $\{\ \}$ or $\varnothing$.

$\{x \mid x \text{ is a month with 32 days}\}$ is $\varnothing$ or $\{\ \}$

because no month has 32 days. The set has no elements.

Helpful Hint

Use $\{\ \}$ or $\varnothing$ alone to write the empty set. $\{\varnothing\}$ is *not* the empty set because it has one element: $\varnothing$.

PRACTICE PROBLEMS 1–2

Write each set in roster form.

1. $\{x \mid x \text{ is a whole number between 0 and 4}\}$

2. $\{x \mid x \text{ is a natural number greater than 80}\}$

EXAMPLES   Write each set in roster form.

1. $\{x \mid x \text{ is a whole number between 1 and 6}\}$

   $\{2, 3, 4, 5\}$

2. $\{x \mid x \text{ is a natural number greater than 100}\}$

   $\{101, 102, 103, \dots\}$

■ **Work Practice Problems 1–2**

The symbol $\in$ is used to denote that an element is in a particular set. The symbol $\in$ is read as "is an element of." For example, the true statement "3 is an element of $\{1, 2, 3, 4, 5\}$" can be written in symbols as

$3 \in \{1, 2, 3, 4, 5\}$

The symbol $\notin$ is read as "is not an element of." In symbols, we write the true statement "p is not an element of $\{a, 5, g, j, q\}$" as

$p \notin \{a, 5, g, j, q\}$

Answers

1. $\{1, 2, 3\}$,   2. $\{81, 82, 83, \dots\}$

✔ **Concept Check Answer**

a number that is zero or positive

EXAMPLES Determine whether each statement is true or false.

3. $3 \in \{x \,|\, x \text{ is a natural number}\}$ True, since 3 is a natural number and therefore an element of the set.

4. $7 \notin \{1, 2, 3\}$ True, since 7 is not an element of the set $\{1, 2, 3\}$.

■ **Work Practice Problems 3–4**

We can use set builder notation to describe three other common sets of numbers.

Identifying Numbers

Real numbers: $\{x \,|\, x \text{ corresponds to a point on the number line}\}$

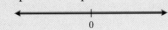

Rational numbers: $\left\{ \dfrac{a}{b} \,\middle|\, a \text{ and } b \text{ are integers and } b \neq 0 \right\}$

Irrational numbers: $\{x \,|\, x \text{ is a real number and } x \text{ is not a rational number}\}$

Notice that every integer is also a rational number since each integer can be written as the quotient of itself and 1:

$$3 = \frac{3}{1}, \quad 0 = \frac{0}{1}, \quad -8 = \frac{-8}{1}$$

Not every rational number, however, is an integer. The rational number $\dfrac{2}{3}$, for example, is not an integer. Some square roots are rational numbers and some are irrational numbers. For example, $\sqrt{2}, \sqrt{3},$ and $\sqrt{7}$ are irrational numbers but $\sqrt{25}$ is a rational number because $\sqrt{25} = 5 = \dfrac{5}{1}$. The number π is an irrational number, To help you make the distinction between rational and irrational numbers, here are a few examples of each.

Rational Numbers		Irrational Numbers
Number	**Equivalent Quotient of Integers, $\dfrac{a}{b}$**	
$-\dfrac{2}{3}$	$\dfrac{-2}{3}$ or $\dfrac{2}{-3}$	$\sqrt{5}$
$\sqrt{36}$	$\dfrac{6}{1}$	$\dfrac{\sqrt{6}}{7}$
5	$\dfrac{5}{1}$	$-\sqrt{3}$
0	$\dfrac{0}{1}$	π
1.2	$\dfrac{12}{10}$	$\dfrac{2}{\sqrt{3}}$
$3\dfrac{7}{8}$	$\dfrac{31}{8}$	

Some rational and irrational numbers are graphed below.

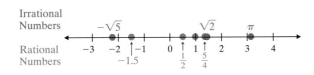

Every rational number can be written as a decimal that either repeats or terminates. For example,

$$\frac{1}{2} = 0.5 \qquad\qquad \frac{5}{4} = 1.25$$

$$\frac{2}{3} = 0.6666666\ldots = 0.\overline{6} \qquad \frac{1}{11} = 0.090909\ldots = 0.\overline{09}$$

An irrational number written as a decimal neither terminates nor repeats. When we perform calculations with irrational numbers, we often use decimal approximations that have been rounded. For example, consider the following irrational numbers along with a four-decimal-place approximation of each:

$$\pi \approx 3.1416 \qquad \sqrt{2} \approx 1.4142$$

Earlier we mentioned that every integer is also a rational number. In other words, all the elements of the set of integers are also elements of the set of rational numbers. When this happens, we say that the set of integers, set I, is a **subset** of the set of rational numbers, set Q. In symbols,

$$\underbrace{I \subseteq Q}_{\text{is a subset of}}$$

The natural numbers, whole numbers, integers, rational numbers, and irrational numbers are each a subset of the set of real numbers. The relationships among these sets of numbers are shown in the following diagram.

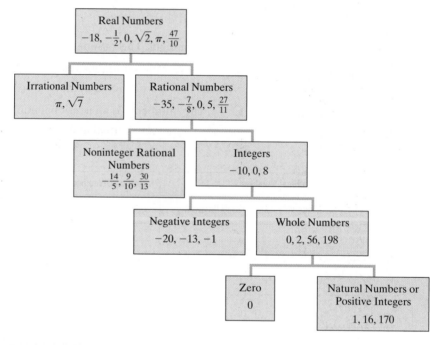

PRACTICE PROBLEMS 5–7

Determine whether each statement is true or false.

5. 0 is a real number.

6. Every integer is a rational number.

7. $\sqrt{3}$ is a rational number.

EXAMPLES Determine whether each statement is true or false.

5. 3 is a real number.

True. Every whole number is a real number.

6. Every rational number is an integer.

False. The number $\frac{2}{3}$, for example, is a rational number, but it is not an integer.

7. $\frac{1}{5}$ is an irrational number.

False. The number $\frac{1}{5}$ is a rational number since it is in the form $\frac{a}{b}$ with a and b integers and $b \neq 0$.

■ **Work Practice Problems 5–7**

Answers

5. true, **6.** true, **7.** false

Objective B Writing Phrases as Algebraic Expressions

Often, solving problems involves translating a phrase into an algebraic expression. The following is a list of key words and phrases and their translations.

Selected Key Words/Phrases and Their Translations			
Addition	**Subtraction**	**Multiplication**	**Division**
sum	difference of	product	quotient
plus	minus	times	divide
added to	subtracted from	multiply	into
more than	less than	twice	ratio
increased by	decreased by	of	
total	less		

EXAMPLES Write each phrase as an algebraic expression. Use the variable x to represent each unknown number.

8. Eight times a number $8 \cdot x$ or $8x$

9. Three more than eight times a number $8x + 3$

10. The quotient of a number and -7 $x \div -7$ or $\dfrac{x}{-7}$

11. One and six-tenths subtracted from twice a number $2x - 1.6$ or $2x - 1\dfrac{6}{10}$

12. Six less than a number $x - 6$

13. Twice the sum of four and a number $2(4 + x)$

🔲 **Work Practice Problems 8–13**

PRACTICE PROBLEMS 8–13

Write each phrase as an algebraic expression. Use the variable x to represent each unknown number.

8. Seventeen times a number
9. Five more than six times a number
10. The quotient of six and a number
11. One-fourth subtracted from three times a number
12. Eleven less than a number
13. Three times the difference of a number and ten

Answers

8. $17 \cdot x$ or $17x$,   9. $6x + 5$,

10. $\dfrac{6}{x}$ or $6 \div x$,   11. $3x - \dfrac{1}{4}$,

12. $x - 11$,   13. $3(x - 10)$

Objective Ⓐ *Write each set in roster form. See Examples 1 and 2.*

1. $\{x \mid x$ is a natural number less than $6\}$

2. $\{x \mid x$ is a natural number greater than $6\}$

3. $\{x \mid x$ is a natural number between 10 and 17$\}$

4. $\{x \mid x$ is an odd natural number$\}$

5. $\{x \mid x$ is a whole number that is not a natural number$\}$

6. $\{x \mid x$ is a natural number less than 1$\}$

7. $\{x \mid x$ is an even whole number less than 9$\}$

8. $\{x \mid x$ is an odd whole number less than 9$\}$

List the elements of the set $\left\{3, 0, \sqrt{7}, \sqrt{36}, \dfrac{2}{5}, -134\right\}$ *that are also elements of the given set. See Examples 3 and 4.*

9. Whole numbers

10. Integers

11. Natural numbers

12. Rational numbers

13. Irrational numbers

14. Real numbers

Place $\in$ *or* $\notin$ *in the space provided to make each statement true. See Examples 3 through 7.*

15. $-11 \quad \{x \mid x$ is an integer$\}$

16. $-6 \quad \{2, 4, 6, \dots\}$

17. $0 \quad \{x \mid x$ is a positive integer$\}$

18. $12 \quad \{1, 2, 3, \dots\}$

19. $12 \quad \{1, 3, 5, \dots\}$

20. $\dfrac{1}{2} \quad \{x \mid x$ is an irrational number$\}$

Determine whether each statement is true or false. See Examples 5 through 7.

21. Every whole number is a real number.

22. Every irrational number is a real number.

23. Some real numbers are irrational numbers.

24. Some real numbers are whole numbers.

25. Every whole number is a natural number.

26. Every irrational number is a rational number.

27. $\dfrac{1}{2}$ is a real number.

28. $-\dfrac{4}{5}$ is a real number.

Mixed Practice *Determine whether each statement is true or false. See Examples 3 through 7.*

29. $0 \in \{x \mid x$ is an integer$\}$

30. $0 \in \{x \mid x$ is a whole number$\}$

31. $\sqrt{7} \notin \{x \mid x$ is an irrational number$\}$

32. $-\dfrac{7}{11} \notin \{x \mid x$ is a rational number$\}$

33. $\{x \mid x$ is a day of the week starting with the letter $B\}$ is $\varnothing$.

34. $\{x \mid x$ is a rational number and an irrational number$\}$ is $\varnothing$.

35. Some real numbers are integers.

36. Every integer is a real number.

37. Some rational numbers are irrational numbers.

38. Every real number is also an integer.

Objective **B** *Write each phrase as an algebraic expression. Use the variable x to represent each unknown number. See Examples 8 through 13.*

39. Twice a number

40. Six times a number

41. Ten less than a number

42. A number minus seven

43. The sum of a number and two

44. The difference of twenty-five and a number

45. A number divided by eleven

46. The quotient of a number and thirteen

47. Four subtracted from a number

48. Seventeen subtracted from a number

49. A number plus two and three-tenths

50. Fifteen and seven-tenths plus a number

51. A number less than one and one-third

52. Two and three-fourths less than a number

53. Nine times a number

54. Nine minus a number

55. Nine added to a number

56. Nine divided by a number

57. Five more than twice a number

58. One more than six times a number

59. Twelve minus three times a number

60. Four subtracted from three times a number

61. One plus twice a number

62. Three less than twice a number

63. Ten subtracted from five times a number

64. Four minus three times a number

65. The quotient of five and the difference of four and a number

66. The quotient of four and the sum of a number and one

67. Twice the sum of a number and three

68. Eight times the difference of a number and nine

For Exercises 69 through 72, fill in the blank so that each is a true statement. There are many possible correct answers.

69. _____ $\in \{1, 3, 5, 7\}$

70. _____ $\notin \{1, 3, 5, 7\}$

71. _____ $\subseteq \{1, 3, 5, 7\}$

72. _____ $\not\subseteq \{1, 3, 5, 7\}$

73. Name a whole number that is not a natural number.

74. Name a rational number that does not simplify to an integer.

Concept Extensions

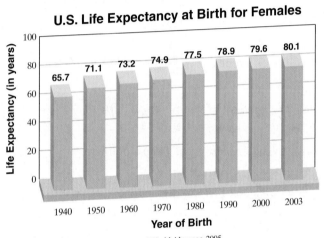

U.S. Life Expectancy at Birth for Females

Life Expectancy (in years)

65.7   71.1   73.2   74.9   77.5   78.9   79.6   80.1

1940   1950   1960   1970   1980   1990   2000   2003

Year of Birth

Source: Social Security Administration and World Almanac, 2005

75. The bar graph to the left shows the U.S. life expectancy at birth for females born in the years shown. Use the graph to calculate the *increase* in life expectancy over each ten-year period shown.

Year	Increase in Life Expectancy (in years) from 10 Years Earlier
1950	
1960	
1970	
1980	
1990	
2000	

76. In your own words, explain why every natural number is also a rational number but not every rational number is a natural number.

77. In your own words, explain why every irrational number is a real number but not every real number is an irrational number.

STUDY SKILLS BUILDER

Learning New Terms?

Many of the terms used in this text may be new to you. It will be helpful to make a list of new mathematical terms and symbols as you encounter them and to review them frequently. Placing these new terms (including page references) on 3 × 5 index cards might help you later when you're preparing for a quiz.

Answer the following.

1. Name one way you might place a word and its definition on a 3 × 5 card.

2. How do new terms stand out in this text so that they can be found?

1.3 EQUATIONS, INEQUALITIES, AND PROPERTIES OF REAL NUMBERS

A Write Sentences as Equations.

B Use Inequality Symbols.

C Find the Opposite, or Additive Inverse, and the Reciprocal, or Multiplicative Inverse, of a Number.

D Identify and Use the Commutative, Associative, and Distributive Properties.

Objective **A** Writing Sentences as Equations

When writing sentences as equations, we use the symbol = to translate the phrase **"is equal to."** All of the following key words and phrases also mean equality.

Equality

equals	is/was	represents	is the same as
gives	yields	amounts to	is equal to

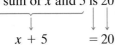 **EXAMPLES** Write each sentence as an equation.

1. The sum of x and 5 is 20

$$x + 5 = 20$$

2. The difference of 8 and x is the same as the product of 2 and x.

$$8 - x = 2 \cdot x$$

3. The quotient of z and 9 amounts to 9 plus z.

$$z \div 9 = 9 + z$$

or

$$\frac{z}{9} = 9 + z$$

◉ Work Practice Problems 1–3

Objective **B** Using Inequality Symbols

If we want to write in symbols that two numbers are not equal, we can use the symbol $\neq$, which means **"is not equal to."** For example,

$$3 \neq 2$$

Graphing two numbers on a number line gives us a way to compare two numbers. For any two real numbers graphed on a number line, the number to the left is less than the number to the right. This means that the number to the right is greater than the number to the left.

The symbol $<$ means **"is less than."** Since -4 is to the left of -1 on the number line, we write $-4 < -1$. The symbol $>$ means **"is greater than."** Since -1 is to the right of -4 on the number line, we write $-1 > -4$.

$$-4 < -1 \text{ or } -1 > -4$$

Notice that since $-4 < -1$, then we also know that $-1 > -4$. This is true for any two numbers, say, a and b.

If $a < b$, then also $b > a$. For example, since $-4 < -1$, then $-1 > -4$.

PRACTICE PROBLEMS 1–3

Write each sentence as an equation.

1. The difference of x and 7 is 45.

2. The product of 5 and x amounts to the sum of x and 14.

3. The quotient of y and 23 is the same as 20 subtracted from y.

15

CHAPTER 1

PRACTICE PROBLEMS 4–11

Insert $<$, $>$, or $=$ between each pair of numbers to form a true statement.

4. 7 $\quad$ -7
5. -1 $\quad$ 11
6. -10 $\quad$ -12
7. -3.25 $\quad$ -3.025
8. 7.206 $\quad$ 7.2060
9. 18.6 $\quad$ -14.2
10. $\dfrac{4}{7}$ $\quad$ $\dfrac{5}{7}$
11. $\dfrac{3}{8}$ $\quad$ $\dfrac{1}{3}$

EXAMPLES Insert $<$, $>$, or $=$ between each pair of numbers to form a true statement.

4. -5 $\quad$ 5 $\qquad$ -5 is to the left of 5 on a number line, so $-5 < 5$.
5. 3 $\quad$ -7 $\qquad$ 3 is to the right of -7, so $3 > -7$.
6. -16 $\quad$ -6 $\qquad$ -16 is to the left of -6, so $-16 < -6$.
7. -2.5 $\quad$ -2.1 $\qquad$ -2.5 is to the left of -2.1, so $-2.5 < -2.1$.
8. 6.36 $\quad$ 6.360 $\qquad$ The true statement is $6.36 = 6.360$.
9. 4.3 $\quad$ -5.2 $\qquad$ 4.3 is to the right of -5.2, so $4.3 > -5.2$.
10. $\dfrac{5}{8}$ $\quad$ $\dfrac{3}{8}$ $\qquad$ The denominators are the same, so $\dfrac{5}{8} > \dfrac{3}{8}$ since $5 > 3$.
11. $\dfrac{2}{3}$ $\quad$ $\dfrac{3}{4}$ $\qquad$ By dividing, we see that $\dfrac{3}{4} = 0.75$ and $\dfrac{2}{3} = 0.666\ldots$.

Thus $\dfrac{2}{3} < \dfrac{3}{4}$ since $0.666\ldots < 0.75$.

◻ **Work Practice Problems 4–11**

Helpful Hint

When inserting the $>$ or $<$ symbol, think of the symbols as arrowheads that "point" toward the smaller number when the statement is true.

In addition to $<$ and $>$, there are the inequality symbols $\leq$ and $\geq$. The symbol $\leq$ means **"is less than or equal to,"** and the symbol $\geq$ means **"is greater than or equal to."**

PRACTICE PROBLEMS 12–15

Determine whether each statement is true or false.

12. $-11 \leq 16$
13. $-7 \leq -7$
14. $-7 \geq -7$
15. $-25 \leq -30$

EXAMPLES Determine whether each statement is true or false.

12. $-9 \leq 7$ $\qquad$ True, since $-9 < 7$ is true.
13. $-5 \leq -5$ $\qquad$ True, since $-5 = -5$ is true.
14. $-5 \geq -5$ $\qquad$ True, since $-5 = -5$ is true.
15. $-24 \geq -20$ $\qquad$ False, since neither $-24 > -20$ nor $-24 = -20$ is true.

◻ **Work Practice Problems 12–15**

Objective **C** Finding Opposites and Reciprocals

Of all the real numbers, two of them stand out as extraordinary: 0 and 1. Zero is the only real number that can be added to *any* real number and result in the same real number. Also, 1 is the only real number that can be multiplied by *any* real number and result in the same real number. This is why 0 is called the **additive identity** and 1 is called the **multiplicative identity.**

Identity Properties

For any real number a,

Identity Property of 0: $\quad a + 0 = 0 + a = a$

Also,

Identity Property of 1: $\quad a \cdot 1 = 1 \cdot a = a$

Answers

4. $>$, 5. $<$, 6. $>$, 7. $<$, 8. $=$,
9. $>$, 10. $<$, 11. $>$, 12. true,
13. true, 14. true, 15. false

Copyright 2007 Pearson Education, Inc.

We use the identity property of 1 when we say that x, for example, means $1 \cdot x$ or $1x$. We also use this property when we write equivalent expressions. For example,

$$\underbrace{\frac{2}{3} = \frac{2}{3} \cdot 1}_{\text{identity property of 1}} = \frac{2}{3} \cdot \frac{5}{5} = \frac{10}{15} \quad \frac{5}{5} \text{ is another name for 1.}$$

Two numbers whose sum is the additive identity 0 are called **opposites** or **additive inverses** of each other. Each real number has a unique opposite.

Opposites or Additive Inverses

If a is a real number, then the unique **opposite,** or **additive inverse,** of a is written as $-a$ and the following is true:

$$a + (-a) = 0 \qquad (\text{Also, } -a + a = 0)$$

On a number line, we picture a real number and its opposite as being the same distance from 0 but on opposite sides of 0.

The opposite of 6 is -6.

The opposite of $\frac{2}{3}$ is $-\frac{2}{3}$.

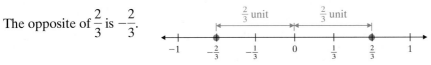

The opposite of -4 is 4.

We stated that the opposite or additive inverse of a number a is $-a$. This means that the opposite of -4 is $-(-4)$. But we stated above that the opposite of -4 is 4. This means that $-(-4) = 4$, and in general, we have the following property.

Double Negative Property

For every real number a, we have $-(-a) = a$.

EXAMPLES Find the opposite, or additive inverse, of each number.

16. 8   The opposite of 8 is -8.

17. $-\frac{1}{5}$ The opposite of $-\frac{1}{5}$ is $-\left(-\frac{1}{5}\right)$ or $\frac{1}{5}$.

18. 0   The opposite of 0 is -0, or 0.

19. -3.5 The opposite of -3.5 is $-(-3.5)$ or 3.5.

▣ **Work Practice Problems 16–19**

Two numbers whose product is 1 are called **reciprocals** or **multiplicative inverses** of each other. Just as each real number has a unique opposite, each nonzero real number also has a unique reciprocal.

PRACTICE PROBLEMS 16–19

Find the opposite, or additive inverse, of each number.

16. 7   **17.** $\frac{2}{13}$

18. $-\frac{5}{7}$ **19.** -4.7

Answers

16. -7,   **17.** $-\frac{2}{13}$,   **18.** $\frac{5}{7}$,   **19.** 4.7

Reciprocals or Multiplicative Inverses

If a is a nonzero real number, then its **reciprocal,** or **multiplicative inverse,** is $\dfrac{1}{a}$ and the following is true:

$$a \cdot \frac{1}{a} = 1 \qquad \left(\text{Also, } \frac{1}{a} \cdot a = 1 \right)$$

PRACTICE PROBLEMS 20–22

Find the reciprocal, or multiplicative inverse, of each number.

20. 13

21. -5

22. $\dfrac{2}{3}$

EXAMPLES Find the reciprocal, or multiplicative inverse, of each number.

20. 11   The reciprocal of 11 is $\dfrac{1}{11}$.

21. -9 The reciprocal of -9 is $-\dfrac{1}{9}$.

22. $\dfrac{7}{4}$ The reciprocal of $\dfrac{7}{4}$ is $\dfrac{4}{7}$ $\left(\text{since } \dfrac{7}{4} \cdot \dfrac{4}{7} = 1 \right)$.

■ **Work Practice Problems 20–22**

Helpful Hint

The number 0 has no reciprocal. Why? There is no number that when multiplied by 0 gives a product of 1.

✔**Concept Check** Can a number's additive inverse and multiplicative inverse ever be the same? Explain.

Objective **D** **Using the Commutative, Associative, and Distributive Properties**

In addition to these special real numbers, all real numbers have certain properties that allow us to write equivalent expressions—that is, expressions that have the same value. These properties will be especially useful in Chapter 2 when we solve equations.

The **commutative properties** state that the order in which two real numbers are added or multiplied does not affect their sum or product.

Commutative Properties

For any real numbers a and b,

Addition: $a + b = b + a$

Multiplication: $a \cdot b = b \cdot a$

For example,

$$7 + 11 = 18 \quad \text{and} \quad 11 + 7 = 18 \quad \text{Addition}$$
$$7 \cdot 11 = 77 \quad \text{and} \quad 11 \cdot 7 = 77 \quad \text{Multiplication}$$

The **associative properties** state that regrouping numbers that are added or multiplied does not affect their sum or product.

Associative Properties

For real numbers $a, b,$ and c,

Addition: $(a + b) + c = a + (b + c)$

Multiplication: $(a \cdot b) \cdot c = a \cdot (b \cdot c)$

Answers

20. $\dfrac{1}{13}$, **21.** $-\dfrac{1}{5}$, **22.** $\dfrac{3}{2}$

✔ **Concept Check Answer**

no; answers may vary

For example,

$$(2 + 3) + 7 = 5 + 7 = 12 \qquad \text{Addition}$$
$$2 + (3 + 7) = 2 + 10 = 12$$
$$(2 \cdot 3) \cdot 7 = 6 \cdot 7 = 42 \qquad \text{Multiplication}$$
$$2 \cdot (3 \cdot 7) = 2 \cdot 21 = 42$$

EXAMPLE 23 Use the commutative property of addition to write an expression equivalent to $7x + 5$.

Solution: $7x + 5 = 5 + 7x$

🖥 **Work Practice Problem 23**

EXAMPLE 24 Use the associative property of multiplication to write an expression equivalent to $4 \cdot (9y)$. Then simplify this equivalent expression.

Solution: $4 \cdot (9y) = (4 \cdot 9)y = 36y$

🖥 **Work Practice Problem 24**

The **distributive property** states that multiplication distributes over addition. In Section 1.4, we learn that subtraction is defined in terms of addition. Because of this, we can also say that multiplication distributes over subtraction.

Distributive Properties

For real numbers a, b, and c,

$$a(b + c) = ab + ac$$

Also,

$$a(b - c) = ab - ac$$

For example,

$$3(6 + 2) = 3(8) = 24$$
$$3(6 + 2) = 3(6) + 3(2) = 18 + 6 = 24$$

EXAMPLES Use the distributive property to multiply.

25. $3(2x - y) = 3 \cdot 2x - 3 \cdot y = 6x - 3y$

26. $4(2y + 5) = 4 \cdot 2y + 4 \cdot 5 = 8y + 20$

27. $0.7x(y - 2) = 0.7x \cdot y - 0.7x \cdot 2 = 0.7xy - 1.4x$

🖥 **Work Practice Problems 25–27**

✔**Concept Check** Is the statement below true? Why or why not?

$$6(2a)(3b) = 6(2a) \cdot 6(3b)$$

PRACTICE PROBLEM 23

Use the commutative property of addition to write an expression equivalent to $9 + 4x$.

PRACTICE PROBLEM 24

Use the associative property of multiplication to write an expression equivalent to $5 \cdot (6x)$. Then simplify this equivalent expression.

Helpful Hint

The distributive property also applies to sums or differences of more than two terms.
For example,

$$a(b + c + d) = ab + ac + ad$$

PRACTICE PROBLEMS 25–27

Use the distributive property to multiply.
25. $7(4x - y)$
26. $8(3 + x)$
27. $5x(y - 4)$

Answers

23. $4x + 9$, **24.** $(5 \cdot 6)x = 30x$,
25. $28x - 7y$, **26.** $24 + 8x$,
27. $5xy - 20x$

✔ **Concept Check Answer**

no; $6(2a)(3b) = 6(6ab) = 36ab$

1.3 EXERCISE SET

FOR EXTRA HELP

Student Solutions Manual

PH Math/Tutor Center

CD/Video for Review

MathXL®

MyMathLab

Objective A *Write each sentence as an equation. See Examples 1 through 3.*

1. The sum of 10 and x is -12.

2. The difference of y and 3 amounts to 12.

3. Twice x plus 5 is the same as -14.

4. Three more than the product of 4 and c is 7.

5. The quotient of n and 5 is 4 times n.

6. The quotient of 8 and y is 3 more than y.

7. The difference of z and one-half is the same as the product of z and one-half.

8. Five added to one-fourth q is the same as 4 more than q.

Objective B *Insert $<$, $>$, or $=$ between each pair of numbers to form a true statement. See Examples 4 through 11.*

9. 0 -2

10. -5 0

11. -16 -17

12. -14 -24

13. $\dfrac{12}{3}$ $\dfrac{12}{2}$

14. $\dfrac{20}{5}$ $\dfrac{20}{4}$

15. 7.4   7.40

16. $\dfrac{12}{4}$ $\dfrac{15}{5}$

17. 8.6 -3.5

18. -4.7 3.8

19. $\dfrac{7}{11}$ $\dfrac{9}{11}$

20. $\dfrac{9}{20}$ $\dfrac{3}{20}$

21. $\dfrac{1}{2}$ $\dfrac{5}{8}$

22. $\dfrac{3}{4}$ $\dfrac{7}{8}$

23. -7.9 -7.09

24. -13.07 -13.7

Determine whether each statement is true or false. See Examples 12 through 15.

25. $-6 \leq 0$

26. $0 \leq -4$

27. $-3 \geq -3$

28. $-8 \leq -8$

29. $-14 \geq -1$

30. $-14 \leq -1$

31. $-3 \leq -3$

32. $-8 \geq -8$

Objective C *Write the opposite (or additive inverse) of each number. See Examples 16 through 19.*

33. 9

34. 15

35. -6.2

36. -7.8

37. $\dfrac{4}{7}$

38. $\dfrac{9}{5}$

39. $-\dfrac{5}{11}$

40. $-\dfrac{14}{3}$

41. 0

42. 10.3

Write the reciprocal (or multiplicative inverse) of each number if one exists. See Examples 20 through 22.

43. 5

44. 9

45. -8

46. -4

47. $-\dfrac{1}{4}$

48. $\dfrac{1}{9}$

49. 0

50. $\dfrac{0}{6}$

51. $\dfrac{7}{8}$

52. $-\dfrac{23}{5}$

Mixed Practice *Fill in the chart. See Examples 16 through 22.*

	Number	Opposite	Reciprocal
53.	25		
54.	7		
55.		10	
56.			$-\dfrac{1}{6}$
57.	$-\dfrac{1}{7}$		
58.	$\dfrac{1}{11}$		
59.	0		
60.	1		
61.			$\dfrac{19}{16}$
62.		$\dfrac{36}{13}$	

Objective **D** *Use a commutative property to write an equivalent expression. See Example 23.*

63. $7x + y$

64. $3a + 2b$

65. $z \cdot w$

66. $r \cdot s$

67. $\dfrac{1}{3} \cdot \dfrac{x}{5}$

68. $\dfrac{x}{2} \cdot \dfrac{9}{10}$

Use an associative property to write an equivalent expression. See Example 24.

69. $5 \cdot (7x)$

70. $3 \cdot (10z)$

71. $(x + 1.2) + y$

72. $5q + (2r + s)$

73. $(14z) \cdot y$

74. $(9.2x) \cdot y$

Use the distributive property to multiply. See Examples 25 through 27.

75. $3(x + 5)$

76. $7(y + 2)$

77. $4(z - 6)$

78. $2(7 - y)$

79. $8(2a + b)$

80. $9(c + 7d)$

81. $6x(y - 4)$

82. $11y(z - 2)$

83. $0.4(2x + 5y)$

84. $0.5(3a - 4b)$

85. $\dfrac{1}{2}(4x - 9y)$

86. $\dfrac{1}{3}(4x + 9y)$

87. $2(6x + 5y + 2z)$

88. $5(3a + b + 9c)$

Complete each statement to illustrate the given property.

89. $3x + 6 =$ _____ Commutative property of addition

90. $8 + 0 =$ _____ Additive identity property

91. $\dfrac{2}{3} + \left(-\dfrac{2}{3}\right) =$ _____ Additive inverse property

92. $4(x + 3) =$ _____ Distributive property

93. $7 \cdot 1 =$ _____ Multiplicative identity property

94. $0 + 5.4 =$ _____ Additive identity property

95. $10(2y) =$ _____ Associative property of multiplication

96. $9y + (x + 3z) =$ _____ Associative property of addition

Concept Extensions

In each statement, a property of real numbers has been incorrectly applied. Correct the right-hand side of each statement. See the second Concept Check in this section.

97. $3(x + 4) = 3x + 4$

98. $5(7y) = (5 \cdot 7)(5 \cdot y)$

99. $4 + 8y = 4y + 8$

100. Name the only real number that has no reciprocal, and explain why this is so.

101. Name the only real number that is its own opposite, and explain why this is so.

102. Is subtraction commutative? Explain why or why not.

103. Is division commutative? Explain why or why not.

104. Evaluate $12 - (5 - 3)$ and $(12 - 5) - 3$. Use these two expressions and discuss whether subtraction is associative.

105. Evaluate $24 \div (6 \div 3)$ and $(24 \div 6) \div 3$. Use these two expressions and discuss whether division is associative.

106. To demonstrate the distributive property geometrically, represent the area of the larger rectangle in two ways: First as length a times width $b + c$, and second as the sum of the areas of the smaller rectangles.

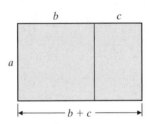

 STUDY SKILLS BUILDER

Are You Familiar with Your Textbook Supplements?

There are many student supplements available for additional study. Below, I have listed some of these. See the preface of this text or your instructor for further information.

- *Chapter Test Prep Video CD*. This material is found in your textbook and is fully explained. The CD contains video clip solutions to the Chapter Test exercises in this text and are excellent help when studying for chapter tests.

- *Lecture Video CDs*. These video segments are keyed to each section of the text. The material is presented by me, Elayn Martin-Gay, and I have placed a video icon by each exercise in the text that I have worked on the video.

- *The Student Solutions Manual*. This contains worked out solutions to odd-numbered exercises as well as every exercise in the Integrated Reviews, Chapter Reviews, Chapter Tests, and Cumulative Reviews.

- *Prentice Hall Tutor Center*. Mathematics questions may be phoned, faxed, or emailed to this center.

- *MyMathLab, MathXL, and Interact Math*. These are computer and Internet tutorials. This supplement may already be available to you somewhere on campus, for example at your local learning resource lab. Take a moment and find the name and location of any such lab on campus.

As usual, your instructor is your best source of information.

Let's see how you are doing with textbook supplements:

1. Name one way the Chapter Test Prep Video can help you prepare for a chapter test.

2. List any textbook supplements that you have found useful.

3. Have you located and visited a learning resource lab located on your campus?

4. List the textbook supplements that are currently housed in your campus' learning resource lab.

1.4 OPERATIONS ON REAL NUMBERS

Objectives

A Find the Absolute Value of a Number.

B Add and Subtract Real Numbers.

C Multiply and Divide Real Numbers.

D Simplify Expressions Containing Exponents.

E Find Roots of Numbers.

Objective A Finding the Absolute Value of a Number

In Section 1.3, we used the number line to compare two real numbers. The number line can also be used to visualize distance, which leads to the concept of absolute value. The **absolute value** of a number is the distance between the number and 0 on a number line. The symbol for absolute value is | |. For example, since -4 and 4 are both 4 units from 0 on the number line, each has an absolute value of 4.

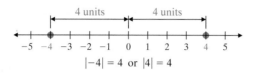

$|-4| = 4$ or $|4| = 4$

An equivalent definition of the absolute value of a real number a is given next.

Absolute Value

The absolute value of a, written as $|a|$, is

$$|a| = \begin{cases} a \text{ if } a \text{ is } 0 \text{ or a positive number} \\ -a \text{ if } a \text{ is a negative number} \end{cases}$$

↑
the opposite of

 EXAMPLES Find each absolute value.

1. $|3| = 3$
2. $|0| = 0$
3. $\left|-\dfrac{1}{7}\right| = -\left(-\dfrac{1}{7}\right) = \dfrac{1}{7}$

   ↑
   the opposite of

4. $-|2.7| = -2.7$
5. $-|-8| = -8$ Since $|-8|$ is 8, we have $-|-8| = -8$.

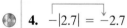 **Work Practice Problems 1–5**

Helpful Hint

Since distance is always positive or zero, the absolute value of a number is always positive or zero.

✔ **Concept Check**   Explain how you know that $|14| = -14$ is a false statement.

Objective B Adding and Subtracting Real Numbers

When solving problems, we often need to add real numbers. For example, if the New Orleans Saints lose 5 yards in one play, then lose another 7 yards in the next play, their total loss may be described by $-5 + (-7)$.

The addition of two real numbers may be summarized by the following.

23

Adding Real Numbers

1. To add two numbers with the *same* sign, add their absolute values and attach their common sign.

2. To add two numbers with *different* signs, subtract the smaller absolute value from the larger absolute value and attach the sign of the number with the larger absolute value.

For example, to add $-5 + (-7)$, we first add their absolute values.

$$|-5| = 5, \quad |-7| = 7, \quad \text{and} \quad 5 + 7 = 12$$

Next, we attach their common negative sign.

$$-5 + (-7) = -12$$

(This represents a total loss of 12 yards for the New Orleans Saints.)

To find $(-4) + 3$, we first subtract their absolute values. (Subtract smaller absolute value from larger absolute value.)

$$|-4| = 4, \quad |3| = 3, \quad \text{and} \quad 4 - 3 = 1$$

Next, we attach the sign of the number with the larger absolute value.

$$(-4) + 3 = -1$$

PRACTICE PROBLEMS 6–11

Add.

6. $-7 + (-10)$

7. $8 + (-12)$

8. $-14 + 20$

9. $-4.6 + (-1.9)$

10. $-\dfrac{2}{3} + \dfrac{1}{6}$

11. $-\dfrac{1}{7} + \dfrac{1}{2}$

EXAMPLES Add.

6. $-3 + (-11) = -(3 + 11) = -14$ Add their absolute values, or $3 + 11 = 14$. Then attach the common negative sign.

7. $3 + (-7) = -4$ Subtract their absolute values, or $7 - 3 = 4$. Since -7 has the larger absolute value, the answer is -4.

8. $-10 + 15 = 5$

9. $-8.3 + (-1.9) = -10.2$

10. $-\dfrac{1}{4} + \dfrac{1}{2} = -\dfrac{1}{4} + \dfrac{1}{2} \cdot \dfrac{2}{2} = -\dfrac{1}{4} + \dfrac{2}{4} = \dfrac{1}{4}$

11. $-\dfrac{2}{3} + \dfrac{3}{7} = -\dfrac{2}{3} \cdot \dfrac{7}{7} + \dfrac{3}{7} \cdot \dfrac{3}{3} = -\dfrac{14}{21} + \dfrac{9}{21} = -\dfrac{5}{21}$

🖥 **Work Practice Problems 6–11**

Subtraction of two real numbers may be defined in terms of addition.

Subtracting Real Numbers

If a and b are real numbers, then the difference of a and b, written $a - b$, is defined by

$$a - b = a + (-b)$$

In other words, to subtract a second real number from a first, we add the first number and the opposite of the second number.

Answers

6. -17, **7.** -4, **8.** 6, **9.** -6.5,

10. $-\dfrac{1}{2}$, **11.** $\dfrac{5}{14}$

EXAMPLES Subtract.

Add the opposite.

12. $2 - 8 = 2 + (-8) = -6$

Add the opposite.

13. $-8 - (-1) = -8 + (1) = -7$

14. $10.7 - (-9.8) = 10.7 + 9.8 = 20.5$

15. $-\dfrac{2}{3} - \dfrac{1}{4} = -\dfrac{2}{3} + \left(-\dfrac{1}{4}\right) = -\dfrac{2}{3} \cdot \dfrac{4}{4} + \left(-\dfrac{1}{4} \cdot \dfrac{3}{3}\right) = -\dfrac{8}{12} + \left(-\dfrac{3}{12}\right) = -\dfrac{11}{12}$

■ **Work Practice Problems 12–15**

To add or subtract three or more real numbers, we add or subtract from left to right.

EXAMPLES Simplify each expression.

16. $11 + 2 - 7 = 13 - 7 = 13 + (-7) = 6$

17. $-5 - 4 + 2 = -5 + (-4) + 2 = -9 + 2 = -7$

■ **Work Practice Problems 16–17**

Objective ◉ Multiplying and Dividing Real Numbers

To discover sign patterns when you multiply real numbers, recall that multiplication by a positive integer is the same as repeated addition. For example,

$$3(2) = 2 + 2 + 2 = 6$$
$$3(-2) = (-2) + (-2) + (-2) = -6$$

Notice here that $3(-2) = -6$. This illustrates that the product of two numbers with different signs is negative. We summarize sign patterns for multiplying any two real numbers as follows.

Multiplying Two Real Numbers

1. The product of two numbers with the *same* sign is positive.

2. The product of two numbers with *different* signs is negative.

Also recall that the product of zero and any real number a is zero.

Product Property of 0

$$0 \cdot a = 0 \qquad \text{Also,} \qquad a \cdot 0 = 0$$

EXAMPLES Multiply.

18. $-8(-1) = 8$

19. $2\left(-\dfrac{1}{6}\right) = \dfrac{2}{1} \cdot \left(-\dfrac{1}{6}\right) = -\dfrac{2}{6} = -\dfrac{1}{3}$

20. $-1.2(0.3) = -0.36$

21. $7(-6) = -42$

22. $-\dfrac{1}{3}\left(-\dfrac{1}{2}\right) = \dfrac{1}{6}$

23. $(-4.6)(-2.5) = 11.5$

24. $0(-6) = 0$

■ **Work Practice Problems 18–24**

PRACTICE PROBLEMS 12–15

Subtract.

12. $7 - 14$

13. $-10 - (-2)$

14. $13.3 - (-8.9)$

15. $-\dfrac{1}{3} - \dfrac{1}{2}$

PRACTICE PROBLEMS 16–17

Simplify each expression.

16. $18 + 3 - 4$

17. $-3 - 11 + 7$

PRACTICE PROBLEMS 18–24

Multiply.

18. $-4(-2)$

19. $5\left(-\dfrac{1}{10}\right)$

20. $-3.2(0.1)$

21. $8(-6)$

22. $-\dfrac{2}{5}\left(-\dfrac{1}{3}\right)$

23. $(-1.3)(-1.5)$

24. $0(-10)$

Answers

12. -7, **13.** -8, **14.** 22.2, **15.** $-\dfrac{5}{6}$,

16. 17, **17.** -7, **18.** 8, **19.** $-\dfrac{1}{2}$,

20. -0.32, **21.** -48, **22.** $\dfrac{2}{15}$,

23. 1.95, **24.** 0

Recall that $\frac{8}{4} = 2$ because $2 \cdot 4 = 8$. Likewise, $\frac{8}{-4} = -2$ because $(-2)(-4) = 8$. Also, $\frac{-8}{4} = -2$ because $(-2)4 = -8$, and $\frac{-8}{-4} = 2$ because $2(-4) = -8$. From these examples, we can see that the sign patterns for division are the same as for multiplication.

Dividing Two Real Numbers

1. The quotient of two numbers with the *same* sign is positive.

2. The quotient of two numbers with *different* signs is negative.

Notice from the previous reasoning that we cannot divide by 0. Why? If $\frac{5}{0}$ did exist, it would equal a number such that the number times 0 would equal 5. There is no such number, so we cannot define division by 0. We say, for example, that $\frac{5}{0}$ is **undefined.**

Divide.

25. $\dfrac{45}{-9}$

26. $\dfrac{-16}{-4}$

27. $\dfrac{25}{-5}$

28. $\dfrac{-3}{0}$

29. $\dfrac{0}{-3}$

30. $\dfrac{-1}{-4}$

EXAMPLES Divide.

25. $\dfrac{20}{-4} = -5$

26. $\dfrac{-9}{-3} = 3$

27. $\dfrac{-40}{10} = -4$

28. $\dfrac{-8}{0}$ is undefined.

29. $\dfrac{0}{-8} = 0$

30. $\dfrac{-10}{-80} = \dfrac{1}{8}$

Work Practice Problems 25–30

With sign rules for division, we can understand why the positioning of the negative sign in a fraction does not change the value of the fraction. For example,

$$\frac{-12}{3} = -4, \qquad \frac{12}{-3} = -4, \qquad \text{and} \qquad -\frac{12}{3} = -4$$

Since all these fractions equal -4, we can say that

$$\frac{-12}{3} = \frac{12}{-3} = -\frac{12}{3}$$

In general, the following holds true:

If a and b are real numbers and $b \neq 0$, then
$$\frac{a}{-b} = \frac{-a}{b} = -\frac{a}{b}$$

Also recall that division by a nonzero real number b is the same as multiplication by its reciprocal $\frac{1}{b}$. In other words,

$$a \div b = a \cdot \frac{1}{b}$$

EXAMPLES Divide.

31. $-\dfrac{1}{10} \div \left(-\dfrac{2}{5}\right) = -\dfrac{1}{10} \cdot \left(-\dfrac{5}{2}\right) = \dfrac{5}{20} = \dfrac{1}{4}$

32. $-\dfrac{1}{4} \div \dfrac{3}{7} = -\dfrac{1}{4} \cdot \dfrac{7}{3} = -\dfrac{7}{12}$

■ **Work Practice Problems 31–32**

PRACTICE PROBLEMS 31–32

Divide.

31. $-\dfrac{3}{4} \div \left(-\dfrac{3}{8}\right)$

32. $-\dfrac{1}{11} \div \dfrac{2}{7}$

Objective D Simplifying Expressions Containing Exponents

Recall that when two numbers are multiplied, each number is called a **factor** of the product. For example, in $3 \cdot 5 = 15$, the 3 and 5 are factors.

A natural number *exponent* is a shorthand notation for repeated multiplication of the same factor. This repeated factor is called the **base**, and the number of times it is used as a factor is indicated by the **exponent**. For example,

$$4^3 = 4 \cdot 4 \cdot 4 = 64$$

base — 4 is a factor 3 times. — exponent

Exponents

If a is a real number and n is a natural number, then the **nth power of a**, or **a raised to the nth power**, written as a^n, is the product of n factors, each of which is a.

$$a^n = \underbrace{a \cdot a \cdot a \cdot a \cdot \cdots \cdot a}_{a \text{ is a factor } n \text{ times.}}$$

base — — exponent

It is not necessary to write an exponent of 1. For example, 3 is assumed to be 3^1.

EXAMPLES Find the value of each expression.

33. $3^2 = 3 \cdot 3 = 9$

34. $-5^2 = -(5 \cdot 5) = -25$

35. $-5^3 = -(5 \cdot 5 \cdot 5) = -125$

36. $\left(\dfrac{1}{2}\right)^4 = \left(\dfrac{1}{2}\right)\left(\dfrac{1}{2}\right)\left(\dfrac{1}{2}\right)\left(\dfrac{1}{2}\right) = \dfrac{1}{16}$

37. $(-5)^2 = (-5)(-5) = 25$

38. $(-5)^3 = (-5)(-5)(-5) = -125$

■ **Work Practice Problems 33–38**

PRACTICE PROBLEMS 33–38

Simplify each expression.

33. 4^2

34. -3^2

35. -3^3

36. $\left(\dfrac{1}{3}\right)^4$

37. $(-3)^2$

38. $(-3)^3$

✔ **Concept Check** When $(-8.2)^7$ is evaluated, will the value be positive or negative? How can you tell without making any calculations?

Helpful Hint

Be very careful when finding the value of expressions such as -5^2 and $(-5)^2$.

$$-5^2 = -(5 \cdot 5) = -25 \quad \text{and} \quad (-5)^2 = (-5)(-5) = 25$$

Without parentheses, the base to square is 5, not -5.

Answers

31. 2, 32. $-\dfrac{7}{22}$, 33. 16, 34. -9,

35. -27, 36. $\dfrac{1}{81}$, 37. 9, 38. -27

✔ **Concept Check Answer**

negative; the exponent is an odd number

Objective **E** Finding the Root of a Number

The opposite of squaring a number is taking the **square root** of a number. For example, since the square of 4, or 4^2, is 16, we say that a square root of 16 is 4. The notation $\sqrt{a}$ is used to denote the **positive,** or **principal square root** of a nonnegative number a. We then have in symbols that

$$\sqrt{16} = 4$$

PRACTICE PROBLEMS 39–41

Find each root.

39. $\sqrt{36}$
40. $\sqrt{4}$
41. $\sqrt{\dfrac{1}{49}}$

EXAMPLES Find each root.

39. $\sqrt{9} = 3$, since 3 is positive and $3^2 = 9$.
40. $\sqrt{25} = 5$, since $5^2 = 25$.
41. $\sqrt{\dfrac{1}{4}} = \dfrac{1}{2}$, since $\left(\dfrac{1}{2}\right)^2 = \dfrac{1}{4}$.

Work Practice Problems 39–41

We can find roots other than square roots. Since 2 cubed, written as 2^3, is 8, we say that the **cube root** of 8 is 2. This is written as

$$\sqrt[3]{8} = 2$$

Also, since $3^4 = 81$ and 3 is positive,

$$\sqrt[4]{81} = 3$$

PRACTICE PROBLEMS 42–44

Find each root.

42. $\sqrt[3]{64}$
43. $\sqrt[4]{1}$
44. $\sqrt[5]{243}$

EXAMPLES Find each root.

42. $\sqrt[3]{27} = 3$, since $3^3 = 27$.
43. $\sqrt[5]{1} = 1$, since $1^5 = 1$.
44. $\sqrt[4]{16} = 2$, since 2 is positive and $2^4 = 16$.

Work Practice Problems 42–44

Of course, as mentioned in Section 1.2, not all roots simplify to rational numbers. We study radicals further in Chapter 7.

Answers
39. 6, **40.** 2, **41.** $\dfrac{1}{7}$, **42.** 4, **43.** 1,
44. 3

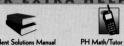
Objective A *Find each absolute value. See Examples 1 through 5.*

1. $|2|$ **2.** $|8|$ **3.** $|-4|$ **4.** $|-6|$ **5.** $|0|$

6. $|-1|$ **7.** $-|3|$ **8.** $-|11|$ **9.** $-\left|-\dfrac{2}{9}\right|$ **10.** $-\left|-\dfrac{5}{13}\right|$

Objective B *Add or subtract as indicated. See Examples 6 through 17.*

11. $-3 + 8$ **12.** $12 + (-7)$ **13.** $-14 + (-10)$ **14.** $-5 + (-9)$

15. $-4.3 - 6.7$ **16.** $-8.2 - (-6.6)$ **17.** $13 - 17$ **18.** $15 - (-1)$

19. $\dfrac{11}{15} - \left(-\dfrac{3}{5}\right)$ **20.** $\dfrac{7}{10} - \dfrac{4}{5}$ **21.** $19 - 10 - 11$ **22.** $-13 - 4 + 9$

23. $-14 - 7$ **24.** $-6 - 31$ **25.** $-\dfrac{4}{5} - \left(-\dfrac{3}{10}\right)$ **26.** $-\dfrac{5}{2} - \left(-\dfrac{2}{3}\right)$

27. Subtract 14 from 8.   **28.** Subtract 9 from -3.

Objective C *Multiply or divide as indicated. See Examples 18 through 32.*

29. $-5 \cdot 12$ **30.** $-3 \cdot 8$ **31.** $-8(-10)$ **32.** $-4(-11)$ **33.** $-17 \cdot 0$

34. $-5 \cdot 0$ **35.** $0(-1)$ **36.** $0(-34)$ **37.** $\dfrac{-9}{3}$ **38.** $\dfrac{-20}{5}$

39. $\dfrac{-12}{-4}$ **40.** $\dfrac{-36}{-6}$ **41.** $3\left(-\dfrac{1}{18}\right)$ **42.** $5\left(-\dfrac{1}{50}\right)$ **43.** $(-0.7)(-0.8)$

44. $(-0.9)(-0.5)$ **45.** $9.1 \div (-1.3)$ **46.** $22.5 \div (-2.5)$ **47.** $-4(-2)(-1)$ **48.** $-5(-3)(-2)$

Objective D *Find the value of each expression. See Examples 33 through 38.*

49. -7^2 **50.** $(-7)^2$ **51.** $(-6)^2$ **52.** -6^2

53. $(-2)^3$ **54.** -2^3 **55.** $\left(-\dfrac{1}{3}\right)^3$ **56.** $\left(-\dfrac{1}{2}\right)^4$

Objective E *Find each root. See Examples 39 through 44.*

57. $\sqrt{49}$ **58.** $\sqrt{81}$ **59.** $\sqrt{64}$ **60.** $\sqrt{100}$ **61.** $\sqrt{\dfrac{1}{9}}$

62. $\sqrt{\dfrac{1}{25}}$ **63.** $\sqrt[3]{64}$ **64.** $\sqrt[5]{32}$ **65.** $\sqrt{\dfrac{4}{25}}$ **66.** $\sqrt{\dfrac{4}{81}}$

Objectives Ⓐ Ⓑ Ⓒ Ⓓ Ⓔ **Mixed Practice** *Perform the indicated operations. See Examples 1 through 44.*

67. $-4 + 7$

68. $-9 + 15$

69. $-9 + (-3)$

70. $-17 + (-2)$

71. $6(-3)$

72. $5(-4)$

73. $-9 \cdot 8$

74. $-6 \cdot 7$

75. $(-11)^2$

76. -11^2

77. $\dfrac{16}{-2}$

78. $\dfrac{35}{-7}$

79. $-18 \div 6$

80. $-42 \div 6$

81. $-\dfrac{2}{7} \cdot \left(-\dfrac{1}{6}\right)$

82. $\dfrac{5}{9} \cdot \left(-\dfrac{3}{5}\right)$

83. $-2(-3.6)$

84. $-5(-4.2)$

85. $-4 - (-19)$

86. $-5 - (-17)$

87. $6.3 - 18.5$

88. $15.9 - 21.7$

89. $\dfrac{0}{-5}$

90. $\dfrac{0}{-11}$

91. $\dfrac{-18}{0}$

92. $\dfrac{-22}{0}$

93. $\sqrt{\dfrac{1}{16}}$

94. $\sqrt{\dfrac{1}{49}}$

95. $\dfrac{-6}{7} \div 2$

96. $\dfrac{-9}{13} \div (-3)$

97. $\dfrac{-5.2}{-1.3}$

98. $\dfrac{-4.2}{-1.4}$

99. $-25 \div (-5)$

100. $-88 \div (-11)$

101. $\sqrt[4]{81}$

102. $\sqrt[3]{1}$

103. $\sqrt[3]{8}$

104. $\sqrt[3]{125}$

105. $-\dfrac{1}{6} \div \dfrac{9}{10}$

106. $\dfrac{4}{7} \div \left(-\dfrac{1}{8}\right)$

107. $-\dfrac{2}{3} \cdot \left(\dfrac{6}{4}\right)$

108. $\dfrac{5}{6} \cdot \left(\dfrac{-12}{15}\right)$

109. $\dfrac{3}{5} \div \left(-\dfrac{2}{5}\right)$

110. $\dfrac{2}{7} \div \left(-\dfrac{1}{14}\right)$

111. $16 - 8 - 9$

112. $-14 - 3 + 6$

113. $-5 + (-7) - 10$

114. $-8 + (-10) - 6$

115. $-7(-1)(5)$

116. $-6(2)(-3)$

117. $-6(-5)(0)$

118. $4(-3)(0)$

119. -4^4

120. $(-4)^4$

Concept Extensions

121. Explain why -3^2 and $(-3)^2$ simplify to different numbers.

122. Explain why -3^3 and $(-3)^3$ simplify to the same number.

Answer each statement true or false.

123. $-7 - 1 < -7(-1)$

124. $\dfrac{-100}{-5} > -100 + (-5)$

Each circle below represents a whole, or 1. Determine the unknown fractional part of each circle.

125.

126.

127. Most of Mauna Kea, a volcano on Hawaii, lies below sea level. If this volcano begins at 5998 meters below sea level and then rises 10,203 meters, find the height of the volcano above sea level.

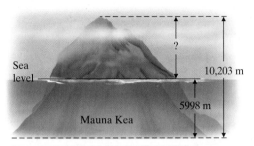

Sea level

?

10,203 m

5998 m

Mauna Kea

128. The highest point on land on Earth is the top of Mt. Everest, in the Himalayas, at an elevation of 29,028 feet above sea level. The lowest point on land is the Dead Sea, between Israel and Jordan, at 1312 feet below sea level. Find the difference in elevations. *(Source:* National Geographic Society)

A fair game is one in which each team or player has the same chance of winning. Suppose that a game consists of three players taking turns spinning a spinner. If the spinner lands on yellow, player 1 gets a point. If the spinner lands on red, player 2 gets a point, and if the spinner lands on blue, player 3 gets a point. After 12 spins, the player with the most points wins. Use this information to answer Exercises 129 through 133.

a   b   c   d

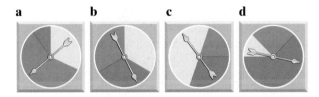

129. Which spinner would lead to a fair game?

130. If you are player 2 and want to win the game, which spinner would you choose?

131. If you are player 1 and want to lose the game, which spinner would you choose?

132. Is it possible for the game to end in a three-way tie? If so, list the possible ending scores.

133. Is it possible for the game to end in a two-way tie? If so, list the possible ending scores.

Use a calculator to approximate each square root. Round to four decimal places.

 134. $\sqrt{10}$ **135.** $\sqrt{273}$ **136.** $\sqrt{7.9}$ **137.** $\sqrt{19.6}$

Investment firms often advertise their gains and losses in the form of bar graphs such as the one that follows. This graph shows investment risk over time for common stocks by showing average annual compound returns for 1 year, 5 years, 10 years, 15 years, and 20 years. For example, after 1 year, the annual compound return in percent for an investor is anywhere from a gain of 56% to a loss of 64%. Use this graph to answer Exercises 138 through 142.

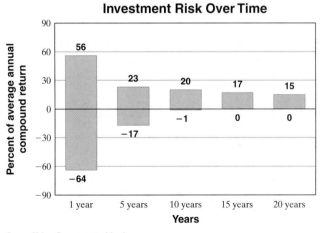

Investment Risk Over Time

Source: Yahoo finance; mutual funds

138. A person investing in common stocks may expect at most an average annual gain of what percent after 15 years?

139. A person investing in common stocks may expect to lose at most an average per year of what percent after 5 years?

140. Find the difference in percent of the highest average annual return and the lowest average annual return after 20 years.

141. Find the difference in percent of the highest average annual return and the lowest average annual return after 5 years.

142. Do you think that the type of investment shown in the figure is recommended for short-term investments or long-term investments? Explain your answer.

Real Numbers

Answers

1. _____
2. _____
3. _____
4. _____
5. _____
6. _____
7. _____
8. _____
9. _____
10. _____
11. _____
12. _____
13. _____
14. _____
15. _____
16. _____
17. _____
18. _____
19. _____
20. _____
21. _____
22. _____
23. _____
24. _____
25. _____
26. _____
27. _____
28. _____
29. _____
30. _____

32

Write each set by listing its elements.

1. $\{x \mid x$ is a natural number less than 4$\}$

2. $\{x \mid x$ is an odd whole number less than 6$\}$

3. $\{x \mid x$ is an even natural number greater than 7$\}$

4. $\{x \mid x$ is a whole number between 10 and 15$\}$

Write each phrase as an algebraic expression. Let x represent the unknown number.

5. Twice the difference of a number and three

6. The quotient of six and the sum of a number and ten

Insert $<, >,$ *or* $=$ *between each pair of numbers to form a true statement.*

7. $-4 \quad -6$

8. $8.6 \quad 8.600$

9. $\dfrac{9}{10} \quad \dfrac{11}{10}$

10. $-6.1 \quad -6.01$

Write each sentence as an equation.

11. The product of 5 and x is the same as 20.

12. The sum of a and 12 amounts to 14.

13. The quotient of y and 10 is the same as the product of y and 10.

14. The sum of x and 1 equals the difference of x and 1.

Perform each indicated operation.

15. $-4 + 7$

16. $-11 + 20$

17. $-4(7)$

18. $-11(20)$

19. $-8 - (-13)$

20. $-12 - 16$

21. $\dfrac{-20}{-4}$

22. $\dfrac{-18}{6}$

23. -5^2

24. $(-5)^2$

25. $-6 - 1 + 20$

26. $18 - 4 - 19$

27. $\dfrac{0}{-3}$

28. $\dfrac{5}{0}$

29. $-4(3)(2)$

30. $-5(-1)(6)$

31. $-\dfrac{1}{2} \cdot \dfrac{6}{7}$

32. $\dfrac{4}{5} \cdot \left(-\dfrac{1}{8}\right)$

33. $\dfrac{3}{10} - \dfrac{4}{5}$

34. $-\dfrac{2}{3} - \dfrac{1}{4}$

35. $\dfrac{1.6}{-0.2}$

36. $\dfrac{-4.8}{16}$

37. $6.7 - (-1.3)$

38. $-4.6 + 9$

39. $\dfrac{1}{2} + \left(-\dfrac{7}{8}\right)$

40. $\dfrac{1}{2} \div \left(-\dfrac{7}{8}\right)$

41. $\sqrt{49}$

42. $\sqrt[3]{27}$

43. -2^2

44. $(-2)^3$

45. $\sqrt{\dfrac{1}{81}}$

46. $\sqrt{\dfrac{1}{100}}$

Fill in the chart.

	Number	Opposite	Reciprocal
47.	-6		
48.	4		
49.			$\dfrac{7}{5}$
50.		$\dfrac{7}{30}$	

Use the distribution property to multiply.

51. $9(m + 5)$

52. $11(7 + r)$

53. $3(2y - 3x)$

54. $8(4m - 7n)$

55. $0.2(3a + 7)$

56. $0.6(2n + 5)$

57. $\dfrac{1}{5}(10x - 19y + 20)$

58. $\dfrac{1}{2}(10x - 19y + 20)$

31. _____

32. _____

33. _____

34. _____

35. _____

36. _____

37. _____

38. _____

39. _____

40. _____

41. _____

42. _____

43. _____

44. _____

45. _____

46. _____

51. _____

52. _____

53. _____

54. _____

55. _____

56. _____

57. _____

58. _____

A Use the Order of Operations.

B Identify and Evaluate Algebraic Expressions.

C Identify Like Terms and Simplify Algebraic Expressions.

1.5 ORDER OF OPERATIONS AND ALGEBRAIC EXPRESSIONS

In this section, we review order of operations and algebraic expressions.

Objective **A** Using the Order of Operations

The expression $3 + 2 \cdot 30$ represents the total number of compact disks (CDs) shown.

Expressions containing more than one operation are written to follow a particular agreed-upon **order of operations.** For example, when we write $3 + 2 \cdot 30$, we mean to multiply first, and then add.

Order of Operations

Simplify expressions using the following order.

1. If grouping symbols such as parentheses are present, simplify expressions within those first, starting with the innermost set.
2. Evaluate exponential expressions, roots, and absolute values.
3. Perform multiplications or divisions in order from left to right.
4. Perform additions or subtractions in order from left to right.

Helpful Hint

Fraction bars, radical signs, and absolute value bars can sometimes be used as grouping symbols. For example,

	Fraction Bar	Radical Sign	Absolute Value Bars
Grouping Symbol	$\dfrac{-1-7}{6-11}$	$\sqrt{15+1}$	$\lvert-7.2-\sqrt{4}\rvert$
Not Grouping Symbol	$-\dfrac{8}{9}$	$\sqrt{9}$	$\lvert-3.2\rvert$

PRACTICE PROBLEM 1

Simplify: $15 - 2 \cdot 5$

EXAMPLE 1 Simplify: $3 + 2 \cdot 30$

Solution: First we multiply; then we add.

$$3 + 2 \cdot 30 = 3 + 60 = 63$$

■ **Work Practice Problem 1**

PRACTICE PROBLEM 2

Simplify: $2 + 5(2 - 6)^2$

EXAMPLE 2 Simplify: $1 + 2(1 - 4)^2$

Solution: Remember order of operations so that you are *not* tempted to add 1 and 2 first. Unless there are grouping symbols, addition is last in order of operations.

$$
\begin{aligned}
1 + 2(1 - 4)^2 &= 1 + 2(-3)^2 && \text{Simplify inside parentheses first.} \\
&= 1 + 2(9) && \text{Write } (-3)^2 \text{ as 9.} \\
&= 1 + 18 && \text{Multiply.} \\
&= 19 && \text{Add.}
\end{aligned}
$$

■ **Work Practice Problem 2**

Answers

1. 5, **2.** 82

EXAMPLE 3 Simplify: $\dfrac{|-2|^3 + 1}{-7 - \sqrt{4}}$

Solution: Here, the fraction bar serves as a grouping symbol. We simplify the numerator and the denominator separately. Then we divide.

$$\frac{|-2|^3 + 1}{-7 - \sqrt{4}} = \frac{2^3 + 1}{-7 - 2} \quad \text{Write } |-2| \text{ as 2 and } \sqrt{4} \text{ as 2.}$$

$$= \frac{8 + 1}{-9} \quad \text{Write } 2^3 \text{ as 8.}$$

$$= \frac{9}{-9} = -1 \quad \text{Simplify the numerator; then divide.}$$

🔲 **Work Practice Problem 3**

PRACTICE PROBLEM 3

Simplify: $\dfrac{|-3|^2 + 5}{\sqrt{9} - 10}$

Besides parentheses, other symbols used for grouping expressions are brackets [ ], braces { }, radical signs, and absolute value bars. Brackets [ ] and braces { } are commonly used when we group expressions that already contain parentheses.

EXAMPLE 4 Simplify: $3 - [6(4 - 6) + 2(5 - 9)]$

Solution:

$$\begin{aligned} 3 - [6(4 - 6) + 2(5 - 9)] &= 3 - [6(-2) + 2(-4)] \quad \text{Simplify within the innermost sets of parentheses.} \\ &= 3 - [-12 + (-8)] \\ &= 3 - [-20] \\ &= 23 \end{aligned}$$

🔲 **Work Practice Problem 4**

PRACTICE PROBLEM 4

Simplify:
$7 - [2(1 - 3) + 5(10 - 12)]$

Helpful Hint
When grouping symbols occur within grouping symbols, remember to perform operations on the innermost set first.

EXAMPLE 5 Simplify: $\dfrac{-5\sqrt{30 - 5} + (-2)^2}{4^2 + |7 - 10|}$

Solution: Here, the fraction bar, radical sign, and absolute value bars serve as grouping symbols. Thus, we simplify within the radical sign and absolute value bars first, remembering to calculate above and below the fraction bar separately.

$$\frac{-5\sqrt{30 - 5} + (-2)^2}{4^2 + |7 - 10|} = \frac{-5\sqrt{25} + (-2)^2}{4^2 + |-3|} = \frac{-5 \cdot 5 + 4}{16 + 3} = \frac{-25 + 4}{16 + 3}$$

$$= \frac{-21}{19} \text{ or } -\frac{21}{19}$$

🔲 **Work Practice Problem 5**

PRACTICE PROBLEM 5

Simplify: $\dfrac{|9 - 16| + 5^2}{-3\sqrt{8 + 1} + (-4)^2}$

✔ **Concept Check** True or false? If two different people use the order of operations to simplify a numerical expression and neither makes a calculation error, it is not possible that they each obtain a different result. Explain.

Objective B Evaluating Algebraic Expressions

Recall from Section 1.2 that an algebraic expression is formed by numbers and variables connected by the operations of addition, subtraction, multiplication, division, raising to powers, or taking roots. Also, if numbers are substituted for the variables in an algebraic expression and the operations performed, the result is called the **value** of the expression for the given replacement values. This entire process is called **evaluating an expression.**

Answers
3. -2, **4.** 21, **5.** $\dfrac{32}{7}$

✔ **Concept Check Answer**
true; answers may vary

PRACTICE PROBLEM 6

Evaluate each expression when $x = 5$ and $y = -4$.

a. $2x - 6y$

b. $-3y^2$

c. $\dfrac{\sqrt{x}}{y} + \dfrac{y}{x}$

EXAMPLE 6 Evaluate each expression when $x = 4$ and $y = -3$.

a. $3x - 7y$ **b.** $-2y^2$ **c.** $\dfrac{\sqrt{x}}{y} - \dfrac{y}{x}$

Solution: For each expression, replace x with 4 and y with -3.

a. $3x - 7y = 3 \cdot 4 - 7(-3)$ Let $x = 4$ and $y = -3$.

$ = 12 - (-21)$ Multiply.

$ = 12 + 21$ Write as an addition.

$ = 33$ Add.

b. $-2y^2 = \underbrace{-2(-3)^2}$ Let $y = -3$.

$ = -2(9)$ Write $(-3)^2$ as 9.

$ = -18$ Multiply.

> **Helpful Hint**
> In $-2(-3)^2$, the exponent 2 goes with the base of -3 only.

c. $\dfrac{\sqrt{x}}{y} - \dfrac{y}{x} = \dfrac{\sqrt{4}}{-3} - \dfrac{-3}{4}$

$\phantom{\dfrac{\sqrt{x}}{y} - \dfrac{y}{x}} = -\dfrac{2}{3} + \dfrac{3}{4}$ Write $\sqrt{4}$ as 2.

$\phantom{\dfrac{\sqrt{x}}{y} - \dfrac{y}{x}} = -\dfrac{2}{3} \cdot \dfrac{4}{4} + \dfrac{3}{4} \cdot \dfrac{3}{3}$ The LCD is 12.

$\phantom{\dfrac{\sqrt{x}}{y} - \dfrac{y}{x}} = -\dfrac{8}{12} + \dfrac{9}{12}$ Write each fraction with a denominator of 12.

$\phantom{\dfrac{\sqrt{x}}{y} - \dfrac{y}{x}} = \dfrac{1}{12}$ Add.

Work Practice Problem 6

PRACTICE PROBLEM 7

Use the algebraic expression given in Example 7 to complete the following table.

Degrees Fahrenheit	x	-13	0	41
Degrees Celsius	$\dfrac{5(x-32)}{9}$			

EXAMPLE 7 **Converting Degrees Fahrenheit to Degrees Celsius**

The algebraic expression $\dfrac{5(x-32)}{9}$ represents the equivalent temperature in degrees Celsius when x is degrees Fahrenheit. Complete the following table by evaluating this expression at the given values of x.

Degrees Fahrenheit	x	-4	10	32
Degrees Celsius	$\dfrac{5(x-32)}{9}$			

Solution: To complete the table, we evaluate $\dfrac{5(x-32)}{9}$ at each given replacement value.

When $x = -4$,

$$\frac{5(x-32)}{9} = \frac{5(-4-32)}{9} = \frac{5(-36)}{9} = -20$$

When $x = 10$,

$$\frac{5(x-32)}{9} = \frac{5(10-32)}{9} = \frac{5(-22)}{9} = \frac{-110}{9} \text{ or } -12\frac{2}{9}$$

When $x = 32$,

$$\frac{5(x-32)}{9} = \frac{5(32-32)}{9} = \frac{5 \cdot 0}{9} = 0$$

Answers

6. a. 34,   **b.** -48 **c.** $-\dfrac{5\sqrt{5}+16}{20}$,

7. $-25; -\dfrac{160}{9}$ or $-17\dfrac{7}{9}; 5$

The completed table is as follows:

Degrees Fahrenheit	x	-4	10	32
Degrees Celsius	$\dfrac{5(x-32)}{9}$	-20	$\dfrac{-110}{9}$ or $-12\dfrac{2}{9}$	0

Thus, $-4°$F is equivalent to $-20°$C, $10°$F is equivalent to $-\dfrac{110°}{9}$ C or $-12\dfrac{2}{9}°$ C, and $32°$F is equivalent to $0°$C.

🔲 **Work Practice Problem 7**

Objective C Simplifying Algebraic Expressions by Combining Like Terms

Often, an algebraic expression may be **simplified** by removing grouping symbols and combining any like terms. The **terms** of an expression are the addends of the expression. For example, in the expression $3x^2 + 4x$, the terms are $3x^2$ and $4x$.

Expression	**Terms**
$-2x + y$	$-2x, \quad y$
$3x^2 - \dfrac{y}{5} + 7$	$3x^2, \quad -\dfrac{y}{5}, \quad 7$

Helpful Hint

The expression $3x^2 - \dfrac{y}{5} + 7$ can be written as $3x^2 + \left(-\dfrac{y}{5}\right) + 7$ so that the addends (terms) are

$$3x^2 \qquad -\dfrac{y}{5} \qquad 7.$$

Terms with the same variable(s) raised to the same power(s) are called **like terms**. We can add or subtract like terms by using the distributive property. This process is called **combining like terms**.

EXAMPLES Simplify by combining like terms.

8. $3x - 5x + 4 = (3 - 5)x + 4$ Use the distributive property.
$$= -2x + 4$$

9. $y + 3y = 1y + 3y = (1 + 3)y$
$$= 4y$$

10. $7x + 9x - 6 - 10 = (7 + 9)x + (-6 - 10)$
$$= 16x - 16$$

🔲 **Work Practice Problems 8–10**

PRACTICE PROBLEMS 8–10

Simplify by combining like terms.

8. $9x - 15x + 7$

9. $8y + y$

10. $4x + 12x - 9 - 10$

Answers

8. $-6x + 7$,   **9.** $9y$,   **10.** $16x - 19$

The associative and commutative properties may sometimes be needed to re-arrange and group like terms when we simplify expressions.

PRACTICE PROBLEMS 11–12

Simplify.

11. $-4x + 7 - 5x - 8$

12. $5y - 6y + 2 - 11 + y$

EXAMPLES Simplify.

11.
$$-7x + 5 + 3x - 2 = -7x + 3x + 5 - 2 \qquad \text{Use the commutative property.}$$
$$= (-7 + 3)x + (5 - 2) \qquad \text{Use the distributive property.}$$
$$= -4x + 3 \qquad \text{Simplify.}$$

12.
$$3y - 2y - 5 - 7 + y = 3y - 2y + y - 5 - 7 \qquad \text{Use the commutative property.}$$
$$= (3 - 2 + 1)y + (-5 - 7) \qquad \text{Use the distributive property.}$$
$$= 2y - 12 \qquad \text{Simplify.}$$

■ **Work Practice Problems 11–12**

PRACTICE PROBLEMS 13–16

Simplify by using the distributive property to multiply and then combining like terms.

13. $-3(y + 1) + 4$

14. $8x + 2 - 4(x - 9)$

15. $(3.2x - 4.1) - (-x + 7.6)$

16. $\dfrac{1}{5}(15m - 40n)$

$\qquad - \dfrac{1}{4}(8m - 4n + 1) + \dfrac{1}{5}$

EXAMPLES Simplify by using the distributive property to multiply and then combining like terms.

13. $-2(x + 3) + 7 = -2(x) + (-2)(3) + 7 = -2x - 6 + 7 = -2x + 1$

14.
$$7x + 3 - 5(x - 4) = 7x + 3 - 5x + 20 \qquad \text{Use the distributive property.}$$
$$= 2x + 23 \qquad \text{Combine like terms.}$$

15.
$$(2.1x - 5.6) - (-x - 5.3) = (2.1x - 5.6) - 1(-x - 5.3)$$
$$= 2.1x - 5.6 + 1x + 5.3 \qquad \text{Use the distributive property.}$$
$$= 3.1x - 0.3 \qquad \text{Combine like terms.}$$

16. $\dfrac{1}{2}(4a - 6b) - \dfrac{1}{3}(9a + 12b - 1) + \dfrac{1}{4}$

$\qquad = 2a - 3b - 3a - 4b + \dfrac{1}{3} + \dfrac{1}{4} \qquad \text{Use the distributive property.}$

$\qquad = -a - 7b + \dfrac{7}{12} \qquad \text{Combine like terms.}$

■ **Work Practice Problems 13–16**

✔ **Concept Check** Find and correct the error in the following:

$$x - 4(x - 5) = x - 4x - 20$$
$$= -3x - 20$$

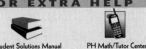

Objective Ⓐ *Simplify each expression. See Examples 1 through 5.*

1. $3(5 - 7)^4$

2. $7(3 - 8)^2$

3. $-3^2 + 2^3$

4. $-5^2 - 2^4$

5. $\dfrac{3.1 - (-1.4)}{-0.5}$

6. $\dfrac{4.2 - (-8.2)}{-0.4}$

7. $|3.6 - 7.2| + |3.6 + 7.2|$

8. $|8.6 - 1.9| - |2.1 + 5.3|$

9. $(-3)^2 + 2^3$

10. $(-15)^2 - 2^4$

11. $-8 \div 4 \cdot 2$

12. $-20 \div 5 \cdot 4$

13. $4[8 - (2 - 4)]$

14. $3[11 - (1 - 3)]$

15. $-8\left(-\dfrac{3}{4}\right) - 8$

16. $-10\left(-\dfrac{2}{5}\right) - 10$

17. $2 - [(7 - 6) + (9 - 19)]$

18. $8 - [(4 - 7) + (8 - 1)]$

19. $\dfrac{(-9 + 6)(-1^2)}{-2 - 2}$

20. $\dfrac{(-1 - 2)(-3^2)}{-6 - 3}$

21. $(\sqrt[3]{8})(-4) - (\sqrt{9})(-5)$

22. $(\sqrt[3]{27})(-5) - (\sqrt{25})(-3)$

23. $12 + \{6 - [5 - 2(-5)]\}$

24. $18 + \{9 - [1 - 6(-3)]\}$

25. $25 - [(3 - 5) + (14 - 18)]^2$

26. $10 - [(4 - 5)^2 + (12 - 14)]^4$

27. $\dfrac{(3 - \sqrt{9}) - (-5 - 1.3)}{-3}$

28. $\dfrac{-\sqrt{16} - (6 - 2.4)}{-2}$

29. $\dfrac{|3 - 9| - |-5|}{-3}$

30. $\dfrac{|-14| - |2 - 7|}{-15}$

31. $\dfrac{3(-2 + 1)}{5} - \dfrac{-7(2 - 4)}{1 - (-2)}$

32. $\dfrac{-1 - 2}{2(-3) + 10} - \dfrac{2(-5)}{-1(8) + 1}$

33. $\dfrac{\dfrac{1}{3} \cdot 9 - 7}{3 + \dfrac{1}{2} \cdot 4}$

34. $\dfrac{\dfrac{1}{5} \cdot 20 - 6}{10 + \dfrac{1}{4} \cdot 12}$

35. $3\{-2 + 5[1 - 2(-2 + 5)]\}$

36. $2\{-1 + 3[7 - 4(-10 + 12)]\}$

37. $\dfrac{-4\sqrt{80 + 1} + (-4)^2}{3^3 + |-2(3)|}$

38. $\dfrac{(-2)^4 + 3\sqrt{120 - 20}}{4^3 + |5(-1)|}$

39. $-150(3.25 - 1.68)$

40. $-290(9.61 - 6.27)$

41. $\left(\dfrac{5.6 - 8.4}{1.9 - 2.7}\right)^2$

42. $\left(\dfrac{9.4 - 10.8}{8.7 - 7.9}\right)^2$

Objective **B** *Evaluate each expression when x = 9 and y = −2. See Example 6.*

43. $9x - 6y$

44. $4x - 10y$

45. $-3y^2$

46. $-7y^2$

47. $\dfrac{\sqrt{x}}{y} - \dfrac{y}{x}$

48. $\dfrac{y}{2x} - \dfrac{\sqrt{x}}{3y}$

49. $\dfrac{3 + 2|x - y|}{x + 2y}$

50. $\dfrac{5 + 2|y - x|}{x + 6y}$

(*Hint:* Remember order of operations.)

51. $\dfrac{y^3 + \sqrt{x - 5}}{|4x - y|}$

52. $\dfrac{y^2 + \sqrt{x + 7}}{|3x - y|}$

Complete each table. See Example 7.

△ **53.** The algebraic expression $8 + 2y$ represents the perimeter of a rectangle with width 4 and length y.

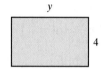

a. Complete the table by evaluating this expression at the given values of y.

Length	y	5	7	10	100
Perimeter	$8 + 2y$				

 b. Use the results of the table in (a) to answer the following question. As the width of a rectangle remains the same and the length increases, does the perimeter increase or decrease? Explain how you arrived at your answer.

△ **54.** The algebraic expression πr^2 represents the area of a circle with radius r.

a. Complete the table by evaluating this expression at the given values of r. (Use 3.14 for π.)

Radius	r	2	3	7	10
Area	πr^2				

b. As the radius of a circle increases, does its area increase or decrease? Explain your answer.

55. The algebraic expression $\dfrac{100x + 5000}{x}$ represents the cost per bookshelf (in dollars) of producing x bookshelves.

a. Complete the table.

Number of Bookshelves	x	10	100	1000
Cost per Bookshelf	$\dfrac{100x + 5000}{x}$			

b. As the number of bookshelves manufactured increases, does the cost per bookshelf increase or decrease? Why do you think that this is so?

56. If C is degrees Celsius, the algebraic expression $1.8C + 32$ represents the equivalent temperature in degrees Fahrenheit.

a. Complete the table.

Degrees Celsius	C	−10	0	50
Degrees Fahrenheit	$1.8C + 32$			

b. As degrees Celsius increase, do degrees Fahrenheit increase or decrease? Explain your answer.

57. The average price for an ounce of gold in the United States during November 2004 was $439.39. The algebraic expression $439.39z$ gives the average cost of z ounces of gold during this period. Find the average cost if 8.4 ounces of gold had been purchased during this time. (*Source:* www.kitco.com)

58. On December 28, 2004, the velocity of the solar wind in Earth's upper atmosphere was 431.2 kilometers per second. At this speed, the algebraic expression $431.2t$ gives the total distance covered in t seconds. Find the distance covered by a proton traveling in the solar wind in 5 seconds. (*Source:* NOAA Space Environment Center)

Objective **C** *Simplify. See Examples 8 through 12.*

59. $6x + 2x$ **60.** $9y - 11y$ **61.** $19y - y$ **62.** $14x - x$

63. $9x - 8 - 10x$ **64.** $14x - 1 - 20x$ **65.** $-9 + 4x + 18 - 10x$ **66.** $5y - 14 + 7y - 20y$

67. $3a - 4b + a - 9b$ **68.** $11x - y + 11x - 6y$ **69.** $x - y + x - y$ **70.** $a - b + 3a - 3b$

71. $1.5x + 2.3 - 0.7x - 5.9$ **72.** $6.3y - 9.7 + 2.2y - 11.1$ **73.** $\frac{3}{4}b - \frac{1}{2} + \frac{1}{6}b - \frac{2}{3}$

74. $\frac{7}{8}a - \frac{11}{12} - \frac{1}{2}a + \frac{5}{6}$ **75.** $8ab - 4.6 - 11ab - 8.2$ **76.** $4mn - 6.01 - 6mn - 8.1$

Simplify. See Examples 13 through 16.

77. $2(3x + 7)$ **78.** $4(5y + 12)$ **79.** $5k - (3k - 10)$ **80.** $-11c - (4 - 2c)$

81. $(3x + 4) - (6x - 1)$ **82.** $(8 - 5y) - (4 - 3y)$ **83.** $3(x - 2) + x + 15$ **84.** $4(y + 3) - 7y + 1$

85. $-(n + 5) + (5n - 3)$ **86.** $-(8 - t) + (2t - 6)$ **87.** $4(6n - 3) - 3(8n + 4)$ **88.** $5(2z - 6) + 10(3 - z)$

89. $\frac{1}{4}(8x - 4) - \frac{1}{5}(20x - 6y)$ **90.** $\frac{1}{2}(10x - 2) - \frac{1}{6}(60x - 5y)$

91. $3x - 2(x - 5) + x$ **92.** $7n + 3(2n - 6) - n$

93. $\frac{1}{6}(24a - 18b) - \frac{1}{7}(7a - 21b - 2) - \frac{1}{5}$ **94.** $\frac{1}{3}(6x - 33y) - \frac{1}{8}(24x - 40y + 1) - \frac{1}{3}$

95. $5.7a + 1.7 - 3(2.1a - 0.6)$ **96.** $6.2b + 5.1 - 2(4.2b - 0.1)$

97. $-4[6(2t + 1) - (9 + 10t)]$ **98.** $-5[3(4x + 2) - (13 + 8x)]$ ▦ **99.** $-1.2(5.7x - 3.6) + 8.75x$

▦ **100.** $5.8(-9.6 - 31.2y) - 18.65$ ▦ **101.** $8.1z + 7.3(z + 5.2) - 6.85$ ▦ **102.** $6.5y - 4.4(1.8y - 3.3) + 10.95$

Concept Extensions

Insert parentheses so that when simplified each expression is equal to the given number.

103. $2 + 7 \cdot 1 + 3;$ 36 **104.** $6 - 5 \cdot 2 + 2;$ -6

105. Write an algebraic expression that simplifies to $-3x - 1$.

106. Write an algebraic expression that simplifies to $-7x - 4$.

Find and correct the error in each expression.

107. $(3x + 2) - (5x + 7) = 3x + 2 - 5x + 7$
$$= -2x + 9$$

108. $2 + 3(7 - 6x) = 5(7 - 6x)$
$$= 35 - 30x$$

The following graph is called a broken-line graph, or simply a line graph. This particular graph shows the past, present, and future predicted U.S. population over 65. Just as with a bar graph, to find the population over 65 for a particular year, read the height of the corresponding point. To read the height, follow the point horizontally to the left until you reach the vertical axis. Use this graph to answer Exercises 109 through 114.

U.S. Population Over 65

Source: U.S. Census Bureau * Projected

109. Estimate the population over 65 in the year 1970.

110. Estimate the predicted population over 65 in the year 2050.

111. Estimate the predicted population over 65 in the year 2030.

112. Estimate the population over 65 in the year 2000.

113. Is the population over 65 increasing as time passes or decreasing? Explain how you arrived at your answer.

114. The percent of Americans over 65 in 1950 was 8.1%. The percent of Americans over 65 in 2050 is expected to be 2.5 times the percent over 65 in 1950. Estimate the percent of Americans expected to be over age 65 in 2050.

Simplify. Round each result to the nearest ten-thousandth.

115. $\dfrac{-1.682 - 17.895}{(-7.102)(-4.691)}$

116. $\dfrac{(-5.161)(3.222)}{7.955 - 19.676}$

1.6 EXPONENTS AND SCIENTIFIC NOTATION

Objectives

A Use the Product Rule for Exponents.

B Simplify Expressions Raised to the Zero Power.

C Use the Quotient Rule for Exponents.

D Simplify Expressions Raised to Negative Powers.

E Simplify Exponential Expressions Containing Variables in the Exponent.

F Convert between Scientific Notation and Standard Notation.

Objective **A** Using the Product Rule

Recall from Section 1.4 that exponents may be used to write repeated factors in a more compact form. As we have seen in the previous sections, exponents can be used when the repeated factor is a number or a variable. For example,

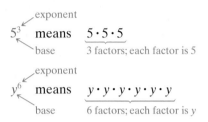

5^3 means $5 \cdot 5 \cdot 5$ — 3 factors; each factor is 5

y^6 means $y \cdot y \cdot y \cdot y \cdot y \cdot y$ — 6 factors; each factor is y

Expressions that contain exponents such as 5^3 and y^6 are called **exponential expressions.**

Exponential expressions can be multiplied, divided, added, subtracted, and themselves raised to powers. In this section, we review operations on exponential expressions.

We review multiplication first. To multiply x^2 by x^3, we use the definition of a^n:

$$x^2 \cdot x^3 = \underbrace{(x \cdot x)(x \cdot x \cdot x)}_{x \text{ is a factor 5 times.}}$$

$$= x^5$$

Notice that the result is exactly the same if we add the exponents.

$$x^2 \cdot x^3 = x^{2+3} = x^5$$

This suggests the following rule.

Product Rule for Exponents

If m and n are integers and a is a real number, then

$$a^m \cdot a^n = a^{m+n}$$

In other words, the *product* of exponential expressions with a common base is the common base raised to a power equal to the *sum* of the exponents of the factors.

EXAMPLES Use the product rule to simplify.

1. $2^2 \cdot 2^5 = 2^{2+5} = 2^7$
2. $x^7 \cdot x^3 = x^{7+3} = x^{10}$
3. $y \cdot y^2 \cdot y^4 = (y^1 \cdot y^2) \cdot y^4$
$\qquad = y^3 \cdot y^4$
$\qquad = y^7$

Work Practice Problems 1–3

EXAMPLES Use the product rule to simplify.

4. $(3x^6)(5x) = 3(5)x^6 x^1 = 15x^7$ Use properties of multiplication to group like bases.
5. $(-2.4x^3p^2)(4xp^{10}) = -2.4(4)x^3 x^1 p^2 p^{10} = -9.6x^4 p^{12}$

Work Practice Problems 4–5

PRACTICE PROBLEMS 1–3

Use the product rule to simplify.
1. $5^2 \cdot 5^6$ **2.** $x^5 \cdot x^9$ **3.** $y \cdot y^4 \cdot y^3$

PRACTICE PROBLEMS 4–5

Use the product rule to simplify.
4. $(7y^5)(6y)$
5. $(-3x^2y^7)(5xy^6)$

Answers
1. 5^8,   **2.** x^{14},   **3.** y^8,   **4.** $42y^6$,
5. $-15x^3y^{13}$

43

Objective B Simplifying Expressions Raised to the Zero Power

The definition of a^n does not include the possibility that n might be 0. But if it did, then, by the product rule,

$$a^0 \cdot a^n = a^{0+n} = a^n = 1 \cdot a^n$$

From this, we reasonably define that $a^0 = 1$, as long as a does not equal 0.

Zero Exponent

If a does not equal 0, then $a^0 = 1$.

EXAMPLES Evaluate each expression.

6. $7^0 = 1$
7. $-7^0 = -7^0 = -1$ Without parentheses, only 7 is raised to the 0 power.
8. $(2x + 5)^0 = 1$
9. $2x^0 = 2(1) = 2$

Work Practice Problems 6–9

PRACTICE PROBLEMS 6–9

Evaluate each expression.

6. 8^0
7. -14^0
8. $(y - 3)^0$
9. $5x^0$

Objective C Using the Quotient Rule

To find quotients of exponential expressions, we again begin with the definition of a^n to simplify $\dfrac{x^9}{x^2}$:

$$\frac{x^9}{x^2} = \frac{x \cdot x \cdot x \cdot x \cdot x \cdot x \cdot x \cdot x \cdot x}{x \cdot x} = \frac{x}{x} \cdot \frac{x}{x} \cdot \frac{x^7}{1} = 1 \cdot 1 \cdot x^7 = x^7$$

(Assume for the next two sections that denominators containing variables are not 0.) Notice that the result is exactly the same if we subtract the exponents.

$$\frac{x^9}{x^2} = x^{9-2} = x^7$$

This suggests the following rule.

Quotient Rule for Exponents

If a is a nonzero real number and m and n are integers, then

$$\frac{a^m}{a^n} = a^{m-n}$$

In other words, the *quotient* of exponential expressions with a common base is the common base raised to a power equal to the *difference* of the exponents.

EXAMPLES Use the quotient rule to simplify.

10. $\dfrac{5^8}{5^2} = 5^{8-2} = 5^6$

11. $\dfrac{x^7}{x^4} = x^{7-4} = x^3$

12. $\dfrac{20x^6}{4x^5} = 5x^{6-5} = 5x^1$, or $5x$

13. $\dfrac{12y^{10}z^7}{14y^8z^7} = \dfrac{6}{7}y^{10-8} \cdot z^{7-7} = \dfrac{6}{7}y^2 \cdot z^0 = \dfrac{6}{7}y^2 \cdot 1 = \dfrac{6}{7}y^2$ or $\dfrac{6y^2}{7}$

Work Practice Problems 10–13

PRACTICE PROBLEMS 10–13

Use the quotient rule to simplify.

10. $\dfrac{6^{10}}{6^2}$ 11. $\dfrac{y^6}{y^2}$

12. $\dfrac{36x^5}{9x}$ 13. $\dfrac{10a^7b^9}{15a^5b^9}$

Answers

6. 1,   7. -1,   8. 1,   9. 5,   10. 6^8,
11. y^4,   12. $4x^4$,   13. $\dfrac{2}{3}a^2$

Objective D Simplifying Expressions Raised to Negative Powers

When the exponent of the denominator is larger than the exponent of the numerator, applying the quotient rule gives a negative exponent. For example,

$$\frac{x^3}{x^5} = x^{3-5} = x^{-2}$$

However, using the definition of a^n gives us

$$\frac{x^3}{x^5} = \frac{x \cdot x \cdot x}{x \cdot x \cdot x \cdot x \cdot x} = 1 \cdot 1 \cdot 1 \cdot \frac{1}{x^2} = \frac{1}{x^2}$$

From this, we reasonably define $x^{-2} = \frac{1}{x^2}$ or, in general, $a^{-n} = \frac{1}{a^n}$.

Negative Exponents

If a is a real number other than 0 and n is a positive integer, then

$$a^{-n} = \frac{1}{a^n}$$

EXAMPLES Simplify and write with positive exponents only.

14. $5^{-2} = \frac{1}{5^2} = \frac{1}{25}$

15. $2x^{-3} = 2 \cdot \frac{1}{x^3} = \frac{2}{x^3}$ Without parentheses, only x is raised to the -3 power.

16. $(3x)^{-1} = \frac{1}{(3x)^1} = \frac{1}{3x}$ With parentheses, both 3 and x are raised to the -1 power.

17. $2^{-1} + 3^{-2} = \frac{1}{2^1} + \frac{1}{3^2} = \frac{1}{2} + \frac{1}{9} = \frac{9}{18} + \frac{2}{18} = \frac{11}{18}$

18. $\frac{1}{t^{-5}} = \frac{1}{\frac{1}{t^5}} = 1 \div \frac{1}{t^5} = 1 \cdot \frac{t^5}{1} = t^5$

🖥 **Work Practice Problems 14–18**

Helpful Hint

Notice that when a factor containing an exponent is moved from the numerator to the denominator or from the denominator to the numerator, the sign of its exponent changes.

$$x^{-3} = \frac{1}{x^3} \qquad 5^{-2} = \frac{1}{5^2} = \frac{1}{25}$$

$$\frac{1}{t^{-5}} = t^5 \qquad \frac{1}{2^{-3}} = 2^3 = 8$$

EXAMPLES Simplify and write using positive exponents only.

19. $\frac{m^5}{m^{15}} = m^{5-15} = m^{-10} = \frac{1}{m^{10}}$

20. $\frac{3^3}{3^6} = 3^{3-6} = 3^{-3} = \frac{1}{3^3} = \frac{1}{27}$

21. $x^{-9} \cdot x^2 = x^{-9+2} = x^{-7} = \frac{1}{x^7}$

Continued on next page

PRACTICE PROBLEMS 14–18

Simplify and write with positive exponents only.

14. 7^{-2}

15. $5x^{-4}$

16. $(2x)^{-1}$

17. $3^{-1} + 2^{-2}$

18. $\frac{1}{y^{-4}}$

PRACTICE PROBLEMS 19–25

Simplify and write using positive exponents only.

19. $\frac{x^3}{x^{10}}$ **20.** $\frac{4^2}{4^5}$ **21.** $y^{-10} \cdot y^3$

22. $\frac{q^5}{q^{-4}}$ **23.** $\frac{5^{-4}}{5^{-2}}$ **24.** $\frac{10x^{-8}y^5}{20xy^{-5}}$

25. $\frac{(4x^{-1})(x^5)}{x^7}$

Answers

14. $\frac{1}{49}$, **15.** $\frac{5}{x^4}$, **16.** $\frac{1}{2x}$, **17.** $\frac{7}{12}$,

18. y^4, **19.** $\frac{1}{x^7}$, **20.** $\frac{1}{64}$, **21.** $\frac{1}{y^7}$,

22. q^9, **23.** $\frac{1}{25}$, **24.** $\frac{y^{10}}{2x^9}$, **25.** $\frac{4}{x^3}$

22. $\dfrac{5p^4}{p^{-3}} = 5 \cdot p^{4-(-3)} = 5p^7$

23. $\dfrac{2^{-3}}{2^{-1}} = 2^{-3-(-1)} = 2^{-2} = \dfrac{1}{2^2} = \dfrac{1}{4}$

24. $\dfrac{2x^{-7}y^2}{10xy^{-5}} = \dfrac{x^{-7-1} \cdot y^{2-(-5)}}{5} = \dfrac{x^{-8}y^7}{5} = \dfrac{y^7}{5x^8}$

25. $\dfrac{(3x^{-3})(x^2)}{x^6} = \dfrac{3x^{-3+2}}{x^6} = \dfrac{3x^{-1}}{x^6} = 3x^{-1-6} = 3x^{-7} = \dfrac{3}{x^7}$

◻ **Work Practice Problems 19–25**

✔ **Concept Check**   Find and correct the error in the following:

$$\frac{y^{-6}}{y^{-2}} = y^{-6-2} = y^{-8} = \frac{1}{y^8}$$

Objective ⓔ Simplifying with Variables in the Exponent

PRACTICE PROBLEMS 26–27

Simplify. Assume that n and m are nonzero integers and that x is not 0.

26. $x^{3m} \cdot x^n$

27. $\dfrac{x^{2m-2}}{x^{m-6}}$

EXAMPLES   Simplify. Assume that a and t are nonzero integers and that x is not 0.

26. $x^{2a} \cdot x^3 = x^{2a+3}$ Use the product rule.

27. $\dfrac{x^{2t-1}}{x^{t-5}} = x^{(2t-1)-(t-5)}$ Use the quotient rule.

         $= x^{2t-1-t+5} = x^{t+4}$

◻ **Work Practice Problems 26–27**

Objective ⓕ Converting between Scientific Notation and Standard Notation

Very large and very small numbers occur frequently in nature. For example, the distance between Earth and the sun is approximately 150,000,000 kilometers. A helium atom has a diameter of 0.000000022 centimeters. It can be tedious to write these very large and very small numbers in standard notation like this. **Scientific notation** is a convenient shorthand notation for writing very large and very small numbers.

Helium atom
0.000000022 cm

150,000,000 km

Scientific Notation

A positive number is written in **scientific notation** if it is written as the product of a number a, where $1 \le a < 10$, and an integer power n of 10: $a \times 10^n$.

Answers

26. x^{3m+n},   **27.** x^{m+4}

✔ Concept Check Answer

$\dfrac{y^{-6}}{y^{-2}} = y^{-6-(-2)} = y^{-4} = \dfrac{1}{y^4}$

For example,

     2.03×10^2 7.362×10^7 8.1×10^{-5}

Writing a Number in Scientific Notation

Step 1: Move the decimal point in the original number until the new number has a value between 1 and 10.

Step 2: Count the number of decimal places the decimal point was moved in Step 1. If the original number is 10 or greater, the count is positive. If the original number is less than 1, the count is negative.

Step 3: Write the product of the new number in Step 1 by 10 raised to an exponent equal to the count found in Step 2.

EXAMPLE 28 Write 730,000 in scientific notation.

Solution:

Step 1. Move the decimal point until the number is between 1 and 10.

730,000.

Step 2. The decimal point is moved 5 places and the original number is 10 or greater, so the count is positive 5.

Step 3. $730,000 = 7.3 \times 10^5$

◻ **Work Practice Problem 28**

EXAMPLE 29 Write 0.00000104 in scientific notation.

Solution:

Step 1. Move the decimal point until the number is between 1 and 10.

0.00000104

Step 2. The decimal point is moved 6 places and the original number is less than 1, so the count is -6.

Step 3. $0.00000104 = 1.04 \times 10^{-6}$

◻ **Work Practice Problem 29**

To write a scientific notation number in standard form, we reverse the preceding steps.

Writing a Scientific Notation Number in Standard Notation

Move the decimal point in the number the same number of places as the exponent on 10. If the exponent is positive, move the decimal point to the right. If the exponent is negative, move the decimal point to the left.

EXAMPLES Write each number in standard notation.

30. $7.7 \times 10^8 = 777,000,000$ Since the exponent is positive, move the decimal point 8 places to the right. Add zeros as needed.

31. $1.025 \times 10^{-3} = 0.001025$ Since the exponent is negative, move the decimal point 3 places to the left. Add zeros as needed.

◻ **Work Practice Problems 30–31**

✔ **Concept Check** Which of the following numbers have values that are less than 1?

a. 3.5×10^{-5} **b.** 3.5×10^5 **c.** -3.5×10^5 **d.** -3.5×10^{-5}

PRACTICE PROBLEM 28

Write 1,760,000 in scientific notation.

PRACTICE PROBLEM 29

Write 0.00028 in scientific notation.

PRACTICE PROBLEMS 30–31

Write each number in standard notation.

30. 8.6×10^7

31. 3.022×10^{-4}

Answers

28. 1.76×10^6,   **29.** 2.8×10^{-4},
30. 86,000,000,   **31.** 0.0003022

✔ **Concept Check Answer**

a, c, d

CALCULATOR EXPLORATIONS

Multiply 5,000,000 by 700,000 on your calculator. The display should read $\boxed{3.5 \quad 12}$ or $\boxed{3.5\,E\,12}$, which is the product written in scientific notation. Both these notations mean 3.5×10^{12}.

To enter a number written in scientific notation on a calculator, find the key marked $\boxed{EE}$. (On some calculators, this key may be marked $\boxed{EXP}$.)

To enter 7.26×10^{13}, press the keys

$\boxed{7.26}$ $\boxed{EE}$ $\boxed{13}$

The display will read $\boxed{7.26 \quad 13}$ or $\boxed{7.26E13}$.

Use your calculator to perform each indicated operation.

1. Multiply 3×10^{11} and 2×10^{32}.
2. Divide 6×10^{14} by 3×10^{9}.
3. Multiply 5.2×10^{23} and 7.3×10^{4}.
4. Divide 4.38×10^{41} by 3×10^{17}.

Mental Math

Write each expression without negative exponents.

1. $5x^{-1}y^{-2}$
2. $7xy^{-4}$
3. $a^2b^{-1}c^{-5}$
4. $a^{-4}b^2c^{-6}$
5. $\dfrac{y^{-2}}{x^{-4}}$
6. $\dfrac{x^{-7}}{z^{-3}}$

1.6 EXERCISE SET

FOR EXTRA HELP

Student Solutions Manual · PH Math/Tutor Center · CD/Video for Review · MathXL® · MyMathLab

Objective A *Use the product rule to simplify each expression. See Examples 1 through 5.*

1. $4^2 \cdot 4^3$
2. $3^3 \cdot 3^5$
3. $x^5 \cdot x^3$
4. $a^2 \cdot a^9$
5. $m \cdot m^7 \cdot m^6$
6. $n \cdot n^{10} \cdot n^{12}$
7. $(4xy)(-5x)$
8. $(-7xy)(7y)$
9. $(-4x^3p^2)(4y^3x^3)$
10. $(-6a^2b^3)(-3ab^3)$

Objective B *Evaluate each expression. See Examples 6 through 9.*

11. -8^0
12. $(-9)^0$
13. $(4x+5)^0$
14. $(3x-1)^0$
15. $-x^0$
16. $-5x^0$
17. $4x^0+5$
18. $8x^0+1$

Objective C *Use the quotient rule to simplify. See Examples 10 through 13.*

19. $\dfrac{a^5}{a^2}$
20. $\dfrac{x^9}{x^4}$
21. $-\dfrac{26z^{11}}{2z^7}$
22. $-\dfrac{16x^5}{8x}$
23. $\dfrac{x^9y^6}{x^8y^6}$
24. $\dfrac{a^{12}b^2}{a^9b}$
25. $\dfrac{12x^4y^7}{9xy^5}$
26. $\dfrac{24a^{10}b^{11}}{10ab^3}$
27. $\dfrac{-36a^5b^7c^{10}}{6ab^3c^4}$
28. $\dfrac{49a^3bc^{14}}{-7abc^8}$

48

Copyright 2007 Pearson Education, Inc.

Objective ⓓ *Simplify and write using positive exponents only. See Examples 14 through 25.*

29. 4^{-2}

30. 2^{-3}

31. $(-3)^{-3}$

32. $(-6)^{-2}$

33. $\dfrac{x^7}{x^{15}}$

34. $\dfrac{z}{z^3}$

35. $5a^{-4}$

36. $10b^{-1}$

37. $\dfrac{x^{-7}}{y^{-2}}$

38. $\dfrac{p^{-13}}{q^{-3}}$

39. $\dfrac{x^{-2}}{x^5}$

40. $\dfrac{z^{-12}}{z^{10}}$

41. $\dfrac{8r^4}{2r^{-4}}$

42. $\dfrac{3s^3}{15s^{-3}}$

43. $\dfrac{x^{-9}x^4}{x^{-5}}$

44. $\dfrac{y^{-7}y}{y^8}$

45. $\dfrac{2a^{-6}b^2}{18ab^{-5}}$

46. $\dfrac{18ab^{-6}}{3a^{-3}b^6}$

47. $\dfrac{(24x^8)(x)}{20x^{-7}}$

48. $\dfrac{(30z^2)(z^5)}{55z^{-4}}$

Objectives ⓐ ⓑ ⓒ ⓓ **Mixed Practice** *Simplify and write using positive exponents only. See Examples 1 through 25.*

49. $-7x^3 \cdot 20x^9$

50. $-3y \cdot -9y^4$

51. $x^7 \cdot x^8 \cdot x$

52. $y^6 \cdot y \cdot y^9$

53. $2x^3 \cdot 5x^7$

54. $-3z^4 \cdot 10z^7$

55. $(5x)^0 + 5x^0$

56. $4y^0 - (4y)^0$

57. $\dfrac{z^{12}}{z^{15}}$

58. $\dfrac{x^{11}}{x^{20}}$

59. $3^0 - 3t^0$

60. $4^0 + 4x^0$

61. $\dfrac{y^{-3}}{y^{-7}}$

62. $\dfrac{y^{-6}}{y^{-9}}$

63. $4^{-1} + 3^{-2}$

64. $1^{-3} - 4^{-2}$

65. $3x^{-1}$

66. $(4x)^{-1}$

67. $\dfrac{r^4}{r^{-4}}$

68. $\dfrac{x^{-5}}{x^3}$

69. $\dfrac{x^{-7}y^{-2}}{x^2y^2}$

70. $\dfrac{a^{-5}b^7}{a^{-2}b^{-3}}$

71. $(-4x^2y)(3x^4)(-2xy^5)$

72. $(-6a^4b)(2b^3)(-3ab^6)$

73. $2^{-4} \cdot x$

74. $5^{-2} \cdot y$

75. $\dfrac{5^{17}}{5^{13}}$

76. $\dfrac{10^{25}}{10^{23}}$

77. $\dfrac{8^{-7}}{8^{-6}}$

78. $\dfrac{13^{-10}}{13^{-9}}$

79. $\dfrac{9^{-5}a^4}{9^{-3}a^{-1}}$

80. $\dfrac{11^{-9}b^3}{11^{-7}b^{-4}}$

81. $\dfrac{14x^{-2}yz^{-4}}{2xyz}$

82. $\dfrac{30x^{-7}yz^{-14}}{3xyz}$

Objective ⓔ *Simplify. Assume that variables in the exponents represent nonzero integers and that x, y, and z are not 0. See Examples 26 and 27.*

83. $x^5 \cdot x^{7a}$

84. $y^{2p} \cdot y^{9p}$

85. $\dfrac{x^{3t-1}}{x^t}$

86. $\dfrac{y^{4p-2}}{y^{3p}}$

87. $x^{4a} \cdot x^7$

88. $x^{9y} \cdot x^{-7y}$

89. $\dfrac{z^{6x}}{z^7}$

90. $\dfrac{y^6}{y^{4z}}$

91. $\dfrac{x^{3t} \cdot x^{4t-1}}{x^t}$

92. $\dfrac{z^{5x} \cdot z^{x-7}}{z^x}$

Objective **F** *Write each number in scientific notation. See Examples 28 and 29.*

93. 31,250,000   **94.** 678,000   **95.** 0.016   **96.** 0.007613   **97.** 67,413

98. 36,800,000   **99.** 0.0125   **100.** 0.00084   **101.** 0.000053   **102.** 98,700,000,000

Write each number in scientific notation.

103. The approximate distance between Jupiter and the sun is 778,300,000 kilometers, (*Source:* National Space Data Center)

104. For the 2004 Major League Baseball season, the World Series Champion Red Sox payroll was approximately $130,395,000. (*Source: The Boston Globe*)

105. The estimated world population in December 2004 was 6,404,000,000 (*Source:* U.S. Census Bureau)

106. Total revenues for Microsoft in fiscal year 2004 were $36,835,000,000. (*Source:* Microsoft Corporation)

107. Lake Mead, created from the Colorado River by the Hoover Dam, has a capacity of 124,000,000,000 cubic feet of water. (*Source:* U.S. Bureau of Reclamation)

108. The temperature of the core of the sun is about 27,000,000°F.

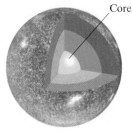

Core

109. A pulsar is a rotating neutron star that gives off sharp, regular pulses of radio waves. For one particular pulsar, the rate of pulses is every 0.001 second.

△ **110.** To convert from cubic inches to cubic meters, multiply by 0.0000164.

Write each number in standard notation. See Examples 30 and 31.

111. 3.6×10^{-9} **112.** 2.7×10^{-5} **113.** 9.3×10^{7} **114.** 6.378×10^{8} **115.** 1.278×10^{6}

116. 7.6×10^{4} **117.** 7.35×10^{12} **118.** 1.66×10^{-5} **119.** 4.03×10^{-7} **120.** 8.007×10^{8}

Write each number in standard notation.

121. The estimated world population in 1 A.D. was 3.0×10^{8}. (*Source: World Almanac and Book of Facts,* 2005)

122. There are 3.949×10^{6} miles of highways, roads, and streets in the United States.(*Source:* Bureau of Transportation Statistics)

123. In 2005, teenagers and children are expected to spend 4.9×10^9 dollars on purchases and transactions made online. *(Source:* Jupiter Research)

124. Each day, an estimated 1.2×10^9 beverages consumed throughout the world are Coca Cola products. *(Source:* Coca Cola)

Concept Extensions

 125. Explain how to convert a number from standard notation to scientific notation.

126. Explain how to convert a number from scientific notation to standard notation.

127. Explain why $(-5)^0$ simplifies to 1 but -5^0 simplifies to -1.

128. Explain why both $4x^0 - 3y^0$ and $(4x - 3y)^0$ simplify to 1.

STUDY SKILLS BUILDER

What to Do the Day of an Exam?

Your first exam may be soon. On the day of an exam, don't forget to try the following:

- Allow yourself plenty of time to arrive.
- Read the directions on the test carefully.
- Read each problem carefully as you take your test. Make sure that you answer the question asked.
- Watch your time and pace yourself so that you may attempt each problem on your test.
- Check your work and answers.
- ***Do not turn your test in early.*** If you have extra time, spend it double-checking your work.

Good luck!

Answer the following questions based on your most recent mathematics exam, whenever that was.

1. How soon before class did you arrive?
2. Did you read the directions on the test carefully?
3. Did you make sure you answered the question asked for each problem on the exam?
4. Were you able to attempt each problem on your exam?
5. If your answer to question 4 is no, list reasons why.
6. Did you have extra time on your exam?
7. If your answer to question 6 is yes, describe how you spent that extra time.

A Use the Power Rules for Exponents.

B Use Exponent Rules and Definitions to Simplify Exponential Expressions.

C Simplify Exponential Expressions Containing Variables in the Exponent.

D Use Scientific Notation to Compute.

1.7 MORE WORK WITH EXPONENTS AND SCIENTIFIC NOTATION

Objective **A** Using the Power Rules

The volume of the cube shown whose side measures x^2 units is $(x^2)^3$ cubic units. To simplify an expression such as $(x^2)^3$, we use the definition of a^n:

$$(x^2)^3 = \underbrace{(x^2)(x^2)(x^2)}_{x^2 \text{ is a factor 3 times.}} = x^{2+2+2} = x^6$$

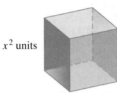

x^2 units

Notice that the result is exactly the same if the exponents are multiplied.

$$(x^2)^3 = x^{2\cdot3} = x^6$$

This suggests that an expression raised to a power that is then all raised to another power is equal to the original expression raised to the product of the powers. Two additional rules for exponents are given in the following box.

Power Rule and Power of a Product or Quotient Rules for Exponents

If a and b are real numbers and m and n are integers, then

$(a^m)^n = a^{m\cdot n}$ Power rule

$(ab)^m = a^m b^m$ Power of a product

$\left(\dfrac{a}{b}\right)^n = \dfrac{a^n}{b^n}$ $(b \neq 0)$ Power of a quotient

---

PRACTICE PROBLEMS 1–4

Use the power rule to simplify each expression. Write each answer using positive exponents only.

1. $(y^2)^8$ 2. $(3^3)^2$
3. $(6^2)^{-1}$ 4. $(x^{-5})^{-7}$

EXAMPLES Use the power rule to simplify each expression. Write each answer using positive exponents only.

1. $(x^5)^7 = x^{5\cdot7} = x^{35}$
2. $(2^2)^3 = 2^{2\cdot3} = 2^6 = 64$
3. $(5^{-1})^2 = 5^{-1\cdot2} = 5^{-2} = \dfrac{1}{5^2} = \dfrac{1}{25}$
4. $(y^{-3})^{-4} = y^{-3(-4)} = y^{12}$

⬛ **Work Practice Problems 1–4**

PRACTICE PROBLEMS 5–9

Use the power rules to simplify each expression. Write each answer using positive exponents only.

5. $(3x^4)^3$ 6. $\left(\dfrac{4}{5}\right)^2$

7. $\left(\dfrac{4m^5}{n^3}\right)^3$ 8. $\left(\dfrac{2^{-1}}{y}\right)^{-3}$

9. $(a^{-4}b^3c^{-2})^6$

EXAMPLES Use the power rules to simplify each expression. Write each answer using positive exponents only.

5. $(5x^2)^3 = 5^3 \cdot (x^2)^3 = 5^3 \cdot x^{2\cdot3} = 125x^6$

6. $\left(\dfrac{2}{3}\right)^3 = \dfrac{2^3}{3^3} = \dfrac{8}{27}$

7. $\left(\dfrac{3p^4}{q^5}\right)^2 = \dfrac{(3p^4)^2}{(q^5)^2} = \dfrac{3^2 \cdot (p^4)^2}{(q^5)^2} = \dfrac{9p^8}{q^{10}}$

Answers

1. y^{16},   2. 729,   3. $\dfrac{1}{36}$,   4. x^{35},

5. $27x^{12}$,   6. $\dfrac{16}{25}$,   7. $\dfrac{64m^{15}}{n^9}$,   8. $8y^3$,

9. $\dfrac{b^{18}}{a^{24}c^{12}}$

8. $\left(\dfrac{2^{-3}}{y}\right)^{-2} = \dfrac{(2^{-3})^{-2}}{y^{-2}}$

$\qquad = \dfrac{2^6}{y^{-2}} = 64y^2$ Use the negative exponent rule.

9. $(x^{-5}y^2z^{-1})^7 = (x^{-5})^7 \cdot (y^2)^7 \cdot (z^{-1})^7$

$\qquad = x^{-35}y^{14}z^{-7} = \dfrac{y^{14}}{x^{35}z^7}$

🔲 **Work Practice Problems 5–9**

Objective B Using Exponent Rules to Simplify Expressions

In the next few examples, we practice the use of several of the rules and definitions for exponents. The following is a summary of these rules and definitions.

Summary of Rules for Exponents

If a and b are real numbers and m and n are integers, then

Product rule	$a^m \cdot a^n = a^{m+n}$	
Zero exponent	$a^0 = 1$	$(a \neq 0)$
Negative exponent	$a^{-n} = \dfrac{1}{a^n}$	$(a \neq 0)$
Quotient rule	$\dfrac{a^m}{a^n} = a^{m-n}$	$(a \neq 0)$
Power rule	$(a^m)^n = a^{m \cdot n}$	
Power of a product	$(ab)^m = a^m \cdot b^m$	
Power of a quotient	$\left(\dfrac{a}{b}\right)^n = \dfrac{a^n}{b^n}$	$(b \neq 0)$

EXAMPLES Simplify each expression. Write each answer using positive exponents only.

10. $(2x^0y^{-3})^{-2} = 2^{-2}(x^0)^{-2}(y^{-3})^{-2}$

$\qquad = 2^{-2}x^0y^6$

$\qquad = \dfrac{1(y^6)}{2^2}$ Write x^0 as 1.

$\qquad = \dfrac{y^6}{4}$

11. $\left(\dfrac{x^{-5}}{x^{-2}}\right)^{-3} = \dfrac{(x^{-5})^{-3}}{(x^{-2})^{-3}} = \dfrac{x^{15}}{x^6} = x^{15-6} = x^9$

12. $\left(\dfrac{2}{7}\right)^{-2} = \dfrac{2^{-2}}{7^{-2}} = \dfrac{7^2}{2^2} = \dfrac{49}{4}$

13. $\dfrac{5^{-2}x^{-3}y^{11}}{x^2y^{-5}} = 5^{-2}x^{-3-2}y^{11-(-5)} = 5^{-2}x^{-5}y^{16} = \dfrac{y^{16}}{5^2x^5} = \dfrac{y^{16}}{25x^5}$

🔲 **Work Practice Problems 10–13**

PRACTICE PROBLEMS 10–13

Simplify each expression. Write each answer using positive exponents only.

10. $(7xy^{-2})^{-2}$

11. $\left(\dfrac{y^{-7}}{y^{-10}}\right)^{-3}$

12. $\left(\dfrac{3}{5}\right)^{-2}$

13. $\dfrac{6^{-2}x^{-4}y^{10}}{x^2y^{-6}}$

Answers

10. $\dfrac{y^4}{49x^2}$, **11.** $\dfrac{1}{y^9}$, **12.** $\dfrac{25}{9}$, **13.** $\dfrac{y^{16}}{36x^6}$

CHAPTER 1

PRACTICE PROBLEMS 14–15

Simplify each expression. Write each answer using positive exponents only.

14. $\left(\dfrac{4a^3b^2}{b^{-6}c}\right)^{-2}$

15. $\left(\dfrac{4x^3}{3y^{-1}}\right)^3\left(\dfrac{y^{-2}}{3x^{-1}}\right)^{-1}$

EXAMPLES Simplify each expression. Write each answer using positive exponents only.

14. $\left(\dfrac{3x^2y}{y^{-9}z}\right)^{-2} = \left(\dfrac{3x^2y^{10}}{z}\right)^{-2} = \dfrac{3^{-2}x^{-4}y^{-20}}{z^{-2}} = \dfrac{z^2}{3^2x^4y^{20}} = \dfrac{z^2}{9x^4y^{20}}$

15. $\left(\dfrac{3a^2}{2x^{-1}}\right)^3\left(\dfrac{x^{-3}}{4a^{-2}}\right)^{-1} = \dfrac{27a^6}{8x^{-3}}\cdot\dfrac{x^3}{4^{-1}a^2}$

$$= \dfrac{27\cdot 4\cdot a^6\cdot x^3\cdot x^3}{8\cdot a^2} = \dfrac{27a^4x^6}{2}$$

◻ **Work Practice Problems 14–15**

Objective **C** Simplifying with Variables in the Exponent

EXAMPLES Simplify. Assume that a and b are integers and that x and y are not 0.

16. $x^{-b}(2x^b)^2 = x^{-b}2^2x^{2b} = 4x^{-b+2b} = 4x^b$

17. $\dfrac{(y^{3a})^2}{y^{a-6}} = \dfrac{y^{2(3a)}}{y^{a-6}} = \dfrac{y^{6a}}{y^{a-6}} = y^{6a-(a-6)} = y^{6a-a+6} = y^{5a+6}$

◻ **Work Practice Problems 16–17**

PRACTICE PROBLEMS 16–17

Simplify. Assume that m and n are integers and that x and y are not 0.

16. $x^{-n}(3x^n)^2$ **17.** $\dfrac{(y^{2m})^2}{y^{m-3}}$

Objective **D** Using Scientific Notation to Compute

To perform operations on numbers written in scientific notation, we use the properties of exponents.

EXAMPLES Perform each indicated operation. Write each answer in scientific notation.

18. $(8.1\times 10^5)(5\times 10^{-7}) = 8.1\times 5\times 10^5\times 10^{-7}$

$$= 40.5\times 10^{-2}$$
$$= (4.05\times 10^1)\times 10^{-2}$$
$$= 4.05\times 10^{-1}$$

19. $\dfrac{1.2\times 10^4}{3\times 10^{-2}} = \left(\dfrac{1.2}{3}\right)\left(\dfrac{10^4}{10^{-2}}\right) = 0.4\times 10^{4-(-2)}$

$$= 0.4\times 10^6 = (4\times 10^{-1})\times 10^6 = 4\times 10^5$$

◻ **Work Practice Problems 18–19**

PRACTICE PROBLEMS 18–19

Perform each indicated operation. Write each answer in scientific notation.

18. $(9.6\times 10^6)(4\times 10^{-8})$

19. $\dfrac{4.2\times 10^7}{7\times 10^{-3}}$

PRACTICE PROBLEM 20

Use scientific notation to simplify:

$$\dfrac{3000\times 0.000012}{400}$$

EXAMPLE 20 Use scientific notation to simplify: $\dfrac{2000\times 0.000021}{700}$

Solution:

$$\dfrac{2000\times 0.000021}{700} = \dfrac{(2\times 10^3)(2.1\times 10^{-5})}{7\times 10^2} = \dfrac{2(2.1)}{7}\cdot\dfrac{10^3\cdot 10^{-5}}{10^2}$$

$$= 0.6\times 10^{-4}$$
$$= (6\times 10^{-1})\times 10^{-4}$$
$$= 6\times 10^{-5}$$

◻ **Work Practice Problem 20**

Answers

14. $\dfrac{c^2}{16a^6b^{16}}$, **15.** $\dfrac{64x^8y^5}{9}$, **16.** $9x^n$,

17. y^{3m+3}, **18.** 3.84×10^{-1},

19. 6×10^9, **20.** 9×10^{-5}

Mental Math

Simplify. See Examples 1 through 4.

1. $(x^4)^5$ **2.** $(5^6)^2$ **3.** $x^4 \cdot x^5$ **4.** $x^7 \cdot x^8$ **5.** $(y^6)^7$

6. $(x^3)^4$ **7.** $(z^4)^9$ **8.** $(z^3)^7$ **9.** $(z^{-6})^{-3}$ **10.** $(y^{-4})^{-2}$

1.7 EXERCISE SET

Objective A *Simplify. Write each answer using positive exponents only. See Examples 1 through 9.*

1. $(3^{-1})^2$ **2.** $(2^{-2})^2$ **3.** $(x^4)^{-9}$ **4.** $(y^7)^{-3}$

5. $(3x^2y^3)^2$ **6.** $(4x^3yz)^2$ **7.** $\left(\dfrac{2x^5}{y^{-3}}\right)^4$ **8.** $\left(\dfrac{3a^{-4}}{b^7}\right)^3$

9. $(2a^2bc^{-3})^{-6}$ **10.** $(6x^{-6}y^7z^0)^{-2}$ **11.** $\left(\dfrac{7}{8}\right)^3$ **12.** $\left(\dfrac{4}{3}\right)^2$

13. $(-2^{-2}y^{-1})^{-3}$ **14.** $(-4^{-6}y^{-6})^{-4}$

Objective B *Simplify. Write each answer using positive exponents only. See Examples 10 through 15.*

15. $\left(\dfrac{a^{-4}}{a^{-5}}\right)^{-2}$ **16.** $\left(\dfrac{x^{-9}}{x^{-4}}\right)^{-3}$ **17.** $\left(\dfrac{6p^6}{p^{12}}\right)^2$ **18.** $\left(\dfrac{4p^6}{p^9}\right)^3$

19. $(-8y^3xa^{-2})^{-3}$ **20.** $(-5y^0x^2a^3)^{-3}$ **21.** $\left(\dfrac{3}{4}\right)^{-3}$ **22.** $\left(\dfrac{5}{8}\right)^{-2}$

23. $\left(\dfrac{2a^{-2}b^5}{4a^2b^7}\right)^{-2}$ **24.** $\left(\dfrac{5x^7y^4}{10x^3y^{-2}}\right)^{-3}$ **25.** $\left(\dfrac{x^{-2}y^{-2}}{a^{-3}}\right)^{-7}$ **26.** $\left(\dfrac{x^{-1}y^{-2}}{z^{-3}}\right)^{-5}$

Objectives A B Mixed Practice *Simplify. Write each answer using positive exponents only. See Examples 1 through 15.*

27. $(y^{-5})^2$ **28.** $(z^{-2})^{13}$ **29.** $(5^{-1})^3$ **30.** $(8^2)^{-1}$

31. $(x^7)^{-9}$ **32.** $(y^{-4})^5$ **33.** $\left(\dfrac{x^7y^{-3}}{z^{-4}}\right)^{-5}$ **34.** $\left(\dfrac{a^{-2}b^{-5}}{c^{-11}}\right)^{-6}$

35. $(4x^2)^2$ **36.** $(-8x^3)^2$ **37.** $\left(\dfrac{4^{-4}}{y^3x}\right)^{-2}$ **38.** $\left(\dfrac{7^{-3}}{ab^2}\right)^{-2}$

39. $\left(\dfrac{2x^{-3}}{y^{-1}}\right)^{-3}$ **40.** $\left(\dfrac{n^5}{2m^{-2}}\right)^{-4}$ **41.** $\dfrac{4^{-1}x^2yz}{x^{-2}yz^3}$ **42.** $\dfrac{8^{-2}x^{-3}y^{11}}{x^2y^{-5}}$

43. $\left(\dfrac{3x^5}{6x^4}\right)^4$ **44.** $\left(\dfrac{8^{-3}}{y^2}\right)^{-2}$ **45.** $\dfrac{(y^3)^{-4}}{y^3}$ **46.** $\dfrac{2(y^3)^{-3}}{y^{-3}}$

47. $\dfrac{3^{-2}a^{-5}b^6}{4^{-2}a^{-7}b^{-3}}$ **48.** $\dfrac{2^{-3}m^{-4}n^{-5}}{5^{-2}m^{-5}n}$ **49.** $(4x^6y^5)^{-2}(6x^4y^3)$ **50.** $(5x^2y^4)^{-2}(3x^9y^4)$

51. $x^6(x^6bc)^{-6}$ **52.** $y^2(y^2bx)^{-4}$ **53.** $\dfrac{2^{-3}x^2y^{-5}}{5^{-2}x^7y^{-1}}$ **54.** $\dfrac{7^{-1}a^{-3}b^5}{a^2b^{-2}}$

55. $\left(\dfrac{2x^2}{y^4}\right)^3\left(\dfrac{2x^5}{y}\right)^{-2}$ **56.** $\left(\dfrac{3z^{-2}}{y}\right)^2\left(\dfrac{9y^{-4}}{z^{-3}}\right)^{-1}$

Objective C *Simplify. Assume that variables in the exponents represent nonzero integers and that all other variables are not 0. See Examples 16 and 17.*

57. $\left(x^{3a+6}\right)^3$

58. $\left(x^{2b+7}\right)^2$

59. $\dfrac{x^{4a}\left(x^{4a}\right)^3}{x}$

60. $\dfrac{x^{-5y+2}x^{2y}}{x}$

61. $\left(b^{5x-2}\right)^2$

62. $\left(c^{2a+3}\right)^3$

63. $\dfrac{\left(y^{2a}\right)^8}{y^{a-3}}$

64. $\dfrac{\left(y^{4a}\right)^7}{y^{2a-1}}$

65. $\left(\dfrac{2x^{3t}}{x^{2t-1}}\right)^4$

66. $\left(\dfrac{3y^{5a}}{y^{-a+1}}\right)^2$

67. $\dfrac{25x^{2a+b}y^{2a-b}}{5x^{a-b}y^{a+b}}$

68. $\dfrac{16x^{3a-b}y^{4a+b}}{2x^{a-2b}y^{a+3b}}$

Objective D *Perform each indicated operation. Write each answer in scientific notation. See Examples 18 through 20.*

69. $(5 \times 10^{11})(2.9 \times 10^{-3})$ **70.** $(3.6 \times 10^{-12})(6 \times 10^9)$ **71.** $(2 \times 10^5)^3$ **72.** $(3 \times 10^{-7})^3$

73. $\dfrac{3.6 \times 10^{-4}}{9 \times 10^2}$

74. $\dfrac{1.2 \times 10^9}{2 \times 10^{-5}}$

75. $\dfrac{0.0069}{0.023}$

76. $\dfrac{0.00048}{0.0016}$

77. $\dfrac{18{,}200 \times 100}{91{,}000}$

78. $\dfrac{0.0003 \times 0.0024}{0.0006 \times 20}$

79. $\dfrac{6000 \times 0.006}{0.009 \times 400}$

80. $\dfrac{0.00016 \times 300}{0.064 \times 100}$

81. $\dfrac{0.00064 \times 2000}{16{,}000}$

82. $\dfrac{0.00072 \times 0.003}{0.00024}$

83. $\dfrac{66{,}000 \times 0.001}{0.002 \times 0.003}$

84. $\dfrac{0.0007 \times 11{,}000}{0.001 \times 0.0001}$

85. $\dfrac{9.24 \times 10^{15}}{(2.2 \times 10^{-2})(1.2 \times 10^{-5})}$

86. $\dfrac{(2.6 \times 10^{-3})(4.8 \times 10^{-4})}{1.3 \times 10^{-12}}$

Solve.

87. A computer can add two numbers in about 10^{-8} second. Express in scientific notation how long it would take this computer to do this task 200,000 times.

88. To convert from square inches to square meters, multiply by 6.452×10^{-4}. The area of the following square is 4×10^{-2} square inches. Convert this area to square meters.

89. To convert from cubic inches to cubic meters, multiply by 1.64×10^{-5}. A grain of salt is in the shape of a cube. If an average size of a grain of salt is 3.8×10^{-6} cubic inches, convert this volume to cubic meters.

4×10^{-2} sq in.

Concept Extensions

90. Each side of the cube shown is $\dfrac{2x^{-2}}{y}$ meters. Find its volume.

$\dfrac{2x^{-2}}{y}$ m

91. The lot shown is in the shape of a parallelogram with base $\dfrac{3x^{-1}}{y^{-3}}$ feet and height $5x^{-7}$ feet. Find its area.

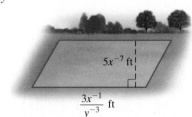

$5x^{-7}$ ft

$\dfrac{3x^{-1}}{y^{-3}}$ ft

92. The density D of an object is equivalent to the quotient of its mass M and volume V. Thus $D = \dfrac{M}{V}$. Express in scientific notation the density of an object whose mass is 500,000 pounds and whose volume is 250 cubic feet.

93. The density of ordinary water is 3.12×10^{-2} tons per cubic foot. The volume of water in the largest of the Great Lakes, Lake Superior, is 4.269×10^{14} cubic feet. Use the formula $D = \dfrac{M}{V}$ (see Exercise 92) to find the mass (in tons) of the water in Lake Superior. Express your answer in scientific notation. (*Source*: National Ocean Service)

94. Is there a number a such that $a^{-1} = a^{1}$? If so, give the value of a.

95. Is there a number a such that a^{-2} is a negative number? If so, give the value of a.

96. Explain whether 0.4×10^{-5} is written in scientific notation.

97. The estimated population of the United States in 2004 was 2.95×10^{8} people. The land area of the United States is 3.536×10^{6} square miles. Find the population density (number of people per square mile) for the United States in 2004. Round to the nearest whole. (*Source:* U.S. Census Bureau)

98. In October 2004, the value of goods and services imported into the United States was $\$1.535 \times 10^{11}$. The estimated population of the United States in 2004 was 2.95×10^{8} people. Find the average value of imports per person in the United States for October 2004. Round to the nearest dollar. (*Sources:* U.S. Census Bureau, Bureau of Economic Analysis)

99. In 2004, the population of Japan was 1.276×10^{8} people. At the same time, the population of Oceania (including the countries of Australia, New Zealand, Fiji, etc.) was 3.3×10^{7} people. How many times greater was the population of Japan than the population of Oceania? Round to the nearest tenth. (*Source:* Population Reference Bureau)

STUDY SKILLS BUILDER

Are You Prepared for a Test on Chapter 1?

Below I have listed some common trouble areas for students in Chapter 1. After studying for your test—but before taking your test—read these.

- Do you remember the meaning of a negative exponent?

$$7^{-2} = \frac{1}{7^{2}} = \frac{1}{49}$$

- Don't forget the order of operations and the distributive property.

$$7 - 3(2x - 6y) + 5 = 7 - 6x + 18y + 5 \quad \text{Use the distributive property.}$$
$$\uparrow$$
$$\text{Notice the sign.}$$
$$= -6x + 18y + 12 \quad \text{Combine like terms.}$$

- Don't forget the difference between $(-3)^{-2}$ and -3^{-2}.

$$(-3)^{-2} = \frac{1}{(-3)^{2}} = \frac{1}{9}$$
$$-3^{-2} = -1 \cdot 3^{-2} = \frac{-1}{3^{2}} = \frac{-1}{9} \text{ or } -\frac{1}{9}$$

- Remember that
$$\frac{0}{8} = 0 \text{ while } \frac{8}{0} \text{ is undefined.}$$

- Don't forget the difference between reciprocal and opposite.

The opposite of $-\dfrac{3}{5}$ is $\dfrac{3}{5}$.

The reciprocal of $-\dfrac{3}{5}$ is $-\dfrac{5}{3}$.

Remember: This is simply a checklist of common trouble areas. For a review of Chapter 1, see the Highlights and Chapter Review at the end of Chapter 1.

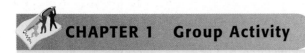

CHAPTER 1   Group Activity

Geometry Investigations

Sections 1.2 through 1.6

Recall that the perimeter of a figure is the distance around the outside of the figure. For a rectangle with length l and width w, the perimeter of the rectangle is given by the expression $2l + 2w$.

Area is a measure of the surface of a region. For example, we measure a plot of land or the floor space of a home by area. For a rectangle with length l and width w, the area of the rectangle is given by the expression lw.

A circular cylinder can be formed by rolling a rectangle into a tube. The surface area of the cylinder (excluding the two ends of the cylinder) is the same as the area of the rectangle used to form the cylinder. Recall that volume is a measure of the space inside a three-dimensional region. The volume of a circular cylinder with height h and radius r is given by the expression $\pi r^2 h$.

Group Activity

1. Work together to discover whether two rectangles with the same perimeter always have the same area. Explain your results. Give examples.

2. Do figures with the same surface area always have the same volume? To see, take two $8\frac{1}{2}$-by-11-inch sheets of paper and construct two cylinders using the following figures as a guide. Verify that both cylinders have the same surface area. Measure the height and radius of each resulting cylinder. Then find the volume of each cylinder to the nearest tenth of a cubic inch. Explain your results.

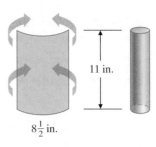

Cylinder 1

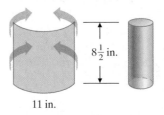

Cylinder 2

Chapter 1 Vocabulary Check

Fill in each blank with one of the words or phrases listed below.

distributive   absolute value   inequality   algebraic expression

real   opposite   commutative   exponent

reciprocals   associative   whole   variable

1. A(n) _____ is formed by numbers and variables connected by the operations of addition, subtraction, multiplication, division, raising to powers, and/or taking roots.
2. The _____ of a number a is $-a$.
3. $3(x - 6) = 3x - 18$ by the _____ property.
4. The _____ of a number is the distance between that number and 0 on the number line.
5. A(n) _____ is a shorthand notation for repeated multiplication of the same factor.
6. A letter that represents a number is called a _____.
7. The symbols $<$ and $>$ are called _____ symbols.
8. If a is not 0, then a and $\frac{1}{a}$ are called _____.
9. $A + B = B + A$ by the _____ property of addition.
10. $(A + B) + C = A + (B + C)$ by the _____ property of addition.
11. The numbers $0, 1, 2, 3, \ldots$ are called _____ numbers.
12. If a number corresponds to a point on the number line, we know that number is a ____ number.

Helpful Hint

Are you preparing for your test? Don't forget to take the Chapter 1 Test on page 67. Then check your answers at the back of the text and use the Chapter Test Prep Video CD to see the fully worked-out solutions to any of the exercises you want to review.

1 Chapter Highlights

DEFINITIONS AND CONCEPTS	EXAMPLES

Section 1.2   Algebraic Expressions and Sets of Numbers

Letters that represent numbers are called **variables.**

An **algebraic expression** is formed by numbers and variables connected by the operations of addition, subtraction, multiplication, division, raising to powers, or taking roots.

Natural numbers: $\{1, 2, 3, \ldots\}$

Whole numbers: $\{0, 1, 2, 3, \ldots\}$

Integers: $\{\ldots, -3, -2, -1, 0, 1, 2, 3, \ldots\}$
Each listing of three dots is called an **ellipsis.**
The objects of a set are called its members or **elements.**

Set builder notation describes the elements of a set but does not list them.

Real numbers: $\{x \mid x$ corresponds to a point on the number line$\}$

Rational numbers: $\left\{\frac{a}{b} \mid a$ and b are integers and $b \neq 0\right\}$

Irrational numbers: $\{x \mid x$ is a real number and x is not a rational number$\}$

If all the elements of set A are also in set B, we say that set A is a **subset** of set B.

$x, \quad a, \quad m, \quad y$

$7y, \quad -3, \quad \frac{x^2 - 9}{-2} + 14x, \quad \sqrt{3} + \sqrt{m}$

Given the set $\left\{-9.6, -5, -\sqrt{2}, 0, \frac{2}{5}, 101\right\}$, list the elements that belong to the set of

Natural numbers   101
Whole numbers $0, 101$
Integers $-5, 0, 101$
Real numbers $-9.6, -5, -\sqrt{2}, 0, \frac{2}{5}, 101$
Rational numbers $-9.6, -5, 0, \frac{2}{5}, 101$
Irrational numbers $-\sqrt{2}$

Write the set $\{x \mid x$ is an integer between -2 and $5\}$ in roster form.

$\{-1, 0, 1, 2, 3, 4\}$

The set of integers is a subset of the set of rational numbers.

DEFINITIONS AND CONCEPTS	EXAMPLES
Section 1.3 Equations, Inequalities, and Properties of Real Numbers	

SYMBOLS

$=$	is equal to		$-5 = -5$
$\neq$	is not equal to		$-5 \neq -3$
$>$	is greater than		$1.7 > 1.2$
$<$	is less than		$-1.7 < -1.2$
$\geq$	is greater than or equal to		$\dfrac{5}{3} \geq \dfrac{5}{3}$
$\leq$	is less than or equal to		$-\dfrac{1}{2} \leq \dfrac{1}{2}$

IDENTITY

$$a + 0 = a \qquad 0 + a = a$$
$$a \cdot 1 = a \qquad 1 \cdot a = a$$

$$3 + 0 = 3 \qquad\qquad 0 + 3 = 3$$
$$-1.8 \cdot 1 = -1.8 \qquad 1 \cdot -1.8 = -1.8$$

INVERSE

$$a + (-a) = 0 \qquad -a + a = 0$$
$$a \cdot \frac{1}{a} = 1 \qquad \frac{1}{a} \cdot a = 1$$

$$7 + (-7) = 0 \qquad -7 + 7 = 0$$
$$5 \cdot \frac{1}{5} = 1 \qquad \frac{1}{5} \cdot 5 = 1$$

COMMUTATIVE

$$a + b = b + a$$
$$a \cdot b = b \cdot a$$

$$x + 7 = 7 + x$$
$$9 \cdot y = y \cdot 9$$

ASSOCIATIVE

$$(a + b) + c = a + (b + c)$$
$$(a \cdot b) \cdot c = a \cdot (b \cdot c)$$

$$(3 + 1) + 10 = 3 + (1 + 10)$$
$$(3 \cdot 1) \cdot 10 = 3 \cdot (1 \cdot 10)$$

DISTRIBUTIVE

$$a(b + c) = ab + ac$$

$$6(x + 5) = 6 \cdot x + 6 \cdot 5$$
$$= 6x + 30$$

Section 1.4 Operations on Real Numbers	

ABSOLUTE VALUE

$$|a| = \begin{cases} a & \text{if } a \text{ is 0 or a positive number} \\ -a & \text{if } a \text{ is a negative number} \end{cases}$$

$$|3| = 3, \quad |0| = 0, \quad |-7.2| = 7.2$$

ADDING REAL NUMBERS

1. To add two numbers with the same sign, add their absolute values and attach their common sign.

2. To add two numbers with different signs, subtract the smaller absolute value from the larger absolute value and attach the sign of the number with the larger absolute value.

$$\frac{2}{7} + \frac{1}{7} = \frac{3}{7}$$
$$-5 + (-2.6) = -7.6$$
$$-18 + 6 = -12$$
$$20.8 + (-10.2) = 10.6$$

SUBTRACTING REAL NUMBERS

$$a - b = a + (-b)$$

$$18 - 21 = 18 + (-21) = -3$$

MULTIPLYING AND DIVIDING REAL NUMBERS

The product or quotient of two numbers with the same sign is positive.

$$(-8)(-4) = 32 \qquad \frac{-8}{-4} = 2$$
$$8 \cdot 4 = 32 \qquad \frac{8}{4} = 2$$

DEFINITIONS AND CONCEPTS	**EXAMPLES**

Section 1.4　Operations on Real Numbers (*continued*)

The product or quotient of two numbers with different signs is negative.	$-17 \cdot 2 = -34 \qquad \dfrac{-14}{2} = -7$ $4(-1.6) = -6.4 \qquad \dfrac{22}{-2} = -11$
A natural number **exponent** is a shorthand notation for repeated multiplication of the same factor.	$3^4 = 3 \cdot 3 \cdot 3 \cdot 3 = 81$
The notation $\sqrt{a}$ is used to denote the **positive,** or **principal square root** of a nonnegative number a. $\sqrt{a} = b$ if $b^2 = a$ and b is positive Also, $\sqrt[3]{a} = b$ if $b^3 = a$ $\sqrt[4]{a} = b$ if $b^4 = a$ and b is positive.	$\sqrt{49} = 7$ $\sqrt[3]{64} = 4$ $\sqrt[4]{16} = 2$

Section 1.5　Order of Operations and Algebraic Expressions

ORDER OF OPERATIONS

Simplify expressions using the order that follows.

1. If grouping symbols such as parentheses are present, simplify expressions within those first, starting with the innermost set.

2. Evaluate exponential expressions, roots, and absolute values.

3. Multiply or divide in order from left to right.

4. Add or subtract in order from left to right.

To **evaluate** an algebraic expression containing variables, substitute the given numbers for the variables and simplify. The result is called the **value** of the expression.

Simplify: $\dfrac{42 - 2(3^2 - \sqrt{16})}{-8}$

$$\dfrac{42 - 2(3^2 - \sqrt{16})}{-8} = \dfrac{42 - 2(9 - 4)}{-8}$$
$$= \dfrac{42 - 2(5)}{-8}$$
$$= \dfrac{42 - 10}{-8}$$
$$= \dfrac{32}{-8} = -4$$

Evaluate:　$2.7x$ when $x = 3$
$$2.7x = 2.7(3)$$
$$= 8.1$$

Section 1.6　Exponents and Scientific Notation

PRODUCT RULE　$a^m \cdot a^n = a^{m+n}$

ZERO EXPONENT　$a^0 = 1 \quad (a \neq 0)$

QUOTIENT RULE　$\dfrac{a^m}{a^n} = a^{m-n} \quad (a \neq 0)$

NEGATIVE EXPONENT　$a^{-n} = \dfrac{1}{a^n} \quad (a \neq 0)$

A positive number is written in **scientific notation** if it is written as the product of a number a, where $1 \leq a < 10$, and an integer power of 10: $a \times 10^n$.

$x^2 \cdot x^3 = x^5$

$7^0 = 1, (-10)^0 = 1$

$\dfrac{y^{10}}{y^4} = y^{10-4} = y^6$

$3^{-2} = \dfrac{1}{3^2} = \dfrac{1}{9}, \dfrac{x^{-5}}{x^{-7}} = x^{-5-(-7)} = x^2$

Numbers written in scientific notation:
$$568{,}000 = 5.68 \times 10^5$$
$$0.0002117 = 2.117 \times 10^{-4}$$

DEFINITIONS AND CONCEPTS	EXAMPLES
Section 1.7 More Work with Exponents and Scientific Notation	

POWER RULES

$$(a^m)^n = a^{m \cdot n}$$

$$(ab)^m = a^m b^m$$

$$\left(\frac{a}{b}\right)^n = \frac{a^n}{b^n}$$

$$(7^8)^2 = 7^{16}$$

$$(2y)^3 = 2^3 y^3 = 8y^3$$

$$\left(\frac{5x^{-3}}{x^2}\right)^{-2} = \frac{5^{-2} x^6}{x^{-4}}$$

$$= 5^{-2} \cdot x^{6-(-4)}$$

$$= \frac{x^{10}}{5^2}, \text{ or } \frac{x^{10}}{25}$$

2

Equations, Inequalities, and Problem Solving

Taken from:
Intermediate Algebra, Third Edition, by Elayn Martin-Gay

A Decide Whether a Number Is a Solution of an Equation.

B Solve Linear Equations Using Properties of Equality.

C Solve Linear Equations That Can Be Simplified by Combining Like Terms.

D Solve Linear Equations Containing Fractions or Decimals.

E Recognize Identities and Equations with No Solution.

2.1 LINEAR EQUATIONS IN ONE VARIABLE

Objective **A** Deciding Whether a Number Is a Solution of an Equation

An **equation** is a statement that two expressions are equal. To solve problems, we need to be able to solve equations. In this section, we will solve a special type of equation called a *linear equation in one variable.*

Linear equations model many real-life problems. For example, we can use a linear equation to calculate the increase in households (in millions) with digital cameras.

With the help of your computer, digital cameras allow you to see your pictures and make copies immediately, send them in e-mail or use them on a Web page. Numbers of households with these cameras for various years are shown in the graph below.

Households with a Digital Camera

Source: Internet Search

To find the increase in households from 2002 to 2003, for example, we can use the equation below.

In words:	Increase in households	is	households in 2003	minus	households in 2002
Translate:	x	$=$	31.5	$-$	22.8

Since our variable x (increase in households) is by itself on one side of the equation, we can find the value of x by simplifying the right side.

$$x = 8.7$$

The increase in households with digital cameras from 2002 to 2003 is $8.7 million.

The **equation,** $x = 31.5 - 22.8$, like every other equation, is a statement that two expressions are equal. Oftentimes, the unknown variable is not by itself on one side of the equation. In these cases, we will use properties of equality to write equivalent equations so that a solution many be found. This is called **solving the equation.** In this section, we concentrate on solving equations such as this one, called **linear equations** in one variable. Linear equations are also called **first-degree equations** since the exponent on the variable is 1.

Linear Equations in One Variable

$$3x = -15 \qquad 7 - y = 3y \qquad 4n - 9n + 6 = 0 \qquad z = -2$$

Linear Equation in One Variable

A **linear equation in one variable** is an equation that can be written in the form

$$ax + b = c$$

where a, b, and c are real numbers and $a \neq 0$.

When a variable in an equation is replaced by a number and the resulting equation is true, then that number is called a **solution** of the equation. For example, 1 is a solution of the equation $3x + 4 = 7$ since $3(1) + 4 = 7$ is a true statement. But 2 is not a solution of this equation since $3(2) + 4 = 7$ is *not* a true statement. The **solution set** of an equation is the set of solutions of the equation. For example, the solution set of $3x + 4 = 7$ is $\{1\}$.

EXAMPLE 1 Determine whether -15 is a solution of $x - 9 = -24$.

Solution: We replace x with -15 and see whether a true statement results.

$$x - 9 = -24$$
$$-15 - 9 \overset{?}{=} -24 \quad \text{Replace } x \text{ with } -15.$$
$$-24 = -24 \quad \text{True}$$

Since a true statement results, -15 is a solution.

🖱 **Work Practice Problem 1**

PRACTICE PROBLEM 1
Determine whether -7 is a solution of $14 - x = 21$.

EXAMPLE 2 Determine whether 5 is a solution of $2x - 3 = x + 3$.

Solution:

$$2x - 3 = x + 3$$
$$2 \cdot 5 - 3 \overset{?}{=} 5 + 3 \quad \text{Replace } x \text{ with } 5.$$
$$7 = 8 \quad \text{False}$$

Since a false statement results, 5 is not a solution.

🖱 **Work Practice Problem 2**

PRACTICE PROBLEM 2
Determine whether 8 is a solution of $x - 10 = 2x - 14$.

Objective B Using the Properties of Equality

To **solve an equation** is to find the solution set of an equation. Equations with the same solution set are called **equivalent equations.** For example,

$$3x + 4 = 7 \qquad 3x = 3 \qquad x = 1$$

are equivalent equations because they all have the same solution set, namely, $\{1\}$. To solve an equation in x, we start with the given equation and write a series of simpler equivalent equations until we obtain an equation of the form

$$x = \textbf{number}$$

To write equivalent equations, we use two important properties.

Addition Property of Equality

If a, b, and c, are real numbers, then

$$a = b \quad \text{and} \quad a + c = b + c$$

are equivalent equations.

Multiplication Property of Equality

If $c \neq 0$, then

$$a = b \quad \text{and} \quad ac = bc$$

are equivalent equations.

The **addition property of equality** guarantees that the same number may be added to both sides of an equation and the result is an equivalent equation. Recall that we define subtraction in terms of addition.

$$7 - 10 = 7 + (-10) = -3$$

This means that the addition property also says we can *subtract* the same number from both sides and the result is an equivalent equation.

The **multiplication property of equality** guarantees that both sides of an equation may be multiplied by the same nonzero number and the result is an equivalent equation. Recall that we define division in terms of multiplication. This means that the multiplication property also says we can *divide* both sides by the same nonzero number and the result is an equivalent equation.

For example, to solve $2x + 5 = 9$, we use the addition and multiplication properties of equality to get x alone—that is, to write an equivalent equation of the form

$$x = \text{number}$$

We will do this in the next example.

PRACTICE PROBLEM 3

Solve: $3x + 6 = 21$

EXAMPLE 3 Solve: $2x + 5 = 9$

Solution: First we use the addition property of equality and subtract 5 from both sides.

$$2x + 5 = 9$$
$$2x + 5 - 5 = 9 - 5 \quad \text{Subtract 5 from both sides.}$$
$$2x = 4 \quad \text{Simplify.}$$

Now we use the multiplication property of equality and divide both sides by 2.

$$\frac{2x}{2} = \frac{4}{2} \quad \text{Divide both sides by 2.}$$
$$x = 2 \quad \text{Simplify.}$$

Check: To check, we replace x in the original equation with 2.

$$2x + 5 = 9 \quad \text{Original equation}$$
$$2(2) + 5 \stackrel{?}{=} 9 \quad \text{Replace } x \text{ with 2.}$$
$$4 + 5 \stackrel{?}{=} 9$$
$$9 = 9 \quad \text{True}$$

The solution set is $\{2\}$.

Work Practice Problem 3

Answer

3. $\{5\}$

EXAMPLE 4 Solve: $0.6 = 2 - 3.5c$

Solution: We use both the addition property and the multiplication property of equality.

$$0.6 = 2 - 3.5c$$
$$0.6 - 2 = 2 - 3.5c - 2 \qquad \text{Subtract 2 from both sides.}$$
$$-1.4 = -3.5c \qquad \text{Simplify.}$$
$$\frac{-1.4}{-3.5} = \frac{-3.5c}{-3.5} \qquad \text{Divide both sides by } -3.5.$$
$$0.4 = c \qquad \text{Simplify } \frac{-1.4}{-3.5}.$$

Check:

$$0.6 = 2 - 3.5c$$
$$0.6 \overset{?}{=} 2 - 3.5(0.4) \qquad \text{Replace } c \text{ with } 0.4.$$
$$0.6 \overset{?}{=} 2 - 1.4 \qquad \text{Multiply.}$$
$$0.6 = 0.6 \qquad \text{True}$$

The solution set is $\{0.4\}$.

■ **Work Practice Problem 4**

Objective C Solving Linear Equations by Combining Like Terms

Often, an equation can be simplified by removing any grouping symbols and combining any like terms.

EXAMPLE 5 Solve: $-4x - 1 + 5x = 9x + 3 - 7x$

Solution: First we simplify both sides of this equation by combining like terms. Then, let's get variable terms on the same side of the equation by using the addition property of equality to subtract $2x$ from both sides. Next, we use this same property to add 1 to both sides of the equation.

$$-4x - 1 + 5x = 9x + 3 - 7x$$
$$x - 1 = 2x + 3 \qquad \text{Combine like terms.}$$
$$x - 1 - 2x = 2x + 3 - 2x \qquad \text{Subtract } 2x \text{ from both sides.}$$
$$-x - 1 = 3 \qquad \text{Simplify.}$$
$$-x - 1 + 1 = 3 + 1 \qquad \text{Add 1 to both sides.}$$
$$-x = 4 \qquad \text{Simplify.}$$

Notice that this equation is not solved for x since we have $-x$, or $-1x$, not x. To get x alone, we divide both sides by -1.

$$\frac{-x}{-1} = \frac{4}{-1} \qquad \text{Divide both sides by } -1.$$
$$x = -4 \qquad \text{Simplify.}$$

Check to see that the solution set is $\{-4\}$.

■ **Work Practice Problem 5**

If an equation contains parentheses, we use the distributive property to remove them.

PRACTICE PROBLEM 6

Solve: $4(x - 2) = 6x - 10$

EXAMPLE 6 Solve: $3(x - 3) = 5x - 9$

Solution: First we use the distributive property.

$$3(x - 3) = 5x - 9$$
$$3x - 9 = 5x - 9 \quad \text{Use the distributive property.}$$

Next we get variable terms on the same side of the equation by using the addition property of equality.

$$3x - 9 - 5x = 5x - 9 - 5x \quad \text{Subtract } 5x \text{ from both sides.}$$
$$-2x - 9 = -9 \quad \text{Simplify.}$$
$$-2x - 9 + 9 = -9 + 9 \quad \text{Add 9 to both sides.}$$
$$-2x = 0 \quad \text{Simplify.}$$
$$\frac{-2x}{-2} = \frac{0}{-2} \quad \text{Divide both sides by } -2.$$
$$x = 0$$

Check to see that $\{0\}$ is the solution set.

■ **Work Practice Problem 6**

Objective **D** **Solving Linear Equations Containing Fractions or Decimals**

If an equation contains fractions, we can first clear the equation of fractions by multiplying both sides of the equation by the *least common denominator* (LCD) of all fractions in the equation.

PRACTICE PROBLEM 7

Solve: $\dfrac{x}{6} - \dfrac{x}{8} = \dfrac{1}{8}$

EXAMPLE 7 Solve: $\dfrac{y}{3} - \dfrac{y}{4} = \dfrac{1}{6}$

Solution: First we clear the equation of fractions by multiplying both sides of the equation by 12, the LCD of the denominators 3, 4, and 6.

$$\frac{y}{3} - \frac{y}{4} = \frac{1}{6}$$
$$12\left(\frac{y}{3} - \frac{y}{4}\right) = 12\left(\frac{1}{6}\right) \quad \text{Multiply both sides by the LCD, 12.}$$
$$12\left(\frac{y}{3}\right) - 12\left(\frac{y}{4}\right) = 2 \quad \text{Use the distributive property.}$$
$$4y - 3y = 2 \quad \text{Simplify.}$$
$$y = 2 \quad \text{Simplify.}$$

Check: To check, we replace y with 2 in the original equation.

$$\frac{y}{3} - \frac{y}{4} = \frac{1}{6} \quad \text{Original equation}$$
$$\frac{2}{3} - \frac{2}{4} \stackrel{?}{=} \frac{1}{6} \quad \text{Replace } y \text{ with 2.}$$
$$\frac{8}{12} - \frac{6}{12} \stackrel{?}{=} \frac{1}{6} \quad \text{Write fractions with the LCD.}$$
$$\frac{2}{12} \stackrel{?}{=} \frac{1}{6} \quad \text{Subtract.}$$
$$\frac{1}{6} = \frac{1}{6} \quad \text{True}$$

Since a true statement results, the solution set is $\{2\}$.

■ **Work Practice Problem 7**

Answers

6. $\{1\}$, **7.** $\{3\}$

As a general guideline, the following steps may be used to solve a linear equation in one variable.

Solving a Linear Equation in One Variable

Step 1: Clear the equation of fractions or decimals by multiplying both sides of the equation by an appropriate nonzero number.

Step 2: Use the distributive property to remove grouping symbols such as parentheses.

Step 3: Combine like terms on each side of the equation.

Step 4: Use the addition property of equality to rewrite the equation as an equivalent equation, with variable terms on one side and numbers on the other side.

Step 5: Use the multiplication property of equality to get the variable alone.

Step 6: Check the proposed solution in the original equation.

EXAMPLE 8 Solve: $\dfrac{x+5}{2} + \dfrac{1}{2} = \dfrac{1}{8}(15x+3)$

Solution: To begin, we multiply both sides of the equation by 8, the LCD of 2 and 8. This will clear the equation of fractions.

$8\left(\dfrac{x+5}{2} + \dfrac{1}{2}\right) = 8\left[\dfrac{1}{8}(15x+3)\right]$ Multiply both sides by 8.

$8\left(\dfrac{x+5}{2}\right) + 8\left(\dfrac{1}{2}\right) = 8 \cdot \dfrac{1}{8}(15x+3)$ Use the distributive property.

$4(x+5) + 4 = 15x + 3$ Multiply.

$4x + 20 + 4 = 15x + 3$ Use the distributive property to remove parentheses.

$4x + 24 = 15x + 3$ Combine like terms.

$4x - 15x = 3 - 24$ Subtract $15x$ and 24 from both sides.

$-11x = -21$ Simplify.

$\dfrac{-11x}{-11} = \dfrac{-21}{-11}$ Divide both sides by -11.

$x = \dfrac{21}{11}$ Simplify.

To check, verify that replacing x with $\dfrac{21}{11}$ makes the original equation true. The solution set is $\left\{\dfrac{21}{11}\right\}$.

■ **Work Practice Problem 8**

If an equation contains decimals, you may want to first clear the equation of decimals by multiplying by an appropriate power of 10.

PRACTICE PROBLEM 8

Solve:

$\dfrac{x-1}{3} + \dfrac{2}{3} = x - \dfrac{2x+3}{9}$

Helpful Hint

When we multiply both sides of an equation by a number, the distributive property tells us that each term of the equation is multiplied by the number.

PRACTICE PROBLEM 9

Solve:

$0.2x + 0.1 = 0.12x - 0.06$

EXAMPLE 9 Solve: $0.3x + 0.1 = 0.27x - 0.02$

Solution: To clear this equation of decimals, we multiply both sides of the equation by 100. Recall that multiplying a number by 100 moves its decimal point two places to the right.

$$100(0.3x + 0.1) = 100(0.27x - 0.02)$$

$$100(0.3x) + 100(0.1) = 100(0.27x) - 100(0.02) \quad \text{Use the distributive property.}$$

$$30x + 10 = 27x - 2 \quad \text{Multiply.}$$

$$30x - 27x = -2 - 10 \quad \text{Subtract } 27x \text{ and } 10 \text{ from both sides.}$$

$$3x = -12 \quad \text{Simplify.}$$

$$\frac{3x}{3} = \frac{-12}{3} \quad \text{Divide both sides by 3.}$$

$$x = -4 \quad \text{Simplify.}$$

Check to see that the solution set is $\{-4\}$.

◻ **Work Practice Problem 9**

✔ **Concept Check** Explain what is wrong with the following:

$$3x - 5 = 16$$
$$3x = 11$$
$$\frac{3x}{3} = \frac{11}{3}$$
$$x = \frac{11}{3}$$

Objective **E** Recognizing Identities and Equations with No Solution

So far, each linear equation that we have solved has had a single solution. We will now look at two other types of equations: *contradictions* and *identities*.

An equation in one variable that has no solution is called a **contradiction,** and an equation in one variable that has every number (for which the equation is defined) as a solution is called an **identity.** The next examples show how to recognize contradictions and identities.

PRACTICE PROBLEM 10

Solve: $5x - 1 = 5(x + 3)$

EXAMPLE 10 Solve: $3x + 5 = 3(x + 2)$

Solution: First we use the distributive property to remove parentheses.

$$3x + 5 = 3(x + 2)$$
$$3x + 5 = 3x + 6 \quad \text{Use the distributive property.}$$
$$3x + 5 - 3x = 3x + 6 - 3x \quad \text{Subtract } 3x \text{ from both sides.}$$
$$5 = 6 \quad \text{False.}$$

The equation $5 = 6$ is a false statement no matter what value the variable x might have. Thus the original equation has no solution. Its solution set is written either as $\{\ \}$ or $\varnothing$. This equation is a contradiction.

◻ **Work Practice Problem 10**

Answers

9. $\{-2\}$, 10. $\varnothing$

✔ **Concept Check Answer**

$$3x - 5 = 16$$
$$3x = 21$$
$$x = 7$$

Therefore the correct solution set is $\{7\}$.

Helpful Hint

A solution set of $\{0\}$ and a solution set of $\{\ \}$ are not the same. The solution set $\{0\}$ means 1 solution, 0. The solution set $\{\ \}$ means no solution.

EXAMPLE 11 Solve: $6x - 4 = 2 + 6(x - 1)$

Solution: First we use the distributive property to remove parentheses.

$$6x - 4 = 2 + 6(x - 1)$$

$6x - 4 = 2 + 6x - 6$ Use the distributive property.

$6x - 4 = 6x - 4$ Combine the terms.

At this point we might notice that both sides of the equation are the same, so replacing x by any real number gives a true statement. Thus the solution set of this equation is the set of real numbers, and the equation is an identity. Continuing to "solve" $6x - 4 = 6x - 4$, we eventually arrive at the same conclusion.

$6x - 4 + 4 = 6x - 4 + 4$ Add 4 to both sides.

$\qquad\qquad 6x = 6x$ Simplify.

$\quad 6x - 6x = 6x - 6x$ Subtract $6x$ from both sides.

$\qquad\qquad 0 = 0$ True

Since $0 = 0$ is a true statement for every value of x, the solution set is the set of all real numbers, which can be written as $\{x \mid x \text{ is a real number}\}$. The equation is called an identity.

▣ **Work Practice Problem 11**

> **Helpful Hint**
>
> For linear equations, *any* false statement such as $5 = 6$, $0 = 1$, or $-2 = 2$ informs us that the original equation has no solution. Also, *any* true statement such as $0 = 0$, $2 = 2$, or $-5 = -5$ informs us that the original equation is an identity.

PRACTICE PROBLEM 11

Solve:

$-4(x - 1) = -4x - 9 + 13$

Answer

11. $\{x \mid x \text{ is a real number}\}$

Mental Math

Solve each equation.

1. $3x = 18$

2. $2x = 60$

3. $x - 7 = 10$

4. $x - 2 = 15$

5. $\dfrac{x}{2} = 4$

6. $\dfrac{x}{3} = 5$

7. $x + 1 = 11$

8. $x + 4 = 20$

2.1 EXERCISE SET

FOR EXTRA HELP

Student Solutions Manual

PH Math/Tutor Center

CD/Video for Review

MathXL®

MyMathLab

Objective Ⓐ *Determine whether each number is a solution of the given equation. See Examples 1 and 2.*

1. $-24;\ \dfrac{x}{-6} = 4$

2. $15;\ \dfrac{x}{-3} = -5$

3. $-3;\ x - 17 = 20$

4. $-8;\ x - 10 = -2$

5. $-2;\ 5 + 3x = -1$

6. $-1;\ 6 - 2x = 4$

7. $5;\ x - 7 = x + 2$

8. $5;\ x - 1 = x - 1$

9. $5;\ 4(x - 3) = 12$

10. $12;\ 5(x - 6) = 30$

11. $-8;\ 4x - 2 = 5x + 6$

12. $2;\ 7x + 1 = 6x - 1$

Objective Ⓑ *Solve each equation and check. See Examples 3 and 4.*

13. $-5x = -30$

14. $-2x = 18$

15. $-10 = x + 12$

16. $-25 = y + 30$

17. $x - 2.8 = 1.9$

18. $y - 8.6 = -6.3$

19. $5x - 4 = 26 + 2x$

20. $5y - 3 = 11 + 3y$

21. $-4.1 - 7z = 3.6$

22. $10.3 - 6x = -2.3$

23. $5y + 12 = 2y - 3$

24. $4x + 14 = 6x + 8$

Objective Ⓒ *Solve each equation and check. See Examples 5 and 6.*

25. $3x - 4 - 5x = x + 4 + x$

26. $13x - 15x + 8 = 4x + 2 - 24$

27. $8x - 5x + 3 = x - 7 + 10$

28. $6 + 3x + x = -x + 8 - 26 + 24$

29. $5x + 12 = 2(2x + 7)$

30. $2(4x + 3) = 7x + 5$

31. $3(x - 6) = 5x$

32. $6x = 4(x - 5)$

33. $-2(5y - 1) - y = -4(y - 3)$

34. $-4(3n - 2) - n = -11(n - 1)$

Objective Ⓓ *Solve each equation and check. See Examples 7 through 9.*

35. $\dfrac{x}{2} + \dfrac{x}{3} = \dfrac{3}{4}$

36. $\dfrac{x}{2} + \dfrac{x}{5} = \dfrac{5}{4}$

37. $\dfrac{3t}{4} - \dfrac{t}{2} = 1$

38. $\dfrac{4r}{5} - 7 = \dfrac{r}{10}$

72

39. $\dfrac{n-3}{4} + \dfrac{n+5}{7} = \dfrac{5}{14}$

40. $\dfrac{2+h}{9} + \dfrac{h-1}{3} = \dfrac{1}{3}$

41. $0.6x - 10 = 1.4x - 14$

42. $0.3x + 2.4 = 0.1x + 4$

43. $\dfrac{3x-1}{9} + x = \dfrac{3x+1}{3} + 4$

44. $\dfrac{2z+7}{8} - 2 = z + \dfrac{z-1}{2}$

45. $1.5(4-x) = 1.3(2-x)$

46. $2.4(2x+3) = -0.1(2x+3)$

Objective **E** *Solve each equation. See Examples 10 and 11.*

47. $4(n+3) = 2(6+2n)$

48. $6(4n+4) = 8(3+3n)$

49. $3(x+1) + 5 = 3x + 2$

50. $4(x+2) + 4 = 4x - 8$

51. $2(x-8) + x = 3(x-6) + 2$

52. $5(x-4) + x = 6(x-2) - 8$

53. $4(x+5) = 3(x-4) + x$

54. $9(x-2) = 8(x-3) + x$

Objectives **B** **C** **D** **E** **Mixed Practice** *Solve each equation. See Examples 3 through 11.*

55. $\dfrac{3}{8} + \dfrac{b}{3} = \dfrac{5}{12}$

56. $\dfrac{a}{2} + \dfrac{7}{4} = 5$

57. $x - 10 = -6x - 10$

58. $4x - 7 = 2x - 7$

59. $5(x-2) + 2x = 7(x+4) - 38$

60. $3x + 2(x+4) = 5(x+1) + 3$

61. $y + 0.2 = 0.6(y+3)$

62. $-(w + 0.2) = 0.3(4 - w)$

63. $\dfrac{1}{4}(a+2) = \dfrac{1}{6}(5-a)$

64. $\dfrac{1}{3}(8+2c) = \dfrac{1}{5}(3c-5)$

65. $2y + 5(y-4) = 4y - 2(y-10)$

66. $9c - 3(6-5c) = c - 2(3c+9)$

67. $6x - 2(x-3) = 4(x+1) + 4$

68. $10x - 2(x+4) = 8(x-2) + 6$

69. $\dfrac{m-4}{3} - \dfrac{3m-1}{5} = 1$

70. $\dfrac{n+1}{8} - \dfrac{2-n}{3} = \dfrac{5}{6}$

71. $8x - 12 - 3x = 9x - 7$

72. $10y - 18 - 4y = 12y - 13$

73. $-(3x-5) - (2x-6) + 1 = -5(x-1) - (3x+2) + 3$

74. $-4(2x-3) - (10x+7) - 2 = -(12x-5) - (4x+9) - 1$

75. $\dfrac{1}{3}(y+4) + 6 = \dfrac{1}{4}(3y-1) - 2$

76. $\dfrac{1}{5}(2y-1) - 2 = \dfrac{1}{2}(3y-5) + 3$

77. $2[7 - 5(1-n)] + 8n = -16 + 3[6(n+1) - 3n]$

78. $3[8 - 4(n-2)] + 5n = -20 + 2[5(1-n) - 6n]$

Review

Translate each phrase into an expression. Use the variable x to represent each unknown number. See Section 1.2.

79. The quotient of 8 and a number

80. The sum of 8 and a number

81. The product of 8 and a number

82. The difference of 8 and a number

83. Five subtracted from twice a number

84. Two more than three times a number

Concept Extensions

Find the error for each proposed solution. Then correct the proposed solution. See the Concept Check in this section.

85. $2x + 19 = 13$
$2x = 32$
$\dfrac{2x}{2} = \dfrac{32}{2}$
$x = 16$

86. $-3(x - 4) = 10$
$-3x - 12 = 10$
$-3x = 22$
$\dfrac{-3x}{-3} = \dfrac{22}{-3}$
$x = -\dfrac{22}{3}$

87. $9x + 1.6 = 4x + 0.4$
$5x = 1.2$
$\dfrac{5x}{5} = \dfrac{1.2}{5}$
$x = 0.24$

88. $\dfrac{x}{3} + 7 = \dfrac{5x}{3}$
$x + 7 = 5x$
$7 = 4x$
$\dfrac{7}{4} = \dfrac{4x}{4}$
$\dfrac{7}{2} = x$

89. a. Simplify the expression $4(x + 1) + 1$.
b. Solve the equation $4(x + 1) + 1 = -7$.
c. Explain the difference between solving an equation for a variable and simplifying an expression.

90. Explain why the multiplication property of equality does not include multiplying both sides of an equation by 0. (*Hint:* Write down a false statement and then multiply both sides by 0. Is the result true or false? What does this mean?)

91. In your own words, explain why the equation $x + 7 = x + 6$ has no solution while the solution set of the equation $x + 7 = x + 7$ contains all real numbers.

92. In your own words, explain why the equation $x = -x$ has one solution—namely, 0—while the solution set of the equation $x = x$ is all real numbers.

Find the value of K such that the equations are equivalent.

93. $3.2x + 4 = 5.4x - 7$
$3.2x = 5.4x + K$

94. $-7.6y - 10 = -1.1y + 12$
$-7.6y = -1.1y + K$

95. $\dfrac{7}{11}x + 9 = \dfrac{3}{11}x - 14$
$\dfrac{7}{11}x = \dfrac{3}{11}x + K$

96. $\dfrac{x}{6} + 4 = \dfrac{x}{3}$
$x + K = 2x$

SOLVING EQUATIONS BY OPPOSITE OPERATIONS
Compiled by Brian Emond

Once you have mastered solving equations using the balanced equation method, you may find it cumbersome on more complicated equations. Another way to solve equations is by the ***Opposite Operation Method***.

From Multiplication to Division

In the equation $2x = 14$ we see that the variable x must be *doubled* to have the left side of the equation equal 14. Therefore, the variable x, without being doubled, must be *one half* of 14, so we divide 14 by 2; thus $x = 7$.

Example 1:

$$2x = 14 \quad (\text{ Since we } \textit{multiply x by 2 } \text{to get } 14)$$
$$x = \frac{14}{2} \quad (\text{ To solve we } \textit{divide 14 by 2 } \text{to get } 7)$$
$$x = 7$$

Rule 1: *When a coefficient is a **multiplier** on one side of the equal sign, it becomes a **divisor** when it moves to the other side of the equal sign.*

From Division to Multiplication

Now lets look at the equation $\frac{x}{7} = 21$.

Notice that x is so large that it must be *divided by 7* to equal 21. So x must be 7 times *larger* than 21; thus $x = 147$.

Example 2:

$$\frac{x}{7} = 21. \quad (\text{ Since we } \textit{divide x by 7 } \text{to get } 21)$$
$$x = 7 \cdot 21 \quad (\text{ To solve we } \textit{multiply 21 by 7 } \text{to get } 147)$$
$$x = 147$$

Rule 2: *When a coefficient is a **divisor** on one side of the equal sign, it becomes a **multiplier** when it moves to the other side of the equal sign.*

From Addition to Subtraction

In the equation $y + 4 = 14$, it is clear that if you need to *add 4* to the variable y to equal 14, y must be *4 less* than 14; thus $y = 10$.

Example 3:

$$y + 4 = 14 \quad (\text{ Since we } \textit{add 4 to y } \text{to get } 14)$$
$$y = 14 - 4 \quad (\text{ To solve we } \textit{subtract 4 from 14 } \text{to get } 10)$$
$$y = 10$$

Rule 3: *When a constant is **positive** on one side of the equal sign, it becomes **negative** when it moves to the other side of the equal sign.*

Subtraction to Addition

Likewise, in the equation $y - 6 = 9$, it is also clear that if you need to *subtract 6* from the variable y to equal 9, y must be *6 larger* than 9; thus $y = 15$.

Example 4:

$$y - 6 = 9 \quad (\text{Since we } \textit{subtract 6 from y } \text{to get } 9)$$
$$y = 9 + 6 \quad (\text{To solve we } \textit{add 6 to 9 } \text{to get } 15)$$
$$y = 15$$

Rule 4: *When a constant is **negative** on one side of the equal sign, it becomes **positive** when it moves to the other side of the equal sign.*

Solving a Multi-Step Equation

Now that you have seen the various ways to solve an equation for one variable, let's put them all together to solve an equation with many steps.

Example 4:
Try solving the following equation for x using the *Opposite Operation Method:*

$$5x - 6 = 27 + 2x$$

Solution:

$$5x - 6 - 2x = 27$$
$$3x - 6 = 27$$
$$3x = 27 + 6$$
$$3x = 33$$
$$x = \frac{33}{3}$$
$$x = 11$$

Check by substituting 11 for x.

$$5(11) - 6 = 27 + 2(11)$$
$$55 - 6 = 27 + 22$$
$$49 = 49 \qquad \text{True}$$

2.2 AN INTRODUCTION TO PROBLEM SOLVING

Objective **A** Writing Algebraic Expressions

In order to prepare for problem solving, we practice writing algebraic expressions that can be simplified.

Our first example involves consecutive integers and perimeter. Recall that *consecutive integers* are integers that follow one another in order. Study the examples of consecutive integers, consecutive even integers, and consecutive odd integers and their representations.

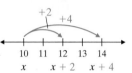

Consecutive Integers:

x $x + 1$ $x + 2$

6   7   8

Consecutive Even Integers:

x $x + 2$ $x + 4$

10   11   12   13   14

Consecutive Odd Integers:

x $x + 2$ $x + 4$

7   8   9   10   11

Helpful Hint

You may want to begin this section by studying key words and phrases and their translations in Sections 1.2 Objective B and 1.3 Objective A.

PRACTICE PROBLEM 1

Write the following as algebraic expressions. Then simplify.

a. The sum of three consecutive even integers, if x is the first even integer.

b. The perimeter of the triangle with sides of length x, $2x + 1$, and $4x$.

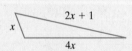

$2x + 1$

x

$4x$

EXAMPLE 1 Write the following as algebraic expressions. Then simplify.

a. The sum of three consecutive integers, if x is the first consecutive integer.

b. The perimeter of the triangle with sides of length x, $5x$, and $6x - 3$.

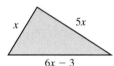

x $5x$

$6x - 3$

Solution:

a. Recall that if x is the first integer, then the next consecutive integer is 1 more, or $x + 1$, and the next consecutive integer is 1 more than $x + 1$, or $x + 1 + 1$, or $x + 2$.

In words:	first integer	plus	next consecutive integer	plus	next consecutive integer
Translate:	x	$+$	$(x + 1)$	$+$	$(x + 2)$

Then $x + (x + 1) + (x + 2) = x + x + 1 + x + 2$

$= 3x + 3$ Simplify by combining like terms.

b. The perimeter of a triangle is the sum of the lengths of the sides.

In words:	side	$+$	side	$+$	side
Translate:	x	$+$	$5x$	$+$	$(6x - 3)$

Then $x + 5x + (6x - 3) = x + 5x + 6x - 3$

$= 12x - 3$ Simplify.

Work Practice Problem 1

EXAMPLE 2 Writing Algebraic Expressions Representing Metropolitan Regions

The most populous metropolitan region in the United States is New York City, although it is only the third most populous metropolitan region in the world. Tokyo is the most populous metropolitan region, followed by Mexico City. Mexico City's population is 0.4 million more than New York, and Tokyo's is twice that of New York decreased by 1.6 million. Write the sum of the populations of these three metropolitan regions as an algebraic expression. Let x be the population of New York (in millions). (*Source:* United Nations, Department of Economic and Social Affairs)

Solution:

If x = the population of New York (in millions) then

$x + 0.4$ = the population of Mexico City (in millions) and

$2x - 1.6$ = the population of Tokyo (in millions)

In words:

population of New York	+	population of Mexico City	+	population of Tokyo

Translate: $\qquad x \qquad + \qquad (x + 0.4) \qquad + \qquad (2x - 1.6)$

Then $x + (x + 0.4) + (2x - 1.6) = x + x + 2x + 0.4 - 1.6$
$$= 4x - 1.2$$

In Exercise 29, we will find the actual populations of these cities.

■ **Work Practice Problem 2**

Objective B Solving Problems

Our main purpose for studying algebra is to solve problems. The following problem-solving strategy will be used throughout this text and may also be used to solve real-life problems that occur outside the mathematics classroom.

General Strategy for Problem Solving

1. UNDERSTAND the problem. During this step, become comfortable with the problem. Some ways of doing this are:

Read and reread the problem.

Choose a variable to represent the unknown.

Construct a drawing if necessary.

Propose a solution and check. Pay careful attention to how you check your proposed solution. This will help when writing an equation to model the problem.

2. TRANSLATE the problem into an equation.

3. SOLVE the equation.

4. INTERPRET the results: If possible, check to see whether your answer is reasonable. Then *check* the proposed solution in the stated problem and *state* your conclusion.

PRACTICE PROBLEM 2

Audience ratings for three new online radio services for an average week in October 2004 were reported by comScore Arbitron Online Radio Ratings. These new online radio stations were AOL® radio Network, Yahoo!®'s LAUNCHcast, and Microsoft's MSN Radio and windowsMedia.com. AOL® radio Network had l359.2 thousand listeners more than the number of listeners Microsoft's MSN Radio and windowsMedia.com had, and Yahoo!®'s LAUNCHcast had 230.l thousand listeners more than four times the number of listeners Microsoft's MSN Radio and windowsMedia.com had. Write the sum of the listeners of these three online radio services as an algebraic expression. Let x be the number of Microsoft's MSN Radio and windowsMedia.com subscribers. (In Exercise 30, we will find the actual number of listeners for each online radio service) (*Source:* comScore Networks, Inc.)

Answer

2. $6x + 1589.3$

Let's review this strategy by solving a problem involving unknown numbers.

EXAMPLE 3 Finding Unknown Numbers

Find three numbers such that the second number is 3 more than twice the first number, and the third number is four times the first number. The sum of the three numbers is 164.

Solution:

1. UNDERSTAND the problem. First let's read and reread the problem and then propose a solution. For example, if the first number is 25, then the second number is 3 more than twice 25, or 53. The third number is four times 25, or 100. The sum of 25, 53, and 100 is 178, not the required sum, but we have gained some valuable information about the problem. First, we know that the first number is less than 25 since our guess led to a sum greater than the required sum. Also, we have gained some information as to how to model the problem.

   Next let's assign a variable and use this variable to represent any other unknown quantities. If we let

$$x = \text{the first number, then}$$
$$\underset{\substack{\uparrow \\ \text{twice the second number}}}{2x} + \underset{\substack{\uparrow \\ \text{3 more than}}}{3} = \text{the second number}$$
$$4x = \text{the third number}$$

2. TRANSLATE the problem into an equation. To do so, we use the fact that the sum of the numbers is 164. First let's write this relationship in words and then translate to an equation.

In words:	first number	added to	second number	added to	third number	is	164
	↓	↓	↓	↓	↓	↓	↓
Translate:	x	$+$	$(2x + 3)$	$+$	$4x$	$=$	164

3. SOLVE the equation.

$$x + (2x + 3) + 4x = 164$$
$$x + 2x + 4x + 3 = 164 \quad \text{Remove parentheses.}$$
$$7x + 3 = 164 \quad \text{Combine like terms.}$$
$$7x = 161 \quad \text{Subtract 3 from both sides.}$$
$$x = 23 \quad \text{Divide both sides by 7.}$$

4. INTERPRET. Here, we *check* our work and *state* the solution. Recall that if the first number $x = 23$, then the second number $2x + 3 = 2 \cdot 23 + 3 = 49$ and the third number $4x = 4 \cdot 23 = 92$.

Check: Is the second number 3 more than twice the first number? Yes, since 3 more than twice 23 is $46 + 3$, or 49. Also, their sum, $23 + 49 + 92 = 164$, is the required sum.

State: The three numbers are 23, 49, and 92.

☐ **Work Practice Problem 3**

Many of today's rates and statistics are given as percents. Interest rates, tax rates, nutrition labeling, and percent of households in a given category are just a few examples. Before we practice solving problems containing percents, let's take a moment to review the meaning of percent and how to find a percent of a number.

The word *percent* means *per hundred,* and the symbol % is used to denote percent. This means that 23% is 23 per one hundred, or $\dfrac{23}{100}$. Also,

$$41\% = \frac{41}{100} = 0.41$$

To find a percent of a number, we multiply.

16% of 25 = 16% $\cdot$ 25 = 0.16 $\cdot$ 25 = 4

Thus, 16% of 25 is 4.

✔**Concept Check** Suppose you are finding 112% of a number x. Which of the following is a correct description of the result? Explain.

a. The result is less than x.

b. The result is equal to x.

c. The result is greater than x.

Next, we solve a problem containing a percent.

EXAMPLE 4 Finding the Original Price of a Computer

Suppose that a computer store just announced an 8% decrease in the price of a particular computer model. If this computer sells for $2162 after the decrease, find its original price.

Solution:

1. UNDERSTAND. Read and reread the problem. Recall that a percent decrease means a percent of the original price. Let's guess that the original price of the computer is $2500. The amount of decrease is then 8% of $2500, or (0.08)($2500) = $200. This means that the new price of the computer is the original price minus the decrease, or $2500 − $200 = $2300. Our guess is incorrect, but we now have an idea of how to model this problem. In our model, we will let x = the original price of the computer.

2. TRANSLATE.

In words:	original price of computer	minus	8% of original price	is	new price
	↓	↓	↓	↓	↓
Translate:	x	−	$0.08x$	=	2162

3. SOLVE the equation.

$x - 0.08x = 2162$

$0.92x = 2162$ Combine like terms.

$x = \dfrac{2162}{0.92} = 2350$ Divide both sides by 0.92.

Continued on next page

PRACTICE PROBLEM 4

The price of a home was just decreased by 6%. If the decreased price is $83,660, find the original price of the home.

Answer

4. $89,000

✔ **Concept Check Answer**

c; the result is greater than x

4. INTERPRET.

Check: The amount $2350 is a reasonable price for a computer. If the original price of the computer was $2350, the new price is

$$\$2350 - (0.08)(\$2350) = \$2350 - \$188$$
$$= \$2162 \quad \text{The given new price}$$

State: The original price of the computer was $2350.

◻ **Work Practice Problem 4**

PRACTICE PROBLEM 5

A rectangle has a perimeter of 106 meters. Its length is 5 meters more than twice its width. Find the length and the width of the rectangle.

△ **EXAMPLE 5** **Finding the Lengths of a Triangle's Sides**

A pennant in the shape of an isosceles triangle is to be constructed for the Slidell High School Athletic Club and sold at a fund-raiser. The company manufacturing the pennant charges according to perimeter, and the athletic club has determined that a perimeter of 149 centimeters should make a nice profit. If each equal side of the triangle is twice the length of the third side, increased by 12 centimeters, find the lengths of the sides of the triangular pennant.

Solution:

1. UNDERSTAND. Read and reread the problem. Recall that the perimeter of a triangle is the distance around. Let's guess that the third side of the triangular pennant is 20 centimeters. This means that each equal side is twice 20 centimeters, increased by 12 centimeters, or $2(20) + 12 = 52$ centimeters.

This gives a perimeter of $20 + 52 + 52 = 124$ centimeters. Our guess is incorrect, but we now have a better understanding of how to model this problem. Now we let

$$x = \text{the third side of the triangle, then}$$
$$2x + 12 = \text{the first side}$$
$$2x + 12 = \text{the second side}$$

2. TRANSLATE.

In words: | first side | + | second side | + | third side | = | 149 |

↓ ↓ ↓ ↓

Translate: $(2x + 12) + (2x + 12) + x = 149$

3. SOLVE the equation.

$$(2x + 12) + (2x + 12) + x = 149$$
$$2x + 12 + 2x + 12 + x = 149 \quad \text{Remove parentheses.}$$
$$5x + 24 = 149 \quad \text{Combine like terms.}$$
$$5x = 125 \quad \text{Subtract 24 from both sides.}$$
$$x = 25 \quad \text{Divide both sides by 5.}$$

Copyright 2007 Pearson Education, Inc.

Answer

5. length: 16 m, width: 37 m

4. INTERPRET. If the third side is 25 centimeters, then the first side is $2(25) + 12 = 62$ centimeters and the second side is 62 centimeters also.

Check: The first and second sides are each twice 25 centimeters increased by 12 centimeters or 62 centimeters. Also, the perimeter is $25 + 62 + 62 = 149$ centimeters, the required perimeter.

State: The dimensions of the triangle are 25 centimeters, 62 centimeters, and 62 centimeters.

▣ **Work Practice Problem 5**

EXAMPLE 6 **Finding Consecutive Integers**

Kelsey Ohleger was helping her friend Benji Burnstine study for an exam. Kelsey told Benji that her three latest art history quiz scores happened to be three consecutive even integers whose sum is 264. Help Benji find the scores.

Solution:

1. UNDERSTAND. Read and reread the problem. Since we are looking for consecutive even integers, let

   x = the first integer. Then

   $x + 2$ = the next consecutive even integer.

   $x + 4 =$ "   "   "   "   "

2. TRANSLATE.

   In words: | first integer | + | next even integer | + | next even integer | = | 264 |

   Translate: $x + (x + 2) + (x + 4) = 264$

3. SOLVE.

   $x + (x + 2) + (x + 4) = 264$

   $3x + 6 = 264$ Combine like terms.

   $3x = 258$ Subtract 6 from both sides.

   $x = 86$ Divide both sides by 3.

4. INTERPRET. If $x = 86$, then $x + 2 = 86 + 2$ or 88, and $x + 4 = 86 + 4$ or 90.

Check: The numbers 86, 88, and 90 are three consecutive even integers. Their sum is 264, the required sum.

State: Kelsey's art history quiz scores are 86, 88, and 90.

▣ **Work Practice Problem 6**

PRACTICE PROBLEM 6

Find three consecutive integers whose sum is 378.

Answer
6. 125, 126, and 127

Objective **A** *Write the following as algebraic expressions. Then simplify. See Examples 1 and 2.*

△ **1.** The perimeter of the square with side length y.

△ **2.** The perimeter of the rectangle with length x and width $x - 5$.

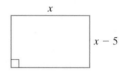

3. The sum of three consecutive integers if the first is z.

4. The sum of three consecutive odd integers if the first integer is x.

5. The total amount of money (in cents) in x nickels, $(x + 3)$ dimes, and $2x$ quarters. (*Hint:* the value of a nickel is 5 cents, the value of a dime is 10 cents, and the value of a quarter is 25 cents)

6. The total amount of money (in cents) in y quarters, $7y$ dimes, and $(2y - 1)$ nickels. (Use the hint for Exercise 5.)

△ **7.** A piece of land along Bayou Liberty is to be fenced and subdivided as shown so that each rectangle has the same dimensions. Express the total amount of fencing needed as an algebraic expression in x.

8. A flooded piece of land near the Mississippi River in New Orleans is to be surveyed and divided into 4 rectangles of equal dimension. Express the total amount of fencing needed as an algebraic expression in y.

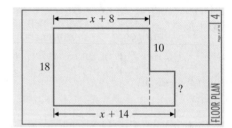

△ **9.** Write the perimeter of the floor plan shown as an algebraic expression in x.

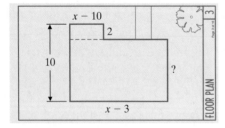

10. Write the perimeter of the floor plan shown as an algebraic expression in x.

Objective **B** *Solve. See Example 3.*

11. Four times the difference of a number and 2 is the same as 2 increased by four times the number plus twice the number. Find the number.

12. Twice the sum of a number and 3 is the same as five times the number minus 1 minus four times the number. Find the number.

13. One number is five times a first number. A third number is 100 more than the first number. If the sum of the three numbers is 415, find the numbers.

14. One number is 6 less than a first number. A third number is twice the first number. If the sum of the three numbers is 306, find the numbers.

Solve. See Examples 4 through 6.

15. The United States consists of 2271 million acres of land. Approximately 29% of this land is federally owned. Find the number of acres that are not federally owned. (*Source:* U.S. General Services Administration)

16. The state of Nevada contains the most federally owned acres of land in the United States. If 90% of the state's 70 million acres of land is federally owned, find the number of acres that are not federally owned. (*Source:* U.S. General Services Administration)

17. In 2004, a total of 3456 earthquakes occurred in the United States. Of these, 91% were minor tremors with magnitudes of 3.9 or less on the Richter scale. How many minor earthquakes occurred in the United States in 2004? Round to the nearest whole. (*Source:* U.S. Geological Survey National Earthquake Information Center)

18. Of the 1376 tornadoes that occurred in the United States during 2003, 39.5% occurred during the month of May. How many tornadoes occurred during May 2003? Round to the nearest whole. (*Source:* Storm Prediction Center)

19. In a recent survey, 15% of online shoppers in the United States say that they prefer to do business only with large, well-known retailers. In a group of 1500 online shoppers, how many are willing to do business with any size retailers? (*Source:* Inc.com)

20. On average 12.8% of American men eat a commercially prepared lunch 5 times or more per week. As of 2003, San Francisco has a male population of 394,828. How many San Francisco men would you expect do not eat a commercially prepared lunch 5 times or more per week? Round to the nearest whole. (*Source:* National Restaurant Association, U.S. Census Bureau)

The following graph is called a circle graph or a pie chart. The circle represents a whole, or in this case, 100%. This particular graph shows the number of minutes per day that people use e-mail at work. Use this graph to answer Exercises 21 through 24.

Time Spent on E-mail at Work

Source: Pew Internet & American Life Project

21. What percent of e-mail users at work spend less than 15 minutes on e-mail per day?

22. Among e-mail users at work, what is the most common time spent on e-mail per day?

23. If it were estimated that a large company has 4633 employees, how many of these would you expect to be using e-mail more than 3 hours per day?

24. If it were estimated that a medium size company has 250 employees, how many of these would you expect to be using e-mail between 2 and 3 hours per day?

25. INVESCO Field at Mile High, home to the Denver Broncos, has 11,675 more seats than Heinz Field, home to the Pittsburgh Steelers. Together, these two stadiums can seat a total of 140,575 NFL fans. How many seats does each stadium have? (*Sources:* Denver Broncos, Pittsburgh Steelers)

26. For the 2001 Major League Baseball season, the opening day payroll for the Minnesota Twins was $46,718,000 less than the opening day payroll for the Colorado Rockies. The total of the opening day payrolls for these two teams was $95,418,000. What was the opening day payroll for each team? (*Source:* Associated Press)

△ 27. The perimeter of the triangle in Example 1b in this section is 483 feet. Find the length of each side.

△ 28. The perimeter of the triangle in Practice Problem 1b in this section is 130.5 meters. Find its dimensions.

29. The sum of the populations of the metropolitan regions of New York, Tokyo and Mexico City is 72 million. Use this information and Example 2 in this section to find the population of each metropolitan region. (*Source:* United Nations Department of Economic and Social Affairs)

30. The total number of listeners to the online radio services AOL® radio Network, Yahoo!®'s LAUNCHcast, and Microsoft's MSN Radio and windowsMedia.com during October 2004 was 4137.5 thousand. Use this information and Practice Problem 2 to find the number of listeners for each online radio service. (*Source:* comScore Networks, Inc.)

Use the diagrams to find the unknown measures of angles or lengths of sides. Recall that the sum of the angle measures of a triangle is 180°.

31.

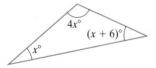

32.

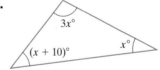

33.

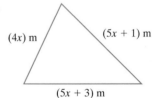

Perimeter is 102 meters.

34.

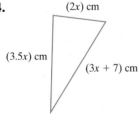

Perimeter is 75 centimeters.

35.

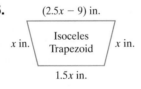

Perimeter is 99 inches.

36.

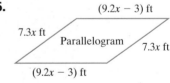

Perimeter is 324 feet.

Many companies and government agencies predict the growth or decline of occupations. The following data are based on information from the U.S. Department of Labor. Notice that the first table is in increase in number of jobs (in thousands) and the second table is in percent increase in number of jobs.

37. Use the table to find the actual number of jobs for each occupation.

Occupation	Increase in Number of Jobs (in thousands) from 2000 to 2012
Security guards	$2x - 51$
Home health aides	$\frac{3}{2}x + 3$
Computer systems analysts	x
Total	780 thousand

38. Use the table to find the actual percent increase in number of jobs for each occupation.

Occupation	Precent Increase in Number of Jobs from 2000 to 2012
Computer software engineers	$\frac{3}{2}x + 1$
Management analysts	x
Receptionist and information clerks	$x - 1$
Total	105%

Solve.

39. The occupations of postsecondary teachers, registered nurses, and medical assistants are among the ten with the largest growth from 2000 to 2012. (See the Chapter 2 opener.) The number of postsecondary teacher jobs will grow 173 thousand more than twice the number of medical assistant jobs. The number of registered nurse jobs will grow 22 thousand less than three times the number of medical assistant jobs. If the total growth of these three jobs is predicted to be 1441 thousand, find the predicted growth of each job.

40. The occupations of telephone operators, fishers, and sewing machine operators are among the ten with the largest job decline from 2000 to 2012, according to the U.S. Department of Labor. The number of telephone operators will decline 8 thousand more than twice the number of fishers. The number of sewing machine operators will decline 1 thousand less than 10 times the number of telephone operators. If the total decline of these three jobs is predicted to be 137 thousand, find the predicted decline of each job.

41. The B767-300ER aircraft has 88 more seats than the B737-200 aircraft. The F-100 has 32 fewer seats than the B737-200 aircraft. If their total number of seats is 413, find the number of seats for each aircraft. (*Source:* Air Transport Association of America)

42. The governor of Delaware makes $36,000 less per year than the governor of Connecticut. The governor of New Jersey makes $7000 more per year than the Connecticut governor. If the total of these salaries is $421,000, find the salary of each governor. (*Source: World Almanac,* 2005)

43. A new fax machine was recently purchased for an office in Hopedale for $464.40 including tax. If the tax rate in Hopedale is 8%, find the price of the fax machine before tax.

44. A premedical student at a local university was complaining that she had just paid $158.60 for her human anatomy book, including tax. Find the price of the book before taxes if the tax rate at this university is 9%.

45. Google, Inc. is a worldwide search engine. On December 28, 2004, shares of Google stock closed at $192.76 per share. This represents a 92.1% increase in stock price from the closing price on August 19, 2004, the day when Google stock was first traded on the NASDAQ exchange. Find the closing price on August 19, 2004. (*Source:* Yahoo! Finance)

46. In 2004, the population of Morocco was 32.2 million. This represented an increase in population of 1.6% from a year earlier. What was the population of Morocco in 2003? Round to the nearest tenth of a million. (*Source:* Population Reference Bureau)

47. The sum of three consecutive integers is 228. Find the integers.

48. The sum of three consecutive odd integers is 327. Find the integers.

Recall that the sum of the angle measures of a triangle is 180°.

△ **49.** Find the measures of the angles of a triangle if the measure of one angle is twice the measure of a second angle and the third angle measures 3 times the second angle decreased by 12.

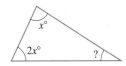

△ **50.** Find the angles of an isoceles triangle whose two base angles are equal and whose third angle is 10° less than three times a base angle.

51. Two frames are needed with the same perimeter: one frame in the shape of a square and one in the shape of an equilateral triangle. Each side of the triangle is 6 centimeters longer than each side of the square. Find the dimensions of each frame. (An equilateral triangle has sides that are the same length.)

52. Two frames are needed with the same perimeter: one frame in the shape of a square and one in the shape of a regular pentagon. Each side of the square is 7 inches longer than each side of the pentagon. Find the dimensions of each frame. (A regular polygon has sides that are the same length.)

53. In 2004, the population of South Africa was 46,900,000 people. From 2004 to 2050, South Africa's population is expected to decrease by 11%. Find the expected population of South Africa in 2050. (*Source:* Population Reference Bureau)

54. Dana, an auto parts supplier headquartered in Toledo, Ohio, recently announced it would be cutting 11,000 jobs worldwide. This is equivalent to 15% of Dana's workforce. Find the size of Dana's workforce prior to this round of job layoffs. Round to the nearest whole. (*Source:* Dana Corporation)

55. The zip codes of three Nevada locations—Fallon, Fernley, and Gardnerville Ranchos—are three consecutive even integers. If twice the first integer added to the third is 268,222, find each zip code.

56. During a recent year, the average SAT scores in math for the states of Alabama, Louisiana, and Michigan were 3 consecutive integers. If the sum of the first integer, second integer, and three times the third integer is 2637, find each score.

Recall that two angles are complements of each other if their sum is 90°. Two angles are supplements of each other if their sum is 180°. Find the measure of each angle.

57. One angle is three times its supplement increased by 20°. Find the measures of the two supplementary angles.

58. One angle is twice its complement increased by 30°. Find the measure of the two complementary angles.

59. Incandescent, fluorescent, and halogen bulbs are lasting longer today than ever before. On average, the number of bulb hours for a fluorescent bulb is 25 times the number of bulb hours for a halogen bulb. The number of bulb hours for an incandescent bulb is 2500 less than the halogen bulb. If the total number of bulb hours for the three types of bulbs is 105,500, find the number of bulb hours for each type. (*Source: Popular Science* magazine)

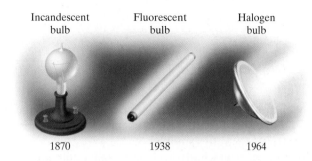

Incandescent bulb 1870   Fluorescent bulb 1938   Halogen bulb 1964

60. Taiwan, Luxembourg, and Italy are the top three countries that have the greatest penetration rate (number of cellular subscriptions per 100 inhabitants) of cellular subscribers in the world. Taiwan has a 9.0 greater penetration rate than Italy. Luxembourg has a 4.3 greater penetration rate than Italy. (*Source: World Almanac and Book of Facts,* 2005)

    a. If the sum of the penetration rates is 318.7, find the number of inhabitants per 100 in each of these countries with cellular subscriptions.

    b. Explain, in your own words, how the penetration rate of cellular subscribers in these three countries is greater than the number of inhabitants.

61. During the 2004 Major League Baseball season, the numbers of home runs hit by Derek Jeter of the New York Yankees, Mark Mulder of the Oakland Athletics, and Geoff Jenkins of the Milwaukee Brewers were three consecutive odd integers. Of these three players, Jenkins hit the most home runs and Jeter hit the fewest home runs. The total number of home runs hit by these three players was 75. How many home runs did each player hit during the 2004 season? (*Source:* Major League Baseball)

62. In the 2004 Summer Olympics, France won more gold medals than Italy, who won more gold medals than Korea. If the total number of gold medals won by these three countries is three consecutive integers whose sum is 30, find the number of gold medals won by each. (*Source:* Athens Olympic Committee)

Review

Find the value of each expression for the given values. See Section 1.5.

63. $4ab - 3bc$; $a = -5$, $b = -8$, and $c = 2$

64. $ab + 6bc$; $a = 0$, $b = -1$, and $c = 9$

65. $n^2 - m^2$; $n = -3$ and $m = -8$

66. $2n^2 + 3m^2$; $n = -2$ and $m = 7$

67. $P + PRT$; $P = 3000$, $R = 0.0325$, and $T = 2$

68. $\frac{1}{3}lwh$; $l = 37.8$, $w = 5.6$, and $h = 7.9$

Concept Extensions

69. For Exercise 38, the percents have a sum of 105%. Is this possible? Why or why not?

70. In your own words, explain the differences in the tables for Exercises 37 and 38.

71. Choose five occupations from the chapter opener graph and define these occupations.

72. Find an angle such that its supplement is equal to twice its complement increased by 50°.

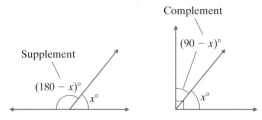

73. The average annual number of cigarettes smoked by an American adult continues to decline. For the years 1990–2002, the equation $y = -72.8x + 2843.5$ approximates this data. Here, x is the number of years after 1990 and y is the average annual number of cigarettes smoked.

   a. If this trend continues, find the year in which the average annual number of cigarettes smoked is 0. To do this, let $y = 0$ and solve for x.

   b. Predict the average annual number of cigarettes smoked by an American adult in 2010. To do so, let $x = 20$ (since $2010 - 1990 = 20$) and find y.

   c. Use the result of part b to predict the average *daily* number of cigarettes smoked by an American adult in 2010. Round to the nearest whole. Do you think this number represents the average daily number of cigarettes smoked by an adult? Why or why not?

74. Determine whether there are three consecutive integers such that their sum is three times the second integer.

75. Determine whether there are two consecutive odd integers such that 7 times the first exceeds 5 times the second by 54.

To break even in a manufacturing business, income or revenue R must equal the cost of production C. Use this information to answer Exercises 76 through 79.

76. The cost C to produce x number of skateboards is $C = 100 + 20x$. The skateboards are sold wholesale for $24 each, so revenue R is given by $R = 24x$. Find how many skateboards the manufacturer needs to produce and sell to break even. (*Hint:* Set the cost expression equal to the revenue expression and solve for x.)

77. The revenue R from selling x number of computer boards is given by $R = 60x$, and the cost C of producing them is given by $C = 50x + 5000$. Find how many boards must be sold to break even. Find how much money is needed to produce the break-even number of boards.

78. In your own words, explain what happens if a company makes and sells fewer products than the break-even number.

79. In your own words, explain what happens if more products than the break-even number are made and sold.

2.3 FORMULAS AND PROBLEM SOLVING

Objectives

A Solve a Formula for a Specified Variable.

B Use Formulas to Solve Problems.

Objective **A** Solving Formulas for Specified Variables

Solving problems that we encounter in the real world sometimes requires us to express relationships among measured quantities. A **formula** is an equation that describes a known relationship among measured phenomena, such as time, area, and gravity. Some examples of formulas follow.

Formula	Meaning
$I = Prt$	Interest = principal · rate · time
$A = lw$	Area of a rectangle = length · width
$d = rt$	Distance = rate · time
$C = 2\pi r$	Circumference of a circle = $2 \cdot \pi \cdot$ radius
$V = lwh$	Volume of a rectangular solid = length · width · height

Other formulas are listed on the inside front cover of this text. Notice that the formula for the volume of a rectangular solid, $V = lwh$, is solved for V since V is by itself on one side of the equation with no Vs on the other side of the equation. Suppose that the volume of a rectangular solid is known as well as its width and its length, and we wish to find its height. One way to find its height is to begin by solving the formula $V = lwh$ for h.

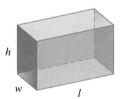

EXAMPLE 1 Solve $V = lwh$ for h.

Solution: To solve $V = lwh$ for h, we want to get h alone on one side of the equation. To do so, we divide both sides of the equation by lw.

$$V = lwh$$

$$\frac{V}{lw} = \frac{lw\ h}{lw} \quad \text{Divide both sides by } lw.$$

$$\frac{V}{lw} = h \text{ or } h = \frac{V}{lw} \quad \text{Simplify.}$$

Thus we see that to find the height of a rectangular solid, we divide its volume by the product of its length and its width.

▣ Work Practice Problem 1

The following steps may be used to solve formulas and equations for a specified variable.

PRACTICE PROBLEM 1

Solve $I = Prt$ for P.

Answer

1. $P = \dfrac{I}{rt}$

89

Solving an Equation for a Specified Variable

Step 1: Clear the equation of fractions or decimals by multiplying each side of the equation by an appropriate nonzero number.

Step 2: Use the distributive property to remove grouping symbols such as parentheses.

Step 3: Combine like terms on each side of the equation.

Step 4: Use the addition property of equality to rewrite the equation as an equivalent equation with terms containing the specified variable on one side and all other terms on the other side.

Step 5: Use the distributive property and the multiplication property of equality to get the specified variable alone.

PRACTICE PROBLEM 2

Solve $2y + 5x = 10$ for y.

EXAMPLE 2 Solve $3y - 2x = 7$ for y.

Solution: This is a linear equation in two variables. Often an equation such as this is solved for y to reveal some properties about the graph of this equation, which we will learn more about in Chapter 3. Since there are no fractions or grouping symbols, we begin with Step 4 and get the term containing the specified variable y on one side by adding $2x$ to both sides of the equation.

$$3y - 2x = 7$$
$$3y - 2x + 2x = 7 + 2x \quad \text{Add } 2x \text{ to both sides.}$$
$$3y = 7 + 2x$$

To solve for y, we divide both sides by 3.

$$\frac{3y}{3} = \frac{7 + 2x}{3} \quad \text{Divide both sides by 3.}$$
$$y = \frac{7 + 2x}{3} \quad \text{or} \quad y = \frac{7}{3} + \frac{2}{3}x$$

▣ **Work Practice Problem 2**

PRACTICE PROBLEM 3

Solve $A = \frac{1}{2}(B + b)h$ for B.

△ **EXAMPLE 3** Solve $A = \frac{1}{2}(B + b)h$ for b.

Solution: Since this formula for finding the area of a trapezoid contains fractions, we begin by multiplying both sides of the equation by the LCD, 2.

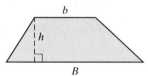

> **Helpful Hint**
> Remember that we may get the specified variable alone on either side of the equation.

$$A = \frac{1}{2}(B + b)h$$

$$2 \cdot A = 2 \cdot \frac{1}{2}(B + b)h \qquad \text{Multiply both sides by 2.}$$

$$2A = (B + b)h \qquad \text{Simplify.}$$

$$2A = Bh + bh \qquad \text{Use the distributive property.}$$

$$2A - Bh = bh \qquad \text{Get the term containing } b \text{ alone by subtracting } Bh \text{ from both sides.}$$

$$\frac{2A - Bh}{h} = \frac{bh}{h} \qquad \text{Divide both sides by } h.$$

$$\frac{2A - Bh}{h} = b \quad \text{or} \quad b = \frac{2A - Bh}{h} \quad \text{or} \quad b = \frac{2A}{h} - B$$

▣ **Work Practice Problem 3**

Answers

2. $y = \dfrac{10 - 5x}{2}$ or $y = 5 - \dfrac{5}{2}x$,

3. $B = \dfrac{2A - bh}{h}$ or $B = \dfrac{2A}{h} - b$

Objective B Using Formulas to Solve Problems

In this section, we also solve problems that can be modeled by known formulas. We use the same problem-solving steps that were introduced in the previous section.

Formulas are very useful in problem solving. For example, the compound interest formula

$$A = P\left(1 + \frac{r}{n}\right)^{nt}$$

is used by banks to compute the amount A in an account that pays compound interest. The variable P represents the principal or amount invested in the account, r is the annual rate of interest, t is the time in years, and n is the number of times compounded per year.

EXAMPLE 4 **Finding the Amount in a Savings Account**

Marial Callier just received an inheritance of $10,000 and plans to place all the money in a savings account that pays 5% compounded quarterly to help her son go to college in 3 years. How much money will be in the account in 3 years?

Solution:

1. **UNDERSTAND.** Read and reread the problem. The appropriate formula needed to solve this problem is the compound interest formula

$$A = P\left(1 + \frac{r}{n}\right)^{nt}$$

Make sure that you understand the meaning of all the variables in this formula:

A = amount in the account after t years

P = principal or amount invested

t = time in years

r = annual rate of interest

n = number of times compounded per year

2. **TRANSLATE.** Use the compound interest formula and let $P = \$10,000$, $r = 5\% = 0.05$, $t = 3$ years, and $n = 4$ since the account is compounded quarterly, or 4 times a year.

Formula: $\quad A = P\left(1 + \frac{r}{n}\right)^{nt}$

Substitute: $\quad A = 10{,}000\left(1 + \frac{0.05}{4}\right)^{4 \cdot 3}$

3. **SOLVE.** We simplify the right side of the equation.

$$A = 10{,}000\left(1 + \frac{0.05}{4}\right)^{4 \cdot 3}$$

$A = 10{,}000(1.0125)^{12}$ Simplify $1 + \dfrac{0.05}{4}$ and write $4 \cdot 3$ as 12.

$A \approx 10{,}000(1.160754518)$ Approximate $(1.0125)^{12}$.

$A \approx 11{,}607.55$ Multiply and round to two decimal places.

4. **INTERPRET.**

Check: Repeat your calculations to make sure that you made no error. Notice that $11,607.55 is a reasonable amount to have in the account after 3 years.

State: In 3 years, the account will contain $11,607.55.

▪ **Work Practice Problem 4**

PRACTICE PROBLEM 4

If $5000 is invested in an account paying 4% compounded monthly, determine how much money will be in the account in 2 years. Use the formula from Example 4.

Answer

4. $5415.71

To solve Example 4, we approximated the expression

$$10{,}000\left(1 + \frac{0.05}{4}\right)^{4\cdot3}.$$

Use the keystrokes (right) to evaluate this expression using a graphing calculator (or graphing utility, or grapher). Notice the use of parentheses.

```
10000(1+(.05/4))
^(4*3)
         11607.54518
```

Mental Math

Solve each equation for the specified variable. See Examples 1 through 3.

1. $2x + y = 5$ for y

2. $7x - y = 3$ for y

3. $a - 5b = 8$ for a

4. $7r + s = 10$ for s

5. $5j + k - h = 6$ for k

6. $w - 4y + z = 0$ for z

2.3 EXERCISE SET

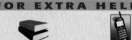
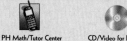

FOR EXTRA HELP

Student Solutions Manual   PH Math/Tutor Center   CD/Video for Review   Math XL   MyMathLab
MathXL®   MyMathLab

Objective Ⓐ *Solve each equation for the specified variable. See Examples 1 through 3.*

1. $d = rt$ for t

2. $W = gh$ for g

3. $I = Prt$ for r

△ **4.** $V = lwh$ for h

△ **5.** $P = a + b + c$ for c

△ **6.** $a^2 + b^2 = c^2$ for b^2

7. $9x - 4y = 16$ for y

8. $2x + 3y = 17$ for y

△ **9.** $P = 2l + 2w$ for l

△ **10.** $P = 2l + 2w$ for w

11. $E = I(r + R)$ for r

12. $A = P(1 + rt)$ for t

13. $5x + 4y = 20$ for y

14. $-9x - 5y = 18$ for y

△ **15.** $S = 2LW + 2LH + 2WH$ for H

△ **16.** $S = 2\pi r^2 + 2\pi rh$ for h

△ **17.** $C = 2\pi r$ for r

△ **18.** $A = \pi r^2$ for π

19. $C = \frac{5}{9}(F - 32)$ for F

20. $F = \frac{9}{5}C + 32$ for C

Objective **B** *Solve. Round all dollar amounts to two decimal places. See Example 4.*

21. Complete the table and find the balance A if $3500 is invested at an annual rate of 3% for 10 years and compounded n times a year.

n	1	2	4	12	365
A					

22. Complete the table and find the balance A if $5000 is invested at an annual rate of 6% for 15 years and compounded n times a year.

n	1	2	4	12	365
A					

23. A principal of $6000 is invested in an account paying an annual rate of 4%. Find the amount in the account after 5 years if the account is compounded

 a. semiannually.
 b. quarterly.
 c. monthly.

24. A principal of $25,000 is invested in an account paying an annual rate of 5%. Find the amount in the account after 2 years if the account is compounded

 a. semiannually.
 b. quarterly.
 c. monthly.

25. One day's high temperature in Phoenix, Arizona, was recorded as 104°F. Write 104°F as degrees Celsius. [Use the formula $C = \dfrac{5}{9}(F - 32)$.]

26. One year's low temperature in Nome, Alaska, was recorded as −15°C. Write −15°C as degrees Fahrenheit. (Use the formula $F = \dfrac{9}{5}C + 32$.)

27. Omaha, Nebraska, is about 90 miles from Lincoln, Nebraska. Irania Schmidt must go to the law library in Lincoln to get a document for the law firm she works for. Find how long it takes her to drive *round-trip* if she averages 50 mph.

28. It took the Selby family $5\dfrac{1}{2}$ hours round-trip to drive from their house to their beach house 154 miles away. Find their average speed.

△ **29.** A package of floor tiles contains 24 one-foot-square tiles. Find how many packages should be bought to cover a square ballroom floor whose side measures 64 feet.

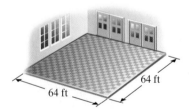
64 ft
64 ft

△ **30.** One-foot-square ceiling tiles are sold in packages of 50. Find how many packages must be bought for a rectangular ceiling 18 feet by 12 feet.

△ **31.** If the area of a triangular kite is 18 square feet and its base is 4 feet, find the height of the kite.

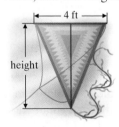
4 ft
height

32. Bryan, Eric, Mandy, and Melissa would like to go to Disneyland in 3 years. The total cost should be $4500. If each invests $1000 in a savings account paying 5.5% interest, compounded semiannually, will they have enough in 3 years?

△ **33.** A gallon of latex paint can cover 500 square feet. Find how many gallon containers of paint should be bought to paint two coats on the walls of a rectangular room whose dimensions are 14 feet by 16 feet. (Assume 8-foot ceilings and disregard any openings such as windows or doors.

△ **34.** A gallon of enamel paint can cover 300 square feet. Find how many gallon containers of paint should be bought to paint three coats on a wall measuring 21 feet by 8 feet.

35. A portion of the external tank of the Space Shuttle *Endeavour* is a liquid hydrogen tank. If the ends of the tank are hemispheres, find the volume of the tank. To do so, answer parts **(a)** through **(c).** (*Source:* NASA/Kennedy Space Center)

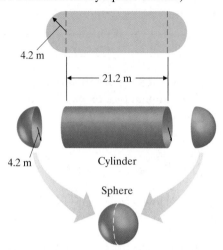

4.2 m

21.2 m

4.2 m   Cylinder

Sphere

  a. Find the volume of the cylinder shown. Round to two decimal places.
  b. Find the volume of the sphere shown. Round to two decimal places.
  c. Add the results of parts **(a)** and **(b).** This sum is the approximate volume of the tank.

36. A different kind of space exploration was launched March 2, 2004. The European Space Agency's *Rosetta* spacecraft is the first to undertake the long-term exploration of a comet, Comet 67P/Churyumov-Gerasimenko, at close quarters. It will take more than 10 years for the spacecraft to reach the comet, arriving in 2014. During its mission, *Rosetta* will travel a total of 490,883,093 miles in 125 months. Find the average speed of the spacecraft in miles per hour. Round to the nearest whole mile per hour. (*Hint:* Convert 125 months to hours using 1 month = 30 days and then use the formula $d = rt$.) (*Source:* European Space Agency)

37. In 1945, Arthur C. Clarke, a scientist and science-fiction writer, predicted that an artificial satellite placed at a height of 22,248 miles directly above the equator would orbit the globe at the same speed with which Earth was rotating. This belt along the equator is known as the Clarke belt. Use the formula for the circumference of a circle and approximate the "length" of the Clarke belt. Round to the nearest whole mile. (*Hint:* Recall that the radius of Earth is approximately 4000 miles.)

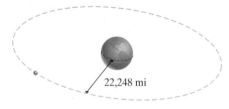

22,248 mi

38. The *Endeavour* Space Shuttle has a cargo bay that is in the shape of a cylinder whose length is 18.3 meters and whose diameter is 4.6 meters. Find its volume.

39. The deepest hole in the ocean floor is beneath the Pacific Ocean and is called Hole 504B. It is located off the coast of Ecuador. Scientists are drilling it to learn more about Earth's history. Currently, the hole is in the shape of a cylinder whose volume is approximately 3800 cubic feet and whose length is 1.3 miles. Find the radius of the hole to the nearest hundredth of a foot. (*Hint:* Make sure the same units of measurement are used.)

40. The deepest man-made hole is called the Kola Superdeep Borehole. It is approximately 8 miles deep and is located near a small Russian town in the Arctic Circle. If it takes 7.5 hours to remove the drill from the bottom of the hole, find the rate that the drill can be retrieved in feet per second. Round to the nearest tenth. (*Hint:* Write 8 miles as feet, 7.5 hours as seconds, and then use the formula $d = rt$.)

△ **41.** Eartha is the world's largest globe. It is located at the headquarters of DeLorme, a mapmaking company in Yarmouth, Maine. Eartha is 41.125 feet in diameter. Find its exact circumference (distance around) and then approximate its circumference using 3.14 for π. (*Source:* DeLorme)

△ **42.** Eartha is in the shape of a sphere. Its radius is about 20.6 feet. Approximate Eartha's volume to the nearest cubic foot. Use the approximation 3.14 for π. (*Source:* DeLorme)

The calorie count of a serving of food can be computed based on its composition of carbohydrate, fat, and protein. The calorie count C for a serving of food can be computed using the formula $C = 4h + 9f + 4p$, where h is the number of grams of carbohydrate contained in the serving, f is the number of grams of fat contained in the serving, and p is the number of grams of protein contained in the serving.

43. Solve this formula for f, the number of grams of fat contained in a serving of food.

44. Solve this formula for h, the number of grams of carbohydrate contained in a serving of food.

45. A serving of cashews contains 14 grams of fat, 7 grams of carbohydrate, and 6 grams of protein. How many calories are in this serving of cashews?

46. A serving of chocolate candies contains 9 grams of fat, 30 grams of carbohydrate, and 2 grams of protein. How many calories are in this serving of chocolate candies?

47. A serving of raisins contains 130 calories and 31 grams of carbohydrate. If raisins are a fat-free food, how much protein is provided by this serving of raisins?

48. A serving of yogurt contains 120 calories, 21 grams of carbohydrate, and 5 grams of protein. How much fat is provided by this serving of yogurt? Round to the nearest tenth of a gram.

Review

Determine which numbers in the set $\{-3, -2, -1, 0, 1, 2, 3\}$ are solutions of each inequality. See Sections 1.3 and 2.1.

49. $x < 0$

50. $x > 1$

51. $x + 5 \leq 6$

52. $x - 3 \geq -7$

53. In your own words, explain what real numbers are solutions of $x < 0$.

54. In your own words, explain what real numbers are solutions of $x > 1$.

Concept Extensions

55. Solar System distances are so great that units other than miles or kilometers are often used. For example, the astronomical unit (AU) is the average distance between Earth and the sun, or 92,900,000 miles. Use this information to convert each planet's distance in miles from the sun to astronomical units. Round to three decimal places. (*Source:* National Space Science Data Center)

Planet	Miles from the Sun	AU from the Sun	Planet	Miles from the Sun	AU from the Sun
Mercury	36 million		Saturn	886.1 million	
Venus	67.2 million		Uranus	1783 million	
Earth	92.9 million		Neptune	2793 million	
Mars	141.5 million		Pluto	3670 million	
Jupiter	483.3 million				

56. An orbit such as Clarke's belt in Exercise 37 is called a geostationary orbit. In your own words, why do you think that communications satellites are placed in geostationary orbits?

57. How much do you think it costs each American to build a Space Shuttle? Write down your estimate. The Space Shuttle *Endeavour* was completed in 1992 and cost approximately $1.7 billion. If the population of the United States in 1992 was 250 million, find the cost per person to build the *Endeavour*. How close was your estimate?

58. Find *how much interest* $10,000 earns in 2 years in a certificate of deposit account paying 8.5% interest compounded quarterly.

59. If you are investing money in a savings account paying a rate of r, which account should you choose — an account compounded 4 times a year or 12 times a year? Explain your choice.

60. To borrow money at a rate of r, which loan plan should you choose — one compounding 4 times a year or 12 times a year? Explain your choice.

61. The Drake Equation is a formula used to estimate the number of technological civilizations that might exist in our own Milky Way Galaxy. The Drake Equation is given as $N = R^* \times f_p \times n_e \times f_l \times f_i \times f_c \times L$. Solve the Drake Equation for the variable n_e. (*Note:* Descriptions of the meaning of each variable in this equation, as well as Drake Equation calculators, exist online. For more information, try doing a Web search on "Drake Equation.")

 STUDY SKILLS BUILDER

How Are Your Homework Assignments Going?

It is very important in mathematics to keep up with homework. Why? Many concepts build on each other. Often your understanding of a day's concepts depends on an understanding of the previous day's material.

Remember that completing your homework assignment involves a lot more than attempting a few of the problems assigned.

To complete a homework assignment, remember these four things:

- Attempt all of it.
- Check it.
- Correct it.
- If needed, ask questions about it.

Take a moment and review your completed homework assignments. Answer the questions below based on this review.

1. Approximate the fraction of your homework you have attempted.

2. Approximate the fraction of your homework you have checked (if possible).

3. If you are able to check your homework, have you corrected it when errors have been found?

4. When working homework, if you do not understand a concept, what do you do?

2.4 LINEAR INEQUALITIES AND PROBLEM SOLVING

Objectives

A Use Interval Notation.

B Solve Linear Inequalities Using the Addition Property of Inequality.

C Solve Linear Inequalities Using the Multiplication Property of Inequality.

D Solve Linear Inequalities Using Both Properties of Inequality.

E Solve Problems That Can Be Modeled by Linear Inequalities.

Relationships among measurable quantities are not always described by equations. For example, suppose that a salesperson earns a base of $600 per month plus a commission of 20% of sales. Suppose we want to find the minimum amount of sales needed to receive a total income of *at least* $1500 per month. Here, the phrase "at least" implies that an income of $1500 *or more* is acceptable. In symbols, we can write

income $\geq$ 1500

This is an example of an inequality, which we will solve in Example 12.

A *linear inequality* in one variable is similar to a linear equation in one variable except that the equality symbol is replaced with an inequality symbol, such as $<, >, \leq,$ or $\geq$.

Linear Inequalities in One Variable

$$3x + 5 \geq 4 \qquad 2y < 0 \qquad 3(x - 4) > 5x \qquad \frac{x}{3} \leq 5$$

↑	↑	↑	↑
is greater than or equal to	is less than	is greater than	is less than or equal to

---

Linear Inequality in One Variable

A **linear inequality in one variable** is an inequality that can be written in the form

$$ax + b < c$$

where a, b, and c are real numbers and $a \neq 0$.

In this section, when we make definitions, state properties, or list steps about an inequality containing the symbol $<$, we mean that the definition, property, or steps apply to an inequality containing the symbols $>$, $\leq$, and $\geq$ also.

Objective **A** Using Interval Notation

A **solution** of an inequality is a value of the variable that makes the inequality a true statement. The **solution set** of an inequality is the set of all solutions. Notice that the solution set of the inequality $x > 2$, for example, contains all numbers greater than 2. Its graph is an interval on the number line since an infinite number of values satisfy the variable. If we use open/closed-circle notation, the graph of $\{x \mid x > 2\}$ looks like:

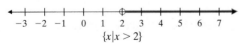

$$\{x \mid x > 2\}$$

In this text, a different graphing notation will be used to help us understand **interval notation.** Instead of an open circle, we use a parenthesis; instead of a closed circle, we use a bracket. With this new notation, the graph of $\{x \mid x > 2\}$ now looks like:

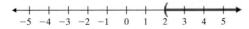

and can be represented in interval notation as $(2, \infty)$. The symbol ∞ is read "infinity" and indicates that the interval includes *all* numbers greater than 2. The left parenthesis indicates that 2 *is not* included in the interval. Using a left bracket, [, would indicate that 2 *is* included in the interval. The following table shows three

97

equivalent ways to describe an interval: in set notation, as a graph, and in interval notation.

Set Notation	Graph	Interval Notation
$\{x \mid x < a\}$		$(-\infty, a)$
$\{x \mid x > a\}$		(a, ∞)
$\{x \mid x \leq a\}$		$(-\infty, a]$
$\{x \mid x \geq a\}$		$[a, \infty)$
$\{x \mid a < x < b\}$		(a, b)
$\{x \mid a \leq x \leq b\}$		$[a, b]$
$\{x \mid a < x \leq b\}$		$(a, b]$
$\{x \mid a \leq x < b\}$		$[a, b)$
$\{x \mid x \text{ is a real number}\}$		$(-\infty, \infty)$

Helpful Hint

Notice that a parenthesis is always used to enclose ∞ and $-\infty$.

PRACTICE PROBLEMS 1–3

Graph each set on a number line and then write it in interval notation.

1. $\{x \mid x > -3\}$

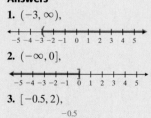

2. $\{x \mid x \leq 0\}$

3. $\{x \mid -0.5 \leq x < 2\}$

EXAMPLES Graph each set on a number line and then write it in interval notation.

1. $\{x \mid x \geq 2\}$ 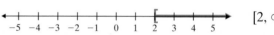 $[2, \infty)$

2. $\{x \mid x < -1\}$  $(-\infty, -1)$

3. $\{x \mid 0.5 < x \leq 3\}$ $(0.5, 3]$

□ **Work Practice Problems 1–3**

✔ **Concept Check** Explain what is wrong with writing the interval $(5, \infty]$.

Objective B Using the Addition Property of Inequality

To solve a linear inequality, we use a process similar to the one used to solve a linear equation. We use properties of inequalities to write equivalent inequalities until the variable is alone on one side of the inequality.

Addition Property of Inequality

If a, b, and c are real numbers, then

$$a < b \quad \text{and} \quad a + c < b + c$$

are equivalent inequalities.

Answers

1. $(-3, \infty)$,

2. $(-\infty, 0]$,

3. $[-0.5, 2)$,

✔ **Concept Check Answer**

should be $(5, \infty)$ since a parenthesis is always used to enclose ∞

In other words, we may add the same real number to both sides of an inequality, and the resulting inequality will have the same solution set. This property also allows us to subtract the same real number from both sides.

EXAMPLE 4 Solve: $x - 2 < 5$. Graph the solution set.

Solution:

$$x - 2 < 5$$
$$x - 2 + 2 < 5 + 2 \quad \text{Add 2 to both sides.}$$
$$x < 7 \quad \text{Simplify.}$$

The solution set is $\{x \mid x < 7\}$, which in interval notation is $(-\infty, 7)$. The graph of the solution set is

🔲 **Work Practice Problem 4**

Helpful Hint

In Example 4, the solution set is $\{x \mid x < 7\}$. This means that *all* numbers less than 7 are solutions. For example, 6.9, 0, $-\pi$, 1, and -56.7 are solutions, just to name a few. To see this, replace x in $x - 2 < 5$ with each of these numbers and see that the result is a true inequality.

EXAMPLE 5 Solve: $4x - 2 < 5x$. Graph the solution set.

Solution: To get x alone on one side of the inequality, we subtract $4x$ from both sides.

$$4x - 2 < 5x$$
$$4x - 2 - 4x < 5x - 4x \quad \text{Subtract } 4x \text{ from both sides.}$$
$$-2 < x \quad \text{or} \quad x > -2 \quad \text{Simplify.}$$

The solution set is $\{x \mid x > -2\}$, which in interval notation is $(-2, \infty)$. The graph is

🔲 **Work Practice Problem 5**

EXAMPLE 6 Solve: $3x + 4 \geq 2x - 6$. Graph the solution set.

Solution:

$$3x + 4 \geq 2x - 6$$
$$3x + 4 - 2x \geq 2x - 6 - 2x \quad \text{Subtract } 2x \text{ from both sides.}$$
$$x + 4 \geq -6 \quad \text{Combine like terms.}$$
$$x + 4 - 4 \geq -6 - 4 \quad \text{Subtract 4 from both sides.}$$
$$x \geq -10 \quad \text{Simplify}$$

The solution set is $\{x \mid x \geq -10\}$, which in interval notation is $[-10, \infty)$. The graph of the solution set is

🔲 **Work Practice Problem 6**

PRACTICE PROBLEM 4

Solve: $x + 3 < 1$. Graph the solution set.

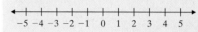

PRACTICE PROBLEM 5

Solve: $3x - 4 < 4x$. Graph the solution set.

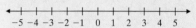

Helpful Hint

Don't forget that $-2 < x$ means the same as $x > -2$.

PRACTICE PROBLEM 6

Solve: $5x - 1 \geq 4x + 4$. Graph the solution set.

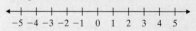

Answers

4. $\{x \mid x < -2\}, (-\infty, -2),$

5. $\{x \mid x > -4\}, (-4, -\infty),$

6. $\{x \mid x \geq 5\}, [5, \infty),$

Objective C Using the Multiplication Property of Inequality

Next, we introduce and use the multiplication property of inequality to solve linear inequalities. To understand this property, let's start with the true statement $-3 < 7$ and multiply both sides by 2.

$$-3 < 7$$
$$2(-3) < 2(7) \quad \text{Multiply both sides by 2.}$$
$$-6 < 14 \quad \text{True}$$

The statement remains true.

Notice what happens if both sides of $-3 < 7$ are multiplied by -2.

$$-3 < 7$$
$$-2(-3) < -2(7) \quad \text{Multiply both sides by 2.}$$
$$6 < -14 \quad \text{False}$$

The inequality $6 < -14$ is a false statement. However, *if the direction of the inequality sign is reversed,* the result is

$$6 > -14 \quad \text{True}$$

These examples suggest the following property.

Multiplication Property of Inequality

If a, b, and c are real numbers and c is **positive,** then

$$a < b \text{ and } ac < bc$$

are equivalent inequalities.

If a, b, and c are real numbers and c is **negative,** then

$$a < b \text{ and } ac > bc$$

are equivalent inequalities.

> **Helpful Hint**
> Whenever both sides of an inequality are multiplied or divided by a negative number, the direction of the inequality symbol *must be* reversed to form an equivalent inequality.

In other words, we may multiply both sides of an inequality by the same positive real number, and the result is an equivalent inequality. We may also multiply both sides of an inequality by the same *negative number* and *reverse the direction of the inequality symbol,* and the result is an equivalent inequality. The multiplication property holds for division also since division is defined in terms of multiplication.

PRACTICE PROBLEM 7

Solve: $\dfrac{1}{6}x \le \dfrac{2}{3}$. Graph the solution set.

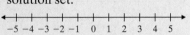

EXAMPLE 7 Solve: $\dfrac{1}{4}x \le \dfrac{3}{2}$. Graph the solution set.

Solution:

$$\dfrac{1}{4}x \le \dfrac{3}{2}$$
$$4 \cdot \dfrac{1}{4}x \le 4 \cdot \dfrac{3}{2} \quad \text{Multiply both sides by 4.}$$
$$x \le 6 \quad \text{Simplify.}$$

> **Helpful Hint**
> The inequality symbol is the same since we are multiplying by a *positive* number.

The solution set is $\{x \mid x \le 6\}$, which in interval notation is $(-\infty, 6]$. The graph of this solution set is

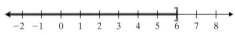

■ **Work Practice Problem 7**

Answer

7. $\{x \mid x \le 4\}, (-\infty, 4],$

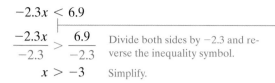 Solve: $-2.3x < 6.9$. Graph the solution set.

Solution:

$$-2.3x < 6.9$$

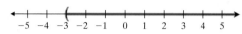 Divide both sides by -2.3 and re-
verse the inequality symbol.

$$x > -3$$ 　Simplify.

> **Helpful Hint**
>
> The inequality symbol is *reversed* since we divided by a *negative* number.

The solution set is $\{x \mid x > -3\}$, which is $(-3, \infty)$ in interval notation. The graph of the solution set is

■ **Work Practice Problem 8**

✔**Concept Check** In which of the following inequalities must the inequality symbol be reversed during the solution process? (If necessary, assume that variable terms are moved to the left and constants are moved to the right.)

a. $-2x > 7$ 　　　　　　　**c.** $-x + 4 + 3x < 5$

b. $2x - 3 > 10$ 　　　　　　**d.** $-x + 4 < 5$

Objective D Using Both Properties of Inequality

Many problems require us to use both properties of inequality. To solve linear inequalities in general, we follow steps similar to those for solving linear equations.

Solving a Linear Inequality in One Variable

Step 1: Clear the equation of fractions or decimals by multiplying both sides of the inequality by an appropriate nonzero number.

Step 2: Use the distributive property to remove grouping symbols such as parentheses.

Step 3: Combine like terms on each side of the inequality.

Step 4: Use the addition property of inequality to rewrite the inequality as an equivalent inequality with variable terms on one side and numbers on the other side.

Step 5: Use the multiplication property of inequality to get the variable alone on one side of the inequality.

EXAMPLE 9 Solve: $-(x - 3) + 2 \leq 3(2x - 5) + x$. Graph the solution set.

Solution:

$$-(x - 3) + 2 \leq 3(2x - 5) + x$$

$$-x + 3 + 2 \leq 6x - 15 + x$$ 　Apply the distributive property.

$$5 - x \leq 7x - 15$$ 　Combine like terms.

$$5 - x + x \leq 7x - 15 + x$$ 　Add x to both sides.

$$5 \leq 8x - 15$$ 　Combine like terms.

$$5 + 15 \leq 8x - 15 + 15$$ 　Add 15 to both sides.

$$20 \leq 8x$$ 　Combine like terms.

Continued on next page

Continued on next page

PRACTICE PROBLEM 8

Solve: $-1.1x < 5.5$. Graph the solution set.

$$\text{-5 -4 -3 -2 -1　0　1　2　3　4　5}$$

PRACTICE PROBLEM 9

Solve:

$-(2x - 6) \leq 4(2x - 4) + 2$. Write the solution in interval notation.

Answers

8. $\{x \mid x > -5\}$, $(-5, \infty)$,

$$\text{-5 -4 -3 -2 -1　0　1　2　3　4　5}$$

9. $[2, \infty)$

✔ **Concept Check Answer**

a, d

Copyright 2007 Pearson Education, Inc.

Helpful Hint

In Example 9, don't forget that $\frac{5}{2} \leq x$ means the same as $x \geq \frac{5}{2}$.

$$\frac{20}{8} \leq \frac{8x}{8} \qquad \text{Divide both sides by 8.}$$

$$\frac{5}{2} \leq x, \quad \text{or} \quad x \geq \frac{5}{2} \qquad \text{Simplify.}$$

The solution set written in interval notation is $\left[\frac{5}{2}, \infty\right)$ and its graph is

■ **Work Practice Problem 9**

PRACTICE PROBLEM 10

Solve: $\frac{3}{4}(x + 2) \geq x - 6$.

Write the solution set in interval notation.

EXAMPLE 10 Solve: $\frac{2}{5}(x - 6) \geq x - 1$. Write the solution set in interval notation.

Solution:

$$\frac{2}{5}(x - 6) \geq x - 1$$

$$5\left[\frac{2}{5}(x - 6)\right] \geq 5(x - 1) \qquad \text{Multiply both sides by 5 to eliminate fractions.}$$

$$2(x - 6) \geq 5(x - 1)$$

$$2x - 12 \geq 5x - 5 \qquad \text{Use the distributive property.}$$

$$-3x - 12 \geq -5 \qquad \text{Subtract } 5x \text{ from both sides.}$$

$$-3x \geq 7 \qquad \text{Add 12 to both sides.}$$

$$\frac{-3x}{-3} \leq \frac{7}{-3} \qquad \text{Divide both sides by } -3 \text{ and reverse the inequality symbol.}$$

$$x \leq -\frac{7}{3} \qquad \text{Simplify.}$$

The solution set is $\left(-\infty, -\frac{7}{3}\right]$.

■ **Work Practice Problem 10**

PRACTICE PROBLEM 11

Solve: $5(x - 3) < 5x + 2$.

EXAMPLE 11 Solve: $2(x + 3) > 2x + 1$.

Solution:

$$2(x + 3) > 2x + 1$$

$$2x + 6 > 2x + 1 \qquad \text{Distribute on the left side.}$$

$$2x + 6 - 2x > 2x + 1 - 2x \qquad \text{Subtract } 2x \text{ from both sides.}$$

$$6 > 1 \qquad \text{Simplify.}$$

$6 > 1$ is a true statement for all values of x, so this inequality and the original inequality are true for all numbers. The solution set is $\{x \mid x \text{ is a real number}\}$, or $(-\infty, \infty)$ in interval notation, and its graph is

■ **Work Practice Problem 11**

Answers

10. $(-\infty, 30]$,

11. $(-\infty, \infty)$

Objective **E** Linear Inequalities and Problem Solving

Problems containing words such as "at least," "at most," "between," "no more than," and "no less than" usually indicate that an inequality is to be solved instead of an equation. In solving applications involving linear inequalities, we use the same four-step strategy as when we solved applications involving linear equations.

EXAMPLE 12 Calculating Income with Commission

A salesperson earns $600 per month plus a commission of 20% of sales. Find the minimum amount of sales needed to receive a total income of at least $1500 per month.

Solution:

1. UNDERSTAND. Read and reread the problem. Let

   x = amount of sales

2. TRANSLATE. Since the income is to be at least $1500, this means, we want the income to be greater than or equal to $1500. To write an inequality, notice that the salesperson's income consists of $600 plus a commission (20% of sales).

   In words: 600 +   commission of 20% of sales $\geq$ 1500

   Translate: 600 + $0.20x$ $\geq$ 1500

3. SOLVE the inequality for x.

$$600 + 0.20x \geq 1500$$
$$600 + 0.20x - 600 \geq 1500 - 600$$
$$0.20x \geq 900$$
$$x \geq 4500$$

4. INTERPRET.

Check: The income for sales of $4500 is

$$600 + 0.20(4500), \text{ or } 1500$$

Thus, if sales are greater than or equal to $4500, income is greater than or equal to $1500.

State: The minimum amount of sales needed for the salesperson to earn at least $1500 per month is $4500.

◼ **Work Practice Problem 12**

EXAMPLE 13 Finding the Annual Consumption

In the United States, the annual consumption of cigarettes is declining. The consumption c in billions of cigarettes per year since 1990 can be approximated by the formula $c = -9.2t + 527.33$, where t is the number of years after 1990. Use this formula to predict the first year that the consumption of cigarettes will be less than 200 billion per year. (*Source:* U.S. Department of Agriculture Economic Research Service.)

Continued on next page

PRACTICE PROBLEM 12

A salesperson earns $1000 a month plus a commission of 15% of sales. Find the minimum amount of sales needed to receive a total income of at least $4000 per month.

PRACTICE PROBLEM 13

Use the formula given in Example 13 to predict when the consumption of cigarettes will be less than 100 billion per year.

Answers

12. $20,000,   **13.** after the year 2037

Solution:

1. UNDERSTAND. Read and reread the problem. To become familiar with the given formula, let's find the cigarette consumption after 20 years, which would be the year 1990 + 20 or 2010. To do so, we substitute 20 for t in the given formula.

$$c = -9.2(20) + 527.33 = 343.33$$

Thus, in 2010, we predict cigarette consumption to be about 343.3 billion. Variables have already been assigned in the given formula. For review, they are

c = the annual consumption of cigarettes in the United States in billions of cigarettes

t = the number of years after 1990

2. TRANSLATE. We are looking for the first year that the consumption of cigarettes *c is less than 200*. Since we are finding years t, we substitute the expression in the formula given for c, or

$$-9.2t + 527.33 < 200$$

3. SOLVE the inequality.

$$-9.2t + 527.33 < 200$$
$$-9.2t < -327.33$$
$$t > \text{approximately } 35.58$$

4. INTERPRET.

Check: Substitute a number greater than 35.58 and see that c is less than 200.

State: The annual consumption of cigarettes will be less than 200 billion more than 35.58 years after 1990, or in approximately 36 + 1990 = 2026.

▣ **Work Practice Problem 13**

Mental Math

Solve each inequality.

1. $x - 2 < 4$ **2.** $x - 1 > 6$ **3.** $x + 5 \geq 15$ **4.** $x + 1 \leq 8$

5. $3x > 12$ **6.** $5x < 20$ **7.** $\dfrac{x}{2} \leq 1$ **8.** $\dfrac{x}{4} \geq 2$

2.4 EXERCISE SET

FOR EXTRA HELP

Student Solutions Manual   PH Math/Tutor Center   CD/Video for Review   MathXL®   MyMathLab

Objective A *Graph the solution set of each inequality on a number line and then write it in interval notation. See Examples 1 through 3.*

1. $\{x \mid x < -3\}$

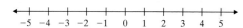

2. $\{x \mid x > 5\}$

3. $\{x \mid x \geq 0.3\}$

4. $\{x \mid x < -0.2\}$

5. $\{x \mid -7 \leq x\}$

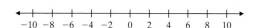

6. $\{x \mid -7 \geq x\}$

7. $\{x \mid -2 < x < 5\}$

8. $\{x \mid -5 \leq x \leq -1\}$

9. $\{x \mid 5 \geq x > -1\}$

10. $\{x \mid -3 > x \geq -7\}$

Objective B *Solve. Graph the solution set and write it in interval notation. See Examples 4 through 6.*

11. $x - 7 \geq -9$

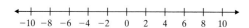

12. $x + 2 \leq -1$

13. $7x < 6x + 1$

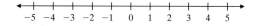

14. $11x < 10x + 5$

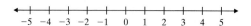

15. $8x - 7 \leq 7x - 5$

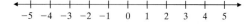

16. $7x - 1 \geq 6x - 1$

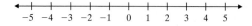

Objective 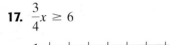 *Solve. Graph the solution set and then write it in interval notation. See Examples 7 and 8.*

17. $\frac{3}{4}x \geq 6$

18. $\frac{5}{6}x \geq 5$

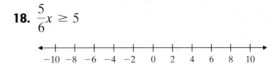

19. $5x < -23.5$

20. $4x > -11.2$

21. $-3x \geq 9$

22. $-4x \geq 8$

Objective 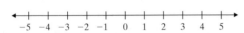 *Solve. Write the solution set using interval notation. See Examples 9 through 11.*

23. $-2x + 7 \geq 9$

24. $8 - 5x \leq 23$

25. $15 + 2x \geq 4x - 7$

26. $20 + x < 6x - 15$

27. $4(2x + 1) > 4$

28. $6(2 - 3x) \geq 12$

29. $3(x - 5) < 2(2x - 1)$

30. $5(x + 4) \leq 4(2x + 3)$

31. $\frac{5x + 1}{7} - \frac{2x - 6}{4} \geq -4$

32. $\frac{1 - 2x}{3} + \frac{3x + 7}{7} > 1$

33. $-3(2x - 1) < -4[2 + 3(x + 2)]$

34. $-2(4x + 2) > -5[1 + 2(x - 1)]$

Objectives **B** **C** **D** **Mixed Practice** *Solve. Write the solution set using interval notation. See Examples 4 through 11.*

35. $x + 9 < 3$

36. $x - 9 < -12$

37. $-x < -4$

38. $-x > -2$

39. $-7x \leq 3.5$

40. $-6x \leq 4.2$

41. $\frac{1}{2} + \frac{2}{3} \geq \frac{x}{6}$

42. $\frac{3}{4} - \frac{2}{3} \geq \frac{x}{6}$

43. $-5x + 4 \leq -4(x - 1)$

44. $-6x + 2 < -3(x + 4)$

45. $\frac{3}{4}(x - 7) \geq x + 2$

46. $\frac{4}{5}(x + 1) \leq x + 1$

47. $0.8x + 0.6x \geq 4.2$

48. $0.7x - x > 0.45$

49. $4(x - 6) + 2x - 4 \geq 3(x - 7) + 10x$

50. $7(2x + 3) + 4x \leq 7 + 5(3x - 4) + x$

51. $14 - (5x - 6) \geq -6(x + 1) - 5$

52. $13y - (9y + 2) \leq 5(y - 6) + 10$

53. $\frac{1}{2}(3x - 4) \leq \frac{3}{4}(x - 6) + 1$

54. $\frac{2}{3}(x + 3) < \frac{1}{6}(2x - 8) + 2$

55. $0.4(4x - 3) < 1.2(x + 2)$

56. $0.2(8x - 2) < 1.2(x - 3)$

57. $\dfrac{2}{5}x - \dfrac{1}{4} \le \dfrac{3}{10}x - \dfrac{4}{5}$

58. $\dfrac{7}{12}x - \dfrac{1}{3} \le \dfrac{3}{8}x - \dfrac{5}{6}$

Objective **E** *Solve. See Examples 12 and 13. For Exercises 59 through 66,* **a.** *answer with an inequality, and* **b.** *in your own words, explain the meaning of your answer to part a.*

Exercises 59 and 60 are written to help you get started.

59. Shureka Washburn has scores of 72, 67, 82, and 79 on her algebra tests.
  a. Use an inequality to find the scores she must make on the final exam to pass the course with an average of 77 or higher, given that the final exam counts as two tests.
  b. In your own words explain the meaning of your answer to part a.

60. In a Winter Olympics 5000-meter speed-skating event, Hans Holden scored times of 6.85, 7.04, and 6.92 minutes on his first three trials.
  a. Use an inequality to find the times he can score on his last trial so that his average time is under 7.0 minutes.
  b. In your own words, explain the meaning of your answer to part a.

61. A small plane's maximum takeoff weight is 2000 pounds or less. Six passengers weigh an average of 160 pounds each. Use an inequality to find the luggage and cargo weights the plane can carry.

62. A shopping mall parking garage charges $1 for the first half-hour and 60 cents for each additional half-hour. Use an inequality to find how long you can park if you have only $4.00 in cash.

63. A clerk must use the elevator to move boxes of paper. The elevator's maximum weight limit is 1500 pounds. If each box of paper weighs 66 pounds and the clerk weighs 147 pounds, use an inequality to find the number of whole boxes she can move on the elevator at one time.

64. To mail an envelope first class, the U.S. Post Office charges 37 cents for the first ounce and 23 cents per ounce for each additional ounce. Use an inequality to find the number of whole ounces that can be mailed for no more than $4.00

65. Northeast Telephone Company offers two billing plans for local calls.

Plan 1: $25 per month for unlimited calls
Plan 2: $13 per month plus $0.06 per call

Use an inequality to find the number of monthly calls for which plan 1 is more economical than plan 2.

66. A car rental company offers two subcompact rental plans.

Plan A: $36 per day and unlimited mileage
Plan B: $24 per day plus $0.15 per mile

Use an inequality to find the number of daily miles for which plan A is more economical than plan B.

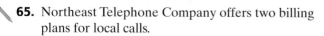

67. At room temperature, glass used in windows actually has some properties of a liquid. It has a very slow, viscous flow. (Viscosity is the property of a fluid that resists internal flow. For example, lemonade flows more easily than fudge syrup. Fudge syrup has a higher viscosity than lemonade.) Glass does not become a true liquid until temperatures are greater than or equal to 500°C. Find the Fahrenheit temperatures for which glass is a liquid. (Use the formula $F = \frac{9}{5}C + 32$.)

68. Stibnite is a silvery white mineral with a metallic luster. It is one of the few minerals that melts easily in a match flame or at temperatures of approximately 977°F or greater. Find the Celsius temperatures for which stibnite melts. [Use the formula $C = \frac{5}{9}(F - 32)$.]

69. Although beginning salaries vary greatly according to your field of study, the equation

$$s = 651.2t + 27{,}821$$

can be used to approximate and to predict average beginning salaries for candidates with bachelor's degrees. The variable s is the starting salary and t is the number of years after 1989.

a. Approximate when beginning salaries for candidates will be greater than $35,000.

b. Determine the year you plan to graduate from college. Use this year to find the corresponding value of t and approximate your beginning salary.

70. a. Use the formula in Example 13 to estimate the years that the consumption of cigarettes will be less than 50 billion per year.

b. Use your answer to part a to describe the limitations of your answer.

The average consumption per person per year of whole milk w can be approximated by the equation

$$w = -1.9t + 70.1$$

where t is the number of years after 1996 and w is measured in pounds. The average consumption of skim milk s per person per year can be approximated by the equation

$$s = -0.8t + 34.3$$

where t is the number of years after 1996 and s is measured in pounds. The consumption of whole milk is shown on the graph in blue and the consumption of skim milk is shown on the graph in red. Use this information to answer Exercises 71 through 79.

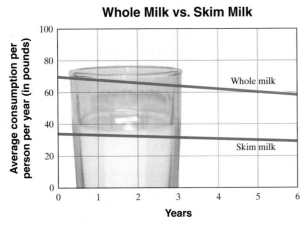

Whole Milk vs. Skim Milk

Source: Based on data from U.S. Department of Agriculture, Economic Research Service

71. Is the consumption of whole milk increasing or decreasing over time? Explain how you arrived at your answer.

72. Is the consumption of skim milk increasing or decreasing over time? Explain how you arrived at your answer.

73. Predict the consumption of whole milk in 2010. (*Hint:* Find the value of t that corresponds to 2010.)

74. Predict the consumption of skim milk in 2010. (*Hint:* Find the value of t that corresponds to 2010.)

75. Determine when the consumption of whole milk will be less than 50 pounds per person per year.

76. For 1996 through 2002, the consumption of whole milk was greater than the consumption of skim milk. Explain how this can be determined from the graph.

77. Both lines have a negative slope, that is, the amount of each type of milk consumed per person per year is decreasing as time goes on. However, the amount of whole milk being consumed is decreasing faster than the amount of skim milk being consumed. Explain how this could be.

78. Do you think it is possible that the consumption of whole milk will eventually be the same as the consumption of skim milk? Explain your answer.

79. The consumption of skim milk will be greater than as the consumption of whole milk when $s > w$.
   a. Find when this will occur by substituting the given equivalent expression for w and the given equivalent expression for s and solving for t.
   b. Estimate to the nearest whole the first year when this will occur.

Review

List or describe the integers that make both inequalities true.

80. $x < 5$ and $x > 1$

81. $x \geq 0$ and $x \leq 7$

82. $x \geq -2$ and $x \geq 2$

83. $x < 6$ and $x < -5$

Solve each equation for x.

84. $2x - 6 = 4$

85. $3x - 12 = 3$

86. $-x + 7 = 5x - 6$

87. $-5x - 4 = -x - 4$

Concept Extensions

In which inequality must the inequality symbol be reversed during the solution process? If necessary, assume that variable terms are moved to the left and constants to the right.

88. $3x > -14$

89. $-3x \leq 14$

90. $-3x < -14$

91. $-x - 17 \geq -23$

92. Write an inequality whose solution set is $\{x \mid x \leq 2\}$.

93. Solve: $2x - 3 = 5$

94. Solve: $2x - 3 < 5$

95. Solve: $2x - 3 > 5$

96. Read the equations and inequalities for Exercises 93, 94, and 95 and their solutions. In your own words, write down your thoughts.

Solve each inequality.

97. $4(x - 1) \geq 4x - 8$

98. $3x + 1 < 3(x - 2)$

99. $7x < 7(x - 2)$

100. $8(x + 3) \leq 7(x + 5) + x$

101. When graphing the solution set of an inequality, explain how you know whether to use a parenthesis or a bracket.

102. Explain what is wrong with the interval notation $(-6, -\infty)$.

103. Explain how solving a linear inequality is similar to solving a linear equation.

104. Explain how solving a linear inequality is different from solving a linear equation.

Linear Equations and Inequalities

Answers

1. _____

2. _____

3. _____

4. _____

5. _____

6. _____

7. _____

8. _____

9. _____

10. _____

11. _____

12. _____

13. _____

14. _____

Solve each equation or inequality.

1. $-4x = 20$

2. $-4x < 20$

3. $\dfrac{3x}{4} \geq 2$

4. $5x + 3 \geq 2 + 4x$

5. $6(y - 4) = 3(y - 8)$

6. $-4x \leq \dfrac{2}{5}$

7. $-3x \geq \dfrac{1}{2}$

8. $5(y + 4) = 4(y + 5)$

9. $7x < 7(x - 2)$

10. $\dfrac{-5x + 11}{2} \leq 7$

11. $-5x + 1.5 = -19.5$

12. $-5x + 4 = -26$

13. $5 + 2x - x = -x + 3 - 14$

14. $12x + 14 < 11x - 2$

15. $\dfrac{x}{5} - \dfrac{x}{4} = \dfrac{x-2}{2}$

16. $12x - 12 = 8(x - 1)$

17. $2(x - 3) > 70$

18. $-3x - 4.7 = 11.8$

19. $-2(b - 4) - (3b - 1) = 5b + 3$

20. $8(x + 3) < 7(x + 5) + x$

21. $\dfrac{3t + 1}{8} = \dfrac{5 + 2t}{7} + 2$

22. $4(x - 6) - x = 8(x - 3) - 5x$

23. $\dfrac{x + 3}{12} + \dfrac{x - 5}{15} < \dfrac{2}{3}$

24. $\dfrac{y}{3} + \dfrac{y}{5} = \dfrac{y + 3}{10}$

25. $5(x - 6) + 2x > 3(2x - 1) - 4$

26. $14(x - 1) - 7x \leq 2(3x - 6) + 4$

27. $\dfrac{1}{4}(3x + 2) - x \geq \dfrac{3}{8}(x - 5) + 2$

28. $\dfrac{1}{3}(x - 10) - 4x > \dfrac{5}{6}(2x + 1) - 1$

15. _____

16. _____

17. _____

18. _____

19. _____

20. _____

21. _____

22. _____

23. _____

24. _____

25. _____

26. _____

27. _____

28. _____

A Find the Intersection of Two Sets.

B Solve Compound Inequalities Containing "*and.*"

C Find the Union of Two Sets.

D Solve Compound Inequalities Containing "*or.*"

2.5 SETS AND COMPOUND INEQUALITIES

Two inequalities joined by the words **and** or **or** are called **compound inequalities.**

Compound Inequalities

$x + 3 < 8$ and $x > 2$

$\dfrac{2x}{3} \geq 5$ or $-x + 10 < 7$

Objective **A** Finding the Intersection of Two Sets

The solution set of a compound inequality formed by the word **and** is the *intersection* of the solution sets of the two inequalities. We use the symbol $\cap$ to denote "intersection."

Intersection of Two Sets

The **intersection** of two sets, A and B, is the set of all elements common to both sets. A intersect B is denoted by

$A \cap B$

PRACTICE PROBLEM 1

Find the intersection:

$\{1, 2, 3, 4, 5\} \cap \{3, 4, 5, 6\}$

EXAMPLE 1 Find the intersection: $\{2, 4, 6, 8\} \cap \{3, 4, 5, 6\}$

Solution: The numbers 4 and 6 are in both sets. The intersection is $\{4, 6\}$.

Work Practice Problem 1

Objective **B** Solving Compound Inequalities Containing "*and*"

A value is a **solution** of a compound inequality formed by the word **and** if it is a solution of *both* inequalities. For example, the solution set of the compound inequality $x \leq 5$ and $x \geq 3$ contains all values of x that make the inequality $x \leq 5$ a true statement **and** the inequality $x \geq 3$ a true statement. The first graph shown below is the graph of $x \leq 5$, the second graph is the graph of $x \geq 3$, and the third graph shows the intersection of the two graphs. The third graph is the graph of $x \leq 5$ **and** $x \geq 3$.

$\{x \mid x \leq 5\}$ (number line from -4 to 6, shaded left of 5) $(-\infty, 5]$

$\{x \mid x \geq 3\}$ (number line from -4 to 6, shaded right of 3) $[3, \infty)$

$\{x \mid x \leq 5 \text{ and } x \geq 3\}$, also $\{x \mid 3 \leq x \leq 5\}$ (see below)   (number line from -4 to 6, shaded between 3 and 5) $[3, 5]$

Since $x \geq 3$ is the same as $3 \leq x$, the compound inequality $3 \leq x$ and $x \leq 5$ can be written in a more compact form as $3 \leq x \leq 5$. The solution set $\{x \mid 3 \leq x \leq 5\}$ includes all numbers that are greater than or equal to 3 and at the same time less than or equal to 5.

In interval notation, the set $\{x \mid x \leq 5 \text{ and } x \geq 3\}$ or $\{x \mid 3 \leq x \leq 5\}$ is written as $[3, 5]$.

Answer

1. $\{3, 4, 5\}$

Helpful Hint

Don't forget that some compound inequalities containing "and" can be written in a more compact form.

Compound Inequality	Compact Form	Interval Notation
$2 \leq x$ and $x \leq 6$	$2 \leq x \leq 6$	$[2, 6]$

Graph:
```
←——┼——┼——┼——┼——┼——■━━━━━■——┼——→
   -3  -2  -1   0   1   2   3   4   5   6   7
```

EXAMPLE 2 Solve: $x - 7 < 2$ and $2x + 1 < 9$

Solution: First we solve each inequality separately.

$$x - 7 < 2 \quad and \quad 2x + 1 < 9$$
$$x < 9 \quad and \quad 2x < 8$$
$$x < 9 \quad and \quad x < 4$$

Now we can graph the two intervals on two number lines and find their intersection.

$\{x \mid x < 9\}$ $(-\infty, 9)$
```
←━━━━━━━━━━━━━━━━━━━━)——┼——→
   0   1   2   3   4   5   6   7   8   9   10
```

$\{x \mid x < 4\}$ $(-\infty, 4)$
```
←━━━━━━━━━━)——┼——┼——┼——┼——┼——→
   0   1   2   3   4   5   6   7   8   9   10
```

$\{x \mid x < 9 \text{ and } x < 4\}$ $(-\infty, 4)$
$= \{x \mid x < 4\}$
```
←━━━━━━━━━━)——┼——┼——┼——┼——┼——→
   0   1   2   3   4   5   6   7   8   9   10
```

The solution set is $(-\infty, 4)$.

▢ Work Practice Problem 2

EXAMPLE 3 Solve: $2x \geq 0$ and $4x - 1 \leq -9$

Solution: First we solve each inequality separately.

$$2x \geq 0 \quad and \quad 4x - 1 \leq -9$$
$$x \geq 0 \quad and \quad 4x \leq -8$$
$$x \geq 0 \quad and \quad x \leq -2$$

Now we can graph the two intervals and find their intersection.

$\{x \mid x \geq 0\}$ $[0, \infty)$
```
←——┼——┼——┼——┼——┼——■━━━━━━━━━→
  -5  -4  -3  -2  -1   0   1   2   3   4   5
```

$\{x \mid x \leq -2\}$ $(-\infty, -2]$
```
←━━━━━━━━■——┼——┼——┼——┼——┼——┼——→
  -5  -4  -3  -2  -1   0   1   2   3   4   5
```

$\{x \mid x \geq 0 \text{ and }$
$x \leq -2\} = \varnothing$
```
←——┼——┼——┼——┼——┼——┼——┼——┼——┼——┼——→
  -5  -4  -3  -2  -1   0   1   2   3   4   5
```

There is no number that is greater than or equal to 0 **and** less than or equal to −2. The solution set is $\varnothing$.

▢ Work Practice Problem 3

Helpful Hint

Example 3 shows that some compound inequalities have no solution. Also, some have all real numbers as solutions.

To solve a compound inequality like $2 < 4 - x < 7$, we get x alone in the middle. Since a compound inequality is really two inequalities in one statement, we must perform the same operation to all three parts of the inequality.

PRACTICE PROBLEM 2

Solve: $x + 5 < 9$ and $3x - 1 < 2$

PRACTICE PROBLEM 3

Solve: $4x \geq 0$ and $2x + 4 \leq 2$

Answers

2. $(-\infty, 1)$, **3.** $\varnothing$

PRACTICE PROBLEM 4

Solve: $5 < 1 - x < 9$

EXAMPLE 4 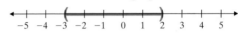 Solve: $2 < 4 - x < 7$

Solution: To get x alone, we first subtract 4 from all three parts.

$$2 < 4 - x < 7$$
$$2 - 4 < 4 - x - 4 < 7 - 4 \quad \text{Subtract 4 from all three parts.}$$
$$-2 < -x < 3 \quad \text{Simplify.}$$
$$\frac{-2}{-1} > \frac{-x}{-1} > \frac{3}{-1} \quad \text{Divide all three parts by } -1 \text{ and reverse the inequality symbols.}$$
$$2 > x > -3$$

> **Helpful Hint**
> Don't forget to reverse both inequality symbols.

This is equivalent to $-3 < x < 2$, and its graph is shown.

The solution set in interval notation is $(-3, 2)$.

■ **Work Practice Problem 4**

PRACTICE PROBLEM 5

Solve: $-2 < \frac{3}{4}x + 2 \le 5$

EXAMPLE 5 Solve: $-1 \le \frac{2}{3}x + 5 < 2$

Solution: First we clear the inequality of fractions by multiplying all three parts by the LCD, 3.

$$-1 \le \frac{2}{3}x + 5 < 2$$
$$3(-1) \le 3\left(\frac{2}{3}x + 5\right) < 3(2) \quad \text{Multiply all three parts by the LCD, 3.}$$
$$-3 \le 2x + 15 < 6 \quad \text{Use the distributive property and multiply.}$$
$$-3 - 15 \le 2x + 15 - 15 < 6 - 15 \quad \text{Subtract 15 from all three parts.}$$
$$-18 \le 2x < -9 \quad \text{Simplify.}$$
$$\frac{-18}{2} \le \frac{2x}{2} < \frac{-9}{2} \quad \text{Divide all three parts by 2.}$$
$$-9 \le x < -\frac{9}{2} \quad \text{Simplify.}$$

The graph of the solution is shown.

The solution set in interval notation is $\left[-9, -\frac{9}{2}\right)$.

■ **Work Practice Problem 5**

Objective **C** Finding the Union of Two Sets

The solution set of a compound inequality formed by the word **or** is the **union** of the solution sets of the two inequalities. We use the symbol $\cup$ to denote "union."

> **Helpful Hint**
> The word "either" in this definition means "one or the other or both."

Union of Two Sets

The **union** of two sets, A and B, is the set of elements that belong to *either* of the sets. A union B is denoted by

$$A \cup B$$

Answers

4. $(-8, -4)$, **5.** $\left(-\frac{16}{3}, 4\right]$

EXAMPLE 6 Find the union: $\{2, 4, 6, 8\} \cup \{3, 4, 5, 6\}$

Solution: The numbers that are in either set are $\{2, 3, 4, 5, 6, 8\}$. This set is the union.

■ **Work Practice Problem 6**

PRACTICE PROBLEM 6
Find the union:
$\{1, 2, 3, 4, 5\} \cup \{3, 4, 5, 6\}$

Objective D Solving Compound Inequalities Containing *"or"*

A value of x is a solution of a compound inequality formed by the word **or** if it is a solution of **either** inequality. For example, the solution set of the compound inequality $x \leq 1$ **or** $x \geq 3$ contains all numbers that make the inequality $x \leq 1$ a true statement **or** the inequality $x \geq 3$ a true statement. In other words, the solution of such an inequality is the *union* of the solutions of the individual inequalities.

$\{x \mid x \leq 1\}$
$(-\infty, 1]$

$\{x \mid x \geq 3\}$
$[3, \infty)$

$\{x \mid x \leq 1$ or $x \geq 3\}$
$(-\infty, 1] \cup [3, \infty)$

In interval notation, the set $\{x \mid x \leq 1 \text{ or } x \geq 3\}$ is written as $(-\infty, 1] \cup [3, \infty)$.

EXAMPLE 7 Solve: $5x - 3 \leq 10 \text{ or } x + 1 \geq 5$

Solution: First we solve each inequality separately.

$$5x - 3 \leq 10 \quad or \quad x + 1 \geq 5$$
$$5x \leq 13 \quad or \quad x \geq 4$$
$$x \leq \frac{13}{5} \quad or \quad x \geq 4$$

Now we can graph each interval and find their union.

$\left\{x \mid x \leq \dfrac{13}{5}\right\}$
$\left(-\infty, \dfrac{13}{5}\right]$

$\{x \mid x \geq 4\}$
$[4, \infty)$

$\left\{x \mid x \leq \dfrac{13}{5} \text{ or } x \geq 4\right\}$

$\left(-\infty, \dfrac{13}{5}\right] \cup [4, \infty)$

The solution set is $\left(-\infty, \dfrac{13}{5}\right] \cup [4, \infty)$.

■ **Work Practice Problem 7**

PRACTICE PROBLEM 7
Solve:
$3x - 2 \geq 10 \text{ or } x - 6 \leq -4$

Answers
6. $\{1, 2, 3, 4, 5, 6\}$,
7. $(-\infty, 2] \cup [4, \infty)$

PRACTICE PROBLEM 8

Solve: $x - 7 \leq -1$ or $2x - 6 \geq 2$

EXAMPLE 8 Solve: $-2x - 5 < -3$ *or* $6x < 0$

Solution: First we solve each inequality separately.

$$-2x - 5 < -3 \quad or \quad 6x < 0$$
$$-2x < 2 \quad or \quad x < 0$$
$$x > -1 \quad or \quad x < 0$$

Now we can graph each interval and find their union.

$\{x \mid x > -1\}$ $(-1, \infty)$

$\{x \mid x < 0\}$ $(-\infty, 0)$

$\{x \mid x > -1 \text{ or } x < 0\}$ $(-\infty, \infty)$
= all real numbers

The solution set is $(-\infty, \infty)$.

Work Practice Problem 8

✔**Concept Check** Which of the following is *not* a correct way to represent the set of all numbers between -3 and 5?
a. $\{x \mid -3 < x < 5\}$
b. $-3 < x$ or $x < 5$
c. $(-3, 5)$
d. $x > -3$ and $x < 5$

Answer
8. $(-\infty, \infty)$

✔ **Concept Check Answer**
b is not correct

2.5 EXERCISE SET

Objectives **A** **C** **Mixed Practice** *If $A = \{x \mid x \text{ is an even integer}\}$, $B = \{x \mid x \text{ is an odd integer}\}$, $C = \{2, 3, 4, 5\}$, and $D = \{4, 5, 6, 7\}$, list the elements of each set. See Examples 1 and 6.*

1. $C \cup D$ **2.** $C \cap D$

3. $A \cap D$ **4.** $A \cup D$

5. $A \cup B$ **6.** $A \cap B$

7. $B \cap D$ **8.** $B \cup D$

9. $B \cup C$ **10.** $B \cap C$

11. $A \cap C$ **12.** $A \cup C$

Objective **B** *Solve each compound inequality. Graph the two inequalities on the first two number lines and the solution set on the third number line. See Examples 2 and 3.*

13. $x < 1$ *and* $x > -3$

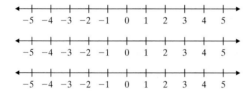

14. $x \leq 0$ *and* $x \geq -2$

15. $x \leq -3$ *and* $x \geq -2$

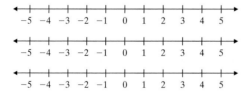

16. $x < 2$ *and* $x > 4$

17. $x < -1$ *and* $x < 1$

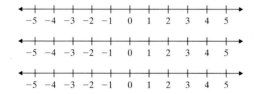

18. $x \geq -4$ *and* $x > 1$

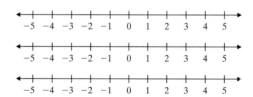

Solve each compound inequality. Write solutions in interval notation. See Examples 2 and 3.

19. $x + 1 \geq 7$ and $3x - 1 \geq 5$ **20.** $x + 2 \geq 3$ and $5x - 1 \geq 9$

21. $4x + 2 \leq -10$ and $2x \leq 0$ **22.** $2x + 4 > 0$ and $4x > 0$

23. $-2x < -8$ and $x - 5 < 5$ **24.** $-7x \leq -21$ and $x - 20 \leq -15$

Solve each compound inequality. See Examples 4 and 5.

25. $5 < x - 6 < 11$ **26.** $-2 \leq x + 3 \leq 0$

27. $-2 \leq 3x - 5 \leq 7$ **28.** $1 < 4 + 2x < 7$ **117**

29. $1 \le \frac{2}{3}x + 3 \le 4$

30. $-2 < \frac{1}{2}x - 5 < 1$

31. $-5 \le \frac{-3x + 1}{4} \le 2$

32. $-4 \le \frac{-2x + 5}{3} \le 1$

Objective **D** *Solve each compound inequality. Graph the two given inequalities on the first two number lines and the solution set on the third number line. See Examples 7 and 8.*

33. $x < 4 \text{ or } x < 5$

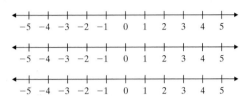

34. $x \ge -2 \text{ or } x \le 2$

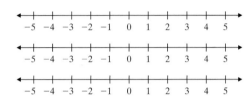

35. $x \le -4 \text{ or } x \ge 1$

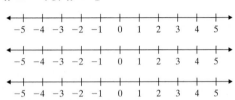

36. $x < 0 \text{ or } x < 1$

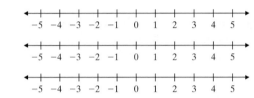

37. $x > 0 \text{ or } x < 3$

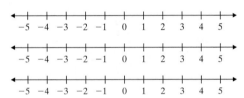

38. $x \ge -3 \text{ or } x \le -4$

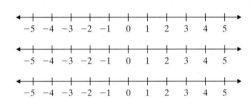

Solve each compound inequality. Write answers in interval notation. See Examples 7 and 8.

39. $-2x \le -4 \text{ or } 5x - 20 \ge 5$

40. $-5x \le 10 \text{ or } 3x - 5 \ge 1$

41. $x + 4 < 0 \text{ or } 6x > -12$

42. $x + 9 < 0 \text{ or } 4x > -12$

43. $3(x - 1) < 12 \text{ or } x + 7 > 10$

44. $5(x - 1) \ge -5 \text{ or } 5 - x \le 11$

Objectives **B** **D** **Mixed Practice** *Solve each compound inequality. Write solutions in interval notation.*

45. $x < \frac{2}{3} \text{ and } x > -\frac{1}{2}$

46. $x < \frac{5}{7} \text{ and } x < 1$

47. $x < \frac{2}{3} \text{ or } x > -\frac{1}{2}$

48. $x < \frac{5}{7} \text{ or } x < 1$

49. $0 \le 2x - 3 \le 9$

50. $3 < 5x + 1 < 11$

51. $\frac{1}{2} < x - \frac{3}{4} < 2$

52. $\frac{2}{3} < x + \frac{1}{2} < 4$

53. $x + 3 \ge 3 \text{ and } x + 3 \le 2$

54. $2x - 1 \ge 3 \text{ and } -x > 2$

55. $3x \ge 5 \text{ or } -\frac{5}{8}x - 6 > 1$

56. $\frac{3}{8}x + 1 \le 0 \text{ or } -2x < -4$

57. $0 < \dfrac{5 - 2x}{3} < 5$

58. $-2 < \dfrac{-2x - 1}{3} < 2$

59. $-6 < 3(x - 2) \le 8$

60. $-5 < 2(x + 4) < 8$

61. $-x + 5 > 6$ and $1 + 2x \le -5$

62. $5x \le 0$ and $-x + 5 < 8$

63. $3x + 2 \le 5$ or $7x > 29$

64. $-x < 7$ or $3x + 1 < -20$

65. $5 - x > 7$ and $2x + 3 \ge 13$

66. $-2x < -6$ or $1 - x > -2$

67. $-\dfrac{1}{2} \le \dfrac{4x - 1}{6} < \dfrac{5}{6}$

68. $-\dfrac{1}{2} \le \dfrac{3x - 1}{10} < \dfrac{1}{2}$

69. $\dfrac{1}{15} < \dfrac{8 - 3x}{15} < \dfrac{4}{5}$

70. $-\dfrac{1}{4} < \dfrac{6 - x}{12} < -\dfrac{1}{6}$

71. $0.3 < 0.2x - 0.9 < 1.5$

72. $-0.7 \le 0.4x + 0.8 < 0.5$

Review

Evaluate. See Section 1.5.

73. $|-7| - |19|$

74. $|-7 - 19|$

75. $-(-6) - |-10|$

76. $|-4| - (-4) + |-20|$

Find by inspection all values for x that make each equation true.

77. $|x| = 7$

78. $|x| = 5$

79. $|x| = 0$

80. $|x| = -2$

Concept Extensions

Use the graph to answer Exercises 81 and 82.

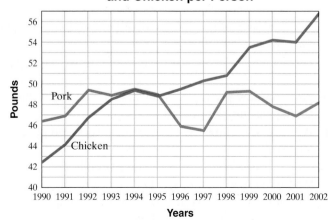

U.S. Consumption of Pork and Chicken per Person

Pounds / Years

Source: Based on data from Economic Research Service, U.S. Department of Agriculture, *Agricultural Outlook*, October 2001

81. For what years was the consumption of pork greater than 48 pounds per person *and* the consumption of chicken greater than 48 pounds per person?

82. For what years was the consumption of pork less than 45 pounds per person *or* the consumption of chicken greater than 55 pounds per person?

83. In your own words, describe how to find the union of two sets.

84. In your own words, describe how to find the intersection of two sets.

To solve a compound inequality such as $x - 6 < 3x < 2x + 5$, *we solve*

$$x - 6 < 3x \quad \text{and} \quad 3x < 2x + 5$$

Use this information to solve the inequalities in Exercises 85 through 88.

85. $x - 6 < 3x < 2x + 5$

86. $2x - 3 < 3x + 1 < 4x - 5$

87. $x + 3 < 2x + 1 < 4x + 6$

88. $-3(x - 2) \leq 3 - 2x \leq 10 - 3x$

The formula for converting Fahrenheit temperatures to Celsius temperatures is $C = \dfrac{5}{9}(F - 32)$. *Use this formula for Exercises 89 and 90.*

89. During a recent year, the temperatures in Chicago ranged from $-29°$ to $35°$ Celsius. Use a compound inequality to convert these temperatures to Fahrenheit temperatures.

90. In Oslo, the average temperature ranges from $-10°$ to $18°$ Celsius. Use a compound inequality to convert these temperatures to the Fahrenheit scale.

Solve.

91. Christian D'Angelo has scores of 68, 65, 75, and 78 on his algebra tests. Use a compound inequality to find the scores he can make on his final exam to receive a C in the course. The final exam counts as two tests, and a C is received if the final course average is from 70 to 79.

92. Wendy Wood has scores of 80, 90, 82, and 75 on her chemistry tests. Use a compound inequality to find the range of scores she can make on her final exam to receive a B in the course. The final exam counts as two tests, and a B is received if the final course average is from 80 to 89.

 STUDY SKILLS BUILDER

Organizing a Notebook

It's never too late to get organized. If you need ideas about organizing a notebook for your mathematics course, try some of these:

- Use a spiral or ring binder notebook with pockets and use it for mathematics only.
- Start each page by writing the book's section number you are working on at the top.
- When your instructor is lecturing, take notes. *Always* include any examples your instructor works for you.
- Place your worked-out homework exercises in your notebook immediately after the lecture notes from that section. This way, a section's worth of material is together.
- Homework exercises: Attempt all assigned homework. For odd-numbered exercises, you are not through until you check your answers against the back of the book. Correct any exercises with incorrect answers. You may want to place a "?" by any homework exercises or notes that you need to ask questions about. Also, consider placing a "!" by any notes or exercises you feel are important.

- Place graded quizzes in the pockets of your notebook. If you are using a binder, you can place your quizzes in a special section of your binder.

Let's check your notebook organization by answering the following questions.

1. Do you have a spiral or ring binder notebook for your mathematics course only?

2. Have you ever had to flip through several sheets of notes and work in your mathematics notebook to determine what section's work you are in?

3. Are you now writing the textbook's section number at the top of each notebook page?

4. Have you ever lost or had trouble finding a graded quiz or test?

5. Are you now placing all your graded work in a dedicated place in your notebook?

6. Are you attempting all of your homework and placing all of your work in your notebook?

7. Are you checking and correcting your homework in your notebook? If not, why not?

8. Are you writing in your notebook the examples your instructor works for you in class?

2.6 ABSOLUTE VALUE EQUATIONS AND INEQUALITIES

In Chapter 1, we defined the absolute value of a number as its distance from 0 on a number line.

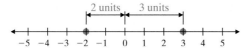

$$|-2| = 2 \quad \text{and} \quad |3| = 3$$

In this section, we concentrate on solving equations and inequalities containing the absolute value of a variable or a variable expression. Examples of absolute value equations and inequalities are

$$|x| = 3 \quad -5 \geq |2y + 7| \quad |z - 6.7| = |3z + 1.2| \quad |x - 3| > 7$$

Absolute value equations and inequalities are extremely useful in data analysis, especially for calculating acceptable measurement error and errors that result from the way numbers are sometimes represented in computers.

Objective **A** Solving Absolute Value Equations

To begin, let's solve a few absolute value equations by inspection.

EXAMPLE 1 Solve: $|x| = 3$

Solution: The solution set of this equation will contain all numbers whose distance from 0 is 3 units. Two numbers are 3 units away from 0 on the number line: 3 and -3.

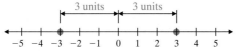

Check: To check, let $x = 3$ and $x = -3$ in the original equation.

$$|x| = 3 \qquad\qquad |x| = 3$$
$$|3| \overset{?}{=} 3 \quad \text{Let } x = 3. \qquad |-3| \overset{?}{=} 3 \quad \text{Let } x = -3.$$
$$3 = 3 \quad \text{True} \qquad\qquad 3 = 3 \quad \text{True}$$

Both solutions check. Thus the solution set of the equation $|x| = 3$ is $\{3, -3\}$.

Work Practice Problem 1

EXAMPLE 2 Solve: $|x| = -2$

Solution: The absolute value of a number is never negative, so this equation has no solution. The solution set is $\{ \ \}$ or $\varnothing$.

Work Practice Problem 2

EXAMPLE 3 Solve: $|y| = 0$

Solution: We are looking for all numbers whose distance from 0 is zero units. The only number is 0. The solution set is $\{0\}$.

Work Practice Problem 3

PRACTICE PROBLEM 1

Solve: $|y| = 5$

PRACTICE PROBLEM 2

Solve: $|p| = -4$

PRACTICE PROBLEM 3

Solve: $|x| = 0$

Answers

1. $\{-5, 5\}$, **2.** $\varnothing$, **3.** $\{0\}$

From the above examples, we have the following.

Absolute Value Property

To solve $|X| = a$,

If a is positive, then solve $X = a$ or $X = -a$.

If a is 0, then $X = 0$.

If a is negative, the equation $|X| = a$ has no solution.

Helpful Hint

For the equation $|X| = a$ in the box above, X can be a single variable or a variable expression.

When we are solving absolute value equations, if $|X|$ is not alone on one side of the equation we first use properties of equality to get $|X|$ alone.

PRACTICE PROBLEM 4

Solve: $|4x + 2| = 6$.

EXAMPLE 4 Solve: $|5w + 3| = 7$

Solution: Here the expression inside the absolute value bars is $5w + 3$. If we think of the expression $5w + 3$ as X in the absolute value property, we see that $|X| = 7$ is equivalent to

$$X = 7 \quad \text{or} \quad X = -7$$

Then substitute $5w + 3$ for X, and we have

$$5w + 3 = 7 \quad \text{or} \quad 5w + 3 = -7$$

Solve these two equations for w.

$$5w + 3 = 7 \quad \text{or} \quad 5w + 3 = -7$$
$$5w = 4 \quad \text{or} \quad 5w = -10$$
$$w = \frac{4}{5} \quad \text{or} \quad w = -2$$

Check: To check, let $w = -2$ and then $w = \frac{4}{5}$ in the original equation.

Let $w = -2$

$$|5(-2) + 3| = 7$$
$$|-10 + 3| = 7$$
$$|-7| = 7$$
$$7 = 7 \quad \text{True}$$

Let $w = \frac{4}{5}$

$$\left|5\left(\frac{4}{5}\right) + 3\right| = 7$$
$$|4 + 3| = 7$$
$$|7| = 7$$
$$7 = 7 \quad \text{True}$$

Both solutions check, and the solution set is $\left\{-2, \frac{4}{5}\right\}$.

Work Practice Problem 4

PRACTICE PROBLEM 5

Solve: $\left|\frac{x}{3} + 4\right| = 1$

EXAMPLE 5 Solve: $\left|\frac{x}{2} - 1\right| = 11$

Solution: $\left|\frac{x}{2} - 1\right| = 11$ is equivalent to

$$\frac{x}{2} - 1 = 11 \quad \text{or} \quad \frac{x}{2} - 1 = -11$$
$$2\left(\frac{x}{2} - 1\right) = 2(11) \quad \text{or} \quad 2\left(\frac{x}{2} - 1\right) = 2(-11) \quad \text{Clear fractions.}$$
$$x - 2 = 22 \quad \text{or} \quad x - 2 = -22 \quad \text{Apply the distributive property.}$$
$$x = 24 \quad \text{or} \quad x = -20$$

The solution set is $\{-20, 24\}$.

Work Practice Problem 5

Answers

4. $\{1, -2\}$, **5.** $\{-9, -15\}$

Don't forget that to use the absolute value property you must first make sure that the absolute value expression is alone on one side of the equation.

> **Helpful Hint**
>
> If the equation has a single absolute value expression containing variables, get the absolute value expression alone. Then use the absolute value property.

EXAMPLE 6 Solve: $|2x - 1| + 5 = 6$

Solution: We want the absolute value expression alone on one side of the equation, so we begin by subtracting 5 from both sides. Then we use the absolute value property.

$$|2x - 1| + 5 = 6$$

$$|2x - 1| = 1 \qquad \text{Subtract 5 from both sides.}$$

$$2x - 1 = 1 \quad \text{or} \quad 2x - 1 = -1 \quad \text{Use the absolute value property.}$$

$$2x = 2 \quad \text{or} \quad 2x = 0$$

$$x = 1 \quad \text{or} \quad x = 0 \qquad \text{Solve.}$$

The solution set is $\{0, 1\}$.

▨ **Work Practice Problem 6**

PRACTICE PROBLEM 6

Solve: $|4x + 2| + 1 = 7$

Given two absolute value expressions, we might ask, when are the absolute values of two expressions equal? To see the answer, notice that

$$|2| = |2| \quad |-2| = |-2| \quad |-2| = |2| \quad |2| = |-2|$$

same   same   opposites   opposites

Two absolute value expressions are equal when the expressions inside the absolute value bars are equal to or are opposites of each other. In otherwords,

---

To solve $|X| = |Y|$, solve $X = Y$ or $X = -Y$.

EXAMPLE 7 Solve: $|3x + 2| = |5x - 8|$

Solution: This equation is true if the expressions inside the absolute value bars are equal to or are opposites of each other.

$$3x + 2 = 5x - 8 \quad \text{or} \quad 3x + 2 = -(5x - 8)$$

Next we solve each equation.

$$3x + 2 = 5x - 8 \quad \text{or} \quad 3x + 2 = -5x + 8$$

$$-2x + 2 = -8 \quad \text{or} \quad 8x + 2 = 8$$

$$-2x = -10 \quad \text{or} \quad 8x = 6$$

$$x = 5 \quad \text{or} \quad x = \frac{3}{4}$$

Check to see that replacing x with 5 or with $\frac{3}{4}$ results in a true statement.

The solution set is $\left\{ \frac{3}{4}, 5 \right\}$.

▨ **Work Practice Problem 7**

PRACTICE PROBLEM 7

Solve: $|4x - 5| = |3x + 5|$

Answers

6. $\{1, -2\}$,   **7.** $\{0, 10\}$

PRACTICE PROBLEM 8

Solve: $|x + 2| = |4 - x|$

EXAMPLE 8   Solve: $|x - 3| = |5 - x|$

Solution:

$$
\begin{array}{llll}
x - 3 = 5 - x & \text{or} & x - 3 = -(5 - x) \\
2x - 3 = 5 & \text{or} & x - 3 = -5 + x \\
2x = 8 & \text{or} & x - 3 - x = -5 + x - x \\
x = 4 & \text{or} & -3 = -5 \quad \text{False}
\end{array}
$$

Recall from Section 2.1 that when an equation simplifies to a false statement, the equation has no solution. Thus the only solution for the original absolute value equation is 4, and the solution set is {4}.

▣ **Work Practice Problem 8**

✔ **Concept Check**   True or false? Absolute value equations always have two solutions. Explain your answer.

Objective B Solving Absolute Value Inequalities

To begin, let's solve a few absolute value inequalities by inspection.

PRACTICE PROBLEM 9

Solve $|x| < 4$ using a number line.

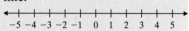

EXAMPLE 9   Solve $|x| < 2$ using a number line.

Solution: The solution set contains all numbers whose distance from 0 is less than 2 units on the number line.

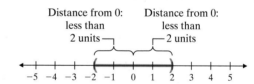

The solution set is $\{x \mid -2 < x < 2\}$, or $(-2, 2)$ in interval notation.

▣ **Work Practice Problem 9**

PRACTICE PROBLEM 10

Solve $|x| \geq 5$ using a number line.

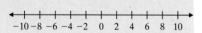

EXAMPLE 10   Solve $|x| \geq 3$ using a number line.

Solution: The solution set contains all numbers whose distance from 0 is 3 or more units. Thus the graph of the solution set contains 3 and all points to the right of 3 on the number line or -3 and all points to the left of -3 on the number line.

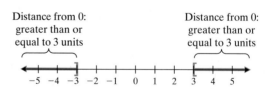

This solution set is $\{x \mid x \leq -3 \text{ or } x \geq 3\}$. In interval notation, the solution set is $(-\infty, -3] \cup [3, \infty)$, since **or** means union.

▣ **Work Practice Problem 10**

Answers

8. {1},

9.

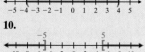

10.

▽ **Concept Check Answer**

false; answers may vary

The following box summarizes solving absolute value equations and inequalities.

Solving Absolute Value Equations and Inequalities

If a is a positive number,

To solve $|X| = a$, solve $X = a$ or $X = -a$.

To solve $|X| = |Y|$, solve $X = Y$ or $X = -Y$.

To solve $|X| < a$, solve $-a < X < a$.

To solve $|X| > a$, solve $X < -a$ or $X > a$.

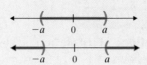

EXAMPLE 11 Solve: $|x - 3| > 7$

Solution: Since 7 is positive, to solve $|x - 3| > 7$, we solve the compound inequality $x - 3 < -7$ or $x - 3 > 7$.

$$x - 3 < -7 \quad \text{or} \quad x - 3 > 7$$
$$x < -4 \quad \text{or} \quad x > 10 \quad \text{Add 3 to both sides.}$$

The solution set is $\{x \mid x < -4 \text{ or } x > 10\}$ or $(-\infty, -4) \cup (10, \infty)$ in interval notation. Its graph is shown.

🔲 **Work Practice Problem 11**

Let's remember the differences between solving absolute value equations and inequalities by solving an absolute value equation.

EXAMPLE 12 Solve: $|x + 1| = 6$

Solution: This is an equation, so we solve

$$x + 1 = 6 \quad \text{or} \quad x + 1 = -6$$
$$x = 5 \quad \text{or} \quad x = -7$$

The solution set is $\{-7, 5\}$. Its graph is shown.

🔲 **Work Practice Problem 12**

Notice that the next example is an absolute value inequality.

EXAMPLE 13 Solve: $|x - 6| \leq 2$

Solution: To solve $|x - 6| \leq 2$, we solve

$$-2 \leq x - 6 \leq 2$$
$$-2 + 6 \leq x - 6 + 6 \leq 2 + 6 \quad \text{Add 6 to all three parts.}$$
$$4 \leq x \leq 8 \quad \text{Simplify.}$$

The solution set is $\{x \mid 4 \leq x \leq 8\}$, or $[4, 8]$ in interval notation. Its graph is shown.

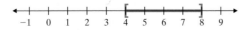

🔲 **Work Practice Problem 13**

PRACTICE PROBLEM 11

Solve: $|x + 2| > 4$. Graph the solution set.

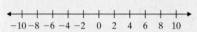

PRACTICE PROBLEM 12

Solve: $|x - 3| = 5$. Graph the solution set.

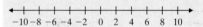

PRACTICE PROBLEM 13

Solve: $|x - 2| \leq 1$. Graph the solution set.

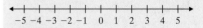

Answers

11. $(-\infty, -6) \cup (2, \infty)$,

12. $\{-2, 8\}$,

13.

> Helpful Hint
>
> As with absolute value equations, before using an absolute value inequality property, get an absolute value expression alone on one side of the inequality.

PRACTICE PROBLEM 14

Solve: $|2x - 5| + 2 \le 9$

EXAMPLE 14 Solve: $|5x + 1| + 1 \le 10$

Solution: First we get the absolute value expression alone by subtracting 1 from both sides.

$$|5x + 1| + 1 \le 10$$
$$|5x + 1| \le 10 - 1 \quad \text{Subtract 1 from both sides.}$$
$$|5x + 1| \le 9 \quad \text{Simplify.}$$

Since 9 is positive, to solve $|5x + 1| \le 9$, we solve

$$-9 \le 5x + 1 \le 9$$
$$-9 - 1 \le 5x + 1 - 1 \le 9 - 1 \quad \text{Subtract 1 from all three parts.}$$
$$-10 \le 5x \le 8 \quad \text{Simplify.}$$
$$-2 \le x \le \frac{8}{5} \quad \text{Divide all three parts by 5.}$$

The solution set is $\left[-2, \frac{8}{5}\right]$.

◻ **Work Practice Problem 14**

The next few examples are special cases of absolute value inequalities.

PRACTICE PROBLEM 15

Solve: $|x| < -1$

EXAMPLE 15 Solve: $|x| \le -3$

Solution: The absolute value of a number is never negative. Thus it will then never be less than or equal to -3. The solution set is { } or $\varnothing$.

◻ **Work Practice Problem 15**

PRACTICE PROBLEM 16

Solve: $|x + 1| \ge -3$

EXAMPLE 16 Solve: $|x - 1| > -2$

Solution: The absolute value of a number is always nonnegative. Thus it will always be greater than -2. The solution set contains all real numbers, or $(-\infty, \infty)$.

◻ **Work Practice Problem 16**

✔ **Concept Check** Without taking any solution steps, how do you know that the absolute value inequality $|3x - 2| > -9$ has a solution? What is its solution?

Answers

14. $[-1, 6]$, **15.** $\varnothing$, **16.** $(-\infty, \infty)$

✔ **Concept Check Answer**

$(-\infty, \infty)$ since the absolute value is always nonnegative

Mental Math

Match each absolute value equation or inequality with an equivalent statement.

1. $|2x + 1| = 3$

2. $|2x + 1| \leq 3$

3. $|2x + 1| < 3$

4. $|2x + 1| \geq 3$

5. $|2x + 1| > 3$

a. $2x + 1 > 3$ or $2x + 1 < -3$

b. $2x + 1 \geq 3$ or $2x + 1 \leq -3$

c. $-3 < 2x + 1 < 3$

d. $2x + 1 = 3$ or $2x + 1 = -3$

e. $-3 \leq 2x + 1 \leq 3$

2.6 EXERCISE SET

FOR EXTRA HELP

Student Solutions Manual   PH Math/Tutor Center   CD/Video for Review   MathXL®   MyMathLab

Objective A *Solve. See Examples 1 through 6.*

1. $|x| = 7$

2. $|y| = 15$

3. $|x| = -4$

4. $|x| = -20$

5. $|3x| = 12.6$

6. $|6n| = 12.6$

7. $3|x| - 5 = 7$

8. $5|x| - 12 = 8$

9. $-6|x| + 44 = -10$

10. $-4|x| + 18 = -22$

11. $|x - 9| = 14$

12. $|x + 2| = 8$

13. $|2x - 5| = 9$

14. $|6 + 2n| = 4$

15. $\left|\dfrac{x}{2} - 3\right| = 1$

16. $\left|\dfrac{n}{3} + 2\right| = 4$

17. $|z| + 4 = 9$

18. $|x| + 1 = 3$

19. $|3x| + 5 = 14$

20. $|2x| - 6 = 4$

21. $\left|\dfrac{4x - 6}{3}\right| = 6$

22. $\left|\dfrac{2x + 1}{5}\right| = 7$

23. $|2x| = 0$

24. $|7z| = 0$

25. $|4n + 1| + 10 = 4$

26. $|3z - 2| + 8 = 1$

27. $3|x - 1| + 19 = 23$

28. $5|x + 1| - 1 = 3$

Solve. See Examples 7 and 8.

29. $|5x - 7| = |3x + 11|$

30. $|9y + 1| = |6y + 4|$

31. $|z + 8| = |z - 3|$

32. $|2x - 5| = |2x + 5|$

33. $|2y - 3| = |9 - 4y|$

34. $|5z - 1| = |7 - z|$

35. $\left|\dfrac{3}{4}x - 2\right| = \left|\dfrac{1}{4}x + 6\right|$

36. $\left|\dfrac{2}{3}x - 5\right| = \left|\dfrac{1}{3}x + 4\right|$

37. $|2x - 6| = |10 - 2x|$

38. $|4n + 5| = |4n + 3|$ **39.** $|x + 4| = |7 - x|$ **40.** $|8 - y| = |y + 2|$

41. $\left|\dfrac{2x + 1}{5}\right| = \left|\dfrac{3x - 7}{3}\right|$ **42.** $\left|\dfrac{5x - 1}{2}\right| = \left|\dfrac{4x + 5}{6}\right|$

43. $|5x + 1| = |4x - 7|$ **44.** $|3 + 6n| = |4n + 11|$

Objective **B** *Solve. Graph the solution set. See Examples 9 through 16.*

 45. $|x| \le 4$

46. $|x| < 6$

 47. $|x| > 3$

48. $|y| \ge 4$

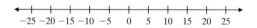

49. $|x + 3| < 2$

50. $|x + 4| < 6$

51. $|y - 6| \ge 7$

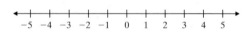

52. $|x - 3| \ge 10$

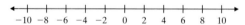

53. $\left|\dfrac{x + 2}{3}\right| < 1$

54. $\left|\dfrac{x - 6}{4}\right| < 1$

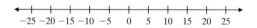

55. $|x| + 7 \le 12$

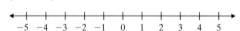

56. $|x| + 6 \le 7$

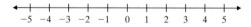

57. $|2x + 3| \le 0$

58. $|7x + 1| \le 0$

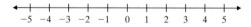

59. $|x| + 2 > 6$

60. $|x| - 1 > 3$

61. $|2x + 7| \le 13$

62. $|5x - 3| \le 18$

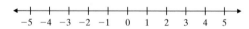

63. $|8 - 3x| < 5$

64. $|7 - 4x| < 5$

Chapter 2 Vocabulary Check

Fill in each blank with one of the words or phrases listed below.

contradiction	linear inequality in one variable	compound inequality	solution
absolute value	consecutive integers	identity	union
formula	linear equation in one variable	intersection	

1. The statement "$x < 5$ or $x > 7$" is called a(n) _____.
2. An equation in one variable that has no solution is called a(n) _____.
3. The _____ of two sets is the set of all elements common to both sets.
4. The _____ of two sets is the set of all elements that belong to either of the sets.
5. An equation in one variable that has every number (for which the equation is defined) as a solution is called a(n) _____.
6. The equation $d = rt$ is also called a(n) _____.
7. A number's distance from 0 is called its _____.
8. When a variable in an equation is replaced by a number and the resulting equation is true, then that number is called a(n) _____ of the equation.
9. The integers 17, 18, 19 are examples of _____.
10. The statement $5x - 0.2 < 7$ is an example of a(n) _____.
11. The statement $5x - 0.2 = 7$ is an example of a(n) _____.

Helpful Hint

Are you preparing for your test? Don't forget to take the Chapter 2 Test on page 149. Then check your answers at the back of the text and use the Chapter Test Prep Video CD to see the fully worked-out solutions to any of the exercises you want to review.

2 Chapter Highlights

DEFINITIONS AND CONCEPTS	EXAMPLES
Section 2.1 Linear Equations in One Variable	
An **equation** is a statement that two expressions are equal.	$5 = 5 \qquad 7x + 2 = -14 \qquad 3(x-1)^2 = 9x^2 - 6$
A **linear equation in one variable** is an equation that can be written in the form $ax + b = c$, where a, b, and c are real numbers and $a \neq 0$.	$7x + 2 = -14 \qquad x = -3$ $5(2y - 7) = -2(8y - 1)$
A **solution** of an equation is a value for the variable that makes the equation a true statement.	Determine whether -1 is a solution of $$3(x - 1) = 4x - 2$$ $$3(-1 - 1) \stackrel{?}{=} 4(-1) - 2$$ $$3(-2) \stackrel{?}{=} -4 - 2$$ $$-6 = -6 \qquad \text{True}$$ Thus, -1 is a solution.

continued

DEFINITIONS AND CONCEPTS	**EXAMPLES**
Section 2.1 Linear Equations in One Variable (*continued*)	

Equivalent equations have the same solution.

The **addition property of equality** guarantees that the same number may be added to (or subtracted from) both sides of an equation and the result is an equivalent equation.

The **multiplication property of equality** guarantees that both sides of an equation may be multiplied by (or divided by) the same nonzero number and the result is an equivalent equation.

$x - 12 = 14$ and $x = 26$ are equivalent equations.

Solve: $-3x - 2 = 10$

$$-3x - 2 + 2 = 10 + 2 \quad \text{Add 2 to both sides.}$$

$$-3x = 12$$

$$\frac{-3x}{-3} = \frac{12}{-3} \quad \text{Divide both sides by } -3$$

$$x = -4$$

SOLVING A LINEAR EQUATION IN ONE VARIABLE

Solve: $x - \dfrac{x-2}{6} = \dfrac{x-7}{3} + \dfrac{2}{3}$

Step 1. Clear the equation of fractions and decimals.

1. $6\left(x - \dfrac{x-2}{6}\right) = 6\left(\dfrac{x-7}{3} + \dfrac{2}{3}\right)$ $\quad$ Multiply both sides by 6.

$\qquad 6x - (x - 2) = 2(x - 7) + 2(2)$ $\quad$ Use the distributive property.

Step 2. Remove grouping symbols such as parentheses.

2. $\quad 6x - x + 2 = 2x - 14 + 4$

Step 3. Simplify by combining like terms.

3. $\qquad 5x + 2 = 2x - 10$

Step 4. Write variable terms on one side and numbers on the other side by using the addition property of equality.

4. $\quad 5x + 2 - 2 = 2x - 10 - 2$ $\quad$ Subtract 2 from both sides.

$\qquad\qquad 5x = 2x - 12$

$\qquad 5x - 2x = 2x - 12 - 2x$ $\quad$ Subtract $2x$ from both sides.

$\qquad\qquad 3x = -12$

Step 5. Get the variable alone by using the multiplication property of equality.

5. $\qquad \dfrac{3x}{3} = \dfrac{-12}{3}$ $\quad$ Divide both sides by 3.

$\qquad\qquad x = -4$

Step 6. Check the proposed solution in the original equation.

6. $\quad -4 - \dfrac{-4-2}{6} \stackrel{?}{=} \dfrac{-4-7}{3} + \dfrac{2}{3}$ $\quad$ Replace x with -4 in the original equation.

$\qquad -4 - \dfrac{-6}{6} \stackrel{?}{=} \dfrac{-11}{3} + \dfrac{2}{3}$

$\qquad -4 - (-1) \stackrel{?}{=} \dfrac{-9}{3}$

$\qquad\qquad -3 = -3 \quad \text{True}$

DEFINITIONS AND CONCEPTS	**EXAMPLES**

Section 2.2   An Introduction to Problem Solving

PROBLEM-SOLVING STRATEGY

1. UNDERSTAND the problem.

Colorado is shaped like a rectangle whose length is about 1.3 times its width. If the perimeter of Colorado is 2070 kilometers, find its dimensions.

1. Read and reread the problem. Guess a solution and check your guess.

Let x = width of Colorado in kilometers. Then $1.3x$ = length of Colorado in kilometers.

2. TRANSLATE the problem.

2. In words:

twice the length	+	twice the width	=	perimeter

Translate: $2(1.3x)$ + $2x$ = 2070

3. SOLVE the equation.

3.
$2.6x + 2x = 2070$
$4.6x = 2070$
$x = 450$

4. INTERPRET the results.

4. If $x = 450$ kilometers, then $1.3x = 1.3(450) = 585$ kilometers. *Check:* The perimeter of a rectangle whose width is 450 kilometers and length is 585 kilometers is $2(450) + 2(585) = 2070$ kilometers, the required perimeter. *State:* The dimensions of Colorado are 450 kilometers by 585 kilometers.

Section 2.3   Formulas and Problem Solving

An equation that describes a known relationship among quantities is called a **formula.**

To solve a formula or equation for a specified variable, use the steps for solving an equation. Treat the specified variable as the only variable of the equation.

$A = \pi r^2$ (area of a circle)

$I = Prt$ (interest = principal $\cdot$ rate $\cdot$ time)

Solve $A = 2HW + 2LW + 2LH$ for H.

$A - 2LW = 2HW + 2LH$	Subtract $2LW$ from both sides.
$A - 2LW = H(2W + 2L)$	Use the distributive property.
$\dfrac{A - 2LW}{2W + 2L} = \dfrac{H(2W + 2L)}{2W + 2L}$	Divide both sides by $2W + 2L$.
$\dfrac{A - 2LW}{2W + 2L} = H$	Simplify.

(continued)

DEFINITIONS AND CONCEPTS	EXAMPLES

Section 2.4   Linear Inequalities and Problem Solving

A **linear inequality in one variable** is an inequality that can be written in the form $ax + b < c$, where a, b, and c are real numbers and $a \neq 0$. (The inequality symbols $>$, $\leq$, and $\geq$ also apply here.)	$5x - 2 \leq -7 \quad 3y > 1 \quad \dfrac{z}{7} < -9(z - 3)$
The **addition property of inequality** guarantees that the same number may be added to (or subtracted from) both sides of an inequality, and the resulting inequality will have the same solution set.	$x - 9 \leq -16$ $x - 9 + 9 \leq -16 + 9$ Add 9 to both sides. $x \leq -7$
The **multiplication property of inequality** guarantees that both sides of an inequality may be multiplied by (or divided by) the same **positive** number, and the resulting inequality will have the same solution set. We may also multiply (or divide) both sides of an inequality by the same **negative** number and **reverse the direction of the inequality symbol,** and the result will be an inequality with the same solution set.	$6x < -66$ Divide both sides by 6. Do not reverse $\dfrac{6x}{6} < \dfrac{-66}{6}$ the direction of the inequality symbol. $x < -11$ $-6x < -66$ Divide both sides by -6. Reverse the $\dfrac{-6x}{-6} > \dfrac{-66}{-6}$ direction of the inequality symbol. $x > 11$
SOLVING A LINEAR INEQUALITY IN ONE VARIABLE **Step 1.** Clear the equation of fractions and decimals. **Step 2.** Remove grouping symbols such as parentheses. **Step 3.** Simplify by combining like terms. **Step 4.** Write variable terms on one side and numbers on the other side using the addition property of inequality. **Step 5.** Get the variable alone using the multiplication property of inequality.	Solve: $\dfrac{3}{7}(x - 4) \geq x + 2$ **1.** $7\left[\dfrac{3}{7}(x - 4)\right] \geq 7(x + 2)$ Multiply both sides by 7. $3(x - 4) \geq 7(x + 2)$ **2.** $3x - 12 \geq 7x + 14$ Use the distributive property. **4.** $-4x - 12 \geq 14$ Subtract $7x$ from both sides. $-4x \geq 26$ Add 12 to both sides. $\dfrac{-4x}{-4} \leq \dfrac{26}{-4}$ Divide both sides by -4. Reverse the direction of the inequality symbol. $x \leq -\dfrac{13}{2}$

Definitions and Concepts	**Examples**

Section 2.5   Sets and Compound Inequalities

Two inequalities joined by the words **and** or **or** are called **compound inequalities.**

The solution set of a compound inequality formed by the word **and** is the **intersection** $\cap$ of the solution sets of the two inequalities.

$x - 7 \le 4$ and $x \ge -21$

$2x + 7 > x - 3$ or $5x + 2 > -3$

Solve:

$x < 5$ and $x < 3$

$\{x \mid x < 5\}$ 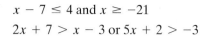 $(-\infty, 5)$

$\{x \mid x < 3\}$ $(-\infty, 3)$

$\{x \mid x < 3$ and $x < 5\}$ $(-\infty, 3)$

The solution set of a compound inequality formed by the word **or** is the **union** $\cup$ of the solution sets of the two inequalities.

Solve:

$x - 2 \ge -3$ or $2x \le -4$

$x \ge -1$ or $x \le -2$

$\{x \mid x \ge -1\}$ $[-1, \infty)$

$\{x \mid x \le -2\}$ $(-\infty, -2]$

$\{x \mid x \le -2$ or $x \ge -1\}$ $(-\infty, -2]$ $\cup [-1, \infty)$

Section 2.6   Absolute Value Equations and Inequalities

If a is a positive number, then $|X| = a$ is equivalent to $X = a$ or $X = -a$.

Solve: $|5y - 1| - 7 = 4$

$\qquad |5y - 1| = 11$ Add 7 to both sides.

$5y - 1 = 11$ or $5y - 1 = -11$

$5y = 12$ or $\qquad 5y = -10$ Add 1 to both sides.

$y = \dfrac{12}{5}$ or $\qquad 5y = -2$ Divide both sides by 5.

The solution set is $\left\{ -2, \dfrac{12}{5} \right\}$.

If a is negative, then $|X| = a$ has no solution.

Solve: $\left| \dfrac{x}{2} - 7 \right| = -1$

The solution set is $\{\ \}$, or $\varnothing$.

(continued)

DEFINITIONS AND CONCEPTS	EXAMPLES
Section 2.6 Absolute Value Equations and Inequalities (*continued*)	

To solve $\lvert X \rvert = \lvert Y \rvert$, solve $X = Y$ or $X = -Y$.	Solve: $\lvert x - 7 \rvert = \lvert 2x + 1 \rvert$ $$x - 7 = 2x + 1 \quad \text{or} \quad x - 7 = -(2x + 1)$$ $$x = 2x + 8 \quad \text{or} \quad x - 7 = -2x - 1$$ $$-x = 8 \qquad\quad \text{or} \qquad\quad x = -2x + 6$$ $$x = -8 \qquad\quad \text{or} \qquad\quad 3x = 6$$ $$x = 2$$ The solution set is $\{-8, 2\}$.
If a is a positive number, then to solve $\lvert X \rvert < a$, solve $-a < X < a$.	Solve: $\lvert y - 5 \rvert \le 3$ $$-3 \le y - 5 \le 3$$ $$-3 + 5 \le y - 5 + 5 \le 3 + 5 \quad \text{\small Add 5 to all three parts.}$$ $$2 \le y \le 8$$ The solution set is $[2, 8]$.
If a is a positive number, then to solve $\lvert X \rvert > a$, solve $X < -a$ or $X > a$.	Solve: $\left\lvert \dfrac{x}{2} - 3 \right\rvert > 7$ $$\frac{x}{2} - 3 < -7 \quad \text{or} \quad \frac{x}{2} - 3 > 7 \quad \text{\small Multiply both sides by 2.}$$ $$x - 6 < -14 \quad \text{or} \quad x - 6 > 14$$ $$x < -8 \qquad \text{or} \qquad x > 20 \quad \text{\small Add 6 to both sides.}$$ The solution set is $(-\infty, -8) \cup (20, \infty)$.

3

Graphs and Functions

Taken from:
Intermediate Algebra, Third Edition, by Elayn Martin-Gay

A Plot Ordered Pairs on a Rectangular Coordinate System.

B Determine Whether an Ordered Pair of Numbers Is a Solution of an Equation in Two Variables.

C Graph Linear Equations.

D Graph Vertical and Horizontal Lines.

3.1 GRAPHING LINEAR EQUATIONS

Graphs are widely used today in newspapers, magazines, and all forms of newsletters as a quick way to display data. A few examples of graphs are shown here.

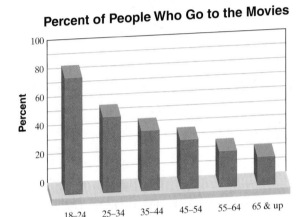

Percent of People Who Go to the Movies

Source: TELENATION/Market Facts, Inc.

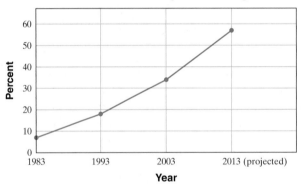

Percent of Sales Completed Using Cards*

Source: The Nilson Report
* These include credit or debit cards, prepaid cards and EBT (electronic benefits transfer) cards.

To help us understand how to read these graphs, we will review their basis—the rectangular coordinate system.

Objective **A** Plotting Ordered Pairs on a Rectangular Coordinate System

One way to locate points on a plane is by using a **rectangular coordinate system,** which is also called a **Cartesian coordinate system** after its inventor, René Descartes (1596–1650). A rectangular coordinate system consists of two number lines that intersect at right angles at their 0 coordinates. We position these axes on paper such that one number line is horizontal and the other number line is then vertical. The horizontal number line is called the **x-axis** (or the axis of the **abscissa**), and the vertical number line is called the **y-axis** (or the axis of the **ordinate**). The point of intersection of these axes is named the **origin.**

Notice that the axes divide the plane into four regions. These regions are called **quadrants.** The top-right region is quadrant I. Quadrants II, III, and IV are numbered counterclockwise from the first quadrant as shown. The x-axis and the y-axis are not in any quadrant.

Each point in the plane can be located, or **plotted,** by describing its position in terms of distances along each axis from the origin. An **ordered pair,** represented by the notation (x, y), records these distances.

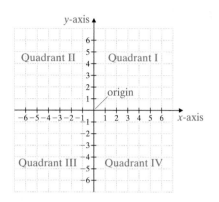

For example, the location of point A in the figure on the right above is described as 2 units to the left of the origin along the x-axis and 5 units upward parallel to the y-axis. Thus, we identify point A with the ordered pair $(-2, 5)$. Notice that the *order* of these numbers is *critical.* The x-value -2 is called the **x-coordinate** and is associated with the x-axis. The y-value 5 is called the **y-coordinate** and is associated with the y-axis.

Compare the location of point A with the location of point B, which corresponds to the ordered pair $(5, -2)$. The x-coordinate 5 indicates that we move 5 units to the right of the origin along the x-axis. The y-coordinate -2 indicates that we move 2 units down parallel to the y-axis. Point A is in a different position than point B. Two ordered pairs are considered equal and correspond to the same point if and only if their x-coordinates are equal and their y-coordinates are equal.

Keep in mind that *each ordered pair corresponds to exactly one point in the coordinate plane and that each point in the plane corresponds to exactly one ordered pair.* Thus, we may refer to the ordered pair (x, y) as the **point** (x, y).

EXAMPLE 1 Plot each ordered pair on a rectangular coordinate system and name the quadrant in which the point is located.

a. $(2, -1)$ **b.** $(0, 5)$ **c.** $(-3, 5)$

d. $(-2, 0)$ **e.** $\left(-\dfrac{1}{2}, -4\right)$ **f.** $(1.5, 1.5)$

Solution: The six points are graphed as shown in the figure.

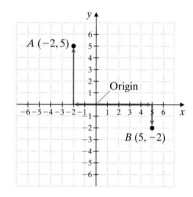

a. $(2, -1)$ lies in quadrant IV.

b. $(0, 5)$ is not in any quadrant.

c. $(-3, 5)$ lies in quadrant II.

d. $(-2, 0)$ is not in any quadrant.

e. $\left(-\dfrac{1}{2}, -4\right)$ is in quadrant III.

f. $(1.5, 1.5)$ is in quadrant I.

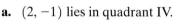 **Work Practice Problem 1**

PRACTICE PROBLEM 1

Plot each ordered pair on a rectangular coordinate system and name the quadrant in which the point is located.

a. $(3, -2)$ **b.** $(3.5, 4.5)$

c. $(0, 3)$ **d.** $(-4, 1)$

e. $(-1, 0)$ **f.** $\left(-2\dfrac{1}{2}, -3\right)$

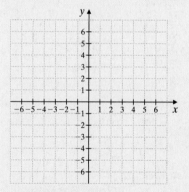

Answers

1.

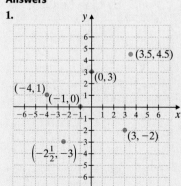

a. quadrant IV,   **b.** quadrant I,
c. not in any quadrant,   **d.** quadrant II,
e. not in any quadrant,   **f.** quadrant III

Notice that the y-coordinate of any point on the x-axis is 0. For example, the point with coordinates $(-2, 0)$ lies on the x-axis. Also, the x-coordinate of any point on the y-axis is 0. For example, the point with coordinates $(0, 5)$ lies on the y-axis. A point on an axis is called a **quadrantal** point.

✔**Concept Check** Which of the following correctly describes the location of the point $(3, -6)$ in a rectangular coordinate system?

a. 3 units to the left of the y-axis and 6 units above the x-axis

b. 3 units above the x-axis and 6 units to the left of the y-axis

c. 3 units to the right of the y-axis and 6 units below the x-axis

d. 3 units below the x-axis and 6 units to the right of the y-axis

Many types of real-world data occur in pairs. For example, the data pairs below are for Walt Disney World ticket prices for the years shown. The graph of paired data, such as the one below, is called a **scatter diagram.** Such diagrams are used to look for patterns and relationships in paired data.

PRACTICE PROBLEM 2

Create a scatter diagram for the given paired data.

3-Point Baskets Made by Lisa Leslie of the Los Angeles Sparks	
WNBA Season	3-Point Baskets Made
2000	7
2001	22
2002	12
2003	12
2004	6
(*Source:* WNBA)	

3-Point Baskets by Lisa Leslie

Paired Data	
Year, x	Price (in dollars), y
0	35.90
1	37.10
2	38.00
3	39.22
4	40.81
5	42.14
6	44.52
7	46.64
8	48.76
9	50.88
10	52.00
11	54.75
12	59.75

Note: The notation $0 \leftrightarrow$ 1992 means that year 0 corresponds to the year 1992, 1 corresponds to 1993, and so on.

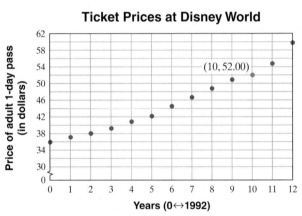

Source: The Walt Disney Company

Helpful Hint
Notice, for example, the paired data (10, 52.00) and its corresponding plotted point, both in blue.

Answer

2.

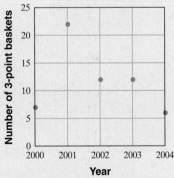

EXAMPLE 2 Create a scatter diagram for the given paired data.

Price of a Big Mac in Russia	
Year	Price (in U.S. dollars)
2001	1.21
2002	1.32
2003	1.43
2004	1.45
(*Sources: The Economist,* McDonald's)	

✔ **Concept Check Answer**

c

Solution: To graph the paired data in the table, we use the first column for the *x*- (or horizontal) axis and the second column for the *y*- (or vertical) axis.

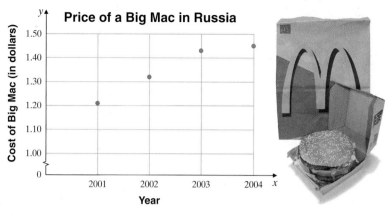

Price of a Big Mac in Russia

■ **Work Practice Problem 2**

Objective B Determining Whether an Ordered Pair of Numbers Is a Solution of an Equation

A **solution** of an equation in two variables consists of two numbers that make the equation true. These two numbers can be written as an ordered pair of numbers. Unless we are told otherwise, we will assume that variable values are written as ordered pairs in alphabetical order (that is, *x* first and then *y*).

EXAMPLE 3   Determine whether $(0, -12)$, $(1, 9)$, and $(2, -6)$ are solutions of the equation $3x - y = 12$.

Solution: To check each ordered pair, we replace *x* with the *x*-coordinate and *y* with the *y*-coordinate and see whether a true statement results.

Let $x = 0$ and $y = -12$.
$$3x - y = 12$$
$$3(0) - (-12) \stackrel{?}{=} 12$$
$$0 + 12 \stackrel{?}{=} 12$$
$$12 = 12 \quad \text{True}$$

Let $x = 1$ and $y = 9$.
$$3x - y = 12$$
$$3(1) - 9 \stackrel{?}{=} 12$$
$$3 - 9 \stackrel{?}{=} 12$$
$$-6 = 12 \quad \text{False}$$

Let $x = 2$ and $y = -6$.
$$3x - y = 12$$
$$3(2) - (-6) \stackrel{?}{=} 12$$
$$6 + 6 \stackrel{?}{=} 12$$
$$12 = 12 \quad \text{True}$$

We see that $(1, 9)$ is not a solution but both $(2, -6)$ and $(0, -12)$ are solutions.

■ **Work Practice Problem 3**

Objective C Graphing Linear Equations

As we saw in Example 3, some linear equations have more than one ordered pair solution. In fact, the equation $3x - y = 12$ has an infinite number of ordered pair solutions. Since it is impossible to list all solutions, we visualize them by graphing them.

A few more ordered pairs that satisfy $3x - y = 12$ are $(4, 0)$, $(3, -3)$, $(5, 3)$, and $(1, -9)$. These ordered pair solutions, along with the ordered pair solutions from Example 3, are plotted on the following graph. The graph of $3x - y = 12$ is the single line containing these points. Every ordered pair solution of the equation

PRACTICE PROBLEM 3

Determine whether $(0, -6)$, $(1, 4)$, and $(-1, -4)$ are solutions of the equation $2x + y = -6$.

Answer

3. yes; no; yes

corresponds to a point on this line, and every point on this line corresponds to an ordered pair solution.

x	y	$3x - y = 12$
5	3	$3 \cdot 5 - 3 = 12$
4	0	$3 \cdot 4 - 0 = 12$
3	-3	$3 \cdot 3 - (-3) = 12$
2	-6	$3 \cdot 2 - (-6) = 12$
1	-9	$3 \cdot 1 - (-9) = 12$
0	-12	$3 \cdot 0 - (-12) = 12$

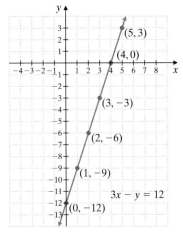

The equation $3x - y = 12$ is called a *linear equation in two variables,* and *the graph of every linear equation in two variables is a line.*

Linear Equation in Two Variables

A **linear equation in two variables** is an equation that can be written in the form

$$Ax + By = C$$

where A, B, and C are real numbers, and A and B are not both 0. This form is called **standard form** and the graph of a linear equation in two variables is a line.

Some examples of linear equations in standard form are:

$$3x - y = 12$$
$$-2.1x + 5.6y = 0$$

> **Helpful Hint**
>
> Remember that in a linear equation in standard form, all of the variable terms are on one side of the equation and the constant is on the other side.

Recall from geometry that a line is determined by two points. This means that to graph a linear equation in two variables, just two solutions are needed. We will find a third solution, just to check our work. To find ordered pair solutions of linear equations in two variables, we can choose an x-value and find its corresponding y-value, or we can choose a y-value and find its corresponding x-value. The number 0 is often a convenient value to choose for x and also for y.

EXAMPLE 4 Graph: $y = -2x + 3$

Solution: This is a linear equation. (In standard form it is $2x + y = 3$.) Find three ordered pair solutions, and plot the ordered pairs. The line through the plotted points is the graph. Since the equation is solved for y, let's choose three x-values. Let's let x be 0, 2, and then -1 to find our three ordered pair solutions.

Let $x = 0$ Let $x = 2$ Let $x = -1$

$y = -2x + 3$ $y = -2x + 3$ $y = -2x + 3$

$y = -2 \cdot 0 + 3$ $y = -2 \cdot 2 + 3$ $y = -2(-1) + 3$

$y = 3$ Simplify. $y = -1$ Simplify. $y = 5$ Simplify.

PRACTICE PROBLEM 4

Graph: $y = 4x - 3$

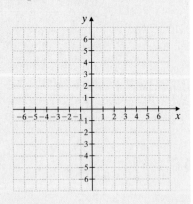

Answer

4.

The three ordered pairs $(0, 3)$, $(2, -1)$ and $(-1, 5)$ are listed in the table and the graph is shown.

x	y
0	3
2	-1
-1	5

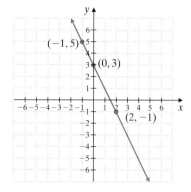

Work Practice Problem 4

Helpful Hint

Since the equation $y = -2x + 3$ is solved for y, we choose x-values for finding points. This way, we simply need to evaluate an expression to find the y-value, as shown.

Notice that the graph crosses the x-axis at the point $\left(\dfrac{3}{2}, 0\right)$. This point is called the **x-intercept.** (You may sometimes see just the number $\dfrac{3}{2}$ called the x-intercept.) This graph also crosses the y-axis at the point $(0, 3)$. This point is called the **y-intercept.** (You may also see just the number 3 called the y-intercept.)

Since every point on the x-axis has an y-value of 0, we can find the x-intercept of a graph by letting $y = 0$ and solving for x. Also, every point on the y-axis has an x-value of 0. To find the y-intercept, we let $x = 0$ and solve for y.

Finding x- and y-Intercepts

To find an x-intercept, let $y = 0$ and solve for x.
To find a y-intercept, let $x = 0$ and solve for y.

We will study intercepts further in Section 3.3.

One way to graph a linear equation in two variables is to find x- and y-intercepts. This provides at most two points, so make sure a third solution point is found to check.

EXAMPLE 5 Find the intercepts and graph: $3x + 4y = -12$

Solution: To find the y-intercept, we let $x = 0$ and solve for y. To find the x-intercept, we let $y = 0$ and solve for x. Let's let $x = 0$, $y = 0$, and then let $x = 2$ to find our third check point.

Let $x = 0$.	Let $y = 0$.	Let $x = 2$.
$3x + 4y = -12$	$3x + 4y = -12$	$3x + 4y = -12$
$3 \cdot 0 + 4y = -12$	$3x + 4 \cdot 0 = -12$	$3 \cdot 2 + 4y = -12$
$4y = -12$	$3x = -12$	$6 + 4y = -12$
$y = -3$	$x = -4$	$4y = -18$
		$y = -\dfrac{18}{4} = -4\dfrac{1}{2}$
$(0, -3)$	$(-4, 0)$	$\left(2, -4\dfrac{1}{2}\right)$

Continued on next page

PRACTICE PROBLEM 5

Find the intercepts and graph:
$2x + 3y = -6$

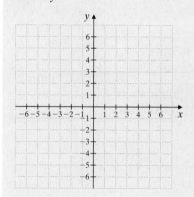

Answer

5.

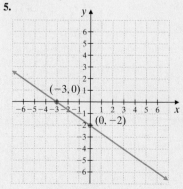

The ordered pairs are $(0, -3), (-4, 0),$ and $\left(2, -4\frac{1}{2}\right)$. We plot these points to obtain the graph shown.

x	y	
0	-3	← y-intercept
x-intercept → -4	0	
2	$-4\frac{1}{2}$	

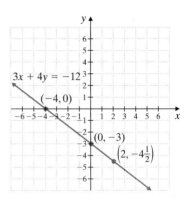

■ **Work Practice Problem 5**

EXAMPLE 6 Graph: $y = \frac{1}{3}x$

Solution: To graph, we find ordered pair solutions, plot the ordered pairs, and draw a line through the plotted points. We will choose x-values and substitute in the equation. To avoid fractions, we choose x-values that are multiples of 3. To find the intercepts, we will also let $x = 0$ and solve for y, then let $y = 0$ and solve for x.

$y = \frac{1}{3}x$

If $x = 6$, then $y = \frac{1}{3}(6)$, or 2.

If $x = -3$, then $y = \frac{1}{3}(-3)$, or -1.

If $x = 0$, then $y = \frac{1}{3}(0)$, or 0.

If $y = 0$, then $0 = \frac{1}{3}x$, or 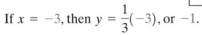 $0 = x$.

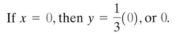 Multiply both sides of $0 = \frac{1}{3}x$ by 3.

x	y
-3	-1
0	0
6	2

This graph crosses the x-axis at $(0, 0)$ and the y-axis at $(0, 0)$. This means that the x-intercept is $(0, 0)$ and that the y-intercept is $(0, 0)$. This happens when the graph passes through the origin.

■ **Work Practice Problem 6**

Objective **D** Graphing Vertical and Horizontal Lines

The equation $x = c$, where c is a real number constant, is a linear equation in two variables because it can be written in the form $x + 0y = c$. The graph of this equation is a vertical line, as shown in the next example.

PRACTICE PROBLEM 6

Graph: $y = \frac{1}{4}x$

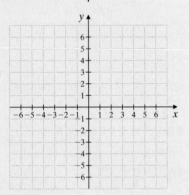

Helpful Hint
Notice that by using multiples of 3 for x, we avoid fractions.

Answer
6.

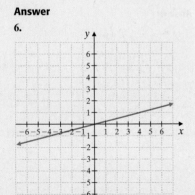

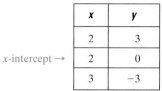 Graph: $x = 2$

Solution: The equation $x = 2$ can be written as $x + 0y = 2$. Notice that for any y-value chosen, x is 2. No other value for x satisfies $x + 0y = 2$. Any ordered pair whose x-coordinate is 2 is a solution to $x + 0y = 2$ because 2 added to 0 times any value of y is $2 + 0$, or 2. We will use the ordered pairs $(2, 3)$, $(2, 0)$ and $(2, -3)$ to graph $x = 2$.

x	y
2	3
2	0
3	-3

x-intercept →

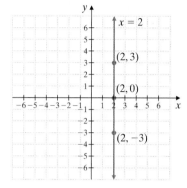

The graph is a vertical line with x-intercept $(2, 0)$. It has no y-intercept because x is never 0.

■ **Work Practice Problem 7**

EXAMPLE 8 Graph: $y = -3$

Solution: The equation $y = -3$ can be written as $0x + y = -3$. For any x-value chosen, y is -3. If we choose 4, 0, and -2 as x-values, the ordered pair solutions are $(4, -3)$, $(0, -3)$, and $(-2, -3)$. We will use these ordered pairs to graph $y = -3$.

x	y
4	-3
0	-3
-2	-3

← y-intercept

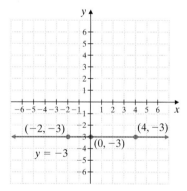

The graph is a horizontal line with y-intercept $(0, -3)$. It has no x-intercept because y is never 0.

■ **Work Practice Problem 8**

From Examples 7 and 8, we have the following generalization.

Graphing Vertical and Horizontal Lines

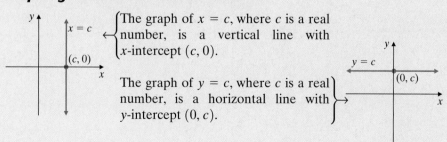

The graph of $x = c$, where c is a real number, is a vertical line with x-intercept $(c, 0)$.

The graph of $y = c$, where c is a real number, is a horizontal line with y-intercept $(0, c)$.

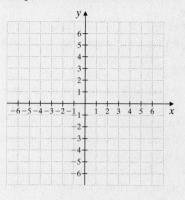
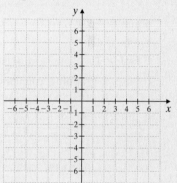
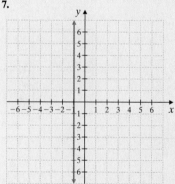
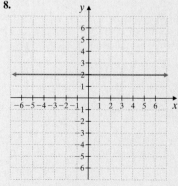

CALCULATOR EXPLORATIONS Graphing

In this section, we begin a study of graphing calculators and graphing software packages for computers.

These graphers use the same point-plotting technique that we introduced in this section. The advantage of this graphing technology is, of course, that graphing calculators and computers can find and plot ordered pair solutions much faster than we can. Note, however, that the features described in these boxes may not be available on all graphing calculators.

The rectangular screen where a portion of the rectangular coordinate system is displayed is called a **window.** We call it a **standard window** for graphing when both the x- and y-axes display coordinates between -10 and 10. This information is often displayed in the window menu on a graphing calculator as

> Xmin = -10
> Xmax = 10
> Xscl = 1 The scale on the x-axis is one unit per tick mark.
> Ymin = -10
> Ymax = 10
> Yscl = 1 The scale on the y-axis is one unit per tick mark.

To use a graphing calculator to graph the equation $y = -5x + 4$, press the Y= key and enter the keystrokes

(-) 5 X + 4

(Check your owner's manual to make sure the "negative" key is pressed here and not the "subtraction" key.)

The top row should now read $Y_1 = -5x + 4$. Next press the GRAPH key, and the display should look like this:

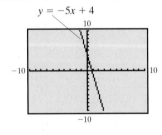

Use a standard window and graph each linear equation. (Unless otherwise stated, we will use a standard window when graphing.)

1. $y = 6x - 1$

2. $y = 3x - 2$

3. $y = -3.2x + 7.9$

4. $y = -x + 5.85$

5. $y = \dfrac{1}{4}x - \dfrac{2}{3}$ (Parentheses may need to be inserted around $\dfrac{1}{4}$.)

6. $y = \dfrac{2}{3}x - \dfrac{1}{5}$ (Parentheses may need to be inserted around $\dfrac{2}{3}$.)

Mental Math

Determine the coordinates of each point on the graph.

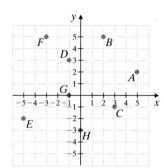

1. Point A

2. Point B

3. Point C

4. Point D

5. Point E

6. Point F

7. Point G

8. Point H

3.1 EXERCISE SET

FOR EXTRA HELP

| Student Solutions Manual | PH Math/Tutor Center | CD/Video for Review | MathXL® | MyMathLab |

Objective Ⓐ *Plot each ordered pair on a rectangular coordinate system and name the quadrant (or axis) in which the point lies. See Example 1.*

1. $(3, 2)$

$(-5, 3)$

$\left(5\dfrac{1}{2}, -4\right)$

$(0, 3.5)$

$(-2, -4)$

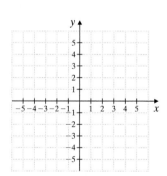

2. $(2, -1)$

$(-3, -1)$

$\left(-2, 6\dfrac{1}{3}\right)$

$(-2, 4)$

$(-4.2, 0)$

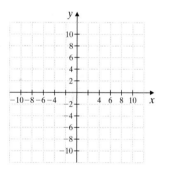

Given that x is a positive number and y is a positive number, determine the quadrant (or axis) in which each point lies. See Example 1.

3. $(x, -y)$

4. $(-x, y)$

5. $(x, 0)$

6. $(0, -y)$

7. $(-x, -y)$

8. $(0, 0)$

Create a scatter diagram for the given paired data. See Example 2.

9. Domestic Airline Revenues in the United States

Year	Revenue (in millions of dollars)
1999	582
2000	610
2001	570
2002	560
2003	593

(*Source: The World Almanac*)

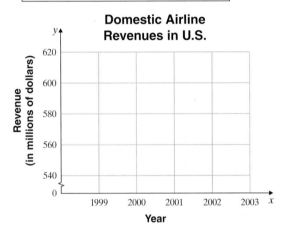

Domestic Airline Revenues in U.S.

10. Median Age at Retirement for U.S. Men

Year	Age (in years)
1950	67
1960	65
1970	63
1980	63
1990	63
2000	62

(*Source:* U.S. Bureau of Labor Statistics)

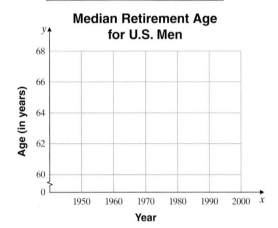

Median Retirement Age for U.S. Men

Objective B *Determine whether each ordered pair is a solution of the given equation. See Example 3.*

11. $y = 3x - 5; (0, 5), (-1, -8)$

12. $y = -2x + 7; (1, 5), (-2, 3)$

13. $-6x + 5y = -6; (1, 0), \left(2, \dfrac{6}{5}\right)$

14. $5x - 3y = 9; (0, 3), \left(\dfrac{12}{5}, -1\right)$

15. $y = -3; (1, -3), (-3, 6)$

16. $y = 2; (2, 5), (0, 2)$

Objectives C D Mixed Practice *Graph each linear equation. See Examples 4 through 8.*

17. $x - 2y = 4$

18. $y - 2x = 4$

19. $3x + 2y = 6$

20. $2x + 4y = 8$

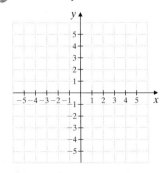

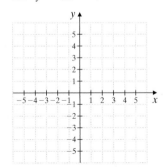

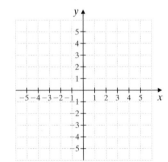

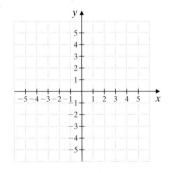

21. $x = 4$
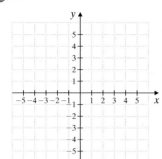

22. $y = 5$
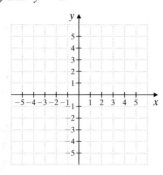

23. $x - 3y = 6$
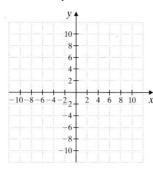

24. $x - 4y = 8$
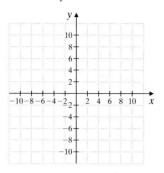

25. $y = 3x$
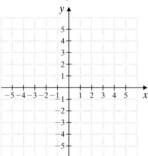

26. $y = -4x$
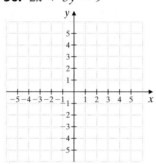

27. $y = -2$
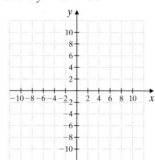

28. $x = -3$
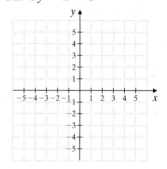

29. $4x + 5y = 15$
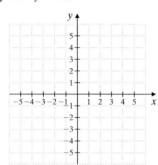

30. $2x + 3y = 9$
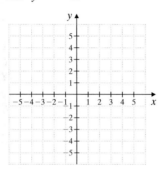

31. $5y = x - 10$
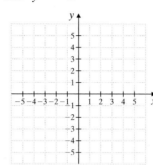

32. $3y = x - 3$
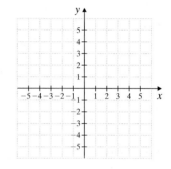

33. $x = \dfrac{1}{2}$
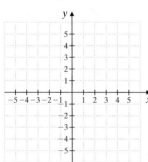

34. $y = -\dfrac{5}{2}$
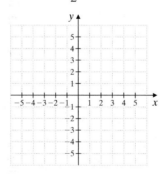

35. $y = 0.5x$
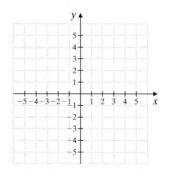

36. $x = 0.5y$
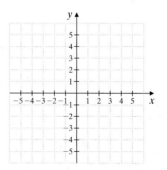

37. $y = -4x + 1$
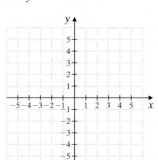

38. $y = -3x + 1$
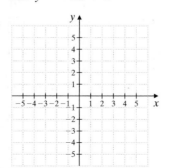

39. $2y - 6 = 0$
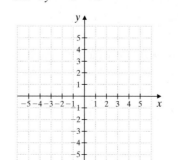

40. $3x + 6 = 0$
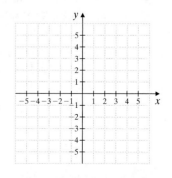

41. $y = -\dfrac{2}{3}x - 4$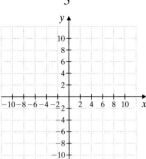

42. $y = -\dfrac{3}{2}x + 6$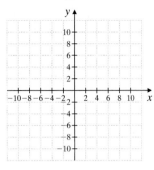

43. $5x - 2y = -10$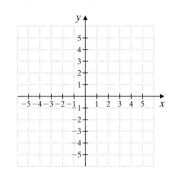

44. $5x - 3y = -15$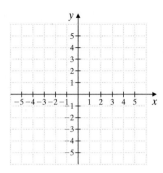

Review

Simplify. See Section 1.5.

45. $\dfrac{-6 - 3}{2 - 8}$

46. $\dfrac{4 - 5}{-1 - 0}$

47. $\dfrac{-8 - (-2)}{-3 - (-2)}$

48. $\dfrac{12 - 3}{10 - 9}$

49. $\dfrac{0 - 6}{5 - 0}$

50. $\dfrac{2 - 2}{3 - 5}$

Concept Extensions

Solve. See the Concept Check in this section.

51. Which correctly describes the location of the point $(-1, 5.3)$ in a rectangular coordinate system?

   a. 1 unit to the right of the y-axis and 5.3 units above the x-axis

   b. 1 unit to the left of the y-axis and 5.3 units above the x-axis

   c. 1 unit to the left of the y-axis and 5.3 units below the x-axis

   d. 1 unit to the right of the y-axis and 5.3 units below the x-axis

52. Which correctly describes the location of the point $\left(0, -\dfrac{3}{4}\right)$ in a rectangular coordinate system?

   a. on the x-axis and $\dfrac{3}{4}$ unit to the left of the y-axis

   b. on the x-axis and $\dfrac{3}{4}$ unit to the right of the y-axis

   c. on the y-axis and $\dfrac{3}{4}$ unit above the x-axis

   d. on the y-axis and $\dfrac{3}{4}$ unit below the x-axis

For Exercises 53 through 56, match each description with the graph that best illustrates it.

53. Moe worked 40 hours per week until the fall semester started. He quit and didn't work again until he worked 60 hours a week during the holiday season starting mid-December.

54. Kawana worked 40 hours a week for her father during the summer. She slowly cut back her hours to not working at all during the fall semester. During the holiday season in December, she started working again and increased her hours to 60 hours per week.

GROUP PROJECTS
Compiled by Brian Emond

Project

COORDINATE GEOMETRY
PLOT TRACKLINE OF RESEARCH VESSEL

Objectives:

- Locate coordinates of Longitude, Latitude and X,Y Loran on a navigation chart;
- To read and interpret tow stations from survey data;
- Graph course/trackline of vessel on navigation chart;
- Calculate distance traveled;
- Convert nautical miles to statute miles.

Materials:

- Navigation chart of survey area
- NOAA fisheries data
- Map of United States
- Drawing materials (pencil, eraser, straightedge)
- Enlarged navigation chart of survey area, or transparency of the chart. (optional).

Activities:

- On the map of the United States find the location of their state and town. Then show how to express the location in longitude and latitude. An explanation of degree and minute intervals will be sufficient. Ask them in what other states and /or towns they have relatives or friends, and locate the longitude and latitude of two or three of them.
- Then explain the similarities of reading locations on the navigation charts in Appendix A and the map of the U.S. with longitude and latitude.
- Now show them how to read the data from a ***Fishermen's Report*** from the Northeast Marine Fisheries Science Center website. Working in pairs, have the students locate the tow locations for ten sequential stations. (Ten pairs of students could track the first one hundred tow stations.)
- Enlarge the navigation chart of the area you are using, or use a transparency of the same area projected on a whiteboard. The students can then draw in their sections of the track line, and connect them together to show the entire trackline.
- Notice the "course" column from the data. This gives the direction the vessel is towing with respect to compass readings. The students can check the "reasonableness" of each line by comparing it to the direction of the tow.
- Students can calculate the distance traveled by their vessel. If the tow duration's are 30 minutes at an average of 4.0 nautical miles per hour, and they located 100 tows, the distance traveled can then be determined. The introduction page of the data will usually have this information. Since the distance is expressed in nautical miles, the students can then convert to statute miles. (1 nautical mile = 1.1515 statute miles).
- A more challenging variation would be to find and draw the trackline using Loran coordinates. These are identified on the navigation chart as crisscrossing diagonal lines. On the data from the Fishermen's Report you will notice the coordinates have either x,y or w,y prefixes. These are the preferred coordinate format by the fishermen. They will often follow the "43000 line" for instance.
- Given that there are approximately 400 commercial scallop vessels in the fleet, and if each vessel fishes for 120 days, how many square miles of ocean floor are dredged for scallops in one fishing season? Take into account that each boat has two 15' wide dredges, and tows at an average speed of 4 nautical miles per hour for 24 hours a day.
- Ask the students to list the similarities and differences in navigation charts, topographical maps and road maps. They can draw a map of their town and label the left side the Y-axis, and the bottom the X-axis. Have them give the coordinates of places of interest. Calculate the distance from their house to school in nautical miles.

3.2 THE SLOPE OF A LINE

You may have noticed by now that different lines often tilt differently. It is very important in many fields to be able to measure and compare the tilt, or **slope,** of lines. For example, a wheelchair ramp with a slope of $\frac{1}{12}$ means that the ramp rises 1 foot for every 12 horizontal feet. A road with a slope or grade of 8% $\left(\text{or } \frac{8}{100}\right)$ means that the road rises 8 feet for every 100 horizontal feet.

We measure the slope of a line as a ratio of **vertical change** to **horizontal change.** Slope is usually designated by the letter m.

Objective **A** Finding Slope from Two Points

Suppose that we want to measure the slope of the following line.

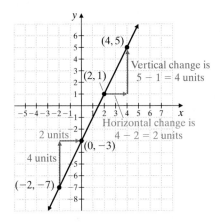

The vertical change between *both* pairs of points on the line is 4 units per horizontal change of 2 units. Then

$$\text{slope } m = \frac{\text{change in } y \text{ (vertical change)}}{\text{change in } x \text{ (horizontal change)}} = \frac{4}{2} = 2$$

Notice that slope is a **rate of change** between points. A slope of 2 or $\frac{2}{1}$ means that between pairs of points on the line, the rate of change is a vertical change of 2 units per horizontal change of 1 unit.

In general, consider the line that passes through the points (x_1, y_1) and (x_2, y_2). (The notation x_1 is read "x-sub-one.") The vertical change, or **rise,** between these points is the difference in the y-coordinates: $y_2 - y_1$. The horizontal change, or **run,** between the points is the difference of the x-coordinates: $x_2 - x_1$.

Slope of a Line

Given a line passing through points (x_1, y_1) and (x_2, y_2) the **slope** m of the line is

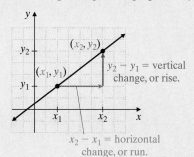

$$m = \frac{\text{rise}}{\text{run}} = \frac{y_2 - y_1}{x_2 - x_1}$$

as long as $x_2 \neq x_1$.

$y_2 - y_1 =$ vertical change, or rise.

$x_2 - x_1 =$ horizontal change, or run.

✔ **Concept Check** In the definition of slope, we state that $x_2 \neq x_1$. Explain why.

EXAMPLE 1 Find the slope of the line containing the points $(0, 3)$ and $(2, 5)$. Graph the line.

Solution: We use the slope formula. It does not matter which point we call (x_1, y_1) and which point we call (x_2, y_2). We'll let $(x_1, y_1) = (0, 3)$ and $(x_2, y_2) = (2, 5)$.

$$m = \frac{y_2 - y_1}{x_2 - x_1}$$

$$= \frac{5 - 3}{2 - 0} = \frac{2}{2} = 1$$

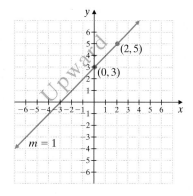

Notice in this example that the slope is *positive* and that the graph of the line containing $(0, 3)$ and $(2, 5)$ moves *upward*—that is, the y-values increase—as we go from left to right.

■ **Work Practice Problem 1**

> **Helpful Hint**
>
> The slope of a line is the same no matter which 2 points of a line you choose to calculate slope. The line in Example 1 also contains the point $(-3, 0)$. Below, we calculate the slope of the line using $(0, 3)$ as (x_1, y_1) and $(-3, 0)$ as (x_2, y_2).
>
> $$m = \frac{y_2 - y_1}{x_2 - x_1} = \frac{0 - 3}{-3 - 0} = \frac{-3}{-3} = 1 \quad \text{Same slope as found in Example 1.}$$

PRACTICE PROBLEM 1

Find the slope of the line containing the points $(-1, -2)$ and $(2, 5)$. Graph the line.

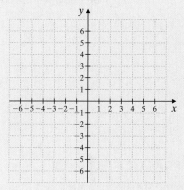

Answer

1. $m = \dfrac{7}{3}$,

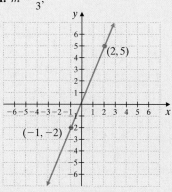

✔ **Concept Check Answer**

so that the denominator is never 0

PRACTICE PROBLEM 2

Find the slope of the line containing the points $(1, -1)$ and $(-2, 4)$. Graph the line.

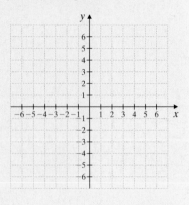

EXAMPLE 2 Find the slope of the line containing the points $(5, -4)$ and $(-3, 3)$. Graph the line.

Solution: We use the slope formula, and let $(x_1, y_1) = (5, -4)$ and $(x_2, y_2) = (-3, 3)$.

$$m = \frac{y_2 - y_1}{x_2 - x_1}$$

$$= \frac{3 - (-4)}{-3 - 5} = \frac{7}{-8} = -\frac{7}{8}$$

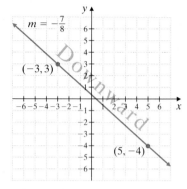

Notice in this example that the slope is negative and that the graph of the line through $(5, -4)$ and $(-3, 3)$ moves downward—that is, the y-values decrease—as we go from left to right.

🔲 **Work Practice Problem 2**

Helpful Hint

When we are trying to find the slope of a line through two given points, it makes no difference which given point is called (x_1, y_1) and which is called (x_2, y_2). Once an x-coordinate is called x_1, however, make sure its corresponding y-coordinate is called y_1.

✔ **Concept Check** Find and correct the error in the following calculation of slope of the line containing the points $(12, 2)$ and $(4, 7)$.

$$m = \frac{12 - 4}{2 - 7} = \frac{8}{-5} = -\frac{8}{5}$$

PRACTICE PROBLEM 3

Find the slope of the line $y = 2x + 4$.

Objective **B** Finding Slope from an Equation

As we have seen, the slope of a line is defined by two points on the line. Thus, if we know the equation of a line, we can find its slope.

Answers

2. $m = -\frac{5}{3}$,

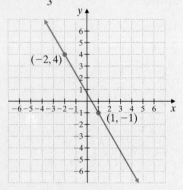

3. $m = 2$

✔ **Concept Check Answer**

$m = \frac{2 - 7}{12 - 4} = \frac{-5}{8} = -\frac{5}{8}$

EXAMPLE 3 Find the slope of the line $y = 3x + 2$.

Solution: We must find two points on the line defined by $y = 3x + 2$ to find its slope. We will let $x = 0$ and then $x = 1$ to find the required points.

Let $x = 0$.

$y = 3x + 2$
$y = 3 \cdot 0 + 2$
$y = 2$

Let $x = 1$.

$y = 3x + 2$
$y = 3 \cdot 1 + 2$
$y = 5$

Now we use the points $(0, 2)$ and $(1, 5)$ to find the slope. We'll let (x_1, y_1) be $(0, 2)$ and (x_2, y_2) be $(1, 5)$. Then

$$m = \frac{y_2 - y_1}{x_2 - x_1} = \frac{5 - 2}{1 - 0} = \frac{3}{1} = 3$$

🔲 **Work Practice Problem 3**

Analyzing the results of Example 3, you may notice a striking pattern:

The slope of $y = 3x + 2$ is 3, the same as the coefficient of x.

The y-coordinate of the y-intercept $(0, 2)$, the same as the constant term.

We have just illustrated, not proved, an amazing pattern with linear equations in two variables. When a linear equation is written in the form $y = mx + b$, m is the slope of the line and $(0, b)$ is its y-intercept. The form $y = mx + b$ is appropriately called the *slope-intercept form*.

Slope-Intercept Form

When a linear equation in two variables is written in **slope-intercept form,**

$$\underset{\underset{\downarrow}{\text{slope}}}{} \quad \underset{\underset{\downarrow}{y\text{-intercept is }(0, b)}}{}$$

$$y = mx + b$$

then m is the slope of the line and $(0, b)$ is the y-intercept of the line.

EXAMPLE 4 Find the slope and the y-intercept of the line $3x - 4y = 4$.

Solution: We write the equation in slope-intercept form by solving for y.

$$3x - 4y = 4$$

$$-4y = -3x + 4 \qquad \text{Subtract } 3x \text{ from both sides.}$$

$$\frac{-4y}{-4} = \frac{-3x}{-4} + \frac{4}{-4} \qquad \text{Divide both sides by } -4.$$

$$y = \frac{3}{4}x - 1 \qquad \text{Simplify.}$$

The coefficient of x, $\frac{3}{4}$, is the slope, and $(0, -1)$, is the y-intercept.

Work Practice Problem 4

PRACTICE PROBLEM 4

Find the slope and the y-intercept of the line $2x - 4y = 8$.

The graphs of $y = \frac{1}{2}x + 1$ and $y = 5x + 1$ are shown below. The graph of $y = \frac{1}{2}x + 1$ has a slope of $\frac{1}{2}$ and the graph of $y = 5x + 1$ has a slope of 5.

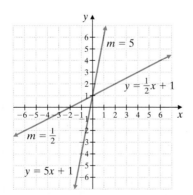

Notice that the line with the slope of 5 is steeper than the line with the slope of $\frac{1}{2}$. This is true in general for positive slopes.

For a line with positive slope m, as m increases the line becomes steeper.

Answer

4. slope: $\frac{1}{2}$; y-intercept: $(0, -2)$

Objective **C** Finding Slopes of Horizontal and Vertical Lines

Next we find the slopes of two special types of lines: vertical lines and horizontal lines.

PRACTICE PROBLEM 5

Find the slope of the line $x = 3$.

EXAMPLE 5 Find the slope of the line $x = -5$.

Solution: Recall that the graph of $x = -5$ is a vertical line with x-intercept $(-5, 0)$. To find the slope, we find two ordered pair solutions of $x = -5$. Of course, solutions of $x = -5$ must have an x-value of -5. We will let $(x_1, y_1) = (-5, 0)$ and $(x_2, y_2) = (-5, 4)$. Then

$$m = \frac{y_2 - y_1}{x_2 - x_1} = \frac{4 - 0}{-5 - (-5)} = \frac{4}{0}$$

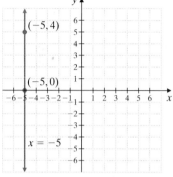

Since $\frac{4}{0}$ is undefined, we say that the slope of the vertical line $x = -5$ is undefined.

🔲 **Work Practice Problem 5**

PRACTICE PROBLEM 6

Find the slope of the line $y = -3$.

EXAMPLE 6 Find the slope of the line $y = 2$.

Solution: Recall that the graph of $y = 2$ is a horizontal line with y-intercept $(0, 2)$. To find the slope, we find two points on the line, such as $(0, 2)$ and $(1, 2)$, and use these points to find the slope.

$$m = \frac{2 - 2}{1 - 0} = \frac{0}{1} = 0$$

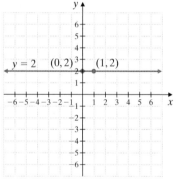

The slope of the horizontal line $y = 2$ is 0.

🔲 **Work Practice Problem 6**

From the above examples, we have the following generalization.

> ### Slopes of Vertical and Horizontal Lines
>
> The slope of any vertical line is undefined.
> The slope of any horizontal line is 0.

Answers

5. undefined, **6.** 0

Helpful Hint

Slope of 0 and undefined slope are not the same. Vertical lines have un-defined slope, whereas horizontal lines have slope of 0.

The following four graphs summarize the overall appearance of lines with positive, negative, zero, and undefined slopes.

Increasing line, positive slope

Decreasing line, negative slope

Horizontal line, zero-slope

Vertical line, undefined slope

Objective D Finding the Slope of a Line Given the Graph of a Line

Now that we know the appearance of lines with positive, negative, zero, and undefined slopes, let's practice finding the slope of a line given its graph.

EXAMPLE 7 Find the slope of the line graphed.

Solution: The two points shown have coordinates $(2, 1)$ and $(0, -4)$. Thus,

$$m = \frac{-4 - 1}{0 - 2} = \frac{-5}{-2} = \frac{5}{2}$$

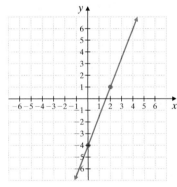

As a quick check, notice that the line goes upward from left to right, so its slope is positive.

The slope of the line is $\frac{5}{2}$.

■ **Work Practice Problem 7**

Objective E Comparing Slopes of Parallel and Perpendicular Lines

Slopes of lines can help us determine whether lines are parallel. Parallel lines are distinct lines with the same steepness, so it follows that they have the same slope.

PRACTICE PROBLEM 7

Find the slope of the line graphed.

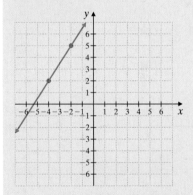

Answer

7. $m = \dfrac{3}{2}$

Parallel Lines

Two nonvertical lines are parallel if they have the same slope and different y-intercepts.

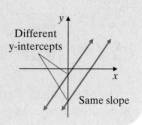

How do the slopes of perpendicular lines compare? (Two lines intersecting at right angles are called **perpendicular lines.**) Suppose that a line has a slope of $\frac{a}{b}$. If the line is rotated 90°, the rise and run are now switched, except that the run is now negative. This means that the new slope is $-\frac{b}{a}$. Notice that

$$\left(\frac{a}{b}\right)\cdot\left(-\frac{b}{a}\right)=-1$$

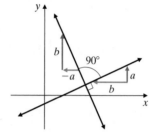

This is how we tell whether two lines are perpendicular.

Perpendicular Lines

Two nonvertical lines are perpendicular if the product of their slopes is −1.

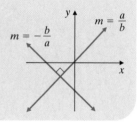

In other words, two nonvertical lines are perpendicular if the slope of one is the negative reciprocal of the slope of the other.

PRACTICE PROBLEM 8

Determine whether the two lines are parallel, perpendicular, or neither.

$2x + 5y = 1$
$4x + 10y = 3$

EXAMPLE 8 Determine whether the two lines are parallel, perpendicular, or neither.

$3x + 7y = 4$
$6x + 14y = 7$

Solution: We find the slope of each line by solving each equation for y.

$3x + 7y = 4$ $6x + 14y = 7$

$7y = -3x + 4$ $14y = -6x + 7$

$\frac{7y}{7} = \frac{-3x}{7} + \frac{4}{7}$ $\frac{14y}{14} = \frac{-6x}{14} + \frac{7}{14}$

$y = -\frac{3}{7}x + \frac{4}{7}$ $y = -\frac{3}{7}x + \frac{1}{2}$

slope   y-intercept $\left(0,\frac{4}{7}\right)$ slope   y-intercept $\left(0,\frac{1}{2}\right)$

Answer
8. parallel

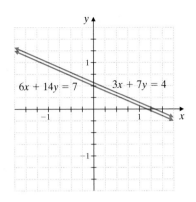

The slopes of both lines are $-\dfrac{3}{7}$. The y-intercepts are different. Therefore, the lines are parallel.

◼ **Work Practice Problem 8**

EXAMPLE 9 Determine whether the two lines are parallel, perpendicular, or neither.

$$-x + 3y = 2$$
$$2x + 6y = 5$$

Solution: When we solve each equation for y, we have

$$\begin{array}{ll}
-x + 3y = 2 & 2x + 6y = 5 \\[4pt]
3y = x + 2 & 6y = -2x + 5 \\[4pt]
\dfrac{3y}{3} = \dfrac{x}{3} + \dfrac{2}{3} & \dfrac{6y}{6} = \dfrac{-2x}{6} + \dfrac{5}{6} \\[6pt]
y = \dfrac{1}{3}x + \dfrac{2}{3} & y = -\dfrac{1}{3}x + \dfrac{5}{6}
\end{array}$$

slope y-intercept $\left(0, \dfrac{2}{3}\right)$ slope y-intercept $\left(0, \dfrac{5}{6}\right)$

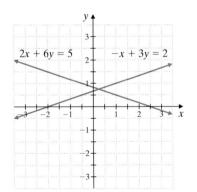

The slopes are not the same and their product is not -1 $\left[\left(\dfrac{1}{3}\right)\cdot\left(-\dfrac{1}{3}\right) = -\dfrac{1}{9}\right]$.

Therefore, the lines are neither parallel nor perpendicular.

◼ **Work Practice Problem 9**

✔ **Concept Check** What is *different* about the equations of two parallel lines?

PRACTICE PROBLEM 9

Determine whether the two lines are parallel, perpendicular, or neither.

$$x - 4y = 3$$
$$3x + 12y = 7$$

Answer
9. neither parallel nor perpendicular

✔ **Concept Check Answer**
y-intercepts are different

▣ CALCULATOR EXPLORATIONS Graphing

It is possible to use a grapher to sketch the graph of more than one equation on the same set of axes. For example, let's graph the equations $y = 2x - 3$ and $y = 2x + 5$ on the same set of axes.

To graph on the same set of axes, press the ⃞Y= key and enter the equations on the first two lines.

$Y_1 = 2x - 3$
$Y_2 = 2x + 5$

Then press the ⃞GRAPH key as usual. The screen should look like this:

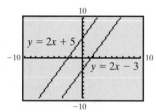

Notice the slopes and y-intercepts of the graphs. Since their slopes are the same and they have different y-intercepts, we have parallel lines, as shown.

Graph each pair of equations on the same set of axes. Describe the similarities and differences in their graphs.

1. $y = 3x, y = 3x + 4$

2. $y = 5x, y = 5x - 2$

3. $y = -\dfrac{2}{3}x + 1, y = -\dfrac{2}{3} + 6$

4. $y = -\dfrac{1}{4}x - 3, y = -\dfrac{1}{4}x + 6$

5. $y = 4.61x - 1.86, y = 4.61x + 2.11$

6. $y = 3.78x + 1.92, y = 3.78x + 8.08$

Mental Math

Determine whether a line with the given slope slants upward, downward, horizontally, or vertically from left to right.

1. $m = \dfrac{7}{6}$

2. $m = -3$

3. $m = 0$

4. m is undefined.

3.2 EXERCISE SET

Objectives Ⓐ Ⓓ **Mixed Practice** *Find the slope of the line containing each pair of points. See Examples 1, 2, and 7.*

1. $(3, 2), (8, 11)$

2. $(1, 6), (7, 11)$

3. $(3, 1), (1, 8)$

4. $(2, 9), (6, 4)$

5. $(-2, 8), (4, 3)$

6. $(3, 7), (-2, 11)$

7. $(-2, -6), (4, -4)$

8. $(-3, -4), (-1, 6)$

9. $(-3, -1), (-12, 11)$

10. $(3, -1), (-6, 5)$

11. $(-2, 5), (3, 5)$

12. $(4, 2), (4, 0)$

13.

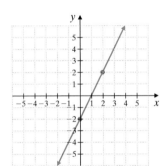

14.

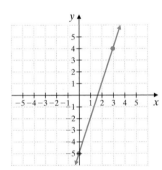

15.

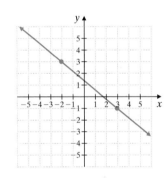

16.

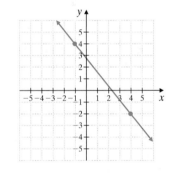

Find each slope. See Examples 1 and 2.

17. Find the pitch, or slope, of the roof shown.

18. Upon takeoff, a Delta Airlines jet climbs to 3 miles as it passes over 25 miles of land below it. Find the slope of its climb.

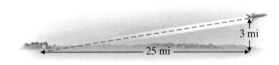

19. Find the grade, or slope, of the road shown.

20. Driving down Bald Mountain in Wyoming, Bob Dean finds that he descends 1600 feet in elevation by the time he is 2.5 miles (horizontally) away from the high point on the mountain road. Find the slope of his descent. (*Hint:* 1 mile = 5280 feet.)

Objectives Ⓑ Ⓒ **Mixed Practice** *Find the slope and the y-intercept of each line. See Examples 3 through 6.*

21. $y = -x + 5$

22. $y = x + 2$

23. $y = 5x - 2$

24. $y = -2x + 6$

25. $2x + y = 7$

26. $-5x + y = 10$

27. $2x - 3y = 10$

28. $-3x - 4y = 6$

29. $x = 4$

30. $x = 7.2$

31. $y = -2$

32. $y = -3.6$

33. $y = \dfrac{1}{2}x$

34. $y = -\dfrac{1}{4}x$

35. $3y + 8 = x$

36. $2y - 7 = x$

37. $-6x + 5y = 30$

38. $4x - 7y = 28$

39. $y = 7x$

40. $y = \dfrac{1}{7}x$

41. $x + 2 = 0$

42. $y - 7 = 0$

Match each graph with its equation.

43. $y = 2x + 3$

44. $y = 2x - 3$

45. $y = -2x + 3$

46. $y = -2x - 3$

A
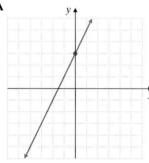

B
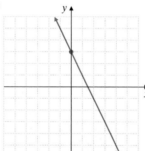

C
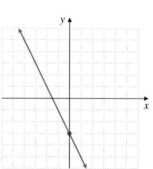

D
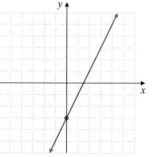

Two lines are graphed on each set of axes. For each graph, determine whether l_1 or l_2 has the greater slope.

47.
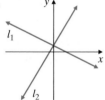

48.
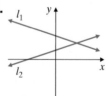

49.
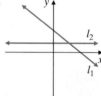

50.
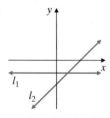

51.
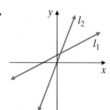

52.
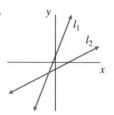

Objective **E** *Determine whether each pair of lines is parallel, perpendicular, or neither. See Examples 8 and 9.*

53. $y = -3x + 6$
$y = 3x + 5$

54. $y = 5x - 6$
$y = 5x + 2$

55. $y = -9x + 3$
$y = \dfrac{3}{2}x - 7$

56. $y = 2x - 12$
$y = \dfrac{1}{2}x - 6$

57. $2x - y = -10$
$2x + 4y = 2$

58. $-2x + 3y = 1$
$3x + 2y = 12$

59. $y = 12x + 6$
$y = 12x - 2$

60. $y = 5x + 8$
$y = \dfrac{1}{5}x - 8$

61. $-4x + 2y = 5$
$2x - y = 7$

62. $8x - 11y = 15$
$11x + 8y = 1$

63. $7x - y = 1$
$x + 7y = 3$

64. $x + 4y = 7$
$-2x - 8y = 0$

65. Line 1 goes through $(0, 5)$ and $(10, 0)$.
Line 2 goes through $(0, -10)$ and $(5, 0)$.

66. Line 1 goes through $(7, 0)$ and $(0, -21)$.
Line 2 goes through $(21, 0)$ and $(0, 7)$.

67. Line 1 goes through $(-3, 8)$ and $(1, -9)$.
Line 2 goes through $(-2, -1)$ and $(-1, 16)$.

68. Line 1 goes through $(-4, 10)$ and $(2, -3)$.
Line 2 goes through $(-3, 8)$ and $(2, -5)$.

Review

Solve. See Section 2.6.

69. $|x - 3| = 6$

70. $|x + 2| < 4$

71. $|2x + 5| > 3$

72. $|5x| = 10$

73. $|3x - 4| \leq 2$

74. $|7x - 2| \geq 5$

Concept Extensions

Determine whether each slope calculation is correct or incorrect. If incorrect, then correct the calculation. See the Concept Check in this section.

75. $(-2, 6)$ and $(7, -14)$

$$m = \frac{-14 - 6}{7 - 2} = \frac{-20}{5} = -4$$

76. $(-1, 4)$ and $(-3, 9)$

$$m = \frac{9 - 4}{-3 - 1} = \frac{5}{-4} \text{ or } -\frac{5}{4}$$

77. $(-8, -10)$ and $(-11, -5)$

$$m = \frac{-10 - (-5)}{-8 - (-11)} = \frac{-5}{3} \text{ or } -\frac{5}{3}$$

78. $(0, -4)$ and $(-6, -6)$

$$m = \frac{0 - (-6)}{-4 - (-6)} = \frac{6}{2} = 3$$

79. Find the slope of a line parallel to the line $y = -\frac{7}{2}x - 6$.

80. Find the slope of a line parallel to the line $y = x$.

81. Find the slope of a line perpendicular to the line $y = -\frac{7}{2}x - 6$.

82. Find the slope of a line perpendicular to the line $y = x$.

83. Find the slope of a line parallel to the line $5x - 2y = 6$.

84. Find the slope of a line parallel to the line $-3x + 4y = 10$.

85. Find the slope of a line perpendicular to the line $5x - 2y = 6$.

The following graph shows the altitude of a seagull in flight over a time period of 30 seconds. Use this graph to answer Exercises 86 through 89.

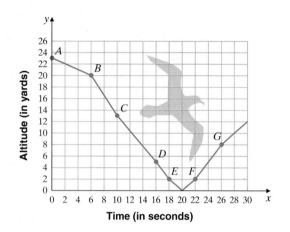

86. Find the coordinates of point *B*.

87. Find the coordinates of point *C*.

88. Find the rate of change of altitude between points *B* and *C*. (Recall that the rate of change between points is the slope between points. This rate of change will be in yards per second.)

89. Find the rate of change of altitude (in yards per second) between points *F* and *G*.

90. Professional plumbers suggest that a sewer pipe should be sloped 0.25 inch for every foot. Find the recommended slope for a sewer pipe. (*Source: Rules of Thumb* by Tom Parker, Houghton Mifflin Company)

91. Explain whether two lines, both with positive slopes, can be perpendicular.

92. Explain how merely looking at a line can tell us whether its slope is negative, positive, undefined, or zero.

93. Each line on the graph has negative slope.
   a. Find the slope of each line.
   b. Use the results of part (a) to fill in the blank: For lines with negative slopes, the steeper line has the _____ (greater/lesser) slope.

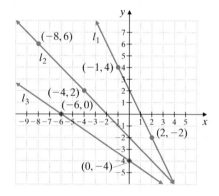

94. a. On a single screen of a graphing calculator, graph $y = \frac{1}{2}x + 1$, $y = x + 1$, and $y = 2x + 1$. Notice the change in slope for each graph.

   b. On a single screen of a graphing calculator, graph $y = -\frac{1}{2}x + 1$, $y = -x + 1$, and $y = -2x + 1$. Notice the change in slope for each graph.

   c. Determine whether the following statement is true or false for slope *m* of a given line: As $|m|$ becomes greater, the line becomes steeper.

3.3 THE SLOPE-INTERCEPT FORM

Objectives

A Graph a Line Using Its Slope and *y*-Intercept.

B Use the Slope-Intercept Form to Write an Equation of the Line.

C Interpret the Slope-Intercept Form in an Application.

Objective **A** Graphing a Line Using Its Slope and *y*-Intercept

In the last section, we learned that the slope-intercept form of a linear equation is $y = mx + b$. Recall that when an equation is written in this form, the slope of the line is the same as the coefficient m of x. Also, the *y*-intercept of the line is $(0, b)$. For example, the slope of the line defined by $y = 2x + 3$ is 2 and its *y*-intercept is $(0, 3)$.

We may also use the slope-intercept form to graph a linear equation.

EXAMPLE 1 Graph: $y = \dfrac{1}{4}x - 3$

Solution: Recall that the slope of the graph of $y = \dfrac{1}{4}x - 3$ is $\dfrac{1}{4}$ and the *y*-intercept is $(0, -3)$. To graph the line, we first plot the *y*-intercept $(0, -3)$. To find another point on the line, we recall that slope is $\dfrac{\text{rise}}{\text{run}} = \dfrac{1}{4}$. We may then plot another point by starting at $(0, -3)$, rising 1 unit up, and then running 4 units to the right. We are now at the point $(4, -2)$. The graph of $y = \dfrac{1}{4}x - 3$ is the line through points $(0, -3)$ and $(4, -2)$, as shown.

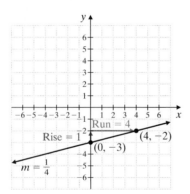

□ **Work Practice Problem 1**

EXAMPLE 2 Graph: $2x + y = 3$

Solution: First, we solve the equation for *y* to write it in slope-intercept form. In slope-intercept form, the equation is $y = -2x + 3$. Next we plot the *y*-intercept $(0, 3)$. To find another point on the line, we use the slope -2, which can be written as $\dfrac{\text{rise}}{\text{run}} = \dfrac{-2}{1}$. We start at $(0, 3)$ and move vertically 2 units down, since the numerator of the slope is -2; then we move horizontally 1 unit to the right since the denominator of the slope is 1. We arrive at the point $(1, 1)$. The line through $(1, 1)$ and $(0, 3)$ will have the required slope of -2.

Continued on next page

PRACTICE PROBLEM 1

Graph: $y = \dfrac{2}{3}x + 1$

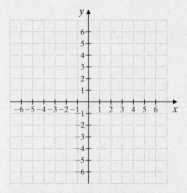

PRACTICE PROBLEM 2

Graph: $3x + y = -2$

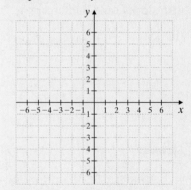

Answers

1.

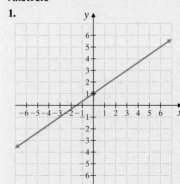

2. See page 164.

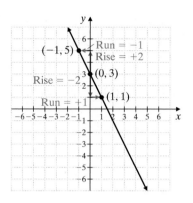

The slope -2 can also be written as $\dfrac{2}{-1}$, so to find another point for Example 2 we could start at $(0, 3)$ and move 2 units up and then 1 unit left. We would stop at the point $(-1, 5)$. The line through $(-1, 5)$ and $(0, 3)$ will have the required slope and will be the same line as shown previously through $(1, 1)$ and $(0, 3)$.

▣ **Work Practice Problem 2**

Objective Ⓑ Using the Slope-Intercept Form to Write an Equation

Given the slope and y-intercept of a line, we may write its equation as well as graph the line.

PRACTICE PROBLEM 3

Write an equation of the line with slope $\dfrac{1}{7}$ and y-intercept $(0, -5)$.

EXAMPLE 3 Write an equation of the line with y-intercept $(0, -7)$ and slope of $\dfrac{2}{3}$.

Solution: We are given the slope and the y-intercept. We let $m = \dfrac{2}{3}$ and $b = -7$, and write the equation in slope-intercept form, $y = mx + b$.

$$y = mx + b$$

$$y = \dfrac{2}{3}x + (-7) \quad \text{Let } m = \dfrac{1}{4} \text{ and } b = -7.$$

$$y = \dfrac{2}{3}x - 7 \quad \text{Simplify.}$$

Notice that the graph of this equation will have slope $\dfrac{2}{3}$ and y-intercept $(0, -7)$ as desired.

▣ **Work Practice Problem 3**

✔ **Concept Check** What is wrong with the following equation of a line with y-intercept $(0, 4)$ and slope 2?

$$y = \cancel{4x + 2}$$

Objective Ⓒ Interpreting the Slope-Intercept Form

Recall from Section 3.1 the graph of an adult one-day pass price for Disney World. Notice that the graph resembles the graph of a line. Often, businesses depend on equations that "closely fit" lines like this one to model the data and predict future trends. For example, by a method called least squares regression, the linear equation

Answers

2.

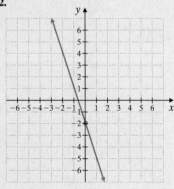

3. $y = \dfrac{1}{7}x - 5$

✔ **Concept Check Answer**

y-intercept and slope were switched, should be $y = 2x + 4$

$y = 1.883x + 34.12$ approximates the data shown, where x is the number of years since 1992 and y is the ticket price for that year.

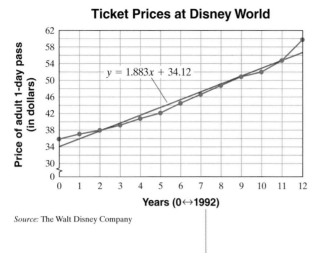

Ticket Prices at Disney World

Source: The Walt Disney Company

Helpful Hint

Don't forget—the notation $0 \leftrightarrow 1992$ means that the number 0 corresponds to the year 1992, 1 corresponds to the year 1993, and so on.

EXAMPLE 4 Predicting Future Prices

The adult one-day pass price y for Disney World is given by

$y = 1.883x + 34.12$

where x is the number of years since 1992.

a. Use this equation to predict the ticket price for 2008.
b. What does the slope of this equation mean?
c. What does the y-intercept of this equation mean?

Solution:

a. To predict the price of a pass in 2008, we need to find y when x is 17. (Since the year 1992 corresponds to $x = 0$, the year 2008 corresponds to $x = 2008 - 1992 = 16$).

$y = 1.883x + 34.12$
$ = 1.883(16) + 34.12$ Let $x = 16$.
$ = 64.248$

We predict that in the year 2008 the price of an adult one-day pass to Disney World will be about $64.25

b. The slope of $y = 1.883x + 34.12$ is 1.883. We can think of this number as $\dfrac{\text{rise}}{\text{run}}$ or $\dfrac{1.883}{1}$. This means that the ticket price increases on the average by $1.883 each year.

c. The y-intercept of $y = 1.883x + 34.12$ is 34.12. Notice that it corresponds to the point of the graph $(0, 34.12)$
           ↑   ↑
       year price

This means that at year $x = 0$, or 1992, the ticket price was about $34.12.

▣ **Work Practice Problem 4**

PRACTICE PROBLEM 4

For the period 1980 through 2020, the number of people y age 85 or older living in the United States is given by the equation $y = 110,520x + 2,127,400$, where x is the number of years since 1980. (*Source:* Based on data and estimates from the U.S. Bureau of the Census)

a. Estimate the number of people age 85 or older living in the United States in 2010.
b. What does the slope of this equation mean?
c. What does the y-intercept of this equation mean?

Answers

a. 5,443,000, **b.** The number of people age 85 or older in the United States increases at a rate of 110,520 per year, **c.** At year $x = 0$, or 1980, there were 2,127,400 people age 85 or older in the United States.

You may have noticed by now that to use the $\boxed{Y=}$ key on a grapher to graph an equation, the equation must be solved for y.

Graph each equation by first solving the equation for y.

1. $x = 3.5y$

2. $-2.7y = x$

3. $5.78x + 2.31y = 10.98$

4. $-7.22x + 3.89y = 12.57$

5. $y - x = 3.78$

6. $3y - 5x = 6x - 4$

7. $y - 5.6x = 7.7x + 1.5$

8. $y + 2.6x = -3.2$

Mental Math

Find the slope and the y-intercept of each line.

1. $y = -4x + 12$

2. $y = \dfrac{2}{3}x - \dfrac{7}{2}$

3. $y = 5x$

4. $y = -x$

5. $y = \dfrac{1}{2}x + 6$

6. $y = -\dfrac{2}{3}x + 5$

Objective **A** *Graph each line passing through the given point with the given slope. See Examples 1 and 2.*

1. Through $(1, 3)$ with slope $\dfrac{3}{2}$

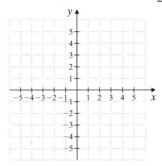

2. Through $(-2, -4)$ with slope $\dfrac{2}{5}$

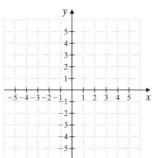

3. Through $(0, 0)$ with slope 5

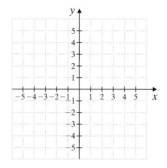

4. Through $(-5, 2)$ with slope 2

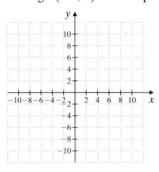

5. Through $(0, 7)$ with slope -1

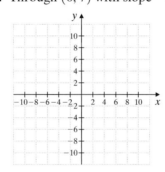

6. Through $(3, 0)$ with slope -3

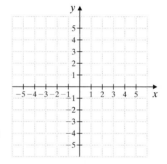

Graph each linear equation using the slope and y-intercept. See Examples 1 and 2.

7. $y = -2x$

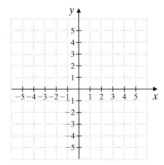

8. $y = 2x$

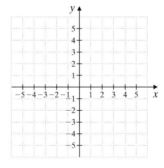

9. $y = -2x + 3$

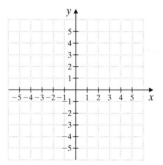

10. $y = 2x + 6$

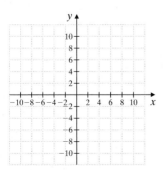

11. $y = \dfrac{1}{2}x$

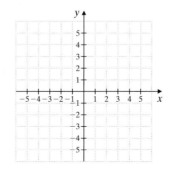

12. $y = \dfrac{1}{3}x$

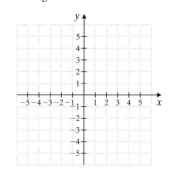

167

13. $y = \frac{1}{2}x - 4$

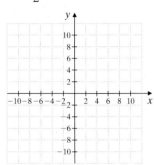

14. $y = \frac{1}{3}x - 2$

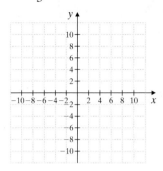

15. $7x - 2y = 10$

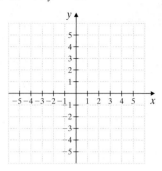

16. $8x - 3y = 9$

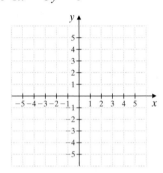

17. $x + 2y = 8$

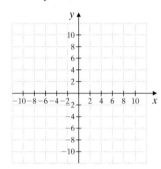

18. $x - 3y = 3$

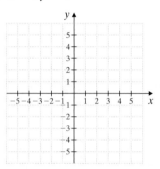

Match each equation with its graph. See Examples 1 and 2.

19. $y = \frac{1}{2}x - 1$

20. $y = \frac{1}{4}x - 1$

21. $y = -2x + 3$

22. $y = -3x + 3$

A

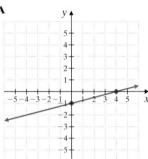

B

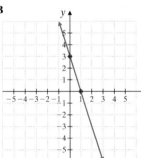

C

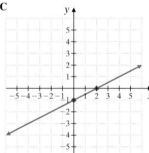

D

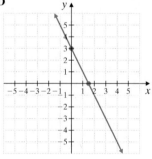

Objective **B** *Use the slope-intercept form of a linear equation to write the equation of each line with the given slope and y-intercept. See Example 3.*

23. Slope -1; y-intercept $(0, 1)$

24. Slope $\frac{1}{2}$; y-intercept $(0, -6)$

25. Slope 2; y-intercept $\left(0, \frac{3}{4}\right)$

26. Slope -3; y-intercept $\left(0, -\frac{1}{5}\right)$

27. Slope $\frac{2}{7}$; y-intercept $(0, 0)$

28. Slope $-\frac{4}{5}$; y-intercept $(0, 0)$

Objective **C** *Solve. See Example 4.*

29. The annual average income y of an American man with an associate's degree is given by the linear equation $y = 1983x + 42{,}972$, where x is the number of years after 1999. (*Source:* Based on data from U.S. Bureau of the Census, 1999–2004)

    a. Find the average income of an American man with an associate's degree in 2000.

    b. Find and interpret the slope of the equation.

    c. Find and interpret the y-intercept of the equation.

30. The annual average income y of an American woman with a bachelor's degree is given by the equation $y = 4174.9x + 42{,}173$, where x is the number of years after 1999. (*Source:* Based on data from U.S. Bureau of the Census, 1999–2004)

    a. Find the average income of an American woman with a bachelor's degree in 2000.

    b. Find and interpret the slope of the equation.

    c. Find and interpret the y-intercept of the equation.

31. One of the top ten occupations in terms of job growth in the next few years is expected to be network systems and data communications analysts. The number of people y, in thousands, employed as network systems and data communications analysts in the United States can be estimated by the linear equation $53x - 5y = -930$, where x is the number of years after 2002. (*Source:* Based on projections from the U.S. Bureau of Labor Statistics, 2002–2012)

    a. Find the slope and the y-intercept of the linear equation.

    b. What does the slope mean in this context?

    c. What does the y-intercept mean in this context?

32. One of the fastest-growing occupations over the next few years is expected to be medical assistant. The number of people y, in thousands, employed as medical assistants in the United States can be estimated by the linear equation $43x - 2y = -730$, where x is the number of years after 2002. (*Source:* Based on projections from the U.S. Bureau of Labor Statistics, 2002–2012)

    a. Find the slope and the y-intercept of the linear equation.

    b. What does the slope mean in this context?

    c. What does the y-intercept mean in this context?

33. The number of cellular subscribers y (in millions) in the United States can be estimated by the linear equation $y = 17.7x + 44.9$, where x is the number of years after 1997. (*Source:* Cellular Telecommunications Industry Association)

    a. Use this equation to estimate the number of cellular telephone subscribers in the United States in 2004.

    b. Use this equation to predict in what year the number of cellular telephone subscribers in the United States will exceed 220 million. (*Hint:* Let $y = 220$ and solve for x.)

    c. Use this equation to estimate the number of cellular telephone subscribers in the present year. Do you have a personal cell phone? Do your friends?

34. The yearly cost of undergraduate tuition and required fees for attending a public two-year college full-time can be estimated by the linear equation $y = 170.5x + 1401$, where x is the number of years after 2000 and y is the total cost in dollars. (*Source:* Based on data from the College Board, 2000–2004).

    a. Use this equation to approximate the yearly cost of attending a public two-year college in 2010.

    b. Use this equation to predict in what year the yearly cost of tuition and required fees will exceed $4000. (*Hint:* Let $y = 4000$ and solve for x)

    c. Use this equation to approximate the yearly cost of attending a two-year college in the present year. If you attend a two-year college, is this amount greater or less than the amount currently charged by the college you attend?

Review

Simplify and solve for y. See Section 2.3.

35. $y - 2 = 5(x + 6)$ **36.** $y - 0 = -3[x - (-10)]$ **37.** $y - (-1) = 2(x - 0)$ **38.** $y - 9 = -8[x - (-4)]$

Concept Extensions

Determine whether each equation is correct or incorrect. If incorrect, then correct. See the Concept Check in this section.

39. The equation of the line with y-intercept $(0, 1.7)$ and slope 3 is $y = 1.7x + 3$.

40. The equation of the line with slope $-\dfrac{1}{9}$ and y-intercept $(0, -5)$ is $y = -\dfrac{1}{9}x + 5$.

41. The equation of the line with slope -5 and y-intercept $\left(0, -\dfrac{1}{3}\right)$ is $y = -5x - \dfrac{1}{3}$.

42. In your own words, explain how to graph an equation using its slope and y-intercept.

43. Suppose that the revenue of a company has increased at a steady rate of $42,000 per year since 1995. Also the company's revenue in 1995 was $2,900,000. Write an equation that describes the company's revenue since 1995.

44. Suppose that a bird dives off a 500-foot cliff and descends at a rate of 7 feet per second. Write an equation that describes the bird's height at any time x.

 STUDY SKILLS BUILDER

Are You Organized?

Have you ever had trouble finding a completed assignment? When it's time to study for a test, are your notes neat and organized? Have you ever had trouble reading your own mathematics handwriting? (Be honest—I have.)

When any of these things happen, it's time to get organized. Here are a few suggestions:

Write your notes and complete your homework assignment in a notebook with pockets (spiral or ring binder.) Take class notes in this notebook, and then follow the notes with your completed homework assignment. When you receive graded papers or handouts, place them in the notebook pocket so that you will not lose them.

Remember to mark (possibly with an exclamation point) any note(s) that seem extra important to you. Also remember to mark (possibly with a question mark) any notes or homework that you are having trouble with. Don't forget to see your instructor or a math tutor to help you with the concepts or exercises that you are having trouble understanding.

Also, if you are having trouble reading your own handwriting, *slow down* and write your mathematics work clearly!

Exercises

1. Have you been completing your assignments on time?

2. Have you been correcting any exercises you may be having difficulty with?

3. If you are having trouble with a mathematical concept or correcting any homework exercises, have you visited your instructor, a tutor, or your campus math lab?

4. Are you taking lecture notes in your mathematics course? (By the way, these notes should include all worked-out examples solved by your instructor.)

5. Is your mathematics course material (handouts, graded papers, lecture notes) organized?

6. If your answer to Exercise 5 is no, take a moment and review your course material. List at least two ways that you might better organize it. Then read the Study Skills Builder on organizing a notebook in Chapter 2.

3.4 MORE EQUATIONS OF LINES

Objectives

A Use the Point-Slope Form to Write the Equation of a Line.

B Write Equations of Vertical and Horizontal Lines.

C Write Equations of Parallel and Perpendicular Lines.

D Use the Point-Slope Form in Real-World Applications.

Objective **A** Using the Point-Slope Form to Write an Equation

When the slope of a line and a point on the line are known, the equation of the line can also be found. To do this, we use the slope formula to write the slope of a line that passes through points (x, y), and (x_1, y_1). We have

$$m = \frac{y - y_1}{x - x_1}$$

We multiply both sides of this equation by $x - x_1$ to obtain

$$y - y_1 = m(x - x_1)$$

This form is called the *point-slope form* of the equation of a line.

Point-Slope Form of the Equation of a Line

The **point-slope form** of the equation of a line is

$$\underset{\text{point}}{y - y_1} = \overset{\text{slope}}{m}(x - x_1)$$

where m is the slope of the line and (x_1, y_1) is a point on the line.

EXAMPLE 1 Write an equation of the line with slope -3 and containing the point $(1, -5)$. Write the equation in slope-intercept form, $y = mx + b$.

Solution: Because we know the slope and a point on the line, we use the point-slope form with $m = -3$ and $(x_1, y_1) = (1, -5)$.

$$y - y_1 = m(x - x_1) \quad \text{Point-slope form}$$
$$y - (-5) = -3(x - 1) \quad \text{Let } m = -3 \text{ and } (x_1, y_1) = (1, -5).$$
$$y + 5 = -3x + 3 \quad \text{Use the distributive property.}$$
$$y = -3x - 2 \quad \text{Write in slope-intercept form (solved for } y\text{).}$$

In slope-intercept form, the equation is $y = -3x - 2$.

■ **Work Practice Problem 1**

PRACTICE PROBLEM 1

Write an equation of the line with slope -2 and containing the point $(2, -4)$. Write the equation in slope-intercept form, $y = mx + b$.

Helpful Hint

Remember, "slope-intercept form" means the equation is "solved for y."

EXAMPLE 2 Write an equation of the line through points $(4, 0)$ and $(-4, -5)$. Write the equation in standard form $Ax + By = C$.

Solution: First we find the slope of the line.

$$m = \frac{-5 - 0}{-4 - 4} = \frac{-5}{-8} = \frac{5}{8}$$

Next we make use of the point-slope form. We replace (x_1, y_1) by either $(4, 0)$ or $(-4, -5)$ in the point-slope equation. We will choose the point $(4, 0)$. The line through $(4, 0)$ with slope $\frac{5}{8}$ is as follows.

PRACTICE PROBLEM 2

Write an equation of the line through points $(3, 0)$ and $(-2, 4)$. Write the equation in standard form, $Ax + By = C$.

Answers
1. $y = -2x$, **2.** $4x + 5y = 12$

Continued on next page

171

$$y - y_1 = m(x - x_1) \quad \text{Point-slope form}$$

$$y - 0 = \frac{5}{8}(x - 4) \quad \text{Let } m = \frac{5}{8} \text{ and } (x_1, y_1) = (4, 0).$$

Let's multiply through by 8 so that the coefficients are integers and are less tedious to work with.

$$8(y - 0) = 8 \cdot \frac{5}{8}(x - 4)$$

$$8y = 5(x - 4) \quad \text{Simplify.}$$

$$8y = 5x - 20 \quad \text{Multiply.}$$

$$-5x + 8y = -20 \quad \text{Write in standard form.}$$

If we multiply both sides of $-5x + 8y = -20$ by -1, we have an equivalent equation in standard form, also. Both $-5x + 8y = -20$ and $5x - 8y = 20$ are acceptable.

■ **Work Practice Problem 2**

Objective B Writing Equations of Vertical and Horizontal Lines

A few special types of linear equations are those whose graphs are vertical and horizontal lines.

PRACTICE PROBLEM 3

Write an equation of the horizontal line containing the point $(-1, 6)$.

EXAMPLE 3 Write an equation of the horizontal line containing the point $(2, 3)$.

Solution: Recall, from Section 3.1, that a horizontal line has an equation of the form $y = b$. Since the line contains the point $(2, 3)$, the equation is $y = 3$.

■ **Work Practice Problem 3**

PRACTICE PROBLEM 4

Write an equation of the line containing the point $(4, 7)$ with undefined slope.

EXAMPLE 4 Write an equation of the line containing the point $(2, 3)$ with undefined slope.

Solution:

Since the line has undefined slope, the line must be vertical. A vertical line has an equation of the form $x = c$, and since the line contains the point $(2, 3)$, the equation is $x = 2$.

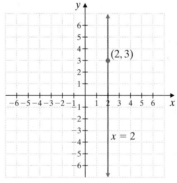

■ **Work Practice Problem 4**

Objective C Writing Equations of Parallel and Perpendicular Lines

Next, we write equations of parallel and perpendicular lines.

Answers

3. $y = 6$, **4.** $x = 4$

EXAMPLE 5 Write an equation of the line containing the point $(4, 4)$ and parallel to the line $2x + y = -6$. Write the equation in slope-intercept form, $y = mx + b$.

Solution: Because the line we want to find is *parallel* to the line $2x + y = -6$, the two lines must have equal slopes. So we first find the slope of $2x + y = -6$ by solving the equation for y to write it in the form $y = mx + b$. Here $y = -2x - 6$, so the slope is -2.

Now we use the point-slope form to write the equation of a line through $(4, 4)$ with slope -2.

$$y - y_1 = m(x - x_1)$$
$$y - 4 = -2(x - 4) \quad \text{Let } m = -2, x_1 = 4, \text{ and } y_1 = 4.$$
$$y - 4 = -2x + 8 \quad \text{Use the distributive property.}$$
$$y = -2x + 12$$

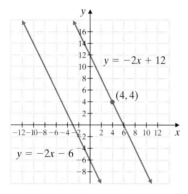

The equation, $y = -2x - 6$, and the new equation, $y = -2x + 12$, have the same slope but different y-intercepts so their graphs are parallel. Also, the graph of $y = -2x + 12$ contains the point $(4, 4)$, as desired.

■ **Work Practice Problem 5**

EXAMPLE 6 Write an equation of the line containing the point $(-2, 1)$ and perpendicular to the line $3x + 5y = 4$. Write the equation in slope-intercept form, $y = mx + b$.

Solution: First we find the slope of $3x + 5y = 4$ by solving the equation for y.

$$5y = -3x + 4$$
$$y = -\frac{3}{5}x + \frac{4}{5}$$

The slope of the given line is $-\frac{3}{5}$. A line perpendicular to this line will have a slope that is the negative reciprocal of $-\frac{3}{5}$, or $\frac{5}{3}$. We use the point-slope form to write an equation of a new line through $(-2, 1)$ with slope $\frac{5}{3}$.

$$y - 1 = \frac{5}{3}[x - (-2)]$$
$$y - 1 = \frac{5}{3}(x + 2) \quad \text{Simplify.}$$
$$y - 1 = \frac{5}{3}x + \frac{10}{3} \quad \text{Use the distributive property.}$$
$$y = \frac{5}{3}x + \frac{13}{3} \quad \text{Add 1 to both sides.}$$

Continued on next page

PRACTICE PROBLEM 5

Write an equation of the line containing the point $(-1, 2)$ and parallel to the line $3x + y = 5$. Write the equation in slope-intercept form $y = mx + b$.

PRACTICE PROBLEM 6

Write an equation of the line containing the point $(3, 4)$ and perpendicular to the line $2x + 4y = 5$. Write the equation in slope-intercept form, $y = mx + b$.

Answers
5. $y = -3x - 1$, **6.** $y = 2x - 2$

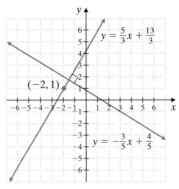

The equation $y = -\dfrac{3}{5}x + \dfrac{4}{5}$ and the new equation $y = \dfrac{5}{3}x + \dfrac{13}{3}$ have negative reciprocal slopes, so their graphs are perpendicular. Also, the graph of $y = \dfrac{5}{3}x + \dfrac{13}{3}$ contains the point $(-2, 1)$, as desired.

■ **Work Practice Problem 6**

Objective D Using the Point-Slope Form in Applications

The point-slope form of an equation is very useful for solving real-world problems.

EXAMPLE 7 Predicting Sales

Southern Star Realty is an established real estate company that has enjoyed constant growth in sales since 1996. In 2000 the company sold 250 houses, and in 2004 the company sold 330 houses. Use these figures to predict the number of houses this company will sell in 2008.

Solution:

1. UNDERSTAND. Read and reread the problem. Then let

    x = the number of years after 1996 and

    y = the number of houses sold in the year corresponding to x

   The information provided than gives the ordered pairs $(4, 250)$ and $(8, 330)$. To better visualize the sales of Southern Star Realty, we graph the line that passes through the points $(4, 250)$ and $(8, 330)$.

2. TRANSLATE. We write the equation of the line that passes through the points $(4, 250)$ and $(8, 330)$. To do so, we first find the slope of the line.

$$m = \frac{330 - 250}{8 - 4} = \frac{80}{4} = 20$$

PRACTICE PROBLEM 7

Southwest Regional is an established office product maintenance company that enjoyed constant growth in new maintenance contracts since 1995. In 1997, the company obtained 15 new contracts, and in 2003, the company obtained 33 new contracts. Use these figures to predict the number of new contracts this company can expect in 2011.

Answer

7. 57 new contracts

Then using the point-slope form to write the equation, we have

$$y - y_1 = m(x - x_1)$$

$y - 250 = 20(x - 4)$ Let $m = 20$ and $(x_1, y_1) = (4, 250)$.

$y - 250 = 20x - 80$ Multiply.

      $y = 20x + 170$ Add 250 to both sides.

3. SOLVE. To predict the number of houses sold in 2008, we use $y = 20x + 170$ and complete the ordered pair (12,), since $2008 - 1996 = 12$.

$y = 20(12) + 170$

$y = 410$

4. INTERPRET.

Check: Verify that the point $(12, 410)$ is a point on the line graphed in Step 1.

State: Southern Star Realty should expect to sell 410 houses in 2008.

◻ **Work Practice Problem 7**

▦ **CALCULATOR EXPLORATIONS** Graphing

Many graphing calculators have a TRACE feature. This feature allows you to trace along a graph and see the corresponding x- and y-coordinates appear on the screen. Use this feature for the following exercises.

Graph each equation and then use the TRACE feature to complete each ordered pair solution. (Many times the tracer will not show the exact x- or y-value asked for. In each case, trace as closely as you can to the given x- or y-coordinate and approximate the other, unknown coordinate to one decimal place.)

1. $y = 2.3x + 6.7$;
$x = 5.1, y = ?$

2. $y = -4.8x + 2.9$;
$x = -1.8, y = ?$

3. $y = -5.9x - 1.6$;
$x = ?, y = 7.2$

4. $y = 0.4x - 8.6$;
$x = ?, y = -4.4$

5. $y = 5.2x - 3.3$;
$x = 2.3, y = ?$
$x = ?, y = 36$

6. $y = -6.2x - 8.3$;
$x = 3.2, y = ?$
$x = ?, y = 12$

Mentalist Math

Find the slope of and a point on the line described by each equation.

1. $y - 4 = -2(x - 1)$

2. $y - 6 = -3(x - 4)$

3. $y - 0 = \dfrac{1}{4}(x - 2)$

4. $y - 1 = -\dfrac{2}{3}(x - 0)$

5. $y + 2 = 5(x - 3)$

6. $y - 7 = 4(x + 6)$

3.4 EXERCISE SET

Objective **A** *Write an equation of each line with the given slope and containing the given point. Write the equation in the slope-intercept form $y = mx + b$. See Example 1.*

1. Slope 3; through $(1, 2)$

2. Slope 4; through $(5, 1)$

3. Slope -2; through $(1, -3)$

4. Slope -4; through $(2, -4)$

5. Slope $\dfrac{1}{2}$; through $(-6, 2)$

6. Slope $\dfrac{2}{3}$; through $(-9, 4)$

7. Slope $-\dfrac{9}{10}$; through $(-3, 0)$

8. Slope $-\dfrac{1}{5}$; through $(4, -6)$

Write an equation of the line passing through the given points. Write the equation in standard form $Ax + By = C$. See Example 2.

9. $(2, 0)$ and $(4, 6)$

10. $(3, 0)$ and $(7, 8)$

11. $(-2, 5)$ and $(-6, 13)$

12. $(7, -4)$ and $(2, 6)$

13. $(-2, -4)$ and $(-4, -3)$

14. $(-9, -2)$ and $(-3, 10)$

15. $(-3, -8)$ and $(-6, -9)$

16. $(8, -3)$ and $(4, -8)$

17. $\left(\dfrac{3}{5}, \dfrac{4}{10}\right)$ and $\left(-\dfrac{1}{5}, \dfrac{7}{10}\right)$

18. $\left(\dfrac{1}{2}, -\dfrac{1}{4}\right)$ and $\left(\dfrac{3}{2}, \dfrac{3}{4}\right)$

Objective **B** *Write an equation of each line. See Examples 3 and 4.*

19. Vertical; through $(2, 6)$

20. Slope 0; through $(-2, -4)$

21. Horizontal; through $(-3, 1)$

22. Vertical; through $(4, 7)$

23. Undefined slope; through $(0, 5)$

24. Horizontal; through $(0, 5)$

Objective **C** *Write an equation of each line. Write the equation in the form $x = a$, $y = b$, or $y = mx + b$. See Examples 5 and 6.*

25. Through $(3, 8)$; parallel to $y = 4x - 2$

26. Through $(1, 5)$; parallel to $y = 3x - 4$

27. Through $(2, -5)$; perpendicular to $3y = x - 6$

28. Through $(-4, 8)$; perpendicular to $2x - 3y = 1$

29. Through $(1, 4)$; parallel to $y = 7$

30. Through $(-2, 6)$; perpendicular to $y = 7$

31. Through $(-2, -3)$; parallel to $3x + 2y = 5$

32. Through $(-2, -3)$; perpendicular to $3x + 2y = 5$

33. Through $(-1, -5)$; perpendicular to $x = 3$

34. Through $(4, -6)$; parallel to $x = -2$

35. Through $(-1, 5)$; perpendicular to $x - 4y = 4$

36. Through $(2, -3)$; perpendicular to $x - 5y = 10$

Objectives **A** **B** **C** **Mixed Practice** *Find the equation of each line. Write the equation in standard form unless indicated otherwise. See Examples 1 through 6.*

37. Slope 2; through $(-2, 3)$

38. Slope 3; through $(-4, 2)$

39. Through $(1, 6)$ and $(5, 2)$; use slope-intercept form.

40. Through $(2, 9)$ and $(8, 6)$; use slope-intercept form.

41. With slope $-\dfrac{1}{2}$; y-intercept $\left(0, \dfrac{3}{8}\right)$; use slope-intercept form.

42. With slope -4; y-intercept $\left(0, \dfrac{2}{9}\right)$; use slope-intercept form.

43. Through $(-7, -4)$ and $(0, -6)$

44. Through $(2, -8)$ and $(-4, -3)$

45. Slope $-\dfrac{4}{3}$; through $(-5, 0)$

46. Slope $-\dfrac{3}{5}$; through $(4, -1)$

47. Vertical line; through $(-2, -10)$

48. Horizontal line; through $(1, 0)$

49. Through $(6, -2)$; parallel to the line $2x + 4y = 9$

50. Through $(8, -3)$; parallel to the line $6x + 2y = 5$

51. Slope 0; through $(-9, 12)$

52. Undefined slope; through $(10, -8)$

53. Through $(6, 1)$; parallel to the line $8x - y = 9$

54. Through $(3, 5)$; perpendicular to the line $2x - y = 8$

55. Through $(5, -6)$; perpendicular to $y = 9$

56. Through $(-3, -5)$; parallel to $y = 9$

57. Through $(2, -8)$ and $(-6, -5)$; use slope-intercept form.

58. Through $(-4, -2)$ and $(-6, 5)$; use slope-intercept form.

Objective **D** *Solve. See Example 7.*

59. A rock is dropped from the top of a 400-foot building. After 1 second, the rock is traveling 32 feet per second. After 3 seconds, the rock is traveling 96 feet per second. Let y be the rate of descent and x be the number of seconds since the rock was dropped.

  a. Write a linear equation that relates time x to rate y. [*Hint:* Use the ordered pairs $(1, 32)$ and $(3, 96)$.]

  b. Use this equation to determine the rate of travel of the rock 4 seconds after it was dropped.

60. The Whammo Company has learned that by pricing a newly released Frisbee at $6, sales will reach 2000 per day. Raising the price to $8 will cause the sales to fall to 1500 per day. Assume that the ratio of change in price to change in daily sales is constant, and let x be the price of the Frisbee and y be number of sales.

  a. Find the linear equation that models the price–sales relationship for this Frisbee. [*Hint:* The line must pass through $(6, 2000)$ and $(8, 1500)$.]

  b. Use this equation to predict the daily sales of Frisbees if the price is set at $7.50.

61. A fruit company recently released a new applesauce. By the end of its first year, profits on this product amounted to $30,000. The anticipated profit for the end of the fourth year is $66,000. The ratio of change in time to change in profit is constant. Let x be years and y be profit.

  a. Write a linear equation that relates profit and time.

  b. Use this equation to predict the company's profit at the end of the seventh year.

  c. Predict when the profit should reach $126,000.

62. The Pool Fun Company has learned that, by pricing a newly released Fun Noodle at $3, sales will reach 10,000 Fun Noodles per day during the summer. Raising the price to $5 will cause the sales to fall to 8000 Fun Noodles per day. Let x be price and y be the number sold.

  a. Assume that the relationship between sales price and number of Fun Noodles sold is linear and write an equation describing this relationship.

  b. Use this equation to predict the daily sales of Fun Noodles if the price is $3.50.

63. In 2000, the median price of an existing home in the United States was $142,200. In 2003, the median price of an existing home was $170,000. Let y be the median price of an existing home in the year x, where $x = 0$ represents the year 2000. (*Source:* National Association of REALTORS)

  a. Write a linear equation that models the median existing home price in terms of the year x. [*Hint:* The line must pass through the point $(0, 142{,}200)$ and $(3, 170{,}000)$.]

  b. Use this equation to predict the median existing home price for 2008.

64. The number of commercial aircraft delivered to customers by Boeing in 1997 was 374. In 2003, Boeing delivered a total of 281 commercial airplanes to customers. Let y be the number of Boeing commercial aircraft delivered to customers in the year x, where $x = 0$ represents 1997. (*Source:* The Boeing Company)

  a. Write a linear equation that models the number of Boeing commercial aircraft delivered to customers in terms of the year x. [*Hint:* The line must pass through $(0, 374)$ and $(6, 281)$.]

  b. Use this information to predict the number of commercial aircraft Boeing delivers to customers in 2007.

65. The number of basic cable TV subscribers in the United States for 2001 was approximately 70.0 million. In 2004, there were 70.3 million basic cable TV subscribers. Let y be the number of basic cable TV subscribers, in millions in year x, where $x = 0$ represents 2001. (*Source:* Cisco Systems)

  a. Write a linear equation that models the number of basic cable TV subscribers (in the millions) in the year x.

  b. Use this equation to estimate the number of basic cable TV subscribers for the year 2008.

66. The number of people employed in the United States as registered nurses was 2284 thousand in 2002. By 2012, this number is expected to rise to 2908 thousand. Let y be the number of registered nurses (in thousands) employed in the United States in the year x, where $x = 0$ represents 2002. (*Source:* U.S. Bureau of Labor Statistics)

  a. Write a linear equation that models the number of people (in thousands) employed as registered nurses in year x.

  b. Use this equation to estimate the number of people who will be employed as registered nurses in 2009.

Review

Complete each ordered pair for the given equation. See Section 3.1.

67. $y = 7x + 3$; (4,)

68. $y = 2x - 6$; (2,)

69. $y = 4.2x$; (−2,)

70. $y = -1.3x$; (6,)

71. $y = x^2 + 2x + 1$; (1,)

72. $y = x^2 - 6x + 4$; (0,)

Concept Extensions

Find an equation of each line graphed. Write the equation in standard form.

73.

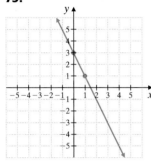

74.

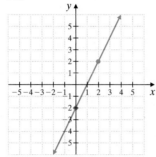

75.

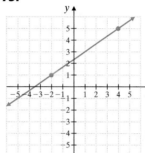

76.

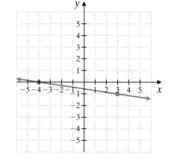

Answer true or false.

77. A vertical line is always perpendicular to a horizontal line.

78. A vertical line is always parallel to another vertical line.

79. Describe how to check to see if the graph of $2x - 4y = 7$ passes through the points $(1.4, -1.05)$ and $(0, -1.75)$. Then follow your directions and check these points.

Use a grapher with a TRACE feature to see the results of each exercise.

80. Exercise 25: Graph the equation and verify that it passes through $(3, 8)$ and is parallel to $y = 4x - 2$.

81. Exercise 26: Graph the equation and verify that it passes through $(1, 5)$ and is parallel to $y = 3x - 4$.

Linear Equations in Two Variables

Below is a review of equations of lines.

Forms of Linear Equations

$Ax + By = C$	**Standard form** of a linear equation. A and B are not both 0.
$y = mx + b$	**Slope-intercept form** of a linear equation. The slope is m, and the y-intercept is $(0, b)$.
$y - y_1 = m(x - x_1)$	**Point-slope form** of a linear equation. The slope is m, and (x_1, y_1) is a point on the line.
$y = c$	**Horizontal line.** The slope is 0, and the y-intercept is $(0, c)$.
$x = c$	**Vertical line.** The slope is undefined and the x-intercept is $(c, 0)$.

Parallel and Perpendicular Lines

Nonvertical parallel lines have the same slope.
The product of the slopes of two nonvertical
perpendicular lines is -1.

Graph each linear equation.

1. $y = -2x$

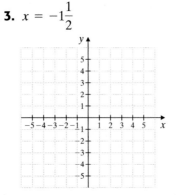

2. $3x - 2y = 6$

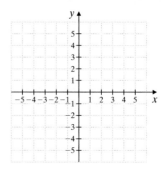

3. $x = -1\frac{1}{2}$

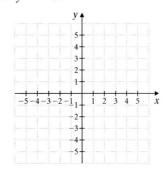

4. $y = 1.5$

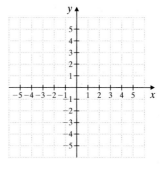

Find the slope of the line containing each pair of points.

5. $(-2, -5), (3, -5)$

6. $(5, 2), (0, 5)$

Find the slope and y-intercept of each line.

7. $y = 3x - 5$

8. $5x - 2y = 7$

Determine whether each pair of lines is parallel, perpendicular, or neither.

9. $y = 8x - 6$
$y = 8x + 6$

10. $y = \dfrac{2}{3}x + 1$
$2y + 3x = 1$

Find the equation of each line. Write the equation in the form $x = a$, $y = b$, or $y = mx + b$.

11. Through $(1, 6)$ and $(5, 2)$

12. Vertical line; through $(-2, -10)$

13. Horizontal line; through $(1, 0)$

14. Through $(2, -8)$ and $(-6, -5)$

15. Through $(-2, 4)$ with slope -5

16. Slope -4; y-intercept $\left(0, \dfrac{1}{3}\right)$

17. Slope $\dfrac{1}{2}$; y-intercept $(0, -1)$

18. Through $\left(\dfrac{1}{2}, 0\right)$ with slope 3

19. Through $(-1, -5)$; parallel to
$3x - y = 5$

20. Through $(0, 4)$; perpendicular to
$4x - 5y = 10$

21. Through $(2, -3)$; perpendicular to
$4x + y = \dfrac{2}{3}$

22. Through $(-1, 0)$; parallel to
$5x + 2y = 2$

23. Undefined slope; through $(-1, 3)$

24. $m = 0$; through $(-1, 3)$

7. _____

8. _____

9. _____

10. _____

11. _____

12. _____

13. _____

14. _____

15. _____

16. _____

17. _____

18. _____

19. _____

20. _____

21. _____

22. _____

23. _____

24. _____

3.5 GRAPHING LINEAR INEQUALITIES

A Graph Linear Inequalities.

B Graph the Intersection or Union of Two Linear Inequalities.

Objective **A** Graphing Linear Inequalities

Recall that the graph of a linear equation in two variables is the graph of all ordered pairs that satisfy the equation and that the graph is a line. Here we graph linear inequalities in two variables; that is, we graph all the ordered pairs that satisfy the inequality.

If the equal sign in a linear equation in two variables is replaced with an inequality symbol, the result is a **linear inequality in two variables.**

Examples of Linear Inequalities in Two Variables

$$x + y < 3 \qquad\qquad 2x - 4y \geq -3$$
$$4x > 2 \qquad\qquad\qquad y \leq 5$$

To graph the linear inequality $x + y < 3$, we first graph the related equation $x + y = 3$. The resulting **boundary line** contains all ordered pairs whose coordinates add up to 3. The line separates the plane into two regions called **half-planes.** All points above the boundary line $x + y = 3$ have coordinates that satisfy the inequality $x + y > 3$, and all points below the line have coordinates that satisfy the inequality $x + y < 3$.

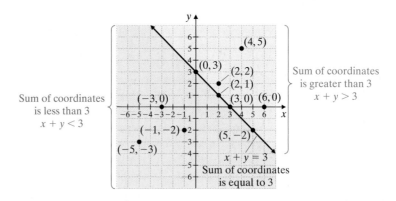

The graph, or **solution region,** for $x + y < 3$, then, is the half-plane below the boundary line and is shown shaded in the figure below. The boundary line is shown dashed since it is not a part of the solution region. The ordered pairs on this line satisfy $x + y = 3$, but not $x + y < 3$.

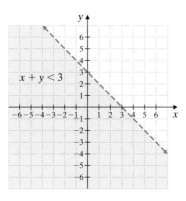

The following steps may be used to graph linear inequalities in two variables.

Graphing a Linear Inequality in Two Variables

Step 1: Graph the boundary line found by replacing the inequality sign with an equal sign. If the inequality sign is $<$ or $>$, graph a dashed line (indicating that points on the line are not solutions of the inequality). If the inequality sign is $\leq$ or $\geq$, graph a solid line (indicating that points on the line are solutions of the inequality).

Step 2: Choose a **test point** *not on the boundary line* and substitute the coordinates of this test point into the *original inequality*.

Step 3: If a true statement is obtained in Step 2, shade the half-plane that contains the test point. If a false statement is obtained, shade the half-plane that does not contain the test point.

EXAMPLE 1 Graph: $2x - y < 6$

Solution: The boundary line for this inequality is the graph of $2x - y = 6$. We graph a dashed boundary line because the inequality symbol is $<$. Next we choose a test point on either side of the boundary line. The point $(0, 0)$ is not on the boundary line, so we use this point. Replacing x with 0 and y with 0 in the *original inequality* $2x - y < 6$ leads to the following:

$$2x - y < 6$$
$$2(0) - 0 < 6 \quad \text{Let } x = 0 \text{ and } y = 0.$$
$$0 < 6 \quad \text{True}$$

Because $(0, 0)$ satisfies the inequality, so does every point on the same side of the boundary line as $(0, 0)$. We shade the half-plane that contains $(0, 0)$, as shown. Every point in the shaded half-plane satisfies the original inequality.

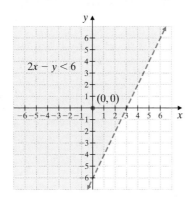

Work Practice Problem 1

EXAMPLE 2 Graph: $3x \geq y$

Solution: The boundary line is the graph of $3x = y$. We graph a solid boundary line because the inequality symbol is $\geq$. We choose a test point not on the boundary line to determine which half-plane contains points that satisfy the inequality. Let's choose $(0, 1)$ as our test point.

$$3x \geq y$$
$$3(0) \geq 1 \quad \text{Let } x = 0 \text{ and } y = 1.$$
$$0 \geq 1 \quad \text{False}$$

Continued on next page

PRACTICE PROBLEM 1

Graph: $x + 3y > 4$

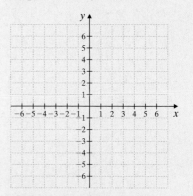

PRACTICE PROBLEM 2

Graph: $x \leq 2y$

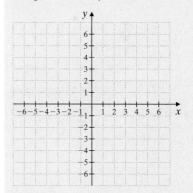

Answers

1.

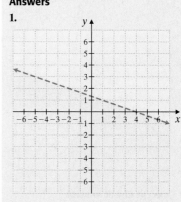

2. See page 184.

This point does not satisfy the inequality, so the correct half-plane is on the opposite side of the boundary line from $(0, 1)$. The graph of $3x \geq y$ is the boundary line together with the shaded region, as shown.

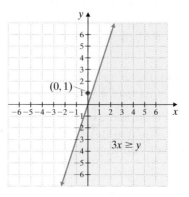

🖥 **Work Practice Problem 2**

✔**Concept Check** If a point on the boundary line is included in the solution of an inequality in two variables, should the graph of the boundary line be solid or dashed?

Objective **B** Graphing Intersections and Unions

The intersections and the unions of linear inequalities can also be graphed, as shown in the next two examples.

EXAMPLE 3 Graph the intersection of $x \geq 1$ and $y \geq 2x - 1$.

Solution: First we graph each inequality. The intersection of the two graphs is all points common to both regions, as shown by the *heaviest* shading in the third graph.

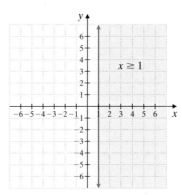

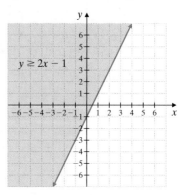

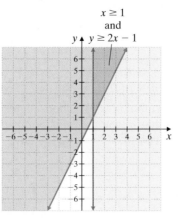

🖥 **Work Practice Problem 3**

PRACTICE PROBLEM 3

Graph the intersection of $x \leq 2$ and $y \geq x + 1$.

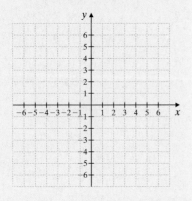

Answers

2.

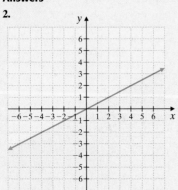

3.

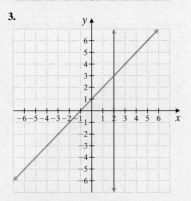

✔ **Concept Check Answer**
Solid

EXAMPLE 4 Graph the union of $2x + y \geq -8$ or $y \leq -2$.

Solution: First we graph each inequality. The union of the two inequalities is both shaded regions, including the solid boundary lines, as shown in the third graph.

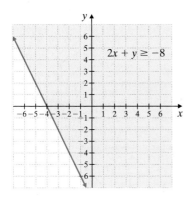

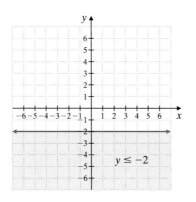

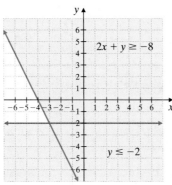

■ **Work Practice Problem 4**

PRACTICE PROBLEM 4

Graph the union of $x + 2y \leq 4$ or $y \geq -1$.

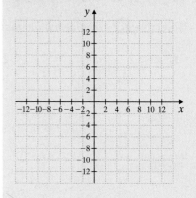

Answer

4.

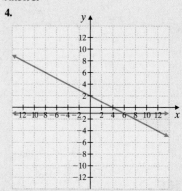

FOR EXTRA HELP

 Student Solutions Manual   PH Math/Tutor Center   CD/Video for Review   Math XL MathXL®   MyMathLab MyMathLab

Objective **A** *Graph each inequality. See Examples 1 and 2.*

1. $x < 2$

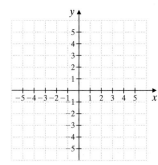

2. $x > -3$

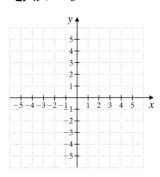

3. $x - y \geq 7$

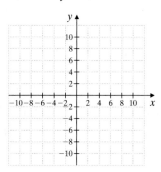

4. $3x + y \leq 1$

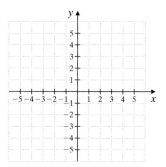

5. $3x + y > 6$

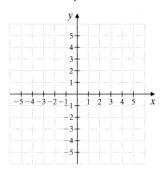

6. $2x + y > 2$

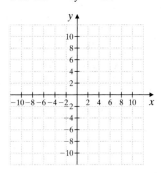

7. $y \leq -2x$

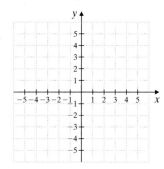

8. $y \leq 3x$

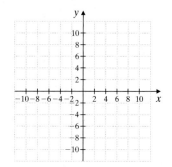

9. $2x + 4y \geq 8$

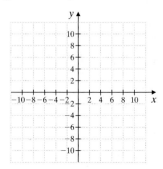

10. $2x + 6y \leq 12$

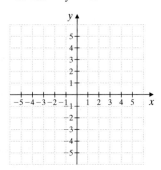

11. $5x + 3y > -15$

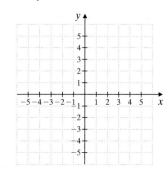

12. $2x + 5y < -20$

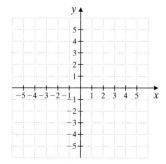

13. $y \leq -4.5$

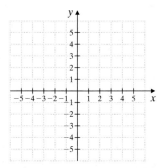

14. $y \geq -2\frac{1}{3}$

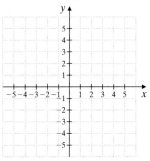

15. $x > 4y$

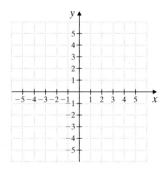

16. $x < -3y$

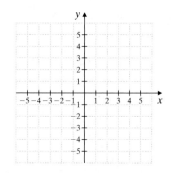

Objective **B** *Graph each union or intersection. See Examples 3 and 4.*

17. The intersection of $x \geq 3$ and $y \leq -2$

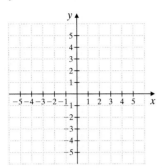

18. The union of $x \geq 3$ or $y \leq -2$

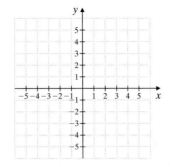

19. The union of $x \leq -2$ or $y \geq 4$

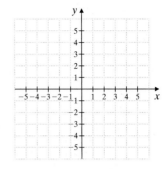

20. The intersection of $x \leq -2$ and $y \geq 4$

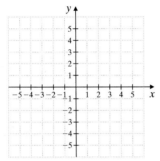

21. The intersection of $x - y < 3$ and $x > 4$

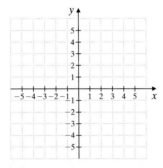

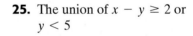 **22.** The intersection of $x + y \leq 1$ and $y \leq -1$

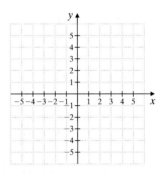

23. The union of $x + y \leq 3$ or $x - y \geq 5$

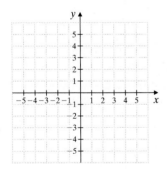

24. The union of $x - y \leq 3$ or $x + y > -1$

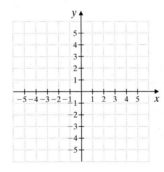

25. The union of $x - y \geq 2$ or $y < 5$

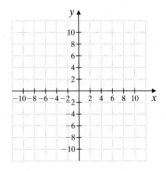

26. The union of $x - y < 3$ or $x > 4$

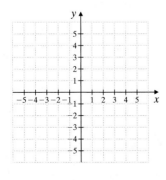

27. The intersection of $2x > y$ and $3x - 9y > 12$

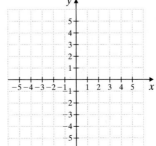

28. The intersection of $y \geq x$ and $2x - 4y \geq 6$

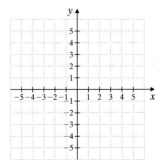

Match each inequality with its graph.

29. $y \leq 2x + 3$ **30.** $y < 2x + 3$ **31.** $y > 2x + 3$ **32.** $y \geq 2x + 3$

A
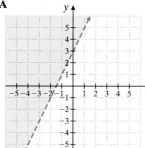

B
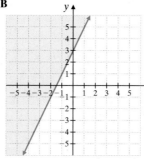

C
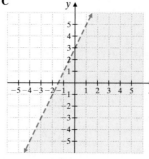

D
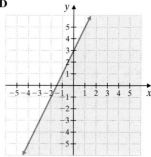

Review

Determine whether the given ordered pair is a solution of both equations. See Section 3.1.

33. $(3, -1)$; $x - y = 4$
$\quad\quad\quad\quad x + 2y = 1$

34. $(0, 2)$; $x + 3y = 6$
$\quad\quad\quad\quad 4x - y = -2$

35. $(-4, 0)$; $3x + 2y = -12$
$\quad\quad\quad\quad\quad x = 4y$

36. $(-5, 2)$; $x + y = -3$
$\quad\quad\quad\quad\quad 2x - y = -8$

Concept Extensions

37. Explain when a dashed boundary line should be used in the graph of an inequality.

38. Explain why, after the boundary line is sketched, we test a point on either side of this boundary in the original inequality.

Solve.

39. Chris-Craft manufactures boats out of Fiberglas and wood. Fiberglas hulls require 2 hours of work, whereas wood hulls require 4 hours of work. Employees work at most 40 hours a week. The following inequalities model these restrictions, where x represents the number of Fiberglas hulls produced and y represents the number of wood hulls produced.

$$x \geq 0$$
$$y \geq 0$$
$$2x + 4y \leq 40$$

Graph the intersection of these inequalities.

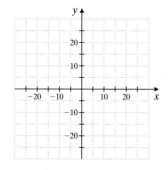

40. Rheem Abo-Zahrah decides that she will study at most 20 hours every week and that she must work at least 10 hours every week. Let x represent the hours studying and y represent the hours working. Write two inequalities that model this situation and graph their intersection.

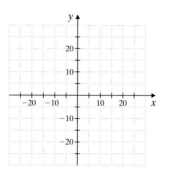

3.6 INTRODUCTION TO FUNCTIONS

Objectives

A Define Relation, Domain, and Range.

B Identify Functions.

C Use the Vertical Line Test for Functions.

D Use Function Notation.

E Graph a Linear Function.

Objective **A** Defining Relation, Domain, and Range

Equations in two variables, such as $y = 2x + 1$, describe **relations** between x-values and y-values. For example, if $x = 1$, then this equation describes how to find the y-value related to $x = 1$. In words, the equation $y = 2x + 1$ says that twice the x-value increased by 1 gives the corresponding y-value. The x-value of 1 corresponds to the y-value of $2(1) + 1 = 3$ for this equation, and we have the ordered pair $(1, 3)$. In other words, for the relationship (or relation) between x and y defined by $y = 2x + 1$, the x-value 1 is paired with the y-value 3.

There are other ways of describing relations or correspondences between two numbers or, in general, a set of first components (sometimes called the set of *inputs*) and a set of second components (sometimes called the set of *outputs*). For example,

First Set: Input	Correspondence	Second Set: Output
People in a certain city	Each person's age	The set of nonnegative integers

A few examples of ordered pairs from this relation might be (Ana, 4); (Bob, 36); (Trey, 21); and so on.

Below are just a few other ways of describing relations between two sets and the ordered pairs that they generate.

First Set: Input **Second Set: Output**

Correspondence

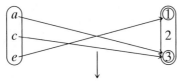

Ordered Pairs

$(a, 3), (c, 3), (e, 1)$

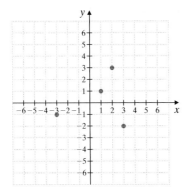

Ordered Pairs

$(-3, -1), (1, 1), (2, 3), (3, -2)$

Some Ordered Pairs

$(1, 3), (0, 1)$, and so on

Relation, Domain, and Range

A **relation** is a set of ordered pairs.

The **domain** of the relation is the set of all first components of the ordered pairs.

The **range** of the relation is the set of all second components of the ordered pairs.

For example, the domain for our middle relation on the previous page is $\{a, c, e\}$ and the range is $\{1, 3\}$. Notice that the range does not include the element 2 of the second set. This is because no element of the first set is assigned to this element. If a relation is defined in terms of x- and y-values, we will agree that the domain corresponds to x-values and that the range corresponds to y-values that are paired with x-values.

Helpful Hint

Remember that the range only includes elements that are paired with domain values. For

| First Set: Input | Correspondence | Second Set: Output |

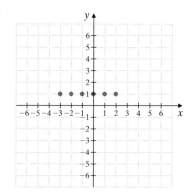

, the range is $\{a\}$.

PRACTICE PROBLEMS 1–3

Determine the domain and range of each relation.

1. $\{(1, 6), (2, 8), (0, 3), (0, -2)\}$

2.

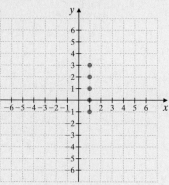

3.

| Input: States | Output: Number of Congressional Representatives |

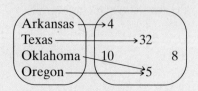

EXAMPLES Determine the domain and range of each relation.

1. $\{(2, 3), (2, 4), (0, -1), (3, -1)\}$

The domain is the set of all first coordinates of the ordered pairs, $\{2, 0, 3\}$. The range is the set of all second coordinates, $\{3, 4, -1\}$.

2.

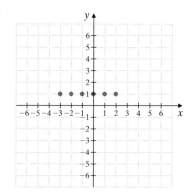

Helpful Hint

Equivalent domain or range elements that occur more than once need only to be listed once.

The relation is $\{(-3, 1), (-2, 1), (-1, 1), (0, 1), (1, 1), (2, 1)\}$.
The domain is $\{-3, -2, -1, 0, 1, 2\}$.
The range is $\{1\}$.

3.

| Input: Cities | Output: Population (in thousands) |

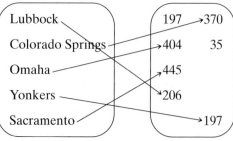

The domain is the set of inputs {Lubbock, Colorado Springs, Omaha, Yonkers, Sacramento}. The range is the numbers in the set of outputs that correspond to elements in the set of inputs {370, 404, 445, 206, 197}.

Work Practice Problems 1–3

Answers

1. domain: $\{1, 2, 0\}$; range: $\{6, 8, 3, -2\}$,

2. domain: $\{1\}$; range: $\{-1, 0, 1, 2, 3\}$,

3. domain: {Arkansas, Texas, Oklahoma, Oregon}; range: $\{4, 5, 32\}$

Objective B Identifying Functions

Now we consider a special kind of relation called a *function*.

Function

A **function** is a relation in which each first component in the ordered pairs corresponds to *exactly one* second component.

EXAMPLES Determine whether each relation is also a function.

4. $\{(-2, 5), (2, 7), (-3, 5), (9, 9)\}$

Although the ordered pairs $(-2, 5)$ and $(-3, 5)$ have the same y-value, each x-value is assigned to only one y-value, so this set of ordered pairs is a function.

5.

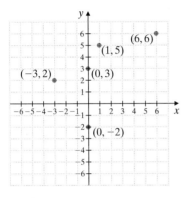

The x-value 0 is assigned to two y-values, -2 and 3, in this graph, so this relation is not a function.

6.

Input	Correspondence	Output
People in a certain city	Each person's age	The set of nonnegative integers

This relation is a function because although two different people may have the same age, each person has only one age. This means that each element in the first set is assigned to only one element in the second set.

▣ **Work Practice Problems 4–6**

✔**Concept Check** Explain why a function can contain both the ordered pairs $(1, 3)$ and $(2, 3)$ but not both $(3, 1)$ and $(3, 2)$.

Recall that an equation such as $y = 2x + 1$ is a relation since this equation defines a set of ordered pair solutions.

EXAMPLE 7 Determine whether the relation $y = 2x + 1$ is also a function.

Solution: The relation $y = 2x + 1$ is a function if each x-value corresponds to just one y-value. For each x-value substituted in the equation $y = 2x + 1$, the multiplication and addition performed gives a single result, so only one y-value will be associated with each x-value. Thus, $y = 2x + 1$ is a function.

▣ **Work Practice Problem 7**

EXAMPLE 8 Determine whether the relation $x = y^2$ is also a function.

Solution: In $x = y^2$, if $y = 3$, then $x = 9$. Also, if $y = -3$, then $x = 9$. In other words, we have the ordered pairs $(9, 3)$ and $(9, -3)$. Since the x-value 9 corresponds to two y-values, 3 and -3, $x = y^2$ is not a function.

▣ **Work Practice Problem 8**

PRACTICE PROBLEMS 4–6

Determine whether each relation is also a function.

4. $\{(-3, 7), (1, 7), (2, 2)\}$

5.

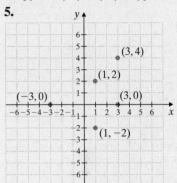

6.

Input	Correspondence	Output
People in a certain state	County/ parish that a person lives in	Counties of that state

---

PRACTICE PROBLEM 7

Determine whether the relation $y = 3x + 2$ is also a function.

PRACTICE PROBLEM 8

Determine whether the relation $x = y^2 + 1$ is also a function.

Answers

4. function, **5.** not a function, **6.** function, **7.** function, **8.** not a function

✔ Concept Check Answer

Two different ordered pairs can have the same y-value, but not the same x-value in a function.

PRACTICE PROBLEMS 9–13

Use the vertical line test to determine which are graphs of functions.

9.

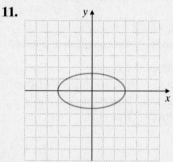

10.

11.

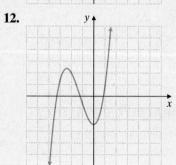

12.

13.

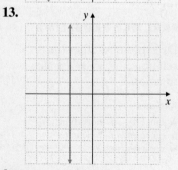

Answers

9. function, **10.** function,
11. not a function, **12.** function,
13. not a function

Objective ⒞ Using the Vertical Line Test

As we have seen, not all relations are functions. Consider the graphs of $y = 2x + 1$ and $x = y^2$ shown next. On the graph of $y = 2x + 1$, notice that each x-value corresponds to only one y-value. Recall from Example 7 that $y = 2x + 1$ is a function.

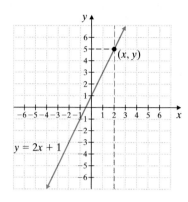

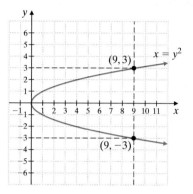

On the graph of $x = y^2$, the x-value 9, for example, corresponds to two y-values, 3 and –3, as shown by the vertical line. Recall from Example 8 that $x = y^2$ is not a function.

Graphs can be used to help determine whether a relation is also a function by the following **vertical line test.**

Vertical Line Test

If no vertical line can be drawn so that it intersects a graph more than once, the graph is the graph of a function. If such a line can be drawn, the graph is not that of a function.

EXAMPLES Use the vertical line test to determine which are graphs of functions.

9.

10.

11.

This is the graph of a function since no vertical line will intersect this graph more than once.

This is the graph of a function.

This is not the graph of a function. Note that vertical lines can be drawn that intersect the graph in two points.

12.

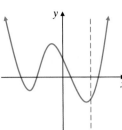

This is the graph of a function.

13.

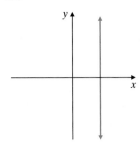

This is not the graph of a function. A vertical line can be drawn that intersects this line at every point.

▣ **Work Practice Problems 9–13**

✔**Concept Check** Determine which equations represent functions. Explain your answer.

a. $y = 14$ **b.** $x = -5$ **c.** $x + y = 6$

Objective D Using Function Notation

Many times letters such as f, g, and h are used to name functions. To denote that y is a function of x, we can write

$$y = f(x)$$

This means that **y is a function of x** or that y *depends on x*. For this reason, y is called the **dependent variable** and x the **independent variable.** The notation $f(x)$ is read "f of x" and is called **function notation.**

For example, to use function notation with the function $y = 4x + 3$, we write $f(x) = 4x + 3$. The notation $f(1)$ means to replace x with 1 and find the resulting y- or function value. Since

$$f(x) = 4x + 3$$

then

$$f(1) = 4(1) + 3 = 7$$

This means that when $x = 1$, y or $f(x) = 7$. The corresponding ordered pair is $(1, 7)$. Here, the input is 1 and the output is $f(1)$ or 7. Now let's find $f(2)$, $f(0)$, and $f(-1)$.

$f(x) = 4x + 3$	$f(x) = 4x + 3$	$f(x) = 4x + 3$
$f(2) = 4(2) + 3$	$f(0) = 4(0) + 3$	$f(-1) = 4(-1) + 3$
$= 8 + 3$	$= 0 + 3$	$= -4 + 3$
$= 11$	$= 3$	$= -1$

Ordered Pairs:

       $(2, 11)$ $(0, 3)$ $(-1, -1)$

Helpful Hint

Note that $f(x)$ is a special symbol in mathematics used to denote a function. The symbol $f(x)$ is read "f of x." It does *not* mean $f \cdot x$ (f times x).

✔ **Concept Check Answers**

a, c

PRACTICE PROBLEMS 14–17

Find each function value.

14. If $g(x) = 4x + 5$, find $g(0)$.

15. If $g(x) = 4x + 5$, find $g(-5)$.

16. If $f(x) = 3x^2 - x + 2$, find $f(2)$.

17. If $f(x) = 3x^2 - x + 2$, find $f(-1)$.

EXAMPLES Find each function value.

14. If $g(x) = 3x - 2$, find $g(1)$.
$$g(1) = 3(1) - 2 = 1$$

15. If $g(x) = 3x - 2$, find $g(0)$.
$$g(0) = 3(0) - 2 = -2$$

16. If $f(x) = 7x^2 - 3x + 1$, find $f(1)$.
$$f(1) = 7(1)^2 - 3(1) + 1 = 5$$

17. If $f(x) = 7x^2 - 3x + 1$, find $f(-2)$.
$$f(-2) = 7(-2)^2 - 3(-2) + 1 = 35$$

▣ **Work Practice Problems 14–17**

✔ **Concept Check** Suppose $y = f(x)$ and we are told that $f(3) = 9$. Which is not true?

a. When $x = 3$, $y = 9$.

b. A possible function is $f(x) = x^2$.

c. A point on the graph of the function is $(3, 9)$.

d. A possible function is $f(x) = 2x + 4$.

Objective **E** **Graphing Linear Functions**

Recall that the graph of a linear equation in two variables is a line, and a line that is not vertical will always pass the vertical line test. Thus, *all linear equations are functions except those whose graphs are vertical lines*. We call such functions *linear functions*.

Linear Function

A **linear function** is a function that can be written in the form
$$f(x) = mx + b$$

EXAMPLE 18 Graph the function $f(x) = 2x + 1$.

Solution: Since $y = f(x)$, we can replace $f(x)$ with y and graph as usual. The graph of $y = 2x + 1$ has slope 2 and y-intercept $(0, 1)$. Its graph is shown.

PRACTICE PROBLEM 18

Graph the function $f(x) = 3x - 2$.

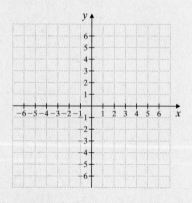

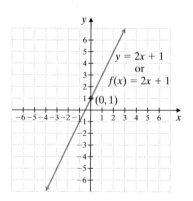

▣ **Work Practice Problem 18**

Answers

14. $g(0) = 5$, **15.** $g(-5) = -15$,
16. $f(2) = 12$, **17.** $f(-1) = 6$,
18.

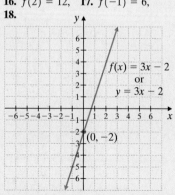

Objectives Ⓐ Ⓑ **Mixed Practice** *Find the domain and the range of each relation. Also determine whether the relation is a function. See Examples 1 through 6.*

1. $\{(-1, 7), (0, 6), (-2, 2), (5, 6)\}$

2. $\{(4, 9), (-4, 9), (2, 3), (10, -5)\}$

3. $\{(-2, 4), (6, 4), (-2, -3), (-7, -8)\}$

4. $\{(6, 6), (5, 6), (5, -2), (7, 6)\}$

 5. $\{(1, 1), (1, 2), (1, 3), (1, 4)\}$

6. $\{(1, 1), (2, 1), (3, 1), (4, 1)\}$

7. $\left\{\left(\dfrac{3}{2}, \dfrac{1}{2}\right), \left(1\dfrac{1}{2}, -7\right), \left(0, \dfrac{4}{5}\right)\right\}$

8. $\{(\pi, 0), (0, \pi), (-2, 4), (4, -2)\}$

9. $\{(-3, -3), (0, 0), (3, 3)\}$

10. $\left\{\left(\dfrac{1}{2}, \dfrac{1}{4}\right), \left(0, \dfrac{7}{8}\right), (0.5, \pi)\right\}$

 11.

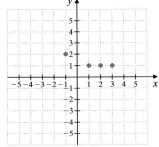

12.

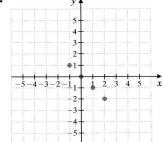

13. Input: **Output:**
States **Number of Congressional Representatives**

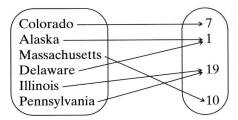

14. Input: **Output:**
Animal **Average Life Span (in years)**

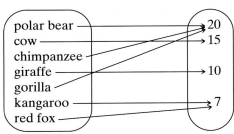

195

15. Input: **Output:**
Degrees Degrees
Fahrenheit Celsius

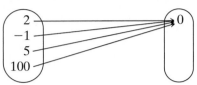

16. Input: **Output:**
Words Number of
Letters

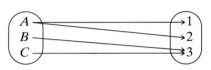

17. Input: **Output:**

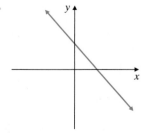

18. Input: **Output:**

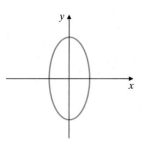

Determine whether each relation is a function. See Examples 4 through 6.

19. First Set: Input	Correspondence	Second Set: Output	20. First Set: Input	Correspondence	Second Set: Output
Class of algebra students	Grade average	Set of nonnegative numbers	People in New Orleans (population 500,000)	Birthdate	Days of the year

Determine whether each relation is also a function. See Examples 7 and 8.

21. $y = x + 1$ **22.** $y = x - 1$ **23.** $x = 2y^2$

24. $y = x^2$ **25.** $y - x = 7$ **26.** $2x - 3y = 9$

Objective **C** *Use the vertical line test to determine whether each graph is the graph of a function. See Examples 9 through 13.*

27.

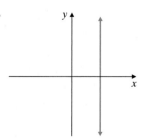

28.

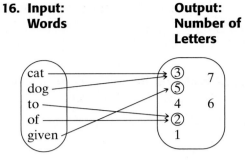

29.

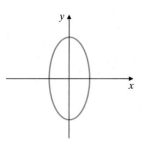

30.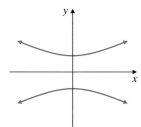

31.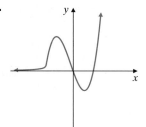

32.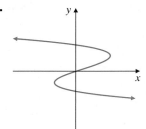

33.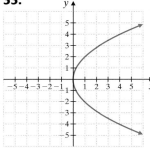

34.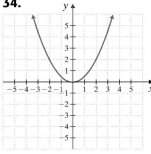

35.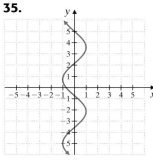

36.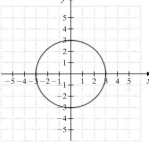

37.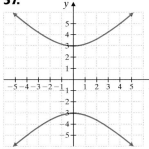

38.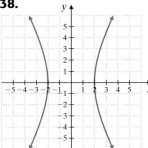

39.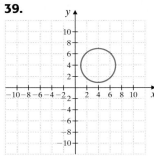

40.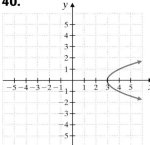

41.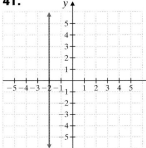

42.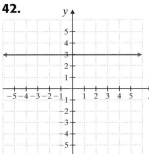

43.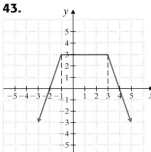

44.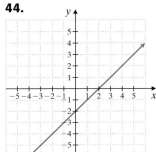

Objective **D** *If* $f(x) = 3x + 3$, $g(x) = 4x^2 - 6x + 3$, *and* $h(x) = 5x^2 - 7$, *find each function value.*
See Examples 14 through 17.

45. $f(4)$ **46.** $f(-1)$ **47.** $h(-3)$ **48.** $h(0)$

49. $g(2)$ **50.** $g(1)$ **51.** $g(0)$ **52.** $h(-2)$

For each function, find the indicated values. See Examples 14 through 17.

53. $f(x) = \frac{1}{2}x;$
  a. $f(0)$
  b. $f(2)$
  c. $f(-2)$

54. $g(x) = -\frac{1}{3}x;$
  a. $g(0)$
  b. $g(-1)$
  c. $g(3)$

55. $f(x) = -5;$
  a. $f(2)$
  b. $f(0)$
  c. $f(606)$

56. $h(x) = 7;$
  a. $h(7)$
  b. $h(542)$
  c. $h\left(-\frac{3}{4}\right)$

The function $A(r) = \pi r^2$ may be used to find the area of a circle if we are given its radius. Use this function to answer Exercises 57 and 58.

△ **57.** Find the area of a circle whose radius is 5 centimeters. (Do not approximate π.)

△ **58.** Find the area of a circular garden whose radius is 8 feet. (Do not approximate π.)

The function $V(x) = x^3$ may be used to find the volume of a cube if we are given the length x of a side. Use this function to answer Exercises 59 and 60.

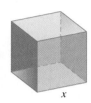

59. Find the volume of a cube whose side is 14 inches.

60. Find the volume of a die whose side is 1.7 centimeters.

Forensic scientists use the following functions to find the height of a woman if they are given the height of her femur bone (f) or her tibia bone (t) in centimeters.

$$H(f) = 2.59f + 47.24$$
$$H(t) = 2.72t + 61.28$$

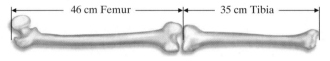

Use these functions to answer Exercises 61 and 62.

61. Find the height of a woman whose femur measures 46 centimeters.

62. Find the height of a woman whose tibia measures 35 centimeters.

The dosage in milligrams D of Ivermectin, a heartworm preventive, for a dog who weighs x pounds is given by

$$D(x) = \frac{136}{25}x$$

Use this function to answer Exercises 63 and 64.

63. Find the proper dosage for a dog that weighs 30 pounds.

64. Find the proper dosage for a dog that weighs 50 pounds.

65. The per capita consumption (in pounds) of all poultry in the United States is given by the function $C(x) = 2.28x + 94.86$, where x is the number of years since 2001. (*Source:* Based on actual and estimated data from the Economic Research Service, U.S. Dept. of Agriculture, 2001–2005)
  a. Find and interpret $C(2)$.
  b. Estimate the per capita consumption of all poultry in the United States in 2007.

66. The amount of money (in billions of dollars) spent by U.S. biotechnology companies on research and development annually is represented by the function $R(x) = 1.84x + 8.57$, where x is the number of years since 1997. (*Source:* Based on data from The Biotechnology Industry Organization)
  a. Find and interpret $R(7)$.
  b. Estimate the amount of money spent on biotechnology research and development in 2000.

Objective **E** *Graph each linear function. See Example 18.*

67. $f(x) = 2x + 3$

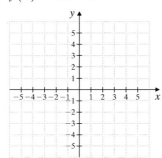

68. $f(x) = 5x - 1$

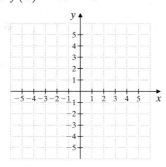

69. $f(x) = -3x$

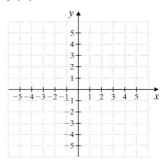

70. $f(x) = -4x$

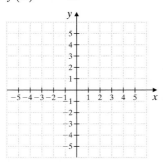

71. $f(x) = -x + 2$

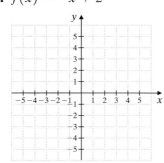

72. $f(x) = -x + 1$

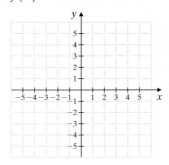

Review

Solve. See Section 2.4.

73. $2x - 7 \leq 21$

74. $-3x + 1 > 0$

75. $5(x - 2) \geq 3(x - 1)$

76. $-2(x + 1) \leq -x + 10$

77. $\dfrac{x}{2} + \dfrac{1}{4} < \dfrac{1}{8}$

78. $\dfrac{x}{5} - \dfrac{3}{10} \geq \dfrac{x}{2} - 1$

Concept Extensions

Think about the appearance of each graph. Without graphing, determine which equations represent functions. Explain each answer. See the first Concept Check in this section.

79. $x = -1$

80. $y = 5$

81. $y = 2x$

82. $x + y = -5$

Suppose that $y = f(x)$ and it is true that $f(7) = 50$. Determine whether each is true or false. See the second Concept Check in this section.

83. An ordered-pair solution of the function is $(7, 50)$.

84. When x is 50, y is 7.

85. A possible function is $f(x) = x^2 + 1$.

86. A possible function is $f(x) = 10x - 20$.

87. Describe a function whose domain is the set of people in your home town.

88. Describe a function whose domain is the set of people in your algebra class.

89. Since $y = x + 7$ describes a function, rewrite the equation using function notation.

90. In your own words, explain how to find the domain of a function given its graph.

91. Explain the vertical line test and how it is used.

For each function, find the indicated values.

92. $f(x) = 2x + 7$
   a. $f(2)$
   b. $f(a)$
   c. $f(-x)$
   d. $f(x + h)$

93. $f(x) = x^2 - 12$;
   a. $f(12)$
   b. $f(a)$
   c. $f(-x)$
   d. $f(x + h)$

94. If $f(x) = 1.3x^2 - 2.6x + 5.1$, the following.
   a. $f(2)$
   b. $f(-2)$
   c. $f(3.1)$

3.7 FIND DOMAINS AND RANGES FROM GRAPHS AND GRAPHING PIECEWISE-DEFINED FUNCTIONS

Objectives

A Find the Domain and Range from a Graph.

B Graph Piecewise-Defined Functions.

Objective **A** Finding the Domain and Range from a Graph

Recall from Section 3.6 that the

> **domain** of a relation is the set of all first components of the ordered pairs of the relation and the
>
> **range** of a relation is the set of all second components of the ordered pairs of the relation.

In this section we use the graph of a relation to find its domain and range. Let's use interval notation to write these domains and ranges. Remember, we use a parenthesis to indicate that a number is not part of the domain and we use a bracket to indicate that a number if part of the domain. Of course, as usual, parentheses are placed about infinity symbols indicating that we approach but never reach infinity.

To find the domain of a function (or relation) from its graph, recall that on the rectangular coordinate system, "domain" is the set of first components of the ordered pairs, so this means what *x*-values are graphed. Similarly, "range" is the set of second components of the ordered pairs, so this means what *y*-values are graphed.

EXAMPLES Find the domain and range of each relation.

1.

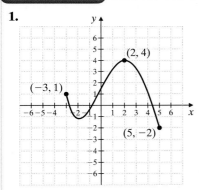

2.

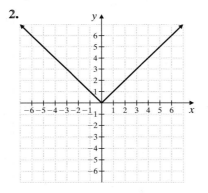

3.

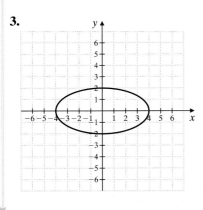

4.

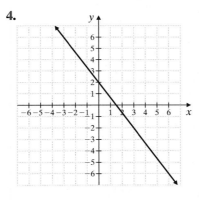

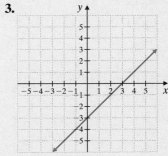
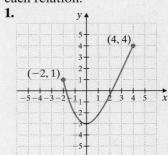
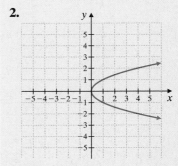

Continued on next page

PRACTICE PROBLEMS 1–4

Find the domain and range of each relation.

1.

2.

3.

Answers

1. domain: [−2, 4]; range: [−3, 4],

2. domain: [0, ∞); range: (−∞, ∞),

3. domain: (−∞, ∞); range: (−∞, ∞),

4.

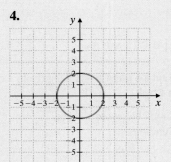

Solution: Notice that the graphs for Examples 1, 2, and 4 are graphs of functions because each passes the vertical line test.

1.

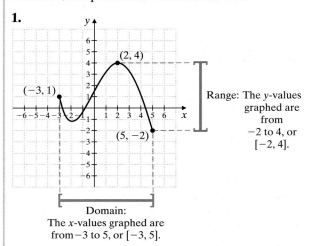

Range: The y-values graphed are from -2 to 4, or $[-2, 4]$.

Domain:
The x-values graphed are from -3 to 5, or $[-3, 5]$.

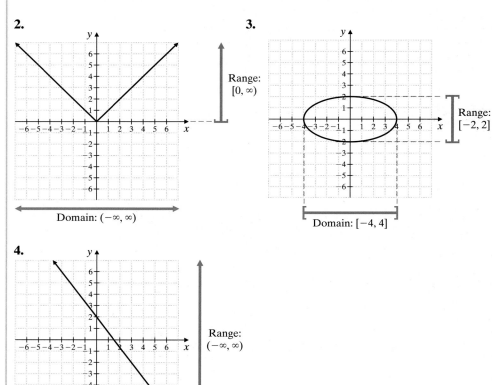

2.

Range: $[0, \infty)$

Domain: $(-\infty, \infty)$

3.

Range: $[-2, 2]$

Domain: $[-4, 4]$

4.

Range: $(-\infty, \infty)$

Domain: $(-\infty, \infty)$

🖳 **Work Practice Problems 1–4**

Objective **B** Graphing Piecewise-Defined Functions

In the last section we graphed functions. There are many special functions. In fact, sometimes a function is defined by two or more expressions. The equation to use depends upon the value of x. Before we actually graph these piecewise-defined functions, let's practice finding function values.

Answer
4. domain: $[-2, 2]$; range: $[-2, 2]$

EXAMPLE 5 Evaluate $f(2), f(-6)$, and $f(0)$ for the function

$$f(x) = \begin{cases} 2x + 3 & \text{if } x \le 0 \\ -x - 1 & \text{if } x > 0 \end{cases}$$

Then write your results in ordered-pair form.

Solution: Take a moment and study this function. It is a single function defined by two expressions depending on the value of x. From above, if $x \le 0$, use $f(x) = 2x + 3$. If $x > 0$, use $f(x) = 3x - 1$. Thus

$f(2) = -(2) - 1$	$f(-6) = 2(-6) + 3$	$f(0) = 2(0) + 3$
$\quad = -3 \quad$ since $2 > 0$	$\quad = -9 \quad$ since $-6 \le 0$	$\quad = 3 \quad$ since $0 \le 0$
$f(2) = -3$	$f(-6) = -9$	$f(0) = 3$
Ordered pairs: $(2, -3)$	$(-6, -9)$	$(0, 3)$

🖥 **Work Practice Problem 5**

Now, let's graph a piecewise-defined function.

EXAMPLE 6 Graph $f(x) = \begin{cases} 2x + 3 & \text{if } x \le 0 \\ -x - 1 & \text{if } x > 0 \end{cases}$

Solution: Let's graph each piece.

If $x \le 0$,
$f(x) = 2x + 3$

Values ≤ 0 $\begin{cases} \\ \\ \\ \end{cases}$

x	$f(x) = 2x + 3$
0	3 Closed circle
−1	1
−2	−1

If $x > 0$,
$f(x) = -x - 1$

Values > 0 $\begin{cases} \\ \\ \\ \end{cases}$

x	$f(x) = -x - 1$
1	−2
2	−3
3	−4

The graph of the first part of $f(x)$ listed will look like a ray with a closed-circle endpoint at $(0, 3)$. The graph of the second part of $f(x)$ listed will look like a ray with an open-circle endpoint. To find the exact location of the open-circle endpoint, use $f(x) = -x - 1$ and find $f(0)$. Since $f(0) = -0 - 1 = -1$, we graph the second table and place an open circle at $(0, -1)$.

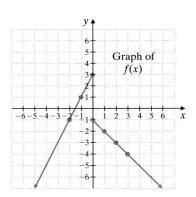

Graph of $f(x)$

Notice that this graph is the graph of a function because it passes the vertical line test. The domain of this function is $(-\infty, \infty)$ and the range is $(-\infty, 3]$.

🖥 **Work Practice Problem 6**

In the next section, we shall graph piecewise-defined functions whose pieces are not necessarily pieces of lines.

PRACTICE PROBLEM 5

Evaluate $f(-4), f(3)$, and $f(0)$ for the function

$$f(x) = \begin{cases} 3x + 4 & \text{if } x < 0 \\ -x + 2 & \text{if } x \ge 0 \end{cases}$$

Then write your results in ordered-pair solution form.

PRACTICE PROBLEM 6

Graph

$$f(x) = \begin{cases} 3x + 4 & \text{if } x < 0 \\ -x + 2 & \text{if } x \ge 0 \end{cases}$$

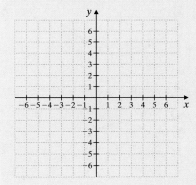

Answers

5. $f(-4) = -8$; $f(3) = -1$; $f(0) = 2$; $(-4, -8)$; $(3, -1)$; $(0, 2)$,

6.

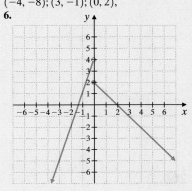

Objective **A** *Find the domain and the range of each relation. See Examples 1 through 4.*

1.

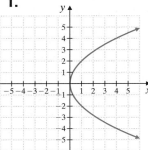

2.

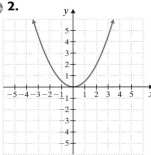

3.

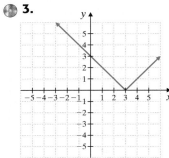

4.

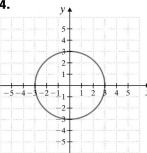

5.

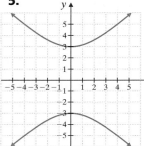

6.

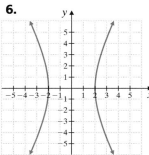

7.

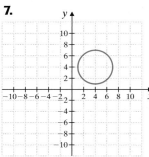

8.

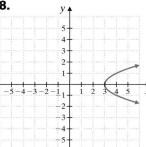

9.

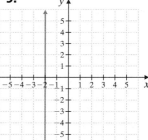

10.

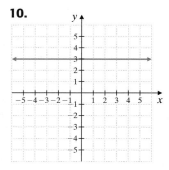

11.

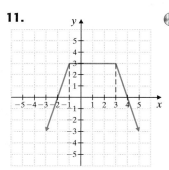

12.

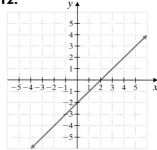

13.

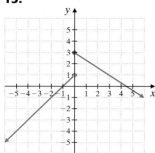

14.

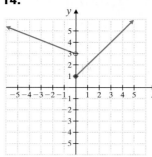

15.

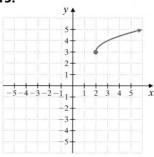

16.

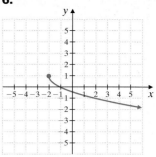

Objective **B** *Graph each piecewise-defined function. See Examples 5 and 6.*

17. $f(x) = \begin{cases} 2x & \text{if } x < 0 \\ x + 1 & \text{if } x \geq 0 \end{cases}$

18. $f(x) = \begin{cases} 3x & \text{if } x < 0 \\ x + 2 & \text{if } x \geq 0 \end{cases}$

19. $f(x) = \begin{cases} 4x + 5 & \text{if } x \leq 0 \\ \dfrac{1}{4}x + 2 & \text{if } x > 0 \end{cases}$

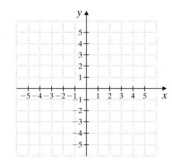

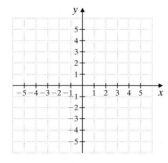

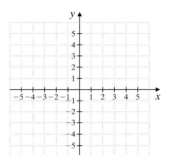

20. $f(x) = \begin{cases} 5x + 4 & \text{if } x \leq 0 \\ \dfrac{1}{3}x - 1 & \text{if } x > 0 \end{cases}$

21. $g(x) = \begin{cases} -x & \text{if } x \leq 1 \\ 2x + 1 & \text{if } x > 1 \end{cases}$

22. $g(x) = \begin{cases} 3x - 1 & \text{if } x \leq 2 \\ -x & \text{if } x > 2 \end{cases}$

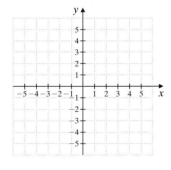

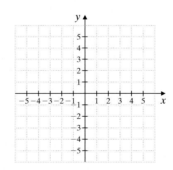

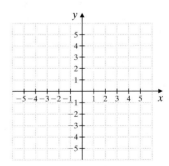

23. $f(x) = \begin{cases} 5 & \text{if } x < -2 \\ 3 & \text{if } x \geq -2 \end{cases}$

24. $f(x) = \begin{cases} 4 & \text{if } x < -3 \\ -2 & \text{if } x \geq -3 \end{cases}$

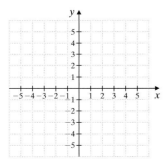

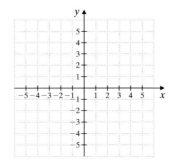

Objectives **A** **B** **Mixed Practice** *Graph each piecewise-defined function. Use the graph to determine the domain and range of the function. See Examples 1 through 6.*

25. $f(x) = \begin{cases} -2x & \text{if } x \le 0 \\ 2x + 1 & \text{if } x > 0 \end{cases}$

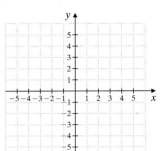

26. $g(x) = \begin{cases} -3x & \text{if } x \le 0 \\ 3x + 2 & \text{if } x > 0 \end{cases}$

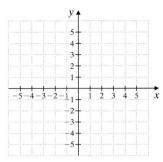

27. $h(x) = \begin{cases} 5x - 5 & \text{if } x < 2 \\ -x + 3 & \text{if } x \ge 2 \end{cases}$

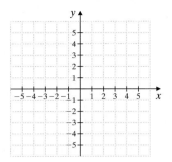

28. $f(x) = \begin{cases} 4x - 4 & \text{if } x < 2 \\ -x + 1 & \text{if } x \ge 2 \end{cases}$

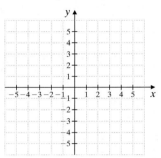

29. $f(x) = \begin{cases} x + 3 & \text{if } x < -1 \\ -2x + 4 & \text{if } x \ge -1 \end{cases}$

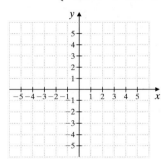

30. $h(x) = \begin{cases} x + 2 & \text{if } x < 1 \\ 2x + 1 & \text{if } x \ge 1 \end{cases}$

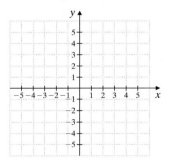

31. $g(x) = \begin{cases} -2 & \text{if } x \le 0 \\ -4 & \text{if } x \ge 1 \end{cases}$

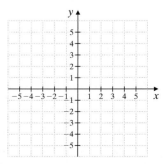

32. $f(x) = \begin{cases} -1 & \text{if } x \le 0 \\ -3 & \text{if } x \ge 2 \end{cases}$

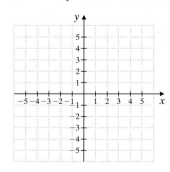

Review

Match each equation with its graph.

33. $y = -1$

A

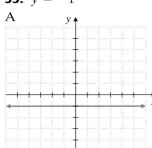

34. $x = -1$

B

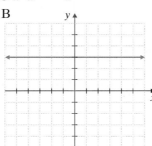

35. $x = 3$

C

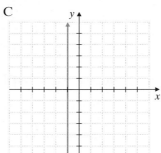

36. $y = 3$

D

Concept Extensions

37. Draw a graph whose domain is $(-\infty, 5]$ and whose range is $[2, \infty)$.

 38. In your own words, describe how to graph a piecewise-defined function.

39. Graph: $f(x) = \begin{cases} -\dfrac{1}{2}x & \text{if } x \le 0 \\ x + 1 & \text{if } 0 < x \le 2 \\ 2x - 1 & \text{if } x > 2 \end{cases}$

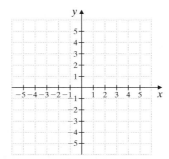

STUDY SKILLS BUILDER

Tips for Studying for an Exam

To prepare for an exam, try the following study techniques:

- Start the study process days before your exam.
- Make sure that you are up-to-date on your assignments.
- If there is a topic that you are unsure of, use one of the many resources that are available to you. For example,

  See your instructor.

  Visit a learning resource center on campus.

  Read the textbook material and examples on the topic.

  View a video on the topic.

- Reread your notes and carefully review the Chapter Highlights at the end of any chapter.
- Work the review exercises at the end of the chapter. Check your answers and correct any mistakes. If you have trouble, use a resource listed above.
- Find a quiet place to take the Chapter Test found at the end of the chapter. Do not use any resources when taking this sample test. This way, you will have a clear

indication of how prepared you are for your exam. Check your answers and make sure that you correct any missed exercises.

- Get lots of rest the night before the exam. It's hard to show how well you know the material if your brain is foggy from lack of sleep.

Good luck and keep a positive attitude.

Let's see how you did on your last exam.

1. How many days before your last exam did you start studying for that exam?

2. Were you up-to-date on your assignments at that time or did you need to catch up on assignments?

3. List the most helpful text supplement (if you used one).

4. List the most helpful campus supplement (if you used one).

5. List your process for preparing for a mathematics test.

6. Was this process helpful? In other words, were you satisfied with your performance on your exam?

7. If not, what changes can you make in your process that will make it more helpful to you?

3.8 SHIFTING AND REFLECTING GRAPHS OF FUNCTIONS

In this section, we take common graphs and learn how more complicated graphs are actually formed by shifting and reflecting these common graphs. These shifts and reflections are called transformations, and it is possible to combine transformations. A knowledge of these transformations will help you simplify future graphs.

Objective **A** Graphing Common Equations

Let's begin with the graphs of four common functions.

First, let's graph the linear function $f(x) = x$, or $y = x$. Ordered-pair solutions of these graphs consist of ordered pairs whose x- and y-values are the same.

x	y or $f(x) = x$
-3	-3
0	0
1	1
4	4

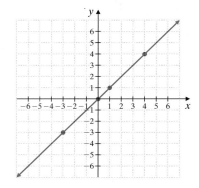

Next, let's graph the nonlinear function $f(x) = x^2$ or $y = x^2$.

This equation is not linear because the x^2 term does not allow us to write it in the form $Ax + By = C$. Its graph is not a line. We begin by finding ordered pair solutions. Because this graph is solved for $f(x)$, or y, we choose x-values and find corresponding $f(x)$, or y-values.

If $x = -3$, then $y = (-3)^2$, or 9.
If $x = -2$, then $y = (-2)^2$, or 4.
If $x = -1$, then $y = (-1)^2$, or 1.
If $x = 0$, then $y = 0^2$, or 0.
If $x = 1$, then $y = 1^2$, or 1.
If $x = 2$, then $y = 2^2$, or 4.
If $x = 3$, then $y = 3^2$, or 9.

x	$f(x)$ or y
-3	9
-2	4
-1	1
0	0
1	1
2	4
3	9

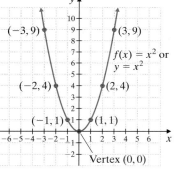

Study the table a moment and look for patterns. Notice that the ordered pair solution $(0, 0)$ contains the smallest y-value because any other x-value squared will give a positive result. This means that the point $(0, 0)$ will be the lowest point on the graph. Also notice that all other y-values correspond to two different x-values. For example, $3^2 = 9$ and also $(-3)^2 = 9$. This means that the graph will be a mirror image of itself across the y-axis. Connect the plotted points with a smooth curve to sketch its graph.

This curve is given a special name, a **parabola.** We will study more about parabolas in later chapters.

Next, let's graph another nonlinear function $f(x) = |x|$ or $y = |x|$.

This is not a linear equation since it cannot be written in the form $Ax + By = C$. Its graph is not a line. Because we do not know the shape of this graph, we find many ordered pair solutions. We will choose x-values and substitute to find corresponding y-values.

If $x = -3$, then $y = |-3|$, or 3.

If $x = -2$, then $y = |-2|$, or 2.

If $x = -1$, then $y = |-1|$, or 1.

If $x = 0$, then $y = |0|$, or 0.

If $x = 1$, then $y = |1|$, or 1.

If $x = 2$, then $y = |2|$, or 2.

If $x = 3$, then $y = |3|$, or 3.

x	y
-3	3
-2	2
-1	1
0	0
1	1
2	2
3	3

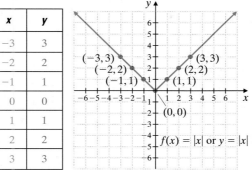

Again, study the table of values for a moment and notice any patterns.

From the plotted ordered pairs, we see that the graph of this absolute value equation is V-shaped.

Finally, a fourth common function, $f(x) = \sqrt{x}$ or $y = \sqrt{x}$. For this graph, you need to recall basic facts about square roots and use your calculator to approximate some square roots to help locate points. Recall also that the square root of a negative number is not a real number, so be careful when finding your domain.

Now let's graph the square root function $f(x) = \sqrt{x}$, or $y = \sqrt{x}$.

To graph, we identify the domain, evaluate the function for several values of x, plot the resulting points, and connect the points with a smooth curve. Since $\sqrt{x}$ represents the nonnegative square root of x, the domain of this function is the set of all nonnegative numbers, $\{x \mid x \geq 0\}$, or $[0, \infty)$. We have approximated $\sqrt{3}$ below to help us locate the point corresponding to $(3, \sqrt{3})$.

If $x = 0$, then $y = \sqrt{0}$, or 0.

If $x = 1$, then $y = \sqrt{1}$, or 1.

If $x = 3$, then $y = \sqrt{3}$, or 1.7.

If $x = 4$, then $y = \sqrt{4}$, or 2.

If $x = 9$, then $y = \sqrt{9}$, or 3.

x	$f(x) = \sqrt{x}$
0	0
1	1
3	$\sqrt{3} \approx 1.7$
4	2
9	3

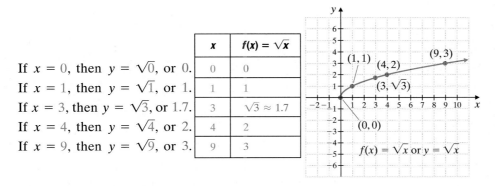

Notice that the graph of this function passes the vertical line test, as expected.

Below is a summary of our four common graphs. Take a moment and study these graphs. Your success in the rest of this section depends on your knowledge of these graphs.

Common Graphs

$f(x) = x$

$f(x) = x^2$

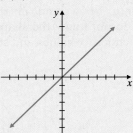

$f(x) = \sqrt{x}$

$f(x) = |x|$

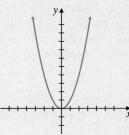

Answers

1.

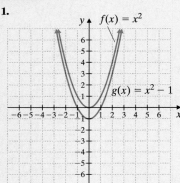

2.

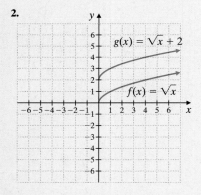

3.

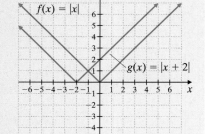

Objective B Vertical and Horizontal Shifting

Your knowledge of the slope-intercept form, $f(x) = mx + b$, will help you understand simple shifting of transformations such as vertical shifts. For example, what is the difference between the graphs of $f(x) = x$ and $g(x) = x + 3$?

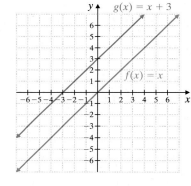

$f(x) = x$ $g(x) = x + 3$
slope, $m = 1$ slope, $m = 1$
y-intercept is $(0, 0)$ y-intercept is $(0, 3)$

Notice that the graph of $g(x) = x + 3$ is the same as the graph of $f(x) = x$, but moved upward 3 units. This is an example of a **vertical shift** and is true for graphs in general.

Vertical Shifts (Upward and Downward) Let k be a Positive Number

Graph of	Same As	Moved
$g(x) = f(x) + k$	$f(x)$	k units upward
$g(x) = f(x) - k$	$f(x)$	k units downward

EXAMPLES Without plotting points, sketch the graph of each pair of functions on the same set of axes.

1. $f(x) = x^2$ and $g(x) = x^2 + 2$

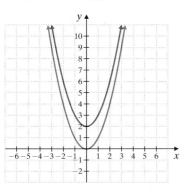

2. $f(x) = \sqrt{x}$ and $g(x) = \sqrt{x} - 3$

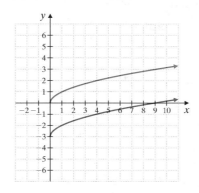

■ **Work Practice Problems 1–2**

A horizontal shift to the left or right may be slightly more difficult to understand. Let's graph $g(x) = |x - 2|$ and compare it with $f(x) = |x|$.

EXAMPLE 3 Without plotting points, sketch the graphs of $f(x) = |x|$ and $g(x) = |x - 2|$ on the same set of axes.

x	$f(x) = |x|$	$g(x) = |x - 2|$
-3	3	5
-2	2	4
-1	1	3
0	0	2
1	1	1
2	2	0
3	3	1

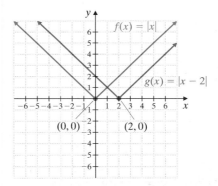

The graph of $g(x) = |x - 2|$ is the same as the graph of $f(x) = |x|$, but moved 2 units to the right. This is an example of a **horizontal shift** and is true for graphs in general.

Horizontal Shift (To the Left or Right) Let h be a Positive Number

Graph of	Same as	Moved
$g(x) = f(x - h)$	$f(x)$	h units to the right
$g(x) = f(x + h)$	$f(x)$	h units to the left

Helpful Hint

Notice that $f(x - h)$ corresponds to a shift to the right and $f(x + h)$ corresponds to a shift to the left.

■ **Work Practice Problem 3**

Vertical and horizontal shifts can be combined.

PRACTICE PROBLEMS 1–2

Without plotting points, sketch the graphs of each pair of functions on the same set of axes.

1. $f(x) = x^2$ and $g(x) = x^2 - 1$

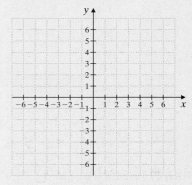

2. $f(x) = \sqrt{x}$ and $g(x) = \sqrt{x} + 2$

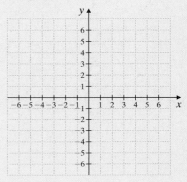

PRACTICE PROBLEM 3

Without plotting points, sketch the graphs of $f(x) = |x|$ and $g(x) = |x + 2|$ on the same set of axes.

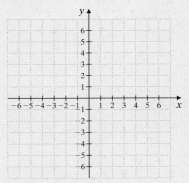

Answers
1–3. See page 210.

PRACTICE PROBLEM 4

Sketch the graphs of $f(x) = x^2$ and $g(x) = (x + 2)^2 - 1$ on the same set of axes.

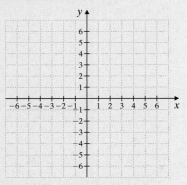

PRACTICE PROBLEM 5

Sketch the graph of $h(x) = -(x - 3)^2 + 2$.

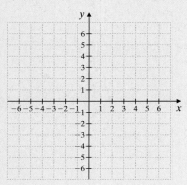

Answers

4.

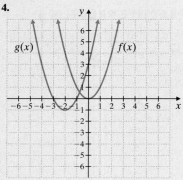

5.

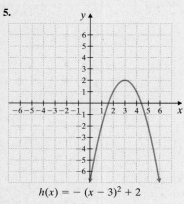

$h(x) = -(x - 3)^2 + 2$

EXAMPLE 4 Sketch the graphs of $f(x) = x^2$ and $g(x) = (x - 2)^2 + 1$ on the same set of axes.

Solution: The graph of $g(x)$ is the same as the graph of $f(x)$ shifted 2 units to the right and 1 unit up.

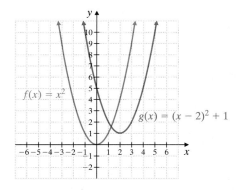

🔲 **Work Practice Problem 4**

Objective C Reflecting Graphs

Another type of transformation is called a **reflection.** In this section, we will study reflections (mirror images) about the x-axis only. For example, take a moment and study these two graphs. The graph of $g(x) = -x^2$ can be found, as usual, by plotting points.

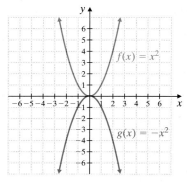

Reflection about the x-axis

The graph of $g(x) = -f(x)$ is the graph of $f(x)$ reflected about the x-axis.

EXAMPLE 5 Sketch the graph of $h(x) = -|x - 3| + 2$.

Solution: The graph of $h(x) = -|x - 3| + 2$ is the same as the graph of $f(x) = |x|$ reflected about the x-axis, then moved three units to the right and two units upward.

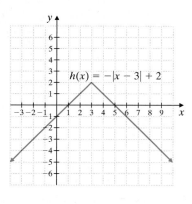

🔲 **Work Practice Problem 5**

There are other transformations, such as stretching that won't be covered in this section. For a review of this transformation, see the Appendix.

Mental Math

Objective A *Match each equation with its graph.*

1. $y = \sqrt{x}$ **2.** $y = x^2$ **3.** $y = x$ **4.** $y = |x|$

a.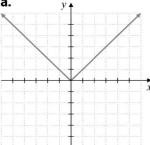

b.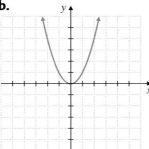

c.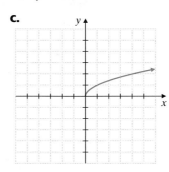

d.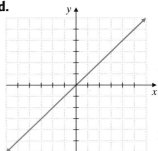

FOR EXTRA HELP

Student Solutions Manual   PH Math/Tutor Center   CD/Video for Review   Math XL MathXL®   MyMathLab MyMathLab

Objectives A B **Mixed Practice**   *Sketch the graph of function. See Examples 1 through 4.*

1. $f(x) = |x| + 3$

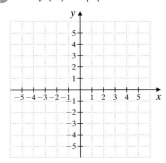

2. $f(x) = |x| - 2$

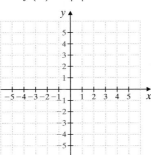

3. $f(x) = \sqrt{x} - 2$

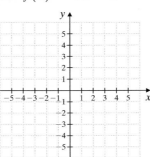

4. $f(x) = \sqrt{x} + 3$

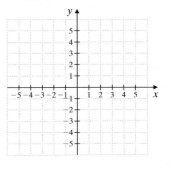

5. $f(x) = |x - 4|$

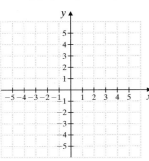

6. $f(x) = |x + 3|$

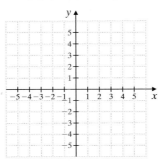

7. $f(x) = \sqrt{x + 2}$

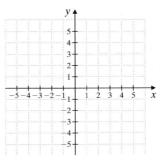

8. $f(x) = \sqrt{x - 2}$

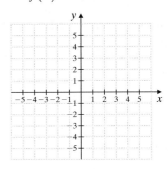

9. $y = (x - 4)^2$

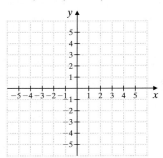

10. $y = (x + 4)^2$

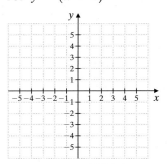

11. $f(x) = x^2 + 4$

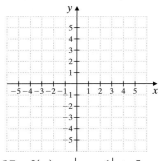

12. $f(x) = x^2 - 4$

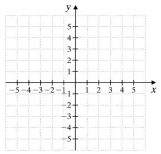

13. $f(x) = \sqrt{x - 2} + 3$

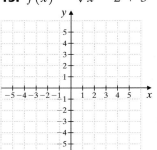

14. $f(x) = \sqrt{x - 1} + 3$

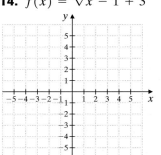

15. $f(x) = |x - 1| + 5$

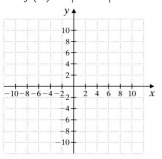

16. $f(x) = |x - 3| + 2$

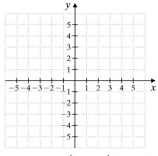

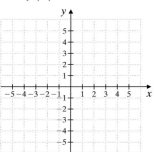 **17.** $f(x) = \sqrt{x + 1} + 1$

18. $f(x) = \sqrt{x + 3} + 2$

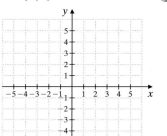

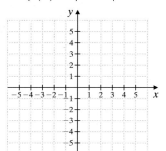 **19.** $f(x) = |x + 3| - 1$

20. $f(x) = |x + 1| - 4$

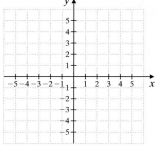

21. $g(x) = (x - 1)^2 - 1$

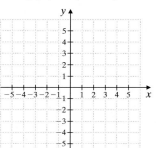

22. $h(x) = (x + 2)^2 + 2$

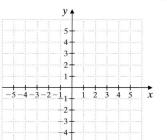

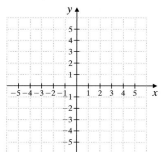 **23.** $f(x) = (x + 3)^2 - 2$

24. $f(x) = (x + 2)^2 + 4$

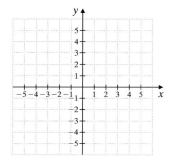

Objectives **A** **B** **C** **Mixed Practice** *Sketch the graph of each function.*

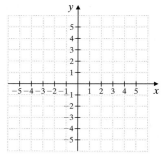 **25.** $f(x) = -(x - 1)^2$

26. $g(x) = -(x + 2)^2$

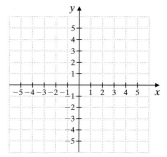

27. $h(x) = -\sqrt{x} + 3$

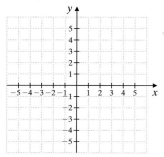

28. $f(x) = -\sqrt{x + 3}$

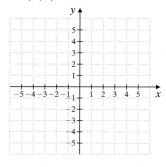

29. $h(x) = -|x + 2| + 3$ **30.** $g(x) = -|x + 1| + 1$ **31.** $f(x) = (x - 3) + 2$ **32.** $f(x) = (x - 1) + 4$

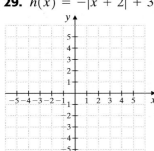 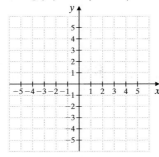

Review

Simplify. See Sections 1.5 through 1.7.

33. $-3x^4 \cdot 5x^4$ **34.** $-3x^4 + 5x^4$ **35.** $y^7 \cdot y^{11}$ **36.** $8(y^7 + y^{11})$

Concept Extensions

Mixed Practice (Sections 3.7, 3.8) *Write the domain and range of each graphed function in this section.*

37. Exercise 13   **38.** Exercise 14

39. Exercise 29   **40.** Exercise 30

Without graphing, find the domain of each function.

41. $f(x) = 5\sqrt{x - 20} + 1$ **42.** $g(x) = -3\sqrt{x + 5}$ **43.** $h(x) = 5|x - 20| + 1$

44. $f(x) = -3|x + 5.7|$ **45.** $g(x) = 9 - \sqrt{x + 103}$ **46.** $h(x) = \sqrt{x - 17} - 3$

Sketch the graph of each piecewise-defined function. Write the domain and range of each function.

47. $f(x) = \begin{cases} |x| & \text{if } x \le 0 \\ x^2 & \text{if } x > 0 \end{cases}$

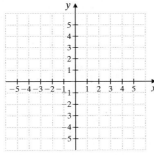

48. $f(x) = \begin{cases} x^2 & \text{if } x < 0 \\ \sqrt{x} & \text{if } x \ge 0 \end{cases}$

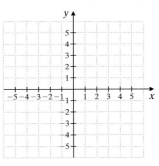

49. $g(x) = \begin{cases} |x - 2| & \text{if } x < 0 \\ -x^2 & \text{if } x \ge 0 \end{cases}$

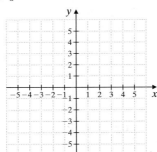

50. $g(x) = \begin{cases} -|x + 1| - 1 & \text{if } x < -2 \\ \sqrt{x + 2} - 4 & \text{if } x \ge -2 \end{cases}$

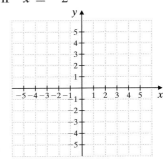

CHAPTER 3   Group Activity

Linear Modeling

As we saw in Sections 3.3 and 3.4, businesses often depend on equations that "closely fit" data. To *model* the data means to find an equation that describes the relationship between the paired data of two variables, such as time in years and profit. A model that accurately summarizes the relationship between two variables can be used to replace a potentially lengthy listing of the raw data. An accurate model might also be used to predict future trends by answering questions such as "If the trend seen in our company's performance in the last several years continues, what level of profit can we reasonably expect in 3 years?"

There are several ways to find a linear equation that models a set of data. If only two ordered pair data points are involved, an exact equation that contains both points can be found using the methods of Section 3.4. When more than two ordered pair data points are involved, it may be impossible to find a linear equation that contains all of the data points. In this case, the graph of the **best fit equation** should have a majority of the plotted ordered pair data points on the graph or close to it. In statistics, a technique called least squares regression is used to determine an equation that best fits a set of data. Various graphing utilities have built-in capabilities for finding an equation (called a regression equation) that best fits a set of ordered pair data points. Regression capabilities are often found with a graphing utility's statistics features.* A best fit equation can also be estimated using an algebraic method, which is outlined in the Group Activity below. In either case, a useful first step when finding a linear equation that models a set of data is creating a scatter diagram of the ordered pair data points to verify that a linear equation is an appropriate model.

Group Activity

Windows operating system is one of the well known products of the Microsoft Corporation. This company develops, manufactures, licenses and supports a wide range of software products for various computing devices. They also provide the MSN network of Internet products and services, and even the Xbox video game system. The table shows Microsoft's total revenues (in billions) for the years 1997 through 2004. Use the table along with your answers to the questions below to find a linear equation $y = mx + b$ that represents total revenue y (in billions) for Microsoft Corporation, where x represents the number of years after 1997.

Year	1997	1998	1999	2000	2001	2002
Total Microsoft Revenues (in billions)	20	23	25	28	32	37

(*Source:* Microsoft Corporation, Reuters Business Reports)

1. Create a scatter diagram of the paired data given in the table. Does a linear model seem appropriate for the data?

2. Use a straightedge to draw on your graph what appears to be the line that "best fits" the data you plotted.

3. Estimate the coordinates of two points that fall on your best fit line. Use these points to find the equation of the line that passes through both points.

4. Use this equation to find the value of y for $x = 11$. Interpret the meaning of this pair of data.

5. How could this equation be useful to accountants who work at Microsoft?

6. Compare your group's linear equation with other groups' equations. Are they the same or different? Explain why.

7. (Optional) Enter the data from the table into a graphing utility and use the linear regression feature to find a linear equation that models the data. Compare this equation with the one you found in Question 3. How are they alike or different?

8. (Optional) Using corporation annual reports or articles from magazines or newspapers, search for a set of business-related data that could be modeled with a linear equation. Explain how modeling this data could be useful to a business. Then find the best fit equation for the data.

*To find out more about using a graphing utility to find a regression equation, consult the user's manual for your graphing utility.

Chapter 3 Vocabulary Check

Fill in each blank with one of the words or phrases listed below.

relation	line	function	standard	parallel
slope-intercept	x	y	range	domain
point-slope	perpendicular	linear inequality	slope	linear function

1. A _____ is a set of ordered pairs.
2. The graph of every linear equation in two variables is a _____.
3. The statement $-x + 2y > 0$ is called a _____ in two variables.
4. _____ form of linear equation in two variables is $Ax + By = C$.
5. The _____ of a relation is the set of all second components of the ordered pairs of the relation.
6. _____ lines have the same slope and different y-intercepts.
7. _____ form of a linear equation in two variables is $y = mx + b$.
8. A _____ is a relation in which each first component in the ordered pairs corresponds to exactly one second component.
9. In the equation $y = 4x - 2$, the coefficient of x is the _____ of its corresponding graph.
10. Two lines are _____ if the product of their slopes is -1.
11. To find the x-intercept of a linear equation, let ___ $= 0$ and solve for the other variable.
12. The _____ of a relation is the set of all first components of the ordered pairs of the relation.
13. A _____ is a function that can be written in the form $f(x) = mx + b$.
14. To find the y-intercept of a linear equation, let ___ $= 0$ and solve for the other variable.
15. The equation $y - 8 = -5(x + 1)$ is written in _____ form.

Helpful Hint

Are you preparing for your test? Don't forget to take the Chapter 3 Test on page 250. Then check your answers at the back of the text and use the Chapter Test Prep Video CD to see the fully worked-out solutions to any of the exercises you want to review.

3 Chapter Highlights

DEFINITIONS AND CONCEPTS	EXAMPLES

Section 3.1   Graphing Linear Equations

The **rectangular coordinate system,** or **Cartesian coordinate system,** consists of a vertical and a horizontal number line on a plane intersecting at their 0 coordinate. The vertical number line is called the **y-axis,** and the horizontal number line is called **x-axis.** The point of intersection of the axes is called the **origin.**

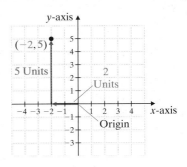

To **plot** or **graph** an ordered pair means to find its corresponding point on a rectangular coordinate system.

An ordered pair is a **solution** of an equation in two variables if replacing the variables by the corresponding coordinates results in a true statement.

Plot or graph the ordered pair $(-2, 5)$.

Start at the origin. Move 2 units to the left along the x-axis, then 5 units upward parallel to the y-axis.

Determine whether $(-2, 3)$ is a solution of $3x + 2y = 0$.

$$3(-2) + 2(3) = 0$$
$$-6 + 6 = 0$$
$$0 = 0 \quad \text{True}$$

$(-2, 3)$ is a solution.

continued

DEFINITIONS AND CONCEPTS	**EXAMPLES**

Section 3.1   Graphing Linear Equations (*continued*)

A **linear equation in two variables** is an equation that can be written in the form $Ax + By = C$, where A, B, and C are real numbers and A and B are not both 0. The form $Ax + By = C$ is called **standard form.**

$y = -2x + 5$, $x = 7$,
$y - 3 = 0$, $6x - 4y = 10$
$6x - 4y = 10$ is in standard form.

The **graph of a linear equation** in two variables is a line. To graph a linear equation in two variables, find three ordered pair solutions. Plot the solution points, and draw the line connecting the points.

Graph: $3x + y = -6$

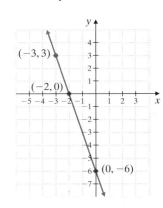

x	y
0	−6
−2	0
−3	3

To find an x-intercept, let $y = 0$ and solve for x.
To find a y-intercept, let $x = 0$ and solve for y.

The graph of $x = c$ is a vertical line with x-intercept c.
The graph of $y = c$ is a horizontal line with y-intercept c.

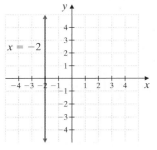 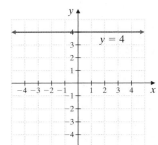

Section 3.2   The Slope of a Line

The **slope** m of the line through (x_1, y_1) and (x_2, y_2) is given by
$$m = \frac{y_2 - y_1}{x_2 - x_1}$$
as long as $x_2 \neq x_1$

Find the slope of the line through $(-1, 7)$ and $(-2, -3)$.
$$m = \frac{y_2 - y_1}{x_2 - x_1} = \frac{-3 - 7}{-2 - (-1)} = \frac{-10}{-1} = 10$$

The **slope-intercept form** of a linear equation is
$$y = mx + b$$
where m is the slope of the line and $(0, b)$ is the y-intercept.

Find the slope and y-intercept of $-3x + 2y = -8$.
$$2y = 3x - 8$$
$$\frac{2y}{2} = \frac{3x}{2} - \frac{8}{2}$$
$$y = \frac{3}{2}x - 4$$

The slope of the line is $\frac{3}{2}$, and the y-intercept is $(0, -4)$.

DEFINITIONS AND CONCEPTS	**EXAMPLES**

Section 3.2   The Slope of a Line (*continued*)

The slope of a horizontal line is 0. The slope of a vertical line is undefined. Parallel lines have the same slope.	The slope of $y = -2$ is 0. The slope of $x = 5$ is undefined. 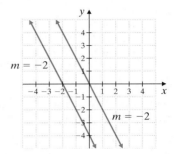
If the product of the slopes of two nonvertical lines is -1, then the lines are perpendicular.	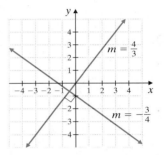

Section 3.3   The Slope-Intercept Form

We can use the slope-intercept form to write an equation
   of a line given its slope and *y*-intercept.
	Write an equation of the line with *y*-intercept $(0, -1)$ and
	   slope $\dfrac{2}{3}$.
	
	$$y = mx + b$$
	$$y = \frac{2}{3}x - 1$$

Section 3.4   More Equations of Lines

The **point-slope form** of the equation of a line is
 	
$$y - y_1 = m(x - x_1)$$
 	
where *m* is the slope of the line and (x_1, y_1) is a point on
   the line.
	Find an equation of the line with slope 2 containing the
	   point $(1, -4)$. Write the equation in standard form:
	   $Ax + By = C$.
	
	$$y - y_1 = m(x - x_1)$$
	$$y - (-4) = 2(x - 1)$$
	$$y + 4 = 2x - 2$$
	$$-2x + y = -6 \quad \text{Standard form}$$

DEFINITIONS AND CONCEPTS	**EXAMPLES**

Section 3.5   Graphing Linear Inequalities

If the equal sign in a linear equation in two variables is replaced with an inequality symbol, the result is a **linear inequality in two variables.**	$x \le -5y, \ y \ge 2,$ $3x - 2y > 7, \ x < -5$

GRAPHING A LINEAR INEQUALITY

Step 1. Graph the **boundary line** by graphing the related equation. Draw a solid line if the inequality symbol is $\le$ or $\ge$. Draw a dashed line if the inequality symbol is $<$ or $>$.	Graph: $2x - 4y > 4$ **1.** Graph $2x - 4y = 4$. Draw a dashed line because the inequality symbol is $>$.
Step 2. Choose a **test point** not on the line. Substitute its coordinates into the original inequality.	**2.** Check the test point $(0, 0)$ in the inequality $2x - 4y > 4$. $\quad\quad 2 \cdot 0 - 4 \cdot 0 > 4 \quad$ Let $x = 0$ and $y = 0$. $\quad\quad\quad\quad\quad 0 > 4 \quad$ False
Step 3. If the resulting inequality is true, shade the **half-plane** that contains the test point. If the inequality is not true, shade the half-plane that does not contain the test point.	**3.** The inequality is false, so shade the half-plane that does not contain $(0, 0)$. 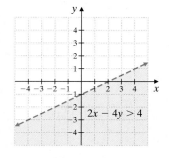

Section 3.6   Introduction to Functions

A **relation** is a set of ordered pairs. The **domain** of the relation is the set of all first components of the ordered pairs. The **range** of the relation is the set of all second components of the ordered pairs.	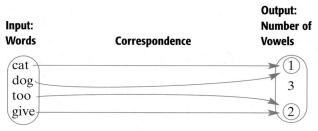 Domain: {cat, dog, too, give} Range: {1, 2}
A **function** is a relation in which each element of the first set corresponds to exactly one element of the second set.	The previous relation is a function. Each word contains one exact number of vowels.

VERTICAL LINE TEST

If no vertical line can be drawn so that it intersects a graph more than once, the graph is the graph of a function. If such a line can be drawn, the graph is not that of a function.	Find the domain and the range of the relation. Also determine whether the relation is a function. 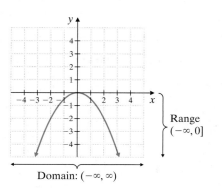 By the vertical line test, this is the graph of a function.

DEFINITIONS AND CONCEPTS	**EXAMPLES**

Section 3.6   Introduction to Functions (*continued*)

The symbol $f(x)$ means **function of x** and is called **function notation.**

A **linear function** is a function that can be written in the form

$$f(x) = mx + b$$

To graph a linear function, use the slope and y-intercept.

If $f(x) = 2x^2 - 5$, find $f(-3)$.

$$f(-3) = 2(-3)^2 - 5 = 2(9) - 5 = 13$$

$$f(x) = -3, g(x) = 5x, h(x) = -\frac{1}{3}x - 7$$

Graph: $f(x) = -2x$
(or $y = -2x + 0$)

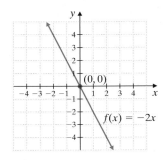

The slope is $\dfrac{2}{-1}$.

The y-intercept is $(0, 0)$.

Section 3.7   Find Domains and Ranges from Graphs and Graphing Piecewise-Defined Functions

To find the domain of a function (or relation) from its graph, recall that on the rectangular coordinate system, "domain" means what x-values are graphed. Similarly, "range" means what y-values are graphed.

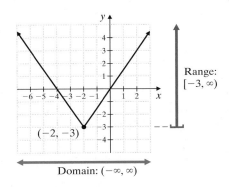

Section 3.8   Shifting and Reflecting Graphs of Functions

Vertical shifts (upward and downward) let k be a positive number.

Graph of	**Same as**	**Moved**
$g(x) = f(x) + k$	$f(x)$	k units upward
$g(x) = f(x) + (-k)$	$f(x)$	k units downward

Horizontal shift (to the left or right) let h be a positive number.

Graph of	**Same as**	**Moved**
$g(x) = f(x - h)$	$f(x)$	h units to the right
$g(x) = f(x + h)$	$f(x)$	h units to the left

Reflection about the x-axis
The graph of $g(x) = -f(x)$ is the graph of $f(x)$ reflected about the x-axis.

The graph of $h(x) = -|x - 3| + 1$ is the same as the graph of $f(x) = |x|$, reflected about the x-axis, shifted 3 units right, then 1 unit up.

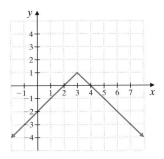

4

Systems of Equations and Inequalities

Taken from:
Intermediate Algebra, Third Edition, by Elayn Martin-Gay
and
Precalculus, Third Edition, by Robert Blitzer

A Determine Whether an Ordered Pair is a Solution of a System of Two Linear Equations.

B Solve a System of Two Equations by Graphing.

C Solve a System Using Substitution.

D Solve a System Using Elimination.

4.1 SOLVING SYSTEMS OF LINEAR EQUATIONS IN TWO VARIABLES

Recall from Chapter 3 that the graph of a linear equation in two variables is a line. Two or more linear equations form a **system of linear equations.** Some examples of systems of linear equations in two variables follow.

$$\begin{cases} x - 2y = -7 \\ 3x + y = 0 \end{cases} \qquad \begin{cases} x = 5 \\ x + \dfrac{y}{2} = 9 \end{cases} \qquad \begin{cases} x - 3 = 2y + 6 \\ y = 1 \end{cases}$$

Objective A Determining Whether an Ordered Pair Is a Solution

Recall that a solution of an equation in two variables is an ordered pair (x, y) that makes the equation true. A **solution of a system** of two equations in two variables is an ordered pair (x, y) that makes both equations true.

PRACTICE PROBLEM 1

Determine whether the ordered pair $(4, 1)$ is a solution of the system.

$$\begin{cases} x - y = 3 \\ 2x - 3y = 5 \end{cases}$$

EXAMPLE 1 Determine whether the ordered pair $(-1, 1)$ is a solution of the system.

$$\begin{cases} -x + y = 2 \\ 2x - y = -3 \end{cases}$$

Solution: We replace x with -1 and y with 1 in each equation.

$$\begin{aligned} -x + y &= 2 \quad &\text{First equation} \\ -(-1) + (1) &\stackrel{?}{=} 2 \quad &\text{Let } x = -1 \text{ and } y = 1. \\ 1 + 1 &\stackrel{?}{=} 2 \\ 2 &= 2 \quad &\text{True} \end{aligned}$$

$$\begin{aligned} 2x - y &= -3 \quad &\text{Second equation} \\ 2(-1) - (1) &\stackrel{?}{=} -3 \quad &\text{Let } x = -1 \text{ and } y = 1. \\ -2 - 1 &\stackrel{?}{=} -3 \\ -3 &= -3 \quad &\text{True} \end{aligned}$$

Since $(-1, 1)$ makes both equations true, it is a solution.

⬛ **Work Practice Problem 1**

PRACTICE PROBLEM 2

Determine whether the ordered pair $(-3, 3)$ is a solution of the system.

$$\begin{cases} 3x - y = -12 \\ x - y = 0 \end{cases}$$

EXAMPLE 2 Determine whether the ordered pair $(-2, 3)$ is a solution of the system.

$$\begin{cases} 5x + 3y = -1 \\ x - y = 1 \end{cases}$$

Solution: We replace x with -2 and y with 3 in each equation.

$$\begin{aligned} 5x + 3y &= -1 \quad &\text{First equation} \\ 5(-2) + 3(3) &\stackrel{?}{=} -1 \quad &\text{Let } x = -2 \text{ and } y = 3. \\ -10 + 9 &\stackrel{?}{=} -1 \\ -1 &= -1 \quad &\text{True} \end{aligned}$$

Answers

1. yes, a solution, **2.** no, not a solution

$$x - y = 1 \quad \text{Second equation}$$
$$(-2) - (3) \overset{?}{=} 1 \quad \text{Let } x = -2 \text{ and } y = 3.$$
$$-5 = 1 \quad \text{False}$$

Since the ordered pair $(-2, 3)$ does not make both equations true, it is not a solution of the system.

🔲 **Work Practice Problem 2**

Objective B Solving a System by Graphing

The graph of each linear equation in a system is a line. Each point on each line corresponds to an ordered pair solution of its equation. If the lines intersect, the point of intersection lies on both lines and corresponds to an ordered pair solution of both equations. In other words, the point of intersection corresponds to an ordered pair solution of the system. Therefore, we can estimate the solutions of a system by graphing the equations on the same rectangular coordinate system and estimating the coordinates of any points of intersection.

EXAMPLE 3 Solve the system by graphing.

$$\begin{cases} x + y = 2 \\ 3x - y = -2 \end{cases}$$

Solution: First we graph the linear equations on the same rectangular coordinate system. These lines intersect at one point as shown. The coordinates of the point of intersection appear to be $(0, 2)$. We check this estimated solution by replacing x with 0 and y with 2 in *both* equations.

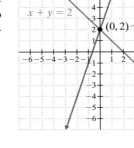

$$x + y = 2 \quad \text{First equation}$$
$$0 + 2 \overset{?}{=} 2 \quad \text{Let } x = 0 \text{ and } y = 2.$$
$$2 = 2 \quad \text{True}$$

$$3x - y = -2 \quad \text{Second equation}$$
$$3(0) - 2 \overset{?}{=} -2 \quad \text{Let } x = 0 \text{ and } y = 2.$$
$$-2 = -2 \quad \text{True}$$

The ordered pair $(0, 2)$ is the solution of the system. A system that has at least one solution, such as this one, is said to be **consistent.**

🔲 **Work Practice Problem 3**

EXAMPLE 4 Solve the system by graphing.

$$\begin{cases} x - 2y = 4 \\ x = 2y \end{cases}$$

Solution: We graph each linear equation.

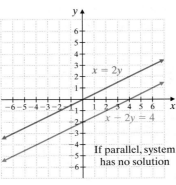

Continued on next page

PRACTICE PROBLEMS 3–4

Solve each system by graphing. If the system has just one solution, estimate the solution.

3. $\begin{cases} x - y = 2 \\ x + 3y = 6 \end{cases}$

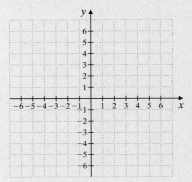

4. $\begin{cases} y = -3x \\ 6x + 2y = 4 \end{cases}$

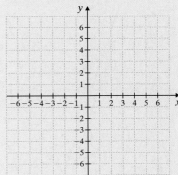

Answers

3. $(3, 1)$,

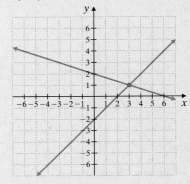

4. See page 226.

The lines appear to be parallel. To be sure, let's write each equation in slope-intercept form, $y = mx + b$. To do so, we solve for y.

$x - 2y = 4$ First equation $x = 2y$ Second equation

$-2y = -x + 4$ Subtract x from both sides. $\dfrac{1}{2}x = y$ Divide both sides by 2.

$y = \dfrac{1}{2}x - 2$ Divide both sides by -2. $y = \dfrac{1}{2}x$

The graphs of these equations have the same slope, $\dfrac{1}{2}$, but different y-intercepts, so these lines are parallel. Therefore, the system has no solution since the equations have no common solution (there are no intersection points). A system that has no solution is said to be **inconsistent.**

🔲 **Work Practice Problem 4**

> **Helpful Hint**
> - If a system of equations has *at least one solution*, the system is *consistent.*
> - If a system of equations has *no solution*, the system is *inconsistent.*

The pairs of equations in Examples 3 and 4 are called independent because their graphs differ. In Example 5, we see an example of dependent equations.

✔ **Concept Check** How can you tell just by looking at the following system that it has no solution?

$$\begin{cases} y = 3x + 5 \\ y = 3x - 7 \end{cases}$$

EXAMPLE 5 Solve the system by graphing.

$$\begin{cases} 2x + 4y = 10 \\ x + 2y = 5 \end{cases}$$

Solution: We graph each linear equation. We see that the graphs of the equations are the same line. To confirm this, notice that if both sides of the second equation are multiplied by 2, the result is the first equation. This means that the equations have identical solutions. Any ordered pair solution of one equation satisfies the other equation also. These equations are said to be **dependent equations.** The solution set of the system is $\{(x, y) \mid x + 2y = 5\}$ or, equivalently, $\{(x, y) \mid 2x + 4y = 10\}$ since the lines describe identical ordered pairs. Written the second way, the solution set is read "the set of all ordered pairs (x, y), such that $2x + 4y = 10$." There are an infinite number of solutions to this system.

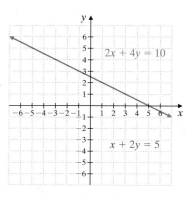

🔲 **Work Practice Problem 5**

> **Helpful Hint**
> - If the graphs of two equations *differ,* they are *independent* equations.
> - If the graphs of two equations are the *same,* they are *dependent* equations.

PRACTICE PROBLEM 5

Solve the system by graphing.

$$\begin{cases} -2x + y = 1 \\ 4x - 2y = -2 \end{cases}$$

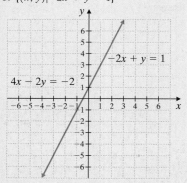

Answers

4. no solution, or $\varnothing$

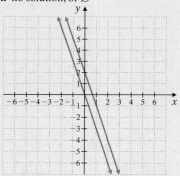

5. $\{(x, y) \mid -2x + y = 1\}$

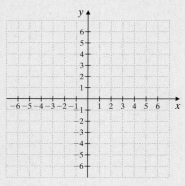

✔ **Concept Check Answer**

answers may vary

✔**Concept Check** How can you tell just by looking at the following system that it has infinitely many solutions?

$$\begin{cases} x + y = 5 \\ 2x + 2y = 10 \end{cases}$$

We can summarize the information discovered in Examples 3 through 5 as follows.

Possible Solutions to Systems of Two Linear Equations

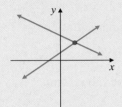

One solution:
consistent system;
independent equations

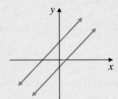

No solution:
inconsistent system;
independent equations

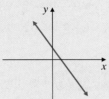

Infinite number
of solutions:
consistent system;
dependent equations

Objective C Solving a System Using Substitution

Graphing the equations of a system by hand is often a good method for finding approximate solutions of a system, but it is not a reliable method for finding exact solutions. To find an exact solution, we need to use *algebra.* One *algebraic* method is called the **substitution method.**

EXAMPLE 6 Use the substitution method to solve the system:

$$\begin{cases} 2x + 4y = -6 & \text{First equation} \\ x = 2y - 5 & \text{Second equation} \end{cases}$$

Solution: In the second equation, we are told that x is equal to $2y - 5$. Since they are equal, we can *substitute* $2y - 5$ for x in the first equation. This will give us an equation in one variable, which we can solve for y.

$$2x + 4y = -6 \qquad \text{First equation}$$

$$2(\overset{\downarrow}{2y - 5}) + 4y = -6 \qquad \text{Substitute } 2y - 5 \text{ for } x.$$

$$4y - 10 + 4y = -6$$

$$8y = 4$$

$$y = \frac{4}{8} = \frac{1}{2} \qquad \text{Solve for } y.$$

The y-coordinate of the solution is $\frac{1}{2}$. To find the x-coordinate, we replace y with $\frac{1}{2}$ in the second equation,

$$x = 2y - 5$$
$$x = 2y - 5$$
$$x = 2\left(\frac{1}{2}\right) - 5 = 1 - 5 = -4$$

The ordered pair solution is $\left(-4, \frac{1}{2}\right)$. Check to see that $\left(-4, \frac{1}{2}\right)$ satisfies both equations of the system.

▨ **Work Practice Problem 6**

PRACTICE PROBLEM 6

Use the substitution method to solve the system:

$$\begin{cases} 6x - 4y = 10 \\ y = 3x - 3 \end{cases}$$

Answer

6. $\left(\frac{1}{3}, -2\right)$

✔ **Concept Check Answer**

answers may vary

228

The substitution method is summarized below. Feel free to use these steps.

Solving a System of Two Equations Using the Substitution Method

Step 1: Solve one of the equations for one of its variables.

Step 2: Substitute the expression for the variable found in Step 1 into the other equation.

Step 3: Find the value of one variable by solving the equation from Step 2.

Step 4: Find the value of the other variable by substituting the value found in Step 3 into the equation from Step 1.

Step 5: Check the ordered pair solution in *both* original equations.

PRACTICE PROBLEM 7

Use the substitution method to solve the system:

$$\begin{cases} -\dfrac{x}{2} + \dfrac{y}{4} = \dfrac{1}{2} \\ \dfrac{x}{2} + \dfrac{y}{2} = -\dfrac{1}{8} \end{cases}$$

EXAMPLE 7 Use the substitution method to solve the system:

$$\begin{cases} -\dfrac{x}{6} + \dfrac{y}{2} = \dfrac{1}{2} \\ \dfrac{x}{3} - \dfrac{y}{6} = -\dfrac{3}{4} \end{cases}$$

Solution: First we multiply each equation by its least common denominator to clear the system of fractions. We multiply the first equation by 6 and the second equation by 12.

$$\begin{cases} 6\left(-\dfrac{x}{6} + \dfrac{y}{2}\right) = 6\left(\dfrac{1}{2}\right) \\ 12\left(\dfrac{x}{3} - \dfrac{y}{6}\right) = 12\left(-\dfrac{3}{4}\right) \end{cases} \quad \text{simplifies to} \quad \begin{cases} -x + 3y = 3 & \text{First equation} \\ 4x - 2y = -9 & \text{Second equation} \end{cases}$$

We now solve the first equation for x so that we may substitute our findings into the second equation.

$$-x + 3y = 3 \quad \text{First equation}$$
$$3y - 3 = x \quad \text{Solve for } x.$$

Next we replace x with $3y - 3$ in the second equation.

$$4x - 2y = -9 \quad \text{Second equation}$$
$$4(3y - 3) - 2y = -9$$
$$12y - 12 - 2y = -9$$
$$10y = 3$$
$$y = \dfrac{3}{10} \quad \text{Solve for } y.$$

Helpful Hint
To avoid tedious fractions, solve for a variable whose coefficient is 1 or −1, if possible.

The y-coordinate is $\dfrac{3}{10}$. To find the x-coordinate, we replace y with $\dfrac{3}{10}$ in the equation $x = 3y - 3$. Then

$$x = 3\left(\dfrac{3}{10}\right) - 3 = \dfrac{9}{10} - 3 = \dfrac{9}{10} - \dfrac{30}{10} = -\dfrac{21}{10}$$

Answer

7. $\left(-\dfrac{3}{4}, \dfrac{1}{2}\right)$

The ordered pair solution is $\left(-\dfrac{21}{10}, \dfrac{3}{10}\right)$. Check to see that this solution satisfies both original equations.

◼ **Work Practice Problem 7**

Helpful Hint

If a system of equations contains equations with fractions, the first step is to clear the equations of fractions.

Objective D Solving a System Using Elimination

The **elimination method,** or **addition method,** is a second algebraic technique for solving systems of equations. For this method, we rely on a version of the addition property of equality, which states that "equals added to equals are equal."

If $A = B$ and $C = D$ then $A + C = B + D$

EXAMPLE 8 Use the elimination method to solve the system:

$$\begin{cases} x - 5y = -12 & \text{First equation} \\ -x + y = 4 & \text{Second equation} \end{cases}$$

Solution: Since the left side of each equation is equal to the right side, we add equal quantities by adding the left sides of the equations and the right sides of the equations. This sum gives us an equation in one variable, y, which we can solve for y.

$$\begin{array}{ll} x - 5y = -12 & \text{First equation} \\ \underline{-x + y = 4} & \text{Second equation} \\ -4y = -8 & \text{Add.} \\ y = 2 & \text{Solve for } y. \end{array}$$

The y-coordinate of the solution is 2. To find the corresponding x-coordinate, we replace y with 2 in either original equation of the system. Let's use the second equation.

$$\begin{array}{ll} -x + y = 4 & \text{Second equation} \\ -x + 2 = 4 & \text{Let } y = 2. \\ -x = 2 & \\ x = -2 & \end{array}$$

The ordered pair solution is $(-2, 2)$. Check to see that $(-2, 2)$ satisfies both equations of the system.

Work Practice Problem 8

The steps below summarize the elimination method.

Solving a System of Two Linear Equations Using the Elimination Method

Step 1: Rewrite each equation in standard form, $Ax + By = C$.

Step 2: If necessary, multiply one or both equations by some nonzero number so that the coefficient of one variable in one equation is the opposite of the coefficient of that variable in the other equation.

Step 3: Add the equations. Your chosen variable should be eliminated.

Step 4: Find the value of the remaining variable by solving the equation from Step 3.

Step 5: Find the value of the other variable by substituting the value found in Step 4 into either original equation.

Step 6: Check the proposed ordered pair solution in *both* original equations.

PRACTICE PROBLEM 8

Use the elimination method to solve the system:

$$\begin{cases} 3x - y = 1 \\ 4x + y = 6 \end{cases}$$

Answer

8. $(1, 2)$

PRACTICE PROBLEM 9

Use the elimination method to solve the system:

$$\begin{cases} \dfrac{x}{3} + 2y = -1 \\ x + 6y = 2 \end{cases}$$

EXAMPLE 9 Use the elimination method to solve the system:

$$\begin{cases} 3x + \dfrac{y}{2} = 2 \\ 6x + y = 5 \end{cases}$$

Solution: If we add the two equations, the sum will still be an equation in two variables. Notice, however, that if we multiply both sides of the first equation by -2, the coefficients of x in the two equations will be opposites. Then

$$\begin{cases} -2\left(3x + \dfrac{y}{2}\right) = -2(2) \\ 6x + y = 5 \end{cases} \text{ simplifies to } \begin{cases} -6x - y = -4 \\ 6x + y = 5 \end{cases}$$

Now we can add the left sides and add the right sides.

$$\begin{array}{r} -6x - y = -4 \\ 6x + y = 5 \\ \hline 0 = 1 \quad \text{False} \end{array}$$

The resulting equation, $0 = 1$, is false for all values of y or x. Thus, the system has no solution. The solution set is $\{\ \}$ or $\varnothing$. This system is inconsistent, and the graphs of the equations are parallel lines.

▣ **Work Practice Problem 9**

PRACTICE PROBLEM 10

Use the elimination method to solve the system:

$$\begin{cases} 2x - 5y = 6 \\ 3x - 4y = 9 \end{cases}$$

EXAMPLE 10 Use the elimination method to solve the system:

$$\begin{cases} 3x - 2y = 10 \\ 4x - 3y = 15 \end{cases}$$

Solution: To eliminate y, our first step is to multiply both sides of the first equation by 3 and both sides of the second equation by -2. Then

$$\begin{cases} 3(3x - 2y) = 3(10) \\ -2(4x - 3y) = -2(15) \end{cases} \text{ simplifies to } \begin{cases} 9x - 6y = 30 \\ -8x + 6y = -30 \end{cases}$$

Next we add the left sides and add the right sides.

$$\begin{array}{r} 9x - 6y = 30 \\ -8x + 6y = -30 \\ \hline x = 0 \end{array}$$

To find y, we let $x = 0$ in either equation of the system

$$\begin{aligned} 3x - 2y &= 10 \quad \text{First equation} \\ 3(0) - 2y &= 10 \quad \text{Let } x = 0. \\ -2y &= 10 \\ y &= -5 \end{aligned}$$

The ordered pair solution is $(0, -5)$. Check to see that $(0, -5)$ satisfies both equations.

▣ **Work Practice Problem 10**

Answers
9. no solution or $\varnothing$, **10.** $(3, 0)$

EXAMPLE 11 Use the elimination method to solve the system:

$$\begin{cases} -5x - 3y = 9 \\ 10x + 6y = -18 \end{cases}$$

Solution: To eliminate x, our first step is to multiply both sides of the first equation by 2. Then

$$\begin{cases} 2(-5x - 3y) = 2(9) \\ 10x + 6y = -18 \end{cases} \quad \text{simplifies to} \quad \begin{cases} -10x - 6y = 18 \\ 10x + 6y = -18 \end{cases}$$

Next we add the equations.

$$\begin{array}{r} -10x - 6y = 18 \\ \underline{10x + 6y = -18} \\ 0 = 0 \end{array}$$

The resulting equation, $0 = 0$, is true for all possible values of y or x. Notice in the original system that if both sides of the first equation are multiplied by -2, the result is the second equation. This means that the two equations are equivalent. They have the same solution set and there are an infinite number of solutions. Thus, the equations of this system are dependent, and the solution set of the system is

$$\{(x, y) \mid -5x - 3y = 9\} \quad \text{or, equivalently,} \quad \{(x, y) \mid 10x + 6y = -18\}$$

☐ **Work Practice Problem 11**

Helpful Hint

Remember that not all ordered pairs are solutions of the system in Example 11. Only the infinite number of ordered pairs that satisfy $-5x - 3y = 9$ or, equivalently, $10x + 6y = -18$.

PRACTICE PROBLEM 11

Use the elimination method to solve the system:

$$\begin{cases} 4x - 7y = 10 \\ -8x + 14y = -20 \end{cases}$$

Answer

11. $\{(x, y) \mid 4x - 7y = 10\}$

📟 CALCULATOR EXPLORATIONS Graphing

We may use a grapher to approximate solutions of systems of equations by graphing both equations on the same set of axes and approximating any points of intersection. For example, let's approximate the solution of the system

$$\begin{cases} y = -2.6x + 5.6 \\ y = 4.3x - 4.9 \end{cases}$$

We use a standard window and graph the equations on a single screen.

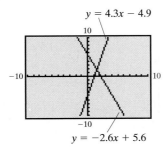

The two lines intersect. To approximate the point of intersection, we trace to the point of intersection and use an INTERSECT feature of the grapher, a ZOOM IN feature of the grapher, or redefine the window to $[0, 3]$ by $[0, 3]$. If we redefine the window to $[0, 3]$ by $[0, 3]$, the screen should look like the following:

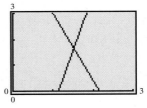

By tracing along the curves, we can see that the point of intersection has an x-value between 1.5 and 1.532. We can continue to zoom and trace or redefine the window until the coordinates of the point of intersection can be determined to the nearest hundredth. The approximate point of intersection is $(1.52, 1.64)$.

Solve each system of equations. Approximate each solution to two decimal places.

1. $y = -1.65x + 3.65$
    $y = 4.56x - 9.44$

2. $y = 7.61x + 3.48$
    $y = -1.26x - 6.43$

3. $2.33x - 4.72y = 10.61$
    $5.86x - 6.22y = -8.89$

4. $-7.89x - 5.68y = 3.26$
    $-3.65x + 4.98y = 11.77$

Mental Math

Match each graph with the solution of the corresponding system.

A
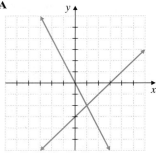

B
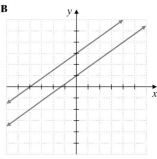

C
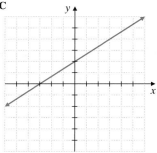

D
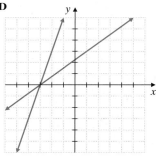

1. No solution

2. Infinite number of solutions

3. $(1, -2)$

4. $(-3, 0)$

4.1 EXERCISE SET

Objective A *Determine whether the given ordered pair is a solution of the system. See Examples 1 and 2.*

1. $\begin{cases} x - y = 3 \\ 2x - 4y = 8 \end{cases}$ $(2, -1)$

2. $\begin{cases} x - y = -4 \\ 2x + 10y = 4 \end{cases}$ $(-3, 1)$

3. $\begin{cases} 2x - 3y = -9 \\ 4x + 2y = -2 \end{cases}$ $(3, 5)$

4. $\begin{cases} 2x - 5y = -2 \\ 3x + 4y = 4 \end{cases}$ $(4, 2)$

5. $\begin{cases} y = -5x \\ x = -2 \end{cases}$ $(-2, 10)$

6. $\begin{cases} y = 6 \\ x = -2y \end{cases}$ $(-12, 6)$

7. $\begin{cases} 3x + 7y = -19 \\ -6x = 5y + 8 \end{cases}$ $\left(\dfrac{2}{3}, -3\right)$

8. $\begin{cases} 4x + 5y = -7 \\ -8x = 3y - 1 \end{cases}$ $\left(\dfrac{3}{4}, -2\right)$

Objective B *Solve each system by graphing. See Examples 3 through 5.*

9. $\begin{cases} x + y = 1 \\ x - 2y = 4 \end{cases}$

10. $\begin{cases} 2x - y = 8 \\ x + 3y = 11 \end{cases}$

 11. $\begin{cases} 2y - 4 = 0 \\ x + 2y = 5 \end{cases}$

12. $\begin{cases} 4x - y = 6 \\ x - y = 0 \end{cases}$

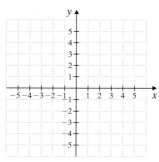

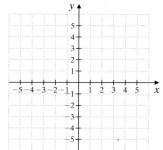

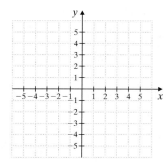

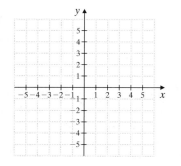

13. $\begin{cases} 3x - y = 4 \\ 6x - 2y = 4 \end{cases}$

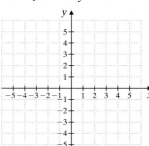

14. $\begin{cases} -x + 3y = 6 \\ 3x - 9y = 9 \end{cases}$

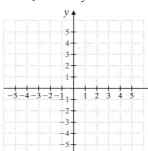

15. $\begin{cases} y = -3x \\ 2x - y = -5 \end{cases}$

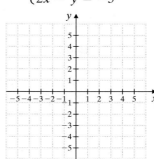

16. $\begin{cases} y = -2x \\ -3x + y = 10 \end{cases}$

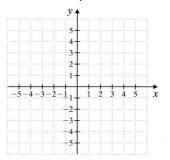

Objective C *Use the substitution method to solve each system of equations. See Examples 6 and 7.*

17. $\begin{cases} x + y = 10 \\ y = 4x \end{cases}$

18. $\begin{cases} 5x + 2y = -17 \\ x = 3y \end{cases}$

19. $\begin{cases} 4x - y = 9 \\ 2x + 3y = -27 \end{cases}$

20. $\begin{cases} 3x - y = 6 \\ -4x + 2y = -8 \end{cases}$

21. $\begin{cases} \dfrac{1}{2}x + \dfrac{3}{4}y = -\dfrac{1}{4} \\ \dfrac{3}{4}x - \dfrac{1}{4}y = 1 \end{cases}$

22. $\begin{cases} \dfrac{2}{5}x + \dfrac{1}{5}y = -1 \\ x + \dfrac{2}{5}y = -\dfrac{8}{5} \end{cases}$

23. $\begin{cases} x = -3y + 4 \\ 3x + 9y = 12 \end{cases}$

24. $\begin{cases} x = 3y - 1 \\ 2x - 6y = -2 \end{cases}$

Objective D *Use the elimination method to solve each system of equations. See Examples 8 through 11.*

25. $\begin{cases} 2x - 4y = 0 \\ x + 2y = 5 \end{cases}$

26. $\begin{cases} 2x - 3y = 0 \\ 2x + 6y = 3 \end{cases}$

27. $\begin{cases} 5x + 2y = 1 \\ x - 3y = 7 \end{cases}$

28. $\begin{cases} 6x - y = -5 \\ 4x - 2y = 6 \end{cases}$

29. $\begin{cases} 5x - 2y = 27 \\ -3x + 5y = 18 \end{cases}$

30. $\begin{cases} 3x + 4y = 2 \\ 2x + 5y = -1 \end{cases}$

31. $\begin{cases} 3x = 5y + 11 \\ 2x = 6y + 2 \end{cases}$

32. $\begin{cases} 6x = 3y - 3 \\ 4x = -5y - 9 \end{cases}$

33. $\begin{cases} x - 2y = 4 \\ 2x - 4y = 4 \end{cases}$

34. $\begin{cases} -x + 3y = 6 \\ 3x - 9y = 9 \end{cases}$

35. $\begin{cases} 3x + y = 1 \\ 2y = 2 - 6x \end{cases}$

36. $\begin{cases} y = 2x - 5 \\ 8x - 4y = 20 \end{cases}$

Objectives C D Mixed Practice *Solve each system of equations.*

37. $\begin{cases} 2x + 5y = 8 \\ 6x + y = 10 \end{cases}$

38. $\begin{cases} x - 4y = -5 \\ -3x - 8y = 0 \end{cases}$

39. $\begin{cases} x + y = 1 \\ x - 2y = 4 \end{cases}$

40. $\begin{cases} 2x - y = 8 \\ x + 3y = 11 \end{cases}$

41. $\begin{cases} \dfrac{1}{3}x + y = \dfrac{4}{3} \\ -\dfrac{1}{4}x - \dfrac{1}{2}y = -\dfrac{1}{4} \end{cases}$

42. $\begin{cases} \dfrac{3}{4}x - \dfrac{1}{2}y = -\dfrac{1}{2} \\ x + y = -\dfrac{3}{2} \end{cases}$

43. $\begin{cases} 4x + 2y = 5 \\ 2x + y = -1 \end{cases}$

44. $\begin{cases} 3x + 6y = 15 \\ 2x + 4y = 3 \end{cases}$

45. $\begin{cases} 10y - 2x = 1 \\ 5y = 4 - 6x \end{cases}$

46. $\begin{cases} 3x + 4y = 0 \\ 7x = 3y \end{cases}$

47. $\begin{cases} \dfrac{3}{4}x + \dfrac{5}{2}y = 11 \\ \dfrac{1}{16}x - \dfrac{3}{4}y = -1 \end{cases}$

48. $\begin{cases} \dfrac{2}{3}x + \dfrac{1}{4}y = -\dfrac{3}{2} \\ \dfrac{1}{2}x - \dfrac{1}{4}y = -2 \end{cases}$

49. $\begin{cases} x = 3y + 2 \\ 5x - 15y = 10 \end{cases}$

50. $\begin{cases} x = 7y - 21 \\ 2x - 14y = -42 \end{cases}$

51. $\begin{cases} \dfrac{x}{3} + y = \dfrac{4}{3} \\ -x + 2y = 11 \end{cases}$

52. $\begin{cases} \dfrac{x}{8} - \dfrac{y}{2} = 1 \\ \dfrac{x}{3} - y = 2 \end{cases}$

53. $\begin{cases} 2x = 6 \\ y = 5 - x \end{cases}$

54. $\begin{cases} x = 3y + 4 \\ -y = 5 \end{cases}$

55. $\begin{cases} \dfrac{x + 5}{2} = \dfrac{6 - 4y}{3} \\ \dfrac{3x}{5} = \dfrac{21 - 7y}{10} \end{cases}$

56. $\begin{cases} \dfrac{y}{5} = \dfrac{8 - x}{2} \\ x = \dfrac{2y - 8}{3} \end{cases}$

57. $\begin{cases} 4x - 7y = 7 \\ 12x - 21y = 24 \end{cases}$

58. $\begin{cases} 2x - 5y = 12 \\ -4x + 10y = 20 \end{cases}$

59. $\begin{cases} \dfrac{2}{3}x - \dfrac{3}{4}y = -1 \\ -\dfrac{1}{6}x + \dfrac{3}{8}y = 1 \end{cases}$

60. $\begin{cases} \dfrac{1}{2}x - \dfrac{1}{3}y = -3 \\ \dfrac{1}{8}x + \dfrac{1}{6}y = 0 \end{cases}$

61. $\begin{cases} 2x - y = -1 \\ y = -2x \end{cases}$

62. $\begin{cases} 4y - x = -1 \\ x = -2y \end{cases}$

63. $\begin{cases} 0.7x - 0.2y = -1.6 \\ 0.2x - y = -1.4 \end{cases}$

64. $\begin{cases} -0.7x + 0.6y = 1.3 \\ 0.5x - 0.3y = -0.8 \end{cases}$

65. $\begin{cases} 4x - 1.5y = 10.2 \\ 2x + 7.8y = -25.68 \end{cases}$

66. $\begin{cases} x - 3y = -5.3 \\ 6.3x + 6y = 3.96 \end{cases}$

Review

Determine whether the given replacement values make each equation true or false. See Section 2.1.

67. $3x - 4y + 2z = 5$;
$x = 1, y = 2$, and $z = 5$

68. $x + 2y - z = 7$;
$x = 2, y = -3$, and $z = 3$

69. $-x - 5y + 3z = 15$;
$x = 0, y = -1$, and $z = 5$

70. $-4x + y - 8z = 4$;
$x = 1, y = 0$, and $z = -1$

Add the equations. See this section.

71. $\begin{cases} 3x + 2y - 5z = 10 \\ -3x + 4y + z = 15 \end{cases}$

72. $\begin{cases} x + 4y - 5z = 20 \\ 2x - 4y - 2z = -17 \end{cases}$

73. $\begin{cases} 10x + 5y + 6z = 14 \\ -9x + 5y - 6z = -12 \end{cases}$

74. $\begin{cases} -9x - 8y - z = 31 \\ 9x + 4y - z = 12 \end{cases}$

Concept Extensions

Without graphing, determine whether each system has one solution, no solution, or an infinite number of solutions. See the Concept Checks in this section.

75. $\begin{cases} y = 2x - 5 \\ y = 2x + 1 \end{cases}$

76. $\begin{cases} y = 3x - \dfrac{1}{2} \\ y = -2x + \dfrac{1}{5} \end{cases}$

77. $\begin{cases} x + y = 3 \\ 5x + 5y = 15 \end{cases}$

78. $\begin{cases} y = 5x - 2 \\ y = -\dfrac{1}{5}x - 2 \end{cases}$

79. Can a system consisting of two linear equations have exactly two solutions? Explain why or why not.

80. Suppose the graph of the equations in a system of two equations in two variables consists of a circle and a line. Discuss the possible number of solutions for this system.

The concept of supply and demand is used often in business. In general, as the unit price of a commodity increases, the demand for that commodity decreases. Also, as a commodity's unit price increases, the manufacturer normally increases the supply. The point where supply is equal to demand is called the equilibrium point. The following shows the graph of a demand equation and the graph of a supply equation for previously rented DVDs. The x-axis represents the number of DVDs in thousands, and the y-axis represents the cost of a DVD. Use this graph to answer Exercises 81 through 84.

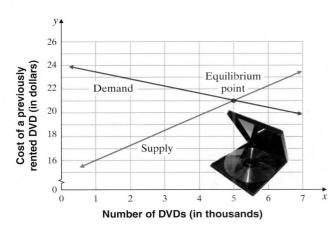

Number of DVDs (in thousands)

81. Find the number of DVDs and the price per DVD when supply equals demand.

82. When x is between 3 and 4, is supply greater than demand or is demand greater than supply?

83. When x is greater than 6, is supply greater than demand or is demand greater than supply?

84. For what x-values are the y-values corresponding to the supply equation greater than the y-values corresponding to the demand equation?

The revenue equation for a certain brand of toothpaste is $y = 2.5x$, where x is the number of tubes of toothpaste sold and y is the total income for selling x tubes. The cost equation is $y = 0.9x + 3000$, where x is the number of tubes of toothpaste manufactured and y is the cost of producing x tubes. The following set of axes shows the graph of the cost and revenue equations. Use this graph for Exercises 85 through 90.

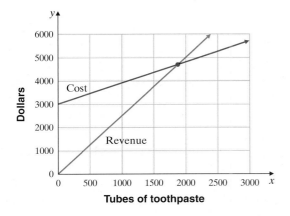

Tubes of toothpaste

85. Find the coordinates of the point of intersection, or break-even point, by solving the system
$$\begin{cases} y = 2.5x \\ y = 0.9x + 3000 \end{cases}$$

86. Explain the meaning of the y-value of the point of intersection.

87. If the company sells 2000 tubes of toothpaste, does the company make money or lose money?

88. If the company sells 1000 tubes of toothpaste, does the company make money or lose money?

89. For what x-values will the company make a profit? (*Hint:* For what x-values is the revenue graph "higher" than the cost graph?)

90. For what x-values will the company lose money? (*Hint:* For what x-values is the revenue graph "lower" than the cost graph?)

91. Write a system of two linear equations in x and y that has the ordered pair solution $(2, 5)$.

92. Which method would you use to solve the system?
$$\begin{cases} 5x - 2y = 6 \\ 2x + 3y = 5 \end{cases}$$
Explain your choice.

93. The amount y of red meat consumed per person in the United States (in pounds) in the year x can be modeled by the linear equation $y = -0.56x + 114$. The amount y of all poultry consumed per person in the United States (in pounds) in the year x can be modeled by the linear equation $y = 0.98x + 67$. In both models, $x = 0$ represents the year 1997. (*Source:* Based on data and forecasts from the Economic Research Service, U.S. Department of Agriculture)

 a. What does the slope of each equation tell you about the patterns of red meat and poultry consumption in the United States?

  b. Solve this system of equations. (Round your final results to the nearest whole numbers.)

  c. Explain the meaning of your answer to part (b).

94. The amount of U.S. federal government income y (in billions of dollars) for the fiscal year x, from 2000 through 2004 ($x = 0$ represents 2000), can be modeled by the linear equation $y = -48.2x + 2025.4$. The amount of U.S. federal government expenditures y (in billions of dollars) for the same period can be modeled by the linear equation $y = 99x + 2165.5$. Did expenses ever equal income during this period? If so, in what year? (*Source:* Based on data from Financial Management Service, U.S. Department of the Treasury, 1995–2000)

Solve each system. To do so you may want to let $a = \dfrac{1}{x}$ (if x is in the denominator) and let $b = \dfrac{1}{y}$ (if y is in the denominator.)

95. $\begin{cases} \dfrac{1}{x} + y = 12 \\ \dfrac{3}{x} - y = 4 \end{cases}$

96. $\begin{cases} x + \dfrac{2}{y} = 7 \\ 3x + \dfrac{3}{y} = 6 \end{cases}$

97. $\begin{cases} \dfrac{1}{x} + \dfrac{1}{y} = 5 \\ \dfrac{1}{x} - \dfrac{1}{y} = 1 \end{cases}$

98. $\begin{cases} \dfrac{2}{x} + \dfrac{3}{y} = 5 \\ \dfrac{5}{x} - \dfrac{3}{y} = 2 \end{cases}$

99. $\begin{cases} \dfrac{2}{x} + \dfrac{3}{y} = -1 \\ \dfrac{3}{x} - \dfrac{2}{y} = 18 \end{cases}$

100. $\begin{cases} \dfrac{3}{x} - \dfrac{2}{y} = -18 \\ \dfrac{2}{x} + \dfrac{3}{y} = 1 \end{cases}$

101. $\begin{cases} \dfrac{2}{x} - \dfrac{4}{y} = 5 \\ \dfrac{1}{x} - \dfrac{2}{y} = \dfrac{3}{2} \end{cases}$

102. $\begin{cases} \dfrac{5}{x} + \dfrac{7}{y} = 1 \\ -\dfrac{10}{x} - \dfrac{14}{y} = 0 \end{cases}$

STUDY SKILLS BUILDER

Are You Getting All the Mathematics Help That You Need?

Remember that, in addition to your instructor, there are many places to get help with your mathematics course. For example,

- This text has an accompanying video lesson for every section and worked out solutions to every Chapter Test exercise on video.

- The back of the book contains answers to odd-numbered exercises and selected solutions.

- A student *Solutions Manual* is available that contains worked-out solutions to odd-numbered exercises as well as solutions to every exercise in the Integrated Reviews, Chapter Reviews, Chapter Tests, and Cumulative Reviews.

- Don't forget to check with your instructor for other local resources available to you, such as a tutor center.

Exercises

1. List items you find helpful in the text and all student supplements to this text.

2. List all the campus help that is available to you for this course.

3. List any help (besides the textbook) from Exercises 1 and 2 above that you are using.

4. List any help (besides the textbook) that you feel you should try.

5. Write a goal for yourself that includes trying anything you listed in Exercise 4 during the next week.

4.2 SOLVING SYSTEMS OF LINEAR EQUATIONS IN THREE VARIABLES

Objective

A Solve a System of Three Linear Equations in Three Variables.

In this section, we solve systems of linear equations in three variables. We call the equation $3x - y + z = -15$, for example, a **linear equation in three variables** since there are three variables and each variable is raised only to the power 1. A solution of this equation is an **ordered triple (x, y, z)** that makes the equation a true statement.

For example, the ordered triple $(2, 0, -21)$ is a solution of $3x - y + z = -15$ since replacing x with 2, y with 0, and z with -21 yields the true statement

$$3(2) - 0 + (-21) = -15$$

The graph of this equation is a plane in three-dimensional space, just as the graph of a linear equation in two variables is a line in two-dimensional space.

Although we will not discuss the techniques for graphing equations in three variables, visualizing the possible patterns of intersecting planes gives us insight into the possible patterns of solutions of a system of three three-variable linear equations. There are four possible patterns.

1. Three planes have a single point in common. This point represents the single solution of the system. This system is **consistent.**

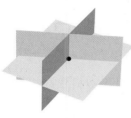

2. Three planes intersect at no point common to all three. This system has no solution. A few ways that this can occur are shown. This system is **inconsistent.**

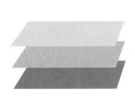  

3. Three planes intersect at all the points of a single line. The system has infinitely many solutions. This system is **consistent.**

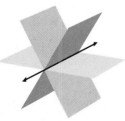

4. Three planes coincide at all points on the plane. The system is **consistent,** and the equations are **dependent.**

Objective Ⓐ Solving a System of Three Linear Equations in Three Variables

Just as with systems of two equations in two variables, we can use the elimination or substitution method to solve a system of three equations in three variables. To use the elimination method, we eliminate a variable and obtain a system of two equations in two variables. Then we use the methods we learned in the previous section to solve the system of two equations.

PRACTICE PROBLEM 1

Solve the system:

$$\begin{cases} 2x - y + 3z = 13 \\ x + y - z = -2 \\ 3x + 2y + 2z = 13 \end{cases}$$

Helpful Hint

Make sure you add two other equations besides equations (1) and (2) and *also* **eliminate the same variable.** You will see why as you follow this example.

EXAMPLE 1 Solve the system:

$$\begin{cases} 3x - y + z = -15 & \text{Equation (1)} \\ x + 2y - z = 1 & \text{Equation (2)} \\ 2x + 3y - 2z = 0 & \text{Equation (3)} \end{cases}$$

Solution: Let's add equations (1) and (2) to eliminate z.

$$\begin{array}{r} 3x - y + z = -15 \\ x + 2y - z = 1 \\ \hline 4x + y = -14 \end{array} \quad \text{Equation (4)}$$

Next we add two *other* equations and *eliminate z again*. To do so, we multiply both sides of equation (1) by 2 and add the resulting equation to equation (3). Then

$$\begin{cases} 2(3x - y + z) = 2(-15) \\ 2x + 3y - 2z = 0 \end{cases} \quad \text{simplifies to} \quad \begin{array}{r} 6x - 2y + 2z = -30 \\ 2x + 3y - 2z = 0 \\ \hline 8x + y = -30 \end{array}$$

$$\text{Equation (5)}$$

We now have two equations (4 and 5) in the same two variables. This means we can solve equations (4) and (5) for x and y. To solve by elimination, we multiply both sides of equation (4) by -1 and add the resulting equation to equation (5). Then

$$\begin{cases} -1(4x + y) = -1(-14) \\ 8x + y = -30 \end{cases} \quad \text{simplifies to} \quad \begin{array}{r} -4x - y = 14 \\ 8x + y = -30 \\ \hline 4x = -16 \\ x = -4 \end{array}$$

Add the equations.
Solve for x.

We now replace x with -4 in equation (4) or (5).

$$\begin{aligned} 4x + y &= -14 \quad \text{Equation (4)} \\ 4(-4) + y &= -14 \quad \text{Let } x = -4. \\ y &= 2 \quad \text{Solve for } y. \end{aligned}$$

Finally, we replace x with -4 and y with 2 in equation (1), (2), or (3).

$$\begin{aligned} x + 2y - z &= 1 \quad \text{Equation (2)} \\ -4 + 2(2) - z &= 1 \quad \text{Let } x = -4 \text{ and } y = 2. \\ -4 + 4 - z &= 1 \\ -z &= 1 \\ z &= -1 \end{aligned}$$

The ordered triple solution is $(-4, 2, -1)$. To check, we let $x = -4$, $y = 2$, and $z = -1$ in *all three* original equations of the system.

Equation (1)

$$\begin{aligned} 3x - y + z &= -15 \\ 3(-4) - 2 + (-1) &\stackrel{?}{=} -15 \\ -12 - 2 - 1 &\stackrel{?}{=} -15 \\ -15 &= -15 \quad \text{True} \end{aligned}$$

Equation (2)

$$\begin{aligned} x + 2y - z &= 1 \\ -4 + 2(2) - (-1) &\stackrel{?}{=} 1 \\ -4 + 4 + 1 &\stackrel{?}{=} 1 \\ 1 &= 1 \quad \text{True} \end{aligned}$$

Answer

1. $(1, 1, 4)$

Equation (3)

$$2x + 3y - 2z = 0$$
$$2(-4) + 3(2) - 2(-1) \overset{?}{=} 0$$
$$-8 + 6 + 2 \overset{?}{=} 0$$
$$0 = 0 \quad \text{True}$$

All three statements are true, so the ordered triple solution is $(-4, 2, -1)$.

▣ **Work Practice Problem 1**

EXAMPLE 2 Solve the system:

$$\begin{cases} 2x - 4y + 8z = 2 & (1) \\ -x - 3y + z = 11 & (2) \\ x - 2y + 4z = 0 & (3) \end{cases}$$

Solution: Add equations (2) and (3) to eliminate x, and the new equation is

$$-5y + 5z = 11 \quad (4)$$

To eliminate x again, we multiply both sides of equation (2) by 2 and add the resulting equation to equation (1). Then

$$\begin{cases} 2x - 4y + 8z = 2 \\ 2(-x - 3y + z) = 2(11) \end{cases} \text{ simplifies to } \begin{cases} 2x - 4y + 8z = 2 \\ \underline{-2x - 6y + 2z = 22} \\ \quad -10y + 10z = 24 \quad (5) \end{cases}$$

Next we solve for y and z using equations (4) and (5). To do so, we multiply both sides of equation (4) by -2 and add the resulting equation to equation (5).

$$\begin{cases} -2(-5y + 5z) = -2(11) \\ -10y + 10z = 24 \end{cases} \text{ simplifies to } \begin{cases} 10y - 10z = -22 \\ \underline{-10y + 10z = 24} \\ \quad\quad 0 = 2 \quad \text{False} \end{cases}$$

Since the statement is false, this system is inconsistent and has no solution. The solution set is the empty set { } or $\varnothing$.

▣ **Work Practice Problem 2**

The elimination method is summarized next.

Solving a System of Three Linear Equations by the Elimination Method

Step 1: Write each equation in standard form, $Ax + By + Cz = D$.

Step 2: Choose a pair of equations and use them to eliminate a variable.

Step 3: Choose any other pair of equations and eliminate the *same variable* as in Step 2.

Step 4: Two equations in two variables should be obtained from Step 2 and Step 3. Use methods from Section 4.1 to solve this system for both variables.

Step 5: To solve for the third variable, substitute the values of the variables found in Step 4 into any of the original equations containing the third variable.

Step 6: Check the ordered triple solution in *all three* original equations.

PRACTICE PROBLEM 2

Solve the system:

$$\begin{cases} 2x + 4y - 2z = 3 \\ -x + y - z = 6 \\ x + 2y - z = 1 \end{cases}$$

Helpful Hint

Make sure you read closely and follow Step 3.

Answer

2. $\varnothing$

✔ **Concept Check** In the system

$$\begin{cases} x + y + z = 6 & \text{Equation (1)} \\ 2x - y + z = 3 & \text{Equation (2)} \\ x + 2y + 3z = 14 & \text{Equation (3)} \end{cases}$$

equations (1) and (2) are used to eliminate y. Which action could be used to finish solving? Why?

a. Use (1) and (2) to eliminate z.

b. Use (2) and (3) to eliminate y.

c. Use (1) and (3) to eliminate x.

PRACTICE PROBLEM 3

Solve the system:

$$\begin{cases} 3x + 2y \quad = -1 \\ 6x \quad - 2z = 4 \\ y - 3z = 2 \end{cases}$$

EXAMPLE 3 Solve the system:

$$\begin{cases} 2x + 4y \quad = 1 & (1) \\ 4x \quad - 4z = -1 & (2) \\ y - 4z = -3 & (3) \end{cases}$$

Solution: Notice that equation (2) has no term containing the variable y. Let's eliminate y using equations (1) and (3). We multiply both sides of equation (3) by -4 and add the resulting equation to equation (1). Then

$$\begin{cases} 2x + 4y \quad = 1 \\ -4(y - 4z) = -4(-3) \end{cases} \text{ simplifies to } \begin{cases} 2x + 4y \quad = 1 \\ \underline{\quad -4y + 16z = 12} \\ 2x \quad + 16z = 13 \quad (4) \end{cases}$$

Next we solve for z using equations (4) and (2). We multiply both sides of equation (4) by -2 and add the resulting equation to equation (2).

$$\begin{cases} -2(2x + 16z) = -2(13) \\ 4x - 4z = -1 \end{cases} \text{ simplifies to } \begin{cases} -4x - 32z = -26 \\ \underline{\quad 4x - 4z = -1} \\ -36z = -27 \\ z = \dfrac{3}{4} \end{cases}$$

Now we replace z with $\dfrac{3}{4}$ in equation (3) and solve for y.

$$y - 4\left(\dfrac{3}{4}\right) = -3 \quad \text{Let } z = \dfrac{3}{4} \text{ in equation (3).}$$
$$y - 3 = -3$$
$$y = 0$$

Finally, we replace y with 0 in equation (1) and solve for x.

$$2x + 4(0) = 1 \quad \text{Let } y = 0 \text{ in equation (1).}$$
$$2x = 1$$
$$x = \dfrac{1}{2}$$

The ordered triple solution is $\left(\dfrac{1}{2}, 0, \dfrac{3}{4}\right)$. Check to see that this solution satisfies *all three* equations of the system.

⬛ **Work Practice Problem 3**

Answer

3. $\left(\dfrac{1}{3}, -1, -1\right)$

✔ **Concept Check Answer**

b; answers may vary

EXAMPLE 4 Solve the system:

$$\begin{cases} x - 5y - 2z = 6 & (1) \\ -2x + 10y + 4z = -12 & (2) \\ \dfrac{1}{2}x - \dfrac{5}{2}y - z = 3 & (3) \end{cases}$$

Solution: We multiply both sides of equation (3) by 2 to eliminate fractions, and we multiply both sides of equation (2) by $-\dfrac{1}{2}$ so that the coefficient of x is 1. The resulting system is then

$$\begin{cases} x - 5y - 2z = 6 & (1) \\ x - 5y - 2z = 6 & \text{Multiply (2) by } -\frac{1}{2}. \\ x - 5y - 2z = 6 & \text{Multiply (3) by 2.} \end{cases}$$

All three resulting equations are identical, and therefore equations (1), (2), and (3) are all equivalent. There are infinitely many solutions of this system. The equations are dependent. The solution set can be written as $\{(x, y, z) \mid x - 5y - 2z = 6\}$.

■ **Work Practice Problem 4**

As mentioned earlier, we can also use the substitution method to solve a system of linear equations in three variables.

EXAMPLE 5 Solve the system:

$$\begin{cases} x - 4y - 5z = 35 & (1) \\ x - 3y = 0 & (2) \\ -y + z = -55 & (3) \end{cases}$$

Solution: Notice in equations (2) and (3) that a variable is missing. Also notice that both equations contain the variable y. Let's use the substitution method by solving equation (2) for x and equation (3) for z and substituting the results in equation (1).

$$x - 3y = 0 \qquad (2)$$
$$x = 3y \qquad \text{Solve equation (2) for } x.$$
$$-y + z = -55 \qquad (3)$$
$$z = y - 55 \qquad \text{Solve equation (3) for } z.$$

Now substitute $3y$ for x and $y - 55$ for z in equation (1).

$$x - 4y - 5z = 35 \qquad (1)$$
$$3y - 4y - 5(y - 55) = 35 \qquad \text{Let } x = 3y \text{ and } z = y - 55.$$
$$3y - 4y - 5y + 275 = 35 \qquad \text{Use the distributive property and multiply.}$$
$$-6y + 275 = 35 \qquad \text{Combine like terms.}$$
$$-6y = -240 \qquad \text{Subtract 275 from both sides.}$$
$$y = 40 \qquad \text{Solve.}$$

To find x, recall that $x = 3y$ and substitute 40 for y. Then $x = 3y$ becomes $x = 3 \cdot 40 = 120$. To find z, recall that $z = y - 55$ and also substitute 40 for y. Then $z = y - 55$ becomes $z = 40 - 55 = -15$. The solution is $(120, 40, -15)$.

■ **Work Practice Problem 5**

PRACTICE PROBLEM 4

Solve the system:

$$\begin{cases} x - 3y + 4z = 2 \\ -2x + 6y - 8z = -4 \\ \dfrac{1}{2}x - \dfrac{3}{2}y + 2z = 1 \end{cases}$$

PRACTICE PROBLEM 5

Solve the system:

$$\begin{cases} 2x + 5y - 3z = 30 & (1) \\ x + y = -3 & (2) \\ 2x - z = 0 & (3) \end{cases}$$

(*Hint:* Equations (2) and (3) each contain the variable x and have a variable missing.)

Helpful Hint

Do not forget to distribute.

Answers

4. $\{(x, y, z) \mid x - 3y + 4z = 2\}$,
5. $(-5, 2, -10)$

Objective A *Solve.*

1. Choose the equation(s) that has $(-1, 3, 1)$ as a solution.
   a. $x + y + z = 3$ **b.** $-x + y + z = 5$
   c. $-x + y + 2z = 0$ **d.** $x + 2y - 3z = 2$

2. Choose the equation(s) that has $(2, 1, -4)$ as a solution.
   a. $x + y + z = -1$ **b.** $x - y - z = -3$
   c. $2x - y + z = -1$ **d.** $-x - 3y - z = -1$

3. Use the result of Exercise 1 to determine whether $(-1, 3, 1)$ is a solution of the system below. Explain your answer.
$$\begin{cases} x + y + z = 3 \\ -x + y + z = 5 \\ x + 2y - 3z = 2 \end{cases}$$

4. Use the result of Exercise 2 to determine whether $(2, 1, -4)$ is a solution of the system below. Explain your answer.
$$\begin{cases} x + y + z = -1 \\ x - y - z = -3 \\ 2x - y + z = -1 \end{cases}$$

Mixed Practice *Solve each system. See Examples 1 through 5.*

5. $\begin{cases} x - y + z = -4 \\ 3x + 2y - z = 5 \\ -2x + 3y - z = 15 \end{cases}$

6. $\begin{cases} x + y - z = -1 \\ -4x - y + 2z = -7 \\ 2x - 2y - 5z = 7 \end{cases}$

7. $\begin{cases} x + y = 3 \\ 2y = 10 \\ 3x + 2y - 3z = 1 \end{cases}$

8. $\begin{cases} 5x = 5 \\ 2x + y = 4 \\ 3x + y - 4z = -15 \end{cases}$

9. $\begin{cases} 2x + 2y + z = 1 \\ -x + y + 2z = 3 \\ x + 2y + 4z = 0 \end{cases}$

10. $\begin{cases} 2x - 3y + z = 5 \\ x + y + z = 0 \\ 4x + 2y + 4z = 4 \end{cases}$

11. $\begin{cases} x - 2y + z = -5 \\ -3x + 6y - 3z = 15 \\ 2x - 4y + 2z = -10 \end{cases}$

12. $\begin{cases} 3x + y - 2z = 2 \\ -6x - 2y + 4z = -2 \\ 9x + 3y - 6z = 6 \end{cases}$

13. $\begin{cases} 4x - y + 2z = 5 \\ 2y + z = 4 \\ 4x + y + 3z = 10 \end{cases}$

14. $\begin{cases} 5y - 7z = 14 \\ 2x + y + 4z = 10 \\ 2x + 6y - 3z = 30 \end{cases}$

15. $\begin{cases} x + 5z = 0 \\ 5x + y = 0 \\ y - 3z = 0 \end{cases}$

16. $\begin{cases} x - 5y = 0 \\ x - z = 0 \\ -x + 5z = 0 \end{cases}$

17. $\begin{cases} 6x - 5z = 17 \\ 5x - y + 3z = -1 \\ 2x + y = -41 \end{cases}$

18. $\begin{cases} x + 2y = 6 \\ 7x + 3y + z = -33 \\ x - z = 16 \end{cases}$

19. $\begin{cases} x + y + z = 8 \\ 2x - y - z = 10 \\ x - 2y - 3z = 22 \end{cases}$

20. $\begin{cases} 5x + y + 3z = 1 \\ x - y + 3z = -7 \\ -x + y = 1 \end{cases}$

21. $\begin{cases} x + 2y - z = 5 \\ 6x + y + z = 7 \\ 2x + 4y - 2z = 5 \end{cases}$

22. $\begin{cases} 4x - y + 3z = 10 \\ x + y - z = 5 \\ 8x - 2y + 6z = 10 \end{cases}$

23. $\begin{cases} 2x - 3y + z = 2 \\ x - 5y + 5z = 3 \\ 3x + y - 3z = 5 \end{cases}$

24. $\begin{cases} 4x + y - z = 8 \\ x - y + 2z = 3 \\ 3x - y + z = 6 \end{cases}$

25. $\begin{cases} -2x - 4y + 6z = -8 \\ x + 2y - 3z = 4 \\ 4x + 8y - 12z = 16 \end{cases}$

26. $\begin{cases} -6x + 12y + 3z = -6 \\ 2x - 4y - z = 2 \\ -x + 2y + \dfrac{z}{2} = -1 \end{cases}$

27. $\begin{cases} 2x + 2y - 3z = 1 \\ y + 2z = -14 \\ 3x - 2y = -1 \end{cases}$

28. $\begin{cases} 7x + 4y = 10 \\ x - 4y + 2z = 6 \\ y - 2z = -1 \end{cases}$

29. $\begin{cases} x + 2y - z = 5 \\ -3x - 2y - 3z = 11 \\ 4x + 4y + 5z = -18 \end{cases}$

30. $\begin{cases} 3x - 3y + z = -1 \\ 3x - y - z = 3 \\ -6x + 4y + 3z = -8 \end{cases}$

31. $\begin{cases} \dfrac{3}{4}x - \dfrac{1}{3}y + \dfrac{1}{2}z = 9 \\ \dfrac{1}{6}x + \dfrac{1}{3}y - \dfrac{1}{2}z = 2 \\ \dfrac{1}{2}x - y + \dfrac{1}{2}z = 2 \end{cases}$

32. $\begin{cases} \dfrac{1}{3}x - \dfrac{1}{4}y + z = -9 \\ \dfrac{1}{2}x - \dfrac{1}{3}y - \dfrac{1}{4}z = -6 \\ x - \dfrac{1}{2}y - z = -8 \end{cases}$

Review

Solve. See Section 2.1.

33. $2(x - 1) - 3x = x - 12$

34. $7(2x - 1) + 4 = 11(3x - 2)$

35. $-y - 5(y + 5) = 3y - 10$

36. $z - 3(z + 7) = 6(2z + 1)$

Solve. See Section 2.2.

37. The sum of two numbers is 45 and one number is twice the other. Find the numbers.

38. The difference between two numbers is 5. Twice the smaller number added to five times the larger number is 53. Find the numbers.

Concept Extensions

39. Write a single linear equation in three variables that has $(-1, 2, -4)$ as a solution. (There are many possibilities.) Explain the process you used to write an equation.

40. Write a system of three linear equations in three variables that has $(2, 1, 5)$ as a solution. (There are many possibilities.) Explain the process you used to write an equation.

41. Write a system of linear equations in three variables that has the solution $(-1, 2, -4)$. Explain the process you used to write your system.

42. When solving a system of three equations in three unknowns, explain how to determine that a system has no solution.

43. The fraction $\dfrac{1}{24}$ can be written as the following sum:

$$\frac{1}{24} = \frac{x}{8} + \frac{y}{4} + \frac{z}{3}$$

where the numbers x, y, and z are solutions of

$$\begin{cases} x + y + z = 1 \\ 2x - y + z = 0 \\ -x + 2y + 2z = -1 \end{cases}$$

Solve the system and see that the sum of the fractions is $\dfrac{1}{24}$.

44. The fraction $\dfrac{1}{18}$ can be written as the following sum:

$$\frac{1}{18} = \frac{x}{2} + \frac{y}{3} + \frac{z}{9}$$

where the numbers x, y, and z are solutions of

$$\begin{cases} x + 3y + z = -3 \\ -x + y + 2z = -14 \\ 3x + 2y - z = 12 \end{cases}$$

Solve the system and see that the sum of the fractions is $\dfrac{1}{18}$.

Solving systems involving more than three variables can be accomplished with methods similar to those encountered in this section. Apply what you already know to solve each system of equations in four variables.

45. $\begin{cases} x + y - w = 0 \\ y + 2z + w = 3 \\ x - z = 1 \\ 2x - y - w = -1 \end{cases}$

46. $\begin{cases} 5x + 4y = 29 \\ y + z - w = -2 \\ 5x + z = 23 \\ y - z + w = 4 \end{cases}$

47. $\begin{cases} x + y + z + w = 5 \\ 2x + y + z + w = 6 \\ x + y + z = 2 \\ x + y = 0 \end{cases}$

48. $\begin{cases} 2x - z = -1 \\ y + z + w = 9 \\ y - 2w = -6 \\ x + y = 3 \end{cases}$

49. Write a system of three linear equations in three variables that are dependent equations.

50. What is the solution to the system in Exercise 49?

4.3 SYSTEMS OF LINEAR EQUATIONS AND PROBLEM SOLVING

Objectives

A Solve Problems That Can Be Modeled by a System of Two Linear Equations.

B Solve Problems with Cost and Revenue Functions.

C Solve Problems That Can Be Modeled by a System of Three Linear Equations.

Objective **A** Solving Problems Modeled by Systems of Two Equations

Thus far, we have solved problems by writing one-variable equations and solving for the variable. Some of these problems can be solved, perhaps more easily, by writing a system of equations, as illustrated in this section.

EXAMPLE 1 Predicting Equal Consumption of Red Meat and Poultry

America's consumption of red meat has decreased most years since 1980 while consumption of poultry has increased. The function $y = -0.71x + 125.6$ approximates the annual pounds of red meat consumed per capita, where x is the number of years since 1980. The function $y = 1.56x + 39.7$ approximates the annual pounds of poultry consumed per capita, where x is also the number of years since 1980. If this trend continues, determine the year when the annual consumption of red meat and poultry are equal.

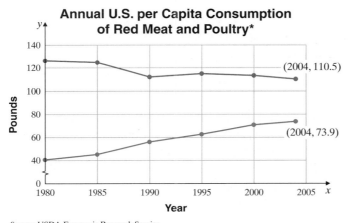

Annual U.S. per Capita Consumption of Red Meat and Poultry*

Source: USDA Economic Research Service

* Excludes shipments to Puerto Rico and other U.S. possessions

Solution:

1. UNDERSTAND. Read and reread the problem and guess a year. Let's guess the year 2010. This year is 30 years since 1980, so $x = 30$. Now let $x = 30$ in each given function.

   Red meat: $y = -0.71x + 125.6 = -0.71(30) + 125.6 = 104.3$ pounds

   Poultry: $y = 1.56x + 39.7 = 1.56(30) + 39.7 = 86.5$ pounds

   Since the projected pounds in 2010 for red meat and poultry are not the same, we guessed incorrectly, but we do have a better understanding of the problem, and we know that the year will be later than 2010.

2. TRANSLATE. We are already given the system of equations.

3. SOLVE. We want to know the year x in which pounds y are the same, so we solve the system:

$$\begin{cases} y = -0.71x + 125.6 \\ y = 1.56x + 39.7 \end{cases}$$

Continued on next page

PRACTICE PROBLEM 1

Read Example 1. If we use the years 2000, 2001, 2002, and 2004 only to write functions approximating the consumption of red meat and poultry, we have the following.

Red meat: $y = -0.7x + 113.5$

Poultry: $y = 2.4x + 66.3$

where x is years since 2000 and y is pounds per year consumed.

a. Assuming this trend continues, predict the year when consumption of red meat and poultry will be the same. Round to the nearest year.

b. Does your answer differ from the answer to Example 1? Why or why not.

Answers

1. a. 2015, **b.** yes; answers may vary

Since both equations are solved for y, one way to solve is to use the substitution method.

$$y = -0.71x + 125.6 \quad \text{First equation}$$

$$1.56x + 39.7 = -0.71x + 125.6 \quad \text{Let } y = 1.56x + 39.7.$$
$$2.27x = 85.9$$
$$x = \frac{85.9}{2.27} \approx 37.84$$

4. INTERPRET. Since we are only asked to find the year, we need only solve for x.

Check: To check, see whether $x \approx 37.84$ gives approximately the same number of pounds of red meat and poultry.

Red meat: $y = -0.71x + 125.6 = -0.71(37.84) + 125.6 \approx 98.73$ pounds
Poultry: $y = 1.56x + 39.7 = 1.56(37.84) + 39.7 \approx 98.73$ pounds

Since we rounded the number of years, the number of pounds do differ slightly. They differ only by 0.0032, so we can assume that we solved correctly.

State: The consumption of red meat and poultry will be the same about 37.84 years after 1980, or 2017.84. Thus, in the year 2017, we predict the consumption will be the same.

■ **Work Practice Problem 1**

EXAMPLE 2 **Finding Unknown Numbers**

A first number is 4 less than a second number. Four times the first number is 6 more than twice the second. Find the numbers.

Solution:

1. UNDERSTAND. Read and reread the problem and guess a solution. If one number is 10 and this is 4 less than a second number, the second number is 14. Four times the first number is 4(10), or 40. This is not equal to 6 more than twice the second number, which is 2(14) + 6 or 34. Although we guessed incorrectly, we now have a better understanding of the problem.

Since we are looking for two numbers, we will let

$x =$ first number
$y =$ second number

2. TRANSLATE. Since we have assigned two variables to this problem, we will translate the given facts into two equations. For the first statement we have

In words: the first number   is   4 less than second number
Translate: x $=$ $y - 4$

Next we translate the second statement into an equation.

In words: four times the first number   is   6 more than twice the second number
Translate: $4x$ $=$ $2y + 6$

3. SOLVE. Now we solve the system
$$\begin{cases} x = y - 4 \\ 4x = 2y + 6 \end{cases}$$

Copyright 2007 Pearson Education, Inc.

PRACTICE PROBLEM 2

A first number is 7 greater than a second number. Twice the first number is 4 more than three times the second. Find the numbers.

Answer
2. 17 and 10

Since the first equation expresses x in terms of y, we will use substitution. We substitute $y - 4$ for x in the second equation and solve for y.

$$4x = 2y + 6 \quad \text{Second equation}$$

$$4(y - 4) = 2y + 6 \quad \text{Let } x = y - 4.$$
$$4y - 16 = 2y + 6$$
$$2y = 22$$
$$y = 11$$

Now we replace y with 11 in the equation $x = y - 4$ and solve for x. Then $x = y - 4$ becomes $x = 11 - 4 = 7$. The ordered pair solution of the system is $(7, 11)$.

4. INTERPRET. Since the solution of the system is $(7, 11)$, the first number we are looking for is 7 and the second number is 11.

Check: Notice that 7 *is* 4 less than 11, and 4 times 7 *is* 6 more than twice 11. The proposed numbers, 7 and 11, are correct.

State: The numbers are 7 and 11.

■ **Work Practice Problem 2**

EXAMPLE 3 **Finding the Rate of Speed**

Two cars leave Indianapolis, one traveling east and the other west. After 3 hours they are 297 miles apart. If one car is traveling 5 mph faster than the other, what is the speed of each?

Solution:

1. UNDERSTAND. Read and reread the problem. Let's guess a solution and use the formula $d = r \cdot t$ to check. Suppose the faster car is traveling at a rate of 55 mph. This means that the other car is traveling at a rate of 50 mph since we are told that one car is traveling 5 mph faster than the other. To find the distance apart after 3 hours, we will first find the distance traveled by each car. One car's distance is rate $\cdot$ time = $55(3) = 165$ miles. The other car's distance is rate $\cdot$ time = $50(3) = 150$ miles. Since one car is traveling east and the other west, their distance apart is the sum of their distances, or 165 miles + 150 miles = 315 miles. Although this distance apart is not the required distance of 297 miles, we now have a better understanding of the problem.

Let's model the problem with a system of equations. We will let

x = speed of one car

y = speed of the other car

We summarize the information on the following chart. Both cars have traveled 3 hours. Since distance = rate $\cdot$ time, their distances are $3x$ and $3y$ miles, respectively.

	Rate	· Time	= Distance
One Car	x	3	$3x$
Other Car	y	3	$3y$

Continued on next page

PRACTICE PROBLEM 3

Two trains leave Tulsa, one traveling north and the other south. After 4 hours, they are 376 miles apart. If one train is traveling 10 mph faster than the other, what is the speed of each?

Answer
3. 42 mph; 52 mph

2. TRANSLATE. We can now translate the stated conditions into two equations.

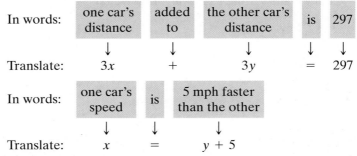

In words:

one car's distance	added to	the other car's distance	is	297
↓	↓	↓	↓	↓

Translate: $3x$ $+$ $3y$ $=$ 297

In words:

one car's speed	is	5 mph faster than the other
↓	↓	↓

Translate: x $=$ $y + 5$

3. SOLVE. Now we solve the system.

$$\begin{cases} 3x + 3y = 297 \\ x = y + 5 \end{cases}$$

Again, the substitution method is appropriate. We replace x with $y + 5$ in the first equation and solve for y.

$$3x + 3y = 297 \quad \text{First equation}$$

$$3\overbrace{(y + 5)} + 3y = 297 \quad \text{Let } x = y + 5.$$
$$3y + 15 + 3y = 297$$
$$6y = 282$$
$$y = 47$$

To find x, we replace y with 47 in the equation $x = y + 5$. Then $x = 47 + 5 = 52$. The ordered pair solution of the system is $(52, 47)$.

4. INTERPRET. The solution $(52, 47)$ means that the cars are traveling at 52 mph and 47 mph, respectively.

Check: Notice that one car is traveling 5 mph faster than the other. Also, if one car travels 52 mph for 3 hours, the distance is $3(52) = 156$ miles. The other car traveling for 3 hours at 47 mph travels a distance of $3(47) = 141$ miles. The sum of the distances $156 + 141$ is 297 miles, the required distance.

State: The cars are traveling at 52 mph and 47 mph.

◼ **Work Practice Problem 3**

Helpful Hint
Don't forget to attach units, if appropriate.

EXAMPLE 4 **Mixing Solutions**

Lynn Pike, a pharmacist, needs 70 liters of a 50% alcohol solution. She has available a 30% alcohol solution and an 80% alcohol solution. How many liters of each solution should she mix to obtain 70 liters of a 50% alcohol solution?

Solution:

1. UNDERSTAND. Read and reread the problem. Next, guess the solution. Suppose that we need 20 liters of the 30% solution. Then we need $70 - 20 = 50$ liters of the 80% solution. To see if this gives us 70 liters of a 50% alcohol solution, let's find the amount of pure alcohol in each solution.

number of liters	×	alcohol strength	=	amount of pure alcohol
↓		↓		↓
20 liters	×	0.30	=	6 liters
50 liters	×	0.80	=	40 liters
70 liters	×	0.50	=	35 liters

PRACTICE PROBLEM 4

One solution contains 20% acid and a second solution contains 50% acid. How many ounces of each solution should be mixed in order to have 60 ounces of a 30% acid solution?

Answer
4. 40 oz of 20% solution; 20 oz of 50% solution

Since 6 liters + 40 liters = 46 liters and not 35 liters, our guess is incorrect, but we have gained some insight as to how to model and check this problem.

We will let

x = amount of 30% solution, in liters

y = amount of 80% solution, in liters

and use a table to organize the given data.

	Number of Liters	Alcohol Strength	Amount of Pure Alcohol
30% Solution	x	30%	$0.30x$
80% Solution	y	80%	$0.80y$
50% Solution Needed	70	50%	$(0.50)(70)$

2. **TRANSLATE.** We translate the stated conditions into two equations.

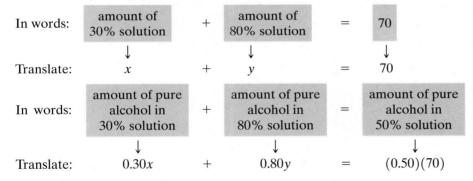

3. **SOLVE.** Now we solve the system

$$\begin{cases} x + \quad y = 70 \\ 0.30x + 0.80y = (0.50)(70) \end{cases}$$

To solve this system, we use the elimination method. We multiply both sides of the first equation by -3 and both sides of the second equation by 10. Then

$$\begin{cases} -3(x+y) = -3(70) \\ 10(0.30x + 0.80y) = 10(0.50)(70) \end{cases} \text{ simplifies to } \begin{cases} -3x - 3y = -210 \\ \underline{3x + 8y = 350} \\ \qquad\quad 5y = 140 \\ \qquad\quad\; y = 28 \end{cases}$$

Now we replace y with 28 in the equation $x + y = 70$ and find that $x + 28 = 70$, or $x = 42$. The ordered pair solution of the system is $(42, 28)$.

4. **INTERPRET.** The solution $(42, 28)$ means that 42 liters of the 30% solution and 28 liters of the 80% solution.

Check:　We check the solution in the same way that we checked our guess.

State:　The pharmacist needs to mix 42 liters of 30% solution and 28 liters of 80% solution to obtain 70 liters of 50% solution.

▣ **Work Practice Problem 4**

✔ **Concept Check** Suppose you mix an amount of 25% acid solution with an amount of 60% acid solution. You then calculate the acid strength of the resulting acid mixture. For which of the following results should you suspect an error in your calculation? Why?

a. 14%   **b.** 32%   **c.** 55%

Objective B Solving Problems with Cost and Revenue Functions

Recall that businesses are often computing cost and revenue functions or equations to predict sales, to determine whether prices need to be adjusted, and to see whether the company is making or losing money. Recall also that the value at which revenue equals cost is called the break-even point. When revenue is less than cost, the company is losing money; when revenue is greater than cost, the company is making money.

EXAMPLE 5 **Finding a Break-Even Point**

A manufacturing company recently purchased $3000 worth of new equipment to create new personalized stationery to sell to its customers. The cost of producing a package of personalized stationery is $3.00, and it is sold for $5.50. Find the number of packages that must be sold for the company to break even.

Solution:

1. UNDERSTAND. Read and reread the problem.

    Notice that the cost to the company will include a one-time cost of $3000 for the equipment and then $3.00 per package produced. The revenue will be $5.50 per package sold.

    To model this problem, we will let

    x = number of packages of personalized stationery

    $C(x)$ = total cost for producing x packages of stationery

    $R(x)$ = total revenue for selling x packages of stationery

2. TRANSLATE. The revenue equation is

In words:	revenue for selling x packages of stationery	=	price per package	·	number of packages
	↓		↓		↓
Translate:	$R(x)$	=	5.5	·	x

The cost equation is

In words:	cost for producing x packages of stationery	=	cost per package	·	number of packages	+	cost for equipment
	↓		↓		↓		↓
Translate:	$C(x)$	=	3	·	x	+	3000

PRACTICE PROBLEM 5

A company that manufactures boxes recently purchased $2000 worth of new equipment to make gift boxes to sell to its customers. The cost of producing a package of gift boxes is $1.50 and it is sold for $4.00. Find the number of packages that must be sold for the company to break even.

Answer

5. 800 packages

✔ **Concept Check Answer**

a; answers may vary

3. SOLVE. Since the break-even point is when $R(x) = C(x)$, we solve the equation $5.5x = 3x + 3000$.

$$5.5x = 3x + 3000$$

| $2.5x = 3000$ | Subtract $3x$ from both sides. |
| $x = 1200$ | Divide both sides by 2.5. |

4. INTERPRET.

Check: To see whether the break-even point occurs when 1200 packages are produced and sold, we check to see if revenue equals cost when $x = 1200$. When $x = 1200$,

$$R(x) = 5.5x = 5.5(1200) = 6600$$
$$C(x) = 3x + 3000 = 3(1200) + 3000 = 6600$$

Since $R(1200) = C(1200) = 6600$, the break-even point is 1200.

State: The company must sell 1200 packages of stationery to break even. The graph of this system is shown.

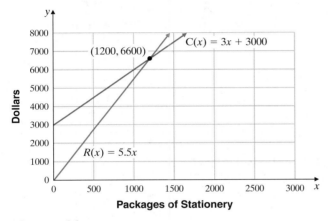

▇ **Work Practice Problem 5**

Objective ◉ Solving Problems Modeled by Systems of Three Equations

To introduce problem solving with systems of three linear equations in three variables, we solve a problem about triangles.

EXAMPLE 6 **Finding Angle Measures**

The measure of the largest angle of a triangle is 80° more than the measure of the smallest angle, and the measure of the remaining angle is 10° more than the measure of the smallest angle. Find the measure of each angle.

Solution:

1. UNDERSTAND. Read and reread the problem. Recall that the sum of the measures of the angles of a triangle is 180°. Then guess a solution. If the smallest angle measures 20°, the measure of the largest angle is 80° more, or 20° + 80° = 100°. The measure of the remaining angle is 10° more than the measure of the smallest angle, or 20° + 10° = 30°. The sum of these three angles is 20° + 100° + 30° = 150°, not the required 180°. We now know that the measure of the smallest angle is greater than 20°.

Continued on next page

To model this problem we will let

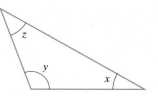

x = degree measure of the smallest angle

y = degree measure of the largest angle

z = degree measure of the remaining angle

2. TRANSLATE. We translate the given information into three equations.

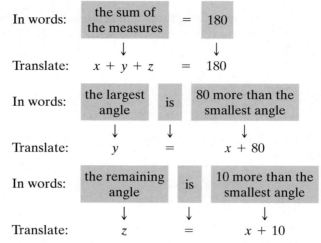

In words: | the sum of the measures | = | 180
Translate: | $x + y + z$ | = | 180

In words: | the largest angle | is | 80 more than the smallest angle
Translate: | y | = | $x + 80$

In words: | the remaining angle | is | 10 more than the smallest angle
Translate: | z | = | $x + 10$

3. SOLVE. We solve the system

$$\begin{cases} x + y + z = 180 \\ y = x + 80 \\ z = x + 10 \end{cases}$$

Since y and z are both expressed in terms of x, we will solve using the substitution method. We substitute $y = x + 80$ and $z = x + 10$ in the first equation. Then

$$x + y + z = 180 \quad \text{First equation}$$

$$x + (x + 80) + (x + 10) = 180 \quad \text{Let } y = x + 80 \text{ and } z = x + 10.$$
$$3x + 90 = 180$$
$$3x = 90$$
$$x = 30$$

Then $y = x + 80 = 30 + 80 = 110$, and $z = x + 10 = 30 + 10 = 40$. The ordered triple solution is $(30, 110, 40)$.

4. INTERPRET.

Check: Notice that $30° + 40° + 110° = 180°$. Also, the measure of the largest angle, $110°$, is $80°$ more than the measure of the smallest angle, $30°$. The measure of the remaining angle, $40°$, is $10°$ more than the measure of the smallest angle, $30°$.

State: The angles measure $30°$, $110°$, and $40°$.

■ **Work Practice Problem 6**

4.3 EXERCISE SET

FOR EXTRA HELP

 Student Solutions Manual

PH Math/Tutor Center

CD/Video for Review

Math XL MathXL®

 MyMathLab MyMathLab

Objective **A** *Solve. See Examples 1 through 4.*

1. One number is two more than a second number. Twice the first is 4 less than 3 times the second. Find the numbers.

2. Three times one number minus a second is 8, and the sum of the numbers is 12. Find the numbers.

3. The U.S.A. has the world's only "large deck" aircraft carriers which can hold up to 72 aircraft. The Enterprise class carrier is longest in length while the Nimitz class carrier is the second longest. The total length of these two carriers is 2193 feet while the difference of their lengths is only 9 feet. (*Source: USA Today,* May, 2001)
   a. Find the length of each class carrier.
   b. If a football field has a length of 100 yards, determine the length of the Enterprise class carrier in terms of number of football fields.

4. The rate of growth of participation (age 6 and older) in sports featured in the X-Games is surpassing that for older sports such as football and baseball. The most popular X-Game sport is in-line roller skating, followed by skateboarding. In 2003, the total number of participants in both sports was 30.3 million. If the number of participants in in-line skating was 3 million less than twice the number of participants in skateboarding, find the number of participants in each sport. (*Source:* April 2004 Sporting Goods Manufacturers Association Sports Participation Topline Report)

5. A Delta 727 traveled 560 mph with the wind and 480 mph against the wind. Find the speed of the plane in still air and the speed of the wind.

6. Terry Watkins can row about 10.6 kilometers in 1 hour downstream and 6.8 kilometers upstream in 1 hour. Find how fast he can row in still water, and find the speed of the current.

7. Find how many quarts of 4% butterfat milk and 1% butterfat milk should be mixed to yield 60 quarts of 2% butterfat milk.

8. A pharmacist needs 500 milliliters of a 20% phenobarbital solution but has only 5% and 25% phenobarbital solutions available. Find how many milliliters of each she should mix to get the desired solution.

9. In recent years, the United Kingdom was the most popular host country for U.S. students traveling abroad to study. Italy was the second most popular destination. A total of 50,642 students visited one of the two countries. If 12,770 more U.S. students studied in the United Kingdom than in Italy, how many students studied abroad in each country? (*Source:* Institute of International Education, Open Doors 2004)

10. Harvard University and Cornell University are each known for their excellent libraries, and each is participating with Google to put their collections into Google's searchable database. In 2003, Harvard libraries contained 584,531 more printed volumes than twice the total number of printed volumes in the libraries of Cornell. Together these two great libraries house 22,479,758 printed volumes. Find the number of printed volumes in each library. (*Source:* Harvard libraries, Cornell libraries)

11. Karen Karlin bought some large frames for $15 each and some small frames for $8 each at a closeout sale. If she bought 22 frames for $239, find how many of each type she bought.

12. Hilton University Drama Club sold 311 tickets for a play. Student tickets cost 50 cents each; nonstudent tickets cost $1.50. If total receipts were $385.50, find how many tickets of each type were sold.

13. One number is two less than a second number. Twice the first is 4 more than 3 times the second. Find the numbers.

14. Twice one number plus a second number is 42, and the first number minus the second number is -6. Find the numbers.

15. In the United States, the percent of women using the Internet is increasing faster than the percent of men. For the years 1998–2003, the function $y = 5.6x + 20.7$ can be used to estimate the percent of females using the Internet while the function $y = 4.8x + 29.4$ can be used to estimate the percent of males. For both functions, x is the number of years since 1998. If this trend continues, predict the year in which the percent of females using the Internet is equal to the percent of males. (*Source:* Pew Internet & American Life Project)

16. The percent of car vehicle sales is decreasing while the percent of light trucks (pickups, sport-utility vehicles, and minivans) is increasing. For the years 1999 through 2003, the function $y = -1.2x + 52.6$ can be used to estimate the percent of vehicle sales being cars while the function $y = 1.2x + 47.4$ can be used to estimate the percent of vehicle sales being light trucks. For both functions, x is the number of years since 1999. (*Source:* Based on data from the Bureau of Transportation Statistics, U.S. Department of Transportation)

    a. If this trend continues, predict the year in which the percent of car sales equals the percent of light truck sales.

    b. Before the actual 2001 vehicle sales data was published, USA today predicted that light truck sales would likely be greater than car sales in the year 2001. Does your prediction from part a agree with this statement? (*Source: USA Today* and Autodata)

17. An office supply store in San Diego sells 7 writing tablets and 4 pens for $6.40. Also, 2 tablets and 19 pens cost $5.40. Find the price of each.

18. A Candy Barrel shop manager mixes M&M's worth $2.00 per pound with trail mix worth $1.50 per pound. Find how many pounds of each she should use to get 50 pounds of a party mix worth $1.80 per pound.

19. An airplane takes 3 hours to travel a distance of 2160 miles with the wind. The return trip takes 4 hours against the wind. Find the speed of the plane in still air and the speed of the wind.

20. Two cyclists start at the same point and travel in opposite directions. One travels 4 mph faster than the other. In 4 hours they are 112 miles apart. Find how fast each is traveling.

21. Two of the major job categories defined by the United States Department of Labor are manufacturing jobs and jobs in the service sector. Jobs in the manufacturing sector have decreased nearly every year since the 1960s. During the same time period, service sector jobs have been steadily increasing. For the years from 1970 through 2003, the function $y = -0.513x + 33.5$ approximates the percent of jobs in the U.S. economy which are manufacturing jobs, while the function $y = 0.56x + 18.4$ approximates the percent of jobs in the United States economy which are service sector jobs. (*Source:* Based on data from the United States Department of Labor)

    a. Explain how the decrease in manufacturing jobs can be verified by the given function, while the increase of service sector jobs can be verified by their given function.

    b. Based on this information, determine the year when the percent of manufacturing jobs and the percent of service sector jobs were the same.

22. The annual U.S. per capita consumption of cheddar cheese has remained about the same since the early 1990s while the consumption of mozzarella cheese has increased. For the years 1997–2003, the function $y = 0.07x + 9.5$ approximates the annual U.S. per capita consumption of cheddar cheese in pounds and the function $y = 0.3x + 8.3$ approximates the annual U.S. per capita consumption of mozzarella cheese in pounds. For both functions, x is the number of years after 1997. Based on this information, determine the year in which the pounds of cheddar cheese consumed equaled the pounds of mozzarella cheese consumed.

△ **23.** The perimeter of a triangle is 93 centimeters. If two sides are equally long and the third side is 9 centimeters longer than the others, find the lengths of the three sides.

24. Jack Reinholt, a car salesman, has a choice of two pay arrangements: a weekly salary of $200 plus 5% commission on sales, or a straight 15% commission. Find the amount of weekly sales for which Jack's earnings are the same regardless of the pay arrangement.

25. Hertz car rental agency charges $25 daily plus 10 cents per mile. Budget charges $20 daily plus 25 cents per mile. Find the daily mileage for which the Budget charge for the day is twice that of the Hertz charge for the day.

26. Carroll Blakemore, a drafting student, bought three templates and a pencil one day for $6.45. Another day he bought two pads of paper and four pencils for $7.50. If the price of a pad of paper is three times the price of a pencil, find the price of each type of item.

△ **27.** In the figure, line l and line m are parallel lines cut by transversal t. Find the values of x and y.

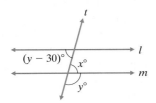

△ **28.** Find the values of x and y in the following isosceles triangle.

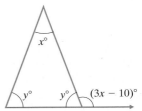

Objective **B** *Given the cost function $C(x)$ and the revenue function $R(x)$, find the number of units x that must be sold to break even. See Example 5.*

29. $C(x) = 30x + 10{,}000$ $R(x) = 46x$

30. $C(x) = 12x + 15{,}000$ $R(x) = 32x$

31. $C(x) = 1.2x + 1500$ $R(x) = 1.7x$

32. $C(x) = 0.8x + 900$ $R(x) = 2x$

33. $C(x) = 75x + 160{,}000$ $R(x) = 200x$

34. $C(x) = 105x + 70{,}000$ $R(x) = 245x$

35. The planning department of Abstract Office Supplies has been asked to determine whether the company should introduce a new computer desk next year. The department estimates that $6000 of new manufacturing equipment will need to be purchased and that the cost of constructing each desk will be $200. The department also estimates that the revenue from each desk will be $450.
   a. Determine the revenue function $R(x)$ from the sale of x desks.
   b. Determine the cost function $C(x)$ for manufacturing x desks.
   c. Find the break-even point.

36. Baskets, Inc., is planning to introduce a new woven basket. The company estimates that $500 worth of new equipment will be needed to manufacture this new type of basket and that it will cost $15 per basket to manufacture. The company also estimates that the revenue from each basket will be $31.
   a. Determine the revenue function $R(x)$ from the sale of x baskets.
   b. Determine the cost function $C(x)$ for manufacturing x baskets.
   c. Find the break-even point. Round up to the nearest whole basket.

Objective **C** *Solve. See Example 6.*

37. Rabbits in a lab are to be kept on a strict daily diet that includes 30 grams of protein, 16 grams of fat, and 24 grams of carbohydrates. The scientist has only three food mixes available with the following grams of nutrients per unit.

	Protein	Fat	Carbohydrate
Mix A	4	6	3
Mix B	6	1	2
Mix C	4	1	12

Find how many units of each mix are needed daily to meet each rabbit's dietary need.

△ **39.** The perimeter of a quadrilateral (four-sided polygon) is 29 inches. The longest side is twice as long as the shortest side. The other two sides are equally long and are 2 inches longer than the shortest side. Find the length of all four sides.

41. The sum of three numbers is 40. One number is five more than a second number. It is also twice the third. Find the numbers.

43. In 2004, the WNBA's top scorer was Lauren Jackson of the Seattle Storm. She scored a total of 738 points during the regular season. The number of two-point field goals Jackson made was 12 more than four times the number of three-point field goals she made. The number of free throws (each worth one point) she made was seventy-eight fewer than the number of two-point field goals she made. Find how many free throws, two-point field goals, and three-point field goals Lauren Jackson made during the 2004 regular WNBA season. (*Source:* Women's National Basketball Association)

△ **45.** Find the values of *x*, *y*, and *z* in the following triangle.

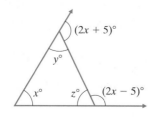

38. Gerry Gundersen mixes different solutions with concentrations of 25%, 40%, and 50% to get 200 liters of a 32% solution. If he uses twice as much of the 25% solution as of the 40% solution, find how many liters of each kind he uses.

△ **40.** The measure of the largest angle of a triangle is 90° more than the measure of the smallest angle, and the measure of the remaining angle is 30° more than the measure of the smallest angle. Find the measure of each angle.

42. The sum of the digits of a three-digit number is 15. The tens-place digit is twice the hundreds-place digit, and the ones-place digit is 1 less than the hundreds-place digit. Find the three-digit number.

44. During the 2003–2004 regular NBA season, the top-scoring player was Kevin Garnett of the Minnesota Timberwolves. Garnett scored a total of 1987 points during the regular season. The number of free throws (each worth one point) he made was five more than thirty-three times the number of three-point field goals he made. The number of two-point field goals that Garnett made was fifty-seven more than twice the number of free throws he made. How many free throws, three-point field goals, and two-point field goals did Kevin Garnett make during the 2003–2004 NBA season? (*Source:* National Basketball Association)

△ **46.** The sum of the measures of the angles of a quadrilateral is 360°. Find the values of *x*, *y*, and *z* in the following quadrilateral.

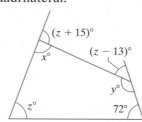

Review

Multiply both sides of equation (1) by 2, and add the resulting equation to equation (2). See Section 4.2.

47. $3x - y + z = 2$ (1)
       $-x + 2y + 3z = 6$ (2)

48. $2x + y + 3z = 7$ (1)
       $-4x + y + 2z = 4$ (2)

Multiply both sides of equation (1) by −3, and add the resulting equation to equation (2). See Section 4.2.

49. $x + 2y - z = 0$ (1)
       $3x + y - z = 2$ (2)

50. $2x - 3y + 2z = 5$ (1)
       $x - 9y + z = -1$ (2)

Concept Extensions

51. The number of personal bankruptcy petitions filed in the United States has been on the rise since the 1980s, but a recent sharper rise has occurred. In 2003, the number of petitions filed was 132,466 less than twice the number of bankruptcy petitions filed in 1993. This is equivalent to an increase of 764,765 petitions filed from 1993 to 2003. Find how many personal bankruptcy petitions were filed in each year. (*Source:* Based on data from the Administrative Office of the United States Courts)

52. In 2003, the median weekly earnings for male janitors was $71 more than the median weekly earnings for female janitors. The median weekly earnings for female janitors was 0.83 times that of their male counterparts. Also in 2003, the median weekly earnings for female pharmacists was $169 less than the median weekly incomes for male pharmacists. The median weekly earning for male pharmacists was 1.12 times that of their female counterparts. (*Source:* Based on data from the U.S. Bureau of Labor Statistics)

  a. Find the median weekly earnings for female janitors in the United States in 2003. (Round to the nearest dollar.)

  b. Find the median weekly earnings for female pharmacists in the United States in 2003. (Round to the nearest dollar.)

  c. Of the four groups of workers described in the problem, which group makes the greatest weekly earnings? Which group makes the least weekly earnings?

53. Find the values of a, b, and c such that the equation $y = ax^2 + bx + c$ has ordered pair solutions $(1, 6)$, $(-1, -2)$, and $(0, -1)$. To do so, substitute each ordered pair solution into the equation. Each time, the result is an equation in three unknowns: a, b, and c. Then solve the resulting system of three linear equations in three unknowns, a, b, and c.

54. Find the values of a, b, and c such that the equation $y = ax^2 + bx + c$ has ordered pair solutions $(1, 2)$, $(2, 3)$, and $(-1, 6)$. (*Hint:* See Exercise 53.)

55. Data (x, y) for the total number (in thousands) of college-bound students who took the ACT assessment in the year x are $(3, 925)$, $(6, 1019)$, and $(11, 1171)$, where $x = 3$ represents 1996 and $x = 6$ represents 1999. Find the values a, b, and c such that the equation $y = ax^2 + bx + c$ models these data. According to your model, how many students will take the ACT in 2009? (*Source:* ACT, Inc.)

56. Monthly normal rainfall data (x, y) for Portland, Oregon, are $(4, 2.47)$, $(7, 0.6)$, $(8, 1.1)$, where x represents time in months (with $x = 1$ representing January) and y represents rainfall in inches. Find the values of a, b, and c rounded to 2 decimal places such that the equation $y = ax^2 + bx + c$ models this data. According to your model, how much rain should Portland expect during September? (*Source:* National Climatic Data Center)

1. _____

2. _____

3. _____

4. _____

5. _____

6. _____

7. _____

8. _____

9. _____

10. _____

11. _____

12. _____

13. _____

14. _____

15. _____

16. _____

17. _____

18. _____

19. _____

20. _____

21. _____

22. _____

INTEGRATED REVIEW **Sections 4.1–4.3**

Systems of Linear Equations

The graphs of various systems of equations are shown. Match each graph with the solution of its corresponding system.

A 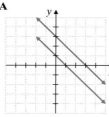 **B** **C** 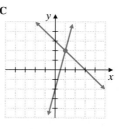 **D**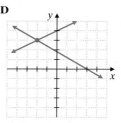

1. Solution: $(1, 2)$ **2.** Solution: $(-2, 3)$

3. No solution   **4.** Infinite number of solutions

Solve each system by elimination or substitution.

5. $\begin{cases} x + y = 4 \\ y = 3x \end{cases}$
6. $\begin{cases} x - y = -4 \\ y = 4x \end{cases}$
7. $\begin{cases} x + y = 1 \\ x - 2y = 4 \end{cases}$
8. $\begin{cases} 2x - y = 8 \\ x + 3y = 11 \end{cases}$

9. $\begin{cases} 2x + 5y = 8 \\ 6x + y = 10 \end{cases}$
10. $\begin{cases} \dfrac{1}{8}x - \dfrac{1}{2}y = -\dfrac{5}{8} \\ -3x - 8y = 0 \end{cases}$
11. $\begin{cases} 4x - 7y = 7 \\ 12x - 21y = 24 \end{cases}$

12. $\begin{cases} 2x - 5y = 3 \\ -4x + 10y = -6 \end{cases}$
13. $\begin{cases} y = \dfrac{1}{3}x \\ 5x - 3y = 4 \end{cases}$
14. $\begin{cases} y = \dfrac{1}{4}x \\ 2x - 4y = 3 \end{cases}$

15. $\begin{cases} x + y = 2 \\ -3y + z = -7 \\ 2x + y - z = -1 \end{cases}$
16. $\begin{cases} y + 2z = -3 \\ x - 2y = 7 \\ 2x - y + z = 5 \end{cases}$
17. $\begin{cases} 2x + 4y - 6z = 3 \\ -x + y - z = 6 \\ x + 2y - 3z = 1 \end{cases}$

18. $\begin{cases} x - y + 3z = 2 \\ -2x + 2y - 6z = -4 \\ 3x - 3y + 9z = 6 \end{cases}$
19. $\begin{cases} x + y - 4z = 5 \\ x - y + 2z = -2 \\ 3x + 2y + 4z = 18 \end{cases}$
20. $\begin{cases} 2x - y + 3z = 2 \\ x + y - 6z = 0 \\ 3x + 4y - 3z = 6 \end{cases}$

21. A first number is 8 less than a second number. Twice the first number is 11 more than the second number. Find the numbers.

△ **22.** The sum of the measures of the angles of a quadrilateral is 360°. The two smallest angles of the quadrilateral have the same measure. The third angle measures 30° more than the measure of one of the smallest angles and the fourth angle measures 50° more than the measure of one of the smallest angles. Find the measure of each angle.

4.4 SOLVING SYSTEMS OF EQUATIONS USING MATRICES

By now, you may have noticed that the solution of a system of equations depends on the coefficients of the equations in the system and not on the variables. In this section, we introduce how to solve a system of equations using a **matrix.**

Objective **A** Using Matrices to Solve a System of Two Equations

A **matrix** (plural: **matrices**) is a rectangular array of numbers. The following are examples of matrices.

$$\begin{bmatrix} 1 & 0 \\ 0 & 1 \end{bmatrix} \quad \begin{bmatrix} 2 & 1 & 3 & -1 \\ 0 & -1 & 4 & 5 \\ -6 & 2 & 1 & 0 \end{bmatrix} \quad \begin{bmatrix} a & b & c \\ d & e & f \end{bmatrix}$$

The numbers aligned horizontally in a matrix are in the same **row.** The numbers aligned vertically are in the same **column.**

Row 1 →
Row 2 → $\begin{bmatrix} 2 & 1 & 0 \\ -1 & 6 & 2 \end{bmatrix}$

Column 1   Column 2   Column 3

This matrix has 2 rows and 3 columns. It is called a 2×3 (read "two by three") matrix.

To see the relationship between systems of equations and matrices, study the example below.

System of Equations (in Standard Form)

$$\begin{cases} 2x - 3y = 6 & \text{Equation 1} \\ x + y = 0 & \text{Equation 2} \end{cases}$$

Corresponding Matrix

$$\begin{bmatrix} 2 & -3 & \vdots & 6 \\ 1 & 1 & \vdots & 0 \end{bmatrix} \begin{matrix} \text{Row 1} \\ \text{Row 2} \end{matrix}$$

> **Helpful Hint**
> Before writing the corresponding matrix associated with a system of equations, make sure that the equations are written in standard form.

Notice that the rows of the matrix correspond to the equations in the system. The coefficients of the variables are placed to the left of a vertical dashed line. The constants are placed to the right. Each of these numbers in the matrix is called an **element.**

The method of solving systems by matrices is to write this matrix as an equivalent matrix from which we can easily identify the solution. Two matrices are equivalent if they represent systems that have the same solution set. The following **row operations** can be performed on matrices, and the result is an equivalent matrix.

Elementary Row Operations

1. Any two rows in a matrix may be interchanged.

2. The elements of any row may be multiplied (or divided) by the same nonzero number.

3. The elements of any row may be multiplied (or divided) by a nonzero number and added to their corresponding elements in any other row.

> **Helpful Hint**
> Notice that these *row* operations are the same operations that we can perform on *equations* in a system.

To solve a system of two equations in x and y by matrices, write the corresponding matrix associated with the system. Then use elementary row operations to write equivalent matrices until you have a matrix of the form

$$\begin{bmatrix} 1 & a & b \\ 0 & 1 & c \end{bmatrix},$$

where a, b, and c are constants. Why? If a matrix associated with a system of equations is in this form, we can easily solve for x and y. For example,

Matrix **System of Equations**

$$\begin{bmatrix} 1 & 2 & -3 \\ 0 & 1 & 5 \end{bmatrix} \text{ corresponds to } \begin{cases} 1x + 2y = -3 \\ 0x + 1y = 5 \end{cases} \text{ or } \begin{cases} x + 2y = -3 \\ y = 5 \end{cases}$$

In the second equation, we have $y = 5$. Substituting this in the first equation, we have $x + 2(5) = -3$ or $x = -13$. The solution of the system is the ordered pair $(-13, 5)$.

PRACTICE PROBLEM 1

Use matrices to solve the system:

$$\begin{cases} x + 2y = -4 \\ 2x - 3y = 13 \end{cases}$$

EXAMPLE 1 Use matrices to solve the system:

$$\begin{cases} x + 3y = 5 \\ 2x - y = -4 \end{cases}$$

Solution: The corresponding matrix is $\begin{bmatrix} 1 & 3 & 5 \\ 2 & -1 & -4 \end{bmatrix}$. We use elementary row operations to write an equivalent matrix that looks like $\begin{bmatrix} 1 & a & b \\ 0 & 1 & c \end{bmatrix}$.

For the matrix given, the element in the first row, first column is already 1, as desired. Next we write an equivalent matrix with a 0 below the 1. To do this, we multiply row 1 by -2 and add to row 2. *We will change only row 2.*

$$\begin{bmatrix} 1 & 3 & 5 \\ -2(1) + 2 & -2(3) + (-1) & -2(5) + (-4) \end{bmatrix} \text{ simplifies to}$$

Row 1 Row 2   Row 1 Row 2   Row 1 Row 2
element element   element element   element element

$$\begin{bmatrix} 1 & 3 & 5 \\ 0 & -7 & -14 \end{bmatrix}$$

Now we change the -7 to a 1 by use of an elementary row operation. We divide row 2 by -7, then

$$\begin{bmatrix} 1 & 3 & 5 \\ \dfrac{0}{-7} & \dfrac{-7}{-7} & \dfrac{-14}{-7} \end{bmatrix} \text{ simplifies to } \begin{bmatrix} 1 & 3 & 5 \\ 0 & 1 & 2 \end{bmatrix}$$

This last matrix corresponds to the system

$$\begin{cases} x + 3y = 5 \\ y = 2 \end{cases}$$

Thus we know that y is 2. To find x, we let $y = 2$ in the first equation, $x + 3y = 5$.

$x + 3y = 5$ First equation

$x + 3(2) = 5$ Let $y = 2$.

$x = -1$

The ordered pair solution is $(-1, 2)$. Check to see that this ordered pair satisfies both original equations.

Work Practice Problem 1

Answer

1. $(2, -3)$

EXAMPLE 2 Use matrices to solve the system:

$$\begin{cases} 2x - y = 3 \\ 4x - 2y = 5 \end{cases}$$

Solution: The corresponding matrix is $\begin{bmatrix} 2 & -1 & \vdots & 3 \\ 4 & -2 & \vdots & 5 \end{bmatrix}$. To get 1 in the row 1, column 1 position, we divide the elements of row 1 by 2.

$$\begin{bmatrix} \dfrac{2}{2} & -\dfrac{1}{2} & \vdots & \dfrac{3}{2} \\ 4 & -2 & \vdots & 5 \end{bmatrix} \text{ simplifies to } \begin{bmatrix} 1 & -\dfrac{1}{2} & \vdots & \dfrac{3}{2} \\ 4 & -2 & \vdots & 5 \end{bmatrix}$$

To get 0 under the 1, we multiply the elements of row 1 by -4 and add the new elements to the elements of row 2.

$$\begin{bmatrix} 1 & -\dfrac{1}{2} & \vdots & \dfrac{3}{2} \\ -4(1) + 4 & -4\left(-\dfrac{1}{2}\right) - 2 & \vdots & -4\left(\dfrac{3}{2}\right) + 5 \end{bmatrix} \begin{array}{c} \text{simplifies} \\ \text{to} \end{array} \begin{bmatrix} 1 & -\dfrac{1}{2} & \vdots & \dfrac{3}{2} \\ 0 & 0 & \vdots & -1 \end{bmatrix}$$

The corresponding system is $\begin{cases} x - \dfrac{1}{2}y = \dfrac{3}{2} \\ 0 = -1 \end{cases}$. The equation $0 = -1$ is false for all y or x values; hence the system is inconsistent and has no solution. The solution set is $\varnothing$ or $\{\ \}$.

■ **Work Practice Problem 2**

✔**Concept Check** Consider the system

$$\begin{cases} 2x - 3y = 8 \\ x + 5y = -3 \end{cases}$$

What is wrong with its corresponding matrix shown below?

$$\begin{bmatrix} 2 & -3 & \vdots & 8 \\ 0 & 5 & \vdots & -3 \end{bmatrix}$$

Objective **B** Using Matrices to Solve a System of Three Equations

To solve a system of three equations in three variables using matrices, we will write the corresponding matrix in the equivalent form

$$\begin{bmatrix} 1 & a & b & \vdots & d \\ 0 & 1 & c & \vdots & e \\ 0 & 0 & 1 & \vdots & f \end{bmatrix}$$

EXAMPLE 3 Use matrices to solve the system:

$$\begin{cases} x + 2y + z = 2 \\ -2x - y + 2z = 5 \\ x + 3y - 2z = -8 \end{cases}$$

Solution: The corresponding matrix is $\begin{bmatrix} 1 & 2 & 1 & \vdots & 2 \\ -2 & -1 & 2 & \vdots & 5 \\ 1 & 3 & -2 & \vdots & -8 \end{bmatrix}$.

Continued on next page

PRACTICE PROBLEM 2

Use matrices to solve the system:

$$\begin{cases} -3x + y = 0 \\ -6x + 2y = 2 \end{cases}$$

PRACTICE PROBLEM 3

Use matrices to solve the system:

$$\begin{cases} x + 3y + z = 5 \\ -3x + y - 3z = 5 \\ x + 2y - 2z = 9 \end{cases}$$

Answers
2. no solution,   **3.** $(1, 2, -2)$

✔ **Concept Check Answer**
matrix should be $\begin{bmatrix} 2 & -3 & \vdots & 8 \\ 1 & 5 & \vdots & -3 \end{bmatrix}$

Our goal is to write an equivalent matrix with 1s along the diagonal (see the numbers in red) and 0s below the 1s. The element in row 1, column 1 is already 1. Next we get 0s for each element in the rest of column 1. To do this, first we multiply the elements of row 1 by 2 and add the new elements to row 2. Also, we multiply the elements of row 1 by -1 and add the new elements to the elements of row 3. *We do not change row 1.* Then

$$\begin{bmatrix} 1 & 2 & 1 & \vdots & 2 \\ 2(1)-2 & 2(2)-1 & 2(1)+2 & \vdots & 2(2)+5 \\ -1(1)+1 & -1(2)+3 & -1(1)-2 & \vdots & -1(2)-8 \end{bmatrix} \quad \text{simplifies to}$$

$$\begin{bmatrix} 1 & 2 & 1 & \vdots & 2 \\ 0 & 3 & 4 & \vdots & 9 \\ 0 & 1 & -3 & \vdots & -10 \end{bmatrix}$$

We continue down the diagonal and use elementary row operations to get 1 where the element 3 is now. To do this, we interchange rows 2 and 3.

$$\begin{bmatrix} 1 & 2 & 1 & \vdots & 2 \\ 0 & 3 & 4 & \vdots & 9 \\ 0 & 1 & -3 & \vdots & -10 \end{bmatrix} \xrightarrow{\text{ is equivalent to }} \begin{bmatrix} 1 & 2 & 1 & \vdots & 2 \\ 0 & 1 & -3 & \vdots & -10 \\ 0 & 3 & 4 & \vdots & 9 \end{bmatrix}$$

Next we want the new row 3, column 2 element to be 0. We multiply the elements of row 2 by -3 and add the result to the elements of row 3.

$$\begin{bmatrix} 1 & 2 & 1 & \vdots & 2 \\ 0 & 1 & -3 & \vdots & -10 \\ -3(0)+0 & -3(1)+3 & -3(-3)+4 & \vdots & -3(-10)+9 \end{bmatrix} \quad \text{simplifies to}$$

$$\begin{bmatrix} 1 & 2 & 1 & \vdots & 2 \\ 0 & 1 & -3 & \vdots & -10 \\ 0 & 0 & 13 & \vdots & 39 \end{bmatrix}$$

Finally, we divide the elements of row 3 by 13 so that the final diagonal element is 1.

$$\begin{bmatrix} 1 & 2 & 1 & \vdots & 2 \\ 0 & 1 & -3 & \vdots & -10 \\ \frac{0}{13} & \frac{0}{13} & \frac{13}{13} & \vdots & \frac{39}{13} \end{bmatrix} \quad \text{simplifies to} \quad \begin{bmatrix} 1 & 2 & 1 & \vdots & 2 \\ 0 & 1 & -3 & \vdots & -10 \\ 0 & 0 & 1 & \vdots & 3 \end{bmatrix}$$

This matrix corresponds to the system

$$\begin{cases} x + 2y + z = 2 \\ \quad\;\; y - 3z = -10 \\ \qquad\quad\; z = 3 \end{cases}$$

We identify the z-coordinate of the solution as 3. Next we replace z with 3 in the second equation and solve for y.

$y - 3z = -10$ Second equation
$y - 3(3) = -10$ Let $z = 3$.
$y = -1$

To find x, we let $z = 3$ and $y = -1$ in the first equation.

$x + 2y + z = 2$ First equation
$x + 2(-1) + 3 = 2$ Let $z = 3$ and $y = -1$.
$x = 1$

The ordered triple solution is $(1, -1, 3)$. Check to see that it satisfies all three equations in the original system.

Work Practice Problem 3

4.4 EXERCISE SET

Objective **A** *Use matrices to solve each system of linear equations. See Example 1.*

1. $\begin{cases} x + y = 1 \\ x - 2y = 4 \end{cases}$

2. $\begin{cases} 2x - y = 8 \\ x + 3y = 11 \end{cases}$

3. $\begin{cases} x + 3y = 2 \\ x + 2y = 0 \end{cases}$

4. $\begin{cases} 4x - y = 5 \\ 3x - 3y = 6 \end{cases}$

Use matrices to solve each system of linear equations. See Example 2.

5. $\begin{cases} x - 2y = 4 \\ 2x - 4y = 4 \end{cases}$

6. $\begin{cases} -x + 3y = 6 \\ 3x - 9y = 9 \end{cases}$

7. $\begin{cases} 3x - 3y = 9 \\ 2x - 2y = 6 \end{cases}$

8. $\begin{cases} 9x - 3y = 6 \\ -18x + 6y = -12 \end{cases}$

Objective **B** *Use matrices to solve each system of linear equations. See Example 3.*

9. $\begin{cases} x + y = 3 \\ 2y = 10 \\ 3x + 2y - 4z = 12 \end{cases}$

10. $\begin{cases} 5x = 5 \\ 2x + y = 4 \\ 3x + y - 5z = -15 \end{cases}$

11. $\begin{cases} 2y - z = -7 \\ x + 4y + z = -4 \\ 5x - y + 2z = 13 \end{cases}$

12. $\begin{cases} 4y + 3z = -2 \\ 5x - 4y = 1 \\ -5x + 4y + z = -3 \end{cases}$

Objectives **A** **B** **Mixed Practice** *Solve each system of linear equations using matrices. See Examples 1 through 3.*

13. $\begin{cases} x - 4 = 0 \\ x + y = 1 \end{cases}$

14. $\begin{cases} 3y = 6 \\ x + y = 7 \end{cases}$

15. $\begin{cases} x + y + z = 2 \\ 2x - z = 5 \\ 3y + z = 2 \end{cases}$

16. $\begin{cases} x + 2y + z = 5 \\ x - y - z = 3 \\ y + z = 2 \end{cases}$

17. $\begin{cases} 5x - 2y = 27 \\ -3x + 5y = 18 \end{cases}$

18. $\begin{cases} 4x - y = 9 \\ 2x + 3y = -27 \end{cases}$

19. $\begin{cases} 4x - 7y = 7 \\ 12x - 21y = 24 \end{cases}$

20. $\begin{cases} 2x - 5y = 12 \\ -4x + 10y = 20 \end{cases}$

21. $\begin{cases} 4x - y + 2z = 5 \\ 2y + z = 4 \\ 4x + y + 3z = 10 \end{cases}$

22. $\begin{cases} 5y - 7z = 14 \\ 2x + y + 4z = 10 \\ 2x + 6y - 3z = 30 \end{cases}$

23. $\begin{cases} 4x + y + z = 3 \\ -x + y - 2z = -11 \\ x + 2y + 2z = -1 \end{cases}$

24. $\begin{cases} x + y + z = 9 \\ 3x - y + z = -1 \\ -2x + 2y - 3z = -2 \end{cases}$

Review

Determine whether each graph is the graph of a function. See Section 3.6.

25.

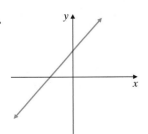

26.

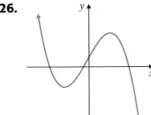

27.

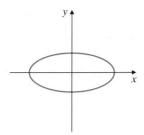

28.

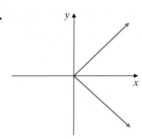

Concept Extensions

Solve. See the Concept Check in this section.

29. For the system $\begin{cases} x \quad + \ z = \ 7 \\ \quad y + 2z = -6 \\ 3x - y \quad = \ 0 \end{cases}$, which is the correct corresponding matrix?

a. $\begin{bmatrix} 1 & 1 & 7 \\ 1 & 2 & -6 \\ 3 & -1 & 0 \end{bmatrix}$ **b.** $\begin{bmatrix} 1 & 0 & 1 & 7 \\ 1 & 2 & 0 & -6 \\ 3 & -1 & 0 & 0 \end{bmatrix}$ **c.** $\begin{bmatrix} 1 & 0 & 1 & 7 \\ 0 & 1 & 2 & -6 \\ 3 & -1 & 0 & 0 \end{bmatrix}$

30. For the system $\begin{cases} x - 6 = 0 \\ 2x - 3y = 1 \end{cases}$, which is the correct corresponding matrix?

a. $\begin{bmatrix} 1 & -6 & 0 \\ 2 & -3 & 1 \end{bmatrix}$ **b.** $\begin{bmatrix} 1 & 0 & 6 \\ 2 & -3 & 1 \end{bmatrix}$ **c.** $\begin{bmatrix} 1 & 0 & -6 \\ 2 & -3 & 1 \end{bmatrix}$

31. The percent y of U.S. households that owned a black-and-white television set between the years 1980 and 1993 can be modeled by the linear equation $2.3x + y = 52$, where x represents the number of years after 1980. Similarly, the percent y of U.S. households that owned a microwave oven during this same period can be modeled by the linear equation $-5.4x + y = 14$. (*Source:* Based on data from the Energy Information Administration, U.S. Department of Energy)

   a. The data used to form these two models were incomplete. It is impossible to tell from the data the year in which the percent of households owning black-and-white television sets was the same as the percent of households owning microwave ovens. Use matrix methods to estimate the year in which this occurred.

   b. Did more households own black-and-white television sets or microwave ovens in 1980? In 1993? What trends do these models show? Does this seem to make sense? Why or why not?

   c. According to the models, when will the percent of households owning black-and-white television sets reach 0%?

   d. Do you think your answer to part **c** is accurate? Why or why not?

32. The most popular amusement park in the world (according to annual attendance) is Tokyo Disneyland, whose yearly attendance in thousands can be approximated by the equation $y = 1201x + 16,507$ where x is the number of years after 2000. In second place is Walt Disney World's Magic Kingdom, whose yearly attendance, in thousands, can be approximated by $y = -616x + 15,400$. Find the last year when attendance in Magic Kingdom was greater than attendance in Tokyo Disneyland. (*Source:* Amusement Business)

33. For the system $\begin{cases} 2x - 3y = \ 8 \\ x + 5y = -3 \end{cases}$, explain what is wrong with writing the corresponding matrix as $\begin{bmatrix} 2 & 3 & 8 \\ 0 & 5 & -3 \end{bmatrix}$.

STUDY SKILLS BUILDER

Are You Satisfied with Your Performance on a Particular Quiz or Exam?

If not, don't forget to analyze your quiz or exam and look for common errors. Were most of your errors a result of:

- *Carelessness?* Did you turn in your quiz or exam before the allotted time expired? If so, resolve next time to use the entire time allotted. Any extra time can be spent checking your work.

- *Running out of time?* If so, make a point to better manage your time on your next quiz or exam. Try completing any questions that you are unsure of last and delay checking your work until all questions have been answered.

- *Not understanding a concept?* If so, review that concept and correct your work. Try to understand how this happened so that you make sure it doesn't happen before the next quiz or exam.

- *Test conditions?* When studying for a quiz or exam, make sure you place yourself in conditions similar to test conditions. For example, before your next quiz or exam, use a few sheets of blank paper and take a sample test without the aid of your notes or text.

(See your instructor or use the Chapter Test at the end of each chapter.)

Exercises

1. Have you corrected all your previous quizzes and exams?

2. List any errors you have found common to two or more of your graded papers.

3. Is one of your common errors not understanding a concept? If so, are you making sure you understand all the concepts for the next quiz or exam?

4. Is one of your common errors making careless mistakes? If so, are you now taking all the time allotted to check over your work so that you can minimize the number of careless mistakes?

5. Are you satisfied with your grades thus far on quizzes and tests?

6. If your answer to Exercise 5 is no, are there any more suggestions you can make to your instructor or yourself to help? If so, list them here and share these with your instructor.

4.5 SYSTEMS OF LINEAR INEQUALITIES

Objective **A** Graphing Systems of Linear Inequalities

In Section 3.5 we solved linear inequalities in two variables. Just as two linear equations make a system of linear equations, two linear inequalities make a **system of linear inequalities.** Systems of inequalities are very important in a process called linear programming. Many businesses use linear programming to find the most profitable way to use limited resources such as employees, machines, or buildings.

A **solution of a system of linear inequalities** is an ordered pair that satisfies each inequality in the system. The set of all such ordered pairs is the solution set of the system. Graphing this set gives us a picture of the solution set. We can graph a system of inequalities by graphing each inequality in the system and identifying the region of overlap.

Graphing the Solutions of a System of Linear Inequalities

Step 1: Graph each inequality in the system on the same set of axes.

Step 2: The solutions of the system are the points common to the graphs of all the inequalities in the system.

EXAMPLE 1 Graph the solutions of the system: $\begin{cases} 3x \geq y \\ x + 2y \leq 8 \end{cases}$

Solution: We begin by graphing each inequality on the *same* set of axes. The graph of the solutions of the system is the region contained in the graphs of both inequalities. In other words, it is their intersection.

First let's graph $3x \geq y$. The boundary line is the graph of $3x = y$. We sketch a solid boundary line since the inequality $3x \geq y$ means $3x > y$ or $3x = y$. The test point $(1, 0)$ satisfies the inequality, so we shade the half-plane that includes $(1, 0)$.

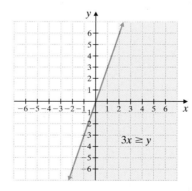

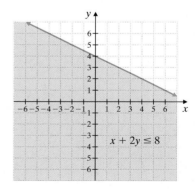

Next we sketch a solid boundary line $x + 2y = 8$ on the same set of axes. The test point $(0, 0)$ satisfies the inequality $x + 2y \leq 8$, so we shade the half-plane that includes $(0, 0)$. (For clarity, the graph of $x + 2y \leq 8$ is shown here on a separate set of axes.) An ordered pair solution of the system must satisfy both inequalities. These solutions are points that lie in both shaded regions. The solution of the system is the darkest shaded region. This solution includes parts of both boundary lines.

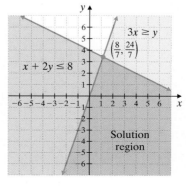

Work Practice Problem 1

PRACTICE PROBLEM 1

Graph the solutions of the system:

$$\begin{cases} 2x \leq y \\ x + 4y \geq 4 \end{cases}$$

Answers

1.

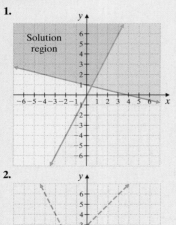

Solution region

2.

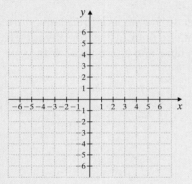

Solution region

In linear programming, it is sometimes necessary to find the coordinates of the **corner point:** the point at which the two boundary lines intersect. To find the corner point for the system of Example 1, we solve the related linear system

$$\begin{cases} 3x = y \\ x + 2y = 8 \end{cases}$$

using either the substitution or the elimination method. The lines intersect at $\left(\dfrac{8}{7}, \dfrac{24}{7} \right)$, the corner point of the graph.

EXAMPLE 2 Graph the solutions of the system:

$$\begin{cases} x - y < 2 \\ x + 2y > -1 \\ y < 2 \end{cases}$$

Solution: First we graph all three inequalities on the same set of axes. All boundary lines are dashed lines since the inequality symbols are $<$ and $>$. The solution of the system is the region shown by the darkest shading. In this example, the boundary lines are *not* a part of the solution.

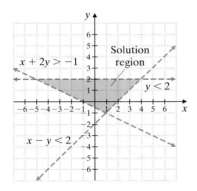

⬛ **Work Practice Problem 2**

✔**Concept Check** Describe the solution of the system of inequalities:

$$\begin{cases} x \le 2 \\ x \ge 2 \end{cases}$$

EXAMPLE 3 Graph the solutions of the system: $\begin{cases} -3x + 4y \le 12 \\ x \le 3 \\ x \ge 0 \\ y \ge 0 \end{cases}$

Solution: We graph the inequalities on the same set of axes. The intersection of the inequalities is the solution region. It is the only region shaded in this graph and includes the portions of all four boundary lines that border the shaded region.

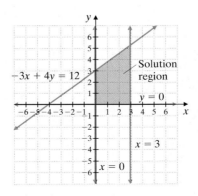

⬛ **Work Practice Problem 3**

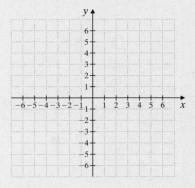
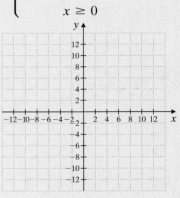
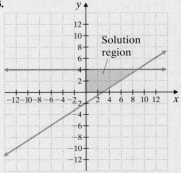

FOR EXTRA HELP

Student Solutions Manual | PH Math/Tutor Center | CD/Video for Review | MathXL® | MyMathLab

Objective **A** *Graph the solutions of each system of linear inequalities. See Examples 1 through 3.*

1. $\begin{cases} y \geq x + 1 \\ y \geq 3 - x \end{cases}$

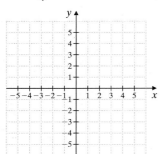

2. $\begin{cases} y \geq x - 3 \\ y \geq -1 - x \end{cases}$

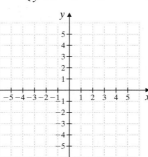

3. $\begin{cases} y < 3x - 4 \\ y \leq x + 2 \end{cases}$

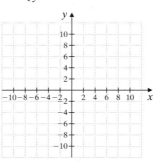

4. $\begin{cases} y \leq 2x + 1 \\ y > x + 2 \end{cases}$

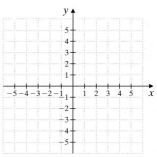

5. $\begin{cases} y < -2x - 2 \\ y > x + 4 \end{cases}$

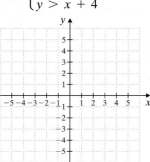

6. $\begin{cases} y \leq 2x + 4 \\ y \geq -x - 5 \end{cases}$

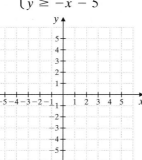

7. $\begin{cases} y \geq -x + 2 \\ y \leq 2x + 5 \end{cases}$

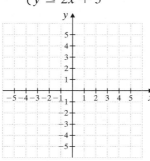

8. $\begin{cases} y \geq x - 5 \\ y \leq -3x + 3 \end{cases}$

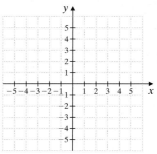

9. $\begin{cases} x \geq 3y \\ x + 3y \leq 6 \end{cases}$

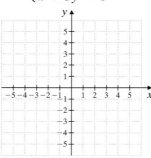

10. $\begin{cases} -2x < y \\ x + 2y < 3 \end{cases}$

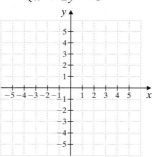

11. $\begin{cases} x \leq 2 \\ y \geq -3 \end{cases}$

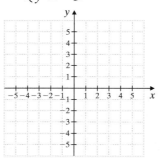

12. $\begin{cases} x \geq -3 \\ y \geq -2 \end{cases}$

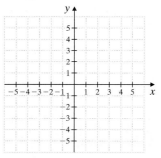

13. $\begin{cases} y \geq 1 \\ x < -3 \end{cases}$

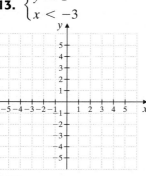

14. $\begin{cases} y > 2 \\ x \geq -1 \end{cases}$

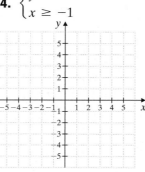

15. $\begin{cases} y + 2x \geq 0 \\ 5x - 3y \leq 12 \\ y \leq 2 \end{cases}$

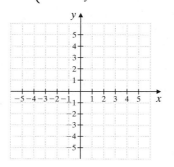

16. $\begin{cases} y + 2x \leq 0 \\ 5x + 3y \geq -2 \\ y \leq 4 \end{cases}$

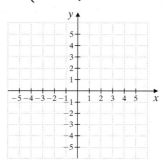

17. $\begin{cases} 3x - 4y \geq -6 \\ 2x + y \leq 7 \\ y \geq -3 \end{cases}$

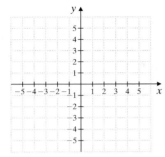

18. $\begin{cases} 4x - y \geq -2 \\ 2x + 3y \leq -8 \\ y \geq -5 \end{cases}$

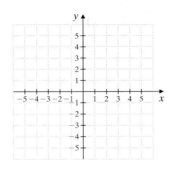

19. $\begin{cases} 2x + y \leq 5 \\ x \leq 3 \\ x \geq 0 \\ y \geq 0 \end{cases}$

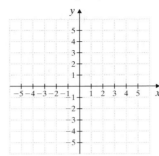

20. $\begin{cases} 3x + y \leq 4 \\ x \leq 4 \\ x \geq 0 \\ y \geq 0 \end{cases}$

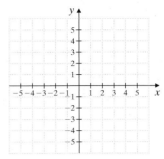

Match each system of inequalities to the corresponding graph.

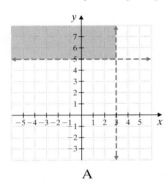

A

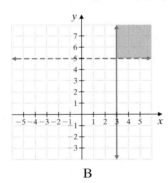

B

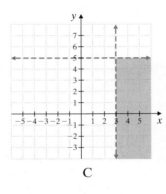

C

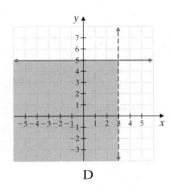

D

21. $\begin{cases} y < 5 \\ x > 3 \end{cases}$

22. $\begin{cases} y > 5 \\ x < 3 \end{cases}$

23. $\begin{cases} y \leq 5 \\ x < 3 \end{cases}$

24. $\begin{cases} y > 5 \\ x \geq 3 \end{cases}$

Review

Evaluate each expression. See Section 1.7.

25. $(-3)^2$

26. $(-5)^3$

27. $\left(\dfrac{2}{3}\right)^2$

28. $\left(\dfrac{3}{4}\right)^3$

Perform each indicated operation. See Section 1.4.

29. $(-2)^2 - (-3) + 2(-1)$ **30.** $5^2 - 11 + 3(-5)$

31. $8^2 + (-13) - 4(-2)$ **32.** $(-12)^2 + (-1)(2) - 6$

Concept Extensions

Solve. See the Concept Check in this section.

33. Describe the solution of the system: $\begin{cases} y \leq 3 \\ y \geq 3 \end{cases}$

34. Describe the solution of the system: $\begin{cases} x \leq 5 \\ x \leq 3 \end{cases}$

35. Explain how to decide which region to shade to show the solution region of the following system.

$$\begin{cases} x \geq 3 \\ y \geq -2 \end{cases}$$

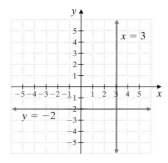

36. Tony Noellert budgets his time at work today. Part of the day he can write bills; the rest of the day he can use to write purchase orders. The total time available is at most 8 hours. Less than 3 hours is to be spent writing bills.

  a. Write a system of inequalities to describe the situation. (Let x = hours available for writing bills and y = hours available for writing purchase orders.)
  b. Graph the solutions of the system.

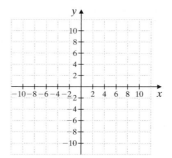

CHAPTER 4 Group Activity

Another Mathematical Model

Sometimes mathematical models other than linear models are appropriate for data. Suppose that an equation of the form $y = ax^2 + bx + c$ is an appropriate model for the ordered pairs (x_1, y_1), (x_2, y_2), and (x_3, y_3). Then it is necessary to find the values of a, b, and c such that the given ordered pairs are solutions of the equation $y = ax^2 + bx + c$. To do so, substitute each ordered pair into the equation. Each time, the result is an equation in three unknowns: a, b, and c. Solving the resulting system of three linear equation in three unknowns will give the required values of a, b, and c.

1. The table gives the total beef supply (in billions of pounds) in the United States in each of the years listed.

  a. Write the data as ordered pairs of the form (x, y), where y is the beef supply (in billions of pounds) in the year $x(x = 0$ represents 1999).
  b. Find the values of a, b, and c such that the equation $y = ax^2 + bx + c$ models this data.
  c. Verify that the model you found in part (b) gives each of the ordered pair solutions from part (a).
  d. According to the model, what was the U.S. beef supply in 2002?

Total U.S. Beef Supply	
Year	**Beef Supply (billions of pounds)**
1999	29.8
2001	29.9
2003	30.1
(*Source:* Economic Research Service, U.S. Department of Agriculture)	

2. The table gives Porsche sales figures for each of the years listed.

  a. Write the data as ordered pairs of the form (x, y), where y is Porsche sales in the year $x(x = 0$ represents 1999).
  b. Find the values of a, b, and c such that the equation $y = ax^2 + bx + c$ models this data.
  c. According to the model, what was the total Porsche sales in 2002?

Total Porsche Sales	
Year	**Number of Porsche Vehicles Produced**
1999	43,982
2001	54,586
2003	66,803
(*Source:* Automotive Intelligence, www.autointell.com)	

3. a. Make up an equation of the form $y = ax^2 + bx + c$.
  b. Find three ordered pair solutions of the equation.
  c. Without revealing your equation from part (a), exchange lists of ordered pair solutions with another group.
  d. Use the method described above to find the values of a, b, and c such that the equation $y = ax^2 + bx + c$ has the ordered pair solutions you received from the other group.
  e. Check with the other group to see if your equation from part (d) is the correct one.

Chapter 4 Vocabulary Check

Fill in each blank with one of the words or phrases listed below.

matrix   consistent   system of equations

solution   inconsistent   square

1. Two or more linear equations in two variables form a _____ .
2. A _____ of a system of two equations in two variables is an ordered pair that makes both equations true.
3. A(n) _____ system of equations has at least one solution.
4. If a matrix has the same number of rows and columns, it is called a _____ matrix.
5. A(n) _____ system of equations has no solution.
6. A _____ is a rectangular array of numbers.

Helpful Hint

  Are you preparing for your test? Don't forget to take the Chapter 4 Test on page 314. Then check your answers at the back of the text and use the Chapter Test Prep Video CD to see the fully worked-out solutions to any of the exercises you want to review.

4 Chapter Highlights

DEFINITIONS AND CONCEPTS	EXAMPLES
Section 4.1 Solving Systems of Linear Equations in Two Variables	

A **system of linear equations** consists of two or more linear equations.

$$\begin{cases} x - 3y = 6 \\ y = \dfrac{1}{2}x \end{cases} \qquad \begin{cases} x + 2y - z = 1 \\ 3x - y + 4z = 0 \\ 5y + z = 6 \end{cases}$$

A **solution** of a system of two equations in two variables is an ordered pair (x, y) that makes both equations true.

Determine whether $(2, -5)$ is a solution of the system.

$$\begin{cases} x + y = -3 \\ 2x - 3y = 19 \end{cases}$$

Replace x with 2 and y with -5 in both equations.

$$x + y = -3 \qquad\qquad 2x - 3y = 19$$
$$2 + (-5) \stackrel{?}{=} -3 \qquad 2(2) - 3(-5) \stackrel{?}{=} 19$$
$$-3 = -3 \quad \text{True} \qquad 4 + 15 \stackrel{?}{=} 19$$
$$19 = 19 \quad \text{True}$$

$(2, -5)$ is a solution of the system.

Geometrically, a solution of a system in two variables is a point of intersection of the graphs of the equations.

Solve by graphing: $\begin{cases} y = 2x - 1 \\ x + 2y = 13 \end{cases}$

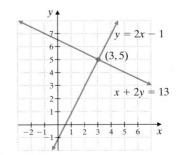

continued

DEFINITIONS AND CONCEPTS	**EXAMPLES**

Section 4.1   Solving Systems of Linear Equations in Two Variables (*continued*)

A system of equations with at least one solution is a **consistent system.** A system that has no solution is an **inconsistent system.**

If the graphs of two linear equations are identical, the equations are **dependent.**

If their graphs are different, the equations are **independent.**

One solution:
Independent equations
Consistent system

No solution:
Independent equations
Inconsistent system

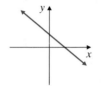

Infinite number of solutions:
Dependent equations
Consistent system

SOLVING A SYSTEM OF LINEAR EQUATIONS BY THE SUBSTITUTION METHOD

Step 1. Solve one equation for a variable.

Step 2. Substitute the expression for the variable into the other equation.

Step 3. Solve the equation from Step 2 to find the value of one variable.

Step 4. Substitute the value from Step 3 in either original equation to find the value of the other variable.

Step 5. Check the solution in both equations.

Solve by substitution:

$$\begin{cases} y = x + 2 \\ 3x - 2y = -5 \end{cases}$$

Since the first equation is solved for y, substitute $x + 2$ for y in the second equation.

$$3x - 2y = -5 \quad \text{Second equation}$$
$$3x - 2(x + 2) = -5 \quad \text{Let } y = x + 2.$$
$$3x - 2x - 4 = -5$$
$$x - 4 = -5 \quad \text{Simplify.}$$
$$x = -1 \quad \text{Add 4.}$$

To find y, let $x = -1$ in $y = x + 2$, so $y = -1 + 2 = 1$. The solution $(-1, 1)$ checks.

SOLVING A SYSTEM OF LINEAR EQUATIONS BY THE ELIMINATION METHOD

Step 1. Rewrite each equation in standard form, $Ax + By = C$.

Step 2. Multiply one or both equations by a nonzero number so that the coefficients of a variable are opposites.

Step 3. Add the equations.

Step 4. Find the value of the remaining variable by solving the resulting equation.

Step 5. Substitute the value from Step 4 into either original equation to find the value of the other variable.

Step 6. Check the solution in both equations.

Solve by elimination:

$$\begin{cases} x - 3y = -3 \\ -2x + y = 6 \end{cases}$$

Multiply both sides of the first equation by 2.

$$\begin{aligned} 2x - 6y &= -6 \\ \underline{-2x + y = 6} \\ -5y &= 0 \quad \text{Add.} \\ y &= 0 \quad \text{Divide by } -5. \end{aligned}$$

To find x, let $y = 0$ in an original equation.

$$x - 3y = -3$$
$$x - 3 \cdot 0 = -3$$
$$x = -3$$

The solution $(-3, 0)$ checks.

DEFINITIONS AND CONCEPTS	**EXAMPLES**
Section 4.2 Solving Systems of Linear Equations in Three Variables	

A **solution** of an equation in three variables x, y, and z is an **ordered triple** (x, y, z) that makes the equation a true statement.

Verify that $(-2, 1, 3)$ is a solution of $2x + 3y - 2z = -7$. Replace x with -2, y with 1, and z with 3.

$$2(-2) + 3(1) - 2(3) \stackrel{?}{=} -7$$
$$-4 + 3 - 6 \stackrel{?}{=} -7$$
$$-7 = -7 \quad \text{True}$$

$(-2, 1, 3)$ is a solution.

SOLVING A SYSTEM OF THREE LINEAR EQUATIONS BY THE ELIMINATION METHOD

Step 1. Write each equation in standard form, $Ax + By + Cz = D$.

Step 2. Choose a pair of equations and use them to eliminate a variable.

Step 3. Choose any other pair of equations and eliminate the same variable.

Step 4. Solve the system of two equations in two variables from Steps 2 and 3.

Step 5. Solve for the third variable by substituting the values of the variables from Step 4 into any of the original equations.

Step 6. Check the solution in all three original equations.

Solve:

$$\begin{cases} 2x + y - z = 0 & (1) \\ x - y - 2z = -6 & (2) \\ -3x - 2y + 3z = -22 & (3) \end{cases}$$

1. Each equation is written in standard form.

2.
$$\begin{array}{rl} 2x + y - z = & 0 \quad (1) \\ \underline{x - y - 2z = -6} & \quad (2) \\ 3x \quad\quad - 3z = -6 & \quad (4) \qquad \text{Add.} \end{array}$$

3. Eliminate y from equations (1) and (3) also.

$$\begin{array}{rl} 4x + 2y - 2z = & 0 \qquad \text{Multiply equation} \\ \underline{-3x - 2y + 3z = -22} \quad (3) & \qquad \text{(1) by 2.} \\ x \quad\quad + z = -22 \quad (5) & \qquad \text{Add.} \end{array}$$

4. Solve.

$$\begin{cases} 3x - 3z = -6 & (4) \\ x + z = -22 & (5) \end{cases}$$

$$\begin{array}{rl} x - z = -2 & \qquad \text{Divide equation (4) by 3.} \\ \underline{x + z = -22} & \qquad \text{(5)} \\ 2x \quad\quad = -24 & \\ x \quad\quad = -12 & \end{array}$$

To find z, use equation (5).

$$x + z = -22$$
$$-12 + z = -22$$
$$z = -10$$

5. To find y, use equation (1).

$$2x + y - z = 0$$
$$2(-12) + y - (-10) = 0$$
$$-24 + y + 10 = 0$$
$$y = 14$$

6. The solution $(-12, 14, -10)$ checks.

DEFINITIONS AND CONCEPTS	EXAMPLES

Section 4.3   Systems of Linear Equations and Problem Solving

	Two numbers have a sum of 11. Twice one number is 3 less than 3 times the other. Find the numbers.
1. UNDERSTAND the problem.	**1.** Read and reread. $x =$ one number $y =$ other number
2. TRANSLATE.	**2.** In words: 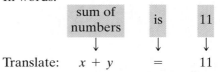 Translate: $x + y$ $=$ 11 In words: 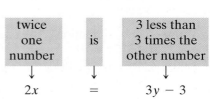 Translate: $2x$ $=$ $3y - 3$
3. SOLVE.	**3.** Solve the system: $\begin{cases} x + y = 11 \\ 2x = 3y - 3 \end{cases}$ In the first equation, $x = 11 - y$. Substitute into the other equation. $$2x = 3y - 3$$ $$2(11 - y) = 3y - 3$$ $$22 - 2y = 3y - 3$$ $$-5y = -25$$ $$y = 5$$ Replace y with 5 in the equation $x = 11 - y$. Then $x = 11 - 5 = 6$. The solution is $(6, 5)$.
4. INTERPRET.	**4.** *Check:* See that $6 + 5 = 11$ is the required sum and that twice 6 is 3 times 5 less 3. *State:* The numbers are 6 and 5.

Section 4.4   Solving Systems of Equations Using Matrices

A **matrix** is a rectangular array of numbers.	$\begin{bmatrix} -7 & 0 & 3 \\ 1 & 2 & 4 \end{bmatrix}$ $\begin{bmatrix} a & b & c \\ d & e & f \\ g & h & i \end{bmatrix}$
The **matrix** corresponding to a system is composed of the coefficients of the variables and the constants of the system.	The matrix corresponding to the system $\begin{cases} x - y = 1 \\ 2x + y = 11 \end{cases}$ is $\begin{bmatrix} 1 & -1 & \vdots & 1 \\ 2 & 1 & \vdots & 11 \end{bmatrix}$

DEFINITIONS AND CONCEPTS	**EXAMPLES**

Section 4.4   Solving Systems of Equations Using Matrices (*continued*)

The following **row operations** can be performed on matrices, and the result is an equivalent matrix.

Elementary row operations:

1. Interchange any two rows.

2. Multiply (or divide) the elements of one row by the same nonzero number.

3. Multiply (or divide) the elements of one row by the same nonzero number and add them to their corresponding elements in any other row.

Use matrices to solve: $\begin{cases} x - y = 1 \\ 2x + y = 11 \end{cases}$

The corresponding matrix is

$$\left[\begin{array}{cc|c} 1 & -1 & 1 \\ 2 & 1 & 11 \end{array}\right]$$

Use row operations to write an equivalent matrix with 1s along the diagonal and 0s below each 1 in the diagonal. Multiply row 1 by -2 and add to row 2. Change row 2 only.

$$\left[\begin{array}{cc|c} 1 & -1 & 1 \\ -2(1) + 2 & -2(-1) + 1 & -2(1) + 11 \end{array}\right]$$

simplifies to $\left[\begin{array}{cc|c} 1 & -1 & 1 \\ 0 & 3 & 9 \end{array}\right]$

Divide row 2 by 3.

$\left[\begin{array}{cc|c} 1 & -1 & 1 \\ \frac{0}{3} & \frac{3}{3} & \frac{9}{3} \end{array}\right]$ simplifies to $\left[\begin{array}{cc|c} 1 & -1 & 1 \\ 0 & 1 & 3 \end{array}\right]$

This matrix corresponds to the system

$$\begin{cases} x - y = 1 \\ y = 3 \end{cases}$$

Let $y = 3$ in the first equation.

$$x - 3 = 1$$
$$x = 4$$

The ordered pair solution is $(4, 3)$.

Section 4. 5   Systems of Linear Inequalities

A **system of linear inequalities** consists of two or more linear inequalities.

To graph a system of inequalities, graph each inequality in the system. The overlapping region is the solution of the system.

$$\begin{cases} x - y \geq 3 \\ y \leq -2x \end{cases}$$

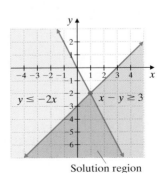

Solution region

SECTION 7.3 *Partial Fractions*

Objectives

❶ Decompose $\frac{P}{Q}$, where Q has only distinct linear factors.

❷ Decompose $\frac{P}{Q}$, where Q has repeated linear factors.

❸ Decompose $\frac{P}{Q}$, where Q has a nonrepeated prime quadratic factor.

❹ Decompose $\frac{P}{Q}$, where Q has a prime, repeated quadratic factor.

The rising and setting of the sun suggest the obvious: Things change over time. Calculus is the study of rates of change, allowing the motion of the rising sun to be measured by "freezing the frame" at one instant in time. If you are given a function, calculus reveals its rate of change at any "frozen" instant. In this section, you will learn an algebraic technique used in calculus to find a function if its rate of change is known. The technique involves expressing a given function in terms of simpler functions.

The Idea behind Partial Fraction Decomposition

We know how to use common denominators to write a sum or difference of rational expressions as a single rational expression. For example,

$$\frac{3}{x-4} - \frac{2}{x+2} = \frac{3(x+2) - 2(x-4)}{(x-4)(x+2)}$$

$$= \frac{3x + 6 - 2x + 8}{(x-4)(x+2)} = \frac{x+14}{(x-4)(x+2)}.$$

For solving the kind of calculus problem described in the section opener, we must reverse this process:

$\frac{x+14}{(x-4)(x+2)}$ is expressed as the sum of two simpler fractions.

$$\frac{x+14}{(x-4)(x+2)} = \underbrace{\frac{3}{x+4} + \frac{-2}{x+2}}_{}.$$

Partial fraction   Partial fraction

This is the partial fraction decomposition of $\frac{x+14}{(x-4)(x+2)}$.

Each of the two fractions on the right is called a **partial fraction**. The sum of these fractions is called the **partial fraction decomposition** of the rational expression on the left-hand side.

    Partial fraction decompositions can be written for rational expressions of the form $\frac{P(x)}{Q(x)}$, where P and Q have no common factors and the highest power in

277

the numerator is less than the highest power in the denominator. In this section, we will show you how to write the partial fraction decompositions for each of the following rational expressions:

$$\frac{9x^2 - 9x + 6}{(2x - 1)(x + 2)(x - 2)}$$

$P(x) = 9x^2 - 9x + 6$; highest power = 2

$Q(x) = (2x - 1)(x + 2)(x - 2)$; multiplying factors, highest power = 3.

$$\frac{5x^3 - 3x^2 + 7x - 3}{(x^2 + 1)^2}.$$

$P(x) = 5x^3 - 3x^2 + 7x - 3$; highest power = 3

$Q(x) = (x^2 + 1)^2$; squaring the expression, highest power = 4.

The partial fraction decomposition of a rational expression depends on the factors of the denominator. We consider four cases involving different kinds of factors in the denominator:

1. The denominator is a product of distinct linear factors.

2. The denominator is a product of linear factors, some of which are repeated.

3. The denominator has prime quadratic factors, none of which is repeated.

4. The denominator has a repeated prime quadratic factor.

① Decompose $\frac{P}{Q}$, where Q has only distinct linear factors.

The Partial Fraction Decomposition of a Rational Expression with Distinct Linear Factors in the Denominator

If the denominator of a rational expression has a linear factor of the form $ax + b$, then the partial fraction decomposition will contain a term of the form

$$\frac{A}{ax + b}.$$

Constant

Linear factor

Each distinct linear factor in the denominator produces a partial fraction of the form *constant over linear factor*. For example,

$$\frac{9x^2 - 9x + 6}{(2x - 1)(x + 2)(x - 2)} = \frac{A}{2x - 1} + \frac{B}{x + 2} + \frac{C}{x - 2}.$$

We write a constant over each linear factor in the denominator.

The Partial Fraction Decomposition of $\dfrac{P(x)}{Q(x)}$: $Q(x)$ Has Distinct Linear Factors

The form of the partial fraction decomposition for a rational expression with distinct linear factors in the denominator is

$$\frac{P(x)}{(a_1x + b_1)(a_2x + b_2)(a_3x + b_3) \cdots (a_nx + b_n)}$$

$$= \frac{A_1}{a_1x + b_1} + \frac{A_2}{a_2x + b_2} + \frac{A_3}{a_3x + b_3} + \cdots + \frac{A_n}{a_nx + b_n}.$$

EXAMPLE 1 **Partial Fraction Decomposition with Distinct Linear Factors**

Find the partial fraction decomposition of

$$\frac{x + 14}{(x - 4)(x + 2)}.$$

Solution   We begin by setting up the partial fraction decomposition with the unknown constants. Write a constant over each of the two distinct linear factors in the denominator.

$$\frac{x + 14}{(x - 4)(x + 2)} = \frac{A}{x - 4} + \frac{B}{x + 2}$$

Our goal is to find A and B. We do this by multiplying both sides of the equation by the least common denominator, $(x - 4)(x + 2)$.

$$(x - 4)(x + 2)\frac{x + 14}{(x - 4)(x + 2)} = (x - 4)(x + 2)\left(\frac{A}{x - 4} + \frac{B}{x + 2}\right)$$

We use the distributive property on the right side.

$$\cancel{(x-4)}\,\cancel{(x+2)}\,\frac{x + 14}{\cancel{(x-4)}\,\cancel{(x+2)}}$$

$$= \cancel{(x-4)}(x + 2)\frac{A}{\cancel{(x-4)}} + (x - 4)\cancel{(x+2)}\frac{B}{\cancel{(x+2)}}$$

Dividing out common factors in numerators and denominators, we obtain

$$x + 14 = A(x + 2) + B(x - 4).$$

To find values for A and B that make both sides equal, we'll express the sides in exactly the same form by writing the variable x-terms and then writing the constant terms. Apply the distributive property on the right side.

$x + 14 = Ax + 2A + Bx - 4B$	Distribute A and B over the parentheses.
$x + 14 = Ax + Bx + 2A - 4B$	Rearrange terms.
$1x + 14 = (A + B)x + (2A - 4B)$	Rewrite to identify the coefficient of x and the constant term.

As shown by the arrows, if two polynomials are equal, coefficients of like powers of x must be equal $(A + B = 1)$ and their constant terms must be equal $(2A - 4B = 14)$. Consequently, A and B satisfy the following two equations:

$$A + B = 1$$
$$2A - 4B = 14.$$

We can use the addition method to solve this linear system in two variables. By multiplying the first equation by -2 and adding equations, we obtain $A = 3$ and $B = -2$. Thus,

$$\frac{x + 14}{(x - 4)(x + 2)} = \frac{A}{x - 4} + \frac{B}{x + 2} = \frac{3}{x - 4} + \frac{-2}{x + 2} \left(\text{or } \frac{3}{x - 4} - \frac{2}{x + 2}\right).$$

Study Tip

You will encounter some examples in which the denominator of the given rational expression is not already factored. If necessary, begin by factoring the denominator. Then apply the six steps needed to obtain the partial fraction decomposition.

Steps in Partial Fraction Decomposition

1. Set up the partial fraction decomposition with the unknown constants A, B, C, etc., in the numerator of the decomposition.
2. Multiply both sides of the resulting equation by the least common denominator.
3. Simplify the right-hand side of the equation.
4. Write both sides in descending powers, equate coefficients of like powers of x, and equate constant terms.
5. Solve the resulting linear system for A, B, C, etc.
6. Substitute the values for A, B, C, etc., into the equation in step 1 and write the partial fraction decomposition.

Check Point 1 Find the partial fraction decomposition of $\dfrac{5x - 1}{(x - 3)(x + 4)}$.

② Decompose $\dfrac{P}{Q}$, where Q has repeated linear factors.

The Partial Fraction Decomposition of a Rational Expression with Linear Factors in the Denominator, Some of Which Are Repeated

Suppose that $(ax + b)^n$ is a factor of the denominator. This means that the linear factor $ax + b$ is repeated n times. When this occurs, the partial fraction decomposition will contain a sum of n fractions for this factor of the denominator.

The Partial Fraction Decomposition of $\dfrac{P(x)}{Q(x)}$: $Q(x)$ Has Repeated Linear Factors

The form of the partial fraction decomposition for a rational expression containing the linear factor $ax + b$ occuring n times as its denominator is

$$\frac{P(x)}{(ax + b)^n} = \frac{A_1}{ax + b} + \frac{A_2}{(ax + b)^2} + \frac{A_3}{(ax + b)^3} + \cdots + \frac{A_n}{(ax + b)^n}.$$

Include one fraction with a constant numerator for each power of $ax + b$.

EXAMPLE 2 Partial Fraction Decomposition with Repeated Linear Factors

Find the partial fraction decomposition of $\dfrac{x - 18}{x(x - 3)^2}$.

Study Tip

Avoid this common error:

INCORRECT!

$$\frac{x - 18}{x(x - 3)^2} = \frac{A}{x} + \frac{B}{x - 3} + \frac{C}{x - 3}$$

Listing $x - 3$ twice does not take into account $(x - 3)^2$.

Solution

Step 1 Set up the partial fraction decomposition with the unknown constants. Because the linear factor $x - 3$ occurs twice, we must include one fraction with a constant numerator for each power of $x - 3$.

$$\frac{x - 18}{x(x - 3)^2} = \frac{A}{x} + \frac{B}{x - 3} + \frac{C}{(x - 3)^2}$$

Step 2 Multiply both sides of the resulting equation by the least common denominator. We clear fractions, multiplying both sides by $x(x - 3)^2$, the least common denominator.

$$x(x - 3)^2 \left[\frac{x - 18}{x(x - 3)^2} \right] = x(x - 3)^2 \left[\frac{A}{x} + \frac{B}{x - 3} + \frac{C}{(x - 3)^2} \right]$$

We use the distributive property on the right side.

$$x(x - 3)^2 \cdot \frac{x - 18}{x(x - 3)^2} = x(x - 3)^2 \cdot \frac{A}{x} + x(x - 3)^2 \cdot \frac{B}{(x - 3)} + x(x - 3)^2 \cdot \frac{C}{(x - 3)^2}$$

Dividing out common factors in numerators and denominators, we obtain

$$x - 18 = A(x - 3)^2 + Bx(x - 3) + Cx.$$

Step 3 Simplify the right side of the equation. Square $x - 3$. Then apply the distributive property.

$$x - 18 = A(x^2 - 6x + 9) + Bx(x - 3) + Cx \qquad \text{Square } x - 3 \text{ using } (A - B)^2 = A^2 - 2AB + B^2.$$

$$x - 18 = Ax^2 - 6Ax + 9A + Bx^2 - 3Bx + Cx \qquad \text{Apply the distributive property.}$$

Step 4 Write both sides in descending powers, equate coefficients of like powers of x, and equate constant terms. The left side, $x - 18$, is in descending powers of x: $x - 18x^0$. We will write the right side in descending powers of x.

$x - 18 = Ax^2 + Bx^2 - 6Ax - 3Bx + Cx + 9A$ Rearrange terms on the right side.

Express both sides in the same form.

$0x^2 + 1x - 18 = (A + B)x^2 + (-6A - 3B + C)x + 9A$ Rewrite to identify coefficients and the constant term.

Equating coefficients of like powers of x and equating constant terms results in the following system of linear equations:

$$A + B = 0$$
$$-6A - 3B + C = 1$$
$$9A = -18.$$

Step 5 Solve the resulting system for A, B, and C. Dividing both sides of the last equation by 9, we obtain $A = -2$. Substituting -2 for A in the first equation, $A + B = 0$, gives $-2 + B = 0$, so $B = 2$. We find C by substituting -2 for A and 2 for B in the middle equation, $-6A - 3B + C = 1$. We obtain $C = -5$.

Step 6 Substitute the values of A, B, and C, and write the partial fraction decomposition. With $A = -2$, $B = 2$, and $C = -5$, the required partial fraction decomposition is

$$\frac{x - 18}{x(x - 3)^2} = \frac{A}{x} + \frac{B}{x - 3} + \frac{C}{(x - 3)^2} = -\frac{2}{x} + \frac{2}{x - 3} - \frac{5}{(x - 3)^2}.$$

Check Point 2 Find the partial fraction decomposition of $\dfrac{x + 2}{x(x - 1)^2}$.

❸ Decompose $\dfrac{P}{Q}$, where Q has a nonrepeated prime quadratic factor.

The Partial Fraction Decomposition of a Rational Expression with Prime, Nonrepeated Quadratic Factors in the Denominator

Our final two cases of partial fraction decomposition involve prime quadratic factors of the form $ax^2 + bx + c$. Based on our work with the discriminant, we know that $ax^2 + bx + c$ is prime and cannot be factored over the integers if $b^2 - 4ac < 0$ or if $b^2 - 4ac$ is not a perfect square.

> **The Partial Fraction Decomposition of $\dfrac{P(x)}{Q(x)}$: $Q(x)$ Has a Nonrepeated, Prime Quadratic Factor**
>
> If $ax^2 + bx + c$ is a prime quadratic factor of $Q(x)$, the partial fraction decomposition will contain a term of the form
>
> $$\frac{Ax + B}{ax^2 + bx + c}.$$
>
> Linear numerator
>
> Quadratic factor

The voice balloons in the box show that each distinct prime quadratic factor in the denominator produces a partial fraction of the form *linear numerator over quadratic factor*. For example,

$$\frac{3x^2 + 17x + 14}{(x - 2)(x^2 + 2x + 4)} = \frac{A}{x - 2} + \frac{Bx + C}{x^2 + 2x + 4}.$$

We write a constant over the linear factor in the denominator.

We write a linear numerator over the prime quadratic factor in the denominator.

Our next example illustrates how a linear system in three variables is used to determine values for A, B, and C.

EXAMPLE 3   Partial Fraction Decomposition

Find the partial fraction decomposition of

$$\frac{3x^2 + 17x + 14}{(x - 2)(x^2 + 2x + 4)}.$$

Solution

Step 1   Set up the partial fraction decomposition with the unknown constants. We put a constant (A) over the linear factor and a linear expression $(Bx + C)$ over the prime quadratic factor.

$$\frac{3x^2 + 17x + 14}{(x - 2)(x^2 + 2x + 4)} = \frac{A}{x - 2} + \frac{Bx + C}{x^2 + 2x + 4}$$

Step 2   Multiply both sides of the resulting equation by the least common denominator. We clear fractions, multiplying both sides by $(x - 2)(x^2 + 2x + 4)$, the least common denominator.

$$(x - 2)(x^2 + 2x + 4)\left[\frac{3x^2 + 17x + 14}{(x - 2)(x^2 + 2x + 4)}\right] = (x - 2)(x^2 + 2x + 4)\left[\frac{A}{x - 2} + \frac{Bx + C}{x^2 + 2x + 4}\right]$$

We use the distributive property on the right side.

$$\cancel{(x - 2)} \, \cancel{(x^2 + 2x + 4)} \cdot \frac{3x^2 + 17x + 14}{\cancel{(x - 2)} \, \cancel{(x^2 + 2x + 4)}}$$

$$= \cancel{(x - 2)}(x^2 + 2x + 4) \cdot \frac{A}{\cancel{x - 2}} + (x - 2)\cancel{(x^2 + 2x + 4)} \cdot \frac{Bx + C}{\cancel{x^2 + 2x + 4}}$$

Dividing out common factors in numerators and denominators, we obtain

$$3x^2 + 17x + 14 = A(x^2 + 2x + 4) + (Bx + C)(x - 2).$$

Step 3   Simplify the right side of the equation. We multiply on the right side by distributing A over each term in parentheses and multiplying $(Bx + C)(x - 2)$ using the FOIL method.

$$3x^2 + 17x + 14 = Ax^2 + 2Ax + 4A + Bx^2 - 2Bx + Cx - 2C$$

Step 4   Write both sides in descending powers, equate coefficients of like powers of x, and equate constant terms. The left side, $3x^2 + 17x + 14$, is in descending powers of x. We write the right side in descending powers of x

$$3x^2 + 17x + 14 = Ax^2 + Bx^2 + 2Ax - 2Bx + Cx + 4A - 2C$$

and express both sides in the same form.

$$3x^2 + 17x + 14 = (A + B)x^2 + (2A - 2B + C)x + (4A - 2C)$$

Equating coefficients of like powers of x and equating constant terms results in the following system of linear equations:

$$A + B = 3$$
$$2A - 2B + C = 17$$
$$4A - 2C = 14.$$

Step 5 Solve the resulting system for A, B, and C. Because the first equation involves A and B, we can obtain another equation in A and B by eliminating C from the second and third equations. Multiply the second equation by 2 and add equations. Solving in this manner, we obtain $A = 5$, $B = -2$, and $C = 3$.

Step 6 Substitute the values of A, B, and C, and write the partial fraction decomposition. With $A = 5$, $B = -2$, and $C = 3$, the required partial fraction decomposition is

$$\frac{3x^2 + 17x + 14}{(x - 2)(x^2 + 2x + 4)} = \frac{A}{x - 2} + \frac{Bx + C}{x^2 + 2x + 4} = \frac{5}{x - 2} + \frac{-2x + 3}{x^2 + 2x + 4}.$$

Technology

You can use the $\boxed{\text{TABLE}}$ feature of a graphing utility to check a partial fraction decomposition. To check the result of Example 3, enter the given rational function and its partial fraction decomposition:

$$y_1 = \frac{3x^2 + 17x + 14}{(x - 2)(x^2 + 2x + 4)}$$

$$y_2 = \frac{5}{x - 2} + \frac{-2x + 3}{x^2 + 2x + 4}.$$

X	Y₁	Y₂
-3	.28571	.28571
-2	.5	.5
-1	0	0
0	-1.75	-1.75
1	-4.857	-4.857
2	ERROR	ERROR
3	4.8421	4.8421

X=-3

No matter how far up or down we scroll, $y_1 = y_2$, so the decomposition appears to be correct.

Check Point 3 Find the partial fraction decomposition of

$$\frac{8x^2 + 12x - 20}{(x + 3)(x^2 + x + 2)}.$$

4 Decompose $\dfrac{P}{Q}$, where Q has a prime, repeated quadratic factor.

The Partial Fraction Decomposition of a Rational Expression with a Prime, Repeated Quadratic Factor in the Denominator

Suppose that $(ax^2 + bx + c)^n$ is a factor of the denominator and that $ax^2 + bx + c$ cannot be factored further. This means that the quadratic factor $ax^2 + bx + c$ occurs n times. When this occurs, the partial fraction decomposition will contain a linear numerator for each power of $ax^2 + bx + c$.

The Partial Fraction Decomposition of $\dfrac{P(x)}{Q(x)}$: $Q(x)$ Has a Prime, Repeated Quadratic Factor

The form of the partial fraction decomposition for a rational expression containing the prime factor $ax^2 + bx + c$ occurring n times as its denominator is

$$\frac{P(x)}{(ax^2 + bx + c)^n} = \frac{A_1x + B_1}{ax^2 + bx + c} + \frac{A_2x + B_2}{(ax^2 + bx + c)^2} + \frac{A_3x + B_3}{(ax^2 + bx + c)^3} + \cdots + \frac{A_nx + B_n}{(ax^2 + bx + c)^n}.$$

Include one fraction with a linear numerator for each power of $ax^2 + bx + c$.

EXAMPLE 4   Partial Fraction Decomposition with a Repeated Quadratic Factor

Find the partial fraction decomposition of

$$\frac{5x^3 - 3x^2 + 7x - 3}{(x^2 + 1)^2}.$$

Solution

Step 1   Set up the partial fraction decomposition with the unknown constants. Because the quadratic factor $x^2 + 1$ occurs twice, we must include one fraction with a linear numerator for each power of $x^2 + 1$.

$$\frac{5x^3 - 3x^2 + 7x - 3}{(x^2 + 1)^2} = \frac{Ax + B}{x^2 + 1} + \frac{Cx + D}{(x^2 + 1)^2}$$

Step 2   Multiply both sides of the resulting equation by the least common denominator. We clear fractions, multiplying both sides by $(x^2 + 1)^2$, the least common denominator.

$$(x^2 + 1)^2\left[\frac{5x^3 - 3x^2 + 7x - 3}{(x^2 + 1)^2}\right] = (x^2 + 1)^2\left[\frac{Ax + B}{x^2 + 1} + \frac{Cx + D}{(x^2 + 1)^2}\right]$$

Now we multiply and simplify.

$$5x^3 - 3x^2 + 7x - 3 = (x^2 + 1)(Ax + B) + Cx + D$$

Step 3   Simplify the right side of the equation. We multiply $(x^2 + 1)(Ax + B)$ using the FOIL method.

$$5x^3 - 3x^2 + 7x - 3 = Ax^3 + Bx^2 + Ax + B + Cx + D$$

Step 4   Write both sides in descending powers, equate coefficients of like powers of x, and equate constant terms.

$$5x^3 - 3x^2 + 7x - 3 = Ax^3 + Bx^2 + Ax + Cx + B + D$$

$$5x^3 - 3x^2 + 7x - 3 = Ax^3 + Bx^2 + (A + C)x + (B + D)$$

Equating coefficients of like powers of x and equating constant terms results in the following system of linear equations:

$$\begin{aligned} A &= 5 \\ B &= -3 \\ A + C &= 7 \\ B + D &= -3. \end{aligned}$$

With $A = 5$, we immediately obtain $C = 2$.
With $B = -3$, we immediately obtain $D = 0$.

Step 5   Solve the resulting system for A, B, C, and D. Based on our observations in step 4, $A = 5, B = -3, C = 2$, and $D = 0$.

Step 6   Substitute the values of A, B, C, and D, and write the partial fraction decomposition.

$$\frac{5x^3 - 3x^2 + 7x - 3}{(x^2 + 1)^2} = \frac{Ax + B}{x^2 + 1} + \frac{Cx + D}{(x^2 + 1)^2} = \frac{5x - 3}{x^2 + 1} + \frac{2x}{(x^2 + 1)^2}$$

Check Point 4 Find the partial fraction decomposition of $\dfrac{2x^3 + x + 3}{(x^2 + 1)^2}$.

EXERCISE SET 7.3

Practice Exercises

In Exercises 1–8, write the form of the partial fraction decomposition of the rational expression. It is not necessary to solve for the constants.

1. $\dfrac{11x - 10}{(x - 2)(x + 1)}$

2. $\dfrac{5x + 7}{(x - 1)(x + 3)}$

3. $\dfrac{6x^2 - 14x - 27}{(x + 2)(x - 3)^2}$

4. $\dfrac{3x + 16}{(x + 1)(x - 2)^2}$

5. $\dfrac{5x^2 - 6x + 7}{(x - 1)(x^2 + 1)}$

6. $\dfrac{5x^2 - 9x + 19}{(x - 4)(x^2 + 5)}$

7. $\dfrac{x^3 + x^2}{(x^2 + 4)^2}$

8. $\dfrac{7x^2 - 9x + 3}{(x^2 + 7)^2}$

In Exercises 9–42, write the partial fraction decomposition of each rational expression.

9. $\dfrac{x}{(x - 3)(x - 2)}$

10. $\dfrac{1}{x(x - 1)}$

11. $\dfrac{3x + 50}{(x - 9)(x + 2)}$

12. $\dfrac{5x - 1}{(x - 2)(x + 1)}$

13. $\dfrac{7x - 4}{x^2 - x - 12}$

14. $\dfrac{9x + 21}{x^2 + 2x - 15}$

15. $\dfrac{4}{2x^2 - 5x - 3}$

16. $\dfrac{x}{x^2 + 2x - 3}$

17. $\dfrac{4x^2 + 13x - 9}{x(x - 1)(x + 3)}$

18. $\dfrac{4x^2 - 5x - 15}{x(x + 1)(x - 5)}$

19. $\dfrac{4x^2 - 7x - 3}{x^3 - x}$

20. $\dfrac{2x^2 - 18x - 12}{x^3 - 4x}$

21. $\dfrac{6x - 11}{(x - 1)^2}$

22. $\dfrac{x}{(x + 1)^2}$

23. $\dfrac{x^2 - 6x + 3}{(x - 2)^3}$

24. $\dfrac{2x^2 + 8x + 3}{(x + 1)^3}$

25. $\dfrac{x^2 + 2x + 7}{x(x - 1)^2}$

26. $\dfrac{3x^2 + 49}{x(x + 7)^2}$

27. $\dfrac{x^2}{(x - 1)^2(x + 1)}$

28. $\dfrac{x^2}{(x - 1)^2(x + 1)^2}$

29. $\dfrac{5x^2 - 6x + 7}{(x - 1)(x^2 + 1)}$

30. $\dfrac{5x^2 - 9x + 19}{(x - 4)(x^2 + 5)}$

31. $\dfrac{5x^2 + 6x + 3}{(x + 1)(x^2 + 2x + 2)}$

32. $\dfrac{9x + 2}{(x - 2)(x^2 + 2x + 2)}$

33. $\dfrac{x + 4}{x^2(x^2 + 4)}$

34. $\dfrac{10x^2 + 2x}{(x - 1)^2(x^2 + 2)}$

35. $\dfrac{6x^2 - x + 1}{x^3 + x^2 + x + 1}$

36. $\dfrac{3x^2 - 2x + 8}{x^3 + 2x^2 + 4x + 8}$

37. $\dfrac{x^3 + x^2 + 2}{(x^2 + 2)^2}$

38. $\dfrac{x^2 + 2x + 3}{(x^2 + 4)^2}$

39. $\dfrac{x^3 - 4x^2 + 9x - 5}{(x^2 - 2x + 3)^2}$

40. $\dfrac{3x^3 - 6x^2 + 7x - 2}{(x^2 - 2x + 2)^2}$

41. $\dfrac{4x^2 + 3x + 14}{x^3 - 8}$

42. $\dfrac{3x - 5}{x^3 - 1}$

Practice Plus

In Exercises 43–46, perform each long division and write the partial fraction decomposition of the remainder term.

43. $\dfrac{x^5 + 2}{x^2 - 1}$

44. $\dfrac{x^5}{x^2 - 4x + 4}$

45. $\dfrac{x^4 - x^2 + 2}{x^3 - x^2}$

46. $\dfrac{x^4 + 2x^3 - 4x^2 + x - 3}{x^2 - x - 2}$

In Exercises 47–50, write the partial fraction decomposition of each rational expression.

47. $\dfrac{1}{x^2 - c^2}$ $(c \neq 0)$

48. $\dfrac{ax + b}{x^2 - c^2}$ $(c \neq 0)$

49. $\dfrac{ax + b}{(x - c)^2}$ $(c \neq 0)$

50. $\dfrac{1}{x^2 - ax - bx + ab}$ $(a \neq b)$

Application Exercises

51. Find the partial fraction decomposition for $\dfrac{1}{x(x + 1)}$ and use the result to find the following sum:

$$\frac{1}{1 \cdot 2} + \frac{1}{2 \cdot 3} + \frac{1}{3 \cdot 4} + \cdots + \frac{1}{99 \cdot 100}.$$

52. Find the partial fraction decomposition for $\dfrac{2}{x(x + 2)}$ and use the result to find the following sum:

$$\frac{2}{1 \cdot 3} + \frac{2}{3 \cdot 5} + \frac{2}{5 \cdot 7} + \cdots + \frac{2}{99 \cdot 101}.$$

Writing in Mathematics

53. Explain what is meant by the partial fraction decomposition of a rational expression.

54. Explain how to find the partial fraction decomposition of a rational expression with distinct linear factors in the denominator.

55. Explain how to find the partial fraction decomposition of a rational expression with a repeated linear factor in the denominator.

56. Explain how to find the partial fraction decomposition of a rational expression with a prime quadratic factor in the denominator.

57. Explain how to find the partial fraction decomposition of a rational expression with a repeated, prime quadratic factor in the denominator.

58. How can you verify your result for the partial fraction decomposition for a given rational expression without using a graphing utility?

Technology Exercise

59. Use the $\boxed{\text{TABLE}}$ feature of a graphing utility to verify any three of the decompositions that you obtained in Exercises 9–42.

Critical Thinking Exercises

60. Use an extension of the Study Tip at the top of page 744 to describe how to set up the partial fraction decomposition of a rational expression that contains powers of a prime cubic factor in the denominator. Give an example of such a decomposition.

61. Find the partial fraction decomposition of

$$\frac{4x^2 + 5x - 9}{x^3 - 6x - 9}.$$

5

Polynomials and Polynomial Functions

Taken from:
Intermediate Algebra, Third Edition, by Elayn Martin-Gay

POLYNOMIAL FUNCTIONS AND ADDING AND SUBTRACTING POLYNOMIALS

A Define Term, Constant, Polynomial, Monomial, Binomial, Trinomial, Degree of a Term, and Degree of a Polynomial.

B Combine Like Terms.

C Add Polynomials.

D Subtract Polynomials.

E Evaluate Polynomial Functions.

Objective **A** Defining a Polynomial and Related Terms

A **term** is a number or the product of a number and one or more variables raised to powers. The **numerical coefficient,** or simply the **coefficient,** is the numerical factor of a term.

Term	Numerical Coefficient of Term
$-1.2x^5$	-1.2
x^3y	1
$-z$	-1
2	2
$\dfrac{x^9}{7}\left(\text{or }\dfrac{1}{7}x^9\right)$	$\dfrac{1}{7}$

If a term contains only a number, it is called a **constant term,** or simply a **constant.**

A **polynomial** is a finite sum of terms in which all variables are raised to non-negative integer powers and no variables appear in any denominator.

Polynomials	Not Polynomials	
$4x^5y + 7xz$	$5x^{-3} + 2x$	Negative integer exponent
$-5x^3 + 2x + \dfrac{2}{3}$	$\dfrac{6}{x^2} - 5x + 1$	Variable in denominator

A polynomial that contains only one variable is called a **polynomial in one variable.** For example, $3x^2 - 2x + 7$ is a **polynomial in x.** This polynomial in x is written in **descending order** since the terms are listed in descending order of the variable's exponents. (The term 7 can be thought of as $7x^0$.) The following examples are polynomials in one variable written in descending order:

$$4x^3 - \frac{7}{8}x^2 + 5 \qquad y^2 - 4.7 \qquad \frac{8a^4}{11} - 7a^2 + \frac{4a}{3}$$

A **monomial** is a polynomial consisting of one term. A **binomial** is a polynomial consisting of two terms. A **trinomial** is a polynomial consisting of three terms.

Helpful Hint
We will write answers that are polynomials in one variable in descending order.

Monomials	Binomials	Trinomials
ax^2	$x + y$	$x^2 + 4xy + y^2$
$-3x$	$6y^2 - 2.9$	$-x^4 + 3x^3 + 0.1$
4	$\dfrac{5}{7}z^3 - 2z$	$8y^2 - 2y - \dfrac{10}{17}$

By definition, all monomials, binomials, and trinomials are also polynomials.
Each term of a polynomial has a **degree.**

Degree of a Term

The **degree of a term** is the sum of the exponents on the *variables* contained in the term.

Copyright 2007 Pearson Education, Inc.

PRACTICE PROBLEMS 1–5

Determine the degree of each term.

1. $2x^3$ **2.** 7^2x^4

3. x **4.** $15xy^2z^4$

5. 9.1

EXAMPLES Determine the degree of each term.

1. $3x^2$ The exponent on x is 2, so the degree of the term is 2.

2. -2^3x^5 The exponent on x is 5, so the degree of the term is 5. (Recall that the degree is the sum of the exponents on *only* the *variables*).

3. y The degree of y, or y^1, is 1.

4. $12x^2yz^3$ The degree is the sum of the exponents on the variables, or $2 + 1 + 3 = 6$.

5. 5.27 The degree of 5.27, which can be written as $5.27x^0$, is 0.

▣ **Work Practice Problems 1–5**

From the preceding examples, we can say that the degree of a constant is 0. Also, the term 0 has no degree.

Each polynomial also has a degree.

Degree of a Polynomial

The **degree of a polynomial** is the greatest degree of any of its terms.

PRACTICE PROBLEMS 6–8

Determine the degree of each polynomial and indicate whether the polynomial is a monomial, binomial, or trinomial.

6. $4x^5 + 7x^3 - 1$

7. $-2xy^2z$

8. $y^3 + 6y$

EXAMPLES Determine the degree of each polynomial and also indicate whether the polynomial is a monomial, binomial, or trinomial.

	Polynomial	Degree	Classification
6.	$7x^3 - \dfrac{3}{4}x + 2$	3	Trinomial
7.	$-xyz$	$1 + 1 + 1 = 3$	Monomial
8.	$x^4 - 16.5$	4	Binomial

▣ **Work Practice Problems 6–8**

PRACTICE PROBLEM 9

Determine the degree of the polynomial $7x^2y - 6x^2yz + 2 - 4y^3$.

EXAMPLE 9 Determine the degree of the polynomial

$$3xy + x^2y^2 - 5x^2 - 6.7$$

Solution: The degree of each term is

$$3xy + x^2y^2 - 5x^2 - 6.7$$
$$\downarrow \qquad \downarrow \qquad \downarrow \qquad \downarrow$$
Degree: 2   4   2   0

The greatest degree of any term is 4, so the degree of this polynomial is 4.

▣ **Work Practice Problem 9**

Objective **B** Combining Like Terms

Before we add polynomials, recall from Section 1.5 that terms are considered to be **like terms** if they contain exactly the same variables raised to exactly the same powers.

Like Terms	**Unlike Terms**
$-5x^2, -x^2$	$4x^2, 3x$
$7xy^3z, -2xzy^3$	$12x^2y^3, -2xy^3$

To simplify a polynomial, we **combine like terms** by using the distributive property. For example, by the distributive property,

$$5x + 7x = (5 + 7)x = 12x$$

EXAMPLES Simplify each polynomial by combining like terms.

10. $-12x^2 + 7x^2 - 6x = (-12 + 7)x^2 - 6x = -5x^2 - 6x$

11. $3xy - 2x + 5xy - x = 3xy + 5xy - 2x - x$
$$= (3 + 5)xy + (-2 - 1)x$$
$$= 8xy - 3x$$

☐ **Work Practice Problems 10–11**

Helpful Hint

These two terms are unlike terms. They cannot be combined.

PRACTICE PROBLEMS 10–11

Simplify each polynomial by combining like terms.

10. $10x^3 - 12x^3 - 3x$

11. $-6ab + 2a + 12ab - a$

Objective ⒞ Adding Polynomials

Now we have reviewed the skills we need to add polynomials.

Adding Polynomials

To add polynomials, combine all like terms.

EXAMPLE 12 Add $11x^3 - 12x^2 + x - 3$ and $x^3 - 10x + 5$.

Solution:

$(11x^3 - 12x^2 + x - 3) + (x^3 - 10x + 5)$
$= 11x^3 + x^3 - 12x^2 + x - 10x - 3 + 5$ Group like terms.
$= 12x^3 - 12x^2 - 9x + 2$ Combine like terms.

☐ **Work Practice Problem 12**

PRACTICE PROBLEM 12

Add $14x^4 - 6x^3 + x^2 - 6$ and $x^3 - 5x^2 + 1$.

Sometimes it is more convenient to add polynomials vertically. To do this, we line up like terms beneath one another and then add like terms.

EXAMPLE 13 Add $11x^3 - 12x^2 + x - 3$ and $x^3 - 10x + 5$ vertically.

Solution:

$$\begin{array}{r} 11x^3 - 12x^2 + x - 3 \\ x^3 \qquad - 10x + 5 \\ \hline 12x^3 - 12x^2 - 9x + 2 \end{array}$$ Line up like terms.
Combine like terms.

This example is the same as Example 12, only here we added vertically.

☐ **Work Practice Problem 13**

PRACTICE PROBLEM 13

Add $10y^3 - y^2 + 4y - 11$ and $y^3 - 4y^2 + 3y$ vertically.

EXAMPLE 14 Add: $(7x^3y - xy^3 + 11) + (6x^3y - 4)$

Solution: To add these polynomials, we remove the parentheses and group like terms.

$(7x^3y - xy^3 + 11) + (6x^3y - 4)$
$= 7x^3y - xy^3 + 11 + 6x^3y - 4$ Remove parentheses.
$= 7x^3y + 6x^3y - xy^3 + 11 - 4$ Group like terms.
$= 13x^3y - xy^3 + 7$ Combine like terms.

☐ **Work Practice Problem 14**

PRACTICE PROBLEM 14

Add:
$(4x^2y - xy^2 + 5) + (-6x^2y - 1)$

Objective ⒟ Subtracting Polynomials

The definition of subtraction of real numbers can be extended to apply to polynomials. To subtract a number, we add its opposite:

$$a - b = a + (-b)$$

Answers

10. $-2x^3 - 3x$, **11.** $6ab + a$,
12. $14x^4 - 5x^3 - 4x^2 - 5$,
13. $11y^3 - 5y^2 + 7y - 11$,
14. $-2x^2y - xy^2 + 4$

Likewise, to subtract a polynomial we add its opposite. In other words, if P and Q are polynomials, then

$$P - Q = P + (-Q)$$

The polynomial $-Q$ is the **opposite,** or **additive inverse,** of the polynomial Q. We can find $-Q$ by changing the sign of each term of Q.

✔**Concept Check**　Which polynomial is the opposite of $16x^3 - 5x + 7$?

a. $-16x^3 - 5x + 7$　　　　　　**b.** $-16x^3 + 5x - 7$
c. $16x^3 + 5x + 7$　　　　　　　**d.** $-16x^3 + 5x + 7$

Subtracting Polynomials

To subtract polynomials, change the signs of the terms of the polynomial being subtracted and then add.

Review the example below.

To subtract, change the signs; then add.

$$(3x^2 + 4x - 7) - (3x^2 - 2x - 5) = (3x^2 + 4x - 7) + (-3x^2 + 2x + 5)$$
$$= 3x^2 + 4x - 7 - 3x^2 + 2x + 5$$
$$= 6x - 2 \qquad \text{Combine like terms.}$$

PRACTICE PROBLEM 15

Subtract:
$(7x^4 - 8x^2 + x)$
$\quad - (-9x^4 + x^2 - 18)$

EXAMPLE 15　Subtract:　$(12z^5 - 12z^3 + z) - (-3z^4 + z^3 + 12z)$

Solution:　First we change the sign of each term of the second polynomial, and then we add the result to the first polynomial.

$(12z^5 - 12z^3 + z) - (-3z^4 + z^3 + 12z)$
$= 12z^5 - 12z^3 + z + 3z^4 - z^3 - 12z$　　Change signs and add.
$= 12z^5 + 3z^4 - 12z^3 - z^3 + z - 12z$　　Group like terms; write in descending order.
$= 12z^5 + 3z^4 - 13z^3 - 11z$　　Combine like terms.

▢ **Work Practice Problem 15**

PRACTICE PROBLEM 16

Subtract
$(2y^4 + 4y) - (6y^4 + 7y^3 - 3y)$
vertically.

EXAMPLE 16　Subtract $(10x^3 - 7x^2) - (4x^3 - 3x^2 + 2)$ vertically.

Solution:　To subtract these polynomials, we add the opposite of the second polynomial to the first one.

$$\begin{array}{r} 10x^3 - 7x^2 \\ -(4x^3 - 3x^2 + 2) \\ \hline \end{array} \quad \text{is equivalent to} \quad \begin{array}{r} 10x^3 - 7x^2 \\ -4x^3 + 3x^2 - 2 \\ \hline 6x^3 - 4x^2 - 2 \end{array} \quad \text{Add.}$$

▢ **Work Practice Problem 16**

Answers

15. $16x^4 - 9x^2 + x + 18$,
16. $-4y^4 - 7y^3 + 7y$

✔ **Concept Check Answers**

b;
With parentheses removed, the expression should be
$7z - 5 - 3z + 4 = 4z - 1$

✔**Concept Check**　Why is the following subtraction incorrect?

$(7z - 5) - (3z - 4)$
$= 7z - 5 - 3z - 4$
$= 4z - 9$

EXAMPLE 17 Subtract $4x^3y^2 - 3x^2y^2 + 2y^2$ from $10x^3y^2 - 7x^2y^2$.

Solution: Notice the order of the expressions, and then write "Subtract $4x^3y^2 - 3x^2y^2 + 2y^2$ from $10x^3y^2 - 7x^2y^2$" as a mathematical expression. (For example, if we subtract 2 from 8, we would write $8 - 2 = 6$.)

$(10x^3y^2 - 7x^2y^2) - (4x^3y^2 - 3x^2y^2 + 2y^2)$

$= 10x^3y^2 - 7x^2y^2 - 4x^3y^2 + 3x^2y^2 - 2y^2$ Remove parentheses.

$= 6x^3y^2 - 4x^2y^2 - 2y^2$ Combine like terms.

◻ **Work Practice Problem 17**

PRACTICE PROBLEM 17

Subtract $3a^2b^3 - 4ab^2 + 6a$ from $7a^2b^3 - ab^2$.

Objective **E** Evaluating Polynomial Functions

Recall function notation first introduced in Section 3.6. At times it is convenient to use function notation to represent polynomials. For example, we may write $P(x)$ to represent the polynomial $3x^4 - 2x^2 - 5$. In symbols, we would write

$P(x) = 3x^4 - 2x^2 - 5$

This function is called a **polynomial function** because the expression $3x^4 - 2x^2 - 5$ is a polynomial.

Helpful Hint

Recall that the symbol $P(x)$ **does not mean** P times x. It is a special symbol used to denote a function.

EXAMPLES If $P(x) = 3x^4 - 2x^2 - 5$, find each function value.

18. $P(1) = 3(1)^4 - 2(1)^2 - 5 = -4$ Let $x = 1$ in the function $P(x)$.

19. $P(-2) = 3(-2)^4 - 2(-2)^2 - 5$ Let $x = -2$ in the function $P(x)$.

$= 3(16) - 2(4) - 5$

$= 35$

◻ **Work Practice Problems 18–19**

PRACTICE PROBLEMS 18–19

If $P(x) = 5x^4 - 3x^2 + 7$, find each function value.

18. $P(2)$
19. $P(-1)$

Many real-world phenomena are modeled by polynomial functions. If the polynomial function model is given, we can often find the solution of a problem by evaluating the function at a certain value.

EXAMPLE 20 Finding the Height of an Object

The Millau Viaduct, at 1125 feet, is the highest bridge in the world and overlooks the river Tarn in France. An object is dropped from the top of this bridge. Neglecting air resistance, the height of the object at time t seconds is given by the polynomial function $P(t) = -16t^2 + 1125$. Find the height of the object when $t = 1$ second and when $t = 8$ seconds.

Solution: To find the height of the object at 1 second, we find $P(1)$.

$P(t) = -16t^2 + 1125$

$P(1) = -16(1)^2 + 1125$

$P(1) = 1109$

Continued on next page

PRACTICE PROBLEM 20

Use the polynomial function in Example 20 to find the height of the object when $t = 3$ seconds and $t = 7$ seconds.

Answers

17. $4a^2b^3 + 3ab^2 - 6a$,
18. $P(2) = 75$,   **19.** $P(-1) = 9$,
20. at 3 sec, height is 981 ft; at 7 sec, height is 341 ft

When $t = 1$ second, the height of the object is 1109 feet.

To find the height of the object at 8 seconds, we find $P(8)$.

$$P(t) = -16t^2 + 1125$$
$$P(8) = -16(8)^2 + 1125$$
$$P(8) = -1024 + 1125$$
$$P(8) = 101$$

When $t = 8$ seconds, the height of the object is 101 feet. Notice that as time t increases, the height of the object decreases.

🔲 **Work Practice Problem 20**

🖩 CALCULATOR EXPLORATIONS Graphing

A graphing calculator may be used to check addition and subtraction of polynomials in one variable. For example, to check the polynomial subtraction statement

$$(3x^2 - 6x + 9) - (x^2 - 5x + 6) = 2x^2 - x + 3$$

graph both

$$Y_1 = (3x^2 - 6x + 9) - (x^2 - 5x + 6) \quad \text{Left side of equation}$$

and

$$Y_2 = 2x^2 - x + 3 \quad \text{Right side of equation}$$

on the same screen and see that their graphs coincide. (*Note:* If the graphs do not coincide, we can be sure that a mistake has been made either in combining polynomials or in calculator keystrokes. However, if the graphs appear to coincide, we cannot be sure that our work is correct. This is because it is possible for the graphs to differ so slightly that we do not notice it.)

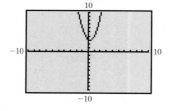

The graphs of Y_1 and Y_2 are shown. The graphs appear to coincide, so the subtraction statement

$$(3x^2 - 6x + 9) - (x^2 - 5x + 6) = 2x^2 - x + 3$$

appears to be correct.

Perform each indicated operation. Then use the procedure described above to check your work.

1. $(2x^2 + 7x + 6) + (x^3 - 6x^2 - 14)$

2. $(-14x^3 - x + 2) + (-x^3 + 3x^2 + 4x)$

3. $(1.8x^2 - 6.8x - 1.7) - (3.9x^2 - 3.6x)$

4. $(-4.8x^2 + 12.5x - 7.8) - (3.1x^2 - 7.8x)$

5. $(1.29x - 5.68) + (7.69x^2 - 2.55x + 10.98)$

6. $(-0.98x^2 - 1.56x + 5.57) + (4.36x - 3.71)$

Mental Math

Add or subtract as indicated.

1. $7x + 3x$ **2.** $8x - 2x$ **3.** $14y - 9y$ **4.** $14y + 9y$ **5.** $3z - 12z$ **6.** $2z - 6z$

5.1 EXERCISE SET

Objective A *Find the degree of each term. See Examples 1 through 5.*

1. 4   **2.** 7   **3.** $5x^2$ **4.** $-z^3$ **5.** $-3xy^2$

6. $12x^3z$ **7.** -8^7y^3 **8.** $-9^{11}y^5$ **9.** $3.78ab^3c^5$ **10.** $9.11r^2st^{12}$

Find the degree of each polynomial and indicate whether the polynomial is a monomial, binomial, trinomial, or none of these. See Examples 6 through 9.

11. $6x + 0.3$

12. $7x - 0.8$

13. $3x^2 - 2x + 5$

14. $5x^2 - 3x - 2$

15. -3^4xy^2

16. -7^5abc

 17. $x^2y - 4xy^2 + 5x + y^4$

18. $-2x^2y - 3y^2 + 4x + y^5$

Objective B *Simplify each polynomial by combining like terms. See Examples 10 and 11.*

19. $5y + y - 6y^2 - y^2$

20. $-x + 3x - 4x^2 - 9x^2$

21. $4x + 7x - 3x^4$

22. $-8y + 9y + 4y^6$

23. $4x^2y + 2x - 3x^2y - \dfrac{1}{2} - 7x$

24. $-8xy^2 + 4x - x + 2xy^2 - \dfrac{11}{15}$

Objective C *Add. See Examples 12 through 14.*

25. $(9y^2 + y - 8) + (9y^2 - y - 9)$

26. $(x^2 + 4x - 7) + (8x^2 + 9x - 7)$

27. $(x^2 + xy - y^2)$ and $(2x^2 - 4xy + 7y^2)$

28. $(6x^2 + 5x + 7)$ and $(x^2 + 6x - 3)$

29. $\begin{array}{r} x^2 - 6x + 3 \\ + \quad\ (2x + 5) \\ \hline \end{array}$

30. $\begin{array}{r} -2x^2 + 3x - 9 \\ + \qquad (2x - 3) \\ \hline \end{array}$

31. $(7x^3y - 4xy + 8) + (5x^3y + 4xy + 8x)$

32. $(9xyz + 4x - y) + (-9xyz - 3x + y + 2)$

33. $(0.6x^3 + 1.2x^2 - 4.5x + 9.1) + (3.9x^3 - x^2 + 0.7x)$ **34.** $(9.3y^2 - y + 12.8) + (2.6y^2 + 4.4y - 8.9)$

Objective **D** *Subtract. See Examples 15 through 17.*

35. $(9y^2 - 7y + 5) - (8y^2 - 7y + 2)$ **36.** $(2x^2 + 3x + 12) - (20x^2 - 5x - 7)$

37. Subtract $(6x^2 - 3x)$ from $(4x^2 + 2x)$.   **38.** Subtract $(8y^2 + 4x)$ from $(y^2 + x)$.

39. $\begin{aligned}6y^2 - 6y + 4 \\ \underline{-(-y^2 + 6y + 7)}\end{aligned}$ **40.** $\begin{aligned}-4x^3 + 4x^2 - 4x \\ \underline{-(2x^3 - 2x^2 + 3x)}\end{aligned}$

41. $(9x^3 - 2x^2 + 4x - 7) - (2x^3 - 6x^2 - 4x + 3)$ **42.** $(3x^2 + 6xy + 3y^2) - (8x^2 - 6xy - y^2)$

43. Subtract $\left(y^2 + 4yx + \dfrac{1}{7}\right)$ from $\left(-19y^2 + 7yx + \dfrac{1}{7}\right)$.   **44.** Subtract $\left(13x^2 + x^2y - \dfrac{1}{4}\right)$ from $\left(3x^2 - 4x^2y - \dfrac{1}{4}\right)$.

Objectives **B** **C** **D** **Mixed Practice** *Perform indicated operations and simplify. See Examples 10 through 17.*

45. $(-3x + 8) + (-3x^2 + 3x - 5)$ **46.** $(-5y^2 - 2y + 4) + (3y + 7)$

47. $(5y^4 - 7y^2 + x^2 - 3) + (-3y^4 + 2y^2 + 4)$ **48.** $(8x^4 - 14x^2 + x + 6) + (-12x^6 - 21x^4 - 9x^2)$

49. $(4x^2 - 6x + 2) - (-x^2 + 3x + 5)$ **50.** $(7x^2 + x + 1) - (6x^2 + x - 1)$

51. $(5x^2 + x + 9) - (2x^2 - 9)$ **52.** $(4x - 4) - (-x - 4)$

53. $(5x - 11) + (-x - 2)$ **54.** $(3x^2 - 2x) + (-5x^2 - 9x)$

55. $(3x^3 - b + 2a - 6) + (-4x^3 + b + 6a - 6)$ **56.** $(9y^3 - a + 7b - 3) + (-2y^3 + a + 6b - 8)$

57. $(14ab - 10a^2b + 6b^2) - (18a^2 - 20a^2b - 6b^2)$ **58.** $(13x^2 - 26x^2y^2 + 4) - (19x^2 + x^2y^2 - 11)$

59. $\begin{aligned}3x^2 + 15x + 8 \\ \underline{+(2x^2 +\ \ 7x + 8)}\end{aligned}$ **60.** $\begin{aligned}9x^2 + 9x - 4 \\ \underline{+(7x^2 - 3x - 4)}\end{aligned}$

61. $(7x^2 - 5) + (-3x^2 - 2) - (4x^2 - 7)$ **62.** $(9y^2 - 3) + (-4y^2 + 1) - (5y^2 - 2)$

63. $(-3 + 4x^2 + 7xy^2) + (2x^3 - x^2 + xy^2)$ **64.** $(-3x^2y + 4) + (-7x^2y - 8y)$

65. $\begin{aligned}3x^2 - 4x + 8 \\ \underline{-\quad\ \ \ (5x - 7)}\end{aligned}$ **66.** $\begin{aligned}-3x^2 - 4x + 8 \\ \underline{-\quad\ \ \ (5x + 12)}\end{aligned}$

67. Subtract $(3x + 7)$ from the sum of $(7x^2 + 4x + 9)$ and $(8x^2 + 7x - 8)$.

68. Subtract $(9x + 8)$ from the sum of $(3x^2 - 2x - x^3 + 2)$ and $(5x^2 - 8x - x^3 + 4)$.

69. $\left(\dfrac{2}{3}x^2 - \dfrac{1}{6}x + \dfrac{5}{6}\right) - \left(\dfrac{1}{3}x^2 + \dfrac{5}{6}x - \dfrac{1}{6}\right)$

70. $\left(\dfrac{3}{16}x^2 + \dfrac{5}{8}x - \dfrac{1}{4}\right) - \left(\dfrac{5}{16}x^2 - \dfrac{3}{8}x + \dfrac{3}{4}\right)$

Objective **E** *If $P(x) = x^2 + x + 1$ and $Q(x) = 5x^2 - 1$, find each function value. See Examples 18 and 19.*

71. $P(7)$ 　　**72.** $Q(4)$ 　　**73.** $Q(-10)$ 　　**74.** $P(-4)$ 　　**75.** $P(0)$ 　　**76.** $Q(0)$

Solve. See Example 20.

The surface area of a rectangular box is given by the polynomial

$$2HL + 2LW + 2HW$$

and is measured in square units. In business, surface area is often calculated to help determine cost of materials.

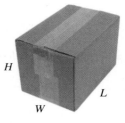

77. A rectangular box is to be constructed to hold a new camcorder. The box is to have dimensions 5 inches by 4 inches by 9 inches. Find the surface area of the box.

78. Suppose it has been determined that a box of dimensions 4 inches by 4 inches by 8.5 inches can be used to contain the camcorder in Exercise 77. Find the surface area of this box and calculate the square inches of material saved by using this box instead of the box in Exercise 77.

79. A projectile is fired upward from the ground with an initial velocity of 300 feet per second. Neglecting air resistance, the height of the projectile at any time t can be described by the polynomial function $P(t) = -16t^2 + 300t$. Find the height of the projectile at each given time.
  a. $t = 1$ second
  b. $t = 2$ seconds
  c. $t = 3$ seconds
  d. $t = 4$ seconds
  e. Explain why the height increases and then decreases as time passes.
  f. Approximate (to the nearest second) how long before the object hits the ground.

80. An object is thrown upward with an initial velocity of 25 feet per second from the top of Washington's head on Mount Rushmore. The height of the object above the ground at any time t can be described by the polynomial function $P(t) = -16t^2 + 25t + 500$. Find the height of the projectile at each given time.
  a. $t = 1$ second
  b. $t = 3$ seconds
  c. $t = 5$ seconds
  d. approximate (to the nearest second) how long before the object hits the ground.

81. The polynomial function $P(x) = 45x - 100,000$ models the relationship between the number of computer briefcases x that a company sells and the profit the company makes, $P(x)$. Find $P(4000)$, the profit from selling 4000 computer briefcases.

82. The total cost (in dollars) for MCD, Inc., Manufacturing Company to produce x blank audio-cassette tapes per week is given by the polynomial function $C(x) = 0.8x + 10,000$. Find the total cost of producing 20,000 tapes per week.

83. The total revenues (in dollars) for MCD, Inc., Manufacturing Company to sell x blank audiocassette tapes per week is given by the polynomial function $R(x) = 2x$. Find the total revenue from selling 20,000 tapes per week.

Review

Use the distributive property to multiply. See Section 1.3.

84. $5(3x - 2)$

85. $-7(2z - 6y)$

86. $-2(x^2 - 5x + 6)$

87. $5(-3y^2 - 2y + 7)$

88. In business, profit equals revenue minus cost, or $P(x) = R(x) - C(x)$. Find the profit function for MCD, Inc. by subtracting the functions given in Exercises 82 and 83.

Concept Extensions

Solve. See the Concept Checks in this section.

89. Which polynomial(s) is the opposite of $8x - 6$?
  a. $-(8x - 6)$
  b. $8x + 6$
  c. $-8x + 6$
  d. $-8x - 6$

90. Which polynomial(s) is the opposite of $-y^5 + 10y^3 - 2.3$?
  a. $y^5 + 10y^3 + 2.3$
  b. $-y^5 - 10y^3 - 2.3$
  c. $y^5 + 10y^3 - 2.3$
  d. $y^5 - 10y^3 + 2.3$

91. Correct the subtraction.
$$(12x - 1.7) - (15x + 6.2) = 12x - 1.7 - 15x + 6.2$$
$$= -3x + 4.5$$

92. Correct the addition.
$$(12x - 1.7) + (15x + 6.2) = 12x - 1.7 + 15x + 6.2$$
$$= 27x + 7.9$$

93. Write a function, $P(x)$, so that $P(0) = 7$.

94. Write a function, $R(x)$, so that $R(1) = 2$.

95. In your own words, describe how to find the degree of a term.

96. In your own words, describe how to find the degree of a polynomial.

97. The function $f(x) = 0.014x^2 + 0.043x + 0.584$ can be used to approximate the amazing growth of the number of Web logs (blogs) appearing on the Internet from June 2003 through December 2004, where x is the number of months after June 2003 and y is the number of new Web logs (in millions). Round answers to the nearest tenth of a million. (*Source:* Clickz.com)
  a. Approximate the number of Web logs on the Internet in June 2003.
  b. Approximate the number of Web logs on the Internet in June 2004.
  c. Use this function to estimate the number of Web logs on the Internet in June 2005.
  d. From parts (a), (b), and (c), determine whether the number of Web logs on the Internet is increasing at a steady rate. Explain why or why not.

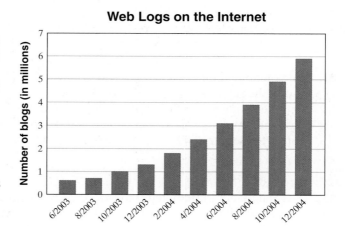

98. The function $f(x) = -1.6x^2 + 9.6x + 67.6$ can be used to approximate the number of Americans enrolled in health maintenance organizations (HMOs) during the period 1997–2003, where x is the number of years after 1997 and $f(x)$ is the number of Americans in millions. Round answers to the nearest tenth of a million. (*Source:* Based on data from *Health, United States, 2004,* National Center for Health Statistics)

    a. Approximate the number of Americans enrolled in HMOs in 1997.
    b. Approximate the number of Americans enrolled in HMOs in 2003.
    c. Use the function to predict the number of Americans enrolled in HMOs in 2006.
    d. From parts (a), (b), and (c), determine whether the number of American enrolled in HMOs is changing at a steady rate. Explain why or why not.

If $P(x) = 3x + 3$, $Q(x) = 4x^2 - 6x + 3$, and $R(x) = 5x^2 - 7$, find each function.

99. $P(x) + Q(x)$ **100.** $Q(x) - R(x)$

101. If $P(x) = 2x - 3$, find $P(a)$, $P(-x)$, and $P(x + h)$.

Perform each indicated operation.

102. $(8x^{2y} - 7x^y + 3) + (-4x^{2y} + 9x^y - 14)$ **103.** $(14z^{5x} + 3z^{2x} + z) - (2z^{5x} - 10z^{2x} + 3z)$

Find each perimeter.

△ **104.**

$(x + y)$ units

$(3x^2 - x + 2y)$ units

△ **105.**

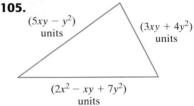

$(5xy - y^2)$ units

$(3xy + 4y^2)$ units

$(2x^2 - xy + 7y^2)$ units

A Multiply Any Two Polynomials.

B Multiply Binomials.

C Square Binomials.

D Multiply the Sum and Difference of Two Terms.

E Multiply Three or More Polynomials.

F Evaluate Polynomial Functions.

PRACTICE PROBLEMS 1–2

Multiply.
1. $(7y^2)(4y^5)$
2. $(-a^2b^3c)(10ab^2c^{12})$

PRACTICE PROBLEMS 3–5

Multiply.
3. $4x(3x - 2)$
4. $-2y^3(5y^2 - 2y + 6)$
5. $-a^2b(4a^3 - 2ab + b^2)$

Answers
1. $28y^7$, 2. $-10a^3b^5c^{13}$, 3. $12x^2 - 8x$,
4. $-10y^5 + 4y^4 - 12y^3$,
5. $-4a^5b + 2a^3b^2 - a^2b^3$

✔ **Concept Check Answer**
$4x(x - 5) + 2x$
$= 4x(x) + 4x(-5) + 2x$
$= 4x^2 - 20x + 2x$
$= 4x^2 - 18x$

5.2 MULTIPLYING POLYNOMIALS

Objective **A** Multiplying Any Two Polynomials

Properties of real numbers and exponents are used continually in the process of multiplying polynomials. To multiply monomials, for example, we apply the commutative and associative properties of real numbers and the product rule for exponents.

EXAMPLES Multiply.

Group like bases and apply the product rule for exponents.

1. $(2x^3)(5x^6) = 2(5)(x^3)(x^6) = 10x^{3+6} = 10x^9$
2. $(7y^4z^4)(-xy^{11}z^5) = 7(-1)x(y^4y^{11})(z^4z^5) = -7xy^{4+11}z^{4+5} = -7xy^{15}z^9$

◙ **Work Practice Problems 1–2**

Helpful Hint

See Sections 1.6 and 1.7 to review exponential expressions further.

To multiply a monomial by a polynomial other than a monomial, we use an expanded form of the distributive property.

$$a(b + c + d + \cdots + z) = ab + ac + ad + \cdots + az$$

Notice that the monomial a is multiplied by each term of the polynomial.

EXAMPLES Multiply.

3. $2x(5x - 4) = 2x(5x) + 2x(-4)$ Use the distributive property.
    $= 10x^2 - 8x$ Multiply.

4. $-3x^2(4x^2 - 6x + 1) = -3x^2(4x^2) + (-3x^2)(-6x) + (-3x^2)(1)$
    $= -12x^4 + 18x^3 - 3x^2$

5. $-xy(7x^2y + 3xy - 11) = -xy(7x^2y) + (-xy)(3xy) + (-xy)(-11)$
    $= -7x^3y^2 - 3x^2y^2 + 11xy$

◙ **Work Practice Problems 3–5**

✔ **Concept Check** Find the error:

$4x(x - 5) + 2x$
$= 4x(x) + 4x(-5) + 4x(2x)$
$= 4x^2 - 20x + 8x^2$
$= 12x^2 - 20x$

To Multiply any two polynomials, we can use the following.

Multiplying Two Polynomials

To multiply any two polynomials, use the distributive property and multiply each term of one polynomial by each term of the other polynomial. Then combine any like terms.

EXAMPLE 6 Multiply: $(x + 3)(2x + 5)$

Solution: We multiply each term of $(x + 3)$ by $(2x + 5)$.

$(x + 3)(2x + 5) = x(2x + 5) + 3(2x + 5)$ Use the distributive property.
$\qquad\qquad\qquad = 2x^2 + 5x + 6x + 15$ Use the distributive property again.
$\qquad\qquad\qquad = 2x^2 + 11x + 15$ Combine like terms.

◻ **Work Practice Problem 6**

EXAMPLE 7 Multiply: $(2x - 3)(5x^2 - 6x + 7)$

Solution: We multiply each term of $(2x - 3)$ by each term of $(5x^2 - 6x + 7)$.

$(2x - 3)(5x^2 - 6x + 7) = 2x(5x^2 - 6x + 7) + (-3)(5x^2 - 6x + 7)$
$\qquad\qquad\qquad\qquad\qquad = 10x^3 - 12x^2 + 14x - 15x^2 + 18x - 21$
$\qquad\qquad\qquad\qquad\qquad = 10x^3 - 27x^2 + 32x - 21$ Combine like terms.

◻ **Work Practice Problem 7**

Sometimes polynomials are easier to multiply vertically, in the same way we multiply real numbers. When multiplying vertically, we line up like terms in the **partial products** vertically. This makes combining like terms easier.

EXAMPLE 8 Multiply vertically: $(4x^2 + 7)(x^2 + 2x + 8)$

Solution:

$$
\begin{array}{r}
x^2 + 2x + 8 \\
4x^2 + 7 \\
\hline
7x^2 + 14x + 56 \\
4x^4 + 8x^3 + 32x^2 \\
\hline
4x^4 + 8x^3 + 39x^2 + 14x + 56
\end{array}
$$

$7(x^2 + 2x + 8)$
$4x^2(x^2 + 2x + 8)$
Combine like terms.

◻ **Work Practice Problem 8**

Objective B Multiplying Binomials

When multiplying a binomial by a binomial, we can follow a special order for multiplying terms, called the **FOIL** order. The letters of FOIL stand for "**F**irst–**O**uter–**I**nner–**L**ast." To illustrate this method, let's multiply $(2x - 3)$ by $(3x + 1)$.

Multiply the **F**irst terms of each binomial. $(2x - 3)(3x + 1)$ F $2x(3x) = 6x^2$

Multiply the **O**uter terms of each binomial. $(2x - 3)(3x + 1)$ O $2x(1) = 2x$

Multiply the **I**nner terms of each binomial. $(2x - 3)(3x + 1)$ I $-3(3x) = -9x$

Multiply the **L**ast terms of each binomial. $(2x - 3)(3x + 1)$ L $-3(1) = -3$

Combine like terms.

$6x^2 + 2x - 9x - 3 = 6x^2 - 7x - 3$

PRACTICE PROBLEM 6
Multiply: $(x + 2)(3x + 1)$

PRACTICE PROBLEM 7
Multiply:
$(5x - 1)(2x^2 - x + 4)$

PRACTICE PROBLEM 8
Multiply vertically:
$(3x^2 + 5)(x^2 - 6x + 1)$

Answers
6. $3x^2 + 7x + 2$,
7. $10x^3 - 7x^2 + 21x - 4$,
8. $3x^4 - 18x^3 + 8x^2 - 30x + 5$

Use the FOIL order to multiply $(x - 7)(x + 5)$.

Helpful Hint

The FOIL *order* is simply that. It is an *order* you may choose to use when multiplying two binomials.

PRACTICE PROBLEMS 10–11

Use the FOIL order to multiply.
10. $(4x - 3)(x - 6)$
11. $(6x^2 + 5y)(2x^2 - y)$

EXAMPLE 9 Use the FOIL order to multiply $(x - 1)(x + 2)$.

Solution:

| First | Outer | Inner | Last |

$$(x - 1)(x + 2) = x \cdot x + x \cdot 2 + (-1)x + (-1)(2)$$
$$= x^2 + 2x - x - 2$$
$$= x^2 + x - 2 \qquad \text{Combine like terms.}$$

☐ **Work Practice Problem 9**

EXAMPLES Use the FOIL order to multiply.

| First | Outer | Inner | Last |

10. $(2x - 7)(3x - 4) = 2x(3x) + 2x(-4) + (-7)(3x) + (-7)(-4)$
$$= 6x^2 - 8x - 21x + 28$$
$$= 6x^2 - 29x + 28$$

| F | O | I | L |

11. $(3x^2 + y)(5x^2 - 2y) = 15x^4 - 6x^2y + 5x^2y - 2y^2$
$$= 15x^4 - x^2y - 2y^2$$

☐ **Work Practice Problems 10–11**

Objective C Squaring Binomials

The **square of a binomial** is a special case of the product of two binomials. By the FOIL order for multiplying two binomials, we have

$$(a + b)^2 = (a + b)(a + b)$$

| F | O | I | L |

$$= a^2 + ab + ba + b^2$$
$$= a^2 + 2ab + b^2$$

We can visualize this product geometrically by analyzing areas.

Area of square in the margin: $(a + b)^2$
Sum of areas of smaller rectangles: $a^2 + 2ab + b^2$
Thus, $(a + b)^2 = a^2 + 2ab + b^2$

The same pattern occurs for the square of a difference. In general, we have the following.

Square of a Binomial

$$(a + b)^2 = a^2 + 2ab + b^2 \qquad (a - b)^2 = a^2 - 2ab + b^2$$

In other words, a binomial squared is the sum of the first term squared, twice the product of both terms, and the second term squared.

Answers
9. $x^2 - 2x - 35$, 10. $4x^2 - 27x + 18$,
11. $12x^4 + 4x^2y - 5y^2$

EXAMPLES Multiply.

$$(a + b)^2 = a^2 + 2 \cdot a \cdot b + b^2$$

12. $(x + 5)^2 = x^2 + 2 \cdot x \cdot 5 + 5^2 = x^2 + 10x + 25$
13. $(x - 9)^2 = x^2 - 2 \cdot x \cdot 9 + 9^2 = x^2 - 18x + 81$
14. $(3x + 2z)^2 = (3x)^2 + 2(3x)(2z) + (2z)^2 = 9x^2 + 12xz + 4z^2$
15. $(4m^2 - 3n)^2 = (4m^2)^2 - 2(4m^2)(3n) + (3n)^2 = 16m^4 - 24m^2n + 9n^2$

▣ **Work Practice Problems 12–15**

Helpful Hint

Note that $(a + b)^2 = a^2 + 2ab + b^2$, not $a^2 + b^2$. Also,
$(a - b)^2 = a^2 - 2ab + b^2$, not $a^2 - b^2$.

Objective ◻ **Multiplying the Sum and Difference of Two Terms**

Another special product applies to the sum and difference of the same two terms. Multiply $(a + b)(a - b)$ to see a pattern.

$$(a + b)(a - b) = a^2 - ab + ba - b^2 = a^2 - b^2$$

Product of the Sum and Difference of Two Terms

$$(a + b)(a - b) = a^2 - b^2$$

In other words, the product of the sum and difference of the same two terms is the difference of the first term squared and the second term squared.

EXAMPLES Multiply.

$$(a + b) \ (a - b) \ = \ a^2 - b^2$$

16. $(x + 3)(x - 3) = x^2 - 3^2 = x^2 - 9$
17. $(4y - 1)(4y + 1) = (4y)^2 - 1^2 = 16y^2 - 1$
18. $(x^2 + 2y)(x^2 - 2y) = (x^2)^2 - (2y)^2 = x^4 - 4y^2$
19. $\left(3m^2 - \dfrac{1}{2}\right)\left(3m^2 + \dfrac{1}{2}\right) = (3m^2)^2 - \left(\dfrac{1}{2}\right)^2 = 9m^4 - \dfrac{1}{4}$

▣ **Work Practice Problems 16–19**

EXAMPLE 20 Multiply $[3 + (2a + b)]^2$.

Solution: Think of 3 as the first term and $(2a + b)$ as the second term, and apply the method for squaring a binomial.

$$[a \ + \ b \ ]^2 = a^2 + 2(a) \cdot b + b^2$$

$$[3 + (2a + b)]^2 = 3^2 + 2(3)(2a + b) + (2a + b)^2$$
$$= 9 + 6(2a + b) + (2a + b)^2$$
$$= 9 + 12a + 6b + (2a)^2 + 2(2a)(b) + b^2 \quad \text{Square } (2a + b).$$
$$= 9 + 12a + 6b + 4a^2 + 4ab + b^2$$

▣ **Work Practice Problem 20**

PRACTICE PROBLEMS 12–15

Multiply.
12. $(x + 3)^2$
13. $(y - 6)^2$
14. $(2x + 5y)^2$
15. $(6a^2 - 2b)^2$

PRACTICE PROBLEMS 16–19

Multiply.
16. $(x + 4)(x - 4)$
17. $(3m - 6)(3m + 6)$
18. $(a^2 + 5y)(a^2 - 5y)$
19. $\left(4y^2 - \dfrac{1}{3}\right)\left(4y^2 + \dfrac{1}{3}\right)$

PRACTICE PROBLEM 20

Multiply:
$$[2 - (3x + y)]^2$$

Answers
12. $x^2 + 6x + 9$, **13.** $y^2 - 12y + 36$,
14. $4x^2 + 20xy + 25y^2$,
15. $36a^4 - 24a^2b + 4b^2$,
16. $x^2 - 16$, **17.** $9m^2 - 36$,
18. $a^4 - 25y^2$, **19.** $16y^4 - \dfrac{1}{9}$,
20. $4 - 12x - 4y + 9x^2 + 6xy + y^2$

PRACTICE PROBLEM 21

Multiply:

$[(2x + 3y) - 2][(2x + 3y) + 2]$

EXAMPLE 21 Multiply: $[(5x - 2y) - 1][(5x - 2y) + 1]$

Solution: We can think of $(5x - 2y)$ as the first term and 1 as the second term. Then we can apply the method for the product of the sum and difference of two terms.

$$
\overbrace{a}^{} \quad - b \quad \overbrace{a}^{} \quad + b \;=\; \overbrace{a^2}^{} \quad - b^2
$$
$$
[\overbrace{(5x - 2y)}^{} - 1][\overbrace{(5x - 2y)}^{} + 1] = \overbrace{(5x - 2y)^2}^{} - 1^2
$$
$$
= (5x)^2 - 2(5x)(2y) + (2y)^2 - 1
$$
$$
\text{Square } (5x - 2y).
$$
$$
= 25x^2 - 20xy + 4y^2 - 1
$$

■ **Work Practice Problem 21**

Objective E **Multiplying Three or More Polynomials**

To multiply three or more polynomials, more than one method may be needed.

PRACTICE PROBLEM 22

Multiply:

$(y - 2)(y + 2)(y^2 - 4)$

EXAMPLE 22 Multiply: $(x - 3)(x + 3)(x^2 - 9)$

Solution: We multiply the first two binomials, the sum and difference of two terms. Then we multiply the resulting two binomials, the square of a binomial.

$$
(x - 3)(x + 3)(x^2 - 9) = (x^2 - 9)(x^2 - 9) \quad \text{Multiply } (x - 3)(x + 3)
$$
$$
= (x^2 - 9)^2
$$
$$
= x^4 - 18x^2 + 81 \quad \text{Square } (x^2 - 9).
$$

■ **Work Practice Problem 22**

Objective F **Evaluating Polynomial Functions**

Our work in multiplying polynomials is often useful in evaluating polynomial functions.

PRACTICE PROBLEM 23

If $f(x) = x^2 - 6x + 1$, find $f(b - 1)$

EXAMPLE 23 If $f(x) = x^2 + 5x - 2$, find $f(a + 1)$.

Solution: To find $f(a + 1)$, replace x with the expression $a + 1$ in the polynomial function $f(x)$.

$$
f(x) = x^2 + 5x - 2
$$
$$
f(a + 1) = (a + 1)^2 + 5(a + 1) - 2
$$
$$
= a^2 + 2a + 1 + 5a + 5 - 2
$$
$$
= a^2 + 7a + 4
$$

■ **Work Practice Problem 23**

Answers

21. $4x^2 + 12xy + 9y^2 - 4$,
22. $y^4 - 8y^2 + 16$, **23.** $b^2 - 8b + 8$

In the previous section, we used a graphing calculator to check addition and subtraction of polynomials in one variable. In this section, we use the same method to check multiplication of polynomials in one variable. For example, to see that

$$(x - 2)(x + 1) = x^2 - x - 2$$

graph both $Y_1 = (x - 2)(x + 1)$ and $Y_2 = x^2 - x - 2$ on the same screen and see whether their graphs coincide.

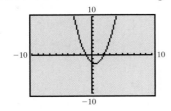

By tracing along both graphs, we see that the graphs of Y_1 and Y_2 appear to coincide, and thus $(x - 2)(x + 1) = x^2 - x - 2$ appears to be correct.

Multiply. Then use a graphing calculator to check the results.

1. $(x + 4)(x - 4)$

2. $(x + 3)(x + 3)$

3. $(3x - 7)^2$

4. $(5x - 2)^2$

5. $(5x + 1)(x^2 - 3x - 2)$

6. $(7x + 4)(2x^2 + 3x - 5)$

5.2 EXERCISE SET

FOR EXTRA HELP

Student Solutions Manual | PH Math/Tutor Center | CD/Video for Review | Math XL MathXL® | MyMathLab MyMathLab

Objective A *Multiply. See Examples 1 through 8.*

1. $(-4x^3)(3x^2)$

2. $(-6a)(4a)$

3. $(8.6a^4b^5c)(10ab^3c^2)$

4. $(7.1xy^2z^{11})(10xy^7z)$

5. $3x(4x + 7)$

6. $5x(6x - 4)$

7. $-6xy(4x + y)$

8. $-8y(6xy + 4x)$

9. $-4ab(xa^2 + ya^2 - 3)$

10. $-6b^2z(z^2a + baz - 3b)$

11. $(x - 3)(2x + 4)$

12. $(y + 5)(3y - 2)$

13. $(2x + 3)(x^3 - x + 2)$

14. $(a + 2)(3a^2 - a + 5)$

15.
$$\begin{array}{r} 3x - 2 \\ \times\; 5x + 1 \end{array}$$

16.
$$\begin{array}{r} 2z - 4 \\ \times\; 6z - 2 \end{array}$$

17.
$$\begin{array}{r} 3m^2 + 2m - 1 \\ \times\qquad\; 5m + 2 \end{array}$$

18.
$$\begin{array}{r} 2x^2 - 3x - 4 \\ \times\qquad\; 4x + 5 \end{array}$$

19. $-6a^2b^2(5a^2b^2 - 6a - 6b)$

20. $7x^2y^3(-3ax - 4xy + z)$

Objective B *Multiply the binomials. See Examples 9 through 11.*

21. $(x - 3)(x + 4)$

22. $(c - 3)(c + 1)$

23. $(5x - 8y)(2x - y)$

24. $(2n - 9m)(n - 7m)$

25. $\left(4x + \dfrac{1}{3}\right)\left(4x - \dfrac{1}{2}\right)$

26. $\left(4y - \dfrac{1}{3}\right)\left(3y - \dfrac{1}{8}\right)$

27. $(5x^2 - 2y^2)(x^2 - 3y^2)$

28. $(4x^2 - 5y^2)(x^2 - 2y^2)$

Objectives **C** **D** *Use special products to multiply. See Examples 12 through 21.*

29. $(x + 4)^2$ **30.** $(x - 5)^2$ **31.** $(6y - 1)(6y + 1)$ **32.** $(7x - 9)(7x + 9)$

33. $(3x - y)^2$ **34.** $(4x + z)^2$ **35.** $(7ab + 3c)(7ab - 3c)$ **36.** $(3xy - 2b)(3xy + 2b)$

37. $\left(3x + \dfrac{1}{2}\right)\left(3x - \dfrac{1}{2}\right)$ **38.** $\left(2x - \dfrac{1}{3}\right)\left(2x + \dfrac{1}{3}\right)$

39. $[3 + (4b + 1)]^2$ **40.** $[5 - (3b - 3)]^2$

41. $[(2s - 3) - 1][(2s - 3) + 1]$ **42.** $[(2y + 5) + 6][(2y + 5) - 6]$

Objective **E** *Multiply. See Example 22.*

43. $(x + y)(2x - 1)(x + 1)$ **44.** $(z + 2)(z - 3)(2z + 1)$ **45.** $(x - 2)^4$

46. $(x - 1)^4$ **47.** $(x - 5)(x + 5)(x^2 + 25)$ **48.** $(x + 3)(x - 3)(x^2 + 9)$

Objectives **A** **B** **C** **D** **E** **Mixed Practice** *Multiply. See Examples 1 through 22.*

49. $-8a^2b(3b^2 - 5b + 20)$ **50.** $-9xy^2(3x^2 - 2x + 10)$ **51.** $(6x + 1)^2$

52. $(4x + 7)^2$ **53.** $(5x^3 + 2y)(5x^3 - 2y)$ **54.** $(3x^4 + 2y)(3x^4 - 2y)$

55. $(2x^3 + 5)(5x^2 + 4x + 1)$ **56.** $(3y^3 - 1)(3y^3 - 6y + 1)$ **57.** $(3x^2 + 2x - 1)^2$

58. $(4x^2 + 4x - 4)^2$ **59.** $(3x - 1)(x + 3)$ **60.** $(5d - 3)(d + 6)$

61. $(3x^4 + 1)(3x^2 + 5)$ **62.** $(4x^3 - 5)(5x^2 + 6)$ **63.** $(3x + 1)^2$

64. $(4x + 6)^2$ **65.** $(3b - 6y)(3b + 6y)$ **66.** $(2x - 4y)(2x + 4y)$

67. $(7x - 3)(7x + 3)$ **68.** $(4x + 1)(4x - 1)$ **69.** $\begin{array}{r} 3x^2 + 4x - 4 \\ \times \quad\quad 3x + 6 \\ \hline \end{array}$

70. $\begin{array}{r} 6x^2 + 2x - 1 \\ \times \quad\quad 3x - 6 \\ \hline \end{array}$ **71.** $(4x^2 - 2x + 5)(3x + 1)$ **72.** $(5x^2 - x - 2)(2x - 1)$

73. $[(xy + 4) - 6]^2$

74. $[(2a^2 + 4) - 1]^2$

75. $(11a^2 + 1)(2a + 1)$

76. $(13x^2 + 1)(3x + 1)$

77. $\left(\dfrac{2}{3}n - 2\right)\left(\dfrac{1}{2}n - 9\right)$

78. $\left(\dfrac{3}{5}y - 6\right)\left(\dfrac{1}{3}y - 10\right)$

79. $(3x + 1)(3x - 1)(2y + 5x)$

80. $(2a + 1)(2a - 1)(6a + 7b)$

Objective ⬛F *If* $f(x) = x^2 - 3x$, *find the following. See Example 23.*

81. $f(a)$

82. $f(c)$

83. $f(a + h)$

84. $f(a + 5)$

85. $f(b - 2)$

86. $f(a - b)$

Review

Simplify. See Section 1.6.

87. $\dfrac{6x^3}{3x}$

88. $\dfrac{4x^7}{x^2}$

89. $\dfrac{20a^3b^5}{18ab^2}$

90. $\dfrac{15x^7y^2}{6xy^2}$

91. $\dfrac{8m^4n}{12mn}$

92. $\dfrac{6n^6p}{8np}$

Concept Extensions

Solve. See the Concept Check in this section.

93. Find the error: $7y(3z - 2) + 1$
$= 21yz - 14y + 7y$
$= 21yz - 7y$

94. Find the error: $2x + 3x(12 - x)$
$= 5x(12 - x)$
$= 60x - 5x^2$

95. Explain how to multiply a polynomial by a polynomial.

96. Explain why $(3x + 2)^2$ does not equal $9x^2 + 4$.

Multiply. Assume that variables represent positive integers.

97. $5x^2y^n(6y^{n+1} - 2)$

98. $-3yz^n(2y^3z^{2n} - 1)$

99. $(x^a + 5)(x^{2a} - 3)$

100. $(x^a + y^{2b})(x^a - y^{2b})$

101. Perform each indicated operation.

    a. $(3x + 5) + (3x + 7)$
    b. $(3x + 5)(3x + 7)$
    c. Explain the difference between the two problems.

102. Explain when the FOIL method can be used to multiply polynomials.

If $R(x) = x + 5, Q(x) = x^2 - 2$, and $P(x) = 5x$, find each function.

103. $P(x) \cdot R(x)$

104. $P(x) \cdot Q(x)$

If $f(x) = x^3 - 2x^2$, find each function value.

105. $f(a)$

106. $f(a + h)$

Find the area of each shaded region.

△ **107.**

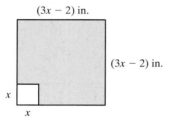

(3x − 2) in.

(3x − 2) in.

x

x

△ **108.**

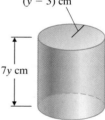

$x - 7$

$2x$ x

△ **109.** Find the area of the circle. Do not approximate π.

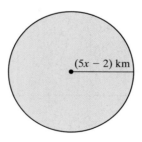

(5x − 2) km

△ **110.** Find the volume of the cylinder. Do not approximate π.

$(y - 3)$ cm

$7y$ cm

 STUDY SKILLS BUILDER

How Are You Doing?

If you haven't done so yet, take a few moments and think about how you are doing in this course. Are you working toward your goal of successfully completing this course? Is your performance on homework, quizzes, and tests satisfactory? If not, you might want to see your instructor to see if he/she has any suggestions on how you can improve your performance. Reread Section 1.1 for ideas on places to get help with your mathematics course.

Answer the following.

1. List any textbook supplements you are using to help you through this course.

2. List any campus resources you are using to help you through this course.

3. Write a short paragraph describing how you are doing in your mathematics course.

4. If improvement is needed, list ways that you can work toward improving your situation as described in Exercise 3.

5.3 DIVIDING POLYNOMIALS AND SYNTHETIC DIVISION

Objectives

A Divide a Polynomial by a Monomial.

B Divide by a Polynomial.

C Use Synthetic Division.

Now that we have added, subtracted, and multiplied polynomials, we will learn how to divide them.

Objective **A** Dividing a Polynomial by a Monomial

Recall the following addition fact for fractions with a common denominator:

$$\frac{a}{c} + \frac{b}{c} = \frac{a+b}{c}$$

If a, b, and c are monomials, we can read this equation from right to left and gain insight into how to divide a polynomial by a monomial.

Dividing a Polynomial by a Monomial

To divide a polynomial by a monomial, divide each term in the polynomial by the monomial.

$$\frac{a+b}{c} = \frac{a}{c} + \frac{b}{c}, \quad c \neq 0$$

EXAMPLE 1 Divide $10x^3 - 5x^2 + 20x$ by $5x$.

Solution: We divide each term of $10x^3 - 5x^2 + 20x$ by $5x$ and simplify.

$$\frac{10x^3 - 5x^2 + 20x}{5x} = \frac{10x^3}{5x} - \frac{5x^2}{5x} + \frac{20x}{5x} = 2x^2 - x + 4$$

To check, see that (quotient)(divisor) = dividend, or

$$(2x^2 - x + 4)(5x) = 10x^3 - 5x^2 + 20x$$

Work Practice Problem 1

EXAMPLE 2 Divide: $\dfrac{3x^5y^2 - 15x^3y - x^2y - 6x}{x^2y}$

Solution: We divide each term in the numerator by x^2y.

$$\frac{3x^5y^2 - 15x^3y - x^2y - 6x}{x^2y} = \frac{3x^5y^2}{x^2y} - \frac{15x^3y}{x^2y} - \frac{x^2y}{x^2y} - \frac{6x}{x^2y}$$

$$= 3x^3y - 15x - 1 - \frac{6}{xy}$$

Work Practice Problem 2

Objective **B** Dividing by a Polynomial

To divide a polynomial by a polynomial other than a monomial, we use **long division.** Polynomial long division is similar to long division of real numbers. We review long division of real numbers by dividing 7 into 296.

Divisor: $7\overline{)296}$ quotient 42

$\begin{array}{r} \quad\; 42 \\ 7\overline{)296} \\ -28 \quad 4(7) = 28 \\ \hline 16 \quad \text{Subtract and bring down the next digit in the dividend.} \\ -14 \quad 2(7) = 14 \\ \hline 2 \quad \text{Subtract. The remainder is 2.} \end{array}$

PRACTICE PROBLEM 1
Divide $16y^3 - 8y^2 + 6y$ by $2y$.

PRACTICE PROBLEM 2
Divide:
$$\frac{9a^3b^3 - 6a^2b^2 + a^2b - 4a}{a^2b}$$

Answers
1. $8y^2 - 4y + 3$,

2. $9ab^2 - 6b + 1 - \dfrac{4}{ab}$

309

The quotient is

$$42\frac{2}{7} \quad \begin{array}{l}\text{remainder}\\ \text{divisor}\end{array}$$

To check, notice that $42(7) + 2 = 296$, which is the dividend. This same division process can be applied to polynomials, as shown next.

PRACTICE PROBLEM 3

Divide $6x^2 + 11x - 2$ by $x + 2$.

EXAMPLE 3 Divide $2x^2 - x - 10$ by $x + 2$.

Solution: $2x^2 - x - 10$ is the dividend, and $x + 2$ is the divisor.

Step 1: Divide $2x^2$ by x.

$$x + 2 \overline{)\begin{array}{c} 2x \\ 2x^2 - x - 10 \end{array}} \qquad \dfrac{2x^2}{x} = 2x, \text{ so } 2x \text{ is the first term of the quotient.}$$

Step 2: Multiply $2x(x + 2)$.

$$\begin{array}{r} 2x \\ x + 2 \overline{)2x^2 - x - 10} \\ 2x^2 + 4x \end{array} \qquad \text{Multiply: } 2x(x + 2). \text{ Like terms are lined up vertically.}$$

Step 3: Subtract $(2x^2 + 4x)$ from $(2x^2 - x - 10)$ by changing the signs of $(2x^2 + 4x)$ and adding.

$$\begin{array}{r} 2x \\ x + 2 \overline{)2x^2 - x - 10} \\ \underline{\cancel{+}2x^2 \; \cancel{+} \; 4x } \\ -5x \end{array}$$

Step 4: Bring down the next term, -10, and start the process over.

$$\begin{array}{r} 2x \\ x + 2 \overline{)2x^2 - x - 10} \\ \underline{\cancel{+}2x^2 \; \cancel{+} \; 4x \downarrow} \\ -5x - 10 \end{array}$$

Step 5: Divide $-5x$ by x.

$$\begin{array}{r} 2x - 5 \\ x + 2 \overline{)2x^2 - x - 10} \\ \underline{\cancel{+}2x^2 \; \cancel{+} \; 4x } \\ -5x - 10 \end{array} \qquad \dfrac{-5x}{x} = -5 \text{ so } -5 \text{ is the second term of the quotient.}$$

Step 6: Multiply $-5(x + 2)$.

$$\begin{array}{r} 2x - 5 \\ x + 2 \overline{)2x^2 - x - 10} \\ \underline{\cancel{+}2x^2 \; \cancel{+} \; 4x } \\ -5x - 10 \\ \underline{-5x - 10} \end{array} \qquad \text{Multiply: } -5(x + 2). \text{ Like terms are lined up vertically.}$$

Step 7: Subtract by changing signs of $-5x - 10$ and adding.

$$\begin{array}{r} 2x - 5 \\ x + 2 \overline{)2x^2 - x - 10} \\ \underline{\cancel{+}2x^2 \; \cancel{+} \; 4x } \\ -5x - 10 \\ \underline{\cancel{+}5x \; \cancel{+} \; 10} \qquad \text{Subtract.} \\ 0 \qquad \text{Remainder.} \end{array}$$

Then $\dfrac{2x^2 - x - 10}{x + 2} = 2x - 5$. There is no remainder.

Check this result by multiplying $2x - 5$ by $x + 2$, the divisor. Their product is $(2x - 5)(x + 2) = 2x^2 - x - 10$, the dividend.

■ **Work Practice Problem 3**

EXAMPLE 4 Divide: $(6x^2 - 19x + 12) \div (3x - 5)$

Solution:

$$
\begin{array}{r}
2x \\
3x - 5 \overline{\smash{)}6x^2 - 19x + 12} \\
\underline{6x^2 - 10x} \downarrow \\
-9x + 12
\end{array}
$$

Divide: $\dfrac{6x^2}{3x} = 2x$

Multiply: $2x(3x - 5)$

Subtract: $(6x^2 - 19x) - (6x^2 - 10x) = -9x$

Bring down the next term, $+12$.

$$
\begin{array}{r}
2x - 3 \\
3x - 5 \overline{\smash{)}6x^2 - 19x + 12} \\
\underline{6x^2 - 10x} \\
-9x + 12 \\
\underline{-9x + 15} \\
-3
\end{array}
$$

Divide: $\dfrac{-9x}{3x} = -3$

Multiply: $-3(3x - 5)$

Subtract: $(-9x + 12) - (-9x + 15) = -3$

Check:

divisor · quotient + remainder

$$(3x - 5)(2x - 3) + (-3) = 6x^2 - 19x + 15 - 3$$
$$= 6x^2 - 19x + 12 \quad \text{The dividend}$$

The division checks, so

$$\frac{6x^2 - 19x + 12}{3x - 5} = 2x - 3 + \frac{-3}{3x - 5}$$

Helpful Hint

This fraction is the remainder over the divisor.

■ **Work Practice Problem 4**

EXAMPLE 5 Divide: $(7x^3 + 16x^2 + 2x - 1) \div (x + 4)$.

Solution:

$$
\begin{array}{r}
7x^2 - 12x + 50 \\
x + 4 \overline{\smash{)}7x^3 + 16x^2 + 2x - 1} \\
\underline{7x^3 + 28x^2} \\
-12x^2 + 2x \\
\underline{-12x^2 - 48x} \\
50x - 1 \\
\underline{50x + 200} \\
-201
\end{array}
$$

Divide $\dfrac{7x^3}{x} = 7x^2$.

$7x^2(x + 4)$

Subtract. Bring down $2x$.

$\dfrac{-12x^2}{x} = -12x$, a term of the quotient.

$-12x(x + 4)$

Subtract. Bring down -1.

$\dfrac{50x}{x} = 50$, a term of the quotient.

$50(x + 4)$.

Subtract.

Thus, $\dfrac{7x^3 + 16x^2 + 2x - 1}{x + 4} = 7x^2 - 12x + 50 + \dfrac{-201}{x + 4}$ or

$$7x^2 - 12x + 50 - \frac{201}{x + 4}.$$

■ **Work Practice Problem 5**

PRACTICE PROBLEM 4

Divide:

$(10x^2 - 17x + 5) \div (5x - 1)$

PRACTICE PROBLEM 5

Divide:

$(5x^3 - 4x^2 + 3x - 4) \div (x - 2)$.

Answers

4. $2x - 3 + \dfrac{2}{5x - 1}$,

5. $5x^2 + 6x + 15 + \dfrac{26}{x - 2}$

Copyright 2007 Pearson Education, Inc.

PRACTICE PROBLEM 6

Divide $3x^4 + 4x^2 - 6x + 1$ by $x^2 + 1$.

EXAMPLE 6 Divide $2x^3 + 3x^4 - 8x + 6$ by $x^2 - 1$.

Solution: Before dividing, we write terms in descending order of powers of x. Also, we represent any "missing powers" by the product of 0 and the variable raised to the missing power. There is no x^2-term in the dividend, so we include $0x^2$ to represent the missing term. Also, there is no x term in the divisor, so we include $0x$ in the divisor.

$$
\begin{array}{r}
3x^2 + 2x + 3 \\
x^2 + 0x - 1 \overline{)3x^4 + 2x^3 + 0x^2 - 8x + 6} \\
\underline{3x^4 \ast 0x^3 \ast 3x^2} \\
2x^3 + 3x^2 - 8x \\
\underline{2x^3 \ast 0x^2 \ast 2x} \\
3x^2 - 6x + 6 \\
\underline{3x^2 \ast 0x \ast 3} \\
-6x + 9
\end{array}
$$

$\dfrac{3x^4}{x^2} = 3x^2$

$3x^2(x^2 + 0x - 1)$

Subtract. Bring down $-8x$.

$2x^3/x^2 = 2x$, a term of the quotient

$2x(x^2 + 0x - 1)$

Subtract. Bring down 6.

$3x^2/x^2 = 3$, a term of the quotient

$3(x^2 + 0x - 1)$

Subtract.

The division process is finished when the degree of the remainder polynomial is less than the degree of the divisor.

Thus,

$$\frac{3x^4 + 2x^3 - 8x + 6}{x^2 - 1} = 3x^2 + 2x + 3 + \frac{-6x + 9}{x^2 - 1}$$

▣ **Work Practice Problem 6**

PRACTICE PROBLEM 7

Divide $64x^3 - 27$ by $4x - 3$.

EXAMPLE 7 Divide $27x^3 + 8$ by $3x + 2$.

Solution: We replace the missing terms in the dividend with $0x^2$ and $0x$.

$$
\begin{array}{r}
9x^2 - 6x + 4 \\
3x + 2 \overline{)27x^3 + 0x^2 + 0x + 8} \\
\underline{27x^3 \ast 18x^2} \\
-18x^2 + 0x \\
\underline{\ast 18x^2 \ast 12x} \\
12x + 8 \\
\underline{12x \ast 8}
\end{array}
$$

$9x^2(3x + 2)$

Subtract. Bring down $0x$.

$-6x(3x + 2)$

Subtract. Bring down 8.

$4(3x + 2)$

Helpful Hint

The degree of the remainder polynomial (1) is the same as the degree of the divisor (1), so we continue the division process.

Thus, $\dfrac{27x^3 + 8}{3x + 2} = 9x^2 - 6x + 4$.

▣ **Work Practice Problem 7**

✔ **Concept Check** In a division problem, the divisor is $4x^3 - 5$. The division process can be stopped when which of these possible remainder polynomials is reached?

a. $2x^4 + x^2 - 3$ **b.** $x^3 - 5^2$ **c.** $4x^2 + 25$

Objective ⓒ Using Synthetic Division

When a polynomial is to be divided by a binomial of the form $x - c$, a shortcut process called **synthetic division** may be used. On the left is an example of long division, and on the right is the same example showing the coefficients of the variables only.

Answers

6. $3x^2 + 1 - \dfrac{6x}{x^2 + 1}$,

7. $16x^2 + 12x + 9$

✔ **Concept Check Answer**

c

$$
\begin{array}{r}
2x^2 + 5x + 2 \\
x - 3\overline{)2x^3 - x^2 - 13x + 1} \\
\underline{2x^3 - 6x^2} \\
5x^2 - 13x \\
\underline{5x^2 - 15x} \\
2x + 1 \\
\underline{2x - 6} \\
7
\end{array}
\qquad
\begin{array}{r}
2 \quad 5 \quad 2 \\
1 - 3\overline{)2 - 1 - 13 + 1} \\
\underline{2 - 6} \\
5 - 13 \\
\underline{5 - 15} \\
2 + 1 \\
\underline{2 - 6} \\
7
\end{array}
$$

Notice that as long as we keep coefficients of powers of x in the same column, we can perform division of polynomials by performing algebraic operations on the coefficients only. This shorter process of dividing with coefficients only in a special format is called synthetic division. To find $(2x^3 - x^2 - 13x + 1) \div (x - 3)$ by synthetic division, follow the next example.

EXAMPLE 8 Use synthetic division to divide $2x^3 - x^2 - 13x + 1$ by $x - 3$.

Solution: To use synthetic division, the divisor must be in the form $x - c$. Since we are dividing by $x - 3$, c is 3. We write down 3 and the coefficients of the dividend.

The quotient is found in the bottom row. The numbers 2, 5, and 2 are the coefficients of the quotient polynomial, and the number 7 is the remainder. The degree of the quotient polynomial is one less than the degree of the dividend. In our example, the degree of the dividend is 3, so the degree of the quotient polynomial is 2. As we found when we performed the long division, the quotient is

$2x^2 + 5x + 2$,   remainder 7

or

$$2x^2 + 5x + 2 + \frac{7}{x - 3}$$

■ **Work Practice Problem 8**

PRACTICE PROBLEM 8

Use synthetic division to divide $3x^3 - 2x^2 + 5x + 4$ by $x - 2$.

Answer

8. $3x^2 + 4x + 13 + \dfrac{30}{x - 2}$

When using synthetic division, if there are missing powers of the variable, insert 0s as coefficients.

PRACTICE PROBLEM 9

Use synthetic division to divide $x^4 + 3x^3 - 5x + 4$ by $x + 1$.

EXAMPLE 9 Use synthetic division to divide $x^4 - 2x^3 - 11x^2 + 34$ by $x + 2$.

Solution: The divisor is $x + 2$, which in the form $x - c$ is $x - (-2)$. Thus, c is -2. There is no x-term in the dividend, so we insert a coefficient of 0. The dividend coefficients are $1, -2, -11, 0$, and 34.

$$
\begin{array}{r|rrrrr}
-2 & 1 & -2 & -11 & 0 & 34 \\
   &   & -2 & 8 & 6 & -12 \\
\hline
   & 1 & -4 & -3 & 6 & 22
\end{array}
$$

The dividend is a fourth-degree polynomial, so the quotient polynomial is a third-degree polynomial. The quotient is $x^3 - 4x^2 - 3x + 6$ with a remainder of 22. Thus,

$$\frac{x^4 - 2x^3 - 11x^2 + 34}{x + 2} = x^3 - 4x^2 - 3x + 6 + \frac{22}{x + 2}$$

☐ **Work Practice Problem 9**

Helpful Hint

 Before dividing by long division or by synthetic division, write the dividend in descending order of variable exponents. Any "missing powers" of the variable must be represented by 0 times the variable raised to the missing power.

✔**Concept Check** Which division problems are candidates for the synthetic division process?

a. $(3x^2 + 5) \div (x + 4)$

b. $(x^3 - x^2 + 2) \div (3x^3 - 2)$

c. $(y^4 + y - 3) \div (x^2 + 1)$

d. $x^5 \div (x - 5)$

Answer

9. $x^3 + 2x^2 - 2x - 3 + \dfrac{7}{x + 1}$

✔ **Concept Check Answer**

a and d

POLYNOMIAL DIVISION: Finding the Remainder

Compiled by Brian Emond

There is another way to determine the remainder of a polynomial division problem. When the polynomial dividend $F(x)$ is divided by a first degree polynomial divisor $x - (b)$, the remainder can be found by evaluating $F(x)$ at $x = b$. Notice that b is *positive*.

Rule 1. If the divisor is $x - b$, b is *positive*. Because $x - b = x - (+b)$.

Example 1:

For $\dfrac{x^2 - 4x - 2}{x - 4}$

$F(x) = x^2 - 4x - 2$ and $x - b = x - 4$, where $b = +4$.

Find the remainder in the form of $F(b)$.

$F(4) = 4^2 - 4(4) - 2$ (Evaluate $F(b)$ at $+4$)

$\quad = 16 - 16 - 2$

$\quad = -2 \quad$ Thus the remainder is -2.

Rule 2. If the divisor is $x + b$, b has to be *negative*. Because $x + b = x - (-b)$.

Example 2:

For $\dfrac{x^2 - 4x - 2}{x + 3}$

$F(x) = x^2 - 4x - 2$ and $x - b = x + 3$, where $b = -3$.

Find the remainder in the form of $F(b)$.

$F(-3) = (-3)^2 - 4(-3) - 2$ (Evaluate $F(b)$ at -3)

$\quad = 9 + 12 - 2$

$\quad = 19 \quad$ Thus the remainder is 19.

5.3 EXERCISE SET

FOR EXTRA HELP

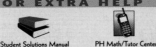
Student Solutions Manual

PH Math/Tutor Center

CD/Video for Review

Math XL
MathXL®

MyMathLab
MyMathLab

Objective **A** *Divide. See Examples 1 and 2.*

1. $4a^2 + 8a$ by $2a$

2. $6x^4 - 3x^3$ by $3x^2$

3. $\dfrac{12a^5b^2 + 16a^4b}{4a^4b}$

4. $\dfrac{4x^3y + 12x^2y^2 - 4xy^3}{4xy}$

5. $\dfrac{4x^2y^2 + 6xy^2 - 4y^2}{2x^2y}$

6. $\dfrac{6x^5y + 75x^4y - 24x^3y^2}{3x^4y}$

Objective **B** *Divide. See Examples 3 through 7.*

7. $(x^2 + 3x + 2) \div (x + 2)$

8. $(y^2 + 7y + 10) \div (y + 5)$

9. $(2x^2 - 6x - 8) \div (x + 1)$

10. $(3x^2 + 19x + 20) \div (x + 5)$

11. $2x^2 + 3x - 2$ by $2x + 4$

12. $6x^2 - 17x - 3$ by $3x - 9$

13. $(4x^3 + 7x^2 + 8x + 20) \div (2x + 4)$

14. $(8x^3 + 18x^2 + 16x + 24) \div (4x + 8)$

15. $(2x^2 + 6x^3 - 18x - 6) \div (3x + 1)$

16. $(4x - 15x^2 + 10x^3 - 6) \div (2x - 3)$

17. $(3x^5 - x^3 + 4x^2 - 12x - 8) \div (x^2 - 2)$

18. $(2x^5 - 6x^4 + x^3 - 4x + 3) \div (x^2 - 3)$

19. $\left(2x^4 + \dfrac{1}{2}x^3 + x^2 + x\right) \div (x - 2)$

20. $\left(x^4 - \dfrac{2}{3}x^3 + x\right) \div (x - 3)$

Objective **C** *Use synthetic division to divide. See Examples 8 and 9.*

21. $\dfrac{x^2 + 3x - 40}{x - 5}$

22. $\dfrac{x^2 - 14x + 24}{x - 2}$

23. $\dfrac{x^2 + 5x - 6}{x + 6}$

24. $\dfrac{x^2 + 12x + 32}{x + 4}$

25. $\dfrac{x^3 - 7x^2 - 13x + 5}{x - 2}$

26. $\dfrac{x^3 + 6x^2 + 4x - 7}{x + 5}$

27. $\dfrac{4x^2 - 9}{x - 2}$

28. $\dfrac{3x^2 - 4}{x - 1}$

Objectives **A** **B** **C** **Mixed Practice** *Divide. See Examples 1–9.*

29. $\dfrac{4x^7y^4 + 8xy^2 + 4xy^3}{4xy^3}$

30. $\dfrac{15x^3y - 5x^2y + 10xy^2}{5x^2y}$

31. $(10x^3 - 5x^2 - 12x + 1) \div (2x - 1)$

32. $(20x^3 - 8x^2 + 5x - 5) \div (5x - 2)$

33. $(2x^3 - 6x^2 - 4) \div (x - 4)$

34. $(3x^3 + 4x - 10) \div (x + 2)$

35. $\dfrac{2x^4 - 13x^3 + 16x^2 - 9x + 20}{x - 5}$

36. $\dfrac{3x^4 + 5x^3 - x^2 + x - 2}{x + 2}$

37. $\dfrac{7x^2 - 4x + 12 + 3x^3}{x + 1}$

38. $\dfrac{4x^3 + x^4 - x^2 - 16x - 4}{x - 2}$

39. $\dfrac{3x^3 + 2x^2 - 4x + 1}{x - \dfrac{1}{3}}$

40. $\dfrac{9y^3 + 9y^2 - y + 2}{y + \dfrac{2}{3}}$

41. $\dfrac{x^3 - 1}{x - 1}$

42. $\dfrac{y^3 - 8}{y - 2}$

43. $(25xy^2 + 75xyz + 125x^2yz) \div (-5x^2y)$

44. $(x^6y^6 - x^3y^3z + 7x^3y) \div (-7yz^2)$

45. $(9x^5 + 6x^4 - 6x^2 - 4x) \div (3x + 2)$

46. $(5x^4 - 5x^2 + 10x^3 - 10x) \div (5x + 10)$

Review

Solve each inequality. See Section 2.6.

47. $|x + 5| < 4$ **48.** $|x - 1| \le 8$ **49.** $|2x + 7| \ge 9$ **50.** $|4x + 2| > 10$

Concept Extensions

Solve. See the Concept Checks in this section. Which division problems are candidates for the synthetic division process?

51. $(5x^2 - 3x + 2) \div (x + 2)$

52. $(x^4 - 6) \div (x^3 + 3x - 1)$

53. $(x^7 - 2) \div (x^5 + 1)$

54. $(3x^2 + 7x - 1) \div \left(x - \dfrac{1}{3}\right)$

55. In a long division exercise, if the divisor is $9x^3 - 2x$, then the division process can be stopped when the degree of the remainder is
    a. 1   **b.** 3   **c.** 9   **d.** 2

56. In a division exercise, if the divisor is $x - 3$, then the division process can be stopped when the degree of the remainder is
    a. 1   **b.** 0   **c.** 2   **d.** 3

△ **57.** A board of length $(3x^4 + 6x^2 - 18)$ meters is to be cut into three pieces of the same length. Find the length of each piece.

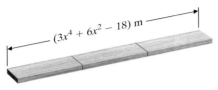 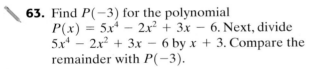

(3x⁴ + 6x² − 18) m

△ **58.** The perimeter of a regular hexagon is given to be $(12x^5 - 48x^3 + 3)$ miles. Find the length of each side.

△ **59.** If the area of the rectangle is $(15x^2 - 29x - 14)$ square inches, and its length is $(5x + 2)$ inches, find its width.

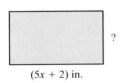

?

$(5x + 2)$ in.

△ **60.** If the area of a parallelogram is $(2x^2 - 17x + 35)$ square centimeters and its base is $(2x - 7)$ centimeters, find its height.

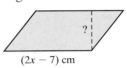

?

$(2x - 7)$ cm

61. Find $P(1)$ for the polynomial function $P(x) = 3x^3 + 2x^2 - 4x + 3$. Next, divide $3x^3 + 2x^2 - 4x + 3$ by $x - 1$. Compare the remainder with $P(1)$.

62. Find $P(-2)$ for the polynomial function $P(x) = x^3 - 4x^2 - 3x + 5$. Next, divide $x^3 - 4x^2 - 3x + 5$ by $x + 2$. Compare the remainder with $P(-2)$.

63. Find $P(-3)$ for the polynomial $P(x) = 5x^4 - 2x^2 + 3x - 6$. Next, divide $5x^4 - 2x^2 + 3x - 6$ by $x + 3$. Compare the remainder with $P(-3)$.

64. Find $P(2)$ for the polynomial function $P(x) = -4x^4 + 2x^3 - 6x + 3$. Next, divide $-4x^4 + 2x^3 - 6x + 3$ by $x - 2$. Compare the remainder with $P(2)$.

65. Write down any patterns you noticed from Exercises 61–64.

66. Explain how to check polynomial long division.

Divide.

67. $\left(x^4 + \dfrac{2}{3}x^3 + x\right) \div (x - 1)$

68. $\left(3x^4 - x - x^3 + \dfrac{1}{2}\right) \div (2x - 1)$

For each given $f(x)$ and $g(x)$, find $\dfrac{f(x)}{g(x)}$. Also find any x-values that are not in the domain of $\dfrac{f(x)}{g(x)}$. (Note: Since $g(x)$ is in the denominator, $g(x)$ cannot be 0).

69. $f(x) = 25x^2 - 5x + 30; g(x) = 5x$

70. $f(x) = 12x^4 - 9x^3 + 3x - 1; g(x) = 3x$

71. $f(x) = 7x^4 - 3x^2 + 2; g(x) = x - 2$

72. $f(x) = 2x^3 - 4x^2 + 1; g(x) = x + 3$

73. Try performing the following division without changing the order of the terms. Describe why this makes the process more complicated. Then perform the division again after putting the terms in the dividend in descending order of exponents.

$$\frac{4x^2 - 12x - 12 + 3x^3}{x - 2}$$

74. Explain how to divide a polynomial in x by $(x - c)$ using synthetic division.

75. Explain an advantage of using synthetic division instead of long division.

76. Dell, Inc., is a provider of products and services required for customers worldwide to build their information-technology and Internet infra-structures. Dell's annual revenues since 1999 can be modeled by the polynomial function $R(x) = 0.4x^3 - 3.6x^2 + 11.6x + 17.9$, where $R(x)$ is revenue in billions of dollars and x is the number of years since 1999. Dell's profit can be modeled by the function $P(x) = 0.2x^3 - 1x^2 + 1.4x + 1.4$, where $P(x)$ is the profit in billions of dollars and x is the number of years since 1999. (*Source:* Based on data from Dell, Inc.)

a. Suppose that a market analyst has found the model $P(x)$ and another analyst at the same firm has found the model $R(x)$. The analysts have been asked by their manager to work together to find a model for Dell's profit margin. The analysts know that a company's profit margin is the ratio of its profit to its revenue. Describe how these two ana-lysts could collaborate to find a function $m(x)$ that models Dell's net profit margin based on the work they have done independently.

b. Without actually finding $m(x)$, give a general description of what you would expect the form of the answer to be.

5.4 THE GREATEST COMMON FACTOR AND FACTORING BY GROUPING

OBJECTIVES

A Factor out the Greatest Common Factor of a Polynomials Terms.

B Factor Polynomials by Grouping.

Factoring is the reverse process of multiplying. It is the process of writing a polynomial as a product

$$6x^2 + 13x - 5 = (3x - 1)(2x + 5)$$

with labels *factoring* (top arrow) and *multiplying* (bottom arrow).

In the next few sections, we review techniques for factoring polynomials.

Objective A Factoring Out the Greatest Common Factor

To factor a polynomial, we first **factor out** the greatest common factor of its terms, using the distributive property. The **greatest common factor** (GCF) of the terms of a polynomial is the product of the GCF of the numerical coefficients and the GCF of each common variable.

Let's find the GCF of $20x^3y$, $10x^2y^2$, and $35x^3$.

The GCF of the numerical coefficients 20, 10, and 35 is 5, the largest integer that is a factor of each integer. The GCF of the variable factors x^3, x^2, and x^3 is x^2 because x^2 is the largest factor common to all three powers of x. The variable y is not a common factor because it does not appear in all three monomials. The GCF is thus

$$5 \cdot x^2, \quad \text{or} \quad 5x^2$$

EXAMPLE 1 Factor: $8x + 4$

Solution: The greatest common factor of the terms $8x$ and 4 is 4.

$$8x + 4 = 4 \cdot 2x + 4 \cdot 1 \quad \text{Factor out 4 from each term.}$$
$$= 4(2x + 1) \quad \text{Use the distributive property.}$$

The factored form of $8x + 4$ is $4(2x + 1)$. To check, multiply $4(2x + 1)$ to see that the product is $8x + 4$.

■ Work Practice Problem 1

EXAMPLES Factor.

2. $6x^2 + 3x^3 = 3x^2 \cdot 2 + 3x^2 \cdot x$ The GCF of 6 and 3 is 3 and the GCF of x^2 and x^3 is x^2. Thus, the GCF of the terms is $3x^2$.

$$= 3x^2(2 + x) \quad \text{Use the distributive property.}$$

3. $3y + 1$ There is no common factor other than 1.

4. $17x^3y^2 - 34x^4y^2 = 17x^3y^2 \cdot 1 - 17x^3y^2 \cdot 2x$ Factor out the greatest common factor, $17x^3y^2$.

$$= 17x^3y^2(1 - 2x) \quad \text{Use the distributive property.}$$

■ Work Practice Problems 2–4

> **Helpful Hint**
>
> If the greatest common factor happens to be one of the terms in the polynomial, a factor of 1 will remain for this term when the greatest common factor is factored out. For example, in the polynomial $21x^2 + 7x$, the greatest common factor of $21x^2$ and $7x$ is $7x$, so
>
> $$21x^2 + 7x = 7x(3x) + 7x(1) = 7x(3x + 1)$$

PRACTICE PROBLEM 1

Factor: $9x + 3$

PRACTICE PROBLEMS 2–4

Factor each polynomial.

2. $20y^2 - 4y^3$
3. $6a - 7$
4. $6a^4b^2 - 3a^2b^2$

Answers

1. $3(3x + 1)$, **2.** $4y^2(5 - y)$,
3. $6a - 7$, **4.** $3a^2b^2(2a^2 - 1)$

319

To check that the greatest common factor has been factored out correctly, multiply the factors together and see that their product is the original polynomial.

PRACTICE PROBLEM 5

Factor: $-2x^2y - 4xy + 10y$

✔**Concept Check** Which factorization of $12x^2 + 9x - 3$ is correct?

a. $3(4x^2 + 3x + 1)$ **b.** $3(4x^2 + 3x - 1)$

c. $3(4x^2 + 3x - 3)$ **d.** $3(4x^2 + 3x)$

EXAMPLE 5 Factor: $-3x^3y + 2x^2y - 5xy$

Solution: Two possibilities are shown for factoring this polynomial.

First, the common factor xy is factored out.

$$-3x^3y + 2x^2y - 5xy = xy(-3x^2 + 2x - 5)$$

Also, the common factor $-xy$ can be factored out as shown.

$$-3x^3y + 2x^2y - 5xy = (-xy)(3x^2) + (-xy)(-2x) + (-xy)(5)$$
$$= -xy(3x^2 - 2x + 5)$$

Both of these are correct.

🔲 **Work Practice Problem 5**

PRACTICE PROBLEM 6

Factor: $3(x + 7) + 5y(x + 7)$

EXAMPLE 6 Factor: $2(x - 5) + 3a(x - 5)$

Solution: The greatest common factor is the binomial factor $(x - 5)$.

$$2(x - 5) + 3a(x - 5) = (x - 5)(2 + 3a)$$

🔲 **Work Practice Problem 6**

PRACTICE PROBLEM 7

Factor:

$6a(2a + 3b) - (2a + 3b)$

EXAMPLE 7 Factor: $7x(x^2 + 5y) - (x^2 + 5y)$

Solution:

$$7x(x^2 + 5y) - (x^2 + 5y) = 7x(x^2 + 5y) - 1(x^2 + 5y)$$
$$= (x^2 + 5y)(7x - 1)$$

Notice that we wrote $-(x^2 + 5y)$ as $-1(x^2 + 5y)$ to aid in factoring.

🔲 **Work Practice Problem 7**

Objective **B** Factoring by Grouping

Sometimes it is possible to factor a polynomial by grouping the terms of the polynomial and looking for common factors in each group. This method of factoring is called **factoring by grouping.**

PRACTICE PROBLEM 8

Factor: $xy - 5y + 3x - 15$

EXAMPLE 8 Factor: $ab - 6a + 2b - 12$

Solution:

$$ab - 6a + 2b - 12 = (ab - 6a) + (2b - 12) \qquad \text{Group pairs of terms.}$$
$$= a(b - 6) + 2(b - 6) \qquad \text{Factor each binomial.}$$
$$= (b - 6)(a + 2) \qquad \text{Factor out the greatest common factor, } (b - 6).$$

To check, multiply $(b - 6)$ and $(a + 2)$ to see that the product is $ab - 6a + 2b - 12$.

🔲 **Work Practice Problem 8**

Answers

5. $-2y(x^2 + 2x - 5)$ or $2y(-x^2 - 2x + 5)$,
6. $(x + 7)(3 + 5y)$,
7. $(2a + 3b)(6a - 1)$,
8. $(x - 5)(y + 3)$

✔ **Concept Check Answer**

b

Helpful Hint

Notice that the polynomial $a(b - 6) + 2(b - 6)$ is *not* in factored form. It is a *sum*, not a *product*. The factored form is $(b - 6)(a + 2)$.

EXAMPLE 9 Factor: $x^3 + 5x^2 + 3x + 15$

Solution:

$$\begin{aligned} x^3 + 5x^2 + 3x + 15 &= (x^3 + 5x^2) + (3x + 15) \quad \text{Group pairs of terms.}\\ &= x^2(x + 5) + 3(x + 5) \quad \text{Factor each binomial.}\\ &= (x + 5)(x^2 + 3) \quad \text{Factor out the common factor, } (x + 5). \end{aligned}$$

⬛ **Work Practice Problem 9**

EXAMPLE 10 Factor: $m^2n^2 + m^2 - 2n^2 - 2$

Solution:

$$\begin{aligned} m^2n^2 + m^2 - 2n^2 - 2 &= (m^2n^2 + m^2) + (-2n^2 - 2) \quad \text{Group pairs of terms.}\\ &= m^2(n^2 + 1) - 2(n^2 + 1) \quad \text{Factor each binomial.}\\ &= (n^2 + 1)(m^2 - 2) \quad \text{Factor out the common factor, } (n^2 + 1). \end{aligned}$$

⬛ **Work Practice Problem 10**

EXAMPLE 11 Factor: $xy + 2x - y - 2$

Solution:

$$\begin{aligned} xy + 2x - y - 2 &= (xy + 2x) + (-y - 2) \quad \text{Group pairs of terms.}\\ &= x(y + 2) - 1(y + 2) \quad \text{Factor each binomial.}\\ &= (y + 2)(x - 1) \quad \text{Factor out the common factor, } y + 2. \end{aligned}$$

⬛ **Work Practice Problem 11**

PRACTICE PROBLEM 9

Factor: $y^3 + 6y^2 + 4y + 24$

PRACTICE PROBLEM 10

Factor: $a^2b^2 + a^2 - 3b^2 - 3$

PRACTICE PROBLEM 11

Factor: $ab + 5a - b - 5$

Answers
9. $(y + 6)(y^2 + 4)$,
10. $(b^2 + 1)(a^2 - 3)$,
11. $(b + 5)(a - 1)$

Mental Math

Find the greatest common factor of each list of monomials.

1. $6, 12$ **2.** $9, 27$ **3.** $15x, 10$ **4.** $9x, 12$

5. $13x, 2x$ **6.** $4y, 5y$ **7.** $7x, 14x$ **8.** $8z, 4z$

5.4 EXERCISE SET

FOR EXTRA HELP

Student Solutions Manual   PH Math/Tutor Center   CD/Video for Review   MathXL®   MyMathLab

Objective A *Factor out the greatest common factor. See Examples 1 through 7.*

1. $18x - 12$ **2.** $21x + 14$ **3.** $4y^2 - 16xy^3$

4. $3z - 21xz^4$ **5.** $6x^5 - 8x^4 + 2x^3$ **6.** $9x + 3x^2 - 6x^3$

7. $8a^3b^3 - 4a^2b^2 + 4ab + 16ab^2$ **8.** $12a^3b - 6ab + 18ab^2 - 18a^2b$ **9.** $6(x + 3) + 5a(x + 3)$

10. $2(x - 4) + 3y(x - 4)$ **11.** $2x(z + 7) + (z + 7)$ **12.** $9x(y - 2) + (y - 2)$

13. $3x(6x^2 + 5) - 2(6x^2 + 5)$ **14.** $4x(2y^2 + 3) - 5(2y^2 + 3)$

Objective B *Factor each polynomial by grouping. See Examples 8 through 11.*

15. $ab + 3a + 2b + 6$ **16.** $ab + 2a + 5b + 10$ **17.** $ac + 4a - 2c - 8$

18. $bc + 8b - 3c - 24$ **19.** $2xy - 3x - 4y + 6$ **20.** $12xy - 18x - 10y + 15$

21. $12xy - 8x - 3y + 2$ **22.** $20xy - 15x - 4y + 3$

Objectives A B Mixed Practice *Factor each polynomial. See Examples 1 through 11.*

23. $6x^3 + 9$ **24.** $6x^2 - 8$ **25.** $x^3 + 3x^2$ **26.** $x^4 - 4x^3$ **27.** $8a^3 - 4a$ **28.** $12b^4 + 3b^2$

29. $-20x^2y + 16xy^3$ **30.** $-18xy^3 + 27x^4y$ **31.** $10a^2b^3 + 5ab^2 - 15ab^3$

32. $10ef - 20e^2f^3 + 30e^3f$ **33.** $9abc^2 + 6a^2bc - 6ab + 3bc$ **34.** $4a^2b^2c - 6ab^2c - 4ac + 8a$

35. $4x(y - 2) - 3(y - 2)$

36. $8y(z + 8) - 3(z + 8)$

37. $6xy + 10x + 9y + 15$

38. $15xy + 20x + 6y + 8$

39. $xy + 3y - 5x - 15$

40. $xy + 4y - 3x - 12$

41. $6ab - 2a - 9b + 3$

42. $16ab - 8a - 6b + 3$

43. $12xy + 18x + 2y + 3$

44. $20xy + 8x + 5y + 2$

45. $2m(n - 8) - (n - 8)$

46. $3a(b - 4) - (b - 4)$

47. $15x^3y^2 - 18x^2y^2$

48. $12x^4y^2 - 16x^3y^3$

49. $2x^2 + 3xy + 4x + 6y$

50. $3x^2 + 12x + 4xy + 16y$

51. $5x^2 + 5xy - 3x - 3y$

52. $4x^2 + 2xy - 10x - 5y$

53. $x^3 + 3x^2 + 4x + 12$

54. $x^3 + 4x^2 + 3x + 12$

55. $x^3 - x^2 - 2x + 2$

56. $x^3 - 2x^2 - 3x + 6$

Review

Find each product by using the FOIL order of multiplying binomials. See Section 5.2.

57. $(x + 2)(x - 5)$

58. $(x - 7)(x - 1)$

59. $(x + 3)(x + 2)$

60. $(x - 4)(x + 2)$

61. $(y - 3)(y - 1)$

62. $(s + 8)(s + 10)$

Concept Extensions

Solve. See the Concept Check in this section.

63. Which factorization of $10x^2 - 2x - 2$ is correct?
   a. $2(5x^2 - x + 1)$
   b. $2(5x^2 - x)$
   c. $2(5x^2 - x - 2)$
   d. $2(5x^2 - x - 1)$

64. Which factorization of $x^4 + 5x^3 - x^2$ is correct?
   a. $-1(x^4 + 5x^3 + x^2)$
   b. $x^2(x^2 + 5x^3 - x^2)$
   c. $x^2(x^2 + 5x - 1)$
   d. $5x^2(x^2 + 5x - 5)$

△ 65. The area of the material needed to manufacture a tin can is given by the polynomial $2\pi r^2 + 2\pi rh$, where the radius is r and height is h. Factor this expression.

66. To estimate the cost of a new product, one expression used by the production department is $4\pi r^2 + \dfrac{4}{3}\pi r^3$. Write an equivalent expression by factoring $4\pi r^2$ from both terms.

67. At the end of T years, the amount of money A in a savings account earning simple interest from an initial investment of \$5600 at rate r is given by the formula $A = 5600 + 5600rt$. Write an equivalent equation by factoring the expression $5600 + 5600rt$.

△ **68.** An open-topped box has a square base and a height of 10 inches. If each of the bottom edges of the box has length x inches, find the amount of material needed to construct the box. Write the answer in factored form.

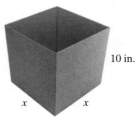

10 in.

x x

69. When $3x^2 - 9x + 3$ is factored, the result is $3(x^2 - 3x + 1)$. Explain why it is necessary to include the term 1 in this factored form.

70. Construct a trinomial whose greatest common factor is $5x^2y^3$.

71. A factored polynomial can be in many forms. For example, a factored form of $xy - 3x - 2y + 6$ is $(x - 2)(y - 3)$. Which of the following is not a factored form of $xy - 3x - 2y + 6$?
 a. $(2 - x)(3 - y)$ **b.** $(-2 + x)(-3 + y)$
 c. $(y - 3)(x - 2)$ **d.** $(-x + 2)(-y + 3)$

72. Consider the following sequence of algebraic steps:
$$x^3 - 6x^2 + 2x - 10 = (x^3 - 6x^2) + (2x - 10)$$
$$= x^2(x - 6) + 2(x - 5)$$
Explain whether the final result is the factored form of the original polynomial.

73. Which factorization of $12x^2 + 9x + 3$ is correct?
 a. $3(4x^2 + 3x + 1)$
 b. $3(4x^2 + 3x - 1)$
 c. $3(4x^2 + 3x - 3)$
 d. $3(4x^2 + 3x)$

74. The amount E of voltage in an electrical circuit is given by the formula
$$IR_1 + IR_2 = E$$
Write an equivalent equation by factoring the expression $IR_1 + IR_2$.

75. At the end of T years, the amount of money A in a savings account earning simple interest from an initial investment of P dollars at rate R is given by the formula
$$A = P + PRT$$
Write an equivalent equation by factoring the expression $P + PRT$.

Factor out the greatest common factor. Assume that variables used as exponents represent positive integers.

76. $x^{3n} - 2x^{2n} + 5x^n$ **77.** $3y^n + 3y^{2n} + 5y^{8n}$ **78.** $6x^{8a} - 2x^{5a} - 4x^{3a}$ **79.** $3x^{5a} - 6x^{3a} + 9x^{2a}$

80. An object is thrown upward from the ground with an initial velocity of 64 feet per second. The height $h(t)$ in feet of the object after t seconds is given by the polynomial function
$$h(t) = -16t^2 + 64t$$
 a. Write an equivalent factored expression for the function $h(t)$ by factoring $-16t^2 + 64t$.
 b. Find $h(1)$ by using
$$h(t) = -16t^2 + 64t$$
   and then by using the factored form of $h(t)$.
 c. Explain why the values found in part (b) are the same.

81. An object is dropped from the gondola of a hot-air balloon at a height of 224 feet. The height $h(t)$ in feet of the object after t seconds is given by the polynomial function

$$h(t) = -16t^2 + 224$$

224 ft

a. Write an equivalent factored expression for the function $h(t)$ by factoring $-16t^2 + 224$.

b. Find $h(2)$ by using

$$h(t) = -16t^2 + 224$$

and then by using the factored form of the function.

c. Explain why the values found in part (b) are the same.

82. The polynomial function $f(x) = 35{,}000x^3 - 171{,}000x^2 + 190{,}000x + 320{,}000$ models the number of applications for trademark registrations for the years 1999–2003, where x represents the number of years after 1999 and $f(x)$ is the number of trademark registration applications. Write an equivalent expression for $f(x)$ by factoring the greatest common factor from the terms of $f(x) = 35{,}000x^3 - 171{,}000x^2 + 190{,}000x + 320{,}000$. (*Source:* International Trademark Association)

83. The percentage of public school instructional rooms with Internet access is increasing. The polynomial function $f(x) = -2x^2 + 22x + 28$ models the percent of public school instructional rooms with Internet access for the years 1997–2003, where x is the years after 1997 and $f(x)$ is the percent of Internet-connected instructional spaces. Write the equivalent expression for $f(x)$ by factoring the greatest common factor from the terms of $f(x) = -2x^2 + 22x + 28$. (*Source:* U.S. Department of Education)

A Factor Trinomials of the Form $x^2 + bx + c$.

B Factor Trinomials of the Form $ax^2 + bx + c$.
   a. Method 1–Trial and Check
   b. Method 2–Grouping

C Factor by Substitution.

5.5 FACTORING TRINOMIALS

Objective **A** Factoring Trinomials of the Form $x^2 + bx + c$

In the previous section, we used factoring by grouping to factor four-term polynomials. In this section, we present techniques for factoring trinomials. Since $(x - 2)(x + 5) = x^2 + 3x - 10$, we say that $(x - 2)(x + 5)$ is a factored form of $x^2 + 3x - 10$. Taking a close look at how $(x - 2)$ and $(x + 5)$ are multiplied suggests a pattern for factoring trinomials of the form $x^2 + bx + c$.

$$(x - 2)(x + 5) = x^2 + 3x - 10$$

The pattern for factoring is summarized next.

Factoring a Trinomial of the Form $x^2 + bx + c$

Find two numbers whose product is c and whose sum is b. The factored form of $x^2 + bx + c$ is

$$(x + \text{one number})(x + \text{other number})$$

PRACTICE PROBLEM 1

Factor: $x^2 + 8x + 15$

EXAMPLE 1 Factor: $x^2 + 10x + 16$

Solution: We look for two integers whose product is 16 and whose sum is 10. Since our integers must have a positive product and a positive sum, we look at only positive factors of 16.

Positive Factors of 16	Sum of Factors
1, 16	$1 + 16 = 17$
4, 4	$4 + 4 = 8$
2, 8	$2 + 8 = 10$ Correct pair

The correct pair of numbers is 2 and 8 because their product is 16 and their sum is 10. Thus,

$$x^2 + 10x + 16 = (x + 2)(x + 8)$$

Check: To check, see that $(x + 2)(x + 8) = x^2 + 10x + 16$.

■ **Work Practice Problem 1**

PRACTICE PROBLEM 2

Factor: $x^2 - 10x + 24$

EXAMPLE 2 Factor: $x^2 - 12x + 35$

Solution: We need to find two integers whose product is 35 and whose sum is -12. Since our integers must have a positive product and a negative sum, we consider only negative factors of 35.

Negative Factors of 35	Sum of Factors
$-1, -35$	$-1 + (-35) = -36$
$-5, -7$	$-5 + (-7) = -12$ Correct pair

The numbers are -5 and -7.

$$x^2 - 12x + 35 = [x + (-5)][x + (-7)]$$
$$= (x - 5)(x - 7)$$

Check: To check, see that $(x - 5)(x - 7) = x^2 - 12x + 35$.

■ **Work Practice Problem 2**

Answers

1. $(x + 5)(x + 3)$,
2. $(x - 4)(x - 6)$

EXAMPLE 3 Factor: $5x^3 - 30x^2 - 35x$

Solution: First we factor out the greatest common factor, $5x$.

$$5x^3 - 30x^2 - 35x = 5x(x^2 - 6x - 7)$$

Next we factor $x^2 - 6x - 7$ by finding two numbers whose product is -7 and whose sum is -6. The numbers are 1 and -7.

$$5x^3 - 30x^2 - 35x = 5x(x^2 - 6x - 7)$$
$$= 5x(x + 1)(x - 7)$$

📱 **Work Practice Problem 3**

> Helpful Hint
>
> If the polynomial to be factored contains a common factor that is factored out, don't forget to include that common factor in the final factored form of the original polynomial.

EXAMPLE 4 Factor: $2n^2 - 38n + 80$

Solution: The terms of this polynomial have a greatest common factor of 2, which we factor out first.

$$2n^2 - 38n + 80 = 2(n^2 - 19n + 40)$$

Next we factor $n^2 - 19n + 40$ by finding two numbers whose product is 40 and whose sum is -19. Both numbers must be negative since their product is positive and their sum is negative. Possibilities are

$$-1 \text{ and } -40, \quad -2 \text{ and } -20, \quad -4 \text{ and } -10, \quad -5 \text{ and } -8$$

None of the pairs has a sum of -19, so no further factoring with integers is possible. The factored form of $2n^2 - 38n + 80$ is

$$2n^2 - 38n + 80 = 2(n^2 - 19n + 40)$$

📱 **Work Practice Problem 4**

We call a polynomial such as $n^2 - 19n + 40$, which cannot be factored further, a **prime polynomial.**

Objective **B** Factoring Trinomials of the Form $ax^2 + bx + c$

Next, we factor trinomials of the form $ax^2 + bx + c$, where the coefficient a of x^2 is not 1. Don't forget that the first step in factoring any polynomial is to factor out the greatest common factor of its terms.

Method 1—Factoring $ax^2 + bx + c$ by Trial and Check

EXAMPLE 5 Factor: $2x^2 + 11x + 15$

Solution: Factors of $2x^2$ are $2x$ and x. Let's try these factors as first terms of the binomials.

$$2x^2 + 11x + 15 = (2x + \quad)(x + \quad)$$

Continued on next page

PRACTICE PROBLEM 3

Factor: $6x^3 + 24x^2 - 30x$

PRACTICE PROBLEM 4

Factor: $3y^2 + 6y + 6$

PRACTICE PROBLEM 5

Factor: $3x^2 + 13x + 4$

Answers
3. $6x(x - 1)(x + 5)$, **4.** $3(y^2 + 2y + 2)$,
5. $(3x + 1)(x + 4)$

Next we try combinations of factors of 15 until the correct middle term, $11x$, is obtained. We will try only positive factors of 15 since the coefficient of the middle term, 11, is positive. Positive factors of 15 are 1 and 15 and 3 and 5.

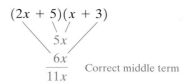

$$(2x + 1)(x + 15)$$
$$1x$$
$$\frac{30x}{31x} \quad \text{Incorrect middle term}$$

$$(2x + 15)(x + 1)$$
$$15x$$
$$\frac{2x}{17x} \quad \text{Incorrect middle term}$$

$$(2x + 3)(x + 5)$$
$$3x$$
$$\frac{10x}{13x} \quad \text{Incorrect middle term}$$

$$(2x + 5)(x + 3)$$
$$5x$$
$$\frac{6x}{11x} \quad \text{Correct middle term}$$

Thus, the factored form of $2x^2 + 11x + 15$ is $(2x + 5)(x + 3)$.

⬛ **Work Practice Problem 5**

Factoring a Trinomial of the Form $ax^2 + bx + c$

Step 1: Write all pairs of factors of ax^2.

Step 2: Write all pairs of factors of c, the constant term.

Step 3: Try various combinations of these factors until the correct middle term bx is found.

Step 4: If no combination exists, the polynomial is **prime**.

PRACTICE PROBLEM 6

Factor: $5x^2 + 13x - 6$

EXAMPLE 6 Factor: $3x^2 - x - 4$

Solution: Factors of $3x^2$: $3x \cdot x$

Factors of -4: $-1 \cdot 4$, $1 \cdot -4$, $-2 \cdot 2$, $2 \cdot -2$

Let's try possible combinations of these factors.

$$(3x - 1)(x + 4)$$
$$-1x$$
$$\frac{12x}{11x} \quad \text{Incorrect middle term}$$

$$(3x + 4)(x - 1)$$
$$4x$$
$$\frac{-3x}{1x} \quad \text{Incorrect middle term}$$

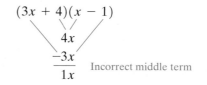

$$(3x - 4)(x + 1)$$
$$-4x$$
$$\frac{3x}{-1x} \quad \text{Correct middle term}$$

Thus, $3x^2 - x - 4 = (3x - 4)(x + 1)$.

⬛ **Work Practice Problem 6**

Answer
6. $(x + 3)(5x - 2)$

Helpful Hint

A positive constant in a trinomial tells us to look for two numbers with the same sign. The sign of the coefficient of the middle term tells us whether the signs are both positive or both negative.

| both positive | same sign | | both negative | same sign |

$$2x^2 + 7x + 3 = (2x + 1)(x + 3) \qquad 2x^2 - 7x + 3 = (2x - 1)(x - 3)$$

A negative constant in a trinomial tells us to look for two numbers with opposite signs.

| opposite signs | | opposite signs |

$$2x^2 - 5x - 3 = (2x + 1)(x - 3) \qquad 2x^2 + 5x - 3 = (2x - 1)(x + 3)$$

EXAMPLE 7 Factor: $12x^3y - 22x^2y + 8xy$

Solution: First we factor out the greatest common factor of the terms of this trinomial, $2xy$.

$$12x^3y - 22x^2y + 8xy = 2xy(6x^2 - 11x + 4)$$

Now we try to factor the trinomial $6x^2 - 11x + 4$.

Factors of $6x^2$: $2x \cdot 3x$, $6x \cdot x$

Let's try $2x$ and $3x$.

$$2xy(6x^2 - 11x + 4) = 2xy(2x + \quad)(3x + \quad)$$

The constant term, 4, is positive and the coefficient of the middle term, -11, is negative, so we factor 4 into negative factors only.

Negative factors of 4: $-4(-1)$, $-2(-2)$

Let's try -4 and -1.

$$2xy(2x - 4)(3x - 1)$$

$$\begin{array}{c} -12x \\ \underline{-2x} \\ -14x \end{array} \quad \text{Incorrect middle term}$$

This combination cannot be correct because one of the factors, $(2x - 4)$, has a common factor of 2. This cannot happen if the polynomial $6x^2 - 11x + 4$ has no common factors.

Now let's try -1 and -4.

$$2xy(2x - 1)(3x - 4)$$

$$\begin{array}{c} -3x \\ \underline{-8x} \\ -11x \end{array} \quad \text{Correct middle term}$$

Thus,

$$12x^3y - 22x^2y + 8xy = 2xy(2x - 1)(3x - 4)$$

If this combination had not worked, we would try -2 and -2 as factors of 4 and then $6x$ and x as factors of $6x^2$.

■ **Work Practice Problem 7**

PRACTICE PROBLEM 7

Factor: $24x^2y^2 - 42xy^2 + 9y^2$

Helpful Hint

If a trinomial has no common factor (other than 1), then none of its binomial factors will contain a common factor (other than 1).

Answer

7. $3y^2(2x - 3)(4x - 1)$

PRACTICE PROBLEM 8

Factor: $4x^2 + 28xy + 49y^2$

EXAMPLE 8 Factor: $16x^2 + 24xy + 9y^2$

Solution: No greatest common factor can be factored out of this trinomial.

Factors of $16x^2$: $16x \cdot x$, $8x \cdot 2x$, $4x \cdot 4x$
Factors of $9y^2$: $y \cdot 9y$, $3y \cdot 3y$

We try possible combinations until the correct factorization is found.

$$16x^2 + 24xy + 9y^2 = (4x + 3y)(4x + 3y) \quad \text{or} \quad (4x + 3y)^2$$

■ **Work Practice Problem 8**

The trinomial $16x^2 + 24xy + 9y^2$ in Example 8 is an example of a **perfect square trinomial** since its factors are two identical binomials. In the next section, we examine a special method for factoring perfect square trinomials.

Method 2—Factoring $ax^2 + bx + c$ by Grouping

There is another method we can use when factoring trinomials of the form $ax^2 + bx + c$: Write the trinomial as a four-term polynomial, and then factor by grouping.

Factoring a Trinomial of the Form $ax^2 + bx + c$ by Grouping

Step 1: Find two numbers whose product is $a \cdot c$ and whose sum is b.

Step 2: Write the term bx as a sum by using the factors found in Step 1.

Step 3: Factor by grouping.

PRACTICE PROBLEM 9

Factor: $12x^2 + 11x + 2$

EXAMPLE 9 Factor: $6x^2 + 13x + 6$

Solution: In this trinomial, $a = 6, b = 13$, and $c = 6$.

Step 1: Find two numbers whose product is $a \cdot c$, or $6 \cdot 6 = 36$, and whose sum is b, 13. The two numbers are 4 and 9.
Step 2: Write the middle term $13x$ as the sum $4x + 9x$.

$$6x^2 + 13x + 6 = 6x^2 + 4x + 9x + 6$$

Step 3: Factor $6x^2 + 4x + 9x + 6$ by grouping.

$$(6x^2 + 4x) + (9x + 6) = 2x(3x + 2) + 3(3x + 2)$$
$$= (3x + 2)(2x + 3)$$

■ **Work Practice Problem 9**

✔ **Concept Check** Name one way that a factorization can be checked.

PRACTICE PROBLEM 10

Factor: $14x^2 - x - 3$

EXAMPLE 10 Factor: $18x^2 - 9x - 2$

Solution: In this trinomial, $a = 18, b = -9$, and $c = -2$.

Step 1: Find two numbers whose product is $a \cdot c$ or $18(-2) = -36$ and whose sum is b, -9. The two numbers are -12 and 3.
Step 2: Write the middle term, $-9x$, as the sum $-12x + 3x$.

$$18x^2 - 9x - 2 = 18x^2 - 12x + 3x - 2$$

Step 3: Factor by grouping.

$$(18x^2 - 12x) + (3x - 2) = 6x(3x - 2) + 1(3x - 2)$$
$$= (3x - 2)(6x + 1)$$

■ **Work Practice Problem 10**

Answers

8. $(2x + 7y)^2$, **9.** $(3x + 2)(4x + 1)$,
10. $(7x + 3)(2x - 1)$

✔ **Concept Check Answer**

Answers may vary. A sample is: By multiplying the factors to see that the product is the original polynomial.

Objective Ⓒ **Factoring by Substitution**

A complicated-looking polynomial may be a simpler trinomial "in disguise." Revealing the simpler trinomial is possible by substitution.

EXAMPLE 11 Factor: $2(a + 3)^2 - 5(a + 3) - 7$

Solution: The quantity $(a + 3)$ is in two of the terms of this polynomial. If we *substitute* x for $(a + 3)$, the result is the following simpler trinomial.

$$2(a + 3)^2 - 5(a + 3) - 7 \quad \text{Original trinomial}$$
$$= \quad 2(x)^2 - 5(x) - 7 \quad \text{Substitute } x \text{ for } (a + 3).$$

Now we can factor $2x^2 - 5x - 7$.

$$2x^2 - 5x - 7 = (2x - 7)(x + 1)$$

But the quantity in the original polynomial was $(a + 3)$, not x. Thus we need to reverse the substitution and replace x with $(a + 3)$.

$$(2x - 7)(x + 1) \qquad \text{Factored expression}$$
$$= [2(a + 3) - 7][(a + 3) + 1] \quad \text{Substitute } (a + 3) \text{ for } x.$$
$$= (2a + 6 - 7)(a + 3 + 1) \qquad \text{Remove inside parentheses.}$$
$$= (2a - 1)(a + 4) \qquad \text{Simplify.}$$

Thus, $2(a + 3)^2 - 5(a + 3) - 7 = (2a - 1)(a + 4)$.

▣ **Work Practice Problem 11**

EXAMPLE 12 Factor: $5x^4 + 29x^2 - 42$

Solution: Again, substitution may help us factor this polynomial more easily. We will let $y = x^2$, so $y^2 = (x^2)^2$, or x^4. Then

$$5x^4 + 29x^2 - 42$$
becomes $\quad\downarrow\qquad\downarrow$
$$5y^2 + 29y - 42$$

which factors as

$$5y^2 + 29y - 42 = (5y - 6)(y + 7)$$

Now we replace y with x^2 to get

$$(5x^2 - 6)(x^2 + 7)$$

▣ **Work Practice Problem 12**

PRACTICE PROBLEM 11

Factor: $3(z + 2)^2 - 19(z + 2) + 6$

PRACTICE PROBLEM 12

Factor: $14x^4 + 23x^2 + 3$

Answers
11. $(3z + 5)(z - 4)$,
12. $(2x^2 + 3)(7x^2 + 1)$

Mental Math

1. Find two numbers whose product is 10 and whose sum is 7.

2. Find two numbers whose product is 12 and whose sum is 8.

3. Find two numbers whose product is 24 and whose sum is 11.

4. Find two numbers whose product is 30 and whose sum is 13.

5.5 EXERCISE SET

FOR EXTRA HELP

Student Solutions Manual   PH Math/Tutor Center   CD/Video for Review   Math XL MathXL®   MyMathLab MyMathLab

Objective A *Factor each trinomial. See Examples 1 through 4.*

 1. $x^2 + 9x + 18$

2. $x^2 + 9x + 20$

3. $x^2 - 12x + 32$

4. $x^2 - 12x + 27$

5. $x^2 + 10x - 24$

6. $x^2 + 3x - 54$

 7. $x^2 - 2x - 24$

8. $x^2 - 9x - 36$

 9. $3x^2 - 18x + 24$

10. $x^2y^2 + 4xy^2 + 3y^2$

11. $4x^2z + 28xz + 40z$

12. $5x^2 - 45x + 70$

13. $2x^2 - 24x - 64$

14. $3n^2 - 6n - 51$

Objective B *Factor each trinomial. See Examples 5 through 9.*

15. $5x^2 + 16x + 3$

16. $3x^2 + 8x + 4$

17. $2x^2 - 11x + 12$

18. $3x^2 - 19x + 20$

19. $2x^2 + 25x - 20$

20. $6x^2 + 13x + 8$

21. $4x^2 - 12x + 9$

22. $25x^2 - 30x + 9$

23. $12x^2 + 10x - 50$

24. $12y^2 - 48y + 45$

25. $3y^4 - y^3 - 10y^2$

26. $2x^2z + 5xz - 12z$

27. $6x^3 + 8x^2 + 24x$

28. $18y^3 + 12y^2 + 2y$

29. $2x^2 - 5xy - 3y^2$

30. $6x^2 + 11xy + 4y^2$

31. $28y^2 + 22y + 4$

32. $24y^3 - 2y^2 - y$

33. $2x^2 + 15x - 27$

34. $3x^2 + 14x + 15$

Objective C *Use substitution to factor each polynomial completely. See Examples 11 and 12.*

35. $x^4 + x^2 - 6$

36. $x^4 - x^2 - 20$

37. $(5x + 1)^2 + 8(5x + 1) + 7$

38. $(3x - 1)^2 + 5(3x - 1) + 6$

39. $x^6 - 7x^3 + 12$

40. $x^6 - 4x^3 - 12$

41. $(a + 5)^2 - 5(a + 5) - 24$

42. $(3c + 6)^2 + 12(3c + 6) - 28$

Objectives A B C Mixed Practice *Factor each polynomial completely. See Examples 1 through 12.*

43. $x^2 - 24x - 81$

44. $x^2 - 48x - 100$

45. $x^2 - 15x - 54$

46. $x^2 - 15x + 54$

47. $3x^2 - 6x + 3$

48. $8x^2 - 8x + 2$

49. $3x^2 - 5x - 2$

50. $5x^2 - 14x - 3$

51. $8x^2 - 26x + 15$ **52.** $12x^2 - 17x + 6$ 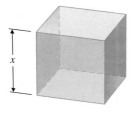 **53.** $18x^4 + 21x^3 + 6x^2$ **54.** $20x^5 + 54x^4 + 10x^3$

55. $x^2 + 8xz + 7z^2$ **56.** $a^2 - 2ab - 15b^2$ **57.** $x^2 - x - 12$ **58.** $x^2 + 4x - 5$

59. $3a^2 + 12ab + 12b^2$ **60.** $2x^2 + 16xy + 32y^2$ **61.** $x^2 + 4x + 5$ **62.** $x^2 + 6x + 8$

63. $2(x + 4)^2 + 3(x + 4) - 5$ **64.** $3(x + 3)^2 + 2(x + 3) - 5$ **65.** $6x^2 - 49x + 30$

66. $4x^2 - 39x + 27$ **67.** $x^4 - 5x^2 - 6$ **68.** $x^4 - 5x^2 + 6$

69. $6x^3 - x^2 - x$ **70.** $12x^3 + x^2 - x$ **71.** $12a^2 - 29ab + 15b^2$

72. $16y^2 + 6yx - 27x^2$ **73.** $9x^2 + 30x + 25$ **74.** $4x^2 + 6x + 9$

75. $3x^2y - 11xy + 8y$ **76.** $5xy^2 - 9xy + 4x$ **77.** $2x^2 + 2x - 12$

78. $3x^2 + 6x - 45$ **79.** $(x - 4)^2 + 3(x - 4) - 18$ **80.** $(x - 3)^2 - 2(x - 3) - 8$

81. $2x^6 + 3x^3 - 9$ **82.** $3x^6 - 14x^3 + 8$ **83.** $72xy^4 - 24xy^2z + 2xz^2$

84. $36xy^2 - 48xyz^2 + 16xz^4$ **85.** $2x^3y + 2x^2y - 12xy$ **86.** $3x^2y^3 + 6x^2y^2 - 45x^2y$

87. $x^2 + 6xy + 5y^2$ **88.** $x^2 + 6xy + 8y^2$

Review

Multiply. See Section 5.2.

89. $(x - 3)(x + 3)$ **90.** $(x - 4)(x + 4)$ **91.** $(2x + 1)^2$

92. $(3x + 5)^2$ **93.** $(x - 2)(x^2 + 2x + 4)$ **94.** $(y + 1)(y^2 - y + 1)$

Concept Extensions

95. Find all positive and negative integers b such that $x^2 + bx + 6$ is factorable.

96. Find all positive and negative integers b such that $x^2 + bx - 10$ is factorable.

△ **97.** The volume $V(x)$ of a box in terms of its height x is given by the function $V(x) = x^3 + 2x^2 - 8x$. Factor this expression for $V(x)$.

△ **98.** Based on your results from Exercise 97, find the length and width of the box if the height is 5 inches and the dimensions of the box are whole numbers.

99. Suppose that a movie is being filmed in New York City. An action shot requires an object to be thrown upward with an initial velocity of 80 feet per second off the top of 1 Madison Square Plaza, a height of 576 feet. The height $h(t)$ in feet of the object after t seconds is given by the function $h(t) = -16t^2 + 80t + 576$. (*Source: The World Almanac, 2001*)

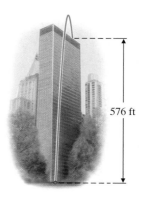

576 ft

  a. Find the height of the object at $t = 0$ seconds, $t = 2$ seconds, $t = 4$ seconds, and $t = 6$ seconds.
  b. Explain why the height of the object increases and then decreases as time passes.
  c. Factor the polynomial $-16t^2 + 80t + 576$.

100. Suppose that an object is thrown upward with an initial velocity of 64 feet per second off the edge of a 960-foot-cliff. The height $h(t)$ in feet of the object after t seconds is given by the function

$$h(t) = -16t^2 + 64t + 960$$

  a. Find the height of the object at $t = 0$ seconds, $t = 3$ seconds, $t = 6$ seconds, and $t = 9$ seconds.
  b. Explain why the height of the object increases and then decreases as time passes.
  c. Factor the polynomial $-16t^2 + 64t + 960$.

Factor. Assume that variables used as exponents represent positive integers.

101. $x^{2n} + 10x^n + 16$ **102.** $x^{2n} - 7x^n + 12$ **103.** $x^{2n} - 3x^n - 18$ **104.** $x^{2n} + 7x^n - 18$

105. $2x^{2n} + 11x^n + 5$ **106.** $3x^{2n} - 8x^n + 4$ **107.** $4x^{2n} - 12x^n + 9$ **108.** $9x^{2n} + 24x^n + 16$

Recall that a graphing calculator may be used to check addition, subtraction, and multiplication of polynomials. In the same manner, a graphing calculator may be used to check factoring of polynomials in one variable. For example, to see that

$$2x^3 - 9x^2 - 5x = x(2x + 1)(x - 5)$$

graph $Y_1 = 2x^3 - 9x^2 - 5x$ *and* $Y_2 = x(2x + 1)(x - 5)$*. Then trace along both graphs to see that they coincide. Factor the following and use this method to check your results.*

109. $x^4 + 6x^3 + 5x^2$ **110.** $x^3 + 6x^2 + 8x$ **111.** $30x^3 + 9x^2 - 3x$ **112.** $-6x^4 + 10x^3 - 4x^2$

STUDY SKILLS BUILDER

Is Your Notebook Still Organized?

It's never too late to organize your material in a course. Let's see how you are doing.

1. Are all your graded papers in one place in your math notebook or binder?

2. Flip through the pages of your notebook. Are your notes neat and readable?

3. Are your notes complete with no sections missing?

4. Are important notes marked in some way (like an exclamation point) so that you will know to review them before a quiz or test?

5. Are your assignments complete?

6. Do exercises that have given you trouble have a mark (like a question mark) so that you will remember to talk to your instructor or a tutor about them?

7. Describe your attitude toward this course.

8. List ways your attitude can improve and make a commitment to work on at least one of these during the next week.

5.6 FACTORING BY SPECIAL PRODUCTS

Objectives

A Factor a Perfect Square Trinomial.

B Factor the Difference of Two Squares.

C Factor the Sum or Difference of Two Cubes.

Objective **A** Factoring Perfect Square Trinomials

In the previous section, we considered a variety of ways to factor trinomials of the form $ax^2 + bx + c$. In Example 8, we factored $16x^2 + 24xy + 9y^2$ as

$$16x^2 + 24xy + 9y^2 = (4x + 3y)^2$$

Recall that we called $16x^2 + 24xy + 9y^2$ a perfect square trinomial because its factors are two identical binomials. A trinomial is a perfect square trinomial if it can be written so that its first term is the square of some quantity a, its last term is the square of some quantity b, and its middle term is twice the product of the quantities a and b.

The following special formulas can be used to factor perfect square trinomials.

Perfect Square Trinomials

$$a^2 + 2ab + b^2 = (a + b)^2$$
$$a^2 - 2ab + b^2 = (a - b)^2$$

Notice that these equations are the same special products from Section 5.2 for the square of a binomial.

From

$$a^2 + 2ab + b^2 = (a + b)^2$$

we see that

$$16x^2 + 24xy + 9y^2 = (4x)^2 + 2(4x)(3y) + (3y)^2 = (4x + 3y)^2$$

EXAMPLE 1 Factor: $m^2 + 10m + 25$

Solution: Notice that the first term is a square: $m^2 = (m)^2$, the last term is a square: $25 = 5^2$, and $10m = 2 \cdot 5 \cdot m$.

This is a perfect square trinomial. Thus,

$$m^2 + 10m + 25 = m^2 + 2(m)(5) + 5^2 = (m + 5)^2$$

Work Practice Problem 1

PRACTICE PROBLEM 1

Factor: $x^2 + 8x + 16$

EXAMPLES Factor each trinomial.

2. $4x^2 + 4x + 1 = (2x)^2 + 2 \cdot 2x \cdot 1 + 1^2$ See whether it is a perfect square trinomial.
           $= (2x + 1)^2$ Factor.

3. $9x^2 - 12x + 4 = (3x)^2 - 2(3x)(2) + 2^2$ See whether it is a perfect square trinomial.
           $= (3x - 2)^2$ Factor.

Work Practice Problems 2–3

PRACTICE PROBLEMS 2–3

Factor.
2. $9x^2 + 6x + 1$
3. $25x^2 - 20x + 4$

EXAMPLE 4 Factor: $3a^2x - 12abx + 12b^2x$

Solution: The terms of this trinomial have a greatest common factor of $3x$, which we factor out first.

$$3a^2x - 12abx + 12b^2x = 3x(a^2 - 4ab + 4b^2)$$

The polynomial $a^2 - 4ab + 4b^2$ is a perfect square trinomial. Notice that the first term is a square: $a^2 = (a)^2$, the last term is a square: $4b^2 = (2b)^2$, and $4ab = 2(a)(2b)$. The factoring can now be completed as

$$3x(a^2 - 4ab + 4b^2) = 3x(a - 2b)^2$$

Work Practice Problem 4

PRACTICE PROBLEM 4

Factor: $4x^3 - 32x^2y + 64xy^2$

Answers
1. $(x + 4)^2$,   **2.** $(3x + 1)^2$,
3. $(5x - 2)^2$,   **4.** $4x(x - 4y)^2$

Objective **B** Factoring the Difference of Two Squares

We now factor special types of binomials, beginning with the **difference of two squares.** The special product pattern presented in Section 5.2 for the product of a sum and a difference of two terms is used again here. However, the emphasis is now on factoring rather than on multiplying.

Difference of Two Squares

$$a^2 - b^2 = (a + b)(a - b)$$

Notice that a binomial is a difference of two squares when it is the difference of the square of some quantity a and the square of some quantity b.

PRACTICE PROBLEMS 5–8

Factor:

5. $x^2 - 49$

6. $4y^2 - 81$

7. $12 - 3a^2$

8. $y^2 - \dfrac{1}{25}$

EXAMPLES Factor.

5. $\begin{aligned} x^2 - 9 &= x^2 - 3^2 \\ &= (x + 3)(x - 3) \end{aligned}$

6. $\begin{aligned} 16y^2 - 9 &= (4y)^2 - 3^2 \\ &= (4y + 3)(4y - 3) \end{aligned}$

7. $\begin{aligned} 50 - 8y^2 &= 2(25 - 4y^2) \\ &= 2[5^2 - (2y)^2] \\ &= 2(5 + 2y)(5 - 2y) \end{aligned}$ Factor out the common factor of 2.

8. $\begin{aligned} x^2 - \dfrac{1}{4} &= x^2 - \left(\dfrac{1}{2}\right)^2 \\ &= \left(x + \dfrac{1}{2}\right)\left(x - \dfrac{1}{2}\right) \end{aligned}$

◻ **Work Practice Problems 5–8**

The binomial $x^2 + 9$ is a **sum of two squares** and cannot be factored by using real numbers. *In general, except for factoring out a greatest common factor, the sum of two squares usually cannot be factored by using real numbers.*

PRACTICE PROBLEM 9

Factor: $a^4 - 81$

EXAMPLE 9 Factor: $p^4 - 16$

Solution:

$$\begin{aligned} p^4 - 16 &= (p^2)^2 - 4^2 \\ &= (p^2 + 4)(p^2 - 4) \end{aligned}$$

The binomial factor $p^2 + 4$ cannot be factored by using real numbers, but the binomial factor $p^2 - 4$ is a difference of squares.

$$(p^2 + 4)(p^2 - 4) = (p^2 + 4)(p + 2)(p - 2)$$

◻ **Work Practice Problem 9**

Answers

5. $(x + 7)(x - 7)$,

6. $(2y + 9)(2y - 9)$,

7. $3(2 + a)(2 - a)$,

8. $\left(y + \dfrac{1}{5}\right)\left(y - \dfrac{1}{5}\right)$,

9. $(a^2 + 9)(a + 3)(a - 3)$

✔**Concept Check** Is $(x - 4)(y^2 - 9)$ completely factored? Why or why not?

EXAMPLE 10 Factor: $(x + 3)^2 - 36$

Solution:

$$
\begin{aligned}
(x + 3)^2 - 36 &= (x + 3)^2 - 6^2 \\
&= [(x + 3) + 6][(x + 3) - 6] \quad \text{Factor as the difference of two squares.} \\
&= [x + 3 + 6][x + 3 - 6] \quad \text{Remove parentheses.} \\
&= (x + 9)(x - 3) \quad \text{Simplify.}
\end{aligned}
$$

◼ **Work Practice Problem 10**

PRACTICE PROBLEM 10

Factor: $(x + 1)^2 - 9$

EXAMPLE 11 Factor: $x^2 + 4x + 4 - y^2$

Solution: Notice that the first three terms form a perfect square trinomial. Let's try factoring by grouping. To do so, let's group and factor the first three terms.

$$
\begin{aligned}
x^2 + 4x + 4 - y^2 &= (x^2 + 4x + 4) - y^2 \quad \text{Group the first three terms.} \\
&= (x + 2)^2 - y^2 \quad \text{Factor the perfect square trinomial.}
\end{aligned}
$$

This is not completely factored yet since we have a *difference,* not a *product.* Since $(x + 2)^2 - y^2$ is a difference of squares, we have

$$
\begin{aligned}
(x + 2)^2 - y^2 &= [(x + 2) + y][(x + 2) - y] \\
&= (x + 2 + y)(x + 2 - y)
\end{aligned}
$$

◼ **Work Practice Problem 11**

PRACTICE PROBLEM 11

Factor: $a^2 + 2a + 1 - b^2$

Objective **C** **Factoring the Sum or Difference of Two Cubes**

Although the sum of two squares usually cannot be factored, the sum of two cubes, as well as the difference of two cubes, can be factored as follows.

Sum and Difference of Two Cubes

$$a^3 + b^3 = (a + b)(a^2 - ab + b^2)$$
$$a^3 - b^3 = (a - b)(a^2 + ab + b^2)$$

To check the first pattern, let's find the product of $(a + b)$ and $(a^2 - ab + b^2)$.

$$
\begin{aligned}
(a + b)(a^2 - ab + b^2) &= a(a^2 - ab + b^2) + b(a^2 - ab + b^2) \\
&= a^3 - a^2b + ab^2 + a^2b - ab^2 + b^3 \\
&= a^3 + b^3
\end{aligned}
$$

EXAMPLE 12 Factor: $x^3 + 8$

Solution: First we write the binomial in the form $a^3 + b^3$. Then we use the formula

$$a^3 + b^3 = (a + b)(a^2 - a \cdot b + b^2), \text{ where } a \text{ is } x \text{ and } b \text{ is } 2.$$

$$x^3 + 8 = x^3 + 2^3 = (x + 2)(x^2 - x \cdot 2 + 2^2)$$

Thus, $x^3 + 8 = (x + 2)(x^2 - 2x + 4)$

◼ **Work Practice Problem 12**

PRACTICE PROBLEM 12

Factor: $z^3 + 27$

Answers
10. $(x - 2)(x + 4)$,
11. $(a + 1 + b)(a + 1 - b)$,
12. $(z + 3)(z^2 - 3z + 9)$

✔ **Concept Check Answer**
no; $(y^2 - 9)$ can be factored

PRACTICE PROBLEM 13

Factor: $x^3 + 64y^3$

EXAMPLE 13 Factor: $p^3 + 27q^3$

Solution:

$$p^3 + 27q^3 = p^3 + (3q)^3$$
$$= (p + 3q)[p^2 - (p)(3q) + (3q)^2]$$
$$= (p + 3q)(p^2 - 3pq + 9q^2)$$

■ **Work Practice Problem 13**

PRACTICE PROBLEM 14

Factor: $y^3 - 8$

EXAMPLE 14 Factor: $y^3 - 64$

Solution: This is a difference of cubes since $y^3 - 64 = y^3 - 4^3$.

From $a^3 - b^3 = (a - b)(a^2 + a \cdot b + b^2)$ we have that

$$y^3 - 4^3 = (y - 4)(y^2 + y \cdot 4 + 4^2)$$
$$= (y - 4)(y^2 + 4y + 16)$$

■ **Work Practice Problem 14**

> **Helpful Hint**
>
> When factoring sums or differences of cubes, be sure to notice the sign patterns.
>
> Same sign
>
> $$x^3 + y^3 = (x + y)(x^2 - xy + y^2)$$
>
> Opposite sign
>
> Always positive
>
> Same sign
>
> $$x^3 - y^3 = (x - y)(x^2 + xy + y^2)$$
>
> Opposite sign

PRACTICE PROBLEM 15

Factor: $27a^2 - b^3a^2$

EXAMPLE 15 Factor: $125q^2 - n^3q^2$

Solution: First we factor out a common factor of q^2.

$$125q^2 - n^3q^2 = q^2(125 - n^3)$$
$$= q^2(5^3 - n^3)$$

Opposite sign   Positive

$$= q^2(5 - n)[5^2 + (5)(n) + (n^2)]$$
$$= q^2(5 - n)(25 + 5n + n^2)$$

Thus, $125q^2 - n^3q^2 = q^2(5 - n)(25 + 5n + n^2)$. The trinomial $25 + 5n + n^2$ cannot be factored further.

■ **Work Practice Problem 15**

Answers

13. $(x + 4y)(x^2 - 4xy + 16y^2)$,
14. $(y - 2)(y^2 + 2y + 4)$,
15. $a^2(3 - b)(9 + 3b + b^2)$

Objective A *Factor. See Examples 1 through 4.*

1. $x^2 + 6x + 9$

2. $x^2 - 10x + 25$

3. $4x^2 - 12x + 9$

4. $25x^2 + 10x + 1$

5. $4a^2 + 12a + 9$

6. $9a^2 - 30a + 25$

7. $3x^2 - 24x + 48$

8. $2x^2 + 28x + 98$

9. $9y^2x^2 + 12yx^2 + 4x^2$

10. $4x^2y^3 - 4xy^3 + y^3$

11. $16x^2 - 56xy + 49y^2$

12. $81x^2 + 36xy + 4y^2$

Objective B *Factor. See Examples 5 through 11.*

13. $x^2 - 25$

14. $y^2 - 100$

15. $\dfrac{1}{9} - 4z^2$

16. $\dfrac{1}{16} - y^2$

17. $(y + 2)^2 - 49$

18. $(x - 1)^2 - z^2$

19. $64x^2 - 100$

20. $4x^2 - 36$

21. $(x + 2y)^2 - 9$

22. $(3x + y)^2 - 25$

23. $x^2 + 16x + 64 - x^4$

24. $x^2 + 20x + 100 - x^4$

Objective C *Factor. See Examples 12 through 15.*

25. $x^3 + 27$

26. $y^3 + 1$

27. $z^3 - 1$

28. $8 - x^3$

29. $m^3 + n^3$

30. $p^3 + 125q^3$

31. $x^3y^2 - 27y^2$

32. $a^3b + 8b^4$

33. $64q^2 - q^2p^3$

34. $8ab^3 + 27a^4$

35. $250y^3 - 16x^3$

36. $54y^3 - 128$

Objectives A B C Mixed Practice *Factor completely. See Examples 1 through 15.*

37. $x^2 - 12x + 36$

38. $x^2 - 18x + 81$

39. $18x^2y - 2y$

40. $12xy^2 - 108x$

41. $9x^2 - 49$

42. $25x^2 - 4$

43. $x^4 - 1$

44. $x^4 - 256$

45. $x^6 - y^3$

46. $x^3 - y^6$

47. $8x^3 + 27y^3$

48. $125x^3 + 8y^3$

49. $4x^2 + 4x + 1 - z^2$

50. $9y^2 + 12y + 4 - x^2$

51. $3x^6y^2 + 81y^2$

52. $x^2y^9 + x^2y^3$

53. $n^3 - \dfrac{1}{27}$

54. $p^3 + \dfrac{1}{125}$

55. $-16y^2 + 64$

56. $-12y^2 + 108$

57. $x^2 - 10x + 25 - y^2$

58. $x^2 - 18x + 81 - y^2$

59. $a^3b^3 + 125$

60. $x^3y^3 + 216$

61. $\dfrac{x^2}{25} - \dfrac{y^2}{9}$

62. $\dfrac{a^2}{4} - \dfrac{b^2}{49}$

63. $(x + y)^3 + 125$

64. $(r + s)^3 + 27$

Review

Solve each equation. See Section 2.1.

65. $x - 5 = 0$

66. $x + 7 = 0$

67. $3x + 1 = 0$

68. $5x - 15 = 0$

69. $-2x = 0$

70. $3x = 0$

71. $-5x + 25 = 0$

72. $-4x - 16 = 0$

Concept Extensions

Determine whether each polynomial is factored completely or not. See the Concept Check in this section.

73. $5x(x^2 - 4)$

74. $x^2y^2(x^3 - y^3)$

75. $7y(a^2 + a + 1)$

76. $9z(x^2 + 4)$

77. A manufacturer of metal washers needs to deter-mine the cross-sectional area of each washer. If the outer radius of the washer is R and the radius of the hole is r, express the area of the washer as a polyno-mial. Factor this polynomial completely.

78. Express the area of the shaded region as a polynomial. Factor the polynomial completely.

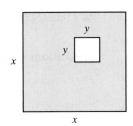

Express the volume of each solid as a polynomial. To do so, subtract the volume of the "hole" from the volume of the larger solid. Then factor the resulting polynomial.

79.

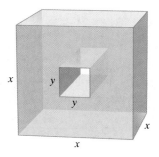

80.

Find the value of c that makes each trinomial a perfect square trinomial.

81. $x^2 + 6x + c$

82. $y^2 + 10y + c$

83. $m^2 - 14m + c$

84. $n^2 - 2n + c$

85. Factor $x^6 - 1$ completely, using the following methods from this chapter.
   a. Factor the expression by treating it as the difference of two squares, $(x^3)^2 - 1^2$.
   b. Factor the expression treating it as the difference of two cubes, $(x^2)^3 - 1^3$.
   c. Are the answers to parts **(a)** and **(b)** the same? Why or why not?

Factor. Assume that variables used as exponents represent positive integers.

86. $x^{2n} - 25$

87. $x^{2n} - 36$

88. $36x^{2n} - 49$

89. $25x^{2n} - 81$

90. $x^{4n} - 16$

91. $x^{4n} - 625$

Operations on Polynomials and Factoring Strategies

Operations on Polynomials

Perform each indicated operation.

1. $(-y^2 + 6y - 1) + (3y^2 - 4y - 10)$

2. $(5z^4 - 6z^2 + z + 1) - (7z^4 - 2z + 1)$

3. Subtract $(x - 5)$ from $(x^2 - 6x + 2)$

4. $(2x^2 + 6x - 5) + (5x^2 - 10x)$

5. $(5x - 3)^2$

6. $(5x^2 - 14x - 3) \div (5x + 1)$

7. $(2x^4 - 3x^2 + 5x - 2) \div (x + 2)$

8. $(4x - 1)(x^2 - 3x - 2)$

Factoring Strategies

The key to proficiency in factoring polynomials is to practice until you are comfortable with each technique. A strategy for factoring polynomials completely is given next.

Factoring a Polynomial

Step 1: Are there any common factors? If so, factor out the greatest common factor.

Step 2: How many terms are in the polynomial?

 a. If there are *two* terms, decide if one of the following formulas may be applied:
  i. Difference of two squares: $a^2 - b^2 = (a - b)(a + b)$
  ii. Difference of two cubes: $a^3 - b^3 = (a - b)(a^2 + ab + b^2)$
  iii. Sum of two cubes: $a^3 + b^3 = (a + b)(a^2 - ab + b^2)$

 b. If there are *three* terms, try one of the following:
  i. Perfect square trinomial: $a^2 + 2ab + b^2 = (a + b)^2$
   $a^2 - 2ab + b^2 = (a - b)^2$
  ii. If not a perfect square trinomial, factor by using the methods presented in Section 5.5.

 c. If there are *four* or more terms, try factoring by grouping.

Step 3: See whether any factors in the factored polynomial can be factored further.

Factor completely.

9. $x^2 - 8x + 16 - y^2$

10. $12x^2 - 22x - 20$

11. $x^4 - x$

12. $(2x + 1)^2 - 3(2x + 1) + 2$

13. $14x^2y - 2xy$

14. $24ab^2 - 6ab$

15. $4x^2 - 16$

16. $9x^2 - 81$

17. $3x^2 - 8x - 11$

18. $5x^2 - 2x - 3$

19. $4x^2 + 8x - 12$

20. $6x^2 - 6x - 12$

21. $4x^2 + 36x + 81$

22. $25x^2 + 40x + 16$

23. $8x^3 + 125y^3$

24. $27x^3 - 64y^3$ **25.** $64x^2y^3 - 8x^2$ **26.** $27x^5y^4 - 216x^2y$

27. $(x + 5)^3 + y^3$ **28.** $(y - 1)^3 + 27x^3$

29. $(5a - 3)^2 - 6(5a - 3) + 9$ **30.** $(4r + 1)^2 + 8(4r + 1) + 16$

31. $7x^2 - 63x$ **32.** $20x^2 + 23x + 6$ **33.** $ab - 6a + 7b - 42$

34. $20x^2 - 220x + 600$ **35.** $x^4 - 1$ **36.** $15x^2 - 20x$

37. $10x^2 - 7x - 33$ **38.** $45m^3n^3 - 27m^2n^2$ **39.** $5a^3b^3 - 50a^3b$

40. $x^4 + x$ **41.** $16x^2 + 25$ **42.** $20x^3 + 20y^3$

43. $10x^3 - 210x^2 + 1100x$ **44.** $9y^2 - 42y + 49$ **45.** $64a^3b^4 - 27a^3b$

46. $y^4 - 16$ **47.** $2x^3 - 54$ **48.** $2sr + 10s - r - 5$

49. $3y^5 - 5y^4 + 6y - 10$ **50.** $64a^2 + b^2$ **51.** $100z^3 + 100$

52. $250x^4 - 16x$ **53.** $4b^2 - 36b + 81$ **54.** $2a^5 - a^4 + 6a - 3$

55. $(y - 6)^2 + 3(y - 6) + 2$ **56.** $(c + 2)^2 - 6(c + 2) + 5$

△ **57.** Express the area of the shaded region as a polynomial. Factor the polynomial completely.

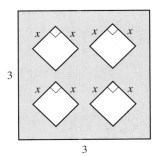

24.	
25.	
26.	
27.	
28.	
29.	
30.	
31.	
32.	
33.	
34.	
35.	
36.	
37.	
38.	
39.	
40.	
41.	
42.	
43.	
44.	
45.	
46.	
47.	
48.	
49.	
50.	
51.	
52.	
53.	
54.	
55.	
56.	
57.	

A Solve Polynomial Equations by Factoring.

B Solve Problems That Can Be Modeled by Polynomial Equations.

5.7 SOLVING EQUATIONS BY FACTORING AND SOLVING PROBLEMS

Objective A Solving Polynomial Equations by Factoring

In this section, your efforts to learn factoring will start to pay off. We use factoring to solve polynomial equations.

A **polynomial equation** is the result of setting two polynomials equal to each other. Examples are shown below.

$$3x^3 - 2x^2 = x^2 + 2x \qquad 2.6x + 7 = -1.3$$
$$-5x^2 - 5 = -9x^2 - 2x + 1$$

A polynomial equation is in **standard form** if one side of the equation is 0, as in the following examples.

$$3x^3 - 3x^2 - 2x + 1 = 0 \qquad 2.6x + 8.3 = 0$$
$$4x^2 + 2x - 6 = 0$$

The degree of a simplified polynomial equation in standard form is the same as the highest degree of any of its terms. A polynomial equation of degree 2 is also called a **quadratic equation.**

A solution of a polynomial equation in one variable is a value of the variable that makes the equation true. The method presented in this section for solving polynomial equations is called the **factoring method.** This method is based on the **zero-factor property.**

Zero-Factor Property

If a and b are real numbers and $a \cdot b = 0$, then $a = 0$ or $b = 0$. This property is true for three or more factors also.

In other words, if the product of two or more real numbers is zero, then at least one of the numbers must be zero.

PRACTICE PROBLEM 1

Solve: $(x - 3)(x + 5) = 0$

EXAMPLE 1 Solve: $(x + 2)(x - 6) = 0$

Solution: By the zero-factor property, $(x + 2)(x - 6) = 0$ only if

$$x + 2 = 0 \quad \text{or} \quad x - 6 = 0.$$

$x + 2 = 0$ or $x - 6 = 0$ Use the zero-factor property.

$\qquad x = -2 \qquad\qquad x = 6$ Solve each linear equation.

To check, let $x = -2$ and then let $x = 6$ in the original equation.

Let $x = -2$.	Let $x = 6$.
$(x + 2)(x - 6) = 0$	$(x + 2)(x - 6) = 0$
$(-2 + 2)(-2 - 6) = 0$	$(6 + 2)(6 - 6) = 0$
$(0)(-8) = 0$	$(8)(0) = 0$
$0 = 0$ True	$0 = 0$ True

Both -2 and 6 check, so the solution set is $\{-2, 6\}$.

Work Practice Problem 1

Answer

1. $\{-5, 3\}$

EXAMPLE 2 Solve: $2x^2 + 9x - 5 = 0$

Solution: To use the zero-factor property, one side of the equation must be 0, and the other side must be in factored form.

$$2x^2 + 9x - 5 = 0$$
$$(2x - 1)(x + 5) = 0 \qquad\qquad \text{Factor.}$$
$$2x - 1 = 0 \quad \text{or} \quad x + 5 = 0 \qquad \text{Set each factor equal to 0.}$$
$$2x = 1 \qquad\qquad x = -5 \qquad \text{Solve each linear equation.}$$
$$x = \frac{1}{2}$$

To check, let $x = \dfrac{1}{2}$ in the original equation; then let $x = -5$ in the original equation. The solution set is $\left\{ -5, \dfrac{1}{2} \right\}$.

📖 **Work Practice Problem 2**

PRACTICE PROBLEM 2

Solve: $3x^2 + 5x - 2 = 0$

Solving a Polynomial Equation by Factoring

Step 1: Write the equation in standard form so that one side of the equation is 0.

Step 2: Factor the polynomial completely.

Step 3: Set each factor containing a variable equal to 0.

Step 4: Solve the resulting equations.

Step 5: Check each solution in the original equation.

Since it is not always possible to factor a polynomial, not all polynomial equations can be solved by factoring. Other methods of solving polynomial equations are presented in Chapter 8.

EXAMPLE 3 Solve: $x(2x - 7) = 4$

Solution: We first write the equation in standard form; then we factor.

$$x(2x - 7) = 4$$
$$2x^2 - 7x = 4 \qquad\qquad \text{Multiply. Write in standard form.}$$
$$2x^2 - 7x - 4 = 0$$
$$(2x + 1)(x - 4) = 0 \qquad\qquad \text{Factor.}$$
$$2x + 1 = 0 \quad \text{or} \quad x - 4 = 0 \qquad \text{Set each factor equal to 0.}$$
$$2x = -1 \qquad\qquad x = 4 \qquad \text{Solve.}$$
$$x = -\frac{1}{2}$$

Check both solutions in the original equation. The solution set is $\left\{ -\dfrac{1}{2}, 4 \right\}$.

📖 **Work Practice Problem 3**

PRACTICE PROBLEM 3

Solve: $x(5x - 7) = -2$

Helpful Hint

To apply the zero-factor property, one side of the equation must be 0, and the other side of the equation must be factored. To solve the equation $x(2x - 7) = 4$, for example, you may *not* set each factor equal to 4.

Answers

2. $\left\{ -2, \dfrac{1}{3} \right\}$, **3.** $\left\{ \dfrac{2}{5}, 1 \right\}$

PRACTICE PROBLEM 4

Solve:

$$2(x^2 + 5) + 10 = -2(x^2 + 10x) - 5$$

EXAMPLE 4 Solve: $3(x^2 + 4) + 5 = -6(x^2 + 2x) + 13$

Solution: We rewrite the equation so that one side is 0.

$$3(x^2 + 4) + 5 = -6(x^2 + 2x) + 13$$

$$3x^2 + 12 + 5 = -6x^2 - 12x + 13 \qquad \text{Use the distributive property.}$$

$$9x^2 + 12x + 4 = 0 \qquad \text{Rewrite the equation in standard form so that one side is 0.}$$

$$(3x + 2)(3x + 2) = 0 \qquad \text{Factor.}$$

$$3x + 2 = 0 \quad \text{or} \quad 3x + 2 = 0 \qquad \text{Set each factor equal to 0.}$$

$$3x = -2 \qquad\qquad 3x = -2 \qquad \text{Solve each equation.}$$

$$x = -\frac{2}{3} \qquad\qquad x = -\frac{2}{3}$$

Check by substituting $-\frac{2}{3}$ into the original equation. The solution set is $\left\{-\frac{2}{3}\right\}$.

■ **Work Practice Problem 4**

If the equation contains fractions, we clear the equation of fractions as a first step.

PRACTICE PROBLEM 5

Solve: $2x^2 + \frac{5}{2}x = 3$

EXAMPLE 5 Solve: $2x^2 = \frac{17}{3}x + 1$

Solution:

$$2x^2 = \frac{17}{3}x + 1$$

$$3(2x^2) = 3\left(\frac{17}{3}x + 1\right) \qquad \text{Clear the equation of fractions.}$$

$$6x^2 = 17x + 3 \qquad \text{Use the distributive property.}$$

$$6x^2 - 17x - 3 = 0 \qquad \text{Rewrite the equation in standard form so that one side is 0.}$$

$$(6x + 1)(x - 3) = 0 \qquad \text{Factor.}$$

$$6x + 1 = 0 \quad \text{or} \quad x - 3 = 0 \qquad \text{Set each factor equal to 0.}$$

$$6x = -1 \qquad\qquad x = 3 \qquad \text{Solve each equation.}$$

$$x = -\frac{1}{6}$$

Check by substituting into the original equation. The solution set is $\left\{-\frac{1}{6}, 3\right\}$.

■ **Work Practice Problem 5**

PRACTICE PROBLEM 6

Solve: $x^3 = x^2 + 6x$

EXAMPLE 6 Solve: $x^3 = 4x$

Solution:

$$x^3 = 4x$$

$$x^3 - 4x = 0 \qquad \text{Rewrite the equation in standard form so that one side is 0.}$$

$$x(x^2 - 4) = 0 \qquad \text{Factor out the greatest common factor.}$$

$$x(x + 2)(x - 2) = 0 \qquad \text{Factor the difference of squares.}$$

$$x = 0 \quad \text{or} \quad x + 2 = 0 \quad \text{or} \quad x - 2 = 0 \qquad \text{Set each factor equal to 0.}$$

$$x = -2 \qquad\qquad x = 2 \qquad \text{Solve each equation.}$$

Check by substituting into the original equation. The solution set is $\{-2, 0, 2\}$.

■ **Work Practice Problem 6**

Notice that the *third*-degree equation of Example 6 yielded *three* solutions.

Answers

4. $\left\{-\frac{5}{2}\right\}$, **5.** $\left\{-2, \frac{3}{4}\right\}$, **6.** $\{-2, 0, 3\}$

EXAMPLE 7   Solve: $x^3 - x = -5x^2 + 5$.

Solution: First, write the equation so that one side is 0.

$$x^3 - x + 5x^2 - 5 = 0$$

$$(x^3 - x) + (5x^2 - 5) = 0 \qquad \text{Factor by grouping.}$$

$$x(x^2 - 1) + 5(x^2 - 1) = 0$$

$$(x^2 - 1)(x + 5) = 0$$

$$(x + 1)(x - 1)(x + 5) = 0 \qquad \text{Factor the difference of squares.}$$

$$x + 1 = 0 \quad \text{or} \quad x - 1 = 0 \quad \text{or} \quad x + 5 = 0 \quad \text{Set each factor equal to 0.}$$

$$x = -1 \quad \text{or} \qquad x = 1 \quad \text{or} \qquad x = -5 \quad \text{Solve each equation.}$$

The solution set is $\{-5, -1, 1\}$. Check in the original equation.

🔲 **Work Practice Problem 7 [[MR 1]]**

✔**Concept Check**   Which solution strategies are incorrect? Why?

a. Solve $(y - 2)(y + 2) = 4$ by setting each factor equal to 4.

b. Solve $(x + 1)(x + 3) = 0$ by setting each factor equal to 0.

c. Solve $z^2 + 5z + 6 = 0$ by factoring $z^2 + 5z + 6$ and setting each factor equal to 0.

d. Solve $x^2 + 6x + 8 = 10$ by factoring $x^2 + 6x + 8$ and setting each factor equal to 0.

Objective 🅱 Solving Problems Modeled by Polynomial Equations

Some problems may be modeled by polynomial equations. To solve these problems, we use the same problem-solving steps that were introduced in Section 2.2. When solving these problems, keep in mind that a solution of an equation that models a problem is not always a solution to the problem. For example, a person's weight or the length of a side of a geometric figure is always a positive number. Discard solutions that do not make sense as solutions of the problem.

EXAMPLE 8   **Finding the Return Time of a Rocket**

An Alpha III model rocket is launched from the ground with an A8-3 engine. Without a parachute the height h in feet of the rocket at time t seconds is approximated by the equation

$$h = -16t^2 + 144t$$

Find how long it takes the rocket to return to the ground.

Solution:

1. UNDERSTAND. Read and reread the problem. The equation $h = -16t^2 + 144t$ models the height of the rocket. Familiarize yourself with this equation by finding a few values.

   When $t = 1$ second, the height of the rocket is

   $$h = -16(1)^2 + 144(1) = 128 \text{ feet}$$

   When $t = 2$ seconds, the height of the rocket is

   $$h = -16(2)^2 + 144(2) = 224 \text{ feet}$$

2. TRANSLATE. To find how long it takes the rocket to return to the ground, we want to know what value of t makes the height h equal to 0. That is, we want to solve for t when $h = 0$.

   $$-16t^2 + 144t = 0$$

Continued on next page

PRACTICE PROBLEM 7

Solve: $x^3 + 7x^2 = 4x + 28$

PRACTICE PROBLEM 8

A model rocket is launched from the ground. Its height h in feet at time t seconds is approximated by the equation

$$h = -16t^2 + 112t$$

Find how long it takes the rocket to return to the ground.

Answers

7. $\{-2, 2, -7\}$,   **8.** 7 sec

✔ **Concept Check Answer**

a and d; the zero-factor property works only if one side of the equation is 0

3. SOLVE the quadratic equation by factoring.

$$-16t^2 + 144t = 0$$
$$-16t(t - 9) = 0$$
$$-16t = 0 \quad \text{or} \quad t - 9 = 0$$
$$t = 0 \qquad\qquad t = 9$$

4. INTERPRET. The height h is 0 feet at time 0 seconds (when the rocket is launched) and at time 9 seconds.

Check: See that the height of the rocket at 9 seconds equals 0.

$$h = -16(9)^2 + 144(9) = -1296 + 1296 = 0$$

State: The rocket returns to the ground 9 seconds after it is launched.

◼ **Work Practice Problem 8**

Some of the exercises at the end of this section make use of the **Pythagorean theorem.** Before we review this theorem, recall that a **right triangle** is a triangle that contains a 90° angle, or right angle. The **hypotenuse** of a right triangle is the side opposite the right angle and is the longest side of the triangle. The **legs** of a right triangle are the other sides of the triangle.

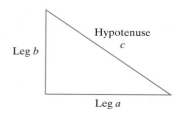

Hypotenuse
c

Leg b

Leg a

Pythagorean Theorem

In a right triangle, the sum of the squares of the lengths of the two legs is equal to the square of the length of the hypotenuse.

$$(\text{leg})^2 + (\text{leg})^2 = (\text{hypotenuse})^2 \quad \text{or} \quad a^2 + b^2 = c^2$$

PRACTICE PROBLEM 9 △

Find a right triangle whose sides are three consecutive even integers.

△ **EXAMPLE 9** Using the Pythagorean Theorem

While framing an addition to an existing home, Kim Menzies, a carpenter, used the Pythagorean theorem to determine whether a wall was "square"—that is, whether the wall formed a right angle with the floor. He used a triangle whose sides are three consecutive integers. Find a right triangle whose sides are three consecutive integers.

?

Solution:

1. UNDERSTAND. Read and reread the problem. Let x, $x + 1$, and $x + 2$ be three consecutive integers. Since these integers represent lengths of the sides of a right triangle, we have

$x = $ one leg,
$x + 1 = $ other leg, and
$x + 2 = $ hypotenuse (longest side)

$x + 2$

x

$x + 1$

Answer

9. 6, 8, and 10 units

2. TRANSLATE. By the Pythagorean theorem, we have

In words: $(\text{leg})^2 + (\text{leg})^2 = (\text{hypotenuse})^2$

$\qquad\qquad\quad\downarrow\qquad\quad\downarrow\qquad\qquad\downarrow$

Translate: $(x)^2 + (x+1)^2 = (x+2)^2$

3. SOLVE the equation.

$$x^2 + (x+1)^2 = (x+2)^2$$
$$x^2 + x^2 + 2x + 1 = x^2 + 4x + 4 \qquad \text{Multiply.}$$
$$2x^2 + 2x + 1 = x^2 + 4x + 4$$
$$x^2 - 2x - 3 = 0 \qquad\qquad \text{Write in standard form.}$$
$$(x-3)(x+1) = 0$$
$$x - 3 = 0 \quad \text{or} \quad x + 1 = 0$$
$$x = 3 \qquad\qquad x = -1$$

4. INTERPRET. Discard $x = -1$ since length cannot be negative. If $x = 3$, then $x + 1 = 4$ and $x + 2 = 5$.

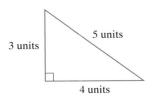

3 units · 4 units · 5 units

Check: To check, see that $(\text{leg})^2 + (\text{leg})^2 = (\text{hypotenuse})^2$.

$$3^2 + 4^2 = 5^2$$
$$9 + 16 = 25 \qquad \text{True}$$

State: The lengths of the sides of the right triangle are 3, 4, and 5 units. Kim used this information by marking off lengths of 3 and 4 feet on the floor and framing, respectively. If the diagonal length between these marks was 5 feet, the wall was square. If not, adjustments were made.

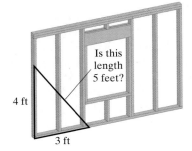

Is this length 5 feet?

4 ft

3 ft

▮ **Work Practice Problem 9**

Recall that to find the x-intercepts of the graph of a function, let $f(x) = 0$, or $y = 0$, and solve for x. This fact gives us a visual interpretation of the results of this section.

From Example 1, we know that the solutions of the equation $(x + 2)$ $(x - 6) = 0$ are -2 and 6. These solutions give us important information about the related polynomial function $p(x) = (x + 2)(x - 6)$. We know that when x is -2 or when x is 6, the value of $p(x)$ is 0.

$$p(x) = (x+2)(x-6)$$
$$p(-2) = (-2+2)(-2-6) = (0)(-8) = 0$$
$$p(6) = (6+2)(6-6) = (8)(0) = 0$$

Thus, we know that $(-2, 0)$ and $(6, 0)$ are the x-intercepts of the graph of $p(x)$.

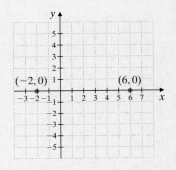

We also know that the graph of $p(x)$ does not cross the x-axis at any other point. For this reason, and the fact that $p(x) = (x + 2)(x - 6) = x^2 - 4x - 12$ has degree 2, we conclude that the graph of p must look something like one of these two graphs:

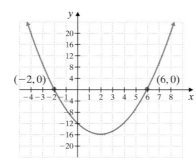
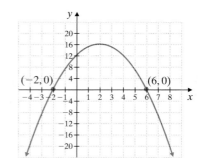

In a later chapter, we explore these graphs more fully. For the moment, know that the solutions of a polynomial equation are the x-intercepts of the graph of the related function and that the x-intercepts of the graph of a polynomial function are the solutions of the related polynomial equation. These values are also called **roots,** or **zeros,** of a polynomial function.

PRACTICE PROBLEM 10

Match each function with its graph.

$f(x) = (x + 1)(x - 3)$
$g(x) = (x - 5)(x - 1)(x + 1)$
$h(x) = x(x - 1)(x + 1)$

a.

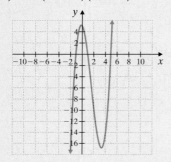

b.

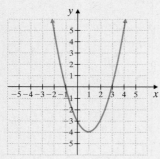

c.

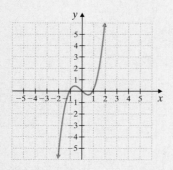

Answers

EXAMPLE 10 **Match Each Function with Its Graph**

$$f(x) = (x - 3)(x + 2) \quad g(x) = x(x + 2)(x - 2)$$
$$h(x) = (x - 2)(x + 2)(x - 1)$$

A

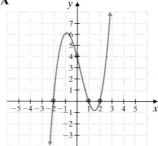

B

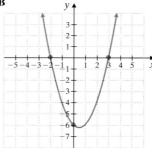

C

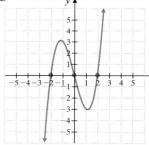

Solution: The graph of the function $f(x) = (x - 3)(x + 2)$ has two x-intercepts, $(3, 0)$ and $(-2, 0)$, because the equation $0 = (x - 3)(x + 2)$ has two solutions, 3 and -2.

The graph of $f(x)$ is graph B.

The graph of the function $g(x) = x(x + 2)(x - 2)$ has three x-intercepts, $(0, 0)$, $(-2, 0)$, and $(2, 0)$, because the equation $0 = x(x + 2)(x - 2)$ has three solutions, $0, -2$, and 2.

The graph of $g(x)$ is graph C.

The graph of the function $h(x) = (x - 2)(x + 2)(x - 1)$ has three x-intercepts, $(-2, 0)$, $(1, 0)$, and $(2, 0)$, because the equation $0 = (x - 2)(x + 2)(x - 1)$ has three solutions, $-2, 1$, and 2.

The graph of $h(x)$ is graph A.

Work Practice Problem 10

CALCULATOR EXPLORATIONS Graphing

We can use a graphing calculator to approximate real number solutions of any quadratic equation in standard form, whether the associated polynomial is factorable or not. For example, let's solve the quadratic equation $x^2 - 2x - 4 = 0$. The solutions of this equation will be the x-intercepts of the graph of the function $f(x) = x^2 - 2x - 4$. (Recall that to find x-intercepts, we let $f(x) = 0$, or $y = 0$.) When we use a standard window, the graph of this function looks like this.

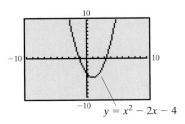

$$y = x^2 - 2x - 4$$

The graph appears to have one x-intercept between -2 and -1 and one between 3 and 4. To find the x-intercept between 3 and 4 to the nearest hundredth, we can use a zero feature, a Zoom feature, which magnifies a portion of the graph around the cursor, or we can redefine our window. If we redefine our window to

Xmin = 2	Ymin = -1
Xmax = 5	Ymax = 1
Xscl = 1	Yscl = 1

the resulting screen is

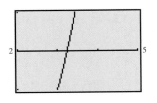

By using the Trace feature, we can now see that one of the intercepts is between 3.21 and 3.25. To approximate to the nearest hundredth, Zoom again or redefine the window to

Xmin = 3.2	Ymin = -0.1
Xmax = 3.3	Ymax = 0.1
Xscl = 1	Yscl = 1

If we use the Trace feature again, we see that, to the nearest hundredth, the x-intercept is 3.24. By repeating this process, we can approximate the other x-intercept to be -1.24.

To check, find $f(3.24)$ and $f(-1.24)$. Both of these values should be close to 0. (They will not be exactly 0 since we approximated these solutions.)

$$f(3.24) = 0.0176 \quad \text{and} \quad f(-1.24) = 0.0176$$

Solve each of these quadratic equations by graphing a related function and approximating the x-intercepts to the nearest thousandth.

1. $x^2 + 3x - 2 = 0$
2. $5x^2 - 7x + 1 = 0$
3. $2.3x^2 - 4.4x - 5.6 = 0$
4. $0.2x^2 + 6.2x + 2.1 = 0$
5. $0.09x^2 - 0.13x - 0.08 = 0$
6. $x^2 + 0.08x - 0.01 = 0$

Mental Math

Solve each equation for the variable.

1. $(x - 3)(x + 5) = 0$

2. $(y + 5)(y + 3) = 0$

3. $(z - 3)(z + 7) = 0$

4. $(c - 2)(c - 4) = 0$

5. $x(x - 9) = 0$

6. $w(w + 7) = 0$

5.7 EXERCISE SET

FOR EXTRA HELP

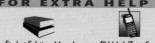

Student Solutions Manual   PH Math/Tutor Center   CD/Video for Review   MathXL®   MyMathLab

Objective **A** *Solve each equation. See Example 1*

1. $(x + 3)(3x - 4) = 0$

2. $(5x + 1)(x - 2) = 0$

3. $3(2x - 5)(4x + 3) = 0$

4. $8(3x - 4)(2x - 7) = 0$

Solve each equation. See Examples 2 through 5.

5. $x^2 + 11x + 24 = 0$

6. $y^2 - 10y + 24 = 0$

7. $12x^2 + 5x - 2 = 0$

8. $3y^2 - y - 14 = 0$

9. $z^2 + 9 = 10z$

10. $n^2 + n = 72$

11. $x(5x + 2) = 3$

12. $n(2n - 3) = 2$

13. $x^2 - 6x = x(8 + x)$

14. $n(3 + n) = n^2 + 4n$

15. $\dfrac{z^2}{6} - \dfrac{z}{2} - 3 = 0$

16. $\dfrac{c^2}{20} - \dfrac{c}{4} + \dfrac{1}{5} = 0$

17. $\dfrac{x^2}{2} + \dfrac{x}{20} = \dfrac{1}{10}$

18. $\dfrac{y^2}{30} = \dfrac{y}{15} + \dfrac{1}{2}$

19. $\dfrac{4t^2}{5} = \dfrac{t}{5} + \dfrac{3}{10}$

20. $\dfrac{5x^2}{6} - \dfrac{7x}{2} + \dfrac{2}{3} = 0$

Solve each equation. See Examples 6 and 7.

21. $(x + 2)(x - 7)(3x - 8) = 0$

22. $(4x + 9)(x - 4)(x + 1) = 0$

23. $y^3 = 9y$

24. $n^3 = 16n$

25. $x^3 - x = 2x^2 - 2$

26. $m^3 = m^2 + 12m$

352

Solve each equation. This section of exercises contains some linear equations. See Examples 1 through 7.

27. $(2x + 7)(x - 10) = 0$

28. $(x + 4)(5x - 1) = 0$

29. $3x(x - 5) = 0$

30. $4x(2x + 3) = 0$

31. $x^2 - 2x - 15 = 0$

32. $x^2 + 6x - 7 = 0$

33. $12x^2 + 2x - 2 = 0$

34. $8x^2 + 13x + 5 = 0$

35. $w^2 - 5w = 36$

36. $x^2 + 32 = 12x$

37. $25x^2 - 40x + 16 = 0$

38. $9n^2 + 30n + 25 = 0$

39. $2r^3 + 6r^2 = 20r$

40. $-2t^3 = 108t - 30t^2$

41. $z(5z - 4)(z + 3) = 0$

42. $2r(r - 3)(5r + 4) = 0$

43. $2z(z + 6) = 2z^2 + 12z - 8$

44. $3c^2 - 8c + 2 = c(3c - 8)$

45. $(x - 1)(x + 4) = 24$

46. $(2x - 1)(x + 2) = -3$

47. $\dfrac{x^2}{4} - \dfrac{5}{2}x + 6 = 0$

48. $\dfrac{x^2}{18} + \dfrac{x}{2} + 1 = 0$

49. $y^2 + \dfrac{1}{4} = -y$

50. $\dfrac{x^2}{10} + \dfrac{5}{2} = x$

51. $y^3 + 4y^2 = 9y + 36$

52. $x^3 + 5x^2 = x + 5$

53. $2x^3 = 50x$

54. $m^5 = 36m^3$

55. $x^2 + (x + 1)^2 = 61$

56. $y^2 + (y + 2)^2 = 34$

57. $m^2(3m - 2) = m$

58. $x^2(5x + 3) = 26x$

59. $3x^2 = -x$

60. $y^2 = -5y$

61. $x(x - 3) = x^2 + 5x + 7$

62. $z^2 - 4z + 10 = z(z - 5)$

63. $3(t - 8) + 2t = 7 + t$

64. $7c - 2(3c + 1) = 5(4 - 2c)$

65. $-3(x - 4) + x = 5(3 - x)$

66. $-4(a + 1) - 3a = -7(2a - 3)$

Objective **B** *Solve. See Examples 8 and 9.*

67. One number exceeds another by five, and their product is 66, Find the numbers.

68. If the sum of two numbers is 4 and their product is $\dfrac{15}{4}$, find the numbers.

69. An electrician needs to run a cable from the top of a 60-foot tower to a transmitter box located 45 feet away from the base of the tower. Find how long he should cut the cable.

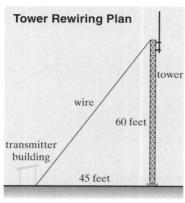

Tower Rewiring Plan

tower

wire

60 feet

transmitter building

45 feet

70. A stereo-system installer needs to run speaker wire above the ceiling along the two diagonals of a rectangular room whose dimensions are 40 feet by 75 feet. Find how much speaker wire she needs.

75 ft

40 ft

71. If the cost, $C(x)$, for manufacturing x units of a certain product is given by $C(x) = x^2 - 15x + 50$, find the number of units manufactured at a cost of $9500.

72. Determine whether any three consecutive integers represent the lengths of the sides of a right triangle.

73. The shorter leg of a right triangle is 3 centimeters less than the other leg. Find the length of the two legs if the hypotenuse is 15 centimeters.

74. The longer leg of a right triangle is 4 feet longer than the other leg. Find the length of the two legs if the hypotenuse is 20 feet.

75. Marie Mulroney has a rectangular board 12 inches by 16 inches around which she wants to put a uniform border of shells. If she has enough shells for a border whose area is 128 square inches, determine the width of the border.

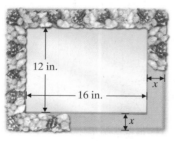

12 in.

16 in.

x

x

76. A gardener has a rose garden that measures 30 feet by 20 feet. He wants to put a uniform border of pine bark around the outside of the garden. Find how wide the border should be if he has enough pine bark to cover 336 square feet.

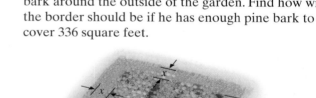

x

x

20 ft

30 ft

77. While hovering near the top of Ribbon Falls in Yosemite National Park at 1600 feet, a helicopter pilot accidentally drops his sunglasses. The height $h(t)$ of the sunglasses after t seconds is given by the polynomial function

$$h(t) = -16t^2 + 1600$$

When will the sunglasses hit the ground?

78. After t seconds, the height $h(t)$ of a model rocket launched from the ground into the air is given by the function

$$h(t) = -16t^2 + 80t$$

Find how long it takes the rocket to reach a height of 96 feet.

△ **79.** The floor of a shed has an area of 90 square feet. The floor is in the shape of a rectangle whose length is 3 feet less than twice the width. Find the length and the width of the floor of the shed.

△ **80.** A vegetable garden with an area of 200 square feet is to be fertilized. If the length of the garden is 1 foot less than three times the width, find the dimensions of the garden.

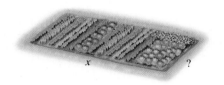

81. The function $W(x) = 0.5x^2$ gives the number of servings of wedding cake that can be obtained from a two-layer x-inch square wedding cake tier. What size square wedding cake tier is needed to serve 50 people? (*Source:* Based on data from the *Wilton 2000 Yearbook of Cake Decorating*)

82. Use the function in Exercise 81 to determine what size wedding cake tier is needed to serve 200 people.

Match each polynomial function with its graph (A–F). See Example 10.

83. $f(x) = (x - 2)(x + 5)$

84. $g(x) = (x + 1)(x - 6)$

85. $h(x) = x(x + 3)(x - 3)$

86. $F(x) = (x + 1)(x - 2)(x + 5)$

87. $G(x) = 2x^2 + 9x + 4$

88. $H(x) = 2x^2 - 7x - 4$

A

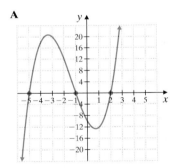

B

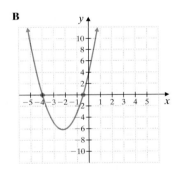

C

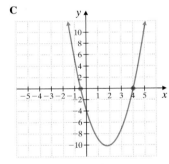

D

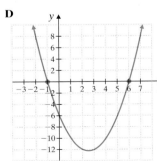

E

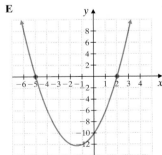

F

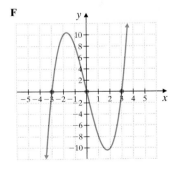

Review

Write the x- and y-intercepts for each graph. See Section 3.1.

89.
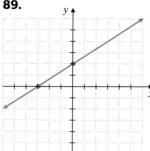

90.
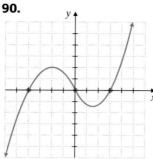

91.
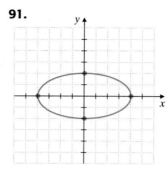

92.
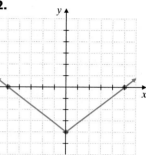

Concept Extensions

Each exercise contains an error. Find and correct the error. See the Concept Check in the section.

93. $(x - 5)(x + 2) = 0$
$x - 5 = 0$ or $x + 2 = 0$
$x = -5$ or $x = -2$

94. $(4x - 5)(x + 7) = 0$
$4x - 5 = 0$ or $x + 7 = 0$
$x = \dfrac{4}{5}$ or $x = -7$

95. $y(y - 5) = -6$
$y = -6$ or $y - 5 = -5$
$y = -7$ or $y = 0$

96. $3x^2 - 19x = 14$
$-16x = 14$
$x = -\dfrac{14}{16}$
$x = -\dfrac{7}{8}$

Solve.

97. $(x^2 + x - 6)(3x^2 - 14x - 5) = 0$

98. $(x^2 - 9)(x^2 + 8x + 16) = 0$

99. Explain how solving $2(x - 3)(x - 1) = 0$ differs from solving $2x(x - 3)(x - 1) = 0$.

100. Explain why the zero-factor property works for more than two numbers whose product is 0.

101. Is the following step correct? Why or why not?

$$x(x - 3) = 5$$
$$x = 5 \quad \text{or} \quad x - 3 = 5$$

Write a quadratic equation that has the given numbers as solutions.

102. 5, 3   **103.** 6, 7

THE BIGGER PICTURE   Solving Equations and Inequalities

Continue the outline started in Section 2.6. Write how to recognize and how to solve quadratic equations by factoring.

Solving Equations and Inequalities

I. Equations

    A. Linear equations (Sec. 2.1)

    B. Absolute value equations (Sec. 2.6)

    C. Quadratic equations: Equation can be written in the standard form $ax^2 + bx + c = 0$, with $a \neq 0$.

    Solve: $2x^2 - 7x = 9$

    $2x^2 - 7x - 9 = 0$ Write in standard form so that equation is equal to 0.

    $(2x - 9)(x + 1) = 0$ Factor.

    $2x - 9 = 0 \quad \text{or} \quad x + 1 = 0$ Set each factor equal to 0.

    $x = \dfrac{9}{2} \quad \text{or} \quad x = -1$ Solve.

II. Inequalities

    A. Linear inequalities (Sec. 2.4)

    B. Compound inequalities (Sec. 2.5)

    C. Absolute value inequalities (Sec. 2.6)

Solve. If an inequality write your answer in interval notation.

1. $|7x - 3| = |5x + 9|$

2. $\left|\dfrac{x + 2}{5}\right| < 1$

3. $3(x - 6) + 2 = 9 + 5(3x - 1)$

4. $(x - 6)(2x + 3) = 0$

5. $|-3x + 10| \geq -2$

6. $|-2x - 5| = 11$

7. $x(x - 7) = 30$

8. $8x - 4 \geq 15x - 4$

CHAPTER 5   Group Activity

Finding the Largest Area

This activity may be completed by working in groups or individually.

A picture framer has a piece of wood that measures 1 inch wide by 50 inches long. She would like to make a picture frame with the largest possible interior area. Complete the following activity to help her determine the dimensions of the frame that she should use to achieve her goal.

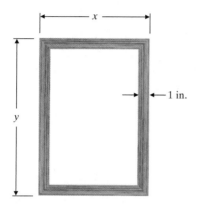

1. Use the situation shown in the figure to write an equation in x and y for the *outer* perimeter of the frame. (Remember that the outer perimeter will equal 50 inches.)

2. Use your equation from Question 1 to help you find the value of y for each value of x given in the table. Complete the y column of the table. (*Note:* The first two columns of the table give possible combinations for the outer dimensions of the frame.)

3. How is the interior width of the frame related to the exterior width of the frame? How is the interior height of the frame related to the exterior height of the frame? Use these relationships to complete the two columns of the table labeled "Interior Width" and "Interior Height."

4. Complete the last column of the table labeled "Interior Area" by using the columns of dimensions for the interior width and height.

5. From the table, what appears to be the largest interior area of the frame? Which exterior dimensions of the frame provide this area?

6. Use the patterns in the table to write an algebraic expression in terms of x for the interior width of the frame.

7. Use the patterns in the table to write an algebraic expression in terms of y for the interior height of the frame.

8. Use the perimeter equation from Question 1 to rewrite the algebraic expression for the interior height of the frame in terms of x.

Frame's Interior Dimensions				
x	y	Interior Width	Interior Height	Interior Area
2.0				
2.5				
3.0				
3.5				
4.0				
4.5				
5.0				
5.5				
6.0				
6.5				
7.0				
7.5				
8.0				
8.5				
9.0				
9.5				
10.0				
10.5				
11.0				
11.5				
12.0				
12.5				
13.0				
13.5				
14.0				
14.5				
15.0				

9. Find a function A that gives the interior area of the frame in terms of its exterior width x. (*Hint:* Study the patterns in the table. How could the expressions from Questions 6 and 8 be used to write this function?)

10. Graph the function A. Locate and label the point from the table that represents the maximum interior area. Describe the location of the point in relation to the rest of the graph.

Chapter 5 Vocabulary Check

Fill in each blank with one of the words or phrases listed below.

| quadratic equation | synthetic division | polynomial | FOIL | 0 | monomial |
| binomial | trinomial | degree of a polynomial | degree of a term | | factoring |

1. A _____ is a finite sum of terms in which all variables are raised to nonnegative integer powers and no variables appear in any denominator.
2. _____ is the process of writing a polynomial as a product.
3. The _____ is the sum of the exponents on the variables contained in the term.
4. A _____ is a polynomial with one term.
5. A _____ is a polynomial with three terms.
6. A polynomial equation of degree 2 is also called a _____.
7. The _____ is the largest degree of all of its terms.
8. A _____ is a polynomial with two terms.
9. If a and b are real numbers and $a \cdot b =$ ___, then $a = 0$ or $b = 0$.
10. The _____ order may be used when multiplying two binomials.
11. A shortcut method called _____ may be used to divide a polynomial by a binomial of the form $x - c$.

Helpful Hint

Are you preparing for your test? Don't forget to take the Chapter 5 Test on page 397. Then check your answers at the back of the text and use the Chapter Test Prep Video CD to see the fully worked-out solutions to any of the exercises you want to review.

5 Chapter Highlights

DEFINITIONS AND CONCEPTS	EXAMPLES
Section 5.1 Polynomial Functions and Adding and Subtracting Polynomials	

A **polynomial** is a finite sum of terms in which all variables have exponents raised to nonnegative integer powers and no variables appear in any denominator.	$1.3x^2$ Monomial $-\frac{1}{3}y + 5$ Binomial $6z^2 - 5z + 7$ Trinomial
To **add polynomials,** combine all like terms.	Add: $(3y^2x - 2yx + 11) + (-5y^2x - 7)$ $= -2y^2x - 2yx + 4$
To **subtract polynomials,** change the signs of the terms of the polynomial being subtracted; then add.	Subtract: $(-2z^3 - z + 1) - (3z^3 + z - 6)$ $= -2z^3 - z + 1 - 3z^3 - z + 6$ $= -5z^3 - 2z + 7$
A function P is a **polynomial function** if $P(x)$ is a polynomial.	For the polynomial function $$P(x) = -x^2 + 6x - 12$$ find $P(-2)$. $$P(-2) = -(-2)^2 + 6(-2) - 12 = -28$$

DEFINITIONS AND CONCEPTS	**EXAMPLES**

Section 5.2   Multiplying Polynomials

MULTIPLYING TWO POLYNOMIALS

Use the distributive property and multiply each term of one polynomial by each term of the other polynomial; then combine like terms.

SPECIAL PRODUCTS

$$(a + b)^2 = a^2 + 2ab + b^2$$
$$(a - b)^2 = a^2 - 2ab + b^2$$
$$(a + b)(a - b) = a^2 - b^2$$

The **FOIL order** may be used when multiplying two binomials.

Multiply.

$$(x^2 - 2x)(3x^2 - 5x + 1)$$
$$= 3x^4 - 5x^3 + x^2 - 6x^3 + 10x^2 - 2x$$
$$= 3x^4 - 11x^3 + 11x^2 - 2x$$

$$(3m + 2n)^2 = 9m^2 + 12mn + 4n^2$$
$$(z^2 - 5)^2 = z^4 - 10z^2 + 25$$
$$(7y + 1)(7y - 1) = 49y^2 - 1$$

Multiply.

$$(x^2 + 5)(2x^2 - 9)$$

$$
\begin{array}{cccc}
\text{F} & \text{O} & \text{I} & \text{L} \\
\downarrow & \downarrow & \downarrow & \downarrow
\end{array}
$$

$$= x^2(2x^2) + x^2(-9) + 5(2x^2) + 5(-9)$$
$$= 2x^4 - 9x^2 + 10x^2 - 45$$
$$= 2x^4 + x^2 - 45$$

Section 5.3   Dividing Polynomials and Synthetic Division

DIVIDING A POLYNOMIAL BY A MONOMIAL

Divide each term in the polynomial by the monomial.

$$\frac{12a^5b^3 - 6a^2b^2 + ab}{6a^2b^2}$$

$$= \frac{12a^5b^3}{6a^2b^2} - \frac{6a^2b^2}{6a^2b^2} + \frac{ab}{6a^2b^2}$$

$$= 2a^3b - 1 + \frac{1}{6ab}$$

DIVIDING A POLYNOMIAL BY A POLYNOMIAL OTHER THAN A MONOMIAL

Use **long division.**

Divide $2x^3 - x^2 - 8x - 1$ by $x - 2$.

$$
\begin{array}{r}
2x^2 + 3x - 2 \\
x - 2 \overline{)\,2x^3 - x^2 - 8x - 1} \\
\underline{2x^3 - 4x^2} \\
3x^2 - 8x \\
\underline{3x^2 - 6x} \\
-2x - 1 \\
\underline{-2x + 4} \\
-5
\end{array}
$$

The quotient is $2x^2 + 3x - 2 - \dfrac{5}{x - 2}$.

A shortcut method called **synthetic division** may be used to divide a polynomial by a binomial of the form $x - c$.

Use synthetic division to divide $2x^3 - x^2 - 8x - 1$ by $x - 2$.

$$
\begin{array}{r|rrrr}
2 & 2 & -1 & -8 & -1 \\
  &   & 4 & 6 & -4 \\
\hline
  & 2 & 3 & -2 & -5
\end{array}
$$

The quotient is $2x^2 + 3x - 2 - \dfrac{5}{x - 2}$.

DEFINITIONS AND CONCEPTS	EXAMPLES
Section 5.4 The Greatest Common Factor and Factoring by Grouping	

The **greatest common factor** of the terms of a polynomial is the product of the greatest common factor of the numerical coefficients and the greatest common factor of the variable factors.

Factor: $14xy^3 - 2xy^2 = 2 \cdot 7 \cdot x \cdot y^3 - 2 \cdot x \cdot y^2$
The greatest common factor is $2 \cdot x \cdot y^2$, or $2xy^2$.

$$14xy^3 - 2xy^2 = 2xy^2(7y - 1)$$

FACTORING A POLYNOMIAL BY GROUPING

Group the terms so that each group has a common factor. Factor out these common factors. Then see if the new groups have a common factor.

Factor: $x^4y - 5x^3 + 2xy - 10$
$$= x^3(xy - 5) + 2(xy - 5)$$
$$= (xy - 5)(x^3 + 2)$$

| **Section 5.5   Factoring Trinomials** ||

FACTORING $ax^2 + bx + c$

Step 1. Write all pairs of factors of ax^2.

Step 2. Write all pairs of factors of c.

Step 3. Try combinations of these factors until the middle term bx is found.

Factor: $28x^2 - 27x - 10$
Factors of $28x^2$: $28x$ and x, $2x$ and $14x$, $4x$ and $7x$.
Factors of -10: -2 and 5, 2 and -5, -10 and 1, 10 and -1.

$$28x^2 - 27x - 10 = (7x + 2)(4x - 5)$$

| **Section 5.6   Factoring by Special Products** ||

PERFECT SQUARE TRINOMIAL
$$a^2 + 2ab + b^2 = (a + b)^2$$
$$a^2 - 2ab + b^2 = (a - b)^2$$

Factor.
$$25x^2 + 30x + 9 = (5x + 3)^2$$
$$49z^2 - 28z + 4 = (7z - 2)^2$$

DIFFERENCE OF TWO SQUARES
$$a^2 - b^2 = (a + b)(a - b)$$

Factor.
$$36x^2 - y^2 = (6x + y)(6x - y)$$

SUM AND DIFFERENCE OF TWO CUBES
$$a^3 + b^3 = (a + b)(a^2 - ab + b^2)$$
$$a^3 - b^3 = (a - b)(a^2 + ab + b^2)$$

Factor.
$$8y^3 + 1 = (2y + 1)(4y^2 - 2y + 1)$$
$$27p^3 - 64q^3 = (3p - 4q)(9p^2 + 12pq + 16q^2)$$

| **Section 5.7   Solving Equations by Factoring and Solving Problems** ||

SOLVING A POLYNOMIAL EQUATION BY FACTORING

Step 1. Write the equation so that one side is 0.

Step 2. Factor the polynomial completely.

Step 3. Set each factor equal to 0.

Step 4. Solve the resulting equations.

Step 5. Check each solution.

Solve: $2x^3 - 5x^2 = 3x$
$$2x^3 - 5x^2 - 3x = 0$$
$$x(2x + 1)(x - 3) = 0$$
$x = 0$ or $2x + 1 = 0$ or $x - 3 = 0$
$x = 0$ $\qquad\qquad$ $x = -\dfrac{1}{2}$ $\qquad\qquad$ $x = 3$

6

Rational Expressions

Taken from:
Intermediate Algebra, Third Edition, by Elayn Martin-Gay

6.1 RATIONAL FUNCTIONS AND MULTIPLYING AND DIVIDING RATIONAL EXPRESSIONS

Objectives

A Find the Domain of a Rational Function.

B Simplify Rational Expressions.

C Multiply Rational Expressions.

D Divide Rational Expressions.

E Use Rational Functions in Real-World Applications.

Recall that a *rational number*, or *fraction*, is a number that can be written as the quotient $\frac{p}{q}$ of two integers p and q as long as q is not 0. A **rational expression** is an expression that can be written as the quotient $\frac{P}{Q}$ of two polynomials P and Q as long as Q is not 0.

Examples of Rational Expressions

$$\frac{8x^3 + 7x^2 + 20}{2} \qquad \frac{5x^2 - 3}{x - 1} \qquad \frac{7x - 2}{x^2 - 2x - 15}$$

Rational expressions are sometimes used to describe functions. For example, we call the function $f(x) = \frac{x^2 + 2}{x - 3}$ a **rational function** since $\frac{x^2 + 2}{x - 3}$ is a rational expression.

Objective **A** Finding Domains of Rational Functions

As with fractions, a rational expression is **undefined** if the denominator is 0. If a variable in a rational expression is replaced with a number that makes the denominator 0, we say that the rational expression is **undefined** for this value of the variable. For example, the rational expression $\frac{x^2 + 2}{x - 3}$ is undefined when x is 3, because replacing x with 3 results in a denominator of 0. For this reason, we must exclude 3 from the domain of the function $f(x) = \frac{x^2 + 2}{x - 3}$.

The domain of f is then

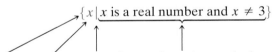

$$\{x \mid x \text{ is a real number and } x \neq 3\}$$

"The set of all x such that x is a real number and x is not equal to 3."
In this section, we will use this set builder notations to write domains.

Unless told otherwise, we assume that the domain of a function described by an equation is the set of all real numbers for which the equation is defined.

EXAMPLE 1 Find the domain of each rational function.

a. $f(x) = \dfrac{8x^3 + 7x^2 + 20}{2}$ **b.** $g(x) = \dfrac{5x^2 - 3}{x - 1}$

c. $f(x) = \dfrac{7x - 2}{x^2 - 2x - 15}$

Solution: The domain of each function will contain all real numbers except those values that make the denominator 0.

a. No matter what the value of x, the denominator of $f(x) = \dfrac{8x^3 + 7x^2 + 20}{2}$ is never 0, so the domain of f is $\{x \mid x \text{ is a real number}\}$.

b. To find the values of x that make the denominator of $g(x)$ equal to 0, we solve the equation "denominator = 0":

$$x - 1 = 0, \quad \text{or} \quad x = 1$$

The domain must exclude 1 since the rational expression is undefined when x is 1. The domain of g is $\{x \mid x \text{ is a real number and } x \neq 1\}$.

PRACTICE PROBLEM 1

Find the domain of each rational function.

a. $f(x) = \dfrac{x^2 + 1}{x - 6}$

b. $g(x) = \dfrac{5x + 4}{x^2 - 3x - 10}$

c. $h(x) = \dfrac{x^2 - 9}{4}$

Answer

1. a. $\{x \mid x \text{ is a real number, } x \neq 6\}$,
b. $\{x \mid x \text{ is a real number, } x \neq 5, x \neq -2\}$,
c. $\{x \mid x \text{ is a real number}\}$

Continued on next page

c. We find the domain by setting the denominator equal to 0.

$$x^2 - 2x - 15 = 0 \quad \text{Set the denominator equal to 0 and solve.}$$
$$(x - 5)(x + 3) = 0$$
$$x - 5 = 0 \quad \text{or} \quad x + 3 = 0$$
$$x = 5 \quad \text{or} \quad x = -3$$

If x is replaced with 5 or with -3, the rational expression is undefined.

The domain of f is $\{x \,|\, x \text{ is a real number and } x \neq 5, x \neq -3\}$.

▣ **Work Practice Problem 1**

Objective **B** Simplifying Rational Expressions

Recall that a fraction is in lowest terms or simplest form if the numerator and denominator have no common factors other than 1 (or -1). For example, $\dfrac{3}{13}$ is in lowest terms since 3 and 13 have no common factors other than 1 (or -1).

To **simplify** a rational expression, or to write it in lowest terms, we use a method similar to simplifying a fraction.

Recall that to simplify a fraction, we essentially "remove factors of 1." Our ability to do this comes from these facts:

- If $c \neq 0$, then $\dfrac{c}{c} = 1$. For example, $\dfrac{7}{7} = 1$ and $\dfrac{-8.65}{-8.65} = 1$.

- $n \cdot 1 = n$. For example, $-5 \cdot 1 = -5$, $126.8 \cdot 1 = 126.8$, and $\dfrac{a}{b} \cdot 1 = \dfrac{a}{b}, b \neq 0$.

In other words, we have the following:

$$\frac{a \cdot c}{b \cdot c} = \frac{a}{b} \cdot \frac{c}{c} = \frac{a}{b}$$

$$\text{Since } \frac{a}{b} \cdot 1 = \frac{a}{b}$$

Let's practice simplifying a fraction by simplifying $\dfrac{15}{65}$.

$$\frac{15}{65} = \frac{3 \cdot 5}{13 \cdot 5} = \frac{3}{13} \cdot \frac{5}{5} = \frac{3}{13} \cdot 1 = \frac{3}{13}$$

Let's use the same technique and simplify the rational expression $\dfrac{(x + 2)^2}{x^2 - 4}$.

$$\frac{(x + 2)^2}{x^2 - 4} = \frac{(x + 2)\,(x + 2)}{(x - 2)\,(x + 2)}$$
$$= \frac{(x + 2)}{(x - 2)} \cdot \frac{x + 2}{x + 2}$$
$$= \frac{x + 2}{x - 2} \cdot 1$$
$$= \frac{x + 2}{x - 2}$$

This means that the rational expression $\dfrac{(x + 2)^2}{x^2 - 4}$ has the same value as the rational expression $\dfrac{x + 2}{x - 2}$ for all values of x except 2 and -2. (Remember that when x is 2, the denominators of both rational expressions are 0 and that when x is -2, the original rational expression has a denominator of 0.)

As we simplify rational expressions, we will assume that the simplified rational expression is equivalent to the original rational expression for all real numbers except those for which either denominator is 0.

Just as for numerical fractions, we can use a shortcut notation. Remember that as long as exact factors in both the numerator and denominator are divided out, we are "removing a factor of 1." We can use the following notation:

$$\frac{(x+2)^2}{x^2-4} = \frac{(x+2)\,(x+2)}{(x-2)\,(x+2)} \qquad \text{A factor of 1 is identified by the shading.}$$

$$= \frac{x+2}{x-2} \qquad \text{"Remove" the factor of 1.}$$

In general, the following steps may be used to simplify rational expressions or to write a rational expression in lowest terms.

Simplifying or Writing a Rational Expression in Lowest Terms

Step 1: Completely factor the numerator and denominator of the rational expression.

Step 2: Divide out factors common to the numerator and denominator. (This is the same as "removing a factor of 1.")

For now, we assume that variables in a rational expression do not represent values that make the denominator 0.

EXAMPLES Simplify each rational expression.

2. $\dfrac{2x^2}{10x^3 - 2x^2} = \dfrac{2x^2 \cdot 1}{2x^2\,(5x-1)}$ Factor the numerator and denominator.

$$= 1 \cdot \frac{1}{5x-1} \qquad \text{Since } \tfrac{2x^2}{2x^2} = 1.$$

$$= \frac{1}{5x-1} \qquad \text{Simplest form.}$$

3. $\dfrac{9x^2 + 13x + 4}{8x^2 + x - 7} = \dfrac{(9x+4)\,(x+1)}{(8x-7)\,(x+1)}$ Factor the numerator and denominator.

$$= \frac{9x+4}{8x-7} \cdot 1 \qquad \text{Since } \tfrac{x+1}{x+1} = 1.$$

$$= \frac{9x+4}{8x-7} \qquad \text{Simplest form.}$$

■ **Work Practice Problems 2–3**

EXAMPLES Simplify each rational expression.

4. $\dfrac{2+x}{x+2} = \dfrac{x+2}{x+2} = 1$ By the commutative property of addition, $2 + x = x + 2$.

5. $\dfrac{2-x}{x-2}$

The terms in the numerator of $\dfrac{2-x}{x-2}$ differ by sign from the terms of the denominator, so the polynomials are opposites of each other and the expression simplifies to -1. To see this, we factor out -1 from the numerator or the denominator.   *Continued on next page*

Continued on next page

PRACTICE PROBLEMS 2–3

Simplify each rational expression.

2. $\dfrac{3y^3}{6y^4 - 3y^3}$

3. $\dfrac{5x^2 + 13x + 6}{6x^2 + 7x - 10}$

PRACTICE PROBLEMS 4–6

Simplify each rational expression.

4. $\dfrac{5+x}{x+5}$ **5.** $\dfrac{5-x}{x-5}$

6. $\dfrac{3-3x^2}{x^2+x-2}$

Answers

2. $\dfrac{1}{2y-1}$,   **3.** $\dfrac{5x+3}{6x-5}$,   **4.** 1,   **5.** -1,

6. $-\dfrac{3(x+1)}{x+2}$

Helpful Hint

When the numerator and the denominator of a rational expression are opposites of each other, the expression simplifies to -1.

If -1 is factored from the *numerator,* then

$$\frac{2-x}{x-2} = \frac{-1(-2+x)}{x-2} = \frac{-1\,(x-2)}{x-2} = \frac{-1}{1} = -1$$

If -1 is factored from the *denominator,* the result is the same.

$$\frac{2-x}{x-2} = \frac{2-x}{-1(-x+2)} = \frac{2-x}{-1\,(2-x)} = \frac{1}{-1} = -1$$

6. $\dfrac{18-2x^2}{x^2-2x-3} = \dfrac{2(9-x^2)}{(x+1)(x-3)}$ Factor.

$$= \frac{2(3+x)(3-x)}{(x+1)(x-3)}$$ Factor completely.

Notice the opposites $3-x$ and $x-3$. We write $3-x$ as $-1(x-3)$ and simplify.

$$\frac{2(3+x)(3-x)}{(x+1)(x-3)} = \frac{2(3+x)\cdot-1\,(x-3)}{(x+1)\,(x-3)} = -\frac{2(3+x)}{x+1}$$

▣ **Work Practice Problems 4–6**

Helpful Hint

Recall that for a fraction.

$$\frac{a}{-b} = \frac{-a}{b} = -\frac{a}{b}$$

For example,

$$\frac{-(x+1)}{(x+2)} = \frac{(x+1)}{-(x+2)} = -\frac{x+1}{x+2}$$

✔ **Concept Check** Which of the following expressions are equivalent to $\dfrac{x}{8-x}$?

a. $\dfrac{-x}{x-8}$ **b.** $\dfrac{-x}{8-x}$ **c.** $\dfrac{x}{x-8}$ **d.** $\dfrac{-x}{-8+x}$

EXAMPLES Simplify each rational expression.

7. $\dfrac{x^3+8}{x+2} = \dfrac{(x+2)\,(x^2-2x+4)}{x+2}$ Factor the sum of the two cubes.

$$= x^2-2x+4$$ Simplest form.

8. $\dfrac{2y^2+2}{y^3-5y^2+y-5} = \dfrac{2(y^2+1)}{(y^3-5y^2)+(y-5)}$ Factor the numerator.

$$= \frac{2(y^2+1)}{y^2(y-5)+1(y-5)}$$ Factor the denominator by grouping.

$$= \frac{2\,(y^2+1)}{(y-5)\,(y^2+1)}$$

$$= \frac{2}{y-5}$$ Simplest form.

▣ **Work Practice Problems 7–8**

PRACTICE PROBLEMS 7–8

Simplify each rational expression.

7. $\dfrac{x^3+27}{x+3}$

8. $\dfrac{3x^2+6}{x^3-3x^2+2x-6}$

Answers

7. x^2-3x+9,   **8.** $\dfrac{3}{x-3}$

✔ **Concept Check Answer**

a and d

✔**Concept Check** Does $\dfrac{n}{n+2}$ simplify to $\dfrac{1}{2}$? Why or why not?

Objective C Multiplying Rational Expressions

Arithmetic operations on rational expressions are performed in the same way as they are on rational numbers. To multiply rational expressions, we multiply numerators and multiply denominators.

Multiplying Rational Expressions

The rule for multiplying rational expressions is

$$\frac{P}{Q} \cdot \frac{R}{S} = \frac{PR}{QS} \quad \text{as long as } Q \neq 0 \text{ and } S \neq 0.$$

To multiply rational expressions, you may use these steps:

Step 1: Completely factor each numerator and denominator.

Step 2: Use the rule above and multiply the numerators and the denominators.

Step 3: Simplify the product.

When we multiply rational expressions, notice that we factor each numerator and denominator first. This helps when we check to see whether the product is in simplest form.

EXAMPLES Multiply.

9. $\dfrac{3n+1}{2n} \cdot \dfrac{2n-4}{3n^2-2n-1} = \dfrac{3n+1}{2n} \cdot \dfrac{2(n-2)}{(3n+1)(n-1)}$ Factor.

$$= \frac{(3n+1) \cdot 2 \,(n-2)}{2\, n\,(3n+1)\,(n-1)} \qquad \text{Multiply.}$$

$$= \frac{n-2}{n(n-1)} \qquad \text{Simplest form.}$$

10. $\dfrac{x^3-1}{-3x+3} \cdot \dfrac{15x^2}{x^2+x+1} = \dfrac{(x-1)(x^2+x+1)}{-3(x-1)} \cdot \dfrac{15x^2}{x^2+x+1}$ Factor.

$$= \frac{(x-1)(x^2+x+1)\cdot 3 \cdot 5x^2}{-1 \cdot 3(x-1)(x^2+x+1)} \qquad \text{Factor.}$$

$$= \frac{5x^2}{-1} = -5x^2 \qquad \text{Simplest form.}$$

◼ **Work Practice Problems 9–10**

Objective D Dividing Rational Expressions

Recall that two numbers are reciprocals of each other if their product is 1. Similarly, if $\dfrac{P}{Q}$ is a rational expression and $P \neq 0$, then $\dfrac{Q}{P}$ is its **reciprocal,** since

$$\frac{P}{Q} \cdot \frac{Q}{P} = \frac{P \cdot Q}{Q \cdot P} = 1$$

PRACTICE PROBLEMS 9–10

Multiply.

9. $\dfrac{2x-3}{5x} \cdot \dfrac{5x+5}{2x^2-x-3}$

10. $\dfrac{x^3+27}{-2x-6} \cdot \dfrac{4x^3}{x^2-3x+9}$

Answers

9. $\dfrac{1}{x}$, **10.** $-2x^3$

✔ **Concept Check Answer**

no; answers may vary

The following are examples of expressions and their reciprocals.

Expression	Reciprocal
$\dfrac{3}{x}$	$\dfrac{x}{3}$
$\dfrac{2 + x^2}{4x - 3}$	$\dfrac{4x - 3}{2 + x^2}$
x^3	$\dfrac{1}{x^3}$
0	no reciprocal

Dividing Rational Expressions

The rule for dividing rational expressions is

$$\frac{P}{Q} \div \frac{R}{S} = \frac{P}{Q} \cdot \frac{S}{R} = \frac{PS}{QR} \quad \text{as long as } Q \neq 0, S \neq 0, \text{ and } R \neq 0.$$

To divide by a rational expression, use the rule above and multiply by its reciprocal. Then simplify if possible.

Notice that division of rational expressions is the same as for rational numbers.

PRACTICE PROBLEMS 11–12

Divide.

11. $\dfrac{12y^3}{5y^2 - 5} \div \dfrac{6}{1 - y}$

12. $\dfrac{8z^2 + 14z + 3}{20z^2 + z - 1}$
$\div \dfrac{2z^2 + 7z + 6}{35z^2 + 3z - 2}$

EXAMPLES Divide.

11. $\dfrac{8m^2}{3m^2 - 12} \div \dfrac{40}{2 - m} = \dfrac{8m^2}{3m^2 - 12} \cdot \dfrac{2 - m}{40}$ Multiply by the reciprocal of the divisor.

$= \dfrac{8m^2(2 - m)}{3(m + 2)(m - 2) \cdot 40}$ Factor and multiply.

$= \dfrac{8 \; m^2 \cdot -1 \, (m - 2)}{3(m + 2) \, (m - 2) \cdot 8 \cdot 5}$ Write $(2 - m)$ as $-1(m - 2)$.

$= -\dfrac{m^2}{15(m + 2)}$ Simplify.

12. $\dfrac{18y^2 + 9y - 2}{24y^2 - 10y + 1} \div \dfrac{3y^2 + 17y + 10}{8y^2 + 18y - 5}$

$= \dfrac{18y^2 + 9y - 2}{24y^2 - 10y + 1} \cdot \dfrac{8y^2 + 18y - 5}{3y^2 + 17y + 10}$ Multiply by the reciprocal.

$= \dfrac{(6y - 1) \; (3y + 2) \cdot (4y - 1) \, (2y + 5)}{(6y - 1) \; (4y - 1) \cdot (3y + 2) \, (y + 5)}$ Factor.

$= \dfrac{2y + 5}{y + 5}$ Simplest form.

Work Practice Problems 11–12

Helpful Hint

When dividing rational expressions, do not divide out common factors until the division problem is rewritten as a multiplication problem.

Answers

11. $-\dfrac{2y^3}{5(y + 1)},$ **12.** $\dfrac{7z + 2}{z + 2}$

EXAMPLE 13 Perform each indicated operation.

$$\frac{x^2 - 25}{(x + 5)^2} \cdot \frac{3x + 15}{4x} \div \frac{x^2 - 3x - 10}{x}$$

Solution:

$$\frac{x^2 - 25}{(x + 5)^2} \cdot \frac{3x + 15}{4x} \div \frac{x^2 - 3x - 10}{x}$$

$$= \frac{x^2 - 25}{(x + 5)^2} \cdot \frac{3x + 15}{4x} \cdot \frac{x}{x^2 - 3x - 10} \quad \text{To divide, multiply by the reciprocal.}$$

$$= \frac{(x + 5) \, (x - 5)}{(x + 5) \, (x + 5)} \cdot \frac{3 \, (x + 5)}{4 \, x} \cdot \frac{x}{(x - 5) \, (x + 2)}$$

$$= \frac{3}{4(x + 2)}$$

Work Practice Problem 13

Objective **E** Applications with Rational Functions

Rational functions are often used to model real-life situations. Don't forget to be aware of the domains of these functions. See the Graphing Calculator Explorations on page 410 for further domain exercises.

EXAMPLE 14 **Finding Unit Cost**

For the ICL Production Company, the rational function $C(x) = \dfrac{2.6x + 10,000}{x}$ describes the company's cost per disc of pressing x compact discs. Find the cost per disc for pressing:

a. 100 compact discs

b. 1000 compact discs

Solution:

a. $C(100) = \dfrac{2.6(100) + 10,000}{100} = \dfrac{10,260}{100} = 102.6$

The cost per disc for pressing 100 compact discs is $102.60.

b. $C(1000) = \dfrac{2.6(1000) + 10,000}{1000} = \dfrac{12,600}{1000} = 12.6$

The cost per disc for pressing 1000 compact discs is $12.60. Notice that as more compact discs are produced, the cost per disc decreases.

Work Practice Problem 14

PRACTICE PROBLEM 13

Perform each indicated operation.

$$\frac{(x + 3)^2}{x^2 - 9} \cdot \frac{2x - 6}{5x}$$

$$\div \frac{x^2 + 7x + 12}{x}$$

PRACTICE PROBLEM 14

A company's cost per book for printing x particular books is given by the rational function $C(x) = \dfrac{0.8x + 5000}{x}$.

Find the cost per book for printing:

a. 100 books

b. 1000 books

Answers

13. $\dfrac{2}{5(x + 4)}$, **14. a.** $50.80, **b.** $5.80

CALCULATOR EXPLORATIONS Graphing

Recall that since the rational expression $\dfrac{7x-2}{(x-2)(x+5)}$ is not defined when $x = 2$ or when $x = -5$, we say that the domain of the rational function $f(x) = \dfrac{7x-2}{(x-2)(x+5)}$ is all real numbers except 2 and -5. This domain can be written as $\{x \mid x \text{ is a real number and } x \neq 2, x \neq -5\}$. This means that the graph of f should not cross the vertical lines $x = 2$ and $x = -5$. The graph of f in *connected* mode is shown below. In connected mode the grapher tries to connect all dots of the graph so that the result is a smooth curve. This is what has happened in the graph. Notice that the graph appears to contain vertical lines at $x = 2$ and at $x = -5$. We know that this cannot happen because the function is not defined at $x = 2$ and at $x = -5$. We also know that this cannot happen because the graph of this function would not pass the vertical line test.

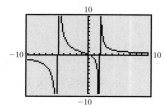

If we graph f in *dot* mode, the graph appears as below. In dot mode the grapher will not connect dots with a smooth curve. Notice that the vertical lines have disappeared, and we have a better picture of the graph. It actually appears more like the hand-drawn graph to its right. By using a TABLE feature, a CALCULATE VALUE feature, or by tracing, we can see that the function is not defined at $x = 2$ and at $x = -5$.

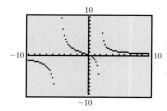

Note: Some calculator manufacturers now offer downloadable operating systems that eliminate the need to use dot mode to graph rational functions.

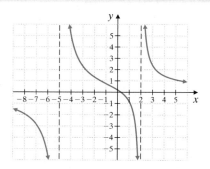

Find the domain of each rational function. Then graph each rational function and use the graph to confirm the domain.

1. $f(x) = \dfrac{5x}{x-6}$

2. $f(x) = \dfrac{x}{x+4}$

3. $f(x) = \dfrac{x+1}{x^2-4}$

4. $g(x) = \dfrac{5x}{x^2-9}$

5. $h(x) = \dfrac{x^2}{2x^2+7x-4}$

6. $f(x) = \dfrac{3x+2}{4x^2-19x-5}$

7. $g(x) = \dfrac{x^2+x+1}{5}$

8. $h(x) = \dfrac{x^2+25}{2}$

Mental Math

Multiply.

1. $\dfrac{x}{5} \cdot \dfrac{y}{2}$ 　　　　**2.** $\dfrac{y}{6} \cdot \dfrac{z}{5}$ 　　　　**3.** $\dfrac{2}{x} \cdot \dfrac{y}{3}$ 　　　　**4.** $\dfrac{a}{5} \cdot \dfrac{7}{b}$ 　　　　**5.** $\dfrac{m}{6} \cdot \dfrac{m}{6}$ 　　　　**6.** $\dfrac{9}{x} \cdot \dfrac{8}{x}$

6.1 EXERCISE SET

Objective A *Find the domain of each rational expression. See Example 1.*

1. $f(x) = \dfrac{5x - 7}{4}$

2. $g(x) = \dfrac{4 - 3x}{2}$

3. $s(t) = \dfrac{t^2 + 1}{2t}$

4. $v(t) = -\dfrac{5t + t^2}{3t}$

5. $f(x) = \dfrac{3x}{7 - x}$

6. $f(x) = \dfrac{-4x}{-2 + x}$

7. $f(x) = \dfrac{x}{3x - 1}$

8. $g(x) = \dfrac{-2}{2x + 5}$

9. $R(x) = \dfrac{3 + 2x}{x^3 + x^2 - 2x}$

10. $h(x) = \dfrac{5 - 3x}{2x^2 - 14x + 20}$

11. $C(x) = \dfrac{x + 3}{x^2 - 4}$

12. $R(x) = \dfrac{5}{x^2 - 7x}$

Objective B *Simplify each rational expression. See Examples 2 through 8.*

13. $\dfrac{8x - 16x^2}{8x}$

14. $\dfrac{3x - 6x^2}{3x}$

15. $\dfrac{x^2 - 9}{3 + x}$

16. $\dfrac{x^2 - 25}{5 + x}$

17. $\dfrac{9y - 18}{7y - 14}$

18. $\dfrac{6y - 18}{2y - 6}$

19. $\dfrac{x^2 + 6x - 40}{x + 10}$

20. $\dfrac{x^2 - 8x + 16}{x - 4}$

21. $\dfrac{x - 9}{9 - x}$

22. $\dfrac{x - 4}{4 - x}$

23. $\dfrac{x^2 - 49}{7 - x}$

24. $\dfrac{x^2 - y^2}{y - x}$

25. $\dfrac{2x^2 - 7x - 4}{x^2 - 5x + 4}$

26. $\dfrac{3x^2 - 11x + 10}{x^2 - 7x + 10}$

27. $\dfrac{x^3 - 125}{2x - 10}$

28. $\dfrac{4x + 4}{x^3 + 1}$

29. $\dfrac{3x^2 - 5x - 2}{6x^3 + 2x^2 + 3x + 1}$

30. $\dfrac{2x^2 - x - 3}{2x^3 - 3x^2 + 2x - 3}$

31. $\dfrac{9x^2 - 15x + 25}{27x^3 + 125}$

32. $\dfrac{8x^3 - 27}{4x^2 + 6x + 9}$

Objective **C** *Multiply and simplify. See Examples 9 and 10.*

33. $\dfrac{2x - 4}{15} \cdot \dfrac{6}{2 - x}$

34. $\dfrac{10 - 2x}{7} \cdot \dfrac{14}{5x - 25}$

35. $\dfrac{18a - 12a^2}{4a^2 + 4a + 1} \cdot \dfrac{4a^2 + 8a + 3}{4a^2 - 9}$

36. $\dfrac{a - 5b}{a^2 + ab} \cdot \dfrac{b^2 - a^2}{10b - 2a}$

37. $\dfrac{9x + 9}{4x + 8} \cdot \dfrac{2x + 4}{3x^2 - 3}$

38. $\dfrac{2x^2 - 2}{10x + 30} \cdot \dfrac{12x + 36}{3x - 3}$

39. $\dfrac{2x^3 - 16}{6x^2 + 6x - 36} \cdot \dfrac{9x + 18}{3x^2 + 6x + 12}$

40. $\dfrac{x^2 - 3x + 9}{5x^2 - 20x - 105} \cdot \dfrac{x^2 - 49}{x^3 + 27}$

41. $\dfrac{a^3 + a^2b + a + b}{5a^3 + 5a} \cdot \dfrac{6a^2}{2a^2 - 2b^2}$

42. $\dfrac{4a^2 - 8a}{ab - 2b + 3a - 6} \cdot \dfrac{8b + 24}{3a + 6}$

43. $\dfrac{x^2 - 6x - 16}{2x^2 - 128} \cdot \dfrac{x^2 + 16x + 64}{3x^2 + 30x + 48}$

44. $\dfrac{2x^2 + 12x - 32}{x^2 + 16x + 64} \cdot \dfrac{x^2 + 10x + 16}{x^2 - 3x - 10}$

Objective **D** *Divide and simplify. See Examples 11 and 12.*

45. $\dfrac{2x}{5} \div \dfrac{6x + 12}{5x + 10}$

46. $\dfrac{7}{3x} \div \dfrac{14 - 7x}{18 - 9x}$

47. $\dfrac{a + b}{ab} \div \dfrac{a^2 - b^2}{4a^3b}$

48. $\dfrac{6a^2b^2}{a^2 - 4} \div \dfrac{3ab^2}{a - 2}$

49. $\dfrac{x^2 - 6x + 9}{x^2 - x - 6} \div \dfrac{x^2 - 9}{4}$

50. $\dfrac{x^2 - 4}{3x + 6} \div \dfrac{2x^2 - 8x + 8}{x^2 + 4x + 4}$

51. $\dfrac{x^2 - 6x - 16}{2x^2 - 128} \div \dfrac{x^2 + 10x + 16}{x^2 + 16x + 64}$

52. $\dfrac{a^2 - a - 6}{a^2 - 81} \div \dfrac{a^2 - 7a - 18}{4a + 36}$

53. $\dfrac{3x - x^2}{x^3 - 27} \div \dfrac{x}{x^2 + 3x + 9}$

54. $\dfrac{x^2 - 3x}{x^3 - 27} \div \dfrac{2x}{2x^2 + 6x + 18}$

55. $\dfrac{8b + 24}{3a + 6} \div \dfrac{ab - 2b + 3a - 6}{a^2 - 4a + 4}$

56. $\dfrac{2a^2 - 2b^2}{a^3 + a^2b + a + b} \div \dfrac{6a^2}{a^3 + a}$

Objectives **B** **C** **D** **Mixed Practice** *Perform each indicated operation. See Examples 2 through 13.*

57. $\dfrac{x^2 - 9}{4} \cdot \dfrac{x^2 - x - 6}{x^2 - 6x + 9}$

58. $\dfrac{x^2 - 4}{9} \cdot \dfrac{x^2 - 6x + 9}{x^2 - 5x + 6}$

59. $\dfrac{2x^2 - 4x - 30}{5x^2 - 40x - 75} \div \dfrac{x^2 - 8x + 15}{x^2 - 6x + 9}$

60. $\dfrac{4a + 36}{a^2 - 7a - 18} \div \dfrac{a^2 - a - 6}{a^2 - 81}$

61. Simplify: $\dfrac{r^3 + s^3}{r + s}$

62. Simplify: $\dfrac{m^3 - n^3}{m - n}$

63. $\dfrac{4}{x} \div \dfrac{3xy}{x^2} \cdot \dfrac{6x^2}{x^4}$

64. $\dfrac{4}{x} \cdot \dfrac{3xy}{x^2} \div \dfrac{6x^2}{x^4}$

65. $\dfrac{3x^2 - 5x - 2}{y^2 + y - 2} \cdot \dfrac{y^2 + 4y - 5}{12x^2 + 7x + 1} \div \dfrac{5x^2 - 9x - 2}{8x^2 - 2x - 1}$

66. $\dfrac{x^2 + x - 2}{3y^2 - 5y - 2} \cdot \dfrac{12y^2 + y - 1}{x^2 + 4x - 5} \div \dfrac{8y^2 - 6y + 1}{5y^2 - 9y - 2}$

Objective **E** *Find each function value. See Example 14.*

67. If $f(x) = \dfrac{x + 8}{2x - 1}$, find $f(2)$, $f(0)$, and $f(-1)$.

68. If $f(x) = \dfrac{x - 2}{-5 + x}$, find $f(-5)$, $f(0)$, and $f(10)$.

69. $g(x) = \dfrac{x^2 + 8}{x^3 - 25x}$; $g(3)$, $g(-2)$, $g(1)$

70. $s(t) = \dfrac{t^3 + 1}{t^2 + 1}$; $s(-1)$, $s(1)$, $s(2)$

71. The total revenue from the sale of a popular book is approximated by the rational function
$$R(x) = \dfrac{1000x^2}{x^2 + 4},$$ where x is the number of years since publication and $R(x)$ is the total revenue in millions of dollars.

   a. Find the total revenue at the end of the first year.
   b. Find the total revenue at the end of the second year.
   c. Find the revenue during the second year only.
   d. Find the domain of function R.

72. The function $f(x) = \dfrac{100{,}000x}{100 - x}$ models the cost in dollars for removing x percent of the pollutants from a bayou in which a nearby company dumped creosol.

   a. Find the cost of removing 20% of the pollutants from the bayou. [*Hint:* Find $f(20)$.]
   b. Find the cost of removing 60% of the pollutants and then 80% of the pollutants.
   c. Find $f(90)$, then $f(95)$, and then $f(99)$. What happens to the cost as x approaches 100%?
   d. Find the domain of function f.

Review

Perform each indicated operation. See Section 1.4.

73. $\dfrac{4}{5} + \dfrac{3}{5}$

74. $\dfrac{4}{10} - \dfrac{7}{10}$

75. $\dfrac{5}{28} - \dfrac{2}{21}$

76. $\dfrac{5}{13} + \dfrac{2}{7}$

77. $\dfrac{3}{8} + \dfrac{1}{2} - \dfrac{3}{16}$

78. $\dfrac{2}{9} - \dfrac{1}{6} + \dfrac{2}{3}$

Concept Extensions

Solve. For Exercises 79 and 80, see the first Concept Check in this section; for Exercises 81 and 82 see the second Concept Check.

79. Which of the expressions are equivalent to $\dfrac{x}{5 - x}$?

    a. $\dfrac{-x}{5 - x}$ **b.** $\dfrac{-x}{-5 + x}$

    c. $\dfrac{x}{x - 5}$ **d.** $\dfrac{-x}{x - 5}$

80. Which of the expressions are equivalent to $\dfrac{-2 + x}{x}$?

    a. $\dfrac{2 - x}{-x}$ **b.** $-\dfrac{2 - x}{x}$

    c. $\dfrac{x - 2}{x}$ **d.** $\dfrac{x - 2}{-x}$

81. Does $\dfrac{x}{x + 5}$ simplify to $\dfrac{1}{5}$? Why or why not?

82. Does $\dfrac{x + 7}{x}$ simplify to 7? Why or why not?

△ **83.** Find the area of the rectangle.

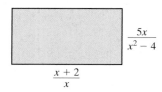

△ **84.** Find the area of the triangle.

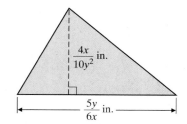

△ **85.** A parallelogram has an area of $\dfrac{x^2 + x - 2}{x^3}$ square feet and a height of $\dfrac{x^2}{x - 1}$ feet. Express the length of its base as a rational expression in x. (*Hint:* Since $A = b \cdot h$, then $b = \dfrac{A}{h}$ or $b = A \div h$.)

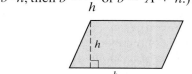

86. A lottery prize of $\dfrac{15x^3}{y^2}$ dollars is to be divided among $5x$ people. Express the amount of money each person is to receive as a rational expression in x and y.

87. In your own words explain how to simplify a rational expression.

88. In your own words, explain the difference between multiplying rational expressions and dividing rational expressions.

89. Decide whether each rational expression equals 1, −1, or neither.

    a. $\dfrac{x + 5}{5 + x}$ **b.** $\dfrac{x - 5}{5 - x}$

    c. $\dfrac{x + 5}{x - 5}$ **d.** $\dfrac{-x - 5}{x + 5}$

    e. $\dfrac{x - 5}{-x + 5}$ **f.** $\dfrac{-5 + x}{x - 5}$

90. In our definition of division for

$$\dfrac{P}{Q} \div \dfrac{R}{S}$$

we stated that $Q \ne 0$, $S \ne 0$, and $R \ne 0$. Explain why R cannot equal 0.

91. Find the polynomial in the second numerator such that the following statement is true.

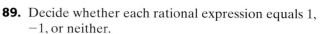

92. In your own words, explain how to find the domain of a rational function.

Simplify. Assume that no denominator is 0.

93. $\dfrac{p^x - 4}{4 - p^x}$

94. $\dfrac{3 + q^n}{q^n + 3}$

95. $\dfrac{x^n + 4}{x^{2n} - 16}$

96. $\dfrac{x^{2k} - 9}{3 + x^k}$

 STUDY SKILLS BUILDER

Are You Satisfied with Your Performance in this Course thus Far?

To see if there is room for improvement, answer these questions:

1. Am I attending all classes and arriving on time?
2. Am I working and checking my homework assignments on time?
3. Am I getting help (from my instructor or a campus learning resource lab) when I need it?

4. In addition to my instructor, am I using the text supplements that might help me?
5. Am I satisfied with my performance on quizzes and exams?

If you answered no to any of these questions, read or reread Section 1.1 for suggestions in these areas. Also, you might want to contact your instructor for additional feedback.

A Add or Subtract Rational Expressions with the Same Denominator.

B Find the Least Common Denominator (LCD) of Two or More Rational Expressions.

C Add and Subtract Rational Expressions with Different Denominators.

Objective **A** Adding or Subtracting Rational Expressions with the Same Denominator

We add or subtract rational expressions just as we add or subtract fractions.

Adding or Subtracting Rational Expressions with Common Denominators

If $\dfrac{P}{Q}$ and $\dfrac{R}{Q}$ are rational expressions, then

$$\frac{P}{Q} + \frac{R}{Q} = \frac{P + R}{Q} \quad \text{and} \quad \frac{P}{Q} - \frac{R}{Q} = \frac{P - R}{Q}$$

To add or subtract rational expressions with common denominators, add or subtract the numerators and write the sum or difference over the common denominator.

PRACTICE PROBLEMS 1–2

Add.

1. $\dfrac{9}{11x^4} + \dfrac{y}{11x^4}$ **2.** $\dfrac{x}{6} + \dfrac{7x}{6}$

EXAMPLES Add.

1. $\dfrac{5}{7z^2} + \dfrac{x}{7z^2} = \dfrac{5 + x}{7z^2}$ Add the numerators and write the result over the common denominator.

2. $\dfrac{x}{4} + \dfrac{5x}{4} = \dfrac{x + 5x}{4} = \dfrac{6x}{4} = \dfrac{3x}{2}$

■ **Work Practice Problems 1–2**

PRACTICE PROBLEMS 3–4

Subtract.

3. $\dfrac{x^2}{x + 3} - \dfrac{9}{x + 3}$

4. $\dfrac{a}{5b^3} - \dfrac{a + 2}{5b^3}$

EXAMPLES Subtract.

3. $\dfrac{x^2}{x + 7} - \dfrac{49}{x + 7} = \dfrac{x^2 - 49}{x + 7}$ Subtract the numerators and write the result over the common denominator.

$$= \frac{(x + 7)(x - 7)}{x + 7}$$ Factor the numerator.

$$= x - 7$$ Simplify.

4. $\dfrac{x}{3y^2} - \dfrac{x + 1}{3y^2} = \dfrac{x - (x + 1)}{3y^2}$ Subtract the numerators.

$$= \frac{x - x - 1}{3y^2}$$ Use the distributive property.

$$= -\frac{1}{3y^2}$$ Simplify.

> **Helpful Hint**
> Be sure to insert parentheses here so that the entire second numerator is subtracted.

■ **Work Practice Problems 3–4**

✔ Concept Check Find and correct the error.

$$\frac{3 + 2y}{y^2 - 1} - \frac{y + 3}{y^2 - 1}$$

$$= \frac{3 + 2y - y + 3}{y^2 - 1}$$

$$= \frac{y + 6}{y^2 - 1}$$

Answers

1. $\dfrac{9 + y}{11x^4}$, **2.** $\dfrac{4x}{3}$, **3.** $x - 3$, **4.** $-\dfrac{2}{5b^3}$

✔ Concept Check Answer

$$\frac{3 + 2y}{y^2 - 1} - \frac{y + 3}{y^2 - 1} = \frac{3 + 2y - y - 3}{y^2 - 1}$$

$$= \frac{y}{y^2 - 1}$$

Objective Ⓑ Finding the LCD of Rational Expressions

To add or subtract rational expressions with unlike, or different, denominators, we first write the rational expressions as equivalent rational expressions with common denominators.

The **least common denominator (LCD)** is usually the easiest common denominator to work with. The LCD of a list of rational expressions is a polynomial of least degree whose factors include all the factors of the denominators in the list.

The following steps can be used to find the LCD.

Finding the Least Common Denominator (LCD)

Step 1: Factor each denominator completely.

Step 2: The LCD is the product of all unique factors each raised to a power equal to the greatest number of times that the factor appears in any one factored denominator.

EXAMPLE 5 Find the LCD of the rational expressions in each list.

a. $\dfrac{2}{3x^5y^2}, \dfrac{3z}{5xy^3}$

b. $\dfrac{7}{z+1}, \dfrac{z}{z-1}$

c. $\dfrac{m-1}{m^2-25}, \dfrac{2m}{2m^2-9m-5}, \dfrac{7}{m^2-10m+25}$

d. $\dfrac{x}{x^2-4}, \dfrac{11}{6-3x}$

Solution:

a. First we factor each denominator.

$3x^5y^2 = 3 \cdot x^5 \cdot y^2$

$5xy^3 = 5 \cdot x \cdot y^3$

$\text{LCD} = 3 \cdot 5 \cdot x^5 \cdot y^3 = 15x^5y^3$

> **Helpful Hint**
> The greatest power of x is 5, so we have a factor of x^5. The greatest power of y is 3, so we have a factor of y^3.

b. The denominators $z+1$ and $z-1$ do not factor further.

$(z+1) = (z+1)$

$(z-1) = (z-1)$

$\text{LCD} = (z+1)(z-1)$

c. We first factor each denominator.

$m^2 - 25 = (m+5)(m-5)$

$2m^2 - 9m - 5 = (2m+1)(m-5)$

$m^2 - 10m + 25 = (m-5)(m-5)$

$\text{LCD} = (m+5)(2m+1)(m-5)^2$

d. We factor each denominator.

$x^2 - 4 = (x+2)(x-2)$

$6 - 3x = 3(2-x) = 3(-1)(x-2)$

$\text{LCD} = 3(-1)(x+2)(x-2)$

$\phantom{\text{LCD}} = -3(x+2)(x-2)$

> **Helpful Hint**
> $(x-2)$ and $(2-x)$ are opposite factors. Notice that a -1 was factored from $(2-x)$ so that the factors are identical.

■ **Work Practice Problem 5**

PRACTICE PROBLEM 5

Find the LCD of the rational expressions in each list.

a. $\dfrac{7}{20a^2b^3}, \dfrac{9}{15ab^4}$

b. $\dfrac{6x}{x-2}, \dfrac{5}{x+2}$

c. $\dfrac{x+4}{x^2-36}, \dfrac{x}{x^2+12x+36}, \dfrac{x^3}{3x^2+19x+6}$

d. $\dfrac{6}{x^2-1}, \dfrac{7}{2-2x}$

Answers
5. **a.** $60a^2b^4$, **b.** $(x-2)(x+2)$,
c. $(x-6)(3x+1)(x+6)^2$,
d. $-2(x+1)(x-1)$

> **Helpful Hint**
>
> If opposite factors occur, do not use both in the LCD. Instead, factor -1 from one of the opposite factors so that the factors are then identical.

Objective **C** Adding or Subtracting Rational Expressions with Different Denominators

To add or subtract rational expressions with different denominators, we write each rational expression as an equivalent rational expression with the LCD as the denominator. To do this, we use the multiplication property of 1 and multiply each rational expression by a form of 1 so that each denominator becomes the LCD.

Adding or Subtracting Rational Expressions with Different Denominators

Step 1: Find the LCD of the rational expressions.

Step 2: Write each rational expression as an equivalent rational expression whose denominator is the LCD found in Step 1.

Step 3: Add or subtract numerators, and write the result over the common denominator.

Step 4: Simplify the resulting rational expression.

PRACTICE PROBLEM 6

Add: $\dfrac{7}{a^3} + \dfrac{9}{2a^4}$

EXAMPLE 6 Add: $\dfrac{2}{x^2} + \dfrac{5}{3x^3}$

Solution: The LCD is $3x^3$. To write the first rational expression as an equivalent rational expression with denominator $3x^3$, we multiply by 1 in the form of $\dfrac{3x}{3x}$.

$$\frac{2}{x^2} + \frac{5}{3x^3} = \frac{2 \cdot 3x}{x^2 \cdot 3x} + \frac{5}{3x^3} \quad \text{The second expression already has a denominator of } 3x^3.$$

$$= \frac{6x}{3x^3} + \frac{5}{3x^3}$$

$$= \frac{6x + 5}{3x^3} \quad \text{Add the numerators.}$$

■ **Work Practice Problem 6**

PRACTICE PROBLEM 7

Add: $\dfrac{1}{x + 5} + \dfrac{6x}{x - 5}$

EXAMPLE 7 Add: $\dfrac{3}{x + 2} + \dfrac{2x}{x - 2}$

Solution: The LCD is the product of the two denominators: $(x + 2)(x - 2)$.

$$\frac{3}{x + 2} + \frac{2x}{x - 2} = \frac{3 \cdot (x - 2)}{(x + 2) \cdot (x - 2)} + \frac{2x \cdot (x + 2)}{(x - 2) \cdot (x + 2)} \quad \begin{array}{l}\text{Write equivalent} \\ \text{rational expressions.}\end{array}$$

$$= \frac{3x - 6}{(x + 2)(x - 2)} + \frac{2x^2 + 4x}{(x + 2)(x - 2)} \quad \begin{array}{l}\text{Multiply in the} \\ \text{numerators.}\end{array}$$

$$= \frac{3x - 6 + 2x^2 + 4x}{(x + 2)(x - 2)} \quad \text{Add the numerators.}$$

$$= \frac{2x^2 + 7x - 6}{(x + 2)(x - 2)} \quad \text{Simplify.}$$

■ **Work Practice Problem 7**

Answers

6. $\dfrac{14a + 9}{2a^4}$, 7. $\dfrac{6x^2 + 31x - 5}{(x + 5)(x - 5)}$

EXAMPLE 8 Subtract: $\dfrac{2x - 6}{x - 1} - \dfrac{4}{1 - x}$

Solution: The LCD is either $x - 1$ or $1 - x$. To get a common denominator of $x - 1$, we factor -1 from the denominator of the second rational expression.

$$\frac{2x - 6}{x - 1} - \frac{4}{1 - x} = \frac{2x - 6}{x - 1} - \frac{4}{-1(x - 1)} \qquad \text{Write } 1 - x \text{ as } -1(x - 1).$$

$$= \frac{2x - 6}{x - 1} - \frac{-1 \cdot 4}{x - 1} \qquad \text{Write } \frac{4}{-1(x - 1)} \text{ as } \frac{-1 \cdot 4}{x - 1}.$$

$$= \frac{2x - 6 - (-4)}{x - 1}$$

$$= \frac{2x - 6 + 4}{x - 1} \qquad \text{Simplify.}$$

$$= \frac{2x - 2}{x - 1}$$

$$= \frac{2(x - 1)}{x - 1}$$

$$= 2$$

■ **Work Practice Problem 8**

EXAMPLE 9 Subtract: $\dfrac{5k}{k^2 - 4} - \dfrac{2}{k^2 + k - 2}$

Solution:

$$\frac{5k}{k^2 - 4} - \frac{2}{k^2 + k - 2} = \frac{5k}{(k + 2)(k - 2)} - \frac{2}{(k + 2)(k - 1)} \qquad \begin{array}{l}\text{Factor each} \\ \text{denominator to} \\ \text{find the LCD.}\end{array}$$

The LCD is $(k + 2)(k - 2)(k - 1)$. We write equivalent rational expressions with the LCD as the denominators.

$$\frac{5k}{(k + 2)(k - 2)} - \frac{2}{(k + 2)(k - 1)}$$

$$= \frac{5k \cdot (k - 1)}{(k + 2)(k - 2) \cdot (k - 1)} - \frac{2 \cdot (k - 2)}{(k + 2)(k - 1) \cdot (k - 2)}$$

$$= \frac{5k^2 - 5k}{(k + 2)(k - 2)(k - 1)} - \frac{2k - 4}{(k + 2)(k - 2)(k - 1)} \qquad \begin{array}{l}\text{Multiply in the} \\ \text{numerators.}\end{array}$$

$$= \frac{5k^2 - 5k - 2k + 4}{(k + 2)(k - 2)(k - 1)} \qquad \begin{array}{l}\text{Subtract the} \\ \text{numerators.}\end{array}$$

$$= \frac{5k^2 - 7k + 4}{(k + 2)(k - 2)(k - 1)} \qquad \text{Simplify.}$$

The numerator is a prime polynomial, so the expression cannot be simplified further.

■ **Work Practice Problem 9**

PRACTICE PROBLEM 8

Subtract: $\dfrac{3m - 26}{m - 6} - \dfrac{8}{6 - m}$

PRACTICE PROBLEM 9

Subtract:

$$\frac{2x}{x^2 - 9} - \frac{3}{x^2 - 4x + 3}$$

Answers

8. 3, **9.** $\dfrac{2x^2 - 5x - 9}{(x + 3)(x - 3)(x - 1)}$

PRACTICE PROBLEM 10

Add:

$$\frac{x + 1}{x^2 + x - 12} + \frac{2x - 1}{x^2 + 6x + 8}$$

EXAMPLE 10 Add: $\dfrac{2x - 1}{2x^2 - 9x - 5} + \dfrac{x + 3}{6x^2 - x - 2}$ Factor the denominators.

Solution:

$$\frac{2x - 1}{2x^2 - 9x - 5} + \frac{x + 3}{6x^2 - x - 2} = \frac{2x - 1}{(2x + 1)(x - 5)} + \frac{x + 3}{(2x + 1)(3x - 2)}$$

The LCD is $(2x + 1)(x - 5)(3x - 2)$.

$$= \frac{(2x - 1) \cdot (3x - 2)}{(2x + 1)(x - 5) \cdot (3x - 2)} + \frac{(x + 3) \cdot (x - 5)}{(2x + 1)(3x - 2) \cdot (x - 5)}$$

$$= \frac{6x^2 - 7x + 2}{(2x + 1)(x - 5)(3x - 2)} + \frac{x^2 - 2x - 15}{(2x + 1)(x - 5)(3x - 2)} \quad \begin{array}{l}\text{Multiply in the}\\\text{numerators.}\end{array}$$

$$= \frac{6x^2 - 7x + 2 + x^2 - 2x - 15}{(2x + 1)(x - 5)(3x - 2)} \quad \begin{array}{l}\text{Add the}\\\text{numerators.}\end{array}$$

$$= \frac{7x^2 - 9x - 13}{(2x + 1)(x - 5)(3x - 2)} \quad \text{Simplify.}$$

The numerator is a prime polynomial, so the expression cannot be simplified further.

▣ **Work Practice Problem 10**

PRACTICE PROBLEM 11

Perform each indicated operation.

$$\frac{6}{x - 5} + \frac{x - 35}{x^2 - 5x} - \frac{2}{x}$$

EXAMPLE 11 Perform each indicated operation:

$$\frac{7}{x - 1} + \frac{10x}{x^2 - 1} - \frac{5}{x + 1}$$

Solution:

$$\frac{7}{x - 1} + \frac{10x}{x^2 - 1} - \frac{5}{x + 1} = \frac{7}{x - 1} + \frac{10x}{(x - 1)(x + 1)} - \frac{5}{x + 1}$$

               The LCD is $(x - 1)(x + 1)$.

$$= \frac{7 \cdot (x + 1)}{(x - 1) \cdot (x + 1)} + \frac{10x}{(x - 1) \cdot (x + 1)} - \frac{5 \cdot (x - 1)}{(x + 1) \cdot (x - 1)}$$

$$= \frac{7x + 7}{(x - 1)(x + 1)} + \frac{10x}{(x - 1)(x + 1)} - \frac{5x - 5}{(x + 1)(x - 1)} \quad \begin{array}{l}\text{Multiply in the}\\\text{numerators.}\end{array}$$

$$= \frac{7x + 7 + 10x - 5x + 5}{(x - 1)(x + 1)} \quad \begin{array}{l}\text{Add and subtract the}\\\text{numerators.}\end{array}$$

$$= \frac{12x + 12}{(x - 1)(x + 1)} \quad \text{Simplify.}$$

$$= \frac{12\,(x + 1)}{(x - 1)\,(x + 1)} \quad \text{Factor the numerator.}$$

$$= \frac{12}{x - 1} \quad \text{Simplify.}$$

▣ **Work Practice Problem 11**

Answers

10. $\dfrac{3x^2 - 4x + 5}{(x + 2)(x - 3)(x + 4)}$,   11. $\dfrac{5}{x}$

▦ CALCULATOR EXPLORATIONS   Graphing

A grapher can be used to support the results of operations on rational expressions. For example, to verify the result of Example 7, graph

$$Y_1 = \frac{3}{x + 2} + \frac{2x}{x - 2} \quad \text{and} \quad Y_2 = \frac{2x^2 + 7x - 6}{(x + 2)(x - 2)}$$

on the same set of axes. The graphs should be the same. Use a TABLE feature or a TRACE feature to see that this is true.

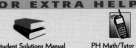
Objective **A** *Add or subtract as indicated. Simplify each answer. See Examples 1 through 4.*

1. $\dfrac{2}{xz^2} - \dfrac{5}{xz^2}$

2. $\dfrac{4}{x^2y} + \dfrac{2}{x^2y}$

 3. $\dfrac{2}{x-2} + \dfrac{x}{x-2}$

4. $\dfrac{x}{5-x} + \dfrac{7}{5-x}$

5. $\dfrac{x^2}{x+2} - \dfrac{4}{x+2}$

6. $\dfrac{x^2}{x+6} - \dfrac{36}{x+6}$

7. $\dfrac{2x-6}{x^2+x-6} + \dfrac{3-3x}{x^2+x-6}$

8. $\dfrac{5x+2}{x^2+2x-8} + \dfrac{2-4x}{x^2+2x-8}$

9. $\dfrac{x-5}{2x} - \dfrac{x+5}{2x}$

10. $\dfrac{x+4}{4x} - \dfrac{x-4}{4x}$

Objective **B** *Find the LCD of the rational expressions in each list. See Example 5.*

11. $\dfrac{2}{7}, \dfrac{3}{5x}$

12. $\dfrac{4}{5y}, \dfrac{3}{4y^2}$

13. $\dfrac{3}{x}, \dfrac{2}{x+1}$

14. $\dfrac{5}{2x}, \dfrac{7}{2+x}$

15. $\dfrac{12}{x+7}, \dfrac{8}{x-7}$

16. $\dfrac{1}{2x-1}, \dfrac{8}{2x+1}$

17. $\dfrac{5}{3x+6}, \dfrac{2x}{2x-4}$

18. $\dfrac{2}{3a+9}, \dfrac{5}{5a-15}$

19. $\dfrac{2a}{a^2-b^2}, \dfrac{1}{a^2-2ab+b^2}$

20. $\dfrac{2a}{a^2+8a+16}, \dfrac{7a}{a^2+a-12}$

21. $\dfrac{x}{x^2-9}, \dfrac{5}{x}, \dfrac{7}{12-4x}$

22. $\dfrac{9}{x^2-25}, \dfrac{1}{50-10x}, \dfrac{6}{x}$

Objective **C** *Add or subtract as indicated. Simplify each answer. See Examples 6 and 7.*

23. $\dfrac{4}{3x} + \dfrac{3}{2x}$

24. $\dfrac{10}{7x} - \dfrac{5}{2x}$

 25. $\dfrac{5}{2y^2} - \dfrac{2}{7y}$

26. $\dfrac{4}{11x^4} - \dfrac{1}{4x^2}$

 27. $\dfrac{x-3}{x+4} - \dfrac{x+2}{x-4}$

28. $\dfrac{x-1}{x-5} - \dfrac{x+2}{x+5}$

29. $\dfrac{1}{x-5} + \dfrac{2x-19}{(x-5)(x+4)}$

30. $\dfrac{4x-2}{(x-5)(x+4)} - \dfrac{2}{x+4}$

Perform the indicated operation. If possible, simplify your answer. See Example 8.

31. $\dfrac{1}{a-b} + \dfrac{1}{b-a}$

32. $\dfrac{1}{a-3} - \dfrac{1}{3-a}$

33. $\dfrac{x + 1}{1 - x} + \dfrac{1}{x - 1}$

34. $\dfrac{5}{1 - x} - \dfrac{1}{x - 1}$

35. $\dfrac{5}{x - 2} + \dfrac{x + 4}{2 - x}$

36. $\dfrac{3}{5 - x} + \dfrac{x + 2}{x - 5}$

Perform each indicated operation. If possible, simplify your answer. See Examples 6 through 10.

37. $\dfrac{y + 1}{y^2 - 6y + 8} - \dfrac{3}{y^2 - 16}$

38. $\dfrac{x + 2}{x^2 - 36} - \dfrac{x}{x^2 + 9x + 18}$

39. $\dfrac{x + 4}{3x^2 + 11x + 6} + \dfrac{x}{2x^2 + x - 15}$

40. $\dfrac{x + 3}{5x^2 + 12x + 4} + \dfrac{6}{x^2 - x - 6}$

41. $\dfrac{7}{x^2 - x - 2} + \dfrac{x}{x^2 + 4x + 3}$

42. $\dfrac{a}{a^2 + 10a + 25} + \dfrac{4}{a^2 + 6a + 5}$

43. $\dfrac{x + 4}{3x^2 + 11x + 6} + \dfrac{x}{2x^2 + x - 15}$

44. $\dfrac{x + 3}{5x^2 + 12x + 4} + \dfrac{6}{x^2 - x - 6}$

45. $\dfrac{2}{a^2 + 2a + 1} + \dfrac{3}{a^2 - 1}$

46. $\dfrac{9x + 2}{3x^2 - 2x - 8} + \dfrac{7}{3x^2 + x - 4}$

Objectives A C Mixed Practice *Add or subtract as indicated. If possible, simplify your answer. See Examples 1 through 10.*

47. $\dfrac{4}{3x^2y^3} + \dfrac{5}{3x^2y^3}$

48. $\dfrac{7}{2xy^4} + \dfrac{1}{2xy^4}$

49. $\dfrac{13x - 5}{2x} - \dfrac{13x + 5}{2x}$

50. $\dfrac{17x + 4}{4x} - \dfrac{17x - 4}{4x}$

51. $\dfrac{3}{2x + 10} + \dfrac{8}{3x + 15}$

52. $\dfrac{10}{3x - 3} + \dfrac{1}{7x - 7}$

53. $\dfrac{-2}{x^2 - 3x} - \dfrac{1}{x^3 - 3x^2}$

54. $\dfrac{-3}{2a + 8} - \dfrac{8}{a^2 + 4a}$

55. $\dfrac{ab}{a^2 - b^2} + \dfrac{b}{a + b}$

56. $\dfrac{x}{25 - x^2} + \dfrac{2}{3x - 15}$

57. $\dfrac{5}{x^2 - 4} - \dfrac{3}{x^2 + 4x + 4}$

58. $\dfrac{3z}{z^2 - 9} - \dfrac{2}{3 - z}$

59. $\dfrac{3x}{2x^2 - 11x + 5} + \dfrac{7}{x^2 - 2x - 15}$

60. $\dfrac{2x}{3x^2 - 13x + 4} + \dfrac{5}{x^2 - 2x - 8}$

Objective **C** *Perform each indicated operation. Simplify each answer. See Example 11.*

61. $\dfrac{2}{x + 1} - \dfrac{3x}{3x + 3} + \dfrac{1}{2x + 2}$

62. $\dfrac{5}{3x - 6} - \dfrac{x}{x - 2} + \dfrac{3 + 2x}{5x - 10}$

63. $\dfrac{3}{x + 3} + \dfrac{5}{x^2 + 6x + 9} - \dfrac{x}{x^2 - 9}$

64. $\dfrac{x + 2}{x^2 - 2x - 3} + \dfrac{x}{x - 3} - \dfrac{x}{x + 1}$

65. $\dfrac{x}{x^2 - 9} + \dfrac{3}{x^2 - 6x + 9} - \dfrac{1}{x + 3}$

66. $\dfrac{3}{x^2 - 9} - \dfrac{x}{x^2 - 6x + 9} + \dfrac{1}{x + 3}$

67. $\left(\dfrac{1}{x} + \dfrac{2}{3}\right) - \left(\dfrac{1}{x} - \dfrac{2}{3}\right)$

68. $\left(\dfrac{1}{2} + \dfrac{2}{x}\right) - \left(\dfrac{1}{2} - \dfrac{1}{x}\right)$

Review

Use the distributive property to multiply each expression. See Section 1.3.

69. $12\left(\dfrac{2}{3} + \dfrac{1}{6}\right)$

70. $14\left(\dfrac{1}{7} + \dfrac{3}{14}\right)$

71. $x^2\left(\dfrac{4}{x^2} + 1\right)$

72. $5y^2\left(\dfrac{1}{y^2} - \dfrac{1}{5}\right)$

Concept Extensions

Find and correct each error. See the Concept Check in this section.

73. $\dfrac{2x - 3}{x^2 + 1} - \dfrac{x - 6}{x^2 + 1} = \dfrac{2x - 3 - x - 6}{x^2 + 1}$
$= \dfrac{x - 9}{x^2 + 1}$

74. $\dfrac{7}{x + 7} - \dfrac{x + 3}{x + 7} = \dfrac{7 - x - 3}{(x + 7)^2}$
$= \dfrac{-x + 4}{(x + 7)^2}$

△ **75.** Find the perimeter and the area of the square.

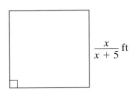

$\dfrac{x}{x + 5}$ ft

△ **76.** Find the perimeter of the quadrilateral.

$\dfrac{3x}{x - 1}$ cm

$\dfrac{5}{x - 1}$ cm

$\dfrac{x^2 - 8}{x - 1}$ cm

$\dfrac{x^2 - 2x}{x - 1}$ cm

77. When is the LCD of two rational expressions equal to the product of their denominators? $\left(\textit{Hint: What}\right.$ is the LCD of $\dfrac{1}{x}$ and $\dfrac{7}{x+5}?\Big)$

78. When is the LCD of two rational expressions with different denominators equal to one of the denominators? $\left(\textit{Hint: What is the LCD of } \dfrac{3x}{x+2} \text{ and }\right.$ $\dfrac{7x+1}{(x+2)^3}?\Big)$

79. In your own words, explain how to add rational expressions with different denominators.

80. In your own words, explain how to multiply rational expressions.

81. In your own words, explain how to divide rational expressions.

82. In your own words, explain how to subtract rational expressions with different denominators.

Mixed Practice (Sections 6.1, 6.2) *Perform the indicated operation. If possible, simplify your answer.*

83. $\left(\dfrac{2}{3}-\dfrac{1}{x}\right)\cdot\left(\dfrac{3}{x}+\dfrac{1}{2}\right)$

84. $\left(\dfrac{2}{3}-\dfrac{1}{x}\right)\div\left(\dfrac{3}{x}+\dfrac{1}{2}\right)$

85. $\left(\dfrac{2a}{3}\right)^2\div\left(\dfrac{a^2}{a+1}-\dfrac{1}{a+1}\right)$

86. $\left(\dfrac{x+2}{2x}-\dfrac{x-2}{2x}\right)\cdot\left(\dfrac{5x}{4}\right)^2$

87. $\left(\dfrac{2x}{3}\right)^2\div\left(\dfrac{x}{3}\right)^2$

88. $\left(\dfrac{2x}{3}\right)^2\cdot\left(\dfrac{3}{x}\right)^2$

89. $\left(\dfrac{x}{x+1}-\dfrac{x}{x-1}\right)\div\dfrac{x}{2x+2}$

90. $\dfrac{x}{2x+2}\div\left(\dfrac{x}{x+1}+\dfrac{x}{x-1}\right)$

91. $\dfrac{4}{x}\cdot\left(\dfrac{2}{x+2}-\dfrac{2}{x-2}\right)$

92. $\dfrac{1}{x+1}\cdot\left(\dfrac{5}{x}+\dfrac{2}{x-3}\right)$

Perform each indicated operation. (Hint: First write each expression with positive exponents.)

93. $x^{-1}+(2x)^{-1}$

94. $y^{-1}+(4y)^{-1}$

95. $4x^{-2}-3x^{-1}$

96. $(4x)^{-2}-(3x)^{-1}$

Use a graphing calculator to support the results of each exercise.

97. Exercise 3

98. Exercise 4

6.3 SIMPLIFYING COMPLEX FRACTIONS

Objectives

A Simplify Complex Fractions by Simplifying the Numerator and Denominator and Then Dividing.

B Simplify Complex Fractions by Multiplying by the Least Common Denominator (LCD).

C Simplify Expressions with Negative Exponents.

A rational expression whose numerator, denominator, or both contain one or more rational expressions is called a **complex rational expression** or a **complex fraction.** Examples are

$$\frac{\dfrac{1}{a}}{\dfrac{b}{2}} \qquad \frac{\dfrac{x}{2y^2}}{\dfrac{6x-2}{9y}} \qquad \frac{x+\dfrac{1}{y}}{y+1}$$

The parts of a complex fraction are

$$\frac{\left.\dfrac{x}{y+2}\right\}}{\left.7+\dfrac{1}{y}\right\}}$$

← Numerator of complex fraction

← Main fraction bar

← Denominator of complex fraction

Our goal in this section is to simplify complex fractions. A complex fraction is simplified when it is in the form $\dfrac{P}{Q}$, where P and Q are polynomials that have no common factors. Two methods of simplifying complex fractions are introduced.

Objective **A** Method 1: Simplifying a Complex Fraction by Simplifying the Numerator and Denominator and Then Dividing

In the first method we study, we simplify complex fractions by simplifying and dividing.

Simplifying a Complex Fraction: Method 1

Step 1: Simplify the numerator and the denominator of the complex fraction so that each is a single fraction.

Step 2: Perform the indicated division by multiplying the numerator of the complex fraction by the reciprocal of the denominator of the complex fraction.

Step 3: Simplify if possible.

EXAMPLE 1 Simplify: $\dfrac{\dfrac{5x}{x+2}}{\dfrac{10}{x-2}}$

Solution:

$$\frac{\dfrac{5x}{x+2}}{\dfrac{10}{x-2}} = \frac{5x}{x+2} \cdot \frac{x-2}{10} \qquad \text{Multiply by the reciprocal of } \frac{10}{x-2}.$$

$$= \frac{\boxed{5}\,x(x-2)}{2 \cdot \boxed{5}\,(x+2)}$$

$$= \frac{x(x-2)}{2(x+2)} \qquad \text{Simplify.}$$

■ **Work Practice Problem 1**

PRACTICE PROBLEM 1

Use Method 1 to simplify:

$$\frac{\dfrac{6x}{x-5}}{\dfrac{12}{x+5}}$$

Answer

1. $\dfrac{x(x+5)}{2(x-5)}$

✔ **Concept Check** Which of the following are equivalent $\dfrac{\dfrac{1}{x}}{\dfrac{3}{y}}$?

a. $\dfrac{1}{x} \div \dfrac{3}{y}$ **b.** $\dfrac{1}{x} \cdot \dfrac{y}{3}$ **c.** $\dfrac{1}{x} \div \dfrac{y}{3}$

PRACTICE PROBLEM 2

Use Method 1 to simplify:

$$\dfrac{\dfrac{x}{y^2} - \dfrac{1}{y}}{\dfrac{y}{x^2} - \dfrac{1}{x}}$$

EXAMPLE 2 Simplify: $\dfrac{\dfrac{x}{y^2} + \dfrac{1}{y}}{\dfrac{y}{x^2} + \dfrac{1}{x}}$

Solution: First we simplify the numerator and the denominator of the complex fraction separately so that each is a single fraction.

$$\dfrac{\dfrac{x}{y^2} + \dfrac{1}{y}}{\dfrac{y}{x^2} + \dfrac{1}{x}} = \dfrac{\dfrac{x}{y^2} + \dfrac{1 \cdot y}{y \cdot y}}{\dfrac{y}{x^2} + \dfrac{1 \cdot x}{x \cdot x}} \qquad \text{The LCD is } y^2.$$

$$\text{The LCD is } x^2.$$

$$= \dfrac{\dfrac{x + y}{y^2}}{\dfrac{y + x}{x^2}} \qquad \begin{array}{l}\text{Add.}\\[1.5em]\text{Add.}\end{array}$$

$$= \dfrac{x + y}{y^2} \cdot \dfrac{x^2}{y + x} \qquad \text{Multiply by the reciprocal of } \dfrac{y + x}{x^2}.$$

$$= \dfrac{x^2\,(x + y)}{y^2\,(y + x)}$$

$$= \dfrac{x^2}{y^2} \qquad \text{Simplify.}$$

◼ **Work Practice Problem 2**

Objective **B** **Method 2: Simplifying a Complex Fraction by Multiplying the Numerator and Denominator by the LCD**

With this method, we multiply the numerator and the denominator of the complex fraction by the least common denominator (LCD) of all fractions in the complex fraction.

Simplifying a Complex Fraction: Method 2

Step 1: Multiply the numerator and the denominator of the complex fraction by the LCD of all the fractions in both the numerator and the denominator.

Step 2: Simplify.

PRACTICE PROBLEM 3

Use Method 2 to simplify:

$$\dfrac{\dfrac{6x}{x - 5}}{\dfrac{12}{x + 5}}$$

Answers

2. $-\dfrac{x^2}{y^2}$, **3.** $\dfrac{x(x + 5)}{2(x - 5)}$

✔ **Concept Check Answer**

a and b

EXAMPLE 3 Simplify: $\dfrac{\dfrac{5x}{x + 2}}{\dfrac{10}{x - 2}}$

Solution: Notice we are reworking Example 1 using Method 2. The least common denominator of $\dfrac{5x}{x + 2}$ and $\dfrac{10}{x - 2}$ is $(x + 2)(x - 2)$. We multiply both the numerator, $\dfrac{5x}{x + 2}$, and the denominator, $\dfrac{10}{x - 2}$, by this LCD.

$$\dfrac{\dfrac{5x}{x+2}}{\dfrac{10}{x-2}} = \dfrac{\left(\dfrac{5x}{x+2}\right) \cdot (x+2)(x-2)}{\left(\dfrac{10}{x-2}\right) \cdot (x+2)(x-2)}$$ Multiply the numerator and denominator by the LCD.

$$= \dfrac{5\,x \cdot (x-2)}{2 \cdot 5 \cdot (x+2)}$$ Simplify.

$$= \dfrac{x(x-2)}{2(x+2)}$$ Simplify.

■ **Work Practice Problem 3**

Examples 1 and 3 are the same and simplify to the same rational expression. Regardless of what method you choose to use, the simplification is the same.

EXAMPLE 4 Simplify: $\dfrac{\dfrac{x}{y^2}+\dfrac{1}{y}}{\dfrac{y}{x^2}+\dfrac{1}{x}}$

Solution: The least common denominator of $\dfrac{x}{y^2}, \dfrac{1}{y}, \dfrac{y}{x^2}$, and $\dfrac{1}{x}$ is $x^2 y^2$.

$$\dfrac{\dfrac{x}{y^2}+\dfrac{1}{y}}{\dfrac{y}{x^2}+\dfrac{1}{x}} = \dfrac{\left(\dfrac{x}{y^2}+\dfrac{1}{y}\right) \cdot x^2 y^2}{\left(\dfrac{y}{x^2}+\dfrac{1}{x}\right) \cdot x^2 y^2}$$ Multiply the numerator and denominator by the LCD.

$$= \dfrac{\dfrac{x}{y^2} \cdot x^2 y^2 + \dfrac{1}{y} \cdot x^2 y^2}{\dfrac{y}{x^2} \cdot x^2 y^2 + \dfrac{1}{x} \cdot x^2 y^2}$$ Use the distributive property.

$$= \dfrac{x^3 + x^2 y}{y^3 + xy^2}$$ Simplify.

$$= \dfrac{x^2(x+y)}{y^2(y+x)}$$ Factor.

$$= \dfrac{x^2}{y^2}$$ Simplify.

■ **Work Practice Problem 4**

PRACTICE PROBLEM 4

Use Method 2 to simplify:

$$\dfrac{\dfrac{x}{y^2}-\dfrac{1}{y}}{\dfrac{y}{x^2}-\dfrac{1}{x}}$$

Helpful Hint

Just as for Examples 1 and 3, Examples 2 and 4 are the same and they simplify to the same rational expression. Note that regardless of what method you use, the result is the same.

Objective C Simplifying Expressions with Negative Exponents

Some expressions containing negative exponents can be written as complex fractions. To simplify these expressions, we first write them as equivalent expressions with positive exponents.

Answer

4. $-\dfrac{x^2}{y^2}$

PRACTICE PROBLEM 5

Simplify: $\dfrac{2x^{-1} + 3y^{-1}}{x^{-1} - 2y^{-1}}$

EXAMPLE 5 Simplify: $\dfrac{x^{-1} + 2xy^{-1}}{x^{-2} - x^{-2}y^{-1}}$

Solution: This fraction does not appear to be a complex fraction. However, if we write it by using only positive exponents we see that it is a complex fraction.

$$\frac{x^{-1} + 2xy^{-1}}{x^{-2} - x^{-2}y^{-1}} = \frac{\dfrac{1}{x} + \dfrac{2x}{y}}{\dfrac{1}{x^2} - \dfrac{1}{x^2y}}$$

The LCD of $\dfrac{1}{x}$, $\dfrac{2x}{y}$, $\dfrac{1}{x^2}$, and $\dfrac{1}{x^2y}$ is x^2y. We multiply both the numerator and denominator by x^2y.

$$\frac{\dfrac{1}{x} + \dfrac{2x}{y}}{\dfrac{1}{x^2} - \dfrac{1}{x^2y}} = \frac{\left(\dfrac{1}{x} + \dfrac{2x}{y}\right) \cdot x^2y}{\left(\dfrac{1}{x^2} - \dfrac{1}{x^2y}\right) \cdot x^2y}$$

$$= \frac{\dfrac{1}{x} \cdot x^2y + \dfrac{2x}{y} \cdot x^2y}{\dfrac{1}{x^2} \cdot x^2y - \dfrac{1}{x^2y} \cdot x^2y} \qquad \text{Use the distributive property.}$$

$$= \frac{xy + 2x^3}{y - 1} \qquad \text{Simplify.}$$

$$\text{or } \frac{x(y + 2x^2)}{y - 1}$$

■ **Work Practice Problem 5**

PRACTICE PROBLEM 6

Simplify: $\dfrac{5 - 3x^{-1}}{2 + (3x)^{-1}}$

EXAMPLE 6 Simplify: $\dfrac{(2x)^{-1} + 1}{2x^{-1} - 1}$

Solution: $\dfrac{(2x)^{-1} + 1}{2x^{-1} - 1} = \dfrac{\dfrac{1}{2x} + 1}{\dfrac{2}{x} - 1}$ Write using positive exponents.

Helpful Hint

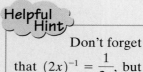

Don't forget that $(2x)^{-1} = \dfrac{1}{2x}$, but $2x^{-1} = 2 \cdot \dfrac{1}{x} = \dfrac{2}{x}$.

$$= \frac{\left(\dfrac{1}{2x} + 1\right) \cdot 2x}{\left(\dfrac{2}{x} - 1\right) \cdot 2x} \qquad \text{The LCD of } \dfrac{1}{2x} \text{ and } \dfrac{2}{x} \text{ is } 2x.$$

$$= \frac{\dfrac{1}{2x} \cdot 2x + 1 \cdot 2x}{\dfrac{2}{x} \cdot 2x - 1 \cdot 2x} \qquad \text{Use distributive property.}$$

$$= \frac{1 + 2x}{4 - 2x} \qquad \text{Simplify.}$$

■ **Work Practice Problem 6**

Answers

5. $\dfrac{2y + 3x}{y - 2x}$,   6. $\dfrac{15x - 9}{6x + 1}$ or $\dfrac{3(5x - 3)}{6x + 1}$

6.3 EXERCISE SET

FOR EXTRA HELP

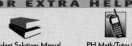 Student Solutions Manual   PH Math/Tutor Center   CD/Video for Review   MathXL®   MyMathLab

Objectives **A** **B** **Mixed Practice** *Simplify each complex fraction. See Examples 1 through 4.*

1. $\dfrac{1 + \dfrac{2}{5}}{2 + \dfrac{3}{5}}$

2. $\dfrac{2 + \dfrac{1}{7}}{3 - \dfrac{4}{7}}$

3. $\dfrac{\dfrac{4}{x-1}}{\dfrac{x}{x-1}}$

4. $\dfrac{\dfrac{x}{x+2}}{\dfrac{2}{x+2}}$

5. $\dfrac{1 - \dfrac{2}{x}}{x + \dfrac{4}{9x}}$

6. $\dfrac{5 - \dfrac{3}{x}}{x + \dfrac{2}{3x}}$

7. $\dfrac{\dfrac{10}{3x}}{\dfrac{5}{6x}}$

8. $\dfrac{\dfrac{15}{2x}}{\dfrac{5}{6x}}$

9. $\dfrac{\dfrac{4x^2 - y^2}{xy}}{\dfrac{2}{y} - \dfrac{1}{x}}$

10. $\dfrac{\dfrac{x^2 - 9y^2}{xy}}{\dfrac{1}{y} - \dfrac{3}{x}}$

11. $\dfrac{\dfrac{x+1}{3}}{\dfrac{2x-1}{6}}$

12. $\dfrac{\dfrac{x+3}{12}}{\dfrac{4x-5}{15}}$

13. $\dfrac{\dfrac{2}{x} + \dfrac{3}{x^2}}{\dfrac{4}{x^2} - \dfrac{9}{x}}$

14. $\dfrac{\dfrac{2}{x^2} + \dfrac{1}{x}}{\dfrac{4}{x^2} - \dfrac{1}{x}}$

15. $\dfrac{\dfrac{1}{x} + \dfrac{2}{x^2}}{x + \dfrac{8}{x^2}}$

16. $\dfrac{\dfrac{1}{y} + \dfrac{3}{y^2}}{y + \dfrac{27}{y^2}}$

17. $\dfrac{\dfrac{4}{5-x} + \dfrac{5}{x-5}}{\dfrac{2}{x} + \dfrac{3}{x-5}}$

18. $\dfrac{\dfrac{3}{x-4} - \dfrac{2}{4-x}}{\dfrac{2}{x-4} - \dfrac{2}{x}}$

19. $\dfrac{\dfrac{x+2}{x} - \dfrac{2}{x-1}}{\dfrac{x+1}{x} + \dfrac{x+1}{x-1}}$

20. $\dfrac{\dfrac{5}{a+2} - \dfrac{1}{a-2}}{\dfrac{3}{2+a} + \dfrac{6}{2-a}}$

21. $\dfrac{\dfrac{2}{x} + 3}{\dfrac{4}{x^2} - 9}$

22. $\dfrac{2 + \dfrac{1}{x}}{4x - \dfrac{1}{x}}$

23. $\dfrac{1 - \dfrac{x}{y}}{\dfrac{x^2}{y^2} - 1}$

24. $\dfrac{1 - \dfrac{2}{x}}{x - \dfrac{4}{x}}$

25. $\dfrac{\dfrac{-2x}{x^2 - xy}}{\dfrac{y}{x^2}}$

26. $\dfrac{\dfrac{7y}{x^2 + xy}}{\dfrac{y^2}{x^2}}$

27. $\dfrac{\dfrac{2}{x} + \dfrac{1}{x^2}}{\dfrac{y}{x^2} + 1}$

28. $\dfrac{\dfrac{5}{x^2} - \dfrac{2}{x}}{\dfrac{1}{x} + 2}$

29. $\dfrac{\dfrac{x}{9} - \dfrac{1}{x}}{1 + \dfrac{3}{x}}$

30. $\dfrac{\dfrac{x}{4} - \dfrac{4}{x}}{1 - \dfrac{4}{x}}$

31. $\dfrac{\dfrac{x-1}{x^2-4}}{1 + \dfrac{1}{x-2}}$

32. $\dfrac{\dfrac{x-2}{x^2-9}}{1+\dfrac{1}{x-3}}$

33. $\dfrac{\dfrac{2}{x+5}+\dfrac{4}{x+3}}{\dfrac{3x+13}{x^2+8x+15}}$

34. $\dfrac{\dfrac{2}{x+2}+\dfrac{6}{x+7}}{\dfrac{4x+13}{x^2+9x+14}}$

Objective **C** *Simplify. See Examples 5 and 6.*

35. $\dfrac{x^{-1}}{x^{-2}+y^{-2}}$

36. $\dfrac{a^{-3}+b^{-1}}{a^{-2}}$

37. $\dfrac{2a^{-1}+3b^{-2}}{a^{-1}-b^{-1}}$

38. $\dfrac{x^{-1}+y^{-1}}{3x^{-2}+5y^{-2}}$

39. $\dfrac{1}{x-x^{-1}}$

40. $\dfrac{x^{-2}}{x+3x^{-1}}$

41. $\dfrac{a^{-1}+1}{a^{-1}-1}$

42. $\dfrac{a^{-1}-4}{4+a^{-1}}$

43. $\dfrac{3x^{-1}+(2y)^{-1}}{x^{-2}}$

44. $\dfrac{5x^{-2}-3y^{-1}}{x^{-1}+y^{-1}}$

45. $\dfrac{2a^{-1}+(2a)^{-1}}{a^{-1}+2a^{-2}}$

46. $\dfrac{a^{-1}+2a^{-2}}{2a^{-1}+(2a)^{-1}}$

47. $\dfrac{5x^{-1}+2y^{-1}}{x^{-2}y^{-2}}$

48. $\dfrac{x^{-2}y^{-2}}{5x^{-1}+2y^{-1}}$

49. $\dfrac{5x^{-1}-2y^{-1}}{25x^{-2}-4y^{-2}}$

50. $\dfrac{3x^{-1}+3y^{-1}}{4x^{-2}-9y^{-2}}$

Review

Solve each equation for x. See Sections 2.1 and 5.7.

51. $7x+2=x-3$

52. $4-2x=17-5x$

53. $x^2=4x-4$

54. $5x^2+10x=15$

55. $\dfrac{x}{3}-5=13$

56. $\dfrac{2x}{9}+1=\dfrac{7}{9}$

Concept Extensions

Solve. See the Concept Check in the section.

57. Which of the following are equivalent to $\dfrac{\dfrac{x+1}{9}}{\dfrac{y-2}{5}}$?

   a. $\dfrac{x+1}{9}\div\dfrac{y-2}{5}$

   b. $\dfrac{x+1}{9}\cdot\dfrac{y-2}{5}$

   c. $\dfrac{x+1}{9}\cdot\dfrac{5}{y-2}$

58. Which of the following are equivalent to $\dfrac{\dfrac{a}{7}}{\dfrac{b}{13}}$?

   a. $\dfrac{a}{7}\cdot\dfrac{b}{13}$

   b. $\dfrac{a}{7}\div\dfrac{b}{13}$

   c. $\dfrac{a}{7}\div\dfrac{13}{b}$

   d. $\dfrac{a}{7}\cdot\dfrac{13}{b}$

59. When the source of a sound is traveling toward a listener, the pitch that the listener hears due to the Doppler effect is given by the complex rational compression $\dfrac{a}{1 - \dfrac{s}{770}}$, where a is the actual pitch of the sound and s is the speed of the sound source. Simplify this expression.

60. In baseball, the earned run average (ERA) statistic gives the average number of earned runs scored on a pitcher per game. It is computed with the following expression: $\dfrac{E}{\dfrac{I}{9}}$, where E is the number of earned runs scored on a pitcher and I is the total number of innings pitched by the pitcher. Simplify this expression.

61. Which of the following are equivalent to $\dfrac{\dfrac{1}{x}}{\dfrac{3}{y}}$?

a. $\dfrac{1}{x} \div \dfrac{3}{y}$ **b.** $\dfrac{1}{x} \cdot \dfrac{y}{3}$ **c.** $\dfrac{1}{x} \div \dfrac{y}{3}$

62. In your own words, explain one method for simplifying a complex fraction.

Simplify.

63. $\dfrac{\dfrac{2}{y^2} - \dfrac{5}{xy} - \dfrac{3}{x^2}}{\dfrac{2}{y^2} + \dfrac{7}{xy} + \dfrac{3}{x^2}}$

64. $\dfrac{\dfrac{2}{x^2} - \dfrac{1}{xy} - \dfrac{1}{y^2}}{\dfrac{1}{x^2} - \dfrac{3}{xy} + \dfrac{2}{y^2}}$

65. $\dfrac{1}{1 + (1 + x)^{-1}}$

66. $\dfrac{(x + 2)^{-1} + (x - 2)^{-1}}{(x^2 - 4)^{-1}}$

67. $\dfrac{x}{1 - \dfrac{1}{1 + \dfrac{1}{x}}}$

68. $\dfrac{x}{1 - \dfrac{1}{1 - \dfrac{1}{x}}}$

*In the study of calculus, the difference quotient $\dfrac{f(a + h) - f(a)}{h}$ is often found and simplified. Find and simplify this quotient for each function $f(x)$ by following steps **a** through **d**.*

a. *Find $(a + h)$.*

b. *Find $f(a)$.*

c. *Use steps **a** and **b** to find $\dfrac{f(a + h) - f(a)}{h}$*

d. *Simplify the result of step **c**.*

69. $f(x) = \dfrac{1}{x}$

70. $f(x) = \dfrac{5}{x}$

71. $\dfrac{3}{x+1}$

72. $\dfrac{2}{x^2}$

 STUDY SKILLS BUILDER

Are You Familiar with Your Textbook Supplements?

Below is a review of some of the student supplements available for additional study. Check to see if you are using the ones most helpful to you.

- Chapter Test Prep Videos on CD. This material is found with your textbook and is fully explained there. The CD contains video clip solutions to the Chapter Test exercises in this text and are excellent help when studying for chapter tests.

- Lecture Videos on CD-ROM. These video segments are keyed to each section of the text. The material is presented by me, Elayn Martin-Gay, and I have placed a 🌐 by the exercises in the text that I have worked on the video.

- The *Student Solutions Manual*. This contains worked out solutions to odd-numbered exercises as well as every exercise in the Integrated Reviews, Chapter Reviews, Chapter Tests, and Cumulative Reviews.

- Prentice Hall Tutor Center. Mathematic questions may be phoned, faxed, or emailed to this center.

- MyMathLab, MathXL, and Interact Math. These are computer and Internet tutorials. This supplement may already be available to you somewhere on campus, for example at your local learning resource lab. Take a moment and find the name and location of any such lab on campus.

As usual, your instructor is your best source of information.

Let's see how you are doing with textbook supplements.

1. Name one way the Lecture Videos can be helpful to you.

2. Name one way the Chapter Test Prep Video can help you prepare for a chapter test.

3. List any textbook supplements that you have found useful.

4. Have you located and visited a learning resource lab located on your campus?

5. List the textbook supplements that are currently housed in your campus' learning resource lab.

Objective **A** Solving Equations Containing Rational Expressions

In this section, we solve rational equations. A *rational equation* is an equation containing at least one rational expression. Before beginning this section, make sure that you understand the difference between an *equation* and an *expression*. An **equation** contains an equal sign and an **expression** does not.

Equation	**Expression**
$\dfrac{x}{2} + \dfrac{x}{6} = \dfrac{2}{3}$ ↑ equal sign	$\dfrac{x}{2} + \dfrac{x}{6}$

Solving an Equation Containing Rational Expressions

To solve an *equation* containing rational expressions, first clear the equation of fractions by multiplying both sides of the equation by the LCD of all rational expressions. Then solve as usual.

Helpful Hint

The method described is for equations only. It may *not* be used for performing operations on expressions.

✔ **Concept Check**   True or false? Clearing fractions is valid when solving an equation and when simplifying rational expressions. Explain.

EXAMPLE 1   Solve: $\dfrac{4x}{5} + \dfrac{3}{2} = \dfrac{3x}{10}$

Solution: The LCD of $\dfrac{4x}{5}, \dfrac{3}{2}$, and $\dfrac{3x}{10}$ is 10. We multiply both sides of the equation by 10.

$$\frac{4x}{5} + \frac{3}{2} = \frac{3x}{10}$$

$$10\left(\frac{4x}{5} + \frac{3}{2}\right) = 10\left(\frac{3x}{10}\right) \quad \text{Multiply both sides by the LCD.}$$

$$10 \cdot \frac{4x}{5} + 10 \cdot \frac{3}{2} = 10 \cdot \frac{3x}{10} \quad \text{Use the distributive property.}$$

$$8x + 15 = 3x \quad \text{Simplify.}$$

$$15 = -5x \quad \text{Subtract } 8x \text{ from both sides.}$$

$$-3 = x \quad \text{Solve.}$$

We verify this solution by replacing x with -3 in the original equation.

Check: $\dfrac{4x}{5} + \dfrac{3}{2} = \dfrac{3x}{10}$

$$\frac{4(-3)}{5} + \frac{3}{2} \stackrel{?}{=} \frac{3(-3)}{10}$$

$$\frac{-12}{5} + \frac{3}{2} \stackrel{?}{=} \frac{-9}{10}$$

$$-\frac{24}{10} + \frac{15}{10} \stackrel{?}{=} -\frac{9}{10}$$

$$-\frac{9}{10} = -\frac{9}{10} \quad \text{True}$$

The solution set is $\{-3\}$.

◼ **Work Practice Problem 1**

Solve: $\dfrac{5x}{6} + \dfrac{1}{2} = \dfrac{x}{3}$

Answer

1. $\{-1\}$

✔ **Concept Check Answer**

false; answers may vary

The important difference about the equations in this section is that the denominator of a rational expression may contain a variable. Recall that a rational expression is undefined for values of the variable that make the denominator 0. If a proposed solution makes the denominator 0, then it must be rejected as a solution of the original equation. Such proposed solutions are called **extraneous solutions.**

PRACTICE PROBLEM 2

Solve: $\dfrac{5}{x} - \dfrac{3x + 6}{2x} = \dfrac{7}{2}$

EXAMPLE 2 Solve: $\dfrac{3}{x} - \dfrac{x + 21}{3x} = \dfrac{5}{3}$

Solution: The LCD of the denominators x, $3x$, and 3 is $3x$. We multiply both sides by $3x$.

$$\frac{3}{x} - \frac{x + 21}{3x} = \frac{5}{3}$$

$$3x\left(\frac{3}{x} - \frac{x + 21}{3x}\right) = 3x\left(\frac{5}{3}\right) \qquad \text{Multiply both sides by the LCD.}$$

$$3x \cdot \frac{3}{x} - 3x \cdot \frac{x + 21}{3x} = 3x \cdot \frac{5}{3} \qquad \text{Use the distributive property.}$$

$$9 - (x + 21) = 5x \qquad \text{Simplify.}$$

$$9 - x - 21 = 5x$$

$$-12 = 6x$$

$$-2 = x \qquad \text{Solve.}$$

The proposed solution is -2.

Check: We check the proposed solution in the original equation.

$$\frac{3}{x} - \frac{x + 21}{3x} = \frac{5}{3}$$

$$\frac{3}{-2} - \frac{-2 + 21}{3(-2)} \stackrel{?}{=} \frac{5}{3}$$

$$-\frac{9}{6} + \frac{19}{6} \stackrel{?}{=} \frac{5}{3}$$

$$\frac{10}{6} = \frac{5}{3} \qquad \text{True}$$

The solution set is $\{-2\}$.

🔲 **Work Practice Problem 2**

The following steps may be used to solve equations containing rational expressions.

> ### To Solve an Equation Containing Rational Expressions
>
> **Step 1:** Multiply both sides of the equation by the LCD of all rational expressions in the equation.
>
> **Step 2:** Simplify both sides.
>
> **Step 3:** Determine whether the equation is linear, quadratic, or higher degree and solve accordingly.
>
> **Step 4:** Check the solution in the original equation.

Let's talk more about multiplying both sides of an equation by the LCD of the rational expressions in the equation. In Example 3 that follows, the LCD is $x - 2$, so we will first multiply both sides of the equation by $x - 2$. Recall that the multiplication property for equations allows us to multiply both sides of an equation by any

Answer

2. $\left\{\dfrac{2}{5}\right\}$

nonzero number. In other words, for Example 3 below, we may multiply both sides of the equation by $x - 2$ *as long as* $x - 2 \neq 0$ or as long as $x \neq 2$. Keep this in mind when solving these equations.

EXAMPLE 3 Solve: $\dfrac{x + 6}{x - 2} = \dfrac{2(x + 2)}{x - 2}$

Solution: First multiply both sides of the equation by the LCD, $x - 2$. (Remember, we can only do this if $x \neq 2$, so that we are not multiplying by 0.)

$$\frac{x + 6}{x - 2} = \frac{2(x + 2)}{x - 2}$$

$$(x - 2) \cdot \frac{x + 6}{x - 2} = (x - 2) \cdot \frac{2(x + 2)}{x - 2} \qquad \text{Multiply both sides by } x - 2.$$

$$x + 6 = 2(x + 2) \qquad \text{Simplify.}$$

$$x + 6 = 2x + 4 \qquad \text{Use the distributive property.}$$

$$2 = x \qquad \text{Solve.}$$

From above, we assumed that $x \neq 2$, so this equation has no solution. This will also show as we attempt to check this proposed solution.

Check: The proposed solution is 2. Notice that 2 makes the denominator 0 in the original equation. This can also be seen in a check. Check the proposed solution 2 in the original equation.

$$\frac{x + 6}{x - 2} = \frac{2(x + 2)}{x - 2}$$

$$\frac{2 + 6}{6 - 2} = \frac{2(2 + 2)}{2 - 2}$$

$$\frac{8}{0} = \frac{2(4)}{0}$$

The denominators are 0, so 2 is not a solution of the original equation. The solution set is $\varnothing$ or $\{\ \}$.

◼ **Work Practice Problem 3**

EXAMPLE 4 Solve: $\dfrac{2x}{2x - 1} + \dfrac{1}{x} = \dfrac{1}{2x - 1}$

Solution: The LCD is $x(2x - 1)$. Multiply both sides by $x(2x - 1)$. By the distributive property, this is the same as multiplying each term by $x(2x - 1)$.

$$x(2x - 1) \cdot \frac{2x}{2x - 1} + x(2x - 1) \cdot \frac{1}{x} = x(2x - 1) \cdot \frac{1}{2x - 1}$$

$$x(2x) + (2x - 1) = x$$

$$2x^2 + 2x - 1 - x = 0$$

$$2x^2 + x - 1 = 0$$

$$(x + 1)(2x - 1) = 0$$

$$x + 1 = 0 \quad \text{or} \quad 2x - 1 = 0$$

$$x = -1 \qquad\qquad x = \frac{1}{2}$$

The number $\dfrac{1}{2}$ makes the denominator $2x - 1$ equal 0, so it is not a solution. The solution set is $\{-1\}$.

◼ **Work Practice Problem 4**

PRACTICE PROBLEM 3

Solve: $\dfrac{x + 5}{x - 3} = \dfrac{2(x + 1)}{x - 3}$

PRACTICE PROBLEM 4

Solve: $\dfrac{3x}{3x - 1} + \dfrac{1}{x} = \dfrac{1}{3x - 1}$

Answers

3. $\varnothing$, **4.** $\{-1\}$

PRACTICE PROBLEM 5

Solve:

$$\frac{2x}{x - 4} + \frac{10 - 5x}{x^2 - 16} = \frac{x}{x + 4}$$

EXAMPLE 5 Solve: $\dfrac{2x}{x - 3} + \dfrac{6 - 2x}{x^2 - 9} = \dfrac{x}{x + 3}$

Solution: We factor the second denominator to find that the LCD is $(x + 3)(x - 3)$. We multiply both sides of the equation by $(x + 3)(x - 3)$. By the distributive property, this is the same as multiplying each term by $(x + 3)(x - 3)$.

$$\frac{2x}{x - 3} + \frac{6 - 2x}{x^2 - 9} = \frac{x}{x + 3}$$

$$(x + 3)(x - 3) \cdot \frac{2x}{x - 3} + (x + 3)(x - 3) \cdot \frac{6 - 2x}{(x + 3)(x - 3)}$$

$$= (x + 3)(x - 3)\left(\frac{x}{x + 3}\right)$$

$$2x(x + 3) + (6 - 2x) = x(x - 3) \quad \text{Simplify.}$$
$$2x^2 + 6x + 6 - 2x = x^2 - 3x \quad \text{Use the distributive property.}$$

Next we solve this quadratic equation by the factoring method. To do so, we first write the equation so that one side is 0.

$$x^2 + 7x + 6 = 0$$
$$(x + 6)(x + 1) = 0 \qquad \text{Factor.}$$
$$x = -6 \quad \text{or} \quad x = -1 \qquad \text{Set each factor equal to 0 and solve.}$$

Neither -6 nor -1 makes any denominator 0. Check to see that the solution set is $\{-6, -1\}$.

🔲 **Work Practice Problem 5**

PRACTICE PROBLEM 6

Solve:

$$\frac{3z}{3z^2 + 7z - 6} - \frac{1}{z} = \frac{4}{3z^2 - 2z}$$

EXAMPLE 6 Solve: $\dfrac{z}{2z^2 + 3z - 2} - \dfrac{1}{2z} = \dfrac{3}{z^2 + 2z}$

Solution: Factor the denominators to find that the LCD is $2z(z + 2)(2z - 1)$. Multiply both sides by the LCD. Remember, by using the distributive property, this is the same as multiplying each term by $2z(z + 2)(2z - 1)$.

$$\frac{z}{2z^2 + 3z - 2} - \frac{1}{2z} = \frac{3}{z^2 + 2z}$$

$$\frac{z}{(2z - 1)(z + 2)} - \frac{1}{2z} = \frac{3}{z(z + 2)}$$

$$2z(z + 2)(2z - 1) \cdot \frac{z}{(2z - 1)(z + 2)} - 2z(z + 2)(2z - 1) \cdot \frac{1}{2z}$$

$$= 2z(z + 2)(2z - 1) \cdot \frac{3}{z(z + 2)} \qquad \begin{array}{l}\text{Apply the distributive}\\\text{property.}\end{array}$$

$$2z(z) - (z + 2)(2z - 1) = 3 \cdot 2(2z - 1) \qquad \text{Simplify.}$$
$$2z^2 - (2z^2 + 3z - 2) = 12z - 6$$
$$2z^2 - 2z^2 - 3z + 2 = 12z - 6$$
$$-3z + 2 = 12z - 6$$
$$-15z = -8$$
$$z = \frac{8}{15} \qquad \text{Solve.}$$

The proposed solution $\dfrac{8}{15}$ does not make any denominator 0; the solution set is $\left\{\dfrac{8}{15}\right\}$.

🔲 **Work Practice Problem 6**

Answers

5. $\{-5, -2\}$,   **6.** $\left\{-\dfrac{6}{11}\right\}$

A graph can be helpful in visualizing solutions of equations. For example, to visualize the solution of the equation $\dfrac{3}{x} - \dfrac{x + 21}{3x} = \dfrac{5}{3}$ in Example 2, the graph of the related rational function $f(x) = \dfrac{3}{x} - \dfrac{x + 21}{3x}$ is shown. A solution of the equation is an x-value that corresponds to a y-value of $\dfrac{5}{3}$.

Notice that an x-value of -2 corresponds to a y-value of $\dfrac{5}{3}$. The solution of the equation is indeed -2 as shown in Example 2.

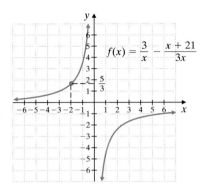

Mental Math

Determine whether each is an equation or an expression. Do not solve or simplify.

1. $\dfrac{x}{2} = \dfrac{3x}{5} + \dfrac{x}{6}$

2. $\dfrac{3x}{5} + \dfrac{x}{6}$

3. $\dfrac{x}{x-1} + \dfrac{2x}{x+1}$

4. $\dfrac{x}{x-1} + \dfrac{2x}{x+1} = 5$

5. $\dfrac{y+7}{2} = \dfrac{y+1}{6} + \dfrac{1}{y}$

6. $\dfrac{y+1}{6} + \dfrac{1}{y}$

6.4 EXERCISE SET

Objective *Solve each equation. See Examples 1 and 2.*

1. $\dfrac{x}{2} - \dfrac{x}{3} = 12$

2. $x = \dfrac{x}{2} - 4$

3. $\dfrac{x}{3} = \dfrac{1}{6} + \dfrac{x}{4}$

4. $\dfrac{x}{2} = \dfrac{21}{10} - \dfrac{x}{5}$

 5. $\dfrac{2}{x} + \dfrac{1}{2} = \dfrac{5}{x}$

6. $\dfrac{5}{3x} + 1 = \dfrac{7}{6}$

7. $\dfrac{x^2 + 1}{x} = \dfrac{5}{x}$

8. $\dfrac{x^2 - 14}{2x} = -\dfrac{5}{2x}$

Solve each equation. See Examples 3 through 6.

9. $\dfrac{x+5}{x+3} = \dfrac{2}{x+3}$

10. $\dfrac{x-7}{x-1} = \dfrac{11}{x-1}$

11. $\dfrac{5}{x-2} - \dfrac{2}{x+4} = \dfrac{-4}{x^2 + 2x - 8}$

12. $\dfrac{1}{x-1} + \dfrac{1}{x+1} = \dfrac{2}{x^2 - 1}$

13. $\dfrac{1}{x-1} = \dfrac{2}{x+1}$

14. $\dfrac{6}{x+3} = \dfrac{4}{x-3}$

15. $\dfrac{x^2 - 23}{2x^2 - 5x - 3} + \dfrac{2}{x-3} = \dfrac{-1}{2x+1}$

16. $\dfrac{4x^2 - 24x}{3x^2 - x - 2} + \dfrac{3}{3x+2} = \dfrac{-4}{x-1}$

17. $\dfrac{1}{x-4} - \dfrac{3x}{x^2 - 16} = \dfrac{2}{x+4}$

18. $\dfrac{3}{2x+3} - \dfrac{1}{2x-3} = \dfrac{4}{4x^2 - 9}$

19. $\dfrac{1}{x-4} = \dfrac{8}{x^2 - 16}$

20. $\dfrac{2}{x^2 - 4} = \dfrac{1}{2x - 4}$

21. $\dfrac{1}{x-2} - \dfrac{2}{x^2 - 2x} = 1$

22. $\dfrac{12}{3x^2 + 12x} = 1 - \dfrac{1}{x+4}$

Mixed Practice *Solve each equation. See Examples 1 through 6.*

23. $\dfrac{5}{x} = \dfrac{20}{12}$

24. $\dfrac{2}{x} = \dfrac{10}{5}$

25. $1 - \dfrac{4}{a} = 5$

26. $7 + \dfrac{6}{a} = 5$

27. $\dfrac{x^2 + 5}{x} - 1 = \dfrac{5(x+1)}{x}$

28. $\dfrac{x^2 + 6}{x} + 5 = \dfrac{2(x+3)}{x}$

29. $\dfrac{1}{2x} - \dfrac{1}{x+1} = \dfrac{1}{3x^2 + 3x}$

30. $\dfrac{2}{x-5} + \dfrac{1}{2x} = \dfrac{5}{3x^2 - 15x}$

31. $\dfrac{1}{x} - \dfrac{x}{25} = 0$

32. $\dfrac{x}{4} + \dfrac{5}{x} = 3$

33. $5 - \dfrac{2}{2y-5} = \dfrac{3}{2y-5}$

34. $1 - \dfrac{5}{y+7} = \dfrac{4}{y+7}$

400

Chapter 6 Vocabulary Check

Fill in each blank with one of the words or phrases listed below.

rational expression   equation   complex fraction   opposites   directly

least common denominator   expression   inversely   jointly

1. A rational expression whose numerator, denominator, or both contain one or more rational expressions is called a <u>complex fraction</u>.

2. In the equation $y = kx$, y varies <u>directly</u> as x.

3. In the equation $y = \dfrac{k}{x}$, y varies <u>inversely</u> as x.

4. The <u>least common denominator</u> of a list of rational expressions is a polynomial of least degree whose factors include the denominator factors in the list.

5. In the equation $y = kxz$, y varies <u>jointly</u> as x and z.

6. The expressions $(x - 5)$ and $(5 - x)$ are called <u>opposites</u>.

7. A <u>rational expression</u> is an expression that can be written as the quotient of $\dfrac{P}{Q}$ of two polynomials P and Q as long as Q is not 0.

8. Which is an expression and which is an equation? An example of an <u>equation</u> is $\dfrac{2}{x} + \dfrac{2}{x^2} = 7$ and an example of an <u>expression</u> is $\dfrac{2}{x} + \dfrac{5}{x^2}$.

Helpful Hint

Are you preparing for your test? Don't forget to take the Chapter 6 Test on page 472. Then check your answers at the back of the text and use the Chapter Test Prep Video CD to see the fully worked-out solutions to any of the exercises you want to review.

6 Chapter Highlights

DEFINITIONS AND CONCEPTS	EXAMPLES
Section 6.1 Rational Functions and Multiplying and Dividing Rational Expressions	

A rational expression is the quotient $\dfrac{P}{Q}$ of two polynomials P and Q, as long as Q is not 0.

$$\frac{2x - 6}{7}, \frac{t^2 - 3t + 5}{t - 1}$$

SIMPLIFYING A RATIONAL EXPRESSION

Step 1. Completely factor the numerator and the denominator.

Step 2. Divide out common factors.

Simplify.

$$\frac{2x^2 + 9x - 5}{x^2 - 25} = \frac{(2x - 1)\,(x + 5)}{(x - 5)\,(x + 5)}$$

$$= \frac{2x - 1}{x - 5}$$

MULTIPLYING RATIONAL EXPRESSIONS

Step 1. Completely factor numerators and denominators.

Step 2. Multiply the numerators and multiply the denominators.

Step 3. Simplify the product.

Multiply: $\dfrac{x^3 + 8}{12x - 18} \cdot \dfrac{14x^2 - 21x}{x^2 + 2x}$

$$= \frac{(x + 2)(x^2 - 2x + 4)}{6(2x - 3)} \cdot \frac{7x(2x - 3)}{x(x + 2)}$$

$$= \frac{7(x^2 - 2x + 4)}{6}$$

DIVIDING RATIONAL EXPRESSIONS

Multiply the first rational expression by the reciprocal of the second rational expression.

Divide: $\dfrac{x^2 + 6x + 9}{5xy - 5y} \div \dfrac{x + 3}{10y}$

$$= \frac{(x + 3)(x + 3)}{5y(x - 1)} \cdot \frac{2 \cdot 5y}{x + 3}$$

$$= \frac{2(x + 3)}{x - 1}$$

A rational function is a function described by a rational expression.

$$f(x) = \frac{2x - 6}{7}, h(t) = \frac{t^2 - 3t + 5}{t - 1}$$

DEFINITIONS AND CONCEPTS	EXAMPLES

Section 6.2   Adding and Subtracting Rational Expressions

ADDING OR SUBTRACTING RATIONAL EXPRESSIONS

Step 1. Find the LCD.

Step 2. Write each rational expression as an equivalent rational expression whose denominator is the LCD.

Step 3. Add or subtract numerators and write the sum or difference over the common denominator.

Step 4. Simplify the result.

Subtract: $\dfrac{3}{x+2} - \dfrac{x+1}{x-3}$

$= \dfrac{3 \cdot (x-3)}{(x+2) \cdot (x-3)} - \dfrac{(x+1) \cdot (x+2)}{(x-3) \cdot (x+2)}$

$= \dfrac{3(x-3) - (x+1)(x+2)}{(x+2)(x-3)}$

$= \dfrac{3x - 9 - (x^2 + 3x + 2)}{(x+2)(x-3)}$

$= \dfrac{3x - 9 - x^2 - 3x - 2}{(x+2)(x-3)}$

$= \dfrac{-x^2 - 11}{(x+2)(x-3)}$

Section 6.3   Simplifying Complex Fractions

Method 1: Simplify the numerator and the denominator so that each is a single fraction. Then perform the indicated division and simplify if possible.

Simplify: $\dfrac{\dfrac{x+2}{x}}{x - \dfrac{4}{x}}$

Method 1: $\dfrac{\dfrac{x+2}{x}}{\dfrac{x \cdot x}{1 \cdot x} - \dfrac{4}{x}} = \dfrac{\dfrac{x+2}{x}}{\dfrac{x^2 - 4}{x}}$

$= \dfrac{x+2}{x} \cdot \dfrac{x}{(x+2)(x-2)} = \dfrac{1}{x-2}$

Method 2: Multiply the numerator and the denominator of the complex fraction by the LCD of the fractions in both the numerator and the denominator. Then simplify if possible.

Method 2: $\dfrac{\left(\dfrac{x+2}{x}\right) \cdot x}{\left(x - \dfrac{4}{x}\right) \cdot x} = \dfrac{x+2}{x \cdot x - \dfrac{4}{x} \cdot x}$

$= \dfrac{x+2}{x^2 - 4} = \dfrac{x+2}{(x+2)(x-2)} = \dfrac{1}{x-2}$

Section 6.4   Solving Equations Containing Rational Expressions

SOLVING AN EQUATION CONTAINING RATIONAL EXPRESSIONS

Multiply both sides of the equation by the LCD of all rational expressions. Then use the distributive property and simplify. Solve the resulting equation and then check each proposed solution to see whether it makes any denominator 0. Discard any solutions that do.

Solve: $x - \dfrac{3}{x} = \dfrac{1}{2}$

$2x\left(x - \dfrac{3}{x}\right) = 2x\left(\dfrac{1}{2}\right)$ The LCD is $2x$.

$2x \cdot x - 2x\left(\dfrac{3}{x}\right) = 2x\left(\dfrac{1}{2}\right)$ Distribute.

$2x^2 - 6 = x$

$2x^2 - x - 6 = 0$ Subtract x from both sides.

$(2x+3)(x-2) = 0$ Factor.

$x = -\dfrac{3}{2}$ or $x = 2$

Both $-\dfrac{3}{2}$ and 2 check. The solution set is $\left\{2, -\dfrac{3}{2}\right\}$.

DEFINITIONS AND CONCEPTS	EXAMPLES
Section 6.5 Rational Equations and Problem Solving	

SOLVING AN EQUATION FOR A SPECIFIED VARIABLE

Treat the specified variable as the only variable of the equation and solve as usual.

Solve for x.

$$A = \frac{2x + 3y}{5}$$

$$5A = 2x + 3y \qquad \text{Multiply both sides by 5.}$$

$$5A - 3y = 2x \qquad \text{Subtract } 3y \text{ from both sides.}$$

$$\frac{5A - 3y}{2} = x \qquad \text{Divide both sides by 2.}$$

SOLVING A PROBLEM THAT INVOLVES A RATIONAL EQUATION

Jeanee and David Dillon volunteer every year to clean a strip of Lake Ponchartrain beach. Jeanee can clean all the trash in this area of beach in 6 hours; David takes 5 hours. Find how long it will take them to clean the area of beach together.

1. UNDERSTAND.

1. Read and reread the problem. Let $x =$ time in hours that it takes Jeanee and David to clean the beach together.

	Hours to Complete	Part Completed in 1 Hour
Jeanee Alone	6	$\frac{1}{6}$
David Alone	5	$\frac{1}{5}$
Together	x	$\frac{1}{x}$

2. TRANSLATE.

2. In words:

$$\boxed{\begin{matrix}\text{part}\\\text{Jeanee}\\\text{can}\\\text{complete}\\\text{in 1 hour}\end{matrix}} \quad + \quad \boxed{\begin{matrix}\text{part}\\\text{David}\\\text{can}\\\text{complete}\\\text{in 1 hour}\end{matrix}} \quad = \quad \boxed{\begin{matrix}\text{part they}\\\text{can}\\\text{complete}\\\text{together}\\\text{in 1 hour}\end{matrix}}$$

$$\downarrow \qquad\qquad \downarrow \qquad\qquad \downarrow$$

Translate:

$$\frac{1}{6} \quad + \quad \frac{1}{5} \quad = \quad \frac{1}{x}$$

3. SOLVE.

3. $\dfrac{1}{6} + \dfrac{1}{5} = \dfrac{1}{x}$

$$5x + 6x = 30 \qquad \text{Multiply both sides by } 30x.$$

$$11x = 30$$

$$x = \frac{30}{11} \quad \text{or} \quad 2\frac{8}{11}$$

4. INTERPRET.

4. *Check* and then *state*. Together, they can clean the beach in $2\frac{8}{11}$ hours.

DEFINITIONS AND CONCEPTS	**EXAMPLES**
Section 6.6 Variation and Problem Solving	
y **varies directly** as *x*, or *y* is **directly proportional** to *x*, if there is a nonzero constant *k* such that $$y = kx$$	The circumference of a circle *C* varies directly as its radius *r*. $$C = \underbrace{2\pi}_{k} r$$
y **varies inversely** as *x*, or *y* is **inversely proportional** to *x*, if there is a nonzero constant *k* such that $$y = \frac{k}{x}$$	Pressure *P* varies inversely with volume *V*. $$P = \frac{k}{V}$$
y **varies jointly** as *x* and *z*, or *y* is **jointly proportional** to *x* and *z*, if there is a nonzero constant *k* such that $$y = kxz$$	The lateral surface area *S* of a cylinder varies jointly as its radius *r* and height *h*. $$S = \underbrace{2\pi}_{k} rh$$

7

Rational Exponents, Radicals, and Complex Numbers

Taken from:
Intermediate Algebra, Third Edition, by Elayn Martin-Gay

A Find Square Roots.

B Approximate Roots Using a Calculator.

C Find Cube Roots.

D Find *n*th Roots.

E Find $\sqrt[n]{a^n}$ when *a* Is Any Real Number.

F Find Function Values of Radical Functions.

PRACTICE PROBLEMS 1-3

Find the square roots of each number.

1. 36 **2.** 81 **3.** -16

7.1 RADICAL EXPRESSIONS AND RADICAL FUNCTIONS

Objective **A** Finding Square Roots

Recall from Section 1.4 that to find a *square root* of a number *a*, we find a number that was squared to get *a*.

Square Root

The number *b* is a **square root** of *a* if $b^2 = a$.

EXAMPLES Find the real square roots of each number.

1. 25 — Since $5^2 = 25$ and $(-5)^2 = 25$, the square roots of 25 are 5 and -5.

2. 49 — Since $7^2 = 49$ and $(-7)^2 = 49$, the square roots of 49 are 7 and -7.

3. -4 — There is no real number whose square is -4. The number -4 has no real number square root.

Work Practice Problems 1-3

Recall that we denote the *nonnegative,* or *principal, square root* with the **radical sign:**

$$\sqrt{25} = 5$$

We denote the *negative square root* with the **negative radical sign:**

$$-\sqrt{25} = -5$$

An expression containing a radical sign is called a **radical expression.** An expression within, or "under," a radical sign is called a **radicand.**

radical expression: $\sqrt{a}$

radical sign

radicand

Principal and Negative Square Roots

The **principal square root** of a nonnegative number *a* is its nonnegative square root. The principal square root is written as $\sqrt{a}$. The **negative square root** of *a* is written as $-\sqrt{a}$.

EXAMPLES Find each square root. Assume that all variables represent non-negative real numbers.

4. $\sqrt{36} = 6$ because $6^2 = 36$.

5. $\sqrt{0} = 0$ because $0^2 = 0$.

6. $\sqrt{\dfrac{4}{49}} = \dfrac{2}{7}$ because $\left(\dfrac{2}{7}\right)^2 = \dfrac{4}{49}$.

7. $\sqrt{0.25} = 0.5$ because $(0.5)^2 = 0.25$.

8. $\sqrt{x^6} = x^3$ because $(x^3)^2 = x^6$.

Answers

1. 6, -6, **2.** 9, -9,

3. no real number square root

9. $\sqrt{9x^{10}} = 3x^5$ because $(3x^5)^2 = 9x^{10}$.

10. $-\sqrt{81} = -9$. The negative in front of the radical indicates the negative square root of 81.

11. $\sqrt{-81}$ is not a real number.

■ **Work Practice Problems 4–11**

> ☁ **Helpful Hint**
>
> • Remember: $\sqrt{0} = 0$.
> • Don't forget that the square root of a negative number is not a real number. For example,
>
> $$\sqrt{-9} \text{ is not a real number}$$
>
> because there is no real number that when multiplied by itself would give a product of -9. In Section 7.7, we will see what kind of a number $\sqrt{-9}$ is.

Objective Ⓑ Approximating Roots

Recall that numbers such as 1, 4, 9, and 25 are called **perfect squares,** since $1 = 1^2, 4 = 2^2, 9 = 3^2$, and $25 = 5^2$. Square roots of perfect square radicands simplify to rational numbers. What happens when we try to simplify a root such as $\sqrt{3}$? Since 3 is not a perfect square, $\sqrt{3}$ is not a rational number. It is called an **irrational number,** and we can find a decimal **approximation** of it. To find decimal approximations, we can use a calculator. For example, an approximation for $\sqrt{3}$ is

$$\sqrt{3} \approx 1.732$$

↑ approximation symbol

To see if the approximation is reasonable, notice that since

$$1 < 3 < 4, \quad \text{then}$$
$$\sqrt{1} < \sqrt{3} < \sqrt{4}, \quad \text{or}$$
$$1 < \sqrt{3} < 2.$$

We found $\sqrt{3} \approx 1.732$, a number between 1 and 2, so our result is reasonable.

EXAMPLE 12

Use a calculator or the appendix to approximate $\sqrt{20}$. Round the approximation to three decimal places and check to see that your approximation is reasonable.

Solution:

$$\sqrt{20} \approx 4.472$$

Is this reasonable? Since $16 < 20 < 25$, then $\sqrt{16} < \sqrt{20} < \sqrt{25}$, or $4 < \sqrt{20} < 5$. The approximation is between 4 and 5 and is thus reasonable.

■ **Work Practice Problem 12**

Objective Ⓒ Finding Cube Roots

Finding roots can be extended to other roots such as cube roots. For example, since $2^3 = 8$, we call 2 the *cube root* of 8. In symbols, we write

$$\sqrt[3]{8} = 2$$

PRACTICE PROBLEMS 4–11

Find each square root. Assume that all variables represent non-negative real numbers.

4. $\sqrt{25}$ 5. $\sqrt{0}$

6. $\sqrt{\dfrac{9}{25}}$ 7. $\sqrt{0.36}$

8. $\sqrt{x^{10}}$ 9. $\sqrt{36x^6}$

10. $-\sqrt{25}$ 11. $\sqrt{-25}$

PRACTICE PROBLEM 12

Use a calculator or the appendix to approximate $\sqrt{30}$. Round the approximation to three decimal places and check to see that your approximation is reasonable.

Answers

4. 5,   **5.** 0,   **6.** $\dfrac{3}{5}$,   **7.** 0.6,   **8.** x^5,

9. $6x^3$,   **10.** -5,   **11.** not a real number,

12. 5.477

Cube Root

The **cube root** of a real number a is written as $\sqrt[3]{a}$, and

$$\sqrt[3]{a} = b \quad \text{only if} \quad b^3 = a$$

From this definition, we have

$\sqrt[3]{64} = 4$ since $4^3 = 64$

$\sqrt[3]{-27} = -3$ since $(-3)^3 = -27$

$\sqrt[3]{x^3} = x$ since $x^3 = x^3$

Notice that, unlike with square roots, *it is possible to have a negative radicand when finding a cube root.* This is so because the *cube* of a negative number is a negative number. Therefore, the *cube root* of a negative number is a negative number.

PRACTICE PROBLEMS 13–17

Find each cube root.

13. $\sqrt[3]{0}$ **14.** $\sqrt[3]{-8}$

15. $\sqrt[3]{\dfrac{1}{64}}$ **16.** $\sqrt[3]{x^9}$

17. $\sqrt[3]{-64x^6}$

EXAMPLES   Find each cube root.

13. $\sqrt[3]{1} = 1$ because $1^3 = 1$.

14. $\sqrt[3]{-64} = -4$ because $(-4)^3 = -64$.

15. $\sqrt[3]{\dfrac{8}{125}} = \dfrac{2}{5}$ because $\left(\dfrac{2}{5}\right)^3 = \dfrac{8}{125}$.

16. $\sqrt[3]{x^6} = x^2$ because $(x^2)^3 = x^6$.

17. $\sqrt[3]{-8x^9} = -2x^3$ because $(-2x^3)^3 = -8x^9$.

▣ **Work Practice Problems 13–17**

Objective D Finding *n*th Roots

Just as we can raise a real number to powers other than 2 or 3, we can find roots other than square roots and cube roots. In fact, we can find the ***n*th root** of a number, where n is any natural number. In symbols, the *n*th root of a is written as $\sqrt[n]{a}$, where n is called the **index.** The index 2 is usually omitted for square roots.

> **Helpful Hint**
>
> If the index is even, such as in $\sqrt{}$, $\sqrt[4]{}$, $\sqrt[6]{}$, and so on, the radicand must be nonnegative for the root to be a real number. For example,
>
> $\sqrt[4]{16} = 2$, but $\sqrt[4]{-16}$ is not a real number,
>
> $\sqrt[6]{64} = 2$, but $\sqrt[6]{-64}$ is not a real number.
>
> If the index is odd, such as in $\sqrt[3]{}$, $\sqrt[5]{}$, and so on, the radicand may be any real number. For example,
>
> $\sqrt[3]{64} = 4$ and $\sqrt[3]{-64} = -4$,
>
> $\sqrt[5]{32} = 2$ and $\sqrt[5]{-32} = -2$.

Answers

13. 0,   **14.** -2,   **15.** $\dfrac{1}{4}$,   **16.** x^3,

17. $-4x^2$

✔ **Concept Check Answer**

b

✔ **Concept Check**   Which one is not a real number?

a. $\sqrt[3]{-15}$ **b.** $\sqrt[4]{-15}$ **c.** $\sqrt[5]{-15}$ **d.** $\sqrt{(-15)^2}$

EXAMPLES Find each root.

18. $\sqrt[4]{81} = 3$ because $3^4 = 81$ and 3 is positive.

19. $\sqrt[5]{-243} = -3$ because $(-3)^5 = -243$.

20. $-\sqrt{25} = -5$ because -5 is the opposite of $\sqrt{25}$.

21. $\sqrt[4]{-81}$ is not a real number. There is no real number that, when raised to the fourth power, is -81.

22. $\sqrt[3]{64x^3} = 4x$ because $(4x)^3 = 64x^3$.

■ **Work Practice Problems 18–22**

PRACTICE PROBLEMS 18–22

Find each root.

18. $\sqrt[4]{16}$ 19. $\sqrt[5]{-32}$

20. $-\sqrt{36}$ 21. $\sqrt[4]{-16}$

22. $\sqrt[3]{8x^6}$

Objective **E** Finding $\sqrt[n]{a^n}$ when a Is Any Real Number

Recall that the notation $\sqrt{a^2}$ indicates the positive square root of a^2 only. For example,

$$\sqrt{(-5)^2} = \sqrt{25} = 5$$

When variables are present in the radicand and it is *unclear whether the variable represents a positive number or a negative number,* absolute value bars are sometimes needed to ensure that the result is a positive number. For example,

$$\sqrt{x^2} = |x|$$

This ensures that the result is positive. This same situation may occur when the index is any *even* positive integer. When the index is any *odd* positive integer, absolute value bars are not necessary.

Finding $\sqrt[n]{a^n}$

If n is an *even* positive integer, then $\sqrt[n]{a^n} = |a|$.

If n is an *odd* positive integer, then $\sqrt[n]{a^n} = a$.

EXAMPLES Simplify. Assume that the variables represent any real number.

23. $\sqrt{(-3)^2} = |-3| = 3$ When the index is even, the absolute value bars ensure that the result is not negative.

24. $\sqrt{x^2} = |x|$

25. $\sqrt[4]{(x-2)^4} = |x-2|$

26. $\sqrt[3]{(-5)^3} = -5$ Absolute value bars are not needed when the index is odd.

27. $\sqrt[5]{(2x-7)^5} = 2x - 7$

28. $\sqrt{25x^2} = 5|x|$

29. $\sqrt{x^2 + 2x + 1} = \sqrt{(x+1)^2} = |x+1|$

■ **Work Practice Problems 23–29**

PRACTICE PROBLEMS 23–29

Simplify. Assume that the variables represent any real number.

23. $\sqrt{(-5)^2}$ 24. $\sqrt{x^6}$

25. $\sqrt[4]{(x+6)^4}$ 26. $\sqrt[3]{(-3)^3}$

27. $\sqrt[5]{(7x-1)^5}$ 28. $\sqrt{36x^2}$

29. $\sqrt{x^2 + 6x + 9}$

Objective **F** Finding Function Values

Functions of the form

$$f(x) = \sqrt[n]{x}$$

are called **radical functions.** Recall that the domain of a function in x is the set of all possible replacement values of x. This means that if n is even, the domain is the set of all nonnegative numbers, or $\{x \mid x \geq 0\}$. If n is odd, the domain is the set of all real numbers. Keep this in mind as we find function values. In Chapter 10, we will graph these functions and discuss their domains further.

Answers

18. 2,   19. -2,   20. -6,

21. not a real number,   22. $2x^2$,

23. 5,   24. $|x^3|$,   25. $|x+6|$,

26. -3,   27. $7x - 1$,   28. $6|x|$,

29. $|x+3|$

PRACTICE PROBLEMS 30–33

If $f(x) = \sqrt{x + 2}$ and $g(x) = \sqrt[3]{x - 1}$, find each function value.

30. $f(7)$ **31.** $g(9)$
32. $f(0)$ **33.** $g(10)$

EXAMPLES If $f(x) = \sqrt{x - 4}$ and $g(x) = \sqrt[3]{x + 2}$, find each function value.

30. $f(8) = \sqrt{8 - 4} = \sqrt{4} = 2$ **31.** $f(6) = \sqrt{6 - 4} = \sqrt{2}$
32. $g(-1) = \sqrt[3]{-1 + 2} = \sqrt[3]{1} = 1$ **33.** $g(1) = \sqrt[3]{1 + 2} = \sqrt[3]{3}$

■ **Work Practice Problems 30–33**

Notice that for the function $f(x) = \sqrt{x - 4}$, the domain includes all real numbers that make the radicand ≥ 0. To see what numbers these are, solve $x - 4 \geq 0$ and find that $x \geq 4$. The domain is $\{x | x \geq 4\}$ or $[4, \infty)$.

The domain of the cube root function $g(x) = \sqrt[3]{x + 2}$ is the set of real numbers or $(-\infty, \infty)$.

See Chapter 9 for further discussions of domains.

Recall from Chapter 3 that the graph of $f(x) = \sqrt{x}$ is

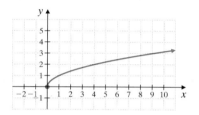

Let's now graph the function $f(x) = \sqrt[3]{x}$.

EXAMPLE 34 Graph the function $f(x) = \sqrt[3]{x}$.

Solution: To graph, we identify the domain, plot points, and connect the points with a smooth curve. The domain of this function is the set of all real numbers. The table comes from the function values obtained earlier. We have approximated $\sqrt[3]{6}$ and $\sqrt[3]{-6}$ for graphing purposes.

PRACTICE PROBLEM 34

Graph the cube root function $h(x) = \sqrt[3]{x} + 2$.

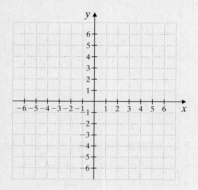

x	$f(x) = \sqrt[3]{x}$
0	0
1	1
-1	-1
6	$\sqrt[3]{6} \approx 1.8$
-6	$\sqrt[3]{-6} \approx -1.8$
8	2
-8	-2

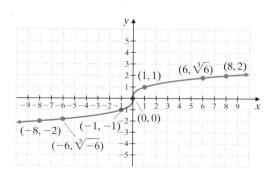

The graph of this function passes the vertical line test, as expected.

■ **Work Practice Problem 34**

Answers

30. 3, **31.** 2, **32.** $\sqrt{2}$, **33.** $\sqrt[3]{9}$,
34.

7.1 EXERCISE SET

FOR EXTRA HELP

Student Solutions Manual

PH Math/Tutor Center

CD/Video for Review

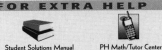

MathXL®

MyMathLab

Objective A *Find the real square roots of each number. See Examples 1 through 3.*

1. 4

2. 9

3. -25

4. -49

5. 100

6. 64

Find each square root. Assume that all variables represent nonnegative real numbers. See Examples 4 through 11.

7. $\sqrt{100}$

8. $\sqrt{400}$

9. $\sqrt{\dfrac{1}{4}}$

10. $\sqrt{\dfrac{9}{25}}$

11. $\sqrt{0.0001}$

12. $\sqrt{0.04}$

13. $-\sqrt{36}$

14. $-\sqrt{9}$

15. $\sqrt{x^{10}}$

16. $\sqrt{x^{16}}$

17. $\sqrt{16y^6}$

18. $\sqrt{64y^{20}}$

Objective B *Use a calculator to approximate each square root to three decimal places. Check to see that each approximation is reasonable. See Example 12.*

19. $\sqrt{7}$

20. $\sqrt{11}$

21. $\sqrt{38}$

22. $\sqrt{56}$

23. $\sqrt{200}$

24. $\sqrt{300}$

Objective C *Find each cube root. See Examples 13 through 17.*

25. $\sqrt[3]{64}$

26. $\sqrt[3]{27}$

27. $\sqrt[3]{\dfrac{1}{8}}$

28. $\sqrt[3]{\dfrac{27}{64}}$

29. $\sqrt[3]{-1}$

30. $\sqrt[3]{-125}$

31. $\sqrt[3]{x^{12}}$

32. $\sqrt[3]{x^{15}}$

33. $\sqrt[3]{-27x^9}$

34. $\sqrt[3]{-64x^6}$

Objective D *Find each root. Assume that all variables represent nonnegative real numbers. See Examples 18 through 22.*

35. $-\sqrt[4]{16}$

36. $\sqrt[5]{-243}$

37. $\sqrt[4]{-16}$

38. $\sqrt{-16}$

39. $\sqrt[5]{-32}$

40. $\sqrt[5]{-1}$

41. $\sqrt[5]{x^{20}}$

42. $\sqrt[4]{x^{20}}$

43. $\sqrt[6]{64x^{12}}$

44. $\sqrt[5]{-32x^{15}}$

45. $\sqrt{81x^4}$

46. $\sqrt[4]{81x^4}$

47. $\sqrt[4]{256x^8}$

48. $\sqrt{256x^8}$

Objective E *Simplify. Assume that the variables represent any real number. See Examples 23 through 29.*

49. $\sqrt{(-8)^2}$

50. $\sqrt{(-7)^2}$

51. $\sqrt[3]{(-8)^3}$

52. $\sqrt[5]{(-7)^5}$

53. $\sqrt{4x^2}$

54. $\sqrt[4]{16x^4}$

55. $\sqrt[3]{x^3}$

56. $\sqrt[5]{x^5}$

57. $\sqrt[4]{(x-2)^4}$

58. $\sqrt[6]{(2x-1)^6}$

59. $\sqrt{x^2 + 4x + 4}$
(*Hint:* Factor the polynomial first.)

60. $\sqrt{x^2 - 8x + 16}$
(*Hint:* Factor the polynomial first.)

Objectives Ⓐ Ⓑ Ⓒ Ⓓ **Mixed Practice** *Simplify each radical. Assume that all variables represent positive real numbers.*

61. $-\sqrt{121}$

62. $-\sqrt[3]{125}$

63. $\sqrt[3]{8x^3}$

64. $\sqrt{16x^8}$

65. $\sqrt{y^{12}}$

66. $\sqrt[3]{y^{12}}$

67. $\sqrt{25a^2b^{20}}$

68. $\sqrt{9x^4y^6}$

69. $\sqrt[3]{-27x^{12}y^9}$

70. $\sqrt[3]{-8a^{21}y^6}$

71. $\sqrt[4]{a^{16}b^4}$

72. $\sqrt[4]{x^8y^{12}}$

73. $\sqrt[5]{-32x^{10}y^5}$

74. $\sqrt[5]{-243z^{15}}$

75. $\sqrt{\dfrac{25}{49}}$

76. $\sqrt{\dfrac{4}{81}}$

77. $\sqrt{\dfrac{x^2}{4y^2}}$

78. $\sqrt{\dfrac{y^{10}}{9x^6}}$

79. $-\sqrt[3]{\dfrac{z^{21}}{27x^3}}$

80. $-\sqrt[3]{\dfrac{64a^3}{b^9}}$

81. $\sqrt[4]{\dfrac{x^4}{16}}$

82. $\sqrt[4]{\dfrac{y^4}{81x^4}}$

Objective Ⓕ *If* $f(x) = \sqrt{2x + 3}$ *and* $g(x) = \sqrt[3]{x - 8}$, *find each function value. See Examples 30 through 33.*

83. $f(0)$

84. $g(0)$

85. $g(7)$

86. $f(-1)$

87. $g(-19)$

88. $f(3)$

89. $f(2)$

90. $g(1)$

Identify the domain and then graph each function. See Example 34.

91. $f(x) = \sqrt[3]{x} + 1$

92. $f(x) = \sqrt[3]{x} - 2$

93. $g(x) = \sqrt[3]{x - 1}$

94. $g(x) = \sqrt[3]{x + 1}$

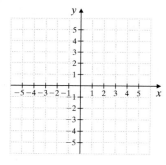

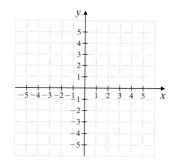

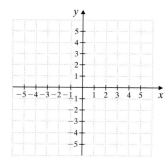

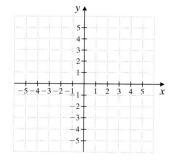

Review

Simplify each exponential expression. See Sections 1.6 and 1.7.

95. $(-2x^3y^2)^5$

96. $(4y^6z^7)^3$

97. $(-3x^2y^3z^5)(20x^5y^7)$

98. $(-14a^5bc^2)(2abc^4)$

99. $\dfrac{7x^{-1}y}{14(x^5y^2)^{-2}}$

100. $\dfrac{(2a^{-1}b^2)^3}{(8a^2b)^{-2}}$

Which of the following are not real numbers? See the Concept Check in this section.

101. $\sqrt{-17}$

102. $\sqrt[3]{-17}$

103. $\sqrt[10]{-17}$

104. $\sqrt[15]{-17}$

Concept Extensions

 105. Explain why $\sqrt{-64}$ is not a real number.

106. Explain why $\sqrt[3]{-64}$ is a real number.

For Exercises 107 through 110, do not use a calculator.

107. $\sqrt{160}$ is closest to
   a. 10   **b.** 13   **c.** 20   **d.** 40

108. $\sqrt{1000}$ is closest to
   a. 10   **b.** 30   **c.** 100   **d.** 500

△ **109.** The perimeter of the triangle is closest to
   a. 12   **b.** 18   **c.** 66   **d.** 132

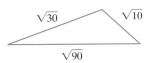

110. The length of the bent wire is closest to
   a. 5   **b.** $\sqrt{28}$ **c.** 7   **d.** 14

The Mosteller formula for calculating adult body surface area is $B = \sqrt{\dfrac{hw}{3131}}$, where B is an individual's body surface area in square meters, h is the individual's height in inches, and w is the individual's weight in pounds. Use this information to answer Exercises 111 and 112. Round answers to 2 decimal places.

△ **111.** Find the body surface area of an individual who is 66 inches tall and who weighs 135 pounds.

△ **112.** Find the body surface area of an individual who is 74 inches tall and who weighs 225 pounds.

113. Suppose that a friend tells you that $\sqrt{13} \approx 5.7$. Without a calculator, how can you convince your friend that he or she must have made an error?

114. Escape velocity is the minimum speed that an object must reach to escape a planet's pull of gravity. Escape velocity v is given by the equation $v = \sqrt{\dfrac{2Gm}{r}}$, where m is the mass of the planet, r is its radius, and G is the universal gravitational constant, which has a value of $G = 6.67 \times 10^{-11}\, m^3/kg \cdot s^2$. The mass of Earth is 5.97×10^{24} kg and its radius is 6.37×10^6 m. Use this information to find the escape velocity for Earth. Round to the nearest whole number. (*Source:* National Space Science Data Center)

STUDY SKILLS BUILDER

How Are Your Homework Assignments Going?

Remember that it is important to keep up with homework. Why? Many concepts in mathematics build on each other. Often, your understanding of a day's lecture depends on an understanding of the previous day's material.

To complete a homework assignment, remember these 4 things:

- Attempt all of it.
- Check it.
- Correct it.
- If needed, ask questions about it.

Take a moment and review your completed homework assignments. Answer the exercises below based on this review.

1. Approximate the fraction of your homework you have attempted.

2. Approximate the fraction of your homework you have checked (if possible).

3. If you are able to check your homework, have you corrected it when errors have been found?

4. When working homework, if you do not understand a concept, what do you personally do?

Objectives

A Understand the Meaning of $a^{1/n}$.

B Understand the Meaning of $a^{m/n}$.

C Understand the Meaning of $a^{-m/n}$.

D Use Rules for Exponents to Simplify Expressions That Contain Rational Exponents.

E Use Rational Exponents to Simplify Radical Expressions.

7.2 RATIONAL EXPONENTS

Objective **A** Understanding $a^{1/n}$

So far in this text, we have not defined expressions with rational exponents such as $3^{1/2}$, $x^{2/3}$, and $-9^{-1/4}$. We will define these expressions so that the rules for exponents shall apply to these rational exponents as well.

Suppose that $x = 5^{1/3}$. Then

$$x^3 = (5^{1/3})^3 = 5^{1/3 \cdot 3} = 5^1 \text{ or } 5$$

using rules for exponents

Since $x^3 = 5$, then x is the number whose cube is 5, or $x = \sqrt[3]{5}$. Notice that we also know that $x = 5^{1/3}$. This means that

$$5^{1/3} = \sqrt[3]{5}$$

Definition of $a^{1/n}$

If n is a positive integer greater than 1 and $\sqrt[n]{a}$ is a real number, then

$$a^{1/n} = \sqrt[n]{a}$$

Notice that the denominator of the rational exponent corresponds to the index of the radical.

PRACTICE PROBLEMS 1–6

Use radical notation to rewrite each expression. Simplify if possible.

1. $25^{1/2}$ 2. $27^{1/3}$
3. $x^{1/5}$ 4. $-25^{1/2}$
5. $(-27y^6)^{1/3}$ 6. $7x^{1/5}$

EXAMPLES Use radical notation to rewrite each expression. Simplify if possible.

1. $4^{1/2} = \sqrt{4} = 2$
2. $64^{1/3} = \sqrt[3]{64} = 4$
3. $x^{1/4} = \sqrt[4]{x}$
4. $-9^{1/2} = -\sqrt{9} = -3$
5. $(81x^8)^{1/4} = \sqrt[4]{81x^8} = 3x^2$
6. $5y^{1/3} = 5\sqrt[3]{y}$

Work Practice Problems 1–6

Objective **B** Understanding $a^{m/n}$

As we expand our use of exponents to include $\dfrac{m}{n}$, we define their meaning so that rules for exponents still hold true. For example, by properties of exponents,

$$8^{2/3} = (8^{1/3})^2 = (\sqrt[3]{8})^2 \quad \text{or} \quad 8^{2/3} = (8^2)^{1/3} = \sqrt[3]{8^2}$$

Definition of $a^{m/n}$

If m and n are positive integers greater than 1 with $\dfrac{m}{n}$ in simplest form, then

$$a^{m/n} = \sqrt[n]{a^m} = (\sqrt[n]{a})^m$$

as long as $\sqrt[n]{a}$ is a real number.

Answers

1. 5, 2. 3, 3. $\sqrt[5]{x}$, 4. -5,
5. $-3y^2$, 6. $7\sqrt[5]{x}$

Notice that the denominator n of the rational exponent corresponds to the index of the radical. The numerator m of the rational exponent indicates that the base is to be raised to the mth power. This means that

$$8^{2/3} = \sqrt[3]{8^2} = \sqrt[3]{64} = 4 \quad \text{or} \quad 8^{2/3} = (\sqrt[3]{8})^2 = 2^2 = 4$$

> **Helpful Hint**
>
> Most of the time, $(\sqrt[n]{a})^m$ will be easier to calculate than $\sqrt[n]{a^m}$.

EXAMPLES Use radical notation to rewrite each expression. Simplify if possible.

7. $4^{3/2} = (\sqrt{4})^3 = 2^3 = 8$

8. $-16^{3/4} = -(\sqrt[4]{16})^3 = -(2)^3 = -8$

9. $(-27)^{2/3} = (\sqrt[3]{-27})^2 = (-3)^2 = 9$

10. $\left(\dfrac{1}{9}\right)^{3/2} = \left(\sqrt{\dfrac{1}{9}}\right)^3 = \left(\dfrac{1}{3}\right)^3 = \dfrac{1}{27}$

11. $(4x - 1)^{3/5} = \sqrt[5]{(4x - 1)^3}$

 Work Practice Problems 7–11

> **Helpful Hint**
>
> The *denominator* of a rational exponent is the index of the corresponding radical. For example, $x^{1/5} = \sqrt[5]{x}$, and $z^{2/3} = \sqrt[3]{z^2}$ or $z^{2/3} = (\sqrt[3]{z})^2$.

Objective C Understanding $a^{-m/n}$

The rational exponents we have given meaning to exclude negative rational numbers. To complete the set of definitions, we define $a^{-m/n}$.

Definition of $a^{-m/n}$

$$a^{-m/n} = \dfrac{1}{a^{m/n}}$$

as long as $a^{m/n}$ is a nonzero real number.

EXAMPLES Write each expression with a positive exponent. Then simplify.

12. $16^{-3/4} = \dfrac{1}{16^{3/4}} = \dfrac{1}{(\sqrt[4]{16})^3} = \dfrac{1}{2^3} = \dfrac{1}{8}$

13. $(-27)^{-2/3} = \dfrac{1}{(-27)^{2/3}} = \dfrac{1}{(\sqrt[3]{-27})^2} = \dfrac{1}{(-3)^2} = \dfrac{1}{9}$

Work Practice Problems 12–13

If an expression contains a negative rational exponent, you may want to first write the expression with a positive exponent, then interpret the rational exponent. Notice that the sign of the base is not affected by the sign of its exponent. For example,

$$9^{-3/2} = \frac{1}{9^{3/2}} = \frac{1}{(\sqrt{9})^3} = \frac{1}{27}$$

Also,

$$(-27)^{-1/3} = \frac{1}{(-27)^{1/3}} = -\frac{1}{3}$$

✔ **Concept Check** Which one is correct?

a. $-8^{2/3} = \frac{1}{4}$ **b.** $8^{-2/3} = -\frac{1}{4}$ **c.** $8^{-2/3} = -4$ **d.** $-8^{-2/3} = -\frac{1}{4}$

Objective D Using Rules for Exponents

It can be shown that the properties of integer exponents hold for rational exponents. By using these properties and definitions, we can now simplify expressions that contain rational exponents. These rules are repeated here for review.

Summary of Exponent Rules

If m and n are rational numbers, and a, b, and c are numbers for which the expressions below exist, then

Product rule for exponents: $a^m \cdot a^n = a^{m+n}$

Power rule for exponents: $(a^m)^n = a^{m \cdot n}$

Power rules for products and quotients: $(ab)^n = a^n b^n$ and

$$\left(\frac{a}{c}\right)^n = \frac{a^n}{c^n}, \quad c \neq 0$$

Quotient rule for exponents: $\frac{a^m}{a^n} = a^{m-n}, \quad a \neq 0$

Zero exponent: $a^0 = 1, \quad a \neq 0$

Negative exponent: $a^{-n} = \frac{1}{a^n}, \quad a \neq 0$

PRACTICE PROBLEMS 14–18

Use the properties of exponents to simplify.

14. $x^{1/3}x^{1/4}$ **15.** $\frac{9^{2/5}}{9^{12/5}}$

16. $y^{-3/10} \cdot y^{6/10}$ **17.** $(11^{2/9})^3$

18. $\frac{(3x^{2/3})^3}{x^2}$

Answers
14. $x^{7/12}$, **15.** $\frac{1}{81}$, **16.** $y^{3/10}$,
17. $11^{2/3}$, **18.** 27

✔ **Concept Check Answer**
d

EXAMPLES Use the properties of exponents to simplify.

14. $x^{1/2}x^{1/3} = x^{1/2+1/3} = x^{3/6+2/6} = x^{5/6}$ Use the product rule.

15. $\frac{7^{1/3}}{7^{4/3}} = 7^{1/3-4/3} = 7^{-3/3} = 7^{-1} = \frac{1}{7}$ Use the quotient rule.

16. $y^{-4/7} \cdot y^{6/7} = y^{-4/7+6/7} = y^{2/7}$ Use the product rule.

17. $(5^{3/8})^4 = 5^{3/8 \cdot 4} = 5^{12/8} = 5^{3/2}$ Use the power rule.

18. $\frac{(2x^{2/5})^5}{x^2} = \frac{2^5(x^{2/5})^5}{x^2}$ Use the power rule.

$$= \frac{32x^2}{x^2}$$ Simplify.

$$= 32x^{2-2}$$ Use the quotient rule.

$$= 32x^0$$ Simplify.

$$= 32 \cdot 1 \quad \text{or} \quad 32$$ Substitute 1 for x^0.

Work Practice Problems 14–18

Objective E Using Rational Exponents to Simplify Radical Expressions

We can simplify some radical expressions by first writing the expression with rational exponents. Use the properties of exponents to simplify, and then convert back to radical notation.

EXAMPLES Use rational exponents to simplify. Assume that all variables represent positive real numbers.

19. $\sqrt[8]{x^4} = x^{4/8}$ Write with rational exponents.

     $= x^{1/2}$ Simplify the exponent.

     $= \sqrt{x}$ Write with radical notation.

20. $\sqrt[6]{25} = 25^{1/6}$ Write with rational exponents.

     $= (5^2)^{1/6}$ Write 25 as 5^2.

     $= 5^{2/6}$ Use the power rule.

     $= 5^{1/3}$ Simplify the exponent.

     $= \sqrt[3]{5}$ Write with radical notation.

21. $\sqrt[6]{r^2 s^4} = (r^2 s^4)^{1/6}$ Write with rational exponents.

     $= r^{2/6} s^{4/6}$ Use the power rule.

     $= r^{1/3} s^{2/3}$ Simplify the exponents.

     $= (rs^2)^{1/3}$ Use $a^n b^n = (ab)^n$.

     $= \sqrt[3]{rs^2}$ Write with radical notation.

■ **Work Practice Problems 19–21**

PRACTICE PROBLEMS 19–21

Use rational exponents to simplify. Assume that all variables represent positive real numbers.

19. $\sqrt[10]{y^5}$ **20.** $\sqrt[4]{9}$

21. $\sqrt[9]{a^6 b^3}$

EXAMPLES Use rational exponents to write as a single radical.

22. $\sqrt{x} \cdot \sqrt[4]{x} = x^{1/2} \cdot x^{1/4} = x^{1/2 + 1/4}$

     $= x^{3/4} = \sqrt[4]{x^3}$

23. $\dfrac{\sqrt{x}}{\sqrt[3]{x}} = \dfrac{x^{1/2}}{x^{1/3}} = x^{1/2 - 1/3} = x^{3/6 - 2/6}$

     $= x^{1/6} = \sqrt[6]{x}$

24. $\sqrt[3]{3} \cdot \sqrt{2} = 3^{1/3} \cdot 2^{1/2}$ Write with rational exponents.

     $= 3^{2/6} \cdot 2^{3/6}$ Write the exponents so that they have the same denominator.

     $= (3^2 \cdot 2^3)^{1/6}$ Use $a^n b^n = (ab)^n$.

     $= \sqrt[6]{3^2 \cdot 2^3}$ Write with radical notation.

     $= \sqrt[6]{72}$ Multiply $3^2 \cdot 2^3$.

■ **Work Practice Problems 22–24**

PRACTICE PROBLEMS 22–24

Use rational exponents to write as a single radical.

22. $\sqrt{y} \cdot \sqrt[3]{y}$ **23.** $\dfrac{\sqrt[3]{x}}{\sqrt[4]{x}}$

24. $\sqrt{5} \cdot \sqrt[3]{2}$

Answers

19. $\sqrt{y}$,   **20.** $\sqrt{3}$,   **21.** $\sqrt[3]{a^2 b}$,

22. $\sqrt[6]{y^5}$,   **23.** $\sqrt[12]{x}$,   **24.** $\sqrt[6]{500}$

7.2 EXERCISE SET

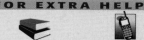

Objective A *Use radical notation to rewrite each expression. Simplify if possible. See Examples 1 through 6.*

1. $49^{1/2}$ **2.** $64^{1/3}$ **3.** $27^{1/3}$ **4.** $8^{1/3}$ **5.** $\left(\dfrac{1}{16}\right)^{1/4}$ **6.** $\left(\dfrac{1}{64}\right)^{1/2}$

7. $169^{1/2}$ **8.** $81^{1/4}$ **9.** $2m^{1/3}$ **10.** $(2m)^{1/3}$ **11.** $(9x^4)^{1/2}$ **12.** $(16x^8)^{1/2}$

13. $(-27)^{1/3}$ **14.** $-64^{1/2}$ **15.** $-16^{1/4}$ **16.** $(-32)^{1/5}$

Objective B *Use radical notation to rewrite each expression. Simplify if possible. See Examples 7 through 11.*

17. $16^{3/4}$ **18.** $4^{5/2}$ **19.** $(-64)^{2/3}$ **20.** $(-8)^{4/3}$ **21.** $(-16)^{3/4}$ **22.** $(-9)^{3/2}$

23. $(2x)^{3/5}$ **24.** $2x^{3/5}$ **25.** $(7x+2)^{2/3}$ **26.** $(x-4)^{3/4}$ **27.** $\left(\dfrac{16}{9}\right)^{3/2}$ **28.** $\left(\dfrac{49}{25}\right)^{3/2}$

Objective C *Write with positive exponents. Simplify if possible. See Examples 12 and 13.*

29. $8^{-4/3}$ **30.** $64^{-2/3}$ **31.** $(-64)^{-2/3}$ **32.** $(-8)^{-4/3}$ **33.** $(-4)^{-3/2}$ **34.** $(-16)^{-5/4}$

35. $x^{-1/4}$ **36.** $y^{-1/6}$ **37.** $\dfrac{1}{a^{-2/3}}$ **38.** $\dfrac{1}{n^{-8/9}}$ **39.** $\dfrac{5}{7x^{-3/4}}$ **40.** $\dfrac{2}{3y^{-5/7}}$

Objective D *Use the properties of exponents to simplify each expression. Write with positive exponents. See Examples 14 through 18.*

41. $a^{2/3}a^{5/3}$ **42.** $b^{9/5}b^{8/5}$ **43.** $x^{-2/5}\cdot x^{7/5}$ **44.** $y^{4/3}\cdot y^{-1/3}$ **45.** $3^{1/4}\cdot 3^{3/8}$

46. $5^{1/2}\cdot 5^{1/6}$ **47.** $\dfrac{y^{1/3}}{y^{1/6}}$ **48.** $\dfrac{x^{3/4}}{x^{1/8}}$ **49.** $(4u^2)^{3/2}$ **50.** $(32^{1/5}x^{2/3})^3$

51. $\dfrac{b^{1/2}b^{3/4}}{-b^{1/4}}$ **52.** $\dfrac{a^{1/4}a^{-1/2}}{a^{2/3}}$ **53.** $\dfrac{(x^3)^{1/2}}{x^{7/2}}$ **54.** $\dfrac{y^{11/3}}{(y^5)^{1/3}}$ **55.** $\dfrac{(3x^{1/4})^3}{x^{1/12}}$

56. $\dfrac{(2x^{1/5})^4}{x^{3/10}}$

57. $\dfrac{(y^3z)^{1/6}}{y^{-1/2}z^{1/3}}$

58. $\dfrac{(m^2n)^{1/4}}{m^{-1/2}n^{5/8}}$

59. $\dfrac{(x^3y^2)^{1/4}}{(x^{-5}y^{-1})^{-1/2}}$

60. $\dfrac{(a^{-2}b^3)^{1/8}}{(a^{-3}b)^{-1/4}}$

Objective **E** *Use rational exponents to simplify each radical. Assume that all variables represent positive real numbers. See Examples 19 through 21.*

61. $\sqrt[6]{x^3}$

62. $\sqrt[9]{a^3}$

63. $\sqrt[6]{4}$

64. $\sqrt[4]{36}$

65. $\sqrt[4]{16x^2}$

66. $\sqrt[8]{4y^2}$

67. $\sqrt[4]{(x+3)^2}$

68. $\sqrt[8]{(y+1)^4}$

69. $\sqrt[8]{x^4y^4}$

70. $\sqrt[9]{y^6z^3}$

71. $\sqrt[12]{a^8b^4}$

72. $\sqrt[10]{a^5b^5}$

Use rational expressions to write as a single radical expression. See Examples 22 through 24.

73. $\sqrt[3]{y}\cdot\sqrt[5]{y^2}$

74. $\sqrt[3]{y^2}\cdot\sqrt[6]{y}$

75. $\dfrac{\sqrt[3]{b^2}}{\sqrt[4]{b}}$

76. $\dfrac{\sqrt[4]{a}}{\sqrt[5]{a}}$

77. $\sqrt[3]{x}\cdot\sqrt[4]{x}\cdot\sqrt[8]{x^3}$

78. $\sqrt[6]{y}\cdot\sqrt[3]{y}\cdot\sqrt[5]{y^2}$

79. $\dfrac{\sqrt[3]{a^2}}{\sqrt[6]{a}}$

80. $\dfrac{\sqrt[5]{b^2}}{\sqrt[10]{b^3}}$

81. $\sqrt{3}\cdot\sqrt[3]{4}$

82. $\sqrt[3]{5}\cdot\sqrt{2}$

83. $\sqrt[5]{7}\cdot\sqrt[3]{y}$

84. $\sqrt[4]{5}\cdot\sqrt[3]{x}$

85. $\sqrt{5r}\cdot\sqrt[3]{s}$

86. $\sqrt[3]{b}\cdot\sqrt[5]{4a}$

Review

Write each integer as a product of two integers such that one of the factors is a perfect square. For example, write 18 as $9\cdot2$, because 9 is a perfect square.

87. 75

88. 20

89. 48

90. 45

Write each integer as a product of two integers such that one of the factors is a perfect cube. For example, write 24 as $8\cdot3$, because 8 is a perfect cube.

91. 16

92. 56

93. 54

94. 80

Concept Extensions

Basal metabolic rate (BMR) is the number of calories per day a person needs to maintain life. A person's basal metabolic rate $B(w)$ in calories per day can be estimated with the function $B(w) = 70w^{3/4}$, where w is the person's weight in kilograms. Use this information to answer Exercises 95 and 96.

95. Estimate the BMR for a person who weighs 60 kilograms. Round to the nearest calorie. (*Note:* 60 kilograms is approximately 132 pounds.)

96. Estimate the BMR for a person who weighs 90 kilograms. Round to the nearest calorie. (*Note:* 90 kilograms is approximately 198 pounds.)

The number of cellular telephone subscriptions in the United States from 1999 through 2004 can be modeled by the function $f(x) = 12x^{7/6}$, where y is the number of cellular telephone subscriptions in millions, x years after 1994. (Source: Based on data from the Cellular Telecommunications & Internet Association, 1985–2004.) Use this information to answer Exercises 97 and 98.

97. Use this model to estimate the number of cellular telephone subscriptions in 2004. Round to the nearest tenth of a million.

98. Predict the number of cellular telephone subscriptions in 2009. Round to the nearest tenth of a million.

99. Explain how writing x^{-7} with positive exponents is similar to writing $x^{-1/4}$ with positive exponents.

100. Explain how writing $2x^{-5}$ with positive exponents is similar to writing $2x^{-3/4}$ with positive exponents.

Fill in each box with the correct expression.

101. $\square \cdot a^{2/3} = a^{3/3}$, or a

102. $\square \cdot x^{1/8} = x^{4/8}$, or $x^{1/2}$

103. $\dfrac{\square}{x^{-2/5}} = x^{3/5}$

104. $\dfrac{\square}{x^{-3/4}} = y^{4/4}$, or y

Use a calculator to write a four-decimal-place approximation of each number.

105. $8^{1/4}$

106. $18^{3/5}$

107. In physics, the speed of a wave traveling over a stretched string with tension t and density u is given by the expression $\dfrac{\sqrt{t}}{\sqrt{u}}$. Write this expression with rational exponents.

108. In electronics, the angular frequency of oscillations in a certain type of circuit is given by the expression $(LC)^{-1/2}$. Use radical notation to write this expression.

7.3 SIMPLIFYING RADICAL EXPRESSIONS

Objective **A** Using the Product Rule

It is possible to simplify some radicals that do not evaluate to rational numbers. To do so, we use a product rule and a quotient rule for radicals. To discover the product rule, notice the following pattern:

$$\sqrt{9} \cdot \sqrt{4} = 3 \cdot 2 = 6$$
$$\sqrt{9 \cdot 4} = \sqrt{36} = 6$$

Since both expressions simplify to 6, it is true that

$$\sqrt{9} \cdot \sqrt{4} = \sqrt{9 \cdot 4}$$

This pattern suggests the following product rule for radicals.

Product Rule for Radicals

If $\sqrt[n]{a}$ and $\sqrt[n]{b}$ are real numbers, then

$$\sqrt[n]{a} \cdot \sqrt[n]{b} = \sqrt[n]{ab}$$

Notice that the product rule is the relationship $a^{1/n} \cdot b^{1/n} = (ab)^{1/n}$ stated in radical notation.

EXAMPLES Use the product rule to multiply.

1. $\sqrt{3} \cdot \sqrt{5} = \sqrt{3 \cdot 5} = \sqrt{15}$

2. $\sqrt{21} \cdot \sqrt{x} = \sqrt{21x}$

3. $\sqrt[3]{4} \cdot \sqrt[3]{2} = \sqrt[3]{4 \cdot 2} = \sqrt[3]{8} = 2$

4. $\sqrt[4]{5} \cdot \sqrt[4]{2x^3} = \sqrt[4]{5 \cdot 2x^3} = \sqrt[4]{10x^3}$

5. $\sqrt{\dfrac{2}{a}} \cdot \sqrt{\dfrac{b}{3}} = \sqrt{\dfrac{2}{a} \cdot \dfrac{b}{3}} = \sqrt{\dfrac{2b}{3a}}$

▢ **Work Practice Problems 1–5**

Objective **B** Using the Quotient Rule

To discover the quotient rule for radicals, notice the following pattern:

$$\sqrt{\dfrac{4}{9}} = \dfrac{2}{3}$$

$$\dfrac{\sqrt{4}}{\sqrt{9}} = \dfrac{2}{3}$$

Since both expressions simplify to $\dfrac{2}{3}$, it is true that

$$\sqrt{\dfrac{4}{9}} = \dfrac{\sqrt{4}}{\sqrt{9}}$$

PRACTICE PROBLEMS 1–5

Use the product rule to multiply.

1. $\sqrt{2} \cdot \sqrt{13}$ 2. $\sqrt{17} \cdot \sqrt{y}$

3. $\sqrt[3]{2} \cdot \sqrt[3]{32}$ 4. $\sqrt[4]{6} \cdot \sqrt[4]{3x^2}$

5. $\sqrt{\dfrac{3}{x}} \cdot \sqrt{\dfrac{y}{2}}$

Answers

1. $\sqrt{26}$,   2. $\sqrt{17y}$,   3. 4,

4. $\sqrt[4]{18x^2}$,   5. $\sqrt{\dfrac{3y}{2x}}$

This pattern suggests the following quotient rule for radicals.

Quotient Rule for Radicals

If $\sqrt[n]{a}$ and $\sqrt[n]{b}$ are real numbers and $\sqrt[n]{b}$ is not zero, then

$$\sqrt[n]{\frac{a}{b}} = \frac{\sqrt[n]{a}}{\sqrt[n]{b}}$$

Notice that the quotient rule is the relationship $\left(\dfrac{a}{b}\right)^{1/n} = \dfrac{a^{1/n}}{b^{1/n}}$ stated in radical notation. We can use the quotient rule to simplify radical expressions by reading the rule from left to right or to divide radicals by reading the rule from right to left.

For example.

$$\sqrt{\frac{x}{16}} = \frac{\sqrt{x}}{\sqrt{16}} = \frac{\sqrt{x}}{4} \qquad \text{Using } \sqrt[n]{\frac{a}{b}} = \frac{\sqrt[n]{a}}{\sqrt[n]{b}}$$

$$\frac{\sqrt{50}}{\sqrt{2}} = \sqrt{\frac{50}{2}} = \sqrt{25} = 5 \qquad \text{Using } \frac{\sqrt[n]{a}}{\sqrt[n]{b}} = \sqrt[n]{\frac{a}{b}}$$

Note: *For the remainder of this chapter, we will assume that variables represent positive real numbers. If this is so, we need not insert absolute value bars when we simplify even roots.*

PRACTICE PROBLEMS 6–9

Use the quotient rule to simplify. Assume that all variables represent positive real numbers.

6. $\sqrt{\dfrac{9}{25}}$ **7.** $\sqrt{\dfrac{y}{36}}$

8. $\sqrt[3]{\dfrac{27}{64}}$ **9.** $\sqrt[5]{\dfrac{7}{32x^5}}$

EXAMPLES Use the quotient rule to simplify.

6. $\sqrt{\dfrac{25}{49}} = \dfrac{\sqrt{25}}{\sqrt{49}} = \dfrac{5}{7}$

7. $\sqrt{\dfrac{x}{9}} = \dfrac{\sqrt{x}}{\sqrt{9}} = \dfrac{\sqrt{x}}{3}$

8. $\sqrt[3]{\dfrac{8}{27}} = \dfrac{\sqrt[3]{8}}{\sqrt[3]{27}} = \dfrac{2}{3}$

9. $\sqrt[4]{\dfrac{3}{16y^4}} = \dfrac{\sqrt[4]{3}}{\sqrt[4]{16y^4}} = \dfrac{\sqrt[4]{3}}{2y}$

▪ **Work Practice Problems 6–9**

Objective **C** Simplifying Radicals

Both the product and quotient rules can be used to simplify a radical. If the product rule is read from right to left, we have that $\sqrt[n]{ab} = \sqrt[n]{a} \cdot \sqrt[n]{b}$. We use this to simplify the following radicals.

PRACTICE PROBLEM 10

Simplify: $\sqrt{18}$

EXAMPLE 10 Simplify: $\sqrt{50}$

Solution: We factor 50 such that one factor is the largest perfect square that divides 50. The largest perfect square factor of 50 is 25, so we write 50 as $25 \cdot 2$ and use the product rule for radicals to simplify.

$$\sqrt{50} = \sqrt{25 \cdot 2} = \sqrt{25} \cdot \sqrt{2} = 5\sqrt{2}$$
$\llcorner$ the largest perfect square factor of 50

▪ **Work Practice Problem 10**

Helpful Hint

Don't forget that, for example, $5\sqrt{2}$ means $5 \cdot \sqrt{2}$.

Answers

6. $\dfrac{3}{5}$, **7.** $\dfrac{\sqrt{y}}{6}$, **8.** $\dfrac{3}{4}$, **9.** $\dfrac{\sqrt[5]{7}}{2x}$,

10. $3\sqrt{2}$

EXAMPLES Simplify.

11. $\sqrt[3]{24} = \sqrt[3]{8 \cdot 3} = \sqrt[3]{8} \cdot \sqrt[3]{3} = 2\sqrt[3]{3}$
   └─ the largest perfect cube factor of 24

12. $\sqrt{26}$ The largest perfect square factor of 26 is 1, so $\sqrt{26}$ cannot be simplified further.

13. $\sqrt[4]{32} = \sqrt[4]{16 \cdot 2} = \sqrt[4]{16} \cdot \sqrt[4]{2} = 2\sqrt[4]{2}$
   └─ the largest 4th power factor of 32

🔲 **Work Practice Problems 11–13**

PRACTICE PROBLEMS 11–13

Simplify.

11. $\sqrt[3]{40}$ 12. $\sqrt{14}$

13. $\sqrt[4]{162}$

After simplifying a radical such as a square root, always check the radicand to see that it contains no other perfect square factors. It may, if the largest perfect square factor of the radicand was not originally recognized. For Example,

$$\sqrt{200} = \sqrt{4 \cdot 50} = \sqrt{4} \cdot \sqrt{50} = 2\sqrt{50}$$

Notice that the radicand 50 still contains the perfect square factor 25. This is because 4 is not the largest perfect square factor of 200. We continue as follows:

$$2\sqrt{50} = 2\sqrt{25 \cdot 2} = 2 \cdot \sqrt{25} \cdot \sqrt{2} = 2 \cdot 5 \cdot \sqrt{2} = 10\sqrt{2}$$

The radical is now simplified since 2 contains no perfect square factors (other than 1).

Helpful Hint
To recognize the largest perfect power factors of a radicand, it will help if you are familiar with some perfect powers. A few are listed below.

Perfect Squares	1, 4, 9, 16, 25, 36, 49, 64, 81, 100, 121, 144
	$1^2 \; 2^2 \; 3^2 \; 4^2 \; 5^2 \; 6^2 \; 7^2 \; 8^2 \; 9^2 \; 10^2 \; 11^2 \; 12^2$
Perfect Cubes	1, 8, 27, 64, 125
	$1^3 \; 2^3 \; 3^3 \; 4^3 \; 5^3$
Perfect 4th powers	1, 16, 81, 256
	$1^4 \; 2^4 \; 3^4 \; 4^4$

Helpful Hint
We say that a radical of the form $\sqrt[n]{a}$ is simplified when the radicand a contains no factors that are perfect nth powers (other than 1 or -1).

EXAMPLES Simplify. Assume that all variables represent positive real numbers.

14. $\sqrt{25x^3} = \sqrt{25 \cdot x^2 \cdot x}$ Find the largest perfect square factor.

   $= \sqrt{25 \cdot x^2} \cdot \sqrt{x}$ Use the product rule.

   $= 5x\sqrt{x}$ Simplify.

15. $\sqrt[3]{54x^6y^8} = \sqrt[3]{27 \cdot 2 \cdot x^6 \cdot y^6 \cdot y^2}$ Factor the radicand and identify perfect cube factors.

   $= \sqrt[3]{27 \cdot x^6 \cdot y^6 \cdot 2y^2}$

   $= \sqrt[3]{27 \cdot x^6 \cdot y^6} \cdot \sqrt[3]{2y^2}$ Use the product rule.

   $= 3x^2y^2\sqrt[3]{2y^2}$ Simplify.

Continued on next page

PRACTICE PROBLEMS 14–16

Simplify. Assume that all variables represent positive real numbers.

14. $\sqrt{49a^5}$ 15. $\sqrt[3]{24x^9y^7}$

16. $\sqrt[4]{16z^9}$

Answers

11. $2\sqrt[3]{5}$,   12. $\sqrt{14}$,   13. $3\sqrt[4]{2}$,
14. $7a^2\sqrt{a}$,   15. $2x^3y^2\sqrt[3]{3y}$,
16. $2z^2\sqrt[4]{z}$

16. $\sqrt[4]{81z^{11}} = \sqrt[4]{81 \cdot z^8 \cdot z^3}$ Factor the radicand and identify perfect 4th power factors.

$\qquad = \sqrt[4]{81 \cdot z^8} \cdot \sqrt[4]{z^3}$ Use the product rule.

$\qquad = 3z^2\sqrt[4]{z^3}$ Simplify.

◾ **Work Practice Problems 14–16**

EXAMPLES   Use the quotient rule to divide. Then simplify if possible. Assume that all variables represent positive real numbers.

17. $\dfrac{\sqrt{20}}{\sqrt{5}} = \sqrt{\dfrac{20}{5}}$ Use the quotient rule.

$\qquad = \sqrt{4}$ Simplify.

$\qquad = 2$ Simplify.

18. $\dfrac{\sqrt{50x}}{2\sqrt{2}} = \dfrac{1}{2} \cdot \sqrt{\dfrac{50x}{2}}$ Use the quotient rule.

$\qquad = \dfrac{1}{2} \cdot \sqrt{25x}$ Simplify.

$\qquad = \dfrac{1}{2} \cdot \sqrt{25} \cdot \sqrt{x}$ Factor $25x$.

$\qquad = \dfrac{1}{2} \cdot 5 \cdot \sqrt{x}$ Simplify.

$\qquad = \dfrac{5}{2}\sqrt{x}$

19. $\dfrac{7\sqrt[3]{48y^4}}{\sqrt[3]{2y}} = 7\sqrt[3]{\dfrac{48y^4}{2y}} = 7\sqrt[3]{24y^3} = 7\sqrt[3]{8 \cdot y^3 \cdot 3}$

$\qquad = 7\sqrt[3]{8 \cdot y^3} \cdot \sqrt[3]{3} = 7 \cdot 2y\sqrt[3]{3} = 14y\sqrt[3]{3}$

20. $\dfrac{2\sqrt[4]{32a^8b^6}}{\sqrt[4]{a^{-1}b^2}} = 2\sqrt[4]{\dfrac{32a^8b^6}{a^{-1}b^2}} = 2\sqrt[4]{32a^9b^4} = 2\sqrt[4]{16 \cdot a^8 \cdot b^4 \cdot 2 \cdot a}$

$\qquad = 2\sqrt[4]{16 \cdot a^8 \cdot b^4} \cdot \sqrt[4]{2 \cdot a} = 2 \cdot 2a^2b \cdot \sqrt[4]{2a} = 4a^2b\sqrt[4]{2a}$

◾ **Work Practice Problems 17–20**

✔**Concept Check**   Find and correct the error:

$$\dfrac{\sqrt[3]{27}}{\sqrt{9}} = \sqrt[3]{\dfrac{27}{9}} = \sqrt[3]{3}$$

Objective **D** **Using the Distance and Midpoint Formulas**

Now that we know how to simplify radicals, we can derive and use the distance formula. The midpoint formula is often confused with the distance formula, so to clarify both, we will also review the midpoint formula.

The Cartesian coordinate system helps us visualize a distance between points. To find the distance between two points, we use the distance formula, which is derived from the Pythagorean theorem.

To find the distance d between two points (x_1, y_1) and (x_2, y_2), draw vertical and horizontal lines so that a right triangle is formed, as shown. Notice that the length of leg a is $x_2 - x_1$ and that

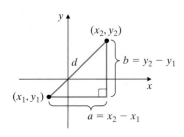

the length of leg b is $y_2 - y_1$. Thus, the Pythagorean theorem tells us that

$$d^2 = a^2 + b^2$$

or

$$d^2 = (x_2 - x_1)^2 + (y_2 - y_1)^2$$

or

$$d = \sqrt{(x_2 - x_1)^2 + (y_2 - y_1)^2}$$

This formula gives us the distance between any two points on the real plane.

Distance Formula

The distance d between two points (x_1, y_1) and (x_2, y_2) is given by

$$d = \sqrt{(x_2 - x_1)^2 + (y_2 - y_1)^2}$$

EXAMPLE 21 Find the distance between $(2, -5)$ and $(1, -4)$. Give an exact distance and a three-decimal-place approximation.

Solution: To use the distance formula, it makes no difference which point we call (x_1, y_1) and which point we call (x_2, y_2). We will let $(x_1, y_1) = (2, -5)$ and $(x_2, y_2) = (1, -4)$.

$$
\begin{aligned}
d &= \sqrt{(x_2 - x_1)^2 + (y_2 - y_1)^2} \\
  &= \sqrt{(1 - 2)^2 + [-4 - (-5)]^2} \\
  &= \sqrt{(-1)^2 + (1)^2} \\
  &= \sqrt{1 + 1} \\
  &= \sqrt{2} \approx 1.414
\end{aligned}
$$

The distance between the two points is exactly $\sqrt{2}$ units, or approximately 1.414 units.

■ **Work Practice Problem 21**

PRACTICE PROBLEM 21

Find the distance between $(-1, 3)$ and $(-2, 6)$. Give an exact distance and a three-decimal-place approximation.

The **midpoint** of a line segment is the **point** located exactly halfway between the two endpoints of the line segment. On the following graph, the point M is the midpoint of line segment PQ. Thus, the distance between M and P equals the distance between M and Q. *Note:* We usually need no knowledge of roots to calculate the midpoint of a line segment. We review midpoint here only because it is often confused with the distance between two points.

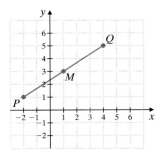

The x-coordinate of M is at half the distance between the x-coordinates of P and Q, and the y-coordinate of M is at half the distance between the y-coordinates of P and Q. That is, the x-coordinate of M is the average of the x-coordinates of P and Q; the y-coordinate of M is the average of the y-coordinates of P and Q.

Answer

21. $\sqrt{10} \approx 3.162$

Midpoint Formula

The midpoint of the line segment whose endpoints are (x_1, y_1) and (x_2, y_2) is the point with coordinates

$$\left(\frac{x_1 + x_2}{2}, \frac{y_1 + y_2}{2} \right)$$

PRACTICE PROBLEM 22

Find the midpoint of the line segment that joins points $P(-2, 5)$ and $Q(4, -6)$.

EXAMPLE 22 Find the midpoint of the line segment that joins points $P(-3, 3)$ and $Q(1, 0)$.

Solution: To use the midpoint formula, it makes no difference which point we call (x_1, y_1) and which point we call (x_2, y_2). We will let $(x_1, y_1) = (-3, 3)$ and $(x_2, y_2) = (1, 0)$.

$$\begin{aligned} \text{midpoint} &= \left(\frac{x_1 + x_2}{2}, \frac{y_1 + y_2}{2} \right) \\ &= \left(\frac{-3 + 1}{2}, \frac{3 + 0}{2} \right) \\ &= \left(\frac{-2}{2}, \frac{3}{2} \right) \\ &= \left(-1, \frac{3}{2} \right) \end{aligned}$$

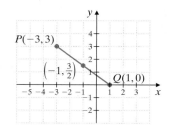

The midpoint of the segment is $\left(-1, \dfrac{3}{2} \right)$.

Work Practice Problem 22

Helpful Hint

The distance between two points is a distance. The midpoint of a line segment is the point halfway between the endpoints of the segment.

distance—measured in units

midpoint—it is a point

Answer

22. $\left(1, -\dfrac{1}{2} \right)$

Objective A *Use the product rule to multiply. Assume that all variables represent positive real numbers. See Examples 1 through 5.*

1. $\sqrt{7} \cdot \sqrt{2}$

2. $\sqrt{11} \cdot \sqrt{10}$

3. $\sqrt[4]{8} \cdot \sqrt[4]{2}$

4. $\sqrt[4]{27} \cdot \sqrt[4]{3}$

5. $\sqrt[3]{4} \cdot \sqrt[3]{9}$

6. $\sqrt[3]{10} \cdot \sqrt[3]{5}$

7. $\sqrt{2} \cdot \sqrt{3x}$

8. $\sqrt{3y} \cdot \sqrt{5x}$

9. $\sqrt{\dfrac{7}{x}} \cdot \sqrt{\dfrac{2}{y}}$

10. $\sqrt{\dfrac{6}{m}} \cdot \sqrt{\dfrac{n}{5}}$

11. $\sqrt[4]{4x^3} \cdot \sqrt[4]{5}$

12. $\sqrt[4]{ab^2} \cdot \sqrt[4]{27ab}$

Objective B *Use the quotient rule to simplify. Assume that all variables represent positive real numbers. See Examples 6 through 9.*

13. $\sqrt{\dfrac{6}{49}}$

14. $\sqrt{\dfrac{8}{81}}$

15. $\sqrt{\dfrac{2}{49}}$

16. $\sqrt{\dfrac{5}{121}}$

17. $\sqrt[4]{\dfrac{x^3}{16}}$

18. $\sqrt[4]{\dfrac{y}{81x^4}}$

19. $\sqrt[3]{\dfrac{4}{27}}$

20. $\sqrt[3]{\dfrac{3}{64}}$

21. $\sqrt[4]{\dfrac{8}{x^8}}$

22. $\sqrt[4]{\dfrac{a^3}{81}}$

23. $\sqrt[3]{\dfrac{2x}{81y^{12}}}$

24. $\sqrt[3]{\dfrac{3}{8x^6}}$

25. $\sqrt{\dfrac{x^2y}{100}}$

26. $\sqrt{\dfrac{y^2z}{400}}$

27. $\sqrt{\dfrac{5x^2}{169y^2}}$

28. $\sqrt{\dfrac{y^{10}}{225x^6}}$

29. $-\sqrt[3]{\dfrac{z^7}{125x^3}}$

30. $-\sqrt[3]{\dfrac{1000a}{b^9}}$

Objective C *Simplify. Assume that all variables represent positive real numbers. See Examples 10 through 16.*

31. $\sqrt{32}$

32. $\sqrt{27}$

33. $\sqrt[3]{192}$

34. $\sqrt[3]{108}$

35. $5\sqrt{75}$

36. $3\sqrt{8}$

37. $\sqrt{24}$

38. $\sqrt{20}$

39. $\sqrt{100x^5}$

40. $\sqrt{64y^9}$

41. $\sqrt[3]{16y^7}$

42. $\sqrt[3]{64y^9}$

43. $\sqrt[4]{a^8b^7}$ **44.** $\sqrt[5]{32z^{12}}$ **45.** $\sqrt{y^5}$ **46.** $\sqrt[3]{y^5}$ **47.** $\sqrt{25a^2b^3}$ **48.** $\sqrt{9x^5y^7}$

49. $\sqrt[5]{-32x^{10}y}$ **50.** $\sqrt[5]{-243z^9}$ **51.** $\sqrt[3]{50x^{14}}$ **52.** $\sqrt[3]{40y^{10}}$ **53.** $-\sqrt{32a^8b^7}$ **54.** $-\sqrt{20ab^6}$

55. $\sqrt{9x^7y^9}$ **56.** $\sqrt{12r^9s^{12}}$ **57.** $\sqrt[3]{125r^9s^{12}}$ **58.** $\sqrt[3]{8a^6b^9}$

Use the quotient rule to divide. Then simplify if possible. Assume that all variables represent positive real numbers. See Examples 17 through 20.

59. $\dfrac{\sqrt{14}}{\sqrt{7}}$ **60.** $\dfrac{\sqrt{45}}{\sqrt{9}}$ **61.** $\dfrac{\sqrt[3]{24}}{\sqrt[3]{3}}$ **62.** $\dfrac{\sqrt[3]{10}}{\sqrt[3]{2}}$

63. $\dfrac{5\sqrt[4]{48}}{\sqrt[4]{3}}$ **64.** $\dfrac{7\sqrt[4]{162}}{\sqrt[4]{2}}$ **65.** $\dfrac{\sqrt{x^5y^3}}{\sqrt{xy}}$ **66.** $\dfrac{\sqrt{a^7b^6}}{\sqrt{a^3b^2}}$

67. $\dfrac{8\sqrt[3]{54m^7}}{\sqrt[3]{2m}}$ **68.** $\dfrac{\sqrt[3]{128x^3}}{-3\sqrt[3]{2x}}$ **69.** $\dfrac{3\sqrt{100x^2}}{2\sqrt{2x^{-1}}}$ **70.** $\dfrac{\sqrt{270y^2}}{5\sqrt{3y^{-4}}}$

71. $\dfrac{\sqrt[4]{96a^{10}b^3}}{\sqrt[4]{3a^2b^3}}$ **72.** $\dfrac{\sqrt[5]{64x^{10}y^3}}{\sqrt[5]{2x^3y^{-7}}}$

Objective **D** *Find the distance between each pair of points. Give an exact distance and a three-decimal-place approximation. See Example 21.*

73. $(5, 1)$ and $(8, 5)$ **74.** $(2, 3)$ and $(14, 8)$ **75.** $(-3, 2)$ and $(1, -3)$

76. $(3, -2)$ and $(-4, 1)$ **77.** $(0, -\sqrt{2})$ and $(\sqrt{3}, 0)$ **78.** $(-\sqrt{5}, 0)$ and $(0, \sqrt{7})$

79. $(1.7, -3.6)$ and $(-8.6, 5.7)$ **80.** $(9.6, 2.5)$ and $(-1.9, -3.7)$

Find the midpoint of each line segment whose endpoints are given. See Example 22.

81. $(6, -8); (2, 4)$ **82.** $(3, 9); (7, 11)$ ● **83.** $(-2, -1); (-8, 6)$ **84.** $(-3, -4); (6, -8)$

85. $\left(\frac{1}{2}, \frac{3}{8}\right); \left(-\frac{3}{2}, \frac{5}{8}\right)$ **86.** $\left(-\frac{2}{5}, \frac{7}{15}\right); \left(-\frac{2}{5}, -\frac{4}{15}\right)$ **87.** $(\sqrt{2}, 3\sqrt{5}); (\sqrt{2}, -2\sqrt{5})$ **88.** $(\sqrt{8}, -\sqrt{12}); (3\sqrt{2}, 7\sqrt{3})$

Review

Perform each indicated operation. See Sections 1.5 and 5.2.

89. $6x + 8x$ **90.** $(6x)(8x)$ **91.** $(2x + 3)(x - 5)$ **92.** $(2x + 3) + (x - 5)$

93. $9y^2 - 8y^2$ **94.** $(9y^2)(-8y^2)$ **95.** $(x - 4)^2$ **96.** $(2x + 1)^2$

Concept Extensions

Find and correct the error. See the Concept Check in this section.

97. $\dfrac{\sqrt[3]{64}}{\sqrt{64}} = \sqrt[3]{\dfrac{64}{64}} = \sqrt[3]{1} = 1$

98. $\dfrac{\sqrt[4]{16}}{\sqrt{4}} = \sqrt[4]{\dfrac{16}{4}} = \sqrt[4]{4}$

99. The formula for the radius r of a sphere with surface area A is given by $r = \sqrt{\dfrac{A}{4\pi}}$. Calculate the radius of a standard zorb whose outside surface area is 32.17 sq m. Round to the nearest tenth. (*Source:* Zorb, Ltd.)

100. Before Mount Vesuvius, a volcano in Italy, erupted violently in 79 A.D., its height was 4190 feet. Vesuvius was roughly cone shaped, and its base had a radius of approximately 25,200 feet. Use the formula $A = \pi r \sqrt{r^2 + h^2}$ for the surface area A of a cone with radius r and height h to approximate the surface area of this volcano before it erupted. (*Source:* Global Volcanism Network)

101. The owner of Knightime Video has determined that the demand equation for renting older released tapes is $F(x) = 0.6\sqrt{49 - x^2}$, where x is the price in dollars per two-day rental and $F(x)$ is the number of times the video is demanded per week.

   a. Approximate to one decimal place the demand per week of an older released video if the rental price is \$3 per two-day rental.

   b. Approximate to one decimal place the demand per week of an older released video if the rental price is \$5 per two-day rental.

   c. Explain how the owner of the video store can use this equation to predict the number of copies of each tape that should be in stock.

Objective **A** Adding or Subtracting Radical Expressions

We have learned that the sum or difference of like terms can be simplified. To simplify these sums or differences, we use the distributive property. For example,

$$2x + 3x = (2 + 3)x = 5x$$

The distributive property can also be used to add *like radicals*.

Like Radicals

Radicals with the same index and the same radicand are **like radicals.** The example below shows how to use the distributive property to simplify an expression containing like radicals.

$$2\sqrt{7} + 3\sqrt{7} = (2 + 3)\sqrt{7} = 5\sqrt{7}$$

Like radicals

> **Helpful Hint**
>
> The expression
>
> $$5\sqrt{7} - 3\sqrt{6}$$
>
> does not contain like radicals and cannot be simplified further.

PRACTICE PROBLEMS 1–3

Add or subtract as indicated.
1. $5\sqrt{15} + 2\sqrt{15}$
2. $9\sqrt[3]{2y} - 15\sqrt[3]{2y}$
3. $6\sqrt{10} - 3\sqrt[3]{10}$

EXAMPLES Add or subtract as indicated.

1. $4\sqrt{11} + 8\sqrt{11} = (4 + 8)\sqrt{11} = 12\sqrt{11}$
2. $5\sqrt[3]{3x} - 7\sqrt[3]{3x} = (5 - 7)\sqrt[3]{3x} = -2\sqrt[3]{3x}$
3. $2\sqrt{7} + 2\sqrt[3]{7}$ This expression cannot be simplified since $2\sqrt{7}$ and $2\sqrt[3]{7}$ do not contain like radicals.

Work Practice Problems 1–3

✔ Concept Check True or false:

$$\sqrt{a} + \sqrt{b} = \sqrt{a + b}$$

Explain.

When adding or subtracting radicals, always check first to see whether any radicals can be simplified.

PRACTICE PROBLEMS 4–8

Add or subtract as indicated. Assume that all variables represent positive real numbers.

4. $\sqrt{50} + 5\sqrt{18}$
5. $\sqrt[3]{24} - 4\sqrt[3]{192} + \sqrt[3]{3}$
6. $\sqrt{20x} - 6\sqrt{16x} + \sqrt{45x}$
7. $\sqrt[4]{32} + \sqrt{32}$
8. $\sqrt[3]{8y^5} + \sqrt[3]{27y^5}$

EXAMPLES Add or subtract as indicated. Assume that all variables represent positive real numbers.

4. $\sqrt{20} + 2\sqrt{45} = \sqrt{4 \cdot 5} + 2\sqrt{9 \cdot 5}$ Factor 20 and 45.

$= \sqrt{4} \cdot \sqrt{5} + 2 \cdot \sqrt{9} \cdot \sqrt{5}$ Use the product rule.

$= 2 \cdot \sqrt{5} + 2 \cdot 3 \cdot \sqrt{5}$ Simplify $\sqrt{4}$ and $\sqrt{9}$.

$= 2\sqrt{5} + 6\sqrt{5}$ Add like radicals.

$= 8\sqrt{5}$

Answers
1. $7\sqrt{15}$, 2. $-6\sqrt[3]{2y}$,
3. $6\sqrt{10} - 3\sqrt[3]{10}$, 4. $20\sqrt{2}$,
5. $-13\sqrt[3]{3}$, 6. $5\sqrt{5x} - 24\sqrt{x}$,
7. $2\sqrt[4]{2} + 4\sqrt{2}$, 8. $5y\sqrt[3]{y^2}$

✔ Concept Check Answer
false; answers may vary

5. $\sqrt[3]{54} - 5\sqrt[3]{16} + \sqrt[3]{2}$

$= \sqrt[3]{27} \cdot \sqrt[3]{2} - 5 \cdot \sqrt[3]{8} \cdot \sqrt[3]{2} + \sqrt[3]{2}$ Factor and use the product rule.

$= 3 \cdot \sqrt[3]{2} - 5 \cdot 2 \cdot \sqrt[3]{2} + \sqrt[3]{2}$ Simplify $\sqrt[3]{27}$ and $\sqrt[3]{8}$.

$= 3\sqrt[3]{2} - 10\sqrt[3]{2} + \sqrt[3]{2}$ Write $5 \cdot 2$ as 10.

$= -6\sqrt[3]{2}$ Combine like radicals.

6. $\sqrt{27x} - 2\sqrt{9x} + \sqrt{72x}$

$= \sqrt{9} \cdot \sqrt{3x} - 2 \cdot \sqrt{9} \cdot \sqrt{x} + \sqrt{36} \cdot \sqrt{2x}$ Factor and use the product rule.

$= 3 \cdot \sqrt{3x} - 2 \cdot 3 \cdot \sqrt{x} + 6 \cdot \sqrt{2x}$ Simplify $\sqrt{9}$ and $\sqrt{36}$.

$= 3\sqrt{3x} - 6\sqrt{x} + 6\sqrt{2x}$ Write $2 \cdot 3$ as 6.

> **Helpful Hint**
>
> None of these terms contain like radicals. We can simplify no further.

7. $\sqrt[3]{98} + \sqrt{98} = \sqrt[3]{98} + \sqrt{49} \cdot \sqrt{2}$ Factor and use the product rule.

$= \sqrt[3]{98} + 7\sqrt{2}$ No further simplification is possible.

8. $\sqrt[3]{48y^4} + \sqrt[3]{6y^4} = \sqrt[3]{8y^3} \cdot \sqrt[3]{6y} + \sqrt[3]{y^3} \cdot \sqrt[3]{6y}$ Factor and use the product rule.

$= 2y\sqrt[3]{6y} + y\sqrt[3]{6y}$ Simplify $\sqrt[3]{8y^3}$ and $\sqrt[3]{y^3}$.

$= 3y\sqrt[3]{6y}$ Combine like radicals.

▢ **Work Practice Problems 4–8**

EXAMPLES   Add or subtract as indicated. Assume that all variables represent positive real numbers.

9. $\dfrac{\sqrt{45}}{4} - \dfrac{\sqrt{5}}{3} = \dfrac{3\sqrt{5}}{4} - \dfrac{\sqrt{5}}{3}$ To subtract, notice that the LCD is 12.

$= \dfrac{3\sqrt{5} \cdot 3}{4 \cdot 3} - \dfrac{\sqrt{5} \cdot 4}{3 \cdot 4}$ Write each expression as an equivalent expression with a denominator of 12.

$= \dfrac{9\sqrt{5}}{12} - \dfrac{4\sqrt{5}}{12}$ Multiply factors in the numerators and the denominators.

$= \dfrac{5\sqrt{5}}{12}$ Subtract.

10. $\sqrt[3]{\dfrac{7x}{8}} + 2\sqrt[3]{7x} = \dfrac{\sqrt[3]{7x}}{\sqrt[3]{8}} + 2\sqrt[3]{7x}$ Use the quotient rule for radicals.

$= \dfrac{\sqrt[3]{7x}}{2} + 2\sqrt[3]{7x}$ Simplify.

$= \dfrac{\sqrt[3]{7x}}{2} + \dfrac{2\sqrt[3]{7x} \cdot 2}{2}$ Write each expression as an equivalent expression with a denominator of 2.

$= \dfrac{\sqrt[3]{7x}}{2} + \dfrac{4\sqrt[3]{7x}}{2}$

$= \dfrac{5\sqrt[3]{7x}}{2}$ Add.

▢ **Work Practice Problems 9–10**

PRACTICE PROBLEMS 9–10

Add or subtract as indicated. Assume that all variables represent positive real numbers.

9. $\dfrac{\sqrt{75}}{9} - \dfrac{\sqrt{3}}{2}$

10. $\sqrt[3]{\dfrac{5x}{27}} + 4\sqrt[3]{5x}$

Answers

9. $\dfrac{\sqrt{3}}{18}$,   **10.** $\dfrac{13\sqrt[3]{5x}}{3}$

Objective **B** Multiplying Radical Expressions

We can multiply radical expressions by using many of the same properties used to multiply polynomial expressions. For instance, to multiply $\sqrt{2}(\sqrt{6} - 3\sqrt{2})$, we use the distributive property and multiply $\sqrt{2}$ by each term inside the parentheses.

$$\sqrt{2}(\sqrt{6} - 3\sqrt{2}) = \sqrt{2}(\sqrt{6}) - \sqrt{2}(3\sqrt{2}) \qquad \text{Use the distributive property.}$$
$$= \sqrt{2 \cdot 6} - 3\sqrt{2 \cdot 2}$$
$$= \sqrt{2 \cdot 2 \cdot 3} - 3 \cdot 2 \qquad \text{Use the product rule for radicals.}$$
$$= 2\sqrt{3} - 6$$

PRACTICE PROBLEM 11

Multiply: $\sqrt{2}(6 + \sqrt{10})$

EXAMPLE 11 Multiply: $\sqrt{3}(5 + \sqrt{30})$

Solution:

$$\sqrt{3}(5 + \sqrt{30}) = \sqrt{3}(5) + \sqrt{3}(\sqrt{30})$$
$$= 5\sqrt{3} + \sqrt{3 \cdot 30}$$
$$= 5\sqrt{3} + \sqrt{3 \cdot 3 \cdot 10}$$
$$= 5\sqrt{3} + 3\sqrt{10}$$

Work Practice Problem 11

PRACTICE PROBLEMS 12–15

Multiply. Assume that all variables represent positive real numbers.

12. $(\sqrt{3} - \sqrt{5})(\sqrt{2} + 7)$
13. $(\sqrt{5y} + 2)(\sqrt{5y} - 2)$
14. $(\sqrt{3} - 7)^2$
15. $(\sqrt{x + 1} + 2)^2$

EXAMPLES Multiply. Assume that all variables represent positive real numbers.

12.
$$\overset{\text{First}}{} \quad \overset{\text{Outer}}{} \quad \overset{\text{Inner}}{} \quad \overset{\text{Last}}{}$$
$$(\sqrt{5} - \sqrt{6})(\sqrt{7} + 1) = \sqrt{5} \cdot \sqrt{7} + \sqrt{5} \cdot 1 - \sqrt{6} \cdot \sqrt{7} - \sqrt{6} \cdot 1$$
$$\text{Using the FOIL order.}$$
$$= \sqrt{35} + \sqrt{5} - \sqrt{42} - \sqrt{6} \qquad \text{Simplify.}$$

13. $(\sqrt{2x} + 5)(\sqrt{2x} - 5) = (\sqrt{2x})^2 - 5^2 \qquad$ Multiply the sum and difference of two terms: $(a + b)(a - b) = a^2 - b^2$
$$= 2x - 25$$

14. $(\sqrt{3} - 1)^2 = (\sqrt{3})^2 - 2 \cdot \sqrt{3} \cdot 1 + 1^2 \qquad$ Square the binomial:
$$= 3 - 2\sqrt{3} + 1 \qquad (a - b)^2 = a^2 - 2ab + b^2$$
$$= 4 - 2\sqrt{3} \qquad \text{Square the binomial:}$$
$$(a + b)^2 = a^2 + 2ab + b^2$$

15. $(\underset{\underset{a}{\uparrow}}{\sqrt{x - 3}} + \underset{\underset{b}{\uparrow}}{5})^2 = \underset{\underset{a^2}{\uparrow}}{(\sqrt{x - 3})^2} + \underset{\underset{+ \, 2 \, \cdot}{\uparrow \uparrow}}{2 \cdot} \underset{\underset{a}{\uparrow}}{\sqrt{x - 3}} \cdot \underset{\underset{\cdot \, b + b^2}{\uparrow \quad \uparrow}}{5 + 5^2}$
$$= x - 3 + 10\sqrt{x - 3} + 25 \qquad \text{Simplify.}$$
$$= x + 22 + 10\sqrt{x - 3} \qquad \text{Combine like terms.}$$

Work Practice Problems 12–15

Answers

11. $6\sqrt{2} + 2\sqrt{5}$,
12. $\sqrt{6} + 7\sqrt{3} - \sqrt{10} - 7\sqrt{5}$,
13. $5y - 4$, 14. $52 - 14\sqrt{3}$,
15. $x + 5 + 4\sqrt{x + 1}$

Mental Math

Simplify. Assume that all variables represent positive real numbers.

1. $2\sqrt{3} + 4\sqrt{3}$

2. $5\sqrt{7} + 3\sqrt{7}$

3. $8\sqrt{x} - 5\sqrt{x}$

4. $3\sqrt{y} + 10\sqrt{y}$

5. $7\sqrt[3]{x} + 5\sqrt[3]{x}$

6. $8\sqrt[3]{z} - 2\sqrt[3]{z}$

7. $(\sqrt{3})^2$

8. $(\sqrt{4x+1})^2$

7.4 EXERCISE SET

 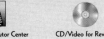

Objective Ⓐ *Add or subtract as indicated. Assume that all variables represent positive real numbers. See Examples 1 through 10.*

1. $\sqrt{8} - \sqrt{32}$

2. $\sqrt{27} - \sqrt{75}$

3. $2\sqrt{2x^3} + 4x\sqrt{8x}$

4. $3\sqrt{45x^3} + x\sqrt{5x}$

5. $2\sqrt{50} - 3\sqrt{125} + \sqrt{98}$

6. $4\sqrt{32} - \sqrt{18} + 2\sqrt{128}$

7. $\sqrt[3]{16x} - \sqrt[3]{54x}$

8. $2\sqrt[3]{3a^4} - 3a\sqrt[3]{81a}$

9. $\sqrt{9b^3} - \sqrt{25b^3} + \sqrt{49b^3}$

10. $\sqrt{4x^7} + 9x^2\sqrt{x^3} - 5x\sqrt{x^5}$

11. $\dfrac{5\sqrt{2}}{3} + \dfrac{2\sqrt{2}}{5}$

12. $\dfrac{\sqrt{3}}{2} + \dfrac{4\sqrt{3}}{3}$

13. $\sqrt[3]{\dfrac{11}{8}} - \dfrac{\sqrt[3]{11}}{6}$

14. $\dfrac{2\sqrt[3]{4}}{7} - \dfrac{\sqrt[3]{4}}{14}$

15. $\dfrac{\sqrt{20x}}{9} + \sqrt{\dfrac{5x}{9}}$

16. $\dfrac{3x\sqrt{7}}{5} + \sqrt{\dfrac{7x^2}{100}}$

17. $7\sqrt{9} - 7 + \sqrt{3}$

18. $\sqrt{16} - 5\sqrt{10} + 7$

19. $2 + 3\sqrt{y^2} - 6\sqrt{y^2} + 5$

20. $3\sqrt{7} - \sqrt[3]{x} + 4\sqrt{7} - 3\sqrt[3]{x}$

21. $3\sqrt{108} - 2\sqrt{18} - 3\sqrt{48}$

22. $-\sqrt{75} + \sqrt{12} - 3\sqrt{3}$

23. $-5\sqrt[3]{625} + \sqrt[3]{40}$

24. $-2\sqrt[3]{108} - \sqrt[3]{32}$

25. $\sqrt{9b^3} - \sqrt{25b^3} + \sqrt{16b^3}$

26. $\sqrt{4x^7y^5} + 9x^2\sqrt{x^3y^5} - 5xy\sqrt{x^5y^3}$

27. $5y\sqrt{8y} + 2\sqrt{50y^3}$

28. $3\sqrt{8x^2y^3} - 2x\sqrt{32y^3}$

29. $\sqrt[3]{54xy^3} - 5\sqrt[3]{2xy^3} + y\sqrt[3]{128x}$

30. $2\sqrt[3]{24x^3y^4} + 4x\sqrt[3]{81y^4}$

31. $6\sqrt[3]{11} + 8\sqrt{11} - 12\sqrt{11}$

32. $3\sqrt[3]{5} + 4\sqrt{5}$

33. $-2\sqrt[4]{x^7} + 3\sqrt[4]{16x^7}$

34. $6\sqrt[3]{24x^3} - 2\sqrt[3]{81x^3} - x\sqrt[3]{3}$

35. $\dfrac{4\sqrt{3}}{3} - \dfrac{\sqrt{12}}{3}$

36. $\dfrac{\sqrt{45}}{10} + \dfrac{7\sqrt{5}}{10}$

37. $\dfrac{\sqrt[3]{8x^4}}{7} + \dfrac{3x\sqrt[3]{x}}{7}$

38. $\dfrac{\sqrt[4]{48}}{5x} - \dfrac{2\sqrt[4]{3}}{10x}$

39. $\sqrt{\dfrac{28}{x^2}} + \sqrt{\dfrac{7}{4x^2}}$

40. $\dfrac{\sqrt{99}}{5x} - \sqrt{\dfrac{44}{x^2}}$

41. $\sqrt[3]{\dfrac{16}{27}} - \dfrac{\sqrt[3]{54}}{6}$

42. $\dfrac{\sqrt[3]{3}}{10} + \sqrt[3]{\dfrac{24}{125}}$

43. $-\dfrac{\sqrt[3]{2x^4}}{9} + \sqrt[3]{\dfrac{250x^4}{27}}$

44. $\dfrac{\sqrt[3]{y^5}}{8} + \dfrac{5y\sqrt[3]{y^2}}{4}$

45. Find the perimeter of the trapezoid.

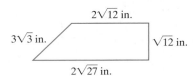

$2\sqrt{12}$ in.

$3\sqrt{3}$ in. $\sqrt{12}$ in.

$2\sqrt{27}$ in.

46. Find the perimeter of the triangle.

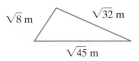

$\sqrt{8}$ m $\sqrt{32}$ m

$\sqrt{45}$ m

Objective Ⓑ *Multiply. Then simplify if possible. Assume that all variables represent positive real numbers. See Examples 11 through 15.*

47. $\sqrt{7}(\sqrt{5} + \sqrt{3})$

48. $\sqrt{5}(\sqrt{15} - \sqrt{35})$

49. $(\sqrt{5} - \sqrt{2})^2$

50. $(3x - \sqrt{2})(3x - \sqrt{2})$

51. $\sqrt{3x}(\sqrt{3} - \sqrt{x})$

52. $\sqrt{5y}(\sqrt{y} + \sqrt{5})$

53. $(2\sqrt{x} - 5)(3\sqrt{x} + 1)$

54. $(8\sqrt{y} + z)(4\sqrt{y} - 1)$

55. $(\sqrt[3]{a} - 4)(\sqrt[3]{a} + 5)$

56. $(\sqrt[3]{a} + 2)(\sqrt[3]{a} + 7)$

57. $6(\sqrt{2} - 2)$

58. $\sqrt{5}(6 - \sqrt{5})$

59. $\sqrt{2}(\sqrt{2} + x\sqrt{6})$

60. $\sqrt{3}(\sqrt{3} - 2\sqrt{5x})$

61. $(2\sqrt{7} + 3\sqrt{5})(\sqrt{7} - 2\sqrt{5})$

62. $(\sqrt{6} - 4\sqrt{2})(3\sqrt{6} + 1)$

63. $(\sqrt{x} - y)(\sqrt{x} + y)$

64. $(3\sqrt{x} + 2)(\sqrt{3x} - 2)$

65. $(\sqrt{3} + x)^2$

66. $(\sqrt{y} - 3x)^2$

67. $(\sqrt{5x} - 3\sqrt{2})(\sqrt{5x} - 3\sqrt{3})$

68. $(5\sqrt{3x} - \sqrt{y})(4\sqrt{x} + 1)$

69. $(\sqrt[3]{4} + 2)(\sqrt[3]{2} - 1)$

70. $(\sqrt[3]{3} + \sqrt[3]{2})(\sqrt[3]{9} - \sqrt[3]{4})$

71. $(\sqrt[3]{x} + 1)(\sqrt[3]{x} - 4\sqrt{x} + 7)$

72. $(\sqrt[3]{3x} + 3)(\sqrt[3]{2x} - 3x - 1)$

73. $(\sqrt{x - 1} + 5)^2$

74. $(\sqrt{3x + 1} + 2)^2$

75. $(\sqrt{2x + 5} - 1)^2$

76. $(\sqrt{x - 6} - 7)^2$

Review

Factor each numerator and denominator. Then simplify if possible. See Section 6.1.

77. $\dfrac{2x - 14}{2}$

78. $\dfrac{8x - 24y}{4}$

79. $\dfrac{7x - 7y}{x^2 - y^2}$

80. $\dfrac{x^3 - 8}{4x - 8}$

81. $\dfrac{6a^2b - 9ab}{3ab}$

82. $\dfrac{14r - 28r^2s^2}{7rs}$

83. $\dfrac{-4 + 2\sqrt{3}}{6}$

84. $\dfrac{-5 + 10\sqrt{7}}{5}$

Concept Extensions

△ **85.** Find the perimeter and area of the rectangle.

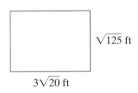

$\sqrt{125}$ ft

$3\sqrt{20}$ ft

△ **86.** Find the area and perimeter of the trapezoid. (*Hint:* The area of a trapezoid is the product of half the height $6\sqrt{3}$ meters and the sum of the bases $2\sqrt{63}$ and $7\sqrt{7}$ meters.)

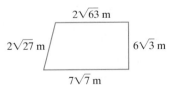

$2\sqrt{63}$ m

$2\sqrt{27}$ m

$6\sqrt{3}$ m

$7\sqrt{7}$ m

87. **a.** Add: $\sqrt{3} + \sqrt{3}$
   b. Multiply: $\sqrt{3} \cdot \sqrt{3}$
   c. Describe the differences in parts a and b.

88. Multiply: $(\sqrt{2} + \sqrt{3} - 1)^2$

STUDY SKILLS BUILDER

Have You Decided to Successfully Complete this Course?

Hopefully by now, one of your current goals is to successfully complete this course.

If it is not a goal of yours, ask yourself why? One common reason is fear of failure. Amazingly enough, fear of failure alone can be strong enough to keep many of us from doing our best in any endeavor. Another common reason is that you simply haven't taken the time to make successfully completing this course one of your goals.

Anytime you are registered for a course, successfully completing this course should probably be a goal. How do you do this? Start by writing this goal in your mathematics notebook. Then list steps you will take to ensure success. A great first step is to read or reread Section 1.1 and make a commitment to try the suggestions in this section.

Good luck and don't forget that a positive attitude will make a big difference.

Let's see how you are doing.

1. Have you made the decision to make "successfully completing this course" a goal of yours? If not, please

list reasons that this has not happened. Study your list and talk to your instructor about this.

2. If your answer to Exercise 1 is yes, take a moment and list, in your notebook, further specific goals that will help you achieve this major goal of successfully completing this course. (For example, my goal this semester is not to miss any of my mathematics classes.)

3. Rate your commitment to this course with a number between 1 and 5. Use the diagram below to help.

High Commitment		Average Commitment		Not Committed at All
5	4	3	2	1

4. If you have rated your personal commitment level (from the exercise above) as a 1, 2, or 3, list the reasons why this is so. Then determine whether it is possible to increase your commitment level to a 4 or 5.

RATIONALIZING NUMERATORS AND DENOMINATORS OF RADICAL EXPRESSIONS

Objective **A** Rationalizing Denominators

Often in mathematics it is helpful to write a radical expression such as $\dfrac{\sqrt{3}}{\sqrt{2}}$ either without a radical in the denominator or without a radical in the numerator. The process of writing this expression as an equivalent expression but without a radical in the denominator is called **rationalizing the denominator.** To rationalize the denominator of $\dfrac{\sqrt{3}}{\sqrt{2}}$, we multiply the numerator and the denominator by $\sqrt{2}$. Recall that this is the same as multiplying by $\dfrac{\sqrt{2}}{\sqrt{2}}$, which simplifies to 1.

$$\frac{\sqrt{3}}{\sqrt{2}} = \frac{\sqrt{3}\cdot\sqrt{2}}{\sqrt{2}\cdot\sqrt{2}} = \frac{\sqrt{6}}{\sqrt{4}} = \frac{\sqrt{6}}{2}$$

EXAMPLE 1 Rationalize the denominator of $\dfrac{2}{\sqrt{5}}$.

Solution: To rationalize the denominator, we multiply the numerator and denominator by a factor that makes the radicand in the denominator a perfect square.

$$\frac{2}{\sqrt{5}} = \frac{2\cdot\sqrt{5}}{\sqrt{5}\cdot\sqrt{5}} = \frac{2\sqrt{5}}{5} \quad \text{The denominator is now rationalized.}$$

▧ **Work Practice Problem 1**

EXAMPLE 2 Rationalize the denominator of $\dfrac{2\sqrt{16}}{\sqrt{9x}}$.

Solution: First we simplify the radicals; then we rationalize the denominator.

$$\frac{2\sqrt{16}}{\sqrt{9x}} = \frac{2(4)}{\sqrt{9}\cdot\sqrt{x}} = \frac{8}{3\sqrt{x}}$$

To rationalize the denominator, we multiply the numerator and the denominator by $\sqrt{x}$.

$$\frac{8}{3\sqrt{x}} = \frac{8\cdot\sqrt{x}}{3\sqrt{x}\cdot\sqrt{x}} = \frac{8\sqrt{x}}{3x}$$

▧ **Work Practice Problem 2**

EXAMPLE 3 Rationalize the denominator of $\sqrt[3]{\dfrac{1}{2}}$.

Solution: $\sqrt[3]{\dfrac{1}{2}} = \dfrac{\sqrt[3]{1}}{\sqrt[3]{2}} = \dfrac{1}{\sqrt[3]{2}}$

Now we rationalize the denominator. Since $\sqrt[3]{2}$ is a cube root, we want to multiply by a value that will make the radicand 2 a perfect cube. If we multiply by $\sqrt[3]{2^2}$, we get $\sqrt[3]{2^3} = 2$. Thus,

$$\frac{1\cdot\sqrt[3]{2^2}}{\sqrt[3]{2}\cdot\sqrt[3]{2^2}} = \frac{\sqrt[3]{4}}{\sqrt[3]{2^3}} = \frac{\sqrt[3]{4}}{2} \quad \text{Multiply numerator and denominator by } \sqrt[3]{2^2} \text{ and then simplify.}$$

▧ **Work Practice Problem 3**

PRACTICE PROBLEM 1

Rationalize the denominator of $\dfrac{7}{\sqrt{2}}$.

PRACTICE PROBLEM 2

Rationalize the denominator of $\dfrac{2\sqrt{9}}{\sqrt{16y}}$.

PRACTICE PROBLEM 3

Rationalize the denominator of $\sqrt[3]{\dfrac{2}{25}}$.

Answers

1. $\dfrac{7\sqrt{2}}{2}$, 2. $\dfrac{3\sqrt{y}}{2y}$, 3. $\dfrac{\sqrt[3]{10}}{5}$

✔ **Concept Check** Determine by which number both the numerator and denominator should be multiplied to rationalize the denominator of the radical expression.

a. $\dfrac{1}{\sqrt[3]{7}}$　　**b.** $\dfrac{1}{\sqrt[4]{8}}$

PRACTICE PROBLEM 4

Rationalize the denominator of $\sqrt{\dfrac{5m}{11n}}$. Assume that all variables represent positive real numbers.

EXAMPLE 4 Rationalize the denominator of $\sqrt{\dfrac{7x}{3y}}$. Assume that all variables represent positive real numbers.

Solution:

$$\sqrt{\dfrac{7x}{3y}} = \dfrac{\sqrt{7x}}{\sqrt{3y}}$$ 　　Use the quotient rule. No radical may be simplified further.

$$= \dfrac{\sqrt{7x}\cdot\sqrt{3y}}{\sqrt{3y}\cdot\sqrt{3y}}$$ 　　Multiply numerator and denominator by $\sqrt{3y}$ so that the radicand in the denominator is a perfect square.

$$= \dfrac{\sqrt{21xy}}{3y}$$ 　　Use the product rule in the numerator and denominator. Remember that $\sqrt{3y}\cdot\sqrt{3y} = 3y$.

▣ **Work Practice Problem 4**

PRACTICE PROBLEM 5

Rationalize the denominator of $\dfrac{\sqrt[5]{a^2}}{\sqrt[5]{32b^{12}}}$. Assume that all variables represent positive real numbers.

EXAMPLE 5 Rationalize the denominator of $\dfrac{\sqrt[4]{x}}{\sqrt[4]{81y^5}}$. Assume that all variables represent positive real numbers.

Solution: First we simplify each radical if possible.

$$\dfrac{\sqrt[4]{x}}{\sqrt[4]{81y^5}} = \dfrac{\sqrt[4]{x}}{\sqrt[4]{81y^4}\cdot\sqrt[4]{y}}$$ 　　Use the product rule in the denominator.

$$= \dfrac{\sqrt[4]{x}}{3y\sqrt[4]{y}}$$ 　　Write $\sqrt[4]{81y^4}$ as $3y$.

$$= \dfrac{\sqrt[4]{x}\cdot\sqrt[4]{y^3}}{3y\sqrt[4]{y}\cdot\sqrt[4]{y^3}}$$ 　　Multiply numerator and denominator by $\sqrt[4]{y^3}$ so that the radicand in the denominator is a perfect 4th power.

$$= \dfrac{\sqrt[4]{xy^3}}{3y\sqrt[4]{y^4}}$$ 　　Use the product rule in the numerator and denominator.

$$= \dfrac{\sqrt[4]{xy^3}}{3y^2}$$ 　　In the denominator, $\sqrt[4]{y^4} = y$ and $3y\cdot y = 3y^2$.

▣ **Work Practice Problem 5**

Objective B Rationalizing Denominators Having Two Terms

Remember the product of the sum and difference of two terms?

$$(a + b)(a - b) = a^2 - b^2$$

These two expressions are called **conjugates** of each other.

Answers

4. $\dfrac{\sqrt{55mn}}{11n}$, 　**5.** $\dfrac{\sqrt[5]{a^2b^3}}{2b^3}$

✔ **Concept Check Answers**

a. $\sqrt[3]{7^2}$ or $\sqrt[3]{49}$, 　b. $\sqrt[4]{2}$

To rationalize a denominator that is a sum or difference of two terms, we use conjugates. To see how and why this works, let's rationalize the denominator of the expression $\dfrac{5}{\sqrt{3} - 2}$. To do so, we multiply both the numerator and the denominator by $\sqrt{3} + 2$, the *conjugate* of the denominator $\sqrt{3} - 2$, and see what happens.

$$\frac{5}{\sqrt{3} - 2} = \frac{5(\sqrt{3} + 2)}{(\sqrt{3} - 2)(\sqrt{3} + 2)}$$

$$= \frac{5(\sqrt{3} + 2)}{(\sqrt{3})^2 - 2^2} \qquad \text{Multiply the sum and difference of two terms:}$$
$$\qquad\qquad\qquad\qquad (a + b)(a - b) = a^2 - b^2.$$

$$= \frac{5(\sqrt{3} + 2)}{3 - 4}$$

$$= \frac{5(\sqrt{3} + 2)}{-1}$$

$$= -5(\sqrt{3} + 2) \quad \text{or} \quad -5\sqrt{3} - 10$$

Notice in the denominator that the product of $(\sqrt{3} - 2)$ and its conjugate, $(\sqrt{3} + 2)$, is -1. In general, the product of an expression and its conjugate will contain no radical terms. This is why, when rationalizing a denominator or a numerator containing two terms, we multiply by its conjugate. Examples of conjugates are

$$\sqrt{a} - \sqrt{b} \quad \text{and} \quad \sqrt{a} + \sqrt{b}$$
$$x + \sqrt{y} \quad \text{and} \quad x - \sqrt{y}$$

EXAMPLE 6 Rationalize the denominator of $\dfrac{2}{3\sqrt{2} + 4}$.

Solution: We multiply the numerator and the denominator by the conjugate of $3\sqrt{2} + 4$.

$$\frac{2}{3\sqrt{2} + 4} = \frac{2(3\sqrt{2} - 4)}{(3\sqrt{2} + 4)(3\sqrt{2} - 4)}$$

$$= \frac{2(3\sqrt{2} - 4)}{(3\sqrt{2})^2 - 4^2} \qquad \text{Multiply the sum and difference}$$
$$\qquad\qquad\qquad\qquad \text{of two terms: } (a + b)(a - b) = a^2 - b^2.$$

$$= \frac{2(3\sqrt{2} - 4)}{18 - 16} \qquad \text{Write } (3\sqrt{2})^2 \text{ as } 9 \cdot 2 \text{ or } 18 \text{ and } 4^2 \text{ as } 16.$$

$$= \frac{2(3\sqrt{2} - 4)}{2} = 3\sqrt{2} - 4$$

■ **Work Practice Problem 6**

As we saw in Example 6, it is often helpful to leave a numerator in factored form to help determine whether the expression can be simplified.

PRACTICE PROBLEM 6

Rationalize the denominator of $\dfrac{3}{2\sqrt{5} + 1}$.

PRACTICE PROBLEM 7

Rationalize the denominator

of $\dfrac{\sqrt{5} + 3}{\sqrt{3} - \sqrt{2}}$.

EXAMPLE 7 Rationalize the denominator of $\dfrac{\sqrt{6} + 2}{\sqrt{5} - \sqrt{3}}$.

Solution: We multiply the numerator and the denominator by the conjugate of $\sqrt{5} - \sqrt{3}$.

$$\frac{\sqrt{6} + 2}{\sqrt{5} - \sqrt{3}} = \frac{(\sqrt{6} + 2)(\sqrt{5} + \sqrt{3})}{(\sqrt{5} - \sqrt{3})(\sqrt{5} + \sqrt{3})}$$

$$= \frac{\sqrt{6}\sqrt{5} + \sqrt{6}\sqrt{3} + 2\sqrt{5} + 2\sqrt{3}}{(\sqrt{5})^2 - (\sqrt{3})^2}$$

$$= \frac{\sqrt{30} + \sqrt{18} + 2\sqrt{5} + 2\sqrt{3}}{5 - 3}$$

$$= \frac{\sqrt{30} + 3\sqrt{2} + 2\sqrt{5} + 2\sqrt{3}}{2}$$

▣ **Work Practice Problem 7**

PRACTICE PROBLEM 8

Rationalize the denominator

of $\dfrac{3}{2 - \sqrt{x}}$. Assume that all

variables represent positive
real numbers.

EXAMPLE 8 Rationalize the denominator of $\dfrac{2\sqrt{m}}{3\sqrt{x} + \sqrt{m}}$. Assume that all variables represent positive real numbers.

Solution: We multiply by the conjugate of $3\sqrt{x} + \sqrt{m}$ to eliminate the radicals from the denominator.

$$\frac{2\sqrt{m}}{3\sqrt{x} + \sqrt{m}} = \frac{2\sqrt{m}(3\sqrt{x} - \sqrt{m})}{(3\sqrt{x} + \sqrt{m})(3\sqrt{x} - \sqrt{m})} = \frac{6\sqrt{mx} - 2m}{(3\sqrt{x})^2 - (\sqrt{m})^2}$$

$$= \frac{6\sqrt{mx} - 2m}{9x - m}$$

▣ **Work Practice Problem 8**

Objective **C** Rationalizing Numerators

As mentioned earlier, it is also often helpful to write an expression such as $\dfrac{\sqrt{3}}{\sqrt{2}}$ as an equivalent expression without a radical in the numerator. This process is called **rationalizing the numerator.** To rationalize the numerator of $\dfrac{\sqrt{3}}{\sqrt{2}}$, we multiply the numerator and the denominator by $\sqrt{3}$.

$$\frac{\sqrt{3}}{\sqrt{2}} = \frac{\sqrt{3} \cdot \sqrt{3}}{\sqrt{2} \cdot \sqrt{3}} = \frac{\sqrt{9}}{\sqrt{6}} = \frac{3}{\sqrt{6}}$$

PRACTICE PROBLEM 9

Rationalize the numerator

of $\dfrac{\sqrt{18}}{\sqrt{75}}$.

EXAMPLE 9 Rationalize the numerator of $\dfrac{\sqrt{7}}{\sqrt{45}}$.

Solution: First we simplify $\sqrt{45}$.

$$\frac{\sqrt{7}}{\sqrt{45}} = \frac{\sqrt{7}}{\sqrt{9 \cdot 5}} = \frac{\sqrt{7}}{3\sqrt{5}}$$

Next we rationalize the numerator by multiplying the numerator and the denominator by $\sqrt{7}$.

$$\frac{\sqrt{7}}{3\sqrt{5}} = \frac{\sqrt{7} \cdot \sqrt{7}}{3\sqrt{5} \cdot \sqrt{7}} = \frac{7}{3\sqrt{5 \cdot 7}} = \frac{7}{3\sqrt{35}}$$

▣ **Work Practice Problem 9**

Answers

7. $\sqrt{15} + \sqrt{10} + 3\sqrt{3} + 3\sqrt{2}$,

8. $\dfrac{6 + 3\sqrt{x}}{4 - x}$,   **9.** $\dfrac{6}{5\sqrt{6}}$

EXAMPLE 10 Rationalize the numerator of $\dfrac{\sqrt[3]{2x^2}}{\sqrt[3]{5y}}$.

Solution:

$$\dfrac{\sqrt[3]{2x^2}}{\sqrt[3]{5y}} = \dfrac{\sqrt[3]{2x^2} \cdot \sqrt[3]{2^2x}}{\sqrt[3]{5y} \cdot \sqrt[3]{2^2x}}$$ Multiply the numerator and denominator by $\sqrt[3]{2^2x}$ so that the radicand in the numerator is a perfect cube.

$$= \dfrac{\sqrt[3]{2^3x^3}}{\sqrt[3]{5y \cdot 2^2x}}$$ Use the product rule in the numerator and denominator.

$$= \dfrac{2x}{\sqrt[3]{20xy}}$$ Simplify.

🔲 **Work Practice Problem 10**

PRACTICE PROBLEM 10

Rationalize the numerator of $\dfrac{\sqrt[3]{3a}}{\sqrt[3]{7b}}$.

Just as for denominators, to rationalize a numerator that is a sum or difference of two terms, we use conjugates.

EXAMPLE 11 Rationalize the numerator of $\dfrac{\sqrt{x} + 2}{5}$. Assume that all variables represent positive real numbers.

Solution: We multiply the numerator and the denominator by the conjugate of $\sqrt{x} + 2$, the numerator.

$$\dfrac{\sqrt{x} + 2}{5} = \dfrac{(\sqrt{x} + 2)(\sqrt{x} - 2)}{5(\sqrt{x} - 2)}$$ Multiply by $\sqrt{x} - 2$, the conjugate of $\sqrt{x} + 2$.

$$= \dfrac{(\sqrt{x})^2 - 2^2}{5(\sqrt{x} - 2)}$$ $(a + b)(a - b) = a^2 - b^2$.

$$= \dfrac{x - 4}{5(\sqrt{x} - 2)}$$

🔲 **Work Practice Problem 11**

PRACTICE PROBLEM 11

Rationalize the numerator of $\dfrac{\sqrt{x} + 5}{3}$. Assume that all variables represent positive real numbers.

Answers

10. $\dfrac{3a}{\sqrt[3]{63a^2b}}$, **11.** $\dfrac{x - 25}{3(\sqrt{x} - 5)}$

Mental Math

Find the conjugate of each expression.

1. $\sqrt{2} + x$

2. $\sqrt{3} + y$

3. $5 - \sqrt{a}$

4. $6 - \sqrt{b}$

5. $7\sqrt{4} + 8\sqrt{x}$

6. $9\sqrt{2} - 6\sqrt{y}$

7.5 EXERCISE SET

Objective A *Rationalize each denominator. Assume that all variables represent positive real numbers. See Examples 1 through 5.*

1. $\dfrac{\sqrt{2}}{\sqrt{7}}$

2. $\dfrac{\sqrt{3}}{\sqrt{2}}$

3. $\sqrt{\dfrac{1}{5}}$

4. $\sqrt{\dfrac{1}{2}}$

5. $\dfrac{4}{\sqrt[3]{3}}$

6. $\dfrac{6}{\sqrt[3]{9}}$

7. $\dfrac{3}{\sqrt{8x}}$

8. $\dfrac{5}{\sqrt{27a}}$

9. $\dfrac{3}{\sqrt[3]{4x^2}}$

10. $\dfrac{5}{\sqrt[3]{3y}}$

11. $\dfrac{9}{\sqrt{3a}}$

12. $\dfrac{x}{\sqrt{5}}$

13. $\dfrac{3}{\sqrt[3]{2}}$

14. $\dfrac{5}{\sqrt[3]{9}}$

15. $\dfrac{2\sqrt{3}}{\sqrt{7}}$

16. $\dfrac{-5\sqrt{2}}{\sqrt{11}}$

17. $\sqrt{\dfrac{2x}{5y}}$

18. $\sqrt{\dfrac{13a}{2b}}$

19. $\sqrt[3]{\dfrac{3}{5}}$

20. $\sqrt[3]{\dfrac{7}{10}}$

21. $\sqrt{\dfrac{3x}{50}}$

22. $\sqrt{\dfrac{11y}{45}}$

23. $\dfrac{1}{\sqrt{12z}}$

24. $\dfrac{1}{\sqrt{32x}}$

25. $\dfrac{\sqrt[3]{2y^2}}{\sqrt[3]{9x^2}}$

26. $\dfrac{\sqrt[3]{3x}}{\sqrt[3]{4y^4}}$

27. $\sqrt[4]{\dfrac{16}{9x^7}}$

28. $\sqrt[5]{\dfrac{32}{m^6 n^{13}}}$

29. $\dfrac{5a}{\sqrt[5]{8a^9 b^{11}}}$

30. $\dfrac{9y}{\sqrt[4]{4y^9}}$

Objective B *Rationalize each denominator. Assume that all variables represent positive real numbers. See Examples 6 through 8.*

31. $\dfrac{6}{2 - \sqrt{7}}$

32. $\dfrac{3}{\sqrt{7} - 4}$

33. $\dfrac{-7}{\sqrt{x} - 3}$

34. $\dfrac{-8}{\sqrt{y} + 4}$

35. $\dfrac{\sqrt{2} - \sqrt{3}}{\sqrt{2} + \sqrt{3}}$

36. $\dfrac{\sqrt{3} + \sqrt{4}}{\sqrt{2} + \sqrt{3}}$

442

37. $\dfrac{\sqrt{a}+1}{2\sqrt{a}-\sqrt{b}}$

38. $\dfrac{2\sqrt{a}-3}{2\sqrt{a}-\sqrt{b}}$

39. $\dfrac{8}{1+\sqrt{10}}$

40. $\dfrac{-3}{\sqrt{6}-2}$

41. $\dfrac{\sqrt{x}}{\sqrt{x}+\sqrt{y}}$

42. $\dfrac{2\sqrt{a}}{2\sqrt{x}-\sqrt{y}}$

43. $\dfrac{2\sqrt{3}+\sqrt{6}}{4\sqrt{3}-\sqrt{6}}$

44. $\dfrac{4\sqrt{5}+\sqrt{2}}{2\sqrt{5}-\sqrt{2}}$

Objective **C** *Rationalize each numerator. Assume that all variables represent positive real numbers. See Examples 9 and 10.*

45. $\sqrt{\dfrac{5}{3}}$

46. $\sqrt{\dfrac{3}{2}}$

47. $\sqrt{\dfrac{18}{5}}$

48. $\sqrt{\dfrac{12}{7}}$

49. $\dfrac{\sqrt{4x}}{7}$

50. $\dfrac{\sqrt{3x^5}}{6}$

51. $\dfrac{\sqrt[3]{5y^2}}{\sqrt[3]{4x}}$

52. $\dfrac{\sqrt[3]{4x}}{\sqrt[3]{z^4}}$

53. $\sqrt{\dfrac{2}{5}}$

54. $\sqrt{\dfrac{3}{7}}$

55. $\dfrac{\sqrt{2x}}{11}$

56. $\dfrac{\sqrt{y}}{7}$

57. $\sqrt[3]{\dfrac{7}{8}}$

58. $\sqrt[3]{\dfrac{25}{2}}$

59. $\dfrac{\sqrt[3]{3x^5}}{10}$

60. $\sqrt[3]{\dfrac{9y}{7}}$

61. $\sqrt{\dfrac{18x^4y^6}{3z}}$

62. $\sqrt{\dfrac{8x^5y}{2z}}$

63. When rationalizing the denominator of $\dfrac{\sqrt{5}}{\sqrt{7}}$, explain why both the numerator and the denominator must be multiplied by $\sqrt{7}$.

64. When rationalizing the numerator of $\dfrac{\sqrt{5}}{\sqrt{7}}$, explain why both the numerator and the denominator must be multiplied by $\sqrt{5}$.

Rationalize each numerator. Assume that all variables represent positive real numbers. See Example 11.

65. $\dfrac{2-\sqrt{11}}{6}$

66. $\dfrac{\sqrt{15}+1}{2}$

67. $\dfrac{2-\sqrt{7}}{-5}$

68. $\dfrac{\sqrt{5}+2}{\sqrt{2}}$

69. $\dfrac{\sqrt{x}+3}{\sqrt{x}}$

70. $\dfrac{5+\sqrt{2}}{\sqrt{2x}}$

71. $\dfrac{\sqrt{x}+1}{\sqrt{x}-1}$

72. $\dfrac{\sqrt{x}+\sqrt{y}}{\sqrt{x}-\sqrt{y}}$

Review

Solve each equation. See Sections 2.1 and 5.7.

73. $2x - 7 = 3(x - 4)$

74. $9x - 4 = 7(x - 2)$

75. $(x - 6)(2x + 1) = 0$

76. $(y + 2)(5y + 4) = 0$

77. $x^2 - 8x = -12$

78. $x^3 = x$

Concept Extensions

△ **79.** The formula of the radius r of a sphere with surface area A is

$$r = \sqrt{\frac{A}{4\pi}}$$

Rationalize the denominator of the radical expression in this formula.

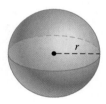

△ **80.** The formula for the radius r of a cone with height 7 centimeters and volume V is

$$r = \sqrt{\frac{3V}{7\pi}}$$

Rationalize the numerator of the radical expression in this formula.

81. Explain why rationalizing the denominator does not change the value of the original expression.

82. Explain why rationalizing the numerator does not change the value of the original expression.

Determine the smallest number both the numerator and denominator should by multiplied by to rationalize the denominator of the radical expression. See the Concept Check in this section.

83. $\dfrac{9}{\sqrt[3]{5}}$

84. $\dfrac{5}{\sqrt{27}}$

Radicals and Rational Exponents

Throughout this review, assume that all variables represent positive real numbers. Find each root.

1. $\sqrt{81}$

2. $\sqrt[3]{-8}$

3. $\sqrt[4]{\dfrac{1}{16}}$

4. $\sqrt{x^6}$

5. $\sqrt[3]{y^9}$

6. $\sqrt{4y^{10}}$

7. $\sqrt[5]{-32y^5}$

8. $\sqrt[4]{81b^{12}}$

Use radical notation to rewrite each expression. Simplify if possible.

9. $36^{1/2}$

10. $(3y)^{1/4}$

11. $64^{-2/3}$

12. $(x+1)^{3/5}$

Use the properties of exponents to simplify each expression. Write with positive exponents.

13. $y^{-1/6} \cdot y^{7/6}$

14. $\dfrac{(2x^{1/3})^4}{x^{5/6}}$

15. $\dfrac{x^{1/4}x^{3/4}}{x^{-1/4}}$

16. $4^{1/3} \cdot 4^{2/5}$

Use rational exponents to simplify each radical.

17. $\sqrt[3]{8x^6}$

18. $\sqrt[12]{a^9b^6}$

Use rational exponents to write each as a single radical expression.

19. $\sqrt[4]{x} \cdot \sqrt{x}$

20. $\sqrt{5} \cdot \sqrt[3]{2}$

Simplify.

21. $\sqrt{40}$

22. $\sqrt[4]{16x^7y^{10}}$

23. $\sqrt[3]{54x^4}$

24. $\sqrt[5]{-64b^{10}}$

1. _____
2. _____
3. _____
4. _____
5. _____
6. _____
7. _____
8. _____
9. _____
10. _____
11. _____
12. _____
13. _____
14. _____
15. _____
16. _____
17. _____
18. _____
19. _____
20. _____
21. _____
22. _____
23. _____
24. _____

25. _____

26. _____

27. _____

28. _____

29. _____

30. _____

31. _____

32. _____

33. _____

34. _____

35. _____

36. _____

37. _____

38. _____

39. _____

40. _____

Multiply or divide. Then simplify if possible.

25. $\sqrt{5} \cdot \sqrt{x}$

26. $\sqrt[3]{8x} \cdot \sqrt[3]{8x^2}$

27. $\dfrac{\sqrt{98y^6}}{\sqrt{2y}}$

28. $\dfrac{\sqrt[4]{48a^9b^3}}{\sqrt[4]{ab^3}}$

Perform each indicated operation.

29. $\sqrt{20} - \sqrt{75} + 5\sqrt{7}$

30. $\sqrt[3]{54y^4} - y\sqrt[3]{16y}$

31. $\sqrt{3}(\sqrt{5} - \sqrt{2})$

32. $(\sqrt{7} + \sqrt{3})^2$

33. $(2x - \sqrt{5})(2x + \sqrt{5})$

34. $(\sqrt{x+1} - 1)^2$

Rationalize each denominator.

35. $\sqrt{\dfrac{7}{3}}$

36. $\dfrac{5}{\sqrt[3]{2x^2}}$

37. $\dfrac{\sqrt{3} - \sqrt{7}}{2\sqrt{3} + \sqrt{7}}$

Rationalize each numerator.

38. $\sqrt{\dfrac{7}{3}}$

39. $\sqrt[3]{\dfrac{9y}{11}}$

40. $\dfrac{\sqrt{x} - 2}{\sqrt{x}}$

7.6 RADICAL EQUATIONS AND PROBLEM SOLVING

Objectives

A Solve Equations That Contain Radical Expressions.

B Use the Pythagorean Theorem to Model Problems.

Objective **A** Solving Equations That Contain Radical Expressions

In this section, we present techniques to solve equations containing radical expressions such as

$$\sqrt{2x - 3} = 9$$

We use the power rule to help us solve these radical equations.

Power Rule

If both sides of an equation are raised to the same power, *all* solutions of the original equation are *among* the solutions of the new equation.

This property *does not* say that raising both sides of an equation to a power yields an equivalent equation. A solution of the new equation *may* or *may not* be a solution of the original equation. Thus, *each solution of the new equation must be checked* to make sure it is a solution of the original equation. Recall that a proposed solution that is not a solution of the original equation is called an extraneous solution.

EXAMPLE 1 Solve: $\sqrt{2x - 3} = 9$

Solution: We use the power rule to square both sides of the equation to eliminate the radical.

$$\sqrt{2x - 3} = 9$$
$$(\sqrt{2x - 3})^2 = 9$$
$$2x - 3 = 81$$
$$2x = 84$$
$$x = 42$$

Now we check the solution in the original equation.

Check: $\sqrt{2x - 3} = 9$
$$\sqrt{2(42) - 3} \stackrel{?}{=} 9 \quad \text{Let } x = 42.$$
$$\sqrt{84 - 3} \stackrel{?}{=} 9$$
$$\sqrt{81} \stackrel{?}{=} 9$$
$$9 = 9 \quad \text{True}$$

The solution checks, so we conclude that the solution set is $\{42\}$.

■ **Work Practice Problem 1**

To solve a radical equation, first isolate a radical on one side of the equation.

PRACTICE PROBLEM 1

Solve: $\sqrt{3x - 2} = 5$

Answer

1. $\{9\}$

447

PRACTICE PROBLEM 2

Solve: $\sqrt{9x - 2} - 2x = 0$

EXAMPLE 2 Solve: $\sqrt{-10x - 1} + 3x = 0$

Solution: First we isolate the radical on one side of the equation. To do this, we subtract $3x$ from both sides.

$$\sqrt{-10x - 1} + 3x = 0$$
$$\sqrt{-10x - 1} + 3x - 3x = 0 - 3x$$
$$\sqrt{-10x - 1} = -3x$$

Next we use the power rule to eliminate the radical.

$$(\sqrt{-10x - 1})^2 = (-3x)^2$$
$$-10x - 1 = 9x^2$$

Since this is a quadratic equation, we can set the equation equal to 0 and try to solve by factoring.

$$9x^2 + 10x + 1 = 0$$
$$(9x + 1)(x + 1) = 0 \qquad \text{Factor.}$$
$$9x + 1 = 0 \quad \text{or} \quad x + 1 = 0 \quad \text{Set each factor equal to 0.}$$
$$x = -\frac{1}{9} \qquad\qquad x = -1$$

Check: Let $x = -\frac{1}{9}$.   Let $x = -1$.

$$\sqrt{-10x - 1} + 3x = 0 \qquad\qquad \sqrt{-10x - 1} + 3x = 0$$
$$\sqrt{-10\left(-\frac{1}{9}\right) - 1} + 3\left(-\frac{1}{9}\right) \stackrel{?}{=} 0 \qquad \sqrt{-10(-1) - 1} + 3(-1) \stackrel{?}{=} 0$$
$$\sqrt{\frac{10}{9} - \frac{9}{9}} - \frac{3}{9} \stackrel{?}{=} 0 \qquad\qquad \sqrt{10 - 1} - 3 \stackrel{?}{=} 0$$
$$\sqrt{\frac{1}{9}} - \frac{1}{3} \stackrel{?}{=} 0 \qquad\qquad\qquad \sqrt{9} - 3 \stackrel{?}{=} 0$$
$$\frac{1}{3} - \frac{1}{3} = 0 \quad \text{True} \qquad\qquad 3 - 3 = 0 \quad \text{True}$$

Both solutions check. The solution set is $\left\{-\frac{1}{9}, -1\right\}$.

■ **Work Practice Problem 2**

The following steps may be used to solve a radical equation.

Solving a Radical Equation

Step 1: Isolate one radical on one side of the equation.

Step 2: Raise each side of the equation to a power equal to the index of the radical and simplify.

Step 3: If the equation still contains a radical term, repeat Steps 1 and 2. If not, solve the equation.

Step 4: Check all proposed solutions in the original equation.

PRACTICE PROBLEM 3

Solve: $\sqrt[3]{x - 5} + 2 = 1$

Answers

2. $\left\{\frac{1}{4}, 2\right\}$, 3. $\{4\}$

EXAMPLE 3 Solve: $\sqrt[3]{x + 1} + 5 = 3$

Solution: First we isolate the radical by subtracting 5 from both sides of the equation.

$$\sqrt[3]{x + 1} + 5 = 3$$
$$\sqrt[3]{x + 1} = -2$$

Next we raise both sides of the equation to the third power to eliminate the radical.

$$(\sqrt[3]{x + 1})^3 = (-2)^3$$
$$x + 1 = -8$$
$$x = -9$$

The solution checks in the original equation, so the solution set is $\{-9\}$.

■ **Work Practice Problem 3**

EXAMPLE 4 Solve: $\sqrt{4 - x} = x - 2$

Solution:
$$\sqrt{4 - x} = x - 2$$
$$(\sqrt{4 - x})^2 = (x - 2)^2$$
$$4 - x = x^2 - 4x + 4 \quad \text{Write the quadratic equation}$$
$$x^2 - 3x = 0 \qquad\qquad \text{in standard form.}$$
$$x(x - 3) = 0 \qquad\qquad \text{Factor.}$$
$$x = 0 \quad \text{or} \quad x - 3 = 0 \qquad \text{Set each factor equal to 0.}$$
$$x = 3$$

Check:

$$\sqrt{4 - x} = x - 2 \qquad\qquad \sqrt{4 - x} = x - 2$$
$$\sqrt{4 - 0} \overset{?}{=} 0 - 2 \quad \text{Let } x = 0. \qquad \sqrt{4 - 3} \overset{?}{=} 3 - 2 \quad \text{Let } x = 3.$$
$$2 = -2 \qquad \text{False} \qquad\qquad 1 = 1 \qquad \text{True}$$

The proposed solution 3 checks, but 0 does not. Since 0 is an extraneous solution, the solution set is $\{3\}$.

■ **Work Practice Problem 4**

> **Helpful Hint**
>
> In Example 4, notice that $(x - 2)^2 = x^2 - 4x + 4$. Make sure binomials are squared correctly.

✔ **Concept Check** How can you immediately tell that the equation $\sqrt{2y + 3} = -4$ has no real solution?

EXAMPLE 5 Solve: $\sqrt{2x + 5} + \sqrt{2x} = 3$

Solution: We get one radical alone by subtracting $\sqrt{2x}$ from both sides.

$$\sqrt{2x + 5} + \sqrt{2x} = 3$$
$$\sqrt{2x + 5} = 3 - \sqrt{2x}$$

Now we use the power rule to begin eliminating the radicals. First we square both sides.

$$(\sqrt{2x + 5})^2 = (3 - \sqrt{2x})^2$$
$$2x + 5 = 9 - 6\sqrt{2x} + 2x \quad \text{Multiply: } (3 - \sqrt{2x})(3 - \sqrt{2x})$$

Continued on next page

PRACTICE PROBLEM 4
Solve: $\sqrt{9 + x} = x + 3$

PRACTICE PROBLEM 5
Solve: $\sqrt{3x + 1} + \sqrt{3x} = 2$

Answers
4. $\{0\}$, 5. $\left\{\dfrac{3}{16}\right\}$

✔ **Concept Check Answer**
answers may vary

There is still a radical in the equation, so we get the radical alone again. Then we square both sides.

$$2x + 5 = 9 - 6\sqrt{2x} + 2x$$

$6\sqrt{2x} = 4$ Get the radical alone.

$(6\sqrt{2x})^2 = 4^2$ Square both sides of the equation to eliminate the radical.

$36(2x) = 16$

$72x = 16$ Multiply.

$x = \dfrac{16}{72}$ Solve.

$x = \dfrac{2}{9}$ Simplify.

The proposed solution $\dfrac{2}{9}$ checks in the original equation. The solution set is $\left\{\dfrac{2}{9}\right\}$.

▣ **Work Practice Problem 5**

Helpful Hint

Make sure expressions are squared correctly. In Example 5, we squared $(3 - \sqrt{2x})$ as

$$(3 - \sqrt{2x})^2 = (3 - \sqrt{2x})(3 - \sqrt{2x})$$
$$= 3 \cdot 3 - 3\sqrt{2x} - 3\sqrt{2x} + \sqrt{2x} \cdot \sqrt{2x}$$
$$= 9 - 6\sqrt{2x} + 2x$$

✔ **Concept Check** What is wrong with the following solution?

$$\sqrt{2x + 5} + \sqrt{4 - x} = 8$$
$$(\sqrt{2x + 5} + \sqrt{4 - x})^2 = 8^2$$
$$(2x + 5) + (4 - x) = 64$$
$$x + 9 = 64$$
$$x = 55$$

Objective **B** Using the Pythagorean Theorem

Recall that the Pythagorean theorem states that in a right triangle, the length of the hypotenuse squared equals the sum of the lengths of each of the legs squared.

Pythagorean Theorem

If a and b are the lengths of the legs of a right triangle and c is the length of the hypotenuse, then $a^2 + b^2 = c^2$.

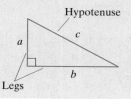

✔ **Concept Check Answer**

From the second line of the solution to the third line of the solution, the left side of the equation is squared incorrectly.

⚠ **EXAMPLE 6** Find the length of the unknown leg of the right triangle.

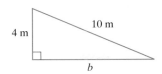

PRACTICE PROBLEM 6

Find the length of the unknown
leg of the right triangle.

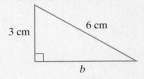

Solution: In the formula $a^2 + b^2 = c^2$, c is the hypotenuse. Here, $c = 10$, the length of the hypotenuse, and $a = 4$. We solve for b. Then $a^2 + b^2 = c^2$ becomes

$$4^2 + b^2 = 10^2$$
$$16 + b^2 = 100$$
$$b^2 = 84 \qquad \text{Subtract 16 from both sides.}$$

Recall from Section 7.1 our definition of square root that if $b^2 = a$, then b is a square root of a. Since b is a length and thus is positive, we have that

$$b = \sqrt{84} = \sqrt{4 \cdot 21} = 2\sqrt{21}$$

The unknown leg of the triangle is exactly $2\sqrt{21}$ meters long. Using a calculator, this is approximately 9.2 meters.

🖳 **Work Practice Problem 6**

⚠ **EXAMPLE 7** **Calculating Placement of a Wire**

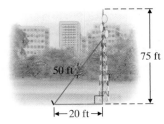

A 50-foot supporting wire is to be attached to a 75-foot antenna. Because of surrounding buildings, sidewalks, and roadways, the wire must be anchored exactly 20 feet from the base of the antenna.

a. How high from the base of the antenna must the wire be attached?

b. Local regulations require that a supporting wire be attached at a height no less than $\dfrac{3}{5}$ of the total height the antenna. From part (a), have local regulations been met?

Solution:

1. UNDERSTAND. Read and reread the problem. From the diagram we notice that a right triangle is formed with hypotenuse 50 feet and one leg 20 feet. We let x = the height from the base of the antenna to the attached wire.

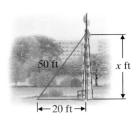

Continued on next page

PRACTICE PROBLEM 7

A furniture upholsterer wishes to cut a strip from a piece of fabric that is 45 inches by 45 inches. The strip must be cut on the bias of the fabric. What is the longest strip that can be cut? Give an exact answer and a two-decimal-place approximation.

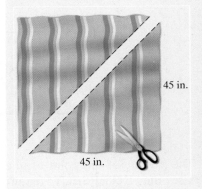

Answers
6. $3\sqrt{3}$ cm, **7.** $45\sqrt{2}$ in. ≈ 63.64 in.

2. TRANSLATE. We'll use the Pythagorean theorem.

$$a^2 + b^2 = c^2$$
$$20^2 + x^2 = 50^2 \quad a = 20, c = 50$$

3. SOLVE.

$$20^2 + x^2 = 50^2$$
$$400 + x^2 = 2500$$
$$x^2 = 2100 \qquad \text{Subtract 400 from both sides.}$$
$$x = \sqrt{2100}$$
$$= 10\sqrt{21}$$

4. INTERPRET. *Check* the work and *state* the solution.

a. The wire is attached exactly $10\sqrt{21}$ feet from the base of the pole, or approximately 45.8 feet.

b. The supporting wire must be attached at a height no less than $\frac{3}{5}$ of the total height of the antenna. This height is $\frac{3}{5}$ (75 feet), or 45 feet.

Since we know from part (a) that the wire is to be attached at a height of approximately 45.8 feet, local regulations have been met.

◼ Work Practice Problem 7

▦ CALCULATOR EXPLORATIONS Graphing

We can use a graphing calculator to solve radical equations. For example, to use a graphing calculator to approximate the solutions of the equation solved in Example 4, we graph the following:

$$Y_1 = \sqrt{4 - x} \quad \text{and} \quad Y_2 = x - 2$$

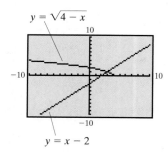

$y = \sqrt{4 - x}$

$y = x - 2$

The *x*-value of the point of intersection is the solution. Use the INTERSECT feature or the ZOOM and TRACE features of your graphing calculator to see that the solution is 3.

Use a graphing calculator to solve each radical equation. Round all solutions to the nearest hundredth.

1. $\sqrt{x + 7} = x$

2. $\sqrt{3x + 5} = 2x$

3. $\sqrt{2x + 1} = \sqrt{2x + 2}$

4. $\sqrt{10x - 1} = \sqrt{-10x + 10} - 1$

5. $1.2x = \sqrt{3.1x + 5}$

6. $\sqrt{1.9x^2 - 2.2} = -0.8x + 3$

7.6 EXERCISE SET

FOR EXTRA HELP

Student Solutions Manual

PH Math/Tutor Center

CD/Video for Review

MathXL
MathXL®

MyMathLab
MyMathLab

Objective A *Solve. See Examples 1 and 2.*

1. $\sqrt{2x} = 4$

2. $\sqrt{3x} = 3$

3. $\sqrt{x-3} = 2$

4. $\sqrt{x+1} = 5$

5. $\sqrt{2x} = -4$

6. $\sqrt{5x} = -5$

7. $\sqrt{4x-3} - 5 = 0$

8. $\sqrt{x-3} - 1 = 0$

9. $\sqrt{2x-3} - 2 = 1$

10. $\sqrt{3x+3} - 4 = 8$

Solve. See Example 3.

11. $\sqrt[3]{6x} = -3$

12. $\sqrt[3]{4x} = -2$

13. $\sqrt[3]{x-2} - 3 = 0$

14. $\sqrt[3]{2x-6} - 4 = 0$

Solve. See Examples 4 and 5.

15. $\sqrt{13-x} = x-1$

16. $\sqrt{2x-3} = 3-x$

17. $x - \sqrt{4-3x} = -8$

18. $2x + \sqrt{x+1} = 8$

19. $\sqrt{y+5} = 2 - \sqrt{y-4}$

20. $\sqrt{x+3} + \sqrt{x-5} = 3$

21. $\sqrt{x-3} + \sqrt{x+2} = 5$

22. $\sqrt{2x-4} - \sqrt{3x+4} = -2$

Solve. See Examples 1 through 5.

23. $\sqrt{3x-2} = 5$

24. $\sqrt{5x-4} = 9$

25. $-\sqrt{2x} + 4 = -6$

26. $-\sqrt{3x+9} = -12$

27. $\sqrt{3x+1} + 2 = 0$

28. $\sqrt{3x+1} - 2 = 0$

29. $\sqrt[4]{4x+1} - 2 = 0$

30. $\sqrt[4]{2x-9} - 3 = 0$

31. $\sqrt{3x+4} = 5$

32. $\sqrt{3x+9} = 12$

33. $\sqrt[3]{6x-3} - 3 = 0$

34. $\sqrt[3]{3x} + 4 = 7$

35. $\sqrt[3]{2x-3} - 2 = -5$

36. $\sqrt[3]{x-4} - 5 = -7$

37. $\sqrt{x+4} = \sqrt{2x-5}$

38. $\sqrt{3y+6} = \sqrt{7y-6}$

39. $x - \sqrt{1-x} = -5$

40. $x - \sqrt{x-2} = 4$

41. $\sqrt[3]{-6x-1} = \sqrt[3]{-2x-5}$

42. $x + \sqrt{x+5} = 7$

43. $\sqrt{5x-1} - \sqrt{x+2} = 3$

44. $\sqrt{2x-1} - 4 = -\sqrt{x-4}$

45. $\sqrt{2x-1} = \sqrt{1-2x}$

46. $\sqrt{7x-4} = \sqrt{4-7x}$

47. $\sqrt{3x+4} - 1 = \sqrt{2x+1}$

48. $\sqrt{x-2} + 3 = \sqrt{4x+1}$

49. $\sqrt{y+3} - \sqrt{y-3} = 1$

50. $\sqrt{x+1} - \sqrt{x-1} = 2$

Objective B *Find the length of the unknown side of each triangle. See Example 6.*

△ **51.**
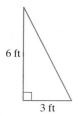
6 ft
3 ft

△ **52.**
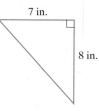
7 in.
8 in.

△ **53.**
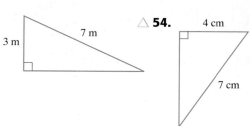
3 m
7 m

△ **54.**
4 cm
7 cm

Find the length of the unknown side of each triangle. Give the exact length and a one-decimal-place approximation. See Example 6.

▦ **55.**
△
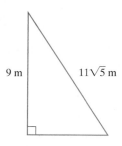
9 m
$11\sqrt{5}$ m

▦ **56.**
△
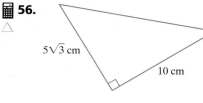
$5\sqrt{3}$ cm
10 cm

▦ **57.**
△

7 mm
7.2 mm

▦ **58.**
△
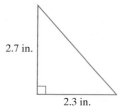
2.7 in.
2.3 in.

Solve. Give exact answers and two-decimal-place approximations where appropriate. See Example 7.

▦ **59.** A wire is needed to support a vertical pole 15 feet
△ high. The cable will be anchored to a stake 8 feet from the base of the pole. How much cable is needed?

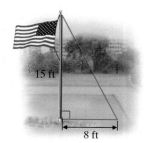
15 ft
8 ft

▦ **60.** The tallest structure in the United States is a TV
△ tower in Blanchard, North Dakota. Its height is 2063 feet. A 2382-foot length of wire is to be used as a guy wire attached to the top of the tower. Approximate to the nearest foot how far from the base of the tower the guy wire must be anchored. (*Source:* U.S. Geological Survey)

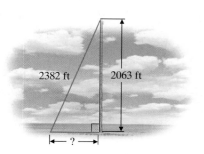
2382 ft
2063 ft
?

△ **61.** A spotlight is mounted on the eaves of a house 12 feet above the ground. A flower bed runs between △ the house and the sidewalk, so the closest the ladder can be placed to the house is 5 feet. How long a ladder is needed so that an electrician can reach the place where the light is mounted?

62. A wire is to be attached to support a telephone pole. Because of surrounding buildings, sidewalks, and roadway, the wire must be anchored exactly 15 feet from the base of the pole. Telephone company workers have only 30 feet of cable, and 2 feet of that must be used to attach the cable to the pole and to the stake on the ground. How high from the base of the pole can the wire be attached?

△ **63.** The radius of the moon is 1080 miles. Use the formula for the radius r of a sphere given its surface area A.

$$r = \sqrt{\frac{A}{4\pi}}$$

to find the surface area of the moon. Round to the nearest square mile. (*Source:* National Space Science Data Center)

64. Police departments find it very useful to be able to approximate driving speeds in skidding accidents. If the road surface is wet concrete, the function $S(x) = \sqrt{10.5x}$ is used, where $S(x)$ is the speed of the car in miles per hour and x is the distance skidded in feet. Find how fast a car was moving if it skidded 280 feet on wet concrete.

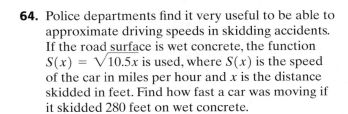

65. The formula $v = \sqrt{2gh}$ relates the velocity v, in feet per second, of an object after it falls h feet accelerated by gravity g, in feet per second squared. If g is approximately 32 feet per second squared, find how far an object has fallen if its velocity is 80 feet per second.

66. Two tractors are pulling a tree stump from a field. If two forces A and B pull at right angles (90°) to each other, the size of the resulting force R is given by the formula $R = \sqrt{A^2 + B^2}$. If tractor A is exerting 600 pounds of force and the resulting force is 850 pounds, find how much force tractor B is exerting.

In psychology, it has been suggested that the number S of nonsense syllables that a person can repeat consecutively depends on his or her IQ score I according to the equation $S = 2\sqrt{I} - 9$.

67. Use this relationship to estimate the IQ of a person who can repeat 11 nonsense syllables consecutively.

68. Use this relationship to estimate the IQ of a person who can repeat 15 nonsense syllables consecutively.

*The **period** of a pendulum is the time it takes for the pendulum to make one full back-and-forth swing. The period of a pendulum depends on the length of the pendulum. The formula for the period P, in seconds, is $P = 2\pi\sqrt{\dfrac{l}{32}}$, where l is the length of the pendulum in feet. Use this formula for Exercises 69 through 74.*

69. Find the period of a pendulum whose length is 2 feet. Give an exact answer and a two-decimal-place approximation.

70. Klockit sells a 43-inch lyre pendulum. Find the period of this pendulum. Round your answer to 2 decimal places. (*Hint:* First convert inches to feet.)

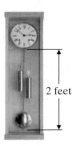

2 feet

71. Find the length of a pendulum whose period is 4 seconds. Round your answer to 2 decimal places.

72. Find the length of a pendulum whose period is 3 seconds. Round your answer to 3 decimal places.

73. Study the relationship between period and pendulum length in Exercises 69 through 72 and make a conjecture about this relationship.

74. Galileo experimented with pendulums. He supposedly made conjectures about pendulums of equal length with different bob weights. Try this experiment. Make two pendulums 3 feet long. Attach a heavy weight (lead) to one and a light weight (a cork) to the other. Pull both pendulums back the same angle measure and release. Make a conjecture from your observations.

If the three lengths of the sides of a triangle are known, Heron's formula can be used to find its area. If a, b, and c are the three lengths of the sides, Heron's formula *for area is*

$$A = \sqrt{s(s-a)(s-b)(s-c)}$$

where s is half the perimeter of the triangle, or $s = \dfrac{1}{2}(a + b + c)$. Use this formula to find the area of each triangle. Give an exact answer and then a 2-decimal place approximation.

△ **75.**

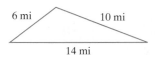

6 mi   10 mi
14 mi

△ **76.**

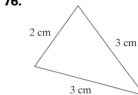

2 cm   3 cm
3 cm

77. Describe when Heron's formula might be useful.

78. In your own words, explain why you think S in *Heron's formula* is called the *semiperimeter*.

The maximum distance $D(h)$ in kilometers that a person can see from a height h kilometers above the ground is given by the function $D(h) = 111.7\sqrt{h}$. Use this function for Exercises 79 and 80. Round your answers to two decimal places.

79. Find the height that would allow a person to see 80 kilometers.

80. Find the height that would allow a person to see 40 kilometers.

Review

Simplify. See Section 6.3.

81. $\dfrac{\dfrac{x}{6}}{\dfrac{2x}{3} + \dfrac{1}{2}}$

82. $\dfrac{\dfrac{1}{y} + \dfrac{4}{5}}{\dfrac{-3}{20}}$

83. $\dfrac{\dfrac{z}{5} + \dfrac{1}{10}}{\dfrac{z}{20} - \dfrac{z}{5}}$

84. $\dfrac{\dfrac{1}{y} + \dfrac{1}{x}}{\dfrac{1}{y} - \dfrac{1}{x}}$

Concept Extensions

85. Solve: $\sqrt{\sqrt{x + 3} + \sqrt{x}} = \sqrt{3}$

86. Explain why proposed solutions of radical equations must be checked.

87. Find the error in the following solution and correct. See the Concept Check in this section.

$$\sqrt{5x - 1} + 4 = 7$$
$$(\sqrt{5x - 1} + 4)^2 = 7^2$$
$$5x - 1 + 16 = 49$$
$$5x = 34$$
$$x = \frac{34}{5}$$

88. Consider the equations $\sqrt{2x} = 4$ and $\sqrt[3]{2x} = 4$.
   a. Explain the difference in solving these equations.
   b. Explain the similarity in solving these equations.

89. The cost $C(x)$ in dollars per day to operate a small delivery service is given by $C(x) = 80\sqrt[3]{x} + 500$, where x is the number of deliveries per day. In July, the manager decides that it is necessary to keep delivery costs below $1620.00. Find the greatest number of deliveries this company can make per day and still keep overhead below $1620.00.

THE BIGGER PICTURE Solving Equations and Inequalities

Continue your outline from Sections 2.6, 5.7, and 6.4. Write how to recognize and how to solve exponential and logarithmic equations in your own words. For example:

Solving Equations and Inequalities

I. Equations

  A. Linear equations (Sec. 2.1)

  B. Absolute value equations (Sec. 2.6)

  C. Quadratic and higher degree equations (Sec. 5.7)

  D. Equations with rational expressions (Sec. 6.4)

  E. Equations with radicals: Equation contains at least one root of a variable expression.

$$\sqrt{5x + 10} - 2 = x \qquad \text{Radical equation.}$$

$$\sqrt{5x + 10} = x + 2 \qquad \text{Isolate the radical.}$$

$$(\sqrt{5x + 10})^2 = (x + 2)^2 \qquad \text{Square both sides.}$$

$$5x + 10 = x^2 + 4x + 4 \qquad \text{Simplify.}$$

$$0 = x^2 - x - 6 \qquad \text{Write in standard form.}$$

$$0 = (x - 3)(x + 2) \qquad \text{Factor.}$$

$$x - 3 = 0 \quad \text{or} \quad x + 2 = 0 \qquad \text{Set each factor equal to 0.}$$

$$x = 3 \quad \text{or} \quad x = -2 \qquad \text{Solve.}$$

Both solutions check.

II. Inequalities

  A. Linear inequalities (Sec. 2.4)

  B. Compound inequalities (Sec. 2.5)

  C. Absolute value inequalities (Sec. 2.6)

Solve. Write inequality solutions in interval notation.

1. $\dfrac{x}{4} + \dfrac{x + 18}{20} = \dfrac{x - 5}{5}$

2. $|3x - 5| = 10$

3. $2x^2 - x = 45$

4. $-6 \le -5x - 1 \le 10$

5. $4(x - 1) + 3x > 1 + 2(x - 6)$

6. $\sqrt{x} + 14 = x - 6$

7. $x \ge 10$ or $-x < 5$

8. $\sqrt{3x - 1} + 4 = 1$

9. $|x - 2| > 15$

10. $5x - 4[x - 2(3x + 1)] = 25$

7.7 COMPLEX NUMBERS

Objectives

A Write Square Roots of Negative Numbers in the Form *bi*.

B Add or Subtract Complex Numbers.

C Multiply Complex Numbers.

D Divide Complex Numbers.

E Raise *i* to Powers.

Objective **A** Writing Numbers in the Form *bi*

Our work with radical expressions has excluded expressions such as $\sqrt{-16}$ because $\sqrt{-16}$ is not a real number; there is no real number whose square is -16. In this section, we discuss a number system that includes roots of negative numbers. This number system is the **complex number system,** and it includes the set of real numbers as a subset. The complex number system allows us to solve equations such as $x^2 + 1 = 0$ that have no real number solutions. The set of complex numbers includes the *imaginary unit.*

Imaginary Unit

The **imaginary unit,** written i, is the number whose square is -1. That is,

$$i^2 = -1 \quad \text{and} \quad i = \sqrt{-1}$$

To write the square root of a negative number in terms of i, we use the property that if a is a positive number, then

$$\sqrt{-a} = \sqrt{-1} \cdot \sqrt{a}$$
$$= i \cdot \sqrt{a}$$

Using i, we can write $\sqrt{-16}$ as

$$\sqrt{-16} = \sqrt{-1 \cdot 16} = \sqrt{-1} \cdot \sqrt{16} = i \cdot 4 \text{ or } 4i$$

EXAMPLES Write using i notation.

1. $\sqrt{-36} = \sqrt{-1 \cdot 36} = \sqrt{-1} \cdot \sqrt{36} = i \cdot 6 \text{ or } 6i$

2. $\sqrt{-5} = \sqrt{-1(5)} = \sqrt{-1} \cdot \sqrt{5} = i\sqrt{5}$

> **Helpful Hint**
> Since $\sqrt{5}i$ can easily be confused with $\sqrt{5i}$, we write $\sqrt{5}i$ as $i\sqrt{5}$.

3. $-\sqrt{-20} = -\sqrt{-1 \cdot 20} = -\sqrt{-1} \cdot \sqrt{4 \cdot 5} = -i \cdot 2\sqrt{5} = -2i\sqrt{5}$

■ **Work Practice Problems 1–3**

The product rule for radicals does not necessarily hold true for imaginary numbers. *To multiply square roots of negative numbers, first we write each number in terms of the imaginary unit i.* For example, to multiply $\sqrt{-4}$ and $\sqrt{-9}$, we first write each number in the form bi:

$$\sqrt{-4} \cdot \sqrt{-9} = 2i(3i) = 6i^2 = 6(-1) = -6 \quad \text{Correct.}$$

Make sure you notice that the product rule does not work for this example. In other words, $\sqrt{-4} \cdot \sqrt{-9} = \sqrt{(-4)(-9)} = \sqrt{36} = 6$ is incorrect!

EXAMPLES Multiply or divide as indicated.

4. $\sqrt{-3} \cdot \sqrt{-5} = i\sqrt{3}(i\sqrt{5}) = i^2\sqrt{15} = -1\sqrt{15} = -\sqrt{15}$

5. $\sqrt{-36} \cdot \sqrt{-1} = 6i(i) = 6i^2 = 6(-1) = -6$

6. $\sqrt{8} \cdot \sqrt{-2} = 2\sqrt{2}(i\sqrt{2}) = 2i(\sqrt{2}\sqrt{2}) = 2i(2) = 4i$

7. $\dfrac{\sqrt{-125}}{\sqrt{5}} = \dfrac{i\sqrt{125}}{\sqrt{5}} = i\sqrt{25} = 5i$

■ **Work Practice Problems 4–7**

PRACTICE PROBLEMS 1–3

Write using i notation.

1. $\sqrt{-25}$

2. $\sqrt{-17}$

3. $-\sqrt{-50}$

PRACTICE PROBLEMS 4–7

Multiply or divide as indicated.

4. $\sqrt{-3} \cdot \sqrt{-7}$

5. $\sqrt{-25} \cdot \sqrt{-1}$

6. $\sqrt{27} \cdot \sqrt{-3}$ **7.** $\dfrac{\sqrt{-8}}{\sqrt{2}}$

Answers

1. $5i$, **2.** $i\sqrt{17}$, **3.** $-5i\sqrt{2}$,
4. $-\sqrt{21}$, **5.** -5, **6.** $9i$, **7.** $2i$

Now that we have practiced working with the imaginary unit, we define *complex numbers*.

Complex Numbers

A **complex number** is a number that can be written in the form $a + bi$, where a and b are real numbers.

Notice that the set of real numbers is a subset of the complex numbers since any real number can be written in the form of a complex number. For example,

$$16 = 16 + 0i$$

In general, a complex number $a + bi$ is a real number if $b = 0$. Also, a complex number is called an **imaginary number** if $a = 0$. For example.

$$3i = 0 + 3i \quad \text{and} \quad i\sqrt{7} = 0 + i\sqrt{7}$$

are imaginary numbers.

The following diagram shows the relationship between complex numbers and their subsets.

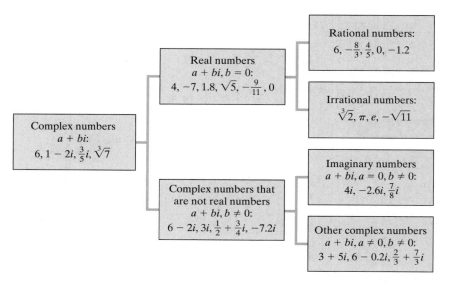

✔**Concept Check** True or false? Every complex number is also a real number.

Objective **B** Adding or Subtracting Complex Numbers

Two complex numbers $a + bi$ and $c + di$ are equal if and only if $a = c$ and $b = d$. Complex numbers can be added or subtracted by adding or subtracting their real parts and then adding or subtracting their imaginary parts.

Sum or Difference of Complex Numbers

If $a + bi$ and $c + di$ are complex numbers, then their sum is

$$(a + bi) + (c + di) = (a + c) + (b + d)i$$

Their difference is

$$(a + bi) - (c + di) = a + bi - c - di = (a - c) + (b - d)i$$

✔ **Concept Check Answer**

false

EXAMPLES Add or subtract as indicated.

8. $(2 + 3i) + (-3 + 2i) = (2 - 3) + (3 + 2)i = -1 + 5i$

9. $5i - (1 - i) = 5i - 1 + i$
$$= -1 + (5 + 1)i$$
$$= -1 + 6i$$

10. $(-3 - 7i) - (-6) = -3 - 7i + 6$
$$= (-3 + 6) - 7i$$
$$= 3 - 7i$$

■ **Work Practice Problems 8–10**

PRACTICE PROBLEMS 8–10

Add or subtract as indicated.
8. $(5 + 2i) + (4 - 3i)$
9. $6i - (2 - i)$
10. $(-2 - 4i) - (-3)$

Objective C Multiplying Complex Numbers

To multiply two complex numbers of the form $a + bi$, we multiply as though they were binomials. Then we use the relationship $i^2 = -1$ to simplify.

EXAMPLES Multiply.

11. $-7i \cdot 3i = -21i^2$
$$= -21(-1) \quad \text{Replace } i^2 \text{ with } -1.$$
$$= 21$$

12. $3i(2 - i) = 3i \cdot 2 - 3i \cdot i \quad \text{Use the distributive property.}$
$$= 6i - 3i^2 \quad \text{Multiply.}$$
$$= 6i - 3(-1) \quad \text{Replace } i^2 \text{ with } -1.$$
$$= 6i + 3$$
$$= 3 + 6i \quad \text{Use the FOIL order. (First, Outer, Inner, Last)}$$

13. $(2 - 5i)(4 + i) = 2(4) + 2(i) - 5i(4) - 5i(i)$
$$\qquad\qquad\qquad \text{F} \qquad \text{O} \qquad \text{I} \qquad \text{L}$$
$$= 8 + 2i - 20i - 5i^2$$
$$= 8 - 18i - 5(-1) \quad i^2 = -1$$
$$= 8 - 18i + 5$$
$$= 13 - 18i$$

14. $(2 - i)^2 = (2 - i)(2 - i)$
$$= 2(2) - 2(i) - 2(i) + i^2$$
$$= 4 - 4i + (-1) \quad i^2 = -1$$
$$= 3 - 4i$$

15. $(7 + 3i)(7 - 3i) = 7(7) - 7(3i) + 3i(7) - 3i(3i)$
$$= 49 - 21i + 21i - 9i^2$$
$$= 49 - 9(-1) \quad i^2 = -1$$
$$= 49 + 9$$
$$= 58$$

PRACTICE PROBLEMS 11–15

Multiply.
11. $-5i \cdot 3i$
12. $-2i(6 - 2i)$
13. $(3 - 4i)(6 + i)$
14. $(1 - 2i)^2$
15. $(6 + 5i)(6 - 5i)$

■ **Work Practice Problems 11–15**

Notice that if you add, subtract, or multiply two complex numbers, the result is a complex number.

Objective D Dividing Complex Numbers

From Example 15, notice that the product of $7 + 3i$ and $7 - 3i$ is a real number. These two complex numbers are called *complex conjugates* of one another. In general, we have the following definition.

Answers
8. $9 - i$, 9. $-2 + 7i$, 10. $1 - 4i$,
11. 15, 12. $-4 - 12i$, 13. $22 - 21i$,
14. $-3 - 4i$, 15. 61

Complex Conjugates

The complex numbers $(a + bi)$ and $(a - bi)$ are called **complex conjugates** of each other, and

$$(a + bi)(a - bi) = a^2 + b^2$$

To see that the product of a complex number $a + bi$ and its conjugate $a - bi$ is the real number $a^2 + b^2$, we multiply:

$$(a + bi)(a - bi) = a^2 - abi + abi - b^2i^2$$
$$= a^2 - b^2(-1)$$
$$= a^2 + b^2$$

We will use complex conjugates to divide by a complex number.

PRACTICE PROBLEM 16

Divide and write in the form
$a + bi$: $\dfrac{3 + i}{2 - 3i}$

EXAMPLE 16 Divide and write in the form $a + bi$: $\dfrac{2 + i}{1 - i}$

Solution: We multiply the numerator and the denominator by the complex conjugate of $1 - i$ to eliminate the imaginary number in the denominator.

$$\frac{2 + i}{1 - i} = \frac{(2 + i)(1 + i)}{(1 - i)(1 + i)}$$
$$= \frac{2(1) + 2(i) + 1(i) + i^2}{1^2 - i^2}$$
$$= \frac{2 + 3i - 1}{1 + 1}$$
$$= \frac{1 + 3i}{2} = \frac{1}{2} + \frac{3}{2}i$$

□ **Work Practice Problem 16**

PRACTICE PROBLEM 17

Divide and write in the form
$a + bi$: $\dfrac{6}{5i}$

EXAMPLE 17 Divide and write in the form $a + bi$: $\dfrac{7}{3i}$

Solution: We multiply the numerator and the denominator by the conjugate of $3i$. Note that $3i = 0 + 3i$, so its conjugate is $0 - 3i$ or $-3i$.

$$\frac{7}{3i} = \frac{7(-3i)}{(3i)(-3i)} = \frac{-21i}{-9i^2} = \frac{-21i}{-9(-1)} = \frac{-21i}{9} = \frac{-7i}{3} = -\frac{7}{3}i$$

□ **Work Practice Problem 17**

Objective **E** Finding Powers of *i*

We can use the fact that $i^2 = -1$ to simplify i^3 and i^4.

$$i^3 = i^2 \cdot i = (-1)i = -i$$
$$i^4 = i^2 \cdot i^2 = (-1) \cdot (-1) = 1$$

We continue this process and use the fact that $i^4 = 1$ and $i^2 = -1$ to simplify i^5 and i^6.

$$i^5 = i^4 \cdot i = 1 \cdot i = i$$
$$i^6 = i^4 \cdot i^2 = 1 \cdot (-1) = -1$$

Answers

16. $\dfrac{3}{13} + \dfrac{11}{13}i$, **17.** $-\dfrac{6}{5}i$

If we continue finding powers of i, we generate the following pattern. Notice that the values i, -1, $-i$, and 1 repeat as i is raised to higher and higher powers.

$i^1 = i$	$i^5 = i$	$i^9 = i$
$i^2 = -1$	$i^6 = -1$	$i^{10} = -1$
$i^3 = -i$	$i^7 = -i$	$i^{11} = -i$
$i^4 = 1$	$i^8 = 1$	$i^{12} = 1$

This pattern allows us to find other powers of i. To do so, we will use the fact that $i^4 = 1$ and rewrite a power of i in terms of i^4. For example,

$$i^{22} = i^{20} \cdot i^2 = (i^4)^5 \cdot i^2 = 1^5 \cdot (-1) = 1 \cdot (-1) = -1$$

EXAMPLES Find each power of i.

18. $i^7 = i^4 \cdot i^3 = 1(-i) = -i$

19. $i^{20} = (i^4)^5 = 1^5 = 1$

20. $i^{46} = i^{44} \cdot i^2 = (i^4)^{11} \cdot i^2 = 1^{11}(-1) = -1$

21. $i^{-12} = \dfrac{1}{i^{12}} = \dfrac{1}{(i^4)^3} = \dfrac{1}{(1)^3} = \dfrac{1}{1} = 1$

■ **Work Practice Problems 18–21**

PRACTICE PROBLEMS 18–21

Find the powers of i.

18. i^{11} **19.** i^{40}

20. i^{50} **21.** i^{-10}

Mental Math

Simplify. See Examples 1 through 3.

 1. $\sqrt{-81}$ **2.** $\sqrt{-49}$ **3.** $\sqrt{-7}$ **4.** $\sqrt{-3}$

5. $-\sqrt{16}$ **6.** $-\sqrt{4}$ **7.** $\sqrt{-64}$ **8.** $\sqrt{-100}$

7.7 EXERCISE SET

FOR EXTRA HELP

Student Solutions Manual   PH Math/Tutor Center   CD/Video for Review   Math XL MathXL®   MyMathLab MyMathLab

Objective A *Write using i notation. See Examples 1 through 3.*

1. $\sqrt{-24}$ **2.** $\sqrt{-32}$ **3.** $-\sqrt{-36}$ **4.** $-\sqrt{-121}$

5. $8\sqrt{-63}$ **6.** $4\sqrt{-20}$ **7.** $-\sqrt{54}$ **8.** $\sqrt{-63}$

Multiply or divide as indicated. See Examples 4 through 7.

9. $\sqrt{-2} \cdot \sqrt{-7}$ **10.** $\sqrt{-11} \cdot \sqrt{-3}$ **11.** $\sqrt{-5} \cdot \sqrt{-10}$

12. $\sqrt{-2} \cdot \sqrt{-6}$ **13.** $\sqrt{16} \cdot \sqrt{-1}$ **14.** $\sqrt{3} \cdot \sqrt{-27}$ **15.** $\dfrac{\sqrt{-9}}{\sqrt{3}}$

16. $\dfrac{\sqrt{49}}{\sqrt{-10}}$ **17.** $\dfrac{\sqrt{-80}}{\sqrt{-10}}$ **18.** $\dfrac{\sqrt{-40}}{\sqrt{-8}}$

Objective B *Add or subtract as indicated. Write your answers in the form a + bi. See Examples 8 through 10.*

19. $(4 - 7i) + (2 + 3i)$ **20.** $(2 - 4i) - (2 - i)$ **21.** $(6 + 5i) - (8 - i)$

22. $(8 - 3i) + (-8 + 3i)$ **23.** $6 - (8 + 4i)$ **24.** $(9 - 4i) - 9$

25. $(6 - 3i) - (4 - 2i)$ **26.** $(-2 - 4i) - (6 - 8i)$ **27.** $(5 - 6i) - 4i$

28. $(6 - 2i) + 7i$ **29.** $(2 + 4i) + (6 - 5i)$ **30.** $(5 - 3i) + (7 - 8i)$

Objective C *Multiply. Write your answers in the form a + bi. See Examples 11 through 15.*

31. $6i \cdot 2i$ **32.** $5i \cdot 7i$ **33.** $-9i \cdot 7i$

34. $-6i \cdot 4i$ **35.** $-10i \cdot -4i$ **36.** $-2i \cdot -11i$

37. $6i(2 - 3i)$ **38.** $5i(4 - 7i)$ **39.** $-3i(-1 + 9i)$

40. $-5i(-2 + i)$ **41.** $(4 + i)(5 + 2i)$ **42.** $(3 + i)(2 + 4i)$

43. $(\sqrt{3} + 2i)(\sqrt{3} - 2i)$ **44.** $(\sqrt{5} - 5i)(\sqrt{5} + 5i)$ **45.** $(4 - 2i)^2$

46. $(6 - 3i)^2$ **47.** $(6 - 2i)(3 + i)$ **48.** $(2 - 4i)(2 - i)$

49. $(1 - i)(1 + i)$ **50.** $(6 + 2i)(6 - 2i)$ **51.** $(9 + 8i)^2$

52. $(4 + 7i)^2$ **53.** $(1 - i)^2$ **54.** $(2 - 2i)^2$

Objective **D** *Divide. Write your answers in the form a + bi. See Examples 16 and 17.*

55. $\dfrac{4}{i}$ 　　　　 **56.** $\dfrac{5}{6i}$ 　　　　 **57.** $\dfrac{7}{4 + 3i}$ 　　　　 **58.** $\dfrac{9}{1 - 2i}$

59. $\dfrac{6i}{1 - 2i}$ 　　　 **60.** $\dfrac{3i}{5 + i}$ 　　　 **61.** $\dfrac{3 + 5i}{1 + i}$ 　　　 **62.** $\dfrac{6 + 2i}{4 - 3i}$

63. $\dfrac{4 - 5i}{2i}$ 　　　 **64.** $\dfrac{6 + 8i}{3i}$ 　　　 **65.** $\dfrac{16 + 15i}{-3i}$ 　　　 **66.** $\dfrac{2 - 3i}{-7i}$

67. $\dfrac{2}{3 + i}$ 　　　 **68.** $\dfrac{5}{3 - 2i}$ 　　　 **69.** $\dfrac{2 - 3i}{2 + i}$ 　　　 **70.** $\dfrac{6 + 5i}{6 - 5i}$

Objective **E** *Find each power of i. See Examples 18 through 21.*

71. i^8 　　 **72.** i^{10} 　　 **73.** i^{21}　i 　　 **74.** i^{15} 　　 **75.** i^{11} 　　 **76.** i^{40}

77. i^{-6} 　　 **78.** i^{-9} 　　 **79.** $(2i)^6$ 　　 **80.** $(5i)^4$ 　　 **81.** $(-3i)^5$ 　　 **82.** $(-2i)^7$

Review

Thirty people were recently polled about the average monthly balance in their checking account. The results of this poll are shown in the bar graph. Use this graph to answer Exercises 83 through 88. See Section 1.2.

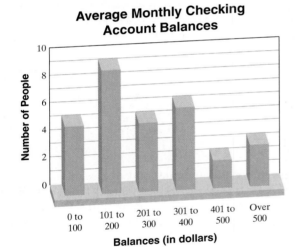

Average Monthly Checking Account Balances

83. How many people polled reported an average checking balance of $201 to $300?

84. How many people polled reported an average checking balance of $0 to $100?

85. How many people polled reported an average checking balance of $200 or less?

86. How many people polled reported an average checking balance of $301 or more?

87. What percent of people polled reported an average checking balance of $201 to $300?

88. What percent of people polled reported an average checking balance of 0 to $100?

Concept Extensions

Write each expression in the form a + bi.

89. $i^3 + i^4$ 　　 **90.** $i^8 - i^7$ 　　 **91.** $i^6 + i^8$ 　　 **92.** $i^4 + i^{12}$ 　　 **93.** $2 + \sqrt{-9}$

94. $5 - \sqrt{-16}$ 　　 **95.** $\dfrac{6 + \sqrt{-18}}{3}$ 　　 **96.** $\dfrac{4 - \sqrt{-8}}{2}$ 　　 **97.** $\dfrac{5 - \sqrt{-75}}{10}$

98. Describe how to find the conjugate of a complex number.

99. Explain why the product of a complex number and its complex conjugate is a real number.

Simplify.

100. $(8 - \sqrt{-3}) - (2 + \sqrt{-12})$ 　　　　 **101.** $(8 - \sqrt{-4}) - (2 + \sqrt{-16})$

102. Determine whether $2i$ is a solution of $x^2 + 4 = 0$.

103. Determine whether $-1 + i$ is a solution of $x^2 + 2x = -2$.

CHAPTER 7   Group Activity

Heron of Alexandria

Heron (also Hero) was a Greek mathematician and engineer. He lived and worked in Alexandria, Egypt, around 75 A.D. During his prolific work life, Heron developed a rotary steam engine called an aeolipile, a surveying tool called a dioptra, as well as a wind organ and a fire engine. As an engineer, he must have had the need to approximate square roots because he described an iterative method for doing so in his work *Metrica*. Heron's method for approximating a square root can be summarized as follows:

Suppose that x is not a perfect square and a^2 is the nearest perfect square to x. For a rough estimate of the value of $\sqrt{x}$, find the value of $y_1 = \frac{1}{2}\left(a + \frac{x}{a}\right)$. This estimate can be improved by calculating a second estimate using the first estimate y_1 in place of a: $y_2 = \frac{1}{2}\left(y_1 + \frac{x}{y_1}\right)$.

Repeating this process several times will give more and more accurate estimates of $\sqrt{x}$.

Critical Thinking

1. **a.** Which perfect square is closest to 80?

   b. Use Heron's method for approximating square roots to calculate the first estimate of the square root of 80.

   c. Use the first estimate of the square root of 80 to find a more refined second estimate.

   d. Use a calculator to find the actual value of the square root of 80. List all digits shown on your calculator's display.

   e. Compare the actual value from part (d) to the values of the first and second estimates. What do you notice?

   f. How many iterations of this process are necessary to get an estimate that differs no more than one digit from the actual value recorded in part (d)?

2. Repeat Question 1 for finding an estimate of the square root of 30.

3. Repeat Question 1 for finding an estimate of the square root of 4572.

4. Why would this iterative method have been important to people of Heron's era? Would you say that this method is as important today? Why or why not?

STUDY SKILLS BUILDER

Are You Prepared for a Test on Chapter 7?

Below I have listed some common trouble areas for students in Chapter 7. After studying for your test, but before taking your test, read these.

- Remember how to convert an expression with rational expressions to one with radicals and one with radicals to one with rational expressions.

$$7^{2/3} = \sqrt[3]{7^2} \text{ or } (\sqrt[3]{7})^2$$
$$\sqrt[5]{4^3} = 4^{3/5}$$

- Remember the difference between $\sqrt{x} + \sqrt{x}$ and $\sqrt{x} \cdot \sqrt{x}, x > 0$.

$$\sqrt{x} + \sqrt{x} = 2\sqrt{x}$$
$$\sqrt{x} \cdot \sqrt{x} = x$$

- Don't forget the difference between rationalizing the denominator of $\sqrt{\dfrac{2}{x}}$ and rationalizing the denominator of $\dfrac{\sqrt{2}}{\sqrt{x} + 1}, x > 0$.

$$\sqrt{\frac{2}{x}} = \frac{\sqrt{2}}{\sqrt{x}} = \frac{\sqrt{2} \cdot}{\sqrt{x} \cdot} = \frac{\sqrt{2x}}{x}$$

$$\frac{\sqrt{2}}{\sqrt{x} + 1} = \frac{\sqrt{2}(\sqrt{x} - 1)}{(\sqrt{x} + 1)(\sqrt{x} - 1)} = \frac{\sqrt{2}(\sqrt{x} - 1)}{x - 1}$$

- Remember that the midpoint of a segment is a *point*. The x-coordinate is the average of the x-coordinates of the endpoints of the segment and the y-coordinate is the average of the y-coordinates of the endpoints of the segment.

   The midpoint of the segment joining $(-1, 5)$ and $(3, 4)$ is $\left(\dfrac{-1 + 3}{2}, \dfrac{5 + 4}{2}\right)$ or $\left(1, \dfrac{9}{2}\right)$.

- Remember that the distance formula gives the *distance* between two points.
   The distance between $(-1, 5)$ and $(3, 4)$ is

$$\sqrt{(3 - (-1))^2 + (4 - 5)^2} = \sqrt{4^2 + (-1)^2}$$
$$= \sqrt{16 + 1} = \sqrt{17} \text{ units}$$

Remember: This is simply a checklist of common trouble areas. For a review of Chapter 7, see the Highlights and Chapter Review at the end of this chapter.

Chapter 7 Vocabulary Check

Fill in each blank with one of the words or phrases listed below.

index	rationalizing	conjugate	principal square root	cube root	midpoint
complex number	like radicals	radicand	imaginary unit	distance	

1. The _____ of $\sqrt{3} + 2$ is $\sqrt{3} - 2$.
2. The _____ of a nonnegative number a is written as $\sqrt{a}$.
3. The process of writing a radical expression as an equivalent expression but without a radical in the denominator is called _____ the denominator.
4. The _____, written i, is the number whose square is -1.
5. The _____ of a number is written as $\sqrt[3]{a}$.
6. In the notation $\sqrt[n]{a}$, n is called the _____ and a is called the _____.
7. Radicals with the same index and the same radicand are called _____.
8. A _____ is a number that can be written in the form $a + bi$, where a and b are real numbers.
9. The _____ formula is $d = \sqrt{(x_2 - x_1)^2 + (y_2 - y_1)^2}$.
10. The _____ formula is $\left(\dfrac{x_1 + x_2}{2}, \dfrac{y_1 + y_2}{2} \right)$.

> **Helpful Hint**
>
> Are you preparing for your test? Don't forget to take the Chapter 7 Test on page 547. Then check your answers at the back of the text and use the Chapter Test Prep Video CD to see the fully worked-out solutions to any of the exercises you want to review.

7 Chapter Highlights

DEFINITIONS AND CONCEPTS	EXAMPLES

Section 7.1   Radical Expressions and Radical Functions

The **positive,** or **principal, square root** of a nonnegative number a is written as $\sqrt{a}$. $\sqrt{a} = b$ only if $b^2 = a$ and $b \geq 0$ The **negative square root** of a is written as $-\sqrt{a}$.	$\sqrt{36} = 6$ $\quad$ $\sqrt{\dfrac{9}{100}} = \dfrac{3}{10}$ $-\sqrt{36} = -6$ $\quad$ $-\sqrt{0.04} = -0.2$
The **cube root** of a real number a is written as $\sqrt[3]{a}$. $\sqrt[3]{a} = b$ only if $b^3 = a$	$\sqrt[3]{27} = 3$ $\quad$ $\sqrt[3]{-\dfrac{1}{8}} = -\dfrac{1}{2}$ $\sqrt[3]{y^6} = y^2$ $\quad$ $\sqrt[3]{64x^9} = 4x^3$
If n is an even positive integer, then $\sqrt[n]{a^n} = |a|$. If n is an odd positive integer, then $\sqrt[n]{a^n} = a$.	$\sqrt{(-3)^2} = |-3| = 3$ $\sqrt[3]{(-7)^3} = -7$
A **radical function** in x is a function defined by an expression containing a root of x.	If $f(x) = \sqrt{x} + 2$, $f(1) = \sqrt{1} + 2 = 1 + 2 = 3$ $f(3) = \sqrt{3} + 2 \approx 3.73$

DEFINITIONS AND CONCEPTS	**EXAMPLES**

Section 7.2   Rational Exponents

$a^{1/n} = \sqrt[n]{a}$ if $\sqrt[n]{a}$ is a real number.

If m and n are positive integers greater than 1 with $\dfrac{m}{n}$ in lowest terms and $\sqrt[n]{a}$ is a real number, then

$$a^{m/n} = (a^{1/n})^m = (\sqrt[n]{a})^m$$

$a^{-m/n} = \dfrac{1}{a^{m/n}}$ as long as $a^{m/n}$ is a nonzero number.

Exponent rules are true for rational exponents.

$$81^{1/2} = \sqrt{81} = 9$$
$$(-8x^3)^{1/3} = \sqrt[3]{-8x^3} = -2x$$
$$4^{5/2} = (\sqrt{4})^5 = 2^5 = 32$$
$$27^{2/3} = (\sqrt[3]{27})^2 = 3^2 = 9$$
$$16^{-3/4} = \frac{1}{16^{3/4}} = \frac{1}{(\sqrt[4]{16})^3} = \frac{1}{2^3} = \frac{1}{8}$$
$$x^{2/3} \cdot x^{-5/6} = x^{2/3-5/6} = x^{-1/6} = \frac{1}{x^{1/6}}$$
$$(8^{14})^{1/7} = 8^2 = 64$$
$$\frac{a^{4/5}}{a^{-2/5}} = a^{4/5-(-2/5)} = a^{6/5}$$

Section 7.3   Simplifying Radical Expressions

PRODUCT AND QUOTIENT RULES

If $\sqrt[n]{a}$ and $\sqrt[n]{b}$ are real numbers,

$$\sqrt[n]{a} \cdot \sqrt[n]{b} = \sqrt[n]{a \cdot b}$$

$$\frac{\sqrt[n]{a}}{\sqrt[n]{b}} = \sqrt[n]{\frac{a}{b}}, \text{provided } \sqrt[n]{b} \neq 0$$

A radical of the form $\sqrt[n]{a}$ is **simplified** when a contains no factors that are perfect nth powers.

Multiply or divide as indicated:
$$\sqrt{11} \cdot \sqrt{3} = \sqrt{33}$$
$$\frac{\sqrt[3]{40x}}{\sqrt[3]{5x}} = \sqrt[3]{8} = 2$$

$$\sqrt{40} = \sqrt{4 \cdot 10} = 2\sqrt{10}$$
$$\sqrt{36x^5} = \sqrt{36x^4 \cdot x} = 6x^2\sqrt{x}$$
$$\sqrt[3]{24x^7y^3} = \sqrt[3]{8x^6y^3 \cdot 3x} = 2x^2y\sqrt[3]{3x}$$

DISTANCE FORMULA

The distance d between two points (x_1, y_1) and (x_2, y_2) is given by
$$d = \sqrt{(x_2 - x_1)^2 + (y_2 - y_1)^2}$$

Find the distance between points $(-1, 6)$ and $(-2, -4)$. Let $(x_1, y_1) = (-1, 6)$ and $(x_2, y_2) = (-2, -4)$.
$$d = \sqrt{(x_2 - x_1)^2 + (y_2 - y_1)^2}$$
$$= \sqrt{(-2 - (-1))^2 + (-4 - 6)^2}$$
$$= \sqrt{1 + 100} = \sqrt{101}$$

MIDPOINT FORMULA

The midpoint of the line segment whose endpoints are (x_1, y_1) and (x_2, y_2) is the point with coordinates
$$\left(\frac{x_1 + x_2}{2}, \frac{y_1 + y_2}{2} \right)$$

Find the midpoint of the line segment whose endpoints are $(-1, 6)$ and $(-2, -4)$.
$$\left(\frac{-1 + (-2)}{2}, \frac{6 + (-4)}{2} \right)$$
The midpoint is $\left(-\dfrac{3}{2}, 1 \right)$.

Section 7.4   Adding, Subtracting, and Multiplying Radical Expressions

Radicals with the same index and the same radicand are **like radicals.**

The distributive property can be used to add like radicals.

Radical expressions are multiplied by using many of the same properties used to multiply polynomials.

$$5\sqrt{6} + 2\sqrt{6} = (5 + 2)\sqrt{6} = 7\sqrt{6}$$
$$-\sqrt[3]{3x} - 10\sqrt[3]{3x} + 3\sqrt[3]{10x}$$
$$= (-1 - 10)\sqrt[3]{3x} + 3\sqrt[3]{10x}$$
$$= -11\sqrt[3]{3x} + 3\sqrt[3]{10x}$$

DEFINITIONS AND CONCEPTS	EXAMPLES

Section 7.4   Adding, Subtracting, and Multiplying Radical Expressions (*continued*)

	Multiply:

$$(\sqrt{5} - \sqrt{2x})(\sqrt{2} + \sqrt{2x})$$
$$= \sqrt{10} + \sqrt{10x} - \sqrt{4x} - 2x$$
$$= \sqrt{10} + \sqrt{10x} - 2\sqrt{x} - 2x$$
$$(2\sqrt{3} - \sqrt{8x})(2\sqrt{3} + \sqrt{8x})$$
$$= 4(3) - 8x = 12 - 8x$$

Section 7.5   Rationalizing Numerators and Denominators of Radical Expressions

The **conjugate** of $a + b$ is $a - b$.
The process of writing the denominator of a radical expression without a radical is called **rationalizing the denominator.**

The conjugate of $\sqrt{7} + \sqrt{3}$ is $\sqrt{7} - \sqrt{3}$.
Rationalize each denominator:

$$\frac{\sqrt{5}}{\sqrt{3}} = \frac{\sqrt{5} \cdot \sqrt{3}}{\sqrt{3} \cdot \sqrt{3}} = \frac{\sqrt{15}}{3}$$

$$\frac{6}{\sqrt{7} + \sqrt{3}} = \frac{6(\sqrt{7} - \sqrt{3})}{(\sqrt{7} + \sqrt{3})(\sqrt{7} - \sqrt{3})}$$

$$= \frac{6(\sqrt{7} - \sqrt{3})}{7 - 3}$$

$$= \frac{6(\sqrt{7} - \sqrt{3})}{4} = \frac{3(\sqrt{7} - \sqrt{3})}{2}$$

The process of writing the numerator of a radical expression without a radical is called **rationalizing the numerator.**

Rationalize each numerator:

$$\frac{\sqrt[3]{9}}{\sqrt[3]{5}} = \frac{\sqrt[3]{9} \cdot \sqrt[3]{3}}{\sqrt[3]{5} \cdot \sqrt[3]{3}} = \frac{\sqrt[3]{27}}{\sqrt[3]{15}} = \frac{3}{\sqrt[3]{15}}$$

$$\frac{\sqrt{9} + \sqrt{3x}}{12} = \frac{(\sqrt{9} + \sqrt{3x})(\sqrt{9} - \sqrt{3x})}{12(\sqrt{9} - \sqrt{3x})}$$

$$= \frac{9 - 3x}{12(\sqrt{9} - \sqrt{3x})}$$

$$= \frac{3(3 - x)}{3 \cdot 4(3 - \sqrt{3x})} = \frac{3 - x}{4(3 - \sqrt{3x})}$$

Section 7.6   Radical Equations and Problem Solving

SOLVING A RADICAL EQUATION

Step 1. Write the equation so that one radical is by itself on one side of the equation.

Step 2. Raise each side of the equation to a power equal to the index of the radical and simplify.

Step 3. If the equation still contains a radical, repeat Steps 1 and 2. If not, solve the equation.

Step 4. Check all proposed solutions in the original equation.

Solve: $x = \sqrt{4x + 9} + 3$

1. $x - 3 = \sqrt{4x + 9}$

2. $(x - 3)^2 = (\sqrt{4x + 9})^2$
$x^2 - 6x + 9 = 4x + 9$

3. $x^2 - 10x = 0$
$x(x - 10) = 0$
$x = 0$ or $x = 10$

4. The proposed solution 10 checks, but 0 does not. The solution set is $\{10\}$.

DEFINITIONS AND CONCEPTS	**EXAMPLES**
Section 7.7 Complex Numbers	

A **complex number** is a number that can be written in the form $a + bi$, where a and b are real numbers. $$i^2 = -1 \quad \text{and} \quad i = \sqrt{-1}$$	Simplify: $\sqrt{-9}$ $$\sqrt{-9} = \sqrt{-1 \cdot 9} = \sqrt{-1} \cdot \sqrt{9} = i \cdot 3, \text{ or } 3i$$ **Complex Numbers Written in Form $a + bi$** $$\begin{array}{ll} 12 & 12 + 0i \\ -5i & 0 + (-5)i \\ -2 - 3i & -2 + (-3)i \end{array}$$ Multiply: $$\sqrt{-3} \cdot \sqrt{-7} = i\sqrt{3} \cdot i\sqrt{7}$$ $$= i^2\sqrt{21}$$ $$= -\sqrt{21}$$
To add or subtract complex numbers, add or subtract their real parts and then add or subtract their imaginary parts.	Perform each indicated operation. $$(-3 + 2i) - (7 - 4i) = -3 + 2i - 7 + 4i$$ $$= -10 + 6i$$
To multiply complex numbers, multiply as though they were binomials.	$$(-7 - 2i)(6 + i) = -42 - 7i - 12i - 2i^2$$ $$= -42 - 19i - 2(-1)$$ $$= -42 - 19i + 2$$ $$= -40 - 19i$$
The complex numbers $(a + bi)$ and $(a - bi)$ are called **complex conjugates.**	The complex conjugate of $$(3 + 6i) \text{ is } (3 - 6i).$$ Their product is a real number: $$(3 - 6i)(3 + 6i) = 9 - 36i^2$$ $$= 9 - 36(-1) = 9 + 36 = 45$$
To divide complex numbers, multiply the numerator and the denominator by the conjugate of the denominator.	Divide: $$\frac{4}{2 - i} = \frac{4(2 + i)}{(2 - i)(2 + i)}$$ $$= \frac{4(2 + i)}{4 - i^2}$$ $$= \frac{4(2 + i)}{4 - (-1)}$$ $$= \frac{8 + 4i}{5} = \frac{8}{5} + \frac{4}{5}i$$

8

Quadratic Equations and Functions

Taken from:
Intermediate Algebra, Third Edition, by Elayn Martin-Gay

8.1 SOLVING QUADRATIC EQUATIONS BY COMPLETING THE SQUARE

Objectives

A Use the Square Root Property to Solve Quadratic Equations.

B Write Perfect Square Trinomials.

C Solve Quadratic Equations by Completing the Square.

D Use Quadratic Equations to Solve Problems.

Objective **A** Using the Square Root Property

In Chapter 5, we solved quadratic equations by factoring. Recall that a **quadratic, or second-degree, equation** is an equation that can be written in the form $ax^2 + bx + c = 0$, where a, b, and c are real numbers and a is not 0. To solve a quadratic equation such as $x^2 = 9$ by factoring, we use the zero-factor property. To use the zero-factor property, the equation must first be written in the standard form $ax^2 + bx + c = 0$.

$$x^2 = 9$$
$$x^2 - 9 = 0 \qquad \text{Subtract 9 from both sides to write in standard form.}$$
$$(x + 3)(x - 3) = 0 \qquad \text{Factor.}$$
$$x + 3 = 0 \quad \text{or} \quad x - 3 = 0 \qquad \text{Set each factor equal to 0.}$$
$$x = -3 \qquad\qquad x = 3 \qquad \text{Solve.}$$

The solution set is $\{-3, 3\}$, the positive and negative square roots of 9.

Not all quadratic equations can be solved by factoring, so we need to explore other methods. Notice that the solutions of the equation $x^2 = 9$ are two numbers whose square is 9:

$$3^2 = 9 \qquad \text{and} \qquad (-3)^2 = 9$$

Thus, we can solve the equation $x^2 = 9$ by taking the square root of both sides. Be sure to include both $\sqrt{9}$ and $-\sqrt{9}$ as solutions since both $\sqrt{9}$ and $-\sqrt{9}$ are numbers whose square is 9.

$$x^2 = 9$$
$$x = \pm\sqrt{9} \qquad \text{The notation } \pm\sqrt{9} \text{ (read as "plus or minus } \sqrt{9}\text{") indicates the pair of}$$
$$x = \pm 3 \qquad\quad \text{numbers } +\sqrt{9} \text{ and } -\sqrt{9}.$$

This illustrates the square root property.

> **Helpful Hint**
>
> The notation ± 3, for example, is read as "plus or minus 3." It is a shorthand notation for the pair of numbers $+3$ and -3.

Square Root Property

If b is a real number and if $a^2 = b$, then $a = \pm\sqrt{b}$.

EXAMPLE 1 Use the square root property to solve $x^2 = 50$.

Solution:

$$x^2 = 50$$
$$x = \pm\sqrt{50} \qquad \text{Use the square root property.}$$
$$x = \pm 5\sqrt{2} \qquad \text{Simplify the radical.}$$

Continued on next page

PRACTICE PROBLEM 1

Use the square root property to solve $x^2 = 45$.

Answer
1. $\{3\sqrt{5}, -3\sqrt{5}\}$

473

Check:

$$\text{Let } x = 5\sqrt{2}.$$
$$x^2 = 50$$
$$(5\sqrt{2})^2 \overset{?}{=} 50$$
$$25 \cdot 2 \overset{?}{=} 50$$
$$50 = 50 \quad \text{True}$$

$$\text{Let } x = -5\sqrt{2}.$$
$$x^2 = 50$$
$$(-5\sqrt{2})^2 \overset{?}{=} 50$$
$$25 \cdot 2 \overset{?}{=} 50$$
$$50 = 50 \quad \text{True}$$

The solution set is $\{5\sqrt{2}, -5\sqrt{2}\}$.

■ **Work Practice Problem 1**

PRACTICE PROBLEM 2

Use the square root property to solve $5x^2 = 55$.

EXAMPLE 2 Use the square root property to solve $2x^2 = 14$.

Solution: First we get the squared variable alone on one side of the equation.

$$2x^2 = 14$$
$$x^2 = 7 \qquad \text{Divide both sides by 2.}$$
$$x = \pm\sqrt{7} \quad \text{Use the square root property.}$$

Check:

$$\text{Let } x = \sqrt{7}.$$
$$2x^2 = 14$$
$$2(\sqrt{7})^2 \overset{?}{=} 14$$
$$2 \cdot 7 \overset{?}{=} 14$$
$$14 = 14 \quad \text{True}$$

$$\text{Let } x = -\sqrt{7}.$$
$$2x^2 = 14$$
$$2(-\sqrt{7})^2 \overset{?}{=} 14$$
$$2 \cdot 7 \overset{?}{=} 14$$
$$14 = 14 \quad \text{True}$$

The solution set is $\{\sqrt{7}, -\sqrt{7}\}$.

■ **Work Practice Problem 2**

PRACTICE PROBLEM 3

Use the square root property to solve $(x + 2)^2 = 18$.

EXAMPLE 3 Use the square root property to solve $(x + 1)^2 = 12$.

Solution:
$$(x + 1)^2 = 12$$
$$x + 1 = \pm\sqrt{12} \qquad \text{Use the square root property.}$$
$$x + 1 = \pm 2\sqrt{3} \qquad \text{Simplify the radical.}$$
$$x = -1 \pm 2\sqrt{3} \quad \text{Subtract 1 from both sides.}$$

Helpful Hint

Don't forget that $-1 \pm 2\sqrt{3}$, for example, means $-1 + 2\sqrt{3}$ and $-1 - 2\sqrt{3}$. In other words, the equation in Example 3 has two solutions.

Check: Below is a check for $-1 + 2\sqrt{3}$. The check for $-1 - 2\sqrt{3}$ is almost the same and is left for you to do on your own.

$$(x + 1)^2 = 12$$
$$(-1 + 2\sqrt{3} + 1)^2 \overset{?}{=} 12$$
$$(2\sqrt{3})^2 \overset{?}{=} 12$$
$$4 \cdot 3 \overset{?}{=} 12$$
$$12 = 12 \quad \text{True}$$

The solution set is $\{-1 + 2\sqrt{3}, -1 - 2\sqrt{3}\}$.

■ **Work Practice Problem 3**

Answers

2. $\{\sqrt{11}, -\sqrt{11}\}$,

3. $\{-2 + 3\sqrt{2}, -2 - 3\sqrt{2}\}$

EXAMPLE 4 Use the square root property to solve $(2x - 5)^2 = -16$.

Solution: $(2x - 5)^2 = -16$

$2x - 5 = \pm\sqrt{-16}$ Use the square root property.

$2x - 5 = \pm 4i$ Simplify the radical.

$2x = 5 \pm 4i$ Add 5 to both sides.

$x = \dfrac{5 \pm 4i}{2}$ Divide both sides by 2.

Check each proposed solution in the original equation to see that the solution set is $\left\{ \dfrac{5 + 4i}{2}, \dfrac{5 - 4i}{2} \right\}$.

■ **Work Practice Problem 4**

✔**Concept Check** How do you know just by looking that $(x - 2)^2 = -81$ has complex solutions?

Objective **B** Writing Perfect Square Trinomials

Notice from Examples 3 and 4 that, if we write a quadratic equation so that one side is the square of a binomial, we can solve by using the square root property. To write the square of a binomial, we must have a perfect square trinomial. Recall that a perfect square trinomial is a trinomial that can be factored into two identical binomial factors, that is, as a binomial squared.

Perfect Square Trinomials	**Factored Form**
$x^2 + 8x + 16$	$(x + 4)^2$
$x^2 - 6x + 9$	$(x - 3)^2$
$x^2 + 3x + \dfrac{9}{4}$	$\left(x + \dfrac{3}{2} \right)^2$

Notice that for each perfect square trinomial, *the constant term of the trinomial is the square of half the coefficient of the x-term.* For example,

$$x^2 + 8x + 16 \qquad\qquad x^2 - 6x + 9$$

$$\dfrac{1}{2}(8) = 4 \text{ and } 4^2 = 16 \qquad \dfrac{1}{2}(-6) = -3 \text{ and } (-3)^2 = 9$$

EXAMPLE 5 Add the proper constant to $x^2 + 6x$ so that the result is a perfect square trinomial. Then factor.

Solution: We add the square of half the coefficient of x.

$$x^2 + 6x + 9 \quad = \quad (x + 3)^2 \quad \text{In factored form}$$

$$\dfrac{1}{2}(6) = 3 \text{ and } 3^2 = 9$$

■ **Work Practice Problem 5**

PRACTICE PROBLEM 4

Use the square root property to solve $(3x - 1)^2 = -4$.

PRACTICE PROBLEM 5

Add the proper constant to $x^2 + 12x$ so that the result is a perfect square trinomial. Then factor.

Answers

4. $\left\{ \dfrac{1 - 2i}{3}, \dfrac{1 + 2i}{3} \right\}$,

5. $x^2 + 12x + 36 = (x + 6)^2$

✔ **Concept Check Answer**

answers may vary

Copyright 2007 Pearson Education, Inc.

PRACTICE PROBLEM 6

Add the proper constant to $y^2 - 5y$ so that the result is a perfect square trinomial. Then factor.

EXAMPLE 6 Add the proper constant to $x^2 - 3x$ so that the result is a perfect square trinomial. Then factor.

Solution: We add the square of half the coefficient of x.

$$x^2 - 3x + \frac{9}{4} = \left(x - \frac{3}{2} \right)^2 \quad \text{In factored form}$$

$$\frac{1}{2}(-3) = -\frac{3}{2} \text{ and } \left(-\frac{3}{2} \right)^2 = \frac{9}{4}$$

Work Practice Problem 6

Objective **C** Solving by Completing the Square

The process of writing a quadratic equation so that one side is a perfect square trinomial is called **completing the square.** We will use this process in the next examples.

PRACTICE PROBLEM 7

Solve $x^2 + 8x = 1$ by completing the square.

EXAMPLE 7 Solve $p^2 + 2p = 4$ by completing the square.

Solution: First we add the square of half the coefficient of p to both sides so that the resulting trinomial will be a perfect square trinomial. The coefficient of p is 2.

$$\frac{1}{2}(2) = 1 \qquad \text{and} \qquad 1^2 = 1$$

Now we add 1 to both sides of the original equation.

$$p^2 + 2p = 4$$
$$p^2 + 2p + 1 = 4 + 1 \quad \text{Add 1 to both sides.}$$
$$(p + 1)^2 = 5 \qquad \text{Factor the trinomial; simplify the right side.}$$

We may now use the square root property and solve for p.

$$p + 1 = \pm\sqrt{5} \qquad \text{Use the square root property.}$$
$$p = -1 \pm \sqrt{5} \qquad \text{Subtract 1 from both sides.}$$

Don't forget that there are two solutions: $-1 + \sqrt{5}$ and $-1 - \sqrt{5}$. The solution set is $\{-1 + \sqrt{5}, -1 - \sqrt{5}\}$.

Work Practice Problem 7

PRACTICE PROBLEM 8

Solve $y^2 - 5y + 2 = 0$ by completing the square.

EXAMPLE 8 Solve $m^2 - 7m - 1 = 0$ by completing the square.

Solution: First we add 1 to both sides of the equation so that the left side has no constant term. We can then add the constant term on both sides that will make the left side a perfect square trinomial.

$$m^2 - 7m - 1 = 0$$
$$m^2 - 7m = 1$$

Now we find the constant term that makes the left side a perfect square trinomial by squaring half the coefficient of m. We add this constant to both sides of the equation.

$$\frac{1}{2}(-7) = -\frac{7}{2} \qquad \text{and} \qquad \left(-\frac{7}{2} \right)^2 = \frac{49}{4}$$

Answers

6. $y^2 - 5y + \frac{25}{4} = \left(y - \frac{5}{2} \right)^2$,

7. $\{-4 - \sqrt{17}, -4 + \sqrt{17}\}$,

8. $\left\{ \dfrac{5 - \sqrt{17}}{2}, \dfrac{5 + \sqrt{17}}{2} \right\}$

$$m^2 - 7m + \frac{49}{4} = 1 + \frac{49}{4}$$ Add $\frac{49}{4}$ to both sides of the equation.

$$\left(m - \frac{7}{2}\right)^2 = \frac{53}{4}$$ Factor the perfect square trinomial and simplify the right side.

$$m - \frac{7}{2} = \pm\sqrt{\frac{53}{4}}$$ Use the square root property.

$$m = \frac{7}{2} \pm \frac{\sqrt{53}}{2}$$ Add $\frac{7}{2}$ to both sides and simplify $\sqrt{\frac{53}{4}}$.

$$m = \frac{7 \pm \sqrt{53}}{2}$$ Simplify.

The solution set is $\left\{\dfrac{7 + \sqrt{53}}{2}, \dfrac{7 - \sqrt{53}}{2}\right\}$.

◼ **Work Practice Problem 8**

The following steps may be used to solve a quadratic equation such as $ax^2 + bx + c = 0$ by completing the square. This method may be used whether or not the polynomial $ax^2 + bx + c$ is factorable.

Solving a Quadratic Equation in x by Completing the Square

Step 1: If the coefficient of x^2 is 1, go to Step 2. Otherwise, divide both sides of the equation by the coefficient of x^2.

Step 2: Get all variable terms alone on one side of the equation.

Step 3: Complete the square for the resulting binomial by adding the square of half of the coefficient of x to both sides of the equation.

Step 4: Factor the resulting perfect square trinomial and write it as the square of a binomial.

Step 5: Use the square root property to solve for x.

EXAMPLE 9 Solve $4x^2 - 24x + 41 = 0$ by completing the square.

Solution: First we divide both sides of the equation by 4 so that the coefficient of x^2 is 1.

$$4x^2 - 24x + 41 = 0$$

Step 1: $x^2 - 6x + \dfrac{41}{4} = 0$ Divide both sides of the equation by 4.

Step 2: $x^2 - 6x = -\dfrac{41}{4}$ Subtract $\dfrac{41}{4}$ from both sides.

Since $\dfrac{1}{2}(-6) = -3$ and $(-3)^2 = 9$, we add 9 to both sides of the equation.

Step 3: $x^2 - 6x + 9 = -\dfrac{41}{4} + 9$ Add 9 to both sides.

Step 4: $(x - 3)^2 = -\dfrac{41}{4} + \dfrac{36}{4}$ Factor the perfect square trinomial.

$$(x - 3)^2 = -\dfrac{5}{4}$$

PRACTICE PROBLEM 9

Solve $2x^2 - 2x + 7 = 0$ by completing the square.

Answer

9. $\left\{\dfrac{1 + i\sqrt{13}}{2}, \dfrac{1 - i\sqrt{13}}{2}\right\}$

Continued on next page

Step 5: $x - 3 = \pm\sqrt{-\dfrac{5}{4}}$ Use the square root property.

$x - 3 = \pm\dfrac{i\sqrt{5}}{2}$ Simplify the radical.

$x = 3 \pm \dfrac{i\sqrt{5}}{2}$ Add 3 to both sides.

$= \dfrac{6}{2} \pm \dfrac{i\sqrt{5}}{2}$ Find a common denominator.

$= \dfrac{6 \pm i\sqrt{5}}{2}$ Simplify.

The solution set is $\left\{ \dfrac{6 + i\sqrt{5}}{2}, \dfrac{6 - i\sqrt{5}}{2} \right\}$.

■ **Work Practice Problem 9**

Objective D Solving Problems Modeled by Quadratic Equations

Recall the **simple interest** formula $I = Prt$, where I is the interest earned, P is the principal, r is the rate of interest, and t is time. If \$100 is invested at a simple interest rate of 5% annually, at the end of 3 years the total interest I earned is

$$I = P \cdot r \cdot t$$

or

$$I = 100 \cdot 0.05 \cdot 3 = \$15$$

and the new principal is

$$\$100 + \$15 = \$115$$

Most of the time, the interest computed on money borrowed or money deposited is **compound interest.** Unlike simple interest, compound interest is computed on original principal *and* on interest already earned. To see the difference between simple interest and compound interest, suppose that \$100 is invested at a rate of 5% compounded annually. To find the total amount of money at the end of 3 years, we calculate as follows:

$$I = P \cdot r \cdot t$$

First year: Interest $= \$100 \cdot 0.05 \cdot 1 = \$5.00$
            New principal $= \$100.00 + \$5.00 = \$105.00$

Second year: Interest $= \$105.00 \cdot 0.05 \cdot 1 = \$5.25$
            New principal $= 105.00 + \$5.25 = \$110.25$

Third year: Interest $= \$110.25 \cdot 0.05 \cdot 1 \approx \$5.51$
            New principal $= \$110.25 + \$5.51 = \$115.76$

At the end of the third year, the total compound interest earned is \$15.76, whereas the total simple interest earned is \$15.

It is tedious to calculate compound interest as we did above, so we use a compound interest formula. The formula for calculating the total amount of money when interest is compounded annually is

$$A = P(1 + r)^t$$

where P is the original investment, r is the interest rate per compounding period, and t is the number of periods. For example, the amount of money A at the end of 3 years if \$100 is invested at 5% compounded annually is

$$A = \$100(1 + 0.05)^3 \approx 100(1.1576) = \$115.76$$

as we previously calculated.

EXAMPLE 10 **Finding an Interest Rate**

Find the interest rate r if \$2000 compounded annually grows to \$2420 in 2 years.

Solution:

1. UNDERSTAND the problem. For this example, make sure that you understand the formula for compounding interest annually.

2. TRANSLATE. We substitute the given values into the formula.

$$A = P(1 + r)^t$$

$$2420 = 2000(1 + r)^2 \quad \text{Let } A = 2420, P = 2000, \text{ and } t = 2.$$

3. SOLVE. We now solve the equation for r.

$$2420 = 2000(1 + r)^2$$

$$\frac{2420}{2000} = (1 + r)^2 \qquad \text{Divide both sides by 2000.}$$

$$\frac{121}{100} = (1 + r)^2 \qquad \text{Simplify the fraction.}$$

$$\pm\sqrt{\frac{121}{100}} = 1 + r \qquad \text{Use the square root property.}$$

$$\pm\frac{11}{10} = 1 + r \qquad \text{Simplify.}$$

$$-1 \pm \frac{11}{10} = r$$

$$-\frac{10}{10} \pm \frac{11}{10} = r$$

$$\frac{1}{10} = r \quad \text{or} \quad -\frac{21}{10} = r$$

4. INTERPRET. The rate cannot be negative, so we reject $-\dfrac{21}{10}$.

Check: $\dfrac{1}{10} = 0.10 = 10\%$ per year. If we invest \$2000 at 10% compounded annually, in 2 years the amount in the account would be $2000(1 + 0.10)^2 = 2420$ dollars, the desired amount.

State: The interest rate is 10% compounded annually.

🔲 **Work Practice Problem 10**

PRACTICE PROBLEM 10

Use the formula from Example 10 to find the interest rate r if \$1600 compounded annually grows to \$1764 in 2 years.

Answer
10. 5%

8.1 EXERCISE SET

FOR EXTRA HELP

Student Solutions Manual   PH Math/Tutor Center   CD/Video for Review

MathXL
MathXL®   MyMathLab
MyMathLab

Objective Ⓐ *Use the square root property to solve each equation. See Examples 1 through 4.*

1. $x^2 = 16$

2. $x^2 = 49$

3. $x^2 - 7 = 0$

4. $x^2 - 11 = 0$

5. $x^2 = 18$

6. $y^2 = 20$

7. $3z^2 - 30 = 0$

8. $2x^2 = 4$

9. $(x + 5)^2 = 9$

10. $(y - 3)^2 = 4$

11. $(z - 6)^2 = 18$

12. $(y + 4)^2 = 27$

13. $(2x - 3)^2 = 8$

14. $(4x + 9)^2 = 6$

15. $x^2 + 9 = 0$

16. $x^2 + 4 = 0$

17. $x^2 - 6 = 0$

18. $y^2 - 10 = 0$

19. $2z^2 + 16 = 0$

20. $3p^2 + 36 = 0$

21. $(3x - 1)^2 = -16$

22. $(4y + 2)^2 = -25$

23. $(z + 7)^2 = 5$

24. $(x + 10)^2 = 11$

25. $(x + 3)^2 + 8 = 0$

26. $(y - 4)^2 + 18 = 0$

Objective Ⓑ *Add the proper constant to each binomial so that the resulting trinomial is a perfect square trinomial. Then factor the trinomial. See Examples 5 and 6.*

27. $x^2 + 16x$

28. $y^2 + 2y$

29. $z^2 - 12z$

30. $x^2 - 8x$

31. $p^2 + 9p$

32. $n^2 + 5n$

33. $r^2 - r$

34. $p^2 - 7p$

Objective **C** *Solve each equation by completing the square. See Examples 7 through 9.*

35. $x^2 + 8x = -15$

36. $y^2 + 6y = -8$

37. $x^2 + 6x + 2 = 0$

38. $x^2 - 2x - 2 = 0$

39. $x^2 + x - 1 = 0$

40. $x^2 + 3x - 2 = 0$

41. $x^2 + 2x - 5 = 0$

42. $x^2 - 6x + 3 = 0$

43. $y^2 + y - 7 = 0$

44. $x^2 - 7x - 1 = 0$

45. $x^2 + 8x + 1 = 0$

46. $x^2 - 10x + 2 = 0$

47. $3p^2 - 12p + 2 = 0$

48. $2x^2 + 14x - 1 = 0$

49. $2x^2 + 7x = 4$

50. $3x^2 - 4x = 4$

51. $3y^2 + 6y - 4 = 0$

52. $2y^2 + 12y + 3 = 0$

53. $y^2 + 2y + 2 = 0$

54. $x^2 + 4x + 6 = 0$

55. $2a^2 + 8a = -12$

56. $3x^2 + 12x = -14$

57. $2x^2 - x + 6 = 0$

58. $4x^2 - 2x + 5 = 0$

59. $x^2 + 10x + 28 = 0$

60. $y^2 + 8y + 18 = 0$

61. $z^2 + 3z - 4 = 0$

62. $y^2 + y - 2 = 0$

63. $2x^2 - 4x + 3 = 0$

64. $9x^2 - 36x = -40$

65. $3x^2 + 3x = 5$

66. $5y^2 - 15y = 1$

Objective **D** *Use the formula $A = P(1 + r)^t$ to solve Exercises 67 through 70. See Example 10.*

67. Find the rate r at which $3000 grows to $4320 in 2 years.

68. Find the rate r at which $800 grows to $882 in 2 years.

69. Find the rate r at which $810 grows to approximately $1000 in 2 years.

70. Find the rate r at which $2000 grows to $2880 in 2 years.

Neglecting air resistance, the distance $s(t)$ in feet traveled by a freely falling object is given by the function $s(t) = 16t^2$, where t is time in seconds. Use this formula to solve Exercises 71 through 74. Round answers to two decimal places.

71. The Petronas Towers in Kuala Lumpur, built in 1997, are the tallest buildings in Malaysia. Each tower is 1483 feet tall. How long would it take an object to fall to the ground from the top of one of the towers? (*Source:* Council on Tall Buildings and Urban Habitat, Lehigh University)

72. The height of the Chicago Beach Tower Hotel, built in 1998 in Dubai, United Arab Emirates, is 1053 feet. How long would it take an object to fall to the ground from the top of the building? (*Source:* Council on Tall Buildings and Urban Habitat, Lehigh University)

73. The Rogun Dam in Tajikistan (part of the former USSR that borders Afghanistan) is the tallest dam in the world at 1100 feet. How long would it take an object to fall from the top to the base of the dam? (*Source:* U.S. Committee on Large Dams of the International Commission on Large Dams)

74. The Hoover Dam, located on the Colorado River on the border of Nevada and Arizona near Las Vegas, is 725 feet tall. How long would it take an object to fall from the top to the base of the dam? (*Source:* U.S. Committee on Large Dams of the International Commission on Large Dams)

Solve.

△ **75.** The area of a square room is 225 square feet. Find the dimensions of the room.

△ **76.** The area of a circle is 36π square inches. Find the radius of the circle.

△ **77.** An isosceles right triangle has legs of equal length. If the hypotenuse is 20 centimeters long, find the length of each leg.

Review

Simplify each expression. See Section 7.5.

78. $\dfrac{6 + 4\sqrt{5}}{2}$

79. $\dfrac{10 - 20\sqrt{3}}{2}$

80. $\dfrac{3 - 9\sqrt{2}}{6}$

81. $\dfrac{12 - 8\sqrt{7}}{16}$

Evaluate $\sqrt{b^2 - 4ac}$ for each set of values. See Section 7.3.

82. $a = 2, b = 4, c = -1$ **83.** $a = 1, b = 6, c = 2$ **84.** $a = 3, b = -1, c = -2$ **85.** $a = 1, b = -3, c = -1$

Concept Extensions

Without solving, determine whether the solutions of each equation are real numbers or complex, but not real numbers. See the Concept Check in this section.

86. $(x + 1)^2 = -1$

87. $(y - 5)^2 = -9$

88. $3z^2 = 10$

89. $4x^2 = 17$

90. $(2y - 5)^2 + 7 = 3$

91. $(3m + 2)^2 + 4 = 1$

92. In your own words, what is the difference between simple interest and compound interest?

93. If you are depositing money in an account that pays 4%, would you prefer the interest to be simple or compound? Explain your answer.

94. If you are borrowing money at a rate of 10%, would you prefer the interest to be simple or compound? Explain your answer.

Find two possible missing terms so that each is a perfect square trinomial.

95. $x^2 + \quad + 16$

96. $y^2 + \quad + 9$

A common equation used in business is a demand equation. It expresses the relationship between the unit price of some commodity and the quantity demanded. For Exercises 97 and 98, p represents the unit price and x represents the quantity demanded in thousands.

97. A manufacturing company has found that the demand equation for a certain type of scissors is given by the equation $p = -x^2 + 47$. Find the demand for the scissors if the price is $11 per pair.

98. Acme, Inc., sells desk lamps and has found that the demand equation for a certain style of desk lamp is given by the equation $p = -x^2 + 15$. Find the demand for the desk lamp if the price is $7 per lamp.

STUDY SKILLS BUILDER

Learning New Terms?

By now, you have encountered many new terms. It's never too late to make a list of new terms and review them frequently. Remember that placing these new terms (including page references) on 3×5 index cards might help you later when you're preparing for a quiz.

Answer the following.

1. How do new terms stand out in this text so that they can be found?

2. Name one way placing a word and its definition on a 3×5 card might be helpful.

8.2 SOLVING QUADRATIC EQUATIONS BY USING THE QUADRATIC FORMULA

Objectives

A Solve Quadratic Equations by Using the Quadratic Formula.

B Determine the Number and Type of Solutions of a Quadratic Equation by Using the Discriminant.

C Solve Problems Modeled by Quadratic Equations.

Objective A Solving Equations by Using the Quadratic Formula

Any quadratic equation can be solved by completing the square. Since the same sequence of steps is repeated each time we complete the square, let's complete the square for a general quadratic equation, $ax^2 + bx + c = 0$. By doing so, we will find a pattern for the solutions of a quadratic equation known as the **quadratic formula.**

Recall that to complete the square for an equation such as $ax^2 + bx + c = 0$, $a \neq 0$, we first divide both sides by the coefficient of x^2.

$$ax^2 + bx + c = 0$$

$$x^2 + \frac{b}{a}x + \frac{c}{a} = 0 \qquad \text{Divide both sides by } a, \text{ the coefficient of } x^2.$$

$$x^2 + \frac{b}{a}x = -\frac{c}{a} \qquad \text{Subtract the constant } \frac{c}{a} \text{ from both sides.}$$

Next we find the square of half $\frac{b}{a}$, the coefficient of x.

$$\frac{1}{2}\left(\frac{b}{a}\right) = \left(\frac{b}{2a}\right) \qquad \text{and} \qquad \left(\frac{b}{2a}\right)^2 = \frac{b^2}{4a^2}$$

Now we add this result to both sides of the equation.

$$x^2 + \frac{b}{a}x + \frac{b^2}{4a^2} = -\frac{c}{a} + \frac{b^2}{4a^2} \qquad \text{Add } \frac{b^2}{4a^2} \text{ to both sides.}$$

$$x^2 + \frac{b}{a}x + \frac{b^2}{4a^2} = \frac{-c \cdot 4a}{a \cdot 4a} + \frac{b^2}{4a^2} \qquad \text{Find a common denominator on the right side.}$$

$$x^2 + \frac{b}{a}x + \frac{b^2}{4a^2} = \frac{b^2 - 4ac}{4a^2} \qquad \text{Simplify the right side.}$$

$$\left(x + \frac{b}{2a}\right)^2 = \frac{b^2 - 4ac}{4a^2} \qquad \text{Factor the perfect square trinomial on the left side.}$$

$$x + \frac{b}{2a} = \pm\sqrt{\frac{b^2 - 4ac}{4a^2}} \qquad \text{Use the square root property.}$$

$$x + \frac{b}{2a} = \pm\frac{\sqrt{b^2 - 4ac}}{2a} \qquad \text{Simplify the radical.}$$

$$x = -\frac{b}{2a} \pm \frac{\sqrt{b^2 - 4ac}}{2a} \qquad \text{Subtract } \frac{b}{2a} \text{ from both sides.}$$

$$x = \frac{-b \pm \sqrt{b^2 - 4ac}}{2a} \qquad \text{Simplify.}$$

The resulting equation identifies the solutions of the general quadratic equation in standard form and is called the quadratic formula. It can be used to solve any equation written in standard form $ax^2 + bx + c = 0$ as long as a is not 0.

Quadratic Formula

A quadratic equation written in the form $ax^2 + bx + c = 0$, $a \neq 0$, has the solutions

$$x = \frac{-b \pm \sqrt{b^2 - 4ac}}{2a}$$

PRACTICE PROBLEM 1

Solve: $2x^2 + 9x + 10 = 0$

EXAMPLE 1   Solve: $3x^2 + 16x + 5 = 0$

Solution: This equation is in standard form with $a = 3$, $b = 16$, and $c = 5$. We substitute these values into the quadratic formula.

$$x = \frac{-b \pm \sqrt{b^2 - 4ac}}{2a} \qquad \text{Quadratic formula}$$

$$= \frac{-16 \pm \sqrt{16^2 - 4(3)(5)}}{2(3)} \qquad \text{Let } a = 3, b = 16, \text{ and } c = 5.$$

$$= \frac{-16 \pm \sqrt{256 - 60}}{6}$$

$$= \frac{-16 \pm \sqrt{196}}{6} = \frac{-16 \pm 14}{6}$$

$$x = \frac{-16 + 14}{6} = -\frac{1}{3} \quad \text{or} \quad x = \frac{-16 - 14}{6} = -\frac{30}{6} = -5$$

The solution set is $\left\{ -\frac{1}{3}, -5 \right\}$.

◼ **Work Practice Problem 1**

> **Helpful Hint**
>
> To replace a, b, and c correctly in the quadratic formula, write the quadratic equation in standard form, $ax^2 + bx + c = 0$.

PRACTICE PROBLEM 2

Solve: $2x^2 - 6x - 1 = 0$

EXAMPLE 2   Solve: $2x^2 - 4x = 3$

Solution: First we write the equation in standard form by subtracting 3 from both sides.

$$2x^2 - 4x - 3 = 0$$

Now $a = 2$, $b = -4$, and $c = -3$. We substitute these values into the quadratic formula.

$$x = \frac{-b \pm \sqrt{b^2 - 4ac}}{2a}$$

$$= \frac{-(-4) \pm \sqrt{(-4)^2 - 4(2)(-3)}}{2(2)}$$

$$= \frac{4 \pm \sqrt{16 + 24}}{4}$$

$$= \frac{4 \pm \sqrt{40}}{4}$$

$$= \frac{4 \pm 2\sqrt{10}}{4}$$

$$= \frac{2\left(2 \pm \sqrt{10}\right)}{2 \cdot 2}$$

$$= \frac{2 \pm \sqrt{10}}{2}$$

The solution set is $\left\{ \dfrac{2 + \sqrt{10}}{2}, \dfrac{2 - \sqrt{10}}{2} \right\}$.

◼ **Work Practice Problem 2**

Answers

1. $\left\{ -\dfrac{5}{2}, -2 \right\}$,

2. $\left\{ \dfrac{3 + \sqrt{11}}{2}, \dfrac{3 - \sqrt{11}}{2} \right\}$

✔**Concept Check** For the quadratic equation $x^2 = 7$, which substitution is correct?

a. $a = 1, b = 0,$ and $c = -7$
b. $a = 1, b = 0,$ and $c = 7$
c. $a = 0, b = 0,$ and $c = 7$
d. $a = 1, b = 1,$ and $c = -7$

Helpful Hint

To simplify the expression $\dfrac{4 \pm 2\sqrt{10}}{4}$ in Example 2, note that we factored 2 out of both terms of the numerator *before* simplifying.

$$\frac{4 \pm 2\sqrt{10}}{4} = \frac{2(2 \pm \sqrt{10})}{2 \cdot 2} = \frac{2 \pm \sqrt{10}}{2}$$

EXAMPLE 3 Solve: $\dfrac{1}{4}m^2 - m + \dfrac{1}{2} = 0$

Solution: We could use the quadratic formula with $a = \dfrac{1}{4}, b = -1,$ and $c = \dfrac{1}{2}$. Instead, let's find a simpler, equivalent, standard-form equation whose coefficients are not fractions.

First we multiply both sides of the equation by 4 to clear the fractions.

$$4\left(\frac{1}{4}m^2 - m + \frac{1}{2}\right) = 4 \cdot 0$$

$$m^2 - 4m + 2 = 0 \quad \text{Simplify.}$$

Now we can substitute $a = 1, b = -4,$ and $c = 2$ into the quadratic formula and simplify.

$$m = \frac{-(-4) \pm \sqrt{(-4)^2 - 4(1)(2)}}{2(1)}$$

$$= \frac{4 \pm \sqrt{16 - 8}}{2}$$

$$= \frac{4 \pm \sqrt{8}}{2} = \frac{4 \pm 2\sqrt{2}}{2} = \frac{2(2 \pm \sqrt{2})}{2} = 2 \pm \sqrt{2}$$

The solution set is $\{2 + \sqrt{2}, 2 - \sqrt{2}\}$.

■ **Work Practice Problem 3**

EXAMPLE 4 Solve: $p = -3p^2 - 3$

Solution: The equation in standard form is $3p^2 + p + 3 = 0$. Thus, $a = 3, b = 1,$ and $c = 3$ in the quadratic formula.

$$p = \frac{-1 \pm \sqrt{1^2 - 4(3)(3)}}{2(3)} = \frac{-1 \pm \sqrt{1 - 36}}{6}$$

$$= \frac{-1 \pm \sqrt{-35}}{6} = \frac{-1 \pm i\sqrt{35}}{6}$$

The solution set is $\left\{\dfrac{-1 + i\sqrt{35}}{6}, \dfrac{-1 - i\sqrt{35}}{6}\right\}$.

■ **Work Practice Problem 4**

PRACTICE PROBLEM 3

Solve: $\dfrac{1}{6}x^2 - \dfrac{1}{3}x - 1 = 0$

PRACTICE PROBLEM 4

Solve: $x = -4x^2 - 4$

Answers
3. $\{1 + \sqrt{7}, 1 - \sqrt{7}\}$,
4. $\left\{\dfrac{-1 - 3i\sqrt{7}}{8}, \dfrac{-1 + 3i\sqrt{7}}{8}\right\}$

✔ **Concept Check Answer**
a

✔**Concept Check** What is the first step in solving $-3x^2 = 5x - 4$ using the quadratic formula?

Objective B Using the Discriminant

In the quadratic formula $x = \dfrac{-b \pm \sqrt{b^2 - 4ac}}{2a}$, the radicand $b^2 - 4ac$ is called the **discriminant** because when we know its value, we can **discriminate** among the possible number and type of solutions of a quadratic equation. Possible values of the discriminant and their meanings are summarized next.

Discriminant

The following table relates the discriminant $b^2 - 4ac$ of a quadratic equation of the form $ax^2 + bx + c = 0$ with the number and type of solutions of the equation.

$b^2 - 4ac$	Number and Type of Solutions
Positive	Two real solutions
Zero	One real solution
Negative	Two complex but not real solutions

PRACTICE PROBLEM 5

Use the discriminant to determine the number and type of solutions of $x^2 + 4x + 4 = 0$.

EXAMPLE 5 Use the discriminant to determine the number and type of solutions of $x^2 + 2x + 1$.

Solution: In $x^2 + 2x + 1 = 0$, $a = 1$, $b = 2$, and $c = 1$. Thus,

$$b^2 - 4ac = 2^2 - 4(1)(1) = 0$$

Since $b^2 - 4ac = 0$, this quadratic equation has one real solution.

▭ **Work Practice Problem 5**

PRACTICE PROBLEM 6

Use the discriminant to determine the number and type of solutions of $5x^2 + 7 = 0$.

EXAMPLE 6 Use the discriminant to determine the number and type of solutions of $3x^2 + 2 = 0$.

Solution: In this equation, $a = 3$, $b = 0$, and $c = 2$. Then

$$b^2 - 4ac = 0^2 - 4(3)(2) = -24$$

Since $b^2 - 4ac$ is negative, this quadratic equation has two complex but not real solutions.

▭ **Work Practice Problem 6**

PRACTICE PROBLEM 7

Use the discriminant to determine the number and type of solutions of $3x^2 - 2x - 2 = 0$.

EXAMPLE 7 Use the discriminant to determine the number and type of solutions of $2x^2 - 7x - 4 = 0$.

Solution: In this equation, $a = 2$, $b = -7$, and $c = -4$. Then

$$b^2 - 4ac = (-7)^2 - 4(2)(-4) = 81$$

Since $b^2 - 4ac$ is positive, this quadratic equation has two real solutions.

▭ **Work Practice Problem 7**

Answers

5. one real solution,
6. two complex but not real solutions,
7. two real solutions

✔ **Concept Check Answer**

Write the equation in standard form.

The discriminant helps us determine the number and type of solutions of a quadratic equation, $ax^2 + bx + c = 0$. Recall from Chapter 5 that the solutions of this equation are the same as the x-intercepts of its related graph $f(x) = ax^2 + bx + c$. This means that the discriminant of $ax^2 + bx + c = 0$ also tells us the number of x-intercepts for the graph of $f(x) = ax^2 + bx + c$, or, equivalently, $y = ax^2 + bx + c$.

Graph of f(x) = ax² + bx + c or y = ax² + bx + c

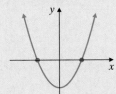
$b^2 - 4ac > 0$,
$f(x)$ has two x-intercepts

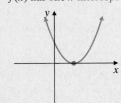
$b^2 - 4ac = 0$,
$f(x)$ has one x-intercept

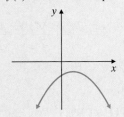
$b^2 - 4ac < 0$,
$f(x)$ has no x-intercepts

Objective C Solving Problems Modeled by Quadratic Equations

The quadratic formula is useful in solving problems that are modeled by quadratic equations.

△ **EXAMPLE 8** **Calculating Distance Saved**

At a local university, students often leave the sidewalk and cut across the lawn to save walking distance. Given the diagram below of a favorite place to cut across the lawn, approximate to the nearest foot how many feet of walking distance a student saves by cutting across the lawn instead of walking on the sidewalk.

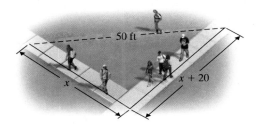

Solution:

1. UNDERSTAND. Read and reread the problem. You may want to review the Pythagorean theorem.
2. TRANSLATE. By the Pythagorean theorem, we have

   In words: $(\text{leg})^2 + (\text{leg})^2 = (\text{hypotenuse})^2$

   Translate: $x^2 + (x + 20)^2 = 50^2$

3. SOLVE. Use the quadratic formula to solve.

   $x^2 + x^2 + 40x + 400 = 2500$ Square $(x + 20)$ and 50.

   $2x^2 + 40x - 2100 = 0$ Write the equation in standard form.

Continued on next page

PRACTICE PROBLEM 8

Given the diagram below, approximate to the nearest foot how many feet of walking distance a person saves by cutting across the lawn instead of walking on the sidewalk.

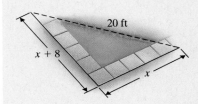

Answer
8. 8 ft

We can use the quadratic formula right now with $a = 2, b = 40,$ and $c = -2100$. Instead, just as in Example 3, you may want to find a simpler, equivalent equation by dividing both sides of the equation by 2.

$x^2 + 20x - 1050 = 0$ Divide by 2.

Here, $a = 1, b = 20,$ and $c = -1050$. By the quadratic formula,

$$x = \frac{-20 \pm \sqrt{20^2 - 4(1)(-1050)}}{2 \cdot 1}$$

$$= \frac{-20 \pm \sqrt{400 + 4200}}{2} = \frac{-20 \pm \sqrt{4600}}{2}$$

$$= \frac{-20 \pm \sqrt{100 \cdot 46}}{2} = \frac{-20 \pm 10\sqrt{46}}{2}$$

$$= -10 \pm 5\sqrt{46} \qquad \text{Simplify.}$$

Check:

4. INTERPRET. We check our calculations from the quadratic formula. The length of a side of a triangle can't be negative, so we reject $-10 - 5\sqrt{46}$. Since $-10 + 5\sqrt{46} \approx 24$ feet, the walking distance along the sidewalk is

$$x + (x + 20) \approx 24 + (24 + 20) = 68 \text{ feet.}$$

State: A person saves about $68 - 50$ or 18 feet of walking distance by cutting across the lawn.

🔲 **Work Practice Problem 8**

PRACTICE PROBLEM 9

How long after the object in Example 9 is thrown will it be 100 feet from the ground? Round to the nearest tenth of a second.

EXAMPLE 9 **Calculating Landing Time**

An object is thrown upward from the top of a 200-foot cliff with a velocity of 12 feet per second. The height above ground h in feet of the object after t seconds is

$$h = -16t^2 + 12t + 200$$

How long after the object is thrown will it strike the ground? Round to the nearest tenth of a second.

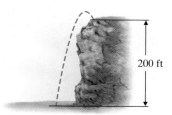

200 ft

Solution:

1. UNDERSTAND. Read and reread the problem.
2. TRANSLATE. Since we want to know when the object strikes the ground, we want to know when the height $h = 0$, or

$$0 = -16t^2 + 12t + 200$$

3. SOLVE. First we divide both sides of the equation by -4.

$$0 = 4t^2 - 3t - 50 \qquad \text{Divide both sides by } -4.$$

Answer

9. 1.7 sec

Here, $a = 4$, $b = -3$, and $c = -50$. By the quadratic formula,

$$t = \frac{-(-3) \pm \sqrt{(-3)^2 - 4(4)(-50)}}{2 \cdot 4}$$

$$= \frac{3 \pm \sqrt{9 + 800}}{8}$$

$$= \frac{3 \pm \sqrt{809}}{8}$$

Check:

4. INTERPRET. We check our calculations from the quadratic formula. Since the time won't be negative, we reject the proposed solution $\dfrac{3 - \sqrt{809}}{8}$.

State: The time it takes for the object to strike the ground is exactly $\dfrac{3 + \sqrt{809}}{8}$ seconds ≈ 3.9 seconds.

⬛ **Work Practice Problem 9**

🔲 **CALCULATOR EXPLORATIONS** Graphing

In Section 5.7, we showed how we can use a grapher to approximate real number solutions of a quadratic equation written in standard form. We can also use a grapher to solve a quadratic equation when it is not written in standard form. For example, to solve $(x + 1)^2 = 12$, the quadratic equation in Example 3 of Section 8.1, we graph the following on the same set of axes. We use Xmin $= -10$, Xmax $= 10$, Ymin $= -13$, and Ymax $= 13$.

$$Y_1 = (x + 1)^2 \quad \text{and} \quad Y_2 = 12$$

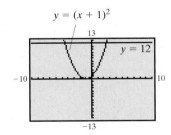

We use the INTERSECT feature or the ZOOM and TRACE features to locate the points of intersection of the graphs. The x-values of these points are the solutions of $(x + 1)^2 = 12$. The solutions, rounded to two decimal points, are 2.46 and -4.46.

Check to see that these numbers are approximations of the exact solutions, $-1 \pm 2\sqrt{3}$.

Use a grapher to solve each quadratic equation. Round all solutions to the nearest hundredth.

1. $x(x - 5) = 8$
2. $x(x + 2) = 5$
3. $x^2 + 0.5x = 0.3x + 1$
4. $x^2 - 2.6x = -2.2x + 3$
5. Use a grapher to solve $(2x - 5)^2 = -16$, (Example 4, Section 8.1) using the window

$$\begin{aligned}
\text{Xmin} &= -20 \\
\text{Xmax} &= 20 \\
\text{Xscl} &= 1 \\
\text{Ymin} &= -20 \\
\text{Ymax} &= 20 \\
\text{Yscl} &= 1
\end{aligned}$$

Explain the results. Compare your results with the solution found in Example 4 of Section 8.1.

6. What are the advantages and disadvantages of using a grapher to solve quadratic equations?

Mental Math

Identify the values of a, b, and c in each quadratic equation.

1. $x^2 + 3x + 1 = 0$

2. $2x^2 - 5x - 7 = 0$

3. $7x^2 - 4 = 0$

4. $x^2 + 9 = 0$

5. $6x^2 - x = 0$

6. $5x^2 + 3x = 0$

8.2 EXERCISE SET

FOR EXTRA HELP

Student Solutions Manual | PH Math/Tutor Center | CD/Video for Review | Math XL MathXL® | MyMathLab MyMathLab

Objective A *Use the quadratic formula to solve each equation. These equations have real number solutions only. See Examples 1 through 3.*

1. $m^2 + 5m - 6 = 0$

2. $p^2 + 11p - 12 = 0$

3. $2y = 5y^2 - 3$

4. $5x^2 - 3 = 14x$

5. $x^2 - 6x + 9 = 0$

6. $y^2 + 10y + 25 = 0$

 7. $x^2 + 7x + 4 = 0$

8. $y^2 + 5y + 3 = 0$

9. $8m^2 - 2m = 7$

10. $11n^2 - 9n = 1$

11. $3m^2 - 7m = 3$

12. $x^2 - 13 = 5x$

13. $\frac{1}{2}x^2 - x - 1 = 0$

14. $\frac{1}{6}x^2 + x + \frac{1}{3} = 0$

15. $\frac{2}{5}y^2 + \frac{1}{5}y = \frac{3}{5}$

16. $\frac{1}{8}x^2 + x = \frac{5}{2}$

17. $\frac{1}{3}y^2 - y - \frac{1}{6} = 0$

18. $\frac{1}{2}y^2 = y + \frac{1}{2}$

19. $x^2 + 5x = -2$

20. $y^2 - 8 = 4y$

21. $(m + 2)(2m - 6) = 5(m - 1) - 12$

22. $7p(p - 2) + 2(p + 4) = 3$

Mixed Practice *Use the quadratic formula to solve each equation. These equations have real solutions and complex, but not real, solutions. See Examples 1 through 4.*

23. $x^2 + 6x + 13 = 0$

24. $x^2 + 2x + 2 = 0$

25. $(x + 5)(x - 1) = 2$

26. $x(x + 6) = 2$

27. $6 = -4x^2 + 3x$

28. $9x^2 + x + 2 = 0$

29. $\dfrac{x^2}{3} - x = \dfrac{5}{3}$

30. $\dfrac{x^2}{2} - 3 = -\dfrac{9}{2}x$

31. $10y^2 + 10y + 3 = 0$

32. $3y^2 + 6y + 5 = 0$

33. $x(6x + 2) = 3$

34. $x(7x + 1) = 2$

35. $\dfrac{2}{5}y^2 + \dfrac{1}{5}y + \dfrac{3}{5} = 0$

36. $\dfrac{1}{8}x^2 + x + \dfrac{5}{2} = 0$

37. $\dfrac{1}{2}y^2 = y - \dfrac{1}{2}$

38. $\dfrac{2}{3}x^2 - \dfrac{20}{3}x = -\dfrac{100}{6}$

39. $(n - 2)^2 = 2n$

40. $\left(p - \dfrac{1}{2}\right)^2 = \dfrac{p}{2}$

Objective **B** *Use the discriminant to determine the number and types of solutions of each equation. See Examples 5 through 7.*

41. $x^2 - 5 = 0$

42. $x^2 - 7 = 0$

43. $4x^2 + 12x = -9$

44. $9x^2 + 1 = 6x$

45. $3x = -2x^2 + 7$

46. $3x^2 = 5 - 7x$

47. $6 = 4x - 5x^2$

48. $8x = 3 - 9x^2$

49. $9x - 2x^2 + 5 = 0$

50. $5 - 4x + 12x^2 = 0$

Objective **C** *Solve. See Examples 8 and 9.*

△ **51.** Nancy, Thelma, and John Varner live on a corner lot. Often, neighborhood children cut across their lot to save walking distance. Given the diagram below, approximate to the nearest foot how many feet of walking distance children save by cutting across their property instead of walking around the lot.

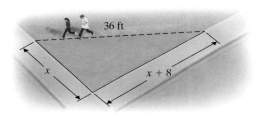

△ **52.** Given the diagram below, approximate to the nearest foot how many feet of walking distance a person saves by cutting across the lawn instead of walking on the sidewalk.

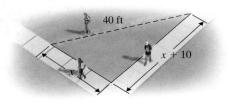

△ **53.** The hypotenuse of an isosceles right triangle is 2 centimeters longer than either of its legs. Find the exact length of each side. (*Hint:* An isosceles right triangle is a right triangle whose legs are the same length.)

△ **54.** The hypotenuse of an isosceles right triangle is one meter longer than either of its legs. Find the length of each side.

△ **55.** Bailey Wilson's rectangular dog pen for her Irish setter must have an area of 400 square feet. Also, the length must be 10 feet longer than the width. Find the dimensions of the pen.

△ **56.** An entry in the Peach Festival Poster Contest must be rectangular and have an area of 1200 square inches. Furthermore, its length must be 20 inches longer than its width. Find the dimensions each entry must have.

△ **57.** A holding pen for cattle must be square and have a diagonal length of 100 meters.
   a. Find the length of a side of the pen.
   b. Find the area of the pen.

△ **58.** A rectangle is three times longer than it is wide. It has a diagonal of length 50 centimeters.
   a. Find the dimensions of the rectangle.
   b. Find the perimeter of the rectangle.

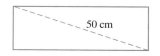

▦ **59.** The heaviest reported door in the world is the
△ 708.6 ton radiation shield door in the National Institute for Fusion Science at Toki, Japan. If the height of the door is 1.1 feet longer than its width, and its front area (neglecting depth) is 1439.9 square feet, find its width and height. [Interesting note: the door is 6.6 feet thick.] (*Source: Guiness World Records*)

▦ **60.** Christi and Robbie Wegmann are constructing a
△ rectangular stained glass window whose length is 7.3 inches longer than its width. If the area of the window is 569.9 square inches, find its width and length.

△ **61.** The base of a triangle is four more than twice its height. If the area of the triangle is 42 square centimeters, find its base and height.

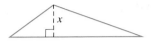

△ **62.** If a point B divides a line segment such that the smaller portion is to the larger portion as the larger is to the whole, the whole is the length of the *golden ratio*.

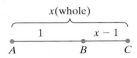

The golden ratio was thought by the Greeks to be the most pleasing to the eye, and many of their buildings contained numerous examples of the golden ratio. The value of the golden ratio is the positive solution of the following equation.

$$\underset{\text{(larger)}}{\overset{\text{(smaller)}}{}}\ \frac{x-1}{1} = \frac{1}{x}\ \underset{\text{(whole)}}{\overset{\text{(larger)}}{}}$$

Find this value.

The Wollomombi Falls in Australia have a height of 1100 feet. A pebble is thrown upward from the top of the falls with an initial velocity of 20 feet per second. The height of the pebble h in feet after t seconds is given by the equation $h = -16t^2 + 20t + 1100$. *Use this equation for Exercises 63 and 64.*

63. How long after the pebble is thrown will it hit the ground? Round to the nearest tenth of a second.

64. How long after the pebble is thrown will it be 550 feet from the ground? Round to the nearest tenth of a second.

A ball is thrown downward from the top of a 180-foot building with an initial velocity of 20 feet per second. The height of the ball h in feet after t seconds is given by the equation $h = -16t^2 - 20t + 180$. *Use this equation to answer Exercises 65 and 66.*

65. How long after the ball is thrown will it strike the ground? Round the result to the nearest tenth of a second.

66. How long after the ball is thrown will it be 50 feet from the ground? Round the result to the nearest tenth of a second.

Review

Solve each equation. See Sections 6.4 and 7.6.

67. $\sqrt{5x - 2} = 3$ **68.** $\sqrt{y + 2} + 7 = 12$ **69.** $\dfrac{1}{x} + \dfrac{2}{5} = \dfrac{7}{x}$ **70.** $\dfrac{10}{z} = \dfrac{5}{z} - \dfrac{1}{3}$

Factor. See Section 5.5 and 5.6.

71. $x^4 + x^2 - 20$ **72.** $2y^4 + 11y^2 - 6$

73. $z^4 - 13z^2 + 36$ **74.** $x^4 - 1$

Concept Extensions

For each quadratic equation, choose the correct substitution for a, b, and c in the standard form $ax^2 + bx + c = 0$.

75. $x^2 = -10$
    a. $a = 1, b = 0, c = -10$
    b. $a = 1, b = 0, c = 10$
    c. $a = 0, b = 1, c = -10$
    d. $a = 1, b = 1, c = 10$

76. $x^2 + 5 = -x$
    a. $a = 1, b = 5, c = -1$
    b. $a = 1, b = -1, c = 5$
    c. $a = 1, b = 5, c = 1$
    d. $a = 1, b = 1, c = 5$

77. Solve Exercise 1 by factoring. Explain the result.

78. Solve Exercise 2 by factoring. Explain the result.

Use the quadratic formula and a calculator to approximate each solution to the nearest tenth.

79. $2x^2 - 6x + 3 = 0$ **80.** $3.6x^2 + 1.8x - 4.3 = 0$

The graph shows the daily low temperatures for one week in New Orleans, Louisiana. Use this graph to answer Exercises 81 through 84.

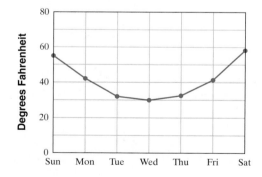

81. Which day of the week shows the greatest decrease in the low temperature?

82. Which day of the week shows the greatest increase in the low temperature?

83. Which day of the week had the lowest temperature?

84. Use the graph to estimate the low temperature on Thursday.

Notice that the shape of the temperature graph for Exercises 81 through 84 is similar to a parabola (see Section 3.8). In fact, this graph can be approximated by the quadratic function $f(x) = 3x^2 - 18x + 57$, where $f(x)$ is the temperature in degrees Fahrenheit and x is the number of days from Sunday. Use this function to answer Exercises 85 and 86.

85. Use the given quadratic function to approximate the low temperature on Thursday. Does your answer agree with the graph?

86. Use the given function and the quadratic formula to find when the low temperature was 35°F. [*Hint:* Let $f(x) = 35$ and solve for x.] Round your answer to one decimal place and interpret your result. Does your answer agree with the graph above?

87. Procter & Gamble's net earnings can be modeled by the quadratic function $f(x) = 213x^2 - 66.4x + 4689$, where $f(x)$ is net earnings in millions of dollars and x is the number of years after 2001. (*Source:* Based on data from The Procter & Gamble Company, 2001–2004)

  a. Find Procter & Gamble's net earnings in 2004.

  b. If the trend described by the model continues, predict the year after 2001 in which Procter & Gamble's net earnings will be $9682 million.

88. The number of inmates in custody in U.S. prisons and jails can be modeled by the quadratic function $p(x) = -18x^2 + 298x + 988$, where $p(x)$ is the number of inmates in thousands and x is the number of years after 1995. (*Source:* Based on data from the Bureau of Justice Statistics, U.S. Department of Justice, 1995–2004)

  a. Find the number of prison and jail inmates in the United States in 1998.
  b. Find the number of prison and jail inmates in the United States in 2000.
  c. If the trend described by the model continues, find a year in which the number of prisoners is 2,212,000 (that is, 2212 thousand).

89. The average total daily supply y of motor gasoline (in thousands of barrels per day) in the United States for the period 2000–2003 can be approximated by the equation $y = -13x^2 + 221x + 8476$, where x is the number of years after 2000. (*Source:* Based on data from the Energy Information Administration)

  a. Find the average total daily supply of motor gasoline in 2001.
  b. According to this model, in what year will the average total daily supply of motor gasoline be 9334 thousand barrels per day?

90. The relationship between body weight and the Recommended Dietary Allowance (RDA) for vitamin A in children up to age 10 is modeled by the quadratic equation $y = 0.149x^2 - 4.475x + 406.478$, where y is the RDA for vitamin A in micrograms for a child whose weight is x pounds. (*Source:* Based on data from the Food and Nutrition Board, National Academy of Sciences—Institute of Medicine, 1989)

  a. Determine the vitamin A requirements of a child who weighs 35 pounds.
  b. What is the weight of a child whose RDA of vitamin A is 600 micrograms? Round your answer to the nearest pound.

91. Use a grapher to solve Exercise 79.

92. Use a grapher to solve Exercise 80.

 STUDY SKILLS BUILDER

How Well Do You Know Your Textbook?

Let's check to see whether you are familiar with your textbook yet. For help, see Section 1.1 in this text.

1. What does the 🌐 icon mean?
2. What does the ✎ icon mean?
3. What does the △ icon mean?
4. Where can you find a review for each chapter? What answers to this review can be found in the back of your text?
5. Each chapter contains an overview of the chapter along with examples. What is this feature called?
6. Each chapter contains a review of vocabulary. What is this feature called?
7. There are free CDs in your text. What content is contained on these CDs?
8. What is the location of the section that is entirely devoted to study skills?
9. There are Practice Problems that are contained in the margin of the text. What are they and how can they be used?

8.3 SOLVING EQUATIONS BY USING QUADRATIC METHODS

Objective **A** Solving Equations That Are Quadratic in Form

In this section, we discuss various types of equations that can be solved in part by using the methods for solving quadratic equations.

Once each equation is simplified, you may want to use these steps when deciding what method to use to solve the quadratic equation.

Solving a Quadratic Equation

Step 1: If the equation is in the form $(ax + b)^2 = c$, use the square root property and solve. If not, go to Step 2.

Step 2: Write the equation in standard form by setting it equal to 0: $ax^2 + bx + c = 0$.

Step 3: Try to solve the equation by the factoring method. If not possible, go to Step 4.

Step 4: Solve the equation by the quadratic formula.

The first example is a radical equation that becomes a quadratic equation once we square both sides.

PRACTICE PROBLEM 1

Solve: $x - \sqrt{x - 1} - 3 = 0$

EXAMPLE 1 Solve: $x - \sqrt{x} - 6 = 0$

Solution: Recall that to solve a radical equation, we first get the radical alone on one side of the equation. Then we square both sides.

$$x - 6 = \sqrt{x} \qquad \text{Add } \sqrt{x} \text{ to both sides.}$$
$$x^2 - 12x + 36 = x \qquad \text{Square both sides.}$$
$$x^2 - 13x + 36 = 0 \qquad \text{Set the equation equal to 0.}$$
$$(x - 9)(x - 4) = 0 \qquad \text{Factor.}$$
$$x - 9 = 0 \quad \text{or} \quad x - 4 = 0 \qquad \text{Set each factor equal to 0.}$$
$$x = 9 \qquad\qquad x = 4 \qquad \text{Solve.}$$

Check: Let $x = 9$. Let $x = 4$.

$$x - \sqrt{x} - 6 = 0 \qquad\qquad x - \sqrt{x} - 6 = 0$$
$$9 - \sqrt{9} - 6 \stackrel{?}{=} 0 \qquad\qquad 4 - \sqrt{4} - 6 \stackrel{?}{=} 0$$
$$9 - 3 - 6 \stackrel{?}{=} 0 \qquad\qquad 4 - 2 - 6 \stackrel{?}{=} 0$$
$$0 = 0 \quad \text{True} \qquad\qquad -4 = 0 \quad \text{False}$$

The solution set is $\{9\}$.

■ **Work Practice Problem 1**

Answer

1. $\{5\}$

EXAMPLE 2 Solve: $\dfrac{3x}{x-2} - \dfrac{x+1}{x} = \dfrac{6}{x(x-2)}$

Solution: In this equation, x cannot be either 2 or 0 because these values cause denominators to equal zero. To solve for x, we first multiply both sides of the equation by $x(x-2)$ to clear the fractions. By the distributive property, this means that we multiply each term by $x(x-2)$.

$$x(x-2)\left(\frac{3x}{x-2}\right) - x(x-2)\left(\frac{x+1}{x}\right) = x(x-2)\left[\frac{6}{x(x-2)}\right]$$

$$3x^2 - (x-2)(x+1) = 6 \quad \text{Simplify.}$$
$$3x^2 - (x^2 - x - 2) = 6 \quad \text{Multiply.}$$
$$3x^2 - x^2 + x + 2 = 6$$
$$2x^2 + x - 4 = 0 \quad \text{Simplify.}$$

This equation cannot be factored using integers, so we solve by the quadratic formula.

$$x = \frac{-1 \pm \sqrt{1^2 - 4(2)(-4)}}{2 \cdot 2} \quad \text{Let } a = 2, b = 1, \text{ and } c = -4, \text{ in the quadratic formula.}$$

$$= \frac{-1 \pm \sqrt{1 + 32}}{4} \quad \text{Simplify.}$$

$$= \frac{-1 \pm \sqrt{33}}{4}$$

Neither proposed solution will make the denominators 0.

The solution set is $\left\{\dfrac{-1 + \sqrt{33}}{4}, \dfrac{-1 - \sqrt{33}}{4}\right\}$.

🖳 **Work Practice Problem 2**

EXAMPLE 3 Solve: $p^4 - 3p^2 - 4 = 0$

Solution: First we factor the trinomial.

$$p^4 - 3p^2 - 4 = 0$$
$$(p^2 - 4)(p^2 + 1) = 0 \quad \text{Factor.}$$
$$(p - 2)(p + 2)(p^2 + 1) = 0 \quad \text{Factor further.}$$
$$p - 2 = 0 \quad \text{or} \quad p + 2 = 0 \quad \text{or} \quad p^2 + 1 = 0 \quad \text{Set each factor equal to 0 and solve.}$$
$$p = 2 \qquad\qquad p = -2 \qquad\qquad p^2 = -1$$
$$p = \pm\sqrt{-1} = \pm i$$

The solution set is $\{2, -2, i, -i\}$.

🖳 **Work Practice Problem 3**

✔**Concept Check**
a. True or false? The maximum number of solutions that a quadratic equation can have is 2.
b. True or false? The maximum number of solutions that an equation in quadratic form can have is 2.

PRACTICE PROBLEM 2

Solve:

$$\frac{2x}{x-1} - \frac{x+2}{x} = \frac{5}{x(x-1)}$$

PRACTICE PROBLEM 3

Solve: $x^4 - 5x^2 - 36 = 0$

Answers

2. $\left\{\dfrac{1 + \sqrt{13}}{2}, \dfrac{1 - \sqrt{13}}{2}\right\}$,

3. $\{3, -3, 2i, -2i\}$

✔ **Concept Check Answers**

a. true,　b. false

PRACTICE PROBLEM 4

Solve:
$(x + 4)^2 - (x + 4) - 6 = 0$

EXAMPLE 4 Solve: $(x - 3)^2 - 3(x - 3) - 4 = 0$

Solution: Notice that the quantity $(x - 3)$ is repeated in this equation. Sometimes it is helpful to substitute a variable (in this case other than x) for the repeated quantity. We will let $u = x - 3$. Then

$$(x - 3)^2 - 3(x - 3) - 4 = 0$$

becomes

$$u^2 - 3u - 4 = 0 \quad \text{Let } x - 3 = u.$$
$$(u - 4)(u + 1) = 0 \quad \text{Factor.}$$

To solve, we use the zero-factor property.

$$u - 4 = 0 \quad \text{or} \quad u + 1 = 0 \quad \text{Set each factor equal to 0.}$$
$$u = 4 \qquad\qquad u = -1 \quad \text{Solve.}$$

To find values of x, we substitute back. That is, we substitute $x - 3$ for u.

$$x - 3 = 4 \quad \text{or} \quad x - 3 = -1$$
$$x = 7 \qquad\qquad x = 2$$

Both 2 and 7 check. The solution is $\{2, 7\}$.

Work Practice Problem 4

> **Helpful Hint**
> When using substitution, don't forget to substitute back to the original variable.

PRACTICE PROBLEM 5

Solve: $x^{2/3} - 7x^{1/3} + 10 = 0$

EXAMPLE 5 Solve: $x^{2/3} - 5x^{1/3} + 6 = 0$

Solution: The key to solving this equation is recognizing that $x^{2/3} = (x^{1/3})^2$. We replace $x^{1/3}$ with m so that

$$(x^{1/3})^2 - 5x^{1/3} + 6 = 0$$

becomes

$$m^2 - 5m + 6 = 0$$

Now we solve by factoring.

$$m^2 - 5m + 6 = 0$$
$$(m - 3)(m - 2) = 0 \quad \text{Factor.}$$
$$m - 3 = 0 \quad \text{or} \quad m - 2 = 0 \quad \text{Set each factor equal to 0.}$$
$$m = 3 \qquad\qquad m = 2$$

Since $m = x^{1/3}$, we have

$$x^{1/3} = 3 \qquad \text{or} \quad x^{1/3} = 2$$
$$x = 3^3 = 27 \quad \text{or} \quad x = 2^3 = 8$$

Both 8 and 27 check. The solution set is $\{8, 27\}$.

Work Practice Problem 5

> **Helpful Hint**
> Example 3 can be solved using substitution also. Think of $p^4 - 3p^2 - 4 = 0$ as
> $$(p^2)^2 - 3p^2 - 4 = 0 \quad \text{Then let } x = p^2, \text{ and solve and substitute back.}$$
> $$\text{The solution set will be the same.}$$
> $$x^2 - 3x - 4 = 0$$

Answers
4. $\{-1, -6\}$, 5. $\{8, 125\}$

Objective B **Solving Problems That Lead to Quadratic Equations**

The next example is a work problem. This problem is modeled by a rational equation that simplifies to a quadratic equation.

EXAMPLE 6 Finding Work Time

Together, an experienced word processor and an apprentice word processor can create a document in 6 hours. Alone, the experienced word processor can process the document 2 hours faster than the apprentice word processor can. Find the time in which each person can create the document alone.

Solution:

1. UNDERSTAND. Read and reread the problem. The key idea here is the relationship between the *time* (hours) it takes to complete the job and the *part of the job* completed in one unit of time (hour). For example, because they can complete the job together in 6 hours, the *part of the job* they can complete in 1 hour is $\frac{1}{6}$. We let

   x = the *time* in hours it takes the apprentice word processor to complete the job alone, and

   $x - 2$ = the *time* in hours it takes the experienced word processor to complete the job alone

We can summarize in a chart the information discussed.

	Total Hours to Complete Job	Part of Job Completed in 1 Hour
Apprentice Word Processor	x	$\frac{1}{x}$
Experienced Word Processor	$x - 2$	$\frac{1}{x - 2}$
Together	6	$\frac{1}{6}$

2. TRANSLATE.

In words:	part of job completed by apprentice word processor in 1 hour	added to	part of job completed by experienced word processor in 1 hour	is equal to	part of job completed together in 1 hour
	↓	↓	↓	↓	↓
Translate:	$\frac{1}{x}$	$+$	$\frac{1}{x - 2}$	$=$	$\frac{1}{6}$

Continued on next page

Continued on next page

PRACTICE PROBLEM 6

Together, Karen and Doug Lewis can clean a strip of beach in 5 hours. Alone, Karen can clean the strip of beach one hour faster than Doug. Find the time that each person can clean the strip of beach alone. Give an exact answer and a one-decimal-place approximation.

Answer

6. Doug: $\frac{11 + \sqrt{101}}{2} \approx 10.5$ hr;

   Karen: $\frac{9 + \sqrt{101}}{2} \approx 9.5$ hr

3. SOLVE.

$$\frac{1}{x} + \frac{1}{x-2} = \frac{1}{6}$$

$$6x(x-2)\left(\frac{1}{x} + \frac{1}{x-2}\right) = 6x(x-2) \cdot \frac{1}{6} \qquad \text{Multiply both sides by the LCD } 6x(x-2).$$

$$6x(x-2) \cdot \frac{1}{x} + 6x(x-2) \cdot \frac{1}{x-2} = 6x(x-2) \cdot \frac{1}{6} \qquad \text{Use the distributive property.}$$

$$6(x-2) + 6x = x(x-2)$$

$$6x - 12 + 6x = x^2 - 2x$$

$$0 = x^2 - 14x + 12$$

Now we can substitute $a = 1, b = -14$, and $c = 12$ into the quadratic formula and simplify.

$$x = \frac{-(-14) \pm \sqrt{(-14)^2 - 4(1)(12)}}{2 \cdot 1} = \frac{14 \pm \sqrt{148}}{2}$$

Using a calculator or a square root table, we see that $\sqrt{148} \approx 12.2$ rounded to one decimal place. Thus,

$$x \approx \frac{14 \pm 12.2}{2}$$

$$x \approx \frac{14 + 12.2}{2} = 13.1 \quad \text{or} \quad x \approx \frac{14 - 12.2}{2} = 0.9$$

4. INTERPRET.

Check: If the apprentice word processor completes the job alone in 0.9 hours, the experienced word processor completes the job alone in $x - 2 = 0.9 - 2 = -1.1$ hours. Since this is not possible, we reject the solution of 0.9. The approximate solution thus is 13.1 hours.

State: The apprentice word processor can complete the job alone in approximately 13.1 hours, and the experienced word processor can complete the job alone in approximately

$$x - 2 = 13.1 - 2 = 11.1 \text{ hours}$$

◻ **Work Practice Problem 6**

Copyright 2007 Pearson Education, Inc.

PRACTICE PROBLEM 7

A family drives 500 miles to the beach for a vacation. The return trip was made at a speed that was 10 miles per hour faster. The total traveling time was $18\frac{1}{3}$ hours. Find the speed to the beach and the return speed.

Answer

7. 50 mph to the beach; 60 mph returning

EXAMPLE 7 **Finding Driving Speeds**

Beach and Fargo are about 400 miles apart. A salesperson travels from Fargo to Beach one day at a certain speed. She returns to Fargo the next day and drives 10 mph faster. Her total travel time was $14\frac{2}{3}$ hours. Find her speed to Beach and the return speed to Fargo.

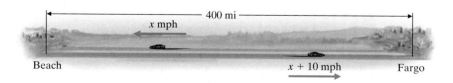

Solution:

1. UNDERSTAND. Read and reread the problem. Let

    $x = $ the speed to Beach, so

    $x + 10 = $ the return speed to Fargo

Then organize the given information in a table.

	Distance	=	Rate	·	Time	
To Beach	400		x		$\dfrac{400}{x}$	← distance ← rate
Return to Fargo	400		$x + 10$		$\dfrac{400}{x + 10}$	← distance ← rate

Helpful Hint
Since $d = rt$, then $t = \dfrac{d}{r}$. The time column was completed using $\dfrac{d}{r}$.

2. TRANSLATE.

In words:

$$\boxed{\text{time to Beach}} \quad + \quad \boxed{\text{return time to Fargo}} \quad = \quad \boxed{14\tfrac{2}{3} \text{ hours}}$$

Translate:

$$\frac{400}{x} \quad + \quad \frac{400}{x + 10} \quad = \quad \frac{44}{3}$$

3. SOLVE.

$$\frac{400}{x} + \frac{400}{x + 10} = \frac{44}{3}$$

This next step is optional. Notice that all three numerators in our equation are divisible by 4. To keep the numbers in our equation as simple as possible, we will take a step and divide through by 4.

$$\frac{100}{x} + \frac{100}{x + 10} = \frac{11}{3} \qquad \text{Divide both sides by 4.}$$

$$3x(x + 10)\left(\frac{100}{x} + \frac{100}{x + 10}\right) = 3x(x + 10) \cdot \frac{11}{3} \qquad \begin{array}{l}\text{Multiply both sides by the LCD,}\\ 3x(x + 10).\end{array}$$

$$3x(x + 10)\frac{100}{x} + 3x(x + 10)\frac{100}{x + 10} = 3x(x + 10) \cdot \frac{11}{3} \qquad \begin{array}{l}\text{Use the distributive property.}\end{array}$$

$$3(x + 10)100 + 3x(100) = x(x + 10)11$$

$$300x + 3000 + 300x = 11x^2 + 110x$$

$$0 = 11x^2 - 490x - 3000 \qquad \begin{array}{l}\text{Set equation equal to 0.}\end{array}$$

$$0 = (11x + 60)(x - 50) \qquad \text{Factor.}$$

$$11x + 60 = 0 \quad \text{or} \quad x - 50 = 0 \qquad \text{Set each factor equal to 0.}$$

$$x = -\frac{60}{11} = -5\frac{5}{11} \qquad x = 50$$

4. INTERPRET.

Check: The speed is not negative, so it's not $-5\frac{5}{11}$. The number 50 does check.

State: The speed to Beach was 50 miles per hour and the return speed to Fargo was 60 miles per hour.

■ **Work Practice Problem 7**

8.3 EXERCISE SET

FOR EXTRA HELP

Student Solutions Manual

PH Math/Tutor Center

CD/Video for Review

Math XL
MathXL®

MyMathLab
MyMathLab

Objective **A** *Solve. See Example 1.*

1. $2x = \sqrt{10 + 3x}$

2. $3x = \sqrt{8x + 1}$

3. $x - 2\sqrt{x} = 8$

4. $x - \sqrt{2x} = 4$

5. $\sqrt{9x} = x + 2$

6. $\sqrt{16x} = x + 3$

Solve. See Example 2.

7. $\dfrac{2}{x} + \dfrac{3}{x - 1} = 1$

8. $\dfrac{6}{x^2} = \dfrac{3}{x + 1}$

9. $\dfrac{3}{x} + \dfrac{4}{x + 2} = 2$

10. $\dfrac{5}{x - 2} + \dfrac{4}{x + 2} = 1$

11. $\dfrac{7}{x^2 - 5x + 6} = \dfrac{2x}{x - 3} - \dfrac{x}{x - 2}$

12. $\dfrac{11}{2x^2 + x - 15} = \dfrac{5}{2x - 5} - \dfrac{x}{x + 3}$

Solve. See Example 3.

13. $p^4 - 16 = 0$

14. $z^4 = 81$

15. $z^4 - 13z^2 + 36 = 0$

16. $x^4 + 2x^2 - 3 = 0$

17. $4x^4 + 11x^2 = 3$

18. $9x^4 + 5x^2 - 4 = 0$

Solve. See Examples 4 and 5.

19. $x^{2/3} - 3x^{1/3} - 10 = 0$

20. $x^{2/3} + 2x^{1/3} + 1 = 0$

21. $(5n + 1)^2 + 2(5n + 1) - 3 = 0$

22. $(m - 6)^2 + 5(m - 6) + 4 = 0$

23. $2x^{2/3} - 5x^{1/3} = 3$

24. $3x^{2/3} + 11x^{1/3} = 4$

25. $1 + \dfrac{2}{3t - 2} = \dfrac{8}{(3t - 2)^2}$

26. $2 - \dfrac{7}{x + 6} = \dfrac{15}{(x + 6)^2}$

27. $20x^{2/3} - 6x^{1/3} - 2 = 0$

28. $4x^{2/3} + 16x^{1/3} = -15$

Mixed Practice *Solve. See Examples 1 through 5.*

29. $a^4 - 5a^2 + 6 = 0$

30. $x^4 - 12x^2 + 11 = 0$

31. $\dfrac{2x}{x - 2} + \dfrac{x}{x + 3} = \dfrac{-5}{x + 3}$

32. $\dfrac{5}{x - 3} + \dfrac{x}{x + 3} = \dfrac{19}{x^2 - 9}$

33. $(p + 2)^2 = 9(p + 2) - 20$

34. $2(4m - 3)^2 - 9(4m - 3) = 5$

35. $2x = \sqrt{11x + 3}$

36. $4x = \sqrt{2x + 3}$

37. $x^{2/3} - 8x^{1/3} + 15 = 0$

38. $x^{2/3} - 2x^{1/3} - 8 = 0$

39. $x - \sqrt{19 - 2x} - 2 = 0$

40. $x - \sqrt{17 - 4x} - 3 = 0$

41. $2x^{2/3} + 3x^{1/3} - 2 = 0$

42. $6x^{2/3} - 25x^{1/3} - 25 = 0$

43. $(t + 3)^2 - 2(t + 3) - 8 = 0$

44. $(2n - 3)^2 - 7(2n - 3) + 12 = 0$

45. $x - \sqrt{x} = 2$

46. $x - \sqrt{3x} = 6$

47. $\dfrac{x}{x - 1} + \dfrac{1}{x + 1} = \dfrac{2}{x^2 - 1}$

48. $\dfrac{x}{x - 5} + \dfrac{5}{x + 5} = \dfrac{-1}{x^2 - 25}$

49. $p^4 - p^2 - 20 = 0$

50. $x^4 - 10x^2 + 9 = 0$

51. $1 = \dfrac{4}{x - 7} + \dfrac{5}{(x - 7)^2}$

52. $3 + \dfrac{1}{2p + 4} = \dfrac{10}{(2p + 4)^2}$

53. $27y^4 + 15y^2 = 2$

54. $8z^4 + 14z^2 = -5$

Objective **B** *Solve. See Examples 6 and 7.*

55. A jogger ran 3 miles, decreased her speed by 1 mile per hour and then ran another 4 miles. If her total time jogging was $1\dfrac{3}{5}$ hours, find her speed for each part of her run.

56. Mark Keaton's workout consists of jogging for 3 miles, and then riding his bike for 5 miles at a speed 4 miles per hour faster than he jogs. If his total workout time is 1 hour, find his jogging speed and his biking speed.

57. A Chinese restaurant in Mandeville, Louisiana, has a large goldfish pond around the restaurant. Suppose that an inlet pipe and a hose together can fill the pond in 8 hours. The inlet pipe alone can complete the job in one hour less time than the hose alone. Find the time that the hose can complete the job alone and the time that the inlet pipe can complete the job alone. Round each to the nearest tenth of an hour.

58. A water tank on a farm in Flatonia, Texas, can be filled with a large inlet pipe and a small inlet pipe in 3 hours. The large inlet pipe alone can fill the tank in 2 hours less time than the small inlet pipe alone. Find the time to the nearest tenth of an hour each pipe can fill the tank alone.

59. Roma Sherry drove 330 miles from her home town to Tucson. During her return trip, she was able to increase her speed by 11 miles per hour. If her return trip took 1 hour less time, find her original speed and her speed returning home.

60. A salesperson drove to Portland, a distance of 300 miles. During the last 80 miles of his trip, heavy rainfall forced him to decrease his speed by 15 miles per hour. If his total driving time was 6 hours, find his original speed and his speed during the rainfall.

61. Bill Shaughnessy and his son Billy can clean the house together in 4 hours. When the son works alone, it takes him an hour longer to clean than it takes his dad alone. Find how long to the nearest tenth of an hour it takes the son to clean alone.

62. Together, Noodles and Freckles eat a 50-pound bag of dog food in 30 days. Noodles by herself eats a 50-pound bag in 2 weeks less time than Freckles does by himself. How many days to the nearest whole day would a 50-pound bag of dog food last Freckles?

63. The product of a number and 4 less than the number is 96. Find the number.

64. A whole number increased by its square is two more than twice itself. Find the number.

△ **65.** Suppose that we want to make an open box from a square sheet of cardboard by cutting out squares from each corner as shown and then folding along the dotted lines. If the box is to have a volume of 300 cubic inches, find the original dimensions of the sheet of cardboard.

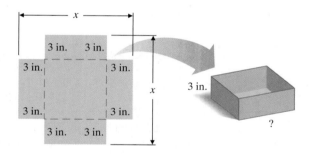

△ **66.** Suppose that we want to make an open box from a square sheet of cardboard by cutting out squares from each corner as shown and then folding along the dotted lines. If the box is to have a volume of 128 cubic inches, find the original dimensions of the sheet of cardboard. (*Hint:* Use Exercise 65 parts (a), (b), and (c) to help you.)

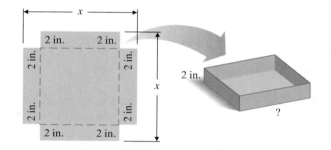

a. The ? in the drawing to the left will be the length (and also the width) of the box as shown in the drawing to the right. Represent this length in terms of x.

b. Use the formula for volume of a box, $V = l \cdot w \cdot h$, to write an equation in x.

c. Solve the equation for x and give the dimensions of the sheet of cardboard. Check your solution.

△ **67.** A sprinkler that sprays water in a circular pattern is to be used to water a square garden. If the area of the garden is 920 square feet, find the smallest whole number *radius* that the sprinkler can be adjusted to so that the entire garden is watered.

△ **68.** Suppose that a square field has an area of 6270 square feet. See Exercise 67 and find a new sprinkler radius.

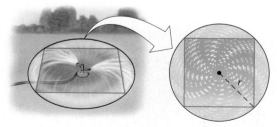

8.5 QUADRATIC FUNCTIONS AND THEIR GRAPHS

Objectives

A Graph Quadratic Functions of the Form $f(x) = x^2 + k$.

B Graph Quadratic Functions of the Form $f(x) = (x - h)^2$.

C Graph Quadratic Functions of the Form $f(x) = (x - h)^2 + k$.

D Graph Quadratic Functions of the Form $f(x) = ax^2$.

E Graph Quadratic Functions of the Form $f(x) = a(x - h)^2 + k$.

Objective **A** Graphing $f(x) = x^2 + k$

We first graphed the quadratic function $f(x) = x^2$ in Section 3.8. In that section, we discovered that the graph of a quadratic function is a parabola opening upward or downward. Now, as we continue our study, we will discover more details about quadratic functions and their graphs.

First, let's recall the definition of a *quadratic function*.

Quadratic Function

A **quadratic function** is a function that can be written in the form $f(x) = ax^2 + bx + c$, where a, b, and c are real numbers and $a \neq 0$.

Notice that equations of the form $y = ax^2 + bx + c$, where $a \neq 0$, also define quadratic functions since y is a function of x or $y = f(x)$.

Recall that if $a > 0$, the parabola opens upward and if $a < 0$, the parabola opens downward. Also, the vertex of a parabola is the lowest point if the parabola opens upward and the highest point if the parabola opens downward. The axis of symmetry is the vertical line that passes through the vertex.

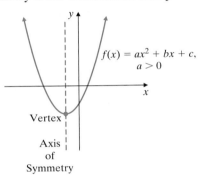
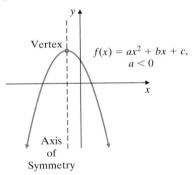

EXAMPLE 1 Graph $f(x) = x^2$ and $g(x) = x^2 + 3$ on the same set of axes.

Solution: First we construct a table of values for f and plot the points. Notice that for each x-value, the corresponding value of $g(x)$ must be 3 more than the corresponding value of $f(x)$ since $f(x) = x^2$ and $g(x) = x^2 + 3$. In other words, the graph of $g(x) = x^2 + 3$ is the same as the graph of $f(x) = x^2$ shifted upward 3 units. The axis of symmetry for both graphs is the y-axis.

x	$f(x) = x^2$	$g(x) = x^2 + 3$
-2	4	7
-1	1	4
0	0	3
1	1	4
2	4	7

Each y-value is increased by 3.

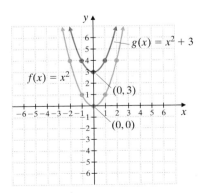

■ **Work Practice Problem 1**

In general, we have the following properties.

PRACTICE PROBLEM 1

Graph $f(x) = x^2$ and $g(x) = x^2 + 4$ on the same set of axes.

Answer

1.

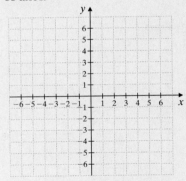

507

Graphing the Parabola Defined by $f(x) = x^2 + k$

If k is positive, the graph of $f(x) = x^2 + k$ is the graph of $y = x^2$ shifted upward k units.

If k is negative, the graph of $f(x) = x^2 + k$ is the graph of $y = x^2$ shifted downward $|k|$ units.

The vertex is $(0, k)$, and the axis of symmetry is the y-axis.

PRACTICE PROBLEMS 2-3

Graph each function.

2. $F(x) = x^2 + 1$

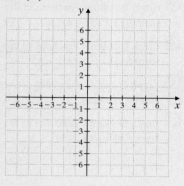

3. $g(x) = x^2 - 2$

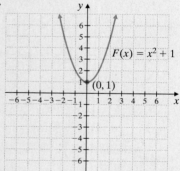

EXAMPLES Graph each function.

2. $F(x) = x^2 + 2$

The graph of $F(x) = x^2 + 2$ is obtained by shifting the graph of $y = x^2$ upward 2 units.

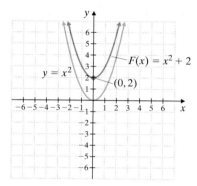

3. $g(x) = x^2 - 3$

The graph of $g(x) = x^2 - 3$ is obtained by shifting the graph of $y = x^2$ downward 3 units.

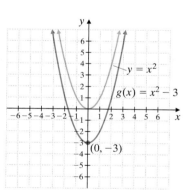

■ **Work Practice Problems 2-3**

Answers

2.

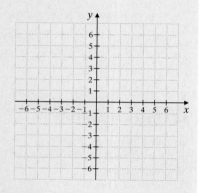

3.

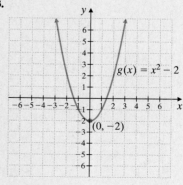

Objective **B** **Graphing $f(x) = (x - h)^2$**

Now we will graph functions of the form $f(x) = (x - h)^2$.

EXAMPLE 4 Graph $f(x) = x^2$ and $g(x) = (x - 2)^2$ on the same set of axes.

Solution: By plotting points, we see that for each x-value, the corresponding value of $g(x)$ is the same as the value of $f(x)$ when the x-value is increased by 2. Thus, the graph of $g(x) = (x - 2)^2$ is the graph of $f(x) = x^2$ shifted to the right 2 units. The axis of symmetry for the graph of $g(x) = (x - 2)^2$ is also shifted 2 units to the right and is the line $x = 2$.

x	$f(x) = x^2$	x	$g(x) = (x - 2)^2$
-2	4	0	4
-1	1	1	1
0	0	2	0
1	1	3	1
2	4	4	4

Each x-value increased by 2 corresponds to same y-value.

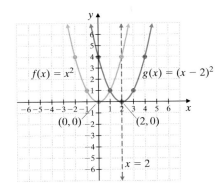

🖳 **Work Practice Problem 4**

In general, we have the following properties.

Graphing the Parabola Defined by $f(x) = (x - h)^2$

If h is positive, the graph of $f(x) = (x - h)^2$ is the graph of $y = x^2$ shifted to the right h units.

If h is negative, the graph of $f(x) = (x - h)^2$ is the graph of $y = x^2$ shifted to the left $|h|$ units.

The vertex is $(h, 0)$, and the axis of symmetry is the vertical line $x = h$.

EXAMPLES Graph each function.

5. $G(x) = (x - 3)^2$

The graph of $G(x) = (x - 3)^2$ is obtained by shifting the graph of $y = x^2$ to the right 3 units.

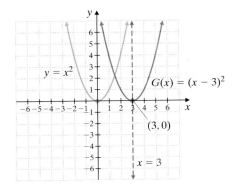

Continued on next page

PRACTICE PROBLEM 4

Graph $f(x) = x^2$ and $g(x) = (x - 1)^2$ on the same set of axes.

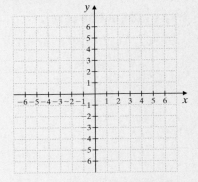

PRACTICE PROBLEMS 5–6

Graph each function.

5. $G(x) = (x - 4)^2$

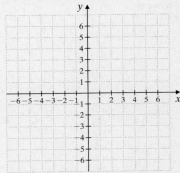

6. $F(x) = (x + 2)^2$

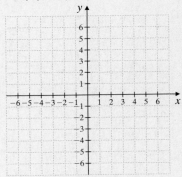

Answers

4.

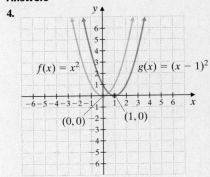

5. See answer on page 602.

6. $F(x) = (x + 1)^2$

The equation $F(x) = (x + 1)^2$ can be written as $F(x) = [x - (-1)]^2$. The graph of $F(x) = [x - (-1)]^2$ is obtained by shifting the graph of $y = x^2$ to the left 1 unit.

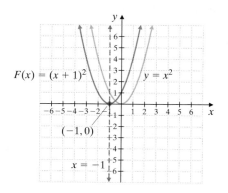

$F(x) = (x + 1)^2$ $y = x^2$
$(-1, 0)$
$x = -1$

□ **Work Practice Problems 5–6**

PRACTICE PROBLEM 7

Graph: $F(x) = (x - 2)^2 + 3$

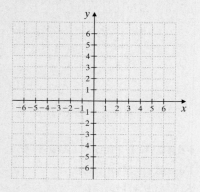

Answers

5.

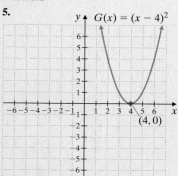

$G(x) = (x - 4)^2$
$(4, 0)$

6.

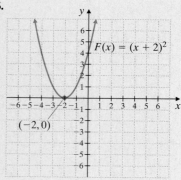

$F(x) = (x + 2)^2$
$(-2, 0)$

7.

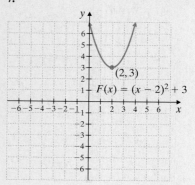

$(2, 3)$
$F(x) = (x - 2)^2 + 3$

Objective C Graphing $f(x) = (x - h)^2 + k$

As we will see in graphing functions of the form $f(x) = (x - h)^2 + k$, it is possible to combine vertical and horizontal shifts.

Graphing the Parabola Defined by $f(x) = (x - h)^2 + k$

The parabola has the same shape as $y = x^2$.

The vertex is (h, k), and the axis of symmetry is the vertical line $x = h$.

EXAMPLE 7 Graph: $F(x) = (x - 3)^2 + 1$

Solution: The graph of $F(x) = (x - 3)^2 + 1$ is the graph of $y = x^2$ shifted 3 units to the right and 1 unit up. The vertex is then $(3, 1)$, and the axis of symmetry is $x = 3$. A few ordered pair solutions are plotted to aid in graphing.

x	$F(x) = (x - 3)^2 + 1$
1	5
2	2
4	2
5	5

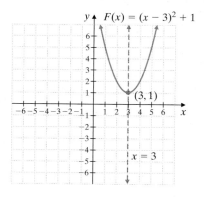

$F(x) = (x - 3)^2 + 1$
$(3, 1)$
$x = 3$

□ **Work Practice Problem 7**

Objective D Graphing $f(x) = ax^2$

Next, we discover the change in the shape of the graph when the coefficient of x^2 is not 1.

EXAMPLE 8 Graph $f(x) = x^2$, $g(x) = 3x^2$, and $h(x) = \frac{1}{2}x^2$ on the same set of axes.

Solution: Comparing the table of values, we see that for each x-value, the corresponding value of $g(x)$ is triple the corresponding value of $f(x)$. Similarly, the value of $h(x)$ is half the value of $f(x)$.

x	$f(x) = x^2$
-2	4
-1	1
0	0
1	1
2	4

x	$g(x) = 3x^2$
-2	12
-1	3
0	0
1	3
2	12

x	$h(x) = \frac{1}{2}x^2$
-2	2
-1	$\frac{1}{2}$
0	0
1	$\frac{1}{2}$
2	2

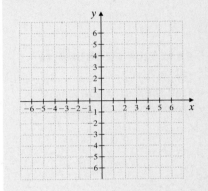

The result is that the graph of $g(x) = 3x^2$ is narrower than the graph of $f(x) = x^2$ and the graph of $h(x) = \frac{1}{2}x^2$ is wider. The vertex for each graph is $(0, 0)$, and the axis of symmetry is the y-axis.

■ **Work Practice Problem 8**

Graphing the Parabola Defined by $f(x) = ax^2$

If a is positive, the parabola opens upward, and if a is negative, the parabola opens downward.
If $|a| > 1$, the graph of the parabola is narrower than the graph of $y = x^2$.
If $|a| < 1$, the graph of the parabola is wider than the graph of $y = x^2$.

EXAMPLE 9 Graph: $f(x) = -2x^2$

Solution: Because $a = -2$, a negative value, this parabola opens downward. Since $|-2| = 2$ and $2 > 1$, the parabola is narrower than the graph of $y = x^2$. The vertex is $(0, 0)$, and the axis of symmetry is the y-axis. We verify this by plotting a few points.

Continued on next page

PRACTICE PROBLEM 8

Graph $f(x) = x^2$, $g(x) = 2x^2$, and $h(x) = \frac{1}{3}x^2$ on the same set of axes.

Answer

8.

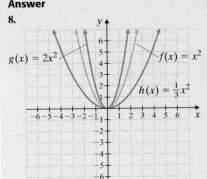

PRACTICE PROBLEM 9

Graph: $f(x) = -3x^2$

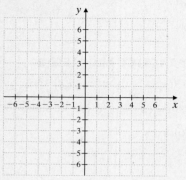

PRACTICE PROBLEM 10

Graph: $f(x) = 2(x + 3)^2 - 4$.
Find the vertex and axis of
symmetry.

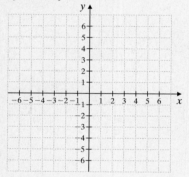

Answers

9.

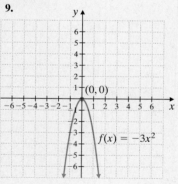

10.

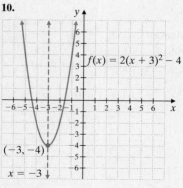

x	$f(x) = -2x^2$
-2	-8
-1	-2
0	0
1	-2
2	-8

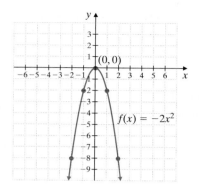

🔲 **Work Practice Problem 9**

Objective **E** **Graphing $f(x) = a(x - h)^2 + k$**

Now we will see the shape of the graph of a quadratic function of the form
$f(x) = a(x - h)^2 + k$.

EXAMPLE 10 Graph: $g(x) = \dfrac{1}{2}(x + 2)^2 + 5$. Find the vertex and the axis
of symmetry.

Solution: The function $g(x) = \dfrac{1}{2}(x + 2)^2 + 5$ may be written as $g(x) = \dfrac{1}{2}[x - (-2)]^2 + 5$. Thus, this graph is the same as the graph of $y = x^2$ shifted
2 units to the left and 5 units upward and widened because a is $\dfrac{1}{2}$. The vertex is
$(-2, 5)$, and the axis of symmetry is $x = -2$. We plot a few points to verify.

x	$g(x) = \dfrac{1}{2}(x + 2)^2 + 5$
-4	7
-3	$5\dfrac{1}{2}$
-2	5
-1	$5\dfrac{1}{2}$
0	7

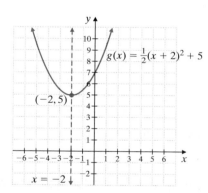

🔲 **Work Practice Problem 10**

In general, the following holds.

Graphing a Quadratic Function

The graph of a quadratic function written in the form $f(x) = a(x - h)^2 + k$ is
a parabola with vertex (h, k).

If $a > 0$, the parabola opens upward.

If $a < 0$, the parabola opens downward. The axis of symmetry is the line
whose equation is $x = h$.

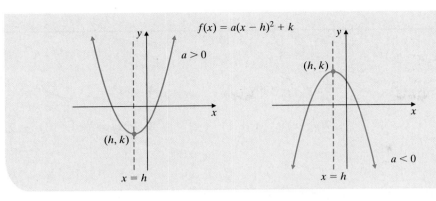

$f(x) = a(x - h)^2 + k$

$a > 0$

(h, k)

$x = h$

(h, k)

$a < 0$

$x = h$

✔ Concept Check

Which description of the graph of $f(x) = -0.35(x + 3)^2 - 4$ is correct?

a. The graph opens downward and has its vertex at $(-3, 4)$.
b. The graph opens upward and has its vertex at $(-3, 4)$.
c. The graph opens downward and has its vertex at $(-3, -4)$.
d. The graph is narrower than the graph of $y = x^2$.

✔ **Concept Check Answer**

c

📇 CALCULATOR EXPLORATIONS   Graphing

Use a graphing calculator to graph the first function of each pair. Then use its graph to predict the graph of the second function. Check your prediction by graphing both on the same set of axes. See this section and Section 3.8.

1. $F(x) = \sqrt{x}; G(x) = \sqrt{x} + 1$

2. $g(x) = x^3; H(x) = x^3 - 2$

3. $H(x) = |x|; f(x) = |x - 5|$

4. $h(x) = x^3 + 2; g(x) = (x - 3)^3 + 2$

5. $f(x) = |x + 4|; F(x) = |x + 4| + 3$

6. $G(x) = \sqrt{x} - 2; g(x) = \sqrt{x - 4} - 2$

Mental Math

State the vertex of the graph of each quadratic function.

1. $f(x) = x^2$

2. $f(x) = -5x^2$

3. $g(x) = (x - 2)^2$

4. $g(x) = (x + 5)^2$

5. $f(x) = 2x^2 + 3$

6. $h(x) = x^2 - 1$

7. $g(x) = (x + 1)^2 + 5$

8. $h(x) = (x - 10)^2 - 7$

8.5 EXERCISE SET

FOR EXTRA HELP

Student Solutions Manual   PH Math/Tutor Center   CD/Video for Review   MathXL   MathXL®   MyMathLab   MyMathLab

Objectives **A** **B** **Mixed Practice** *Graph each quadratic function. Label the vertex and sketch and label the axis of symmetry. See Examples 1 through 6.*

1. $f(x) = x^2 - 1$

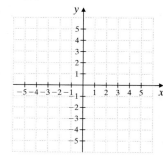

2. $h(x) = x^2 + 3$

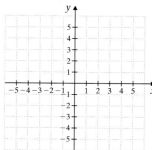

3. $f(x) = (x - 5)^2$

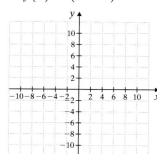

4. $g(x) = (x + 5)^2$

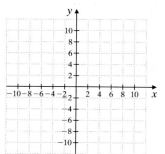

5. $h(x) = x^2 + 5$

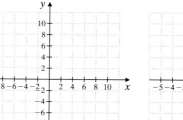

6. $h(x) = x^2 - 4$

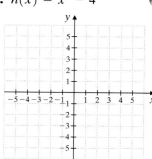

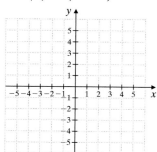 **7.** $h(x) = (x + 2)^2$

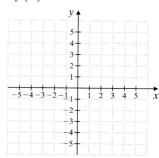

8. $H(x) = (x - 1)^2$

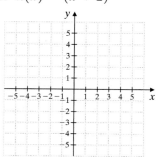

9. $g(x) = x^2 + 7$

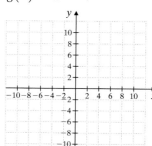

10. $f(x) = x^2 - 2$

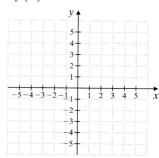

11. $G(x) = (x + 3)^2$

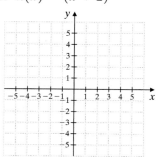

12. $f(x) = (x - 6)^2$

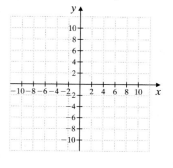

514

Objective **C** *Graph each quadratic function. Label the vertex and sketch and label the axis of symmetry. See Example 7.*

13. $f(x) = (x - 2)^2 + 5$

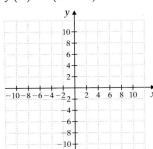

14. $g(x) = (x - 6)^2 + 1$

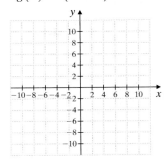

15. $h(x) = (x + 1)^2 + 4$

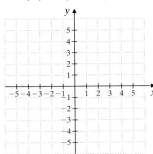

16. $G(x) = (x + 3)^2 + 3$

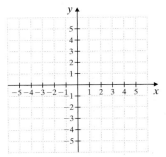

17. $g(x) = (x + 2)^2 - 5$

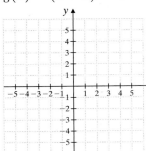

18. $h(x) = (x + 4)^2 - 6$

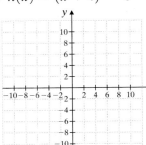

19. $h(x) = (x - 3)^2 + 2$

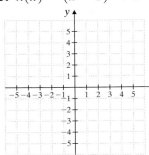

20. $F(x) = (x - 2)^2 - 3$

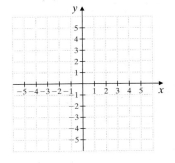

Objective **D** *Graph each quadratic function. Label the vertex and sketch and label the axis of symmetry. See Examples 8 and 9.*

21. $g(x) = -x^2$

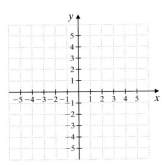

22. $f(x) = 5x^2$

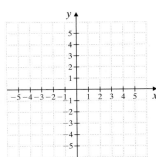

23. $h(x) = \frac{1}{3}x^2$

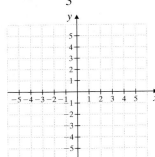

24. $g(x) = -3x^2$

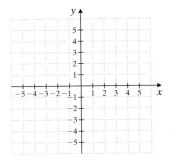

25. $H(x) = 2x^2$

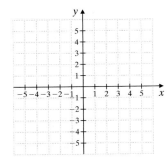

26. $f(x) = -\frac{1}{4}x^2$

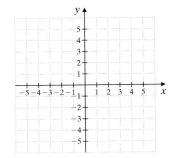

27. $F(x) = -4x^2$

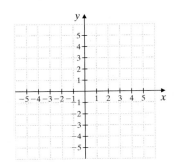

28. $G(x) = \frac{1}{5}x^2$

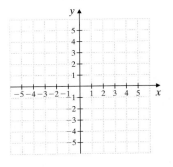

Objective **E** *Graph each quadratic function. Label the vertex and sketch and label the axis of symmetry. See Example 10.*

29. $f(x) = 10(x + 4)^2 - 6$

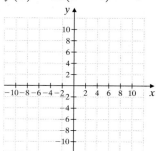

30. $g(x) = 4(x - 4)^2 + 2$

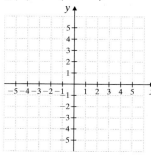

31. $h(x) = -3(x + 3)^2 + 1$

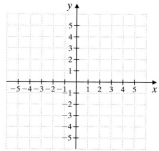

32. $f(x) = -(x - 2)^2 - 6$

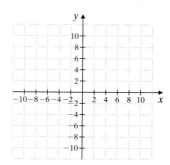

33. $H(x) = \frac{1}{2}(x - 6)^2 - 3$

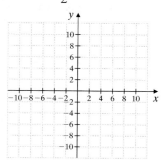

34. $G(x) = \frac{1}{5}(x + 4)^2 + 3$

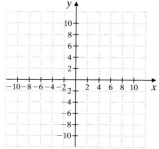

35. $f(x) = -(x - 1)^2$

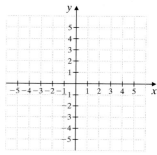

36. $f(x) = 2(x + 3)^2$

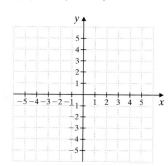

37. $F(x) = \left(x + \frac{1}{2}\right)^2 - 2$

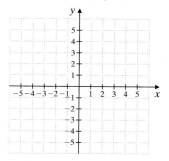

38. $H(x) = \left(x + \frac{1}{4}\right)^2 - 3$

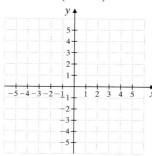

39. $F(x) = -x^2 + 2$

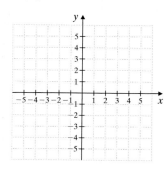

40. $G(x) = 3x^2 + 1$

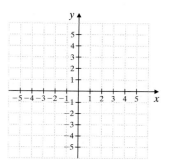

Review

Add the proper constant to each binomial so that the resulting trinomial is a perfect square trinomial. See Section 8.1.

41. $x^2 + 8x$

42. $y^2 + 4y$

43. $z^2 - 16z$

44. $x^2 - 10x$

45. $y^2 + y$

46. $z^2 - 3z$

Concept Extensions

Write the equation of the parabola that has the same shape as $f(x) = 5x^2$ *but with each given vertex. Call each function* $g(x)$.

47. $(2, 3)$ **48.** $(1, 6)$ **49.** $(-3, 6)$ **50.** $(4, -1)$

Recall from Section 3.8 that the shifting properties covered in this section apply to the graphs of all functions. Given the accompanying graph of $y = f(x)$, *graph each function.*

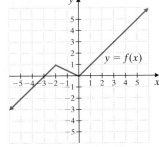

51. $y = f(x) + 1$ **52.** $y = f(x) - 2$ **53.** $y = f(x - 3)$

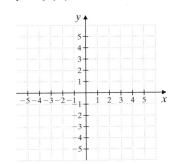   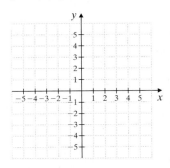   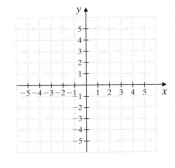

54. $y = f(x + 3)$ **55.** $y = f(x + 2) + 2$ **56.** $y = f(x - 1) + 1$

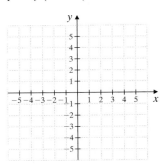   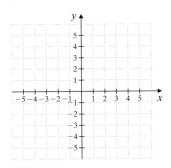   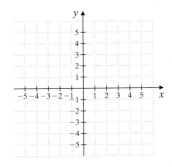

Solve. See the Concept Check in this section.

57. Which description of $f(x) = -213(x - 0.1)^2 + 3.6$ is correct?

Graph Opens	Vertex
a. upward	$(0.1, 3.6)$
b. upward	$(-213, 3.6)$
c. downward	$(0.1, 3.6)$
d. downward	$(-0.1, 3.6)$

58. Which description of $f(x) = 5\left(x + \dfrac{1}{2}\right)^2 + \dfrac{1}{2}$ is correct?

Graph Opens	Vertex
a. upward	$\left(\dfrac{1}{2}, \dfrac{1}{2}\right)$
b. upward	$\left(-\dfrac{1}{2}, \dfrac{1}{2}\right)$
c. downward	$\left(\dfrac{1}{2}, -\dfrac{1}{2}\right)$
d. downward	$\left(-\dfrac{1}{2}, -\dfrac{1}{2}\right)$

A Write Quadratic Functions in the Form $y = a(x - h)^2 + k$.

B Derive a Formula for Finding the Vertex of a Parabola.

C Find the Minimum or Maximum Value of a Quadratic Function.

8.6 FURTHER GRAPHING OF QUADRATIC FUNCTIONS

Objective **A** Writing Quadratic Functions in the Form $y = a(x - h)^2 + k$

We know that the graph of a quadratic function is a parabola. If a quadratic function is written in the form

$$f(x) = a(x - h)^2 + k$$

we can easily find the vertex (h, k) and graph the parabola. To write a quadratic function in this form, we need to complete the square. (See Section 8.1 for a review of completing the square.)

EXAMPLE 1 Graph: $f(x) = x^2 - 4x - 12$. Find the vertex and any intercepts.

Solution: The graph of this quadratic function is a parabola. To find the vertex of the parabola, we complete the square on the binomial $x^2 - 4x$. To simplify our work, we let $f(x) = y$.

$$y = x^2 - 4x - 12 \quad \text{Let } f(x) = y.$$
$$y + 12 = x^2 - 4x \quad \text{Add 12 to both sides to get the } x\text{-variable terms alone.}$$

Now we add the square of half of -4 to both sides.

$$\frac{1}{2}(-4) = -2 \quad \text{and} \quad (-2)^2 = 4$$

$$y + 12 + 4 = x^2 - 4x + 4 \quad \text{Add 4 to both sides.}$$
$$y + 16 = (x - 2)^2 \quad \text{Factor the trinomial.}$$
$$y = (x - 2)^2 - 16 \quad \text{Subtract 16 from both sides.}$$
$$f(x) = (x - 2)^2 - 16 \quad \text{Replace } y \text{ with } f(x).$$

From this equation, we can see that the vertex of the parabola is $(2, -16)$, a point in quadrant IV, and the axis of symmetry is the line $x = 2$.

Notice that $a = 1$. Since $a > 0$, the parabola opens upward. This parabola opening upward with vertex $(2, -16)$ will have two x-intercepts.

To find the x-intercepts, we let $f(x)$ or $y = 0$.

$$0 = x^2 - 4x - 12$$
$$0 = (x - 6)(x + 2)$$
$$0 = x - 6 \quad \text{or} \quad 0 = x + 2$$
$$6 = x \qquad \qquad -2 = x$$

The two x-intercepts are $(6, 0)$ and $(-2, 0)$. To find the y-intercept, we let $x = 0$.

$$f(0) = 0^2 - 4 \cdot 0 - 12 = -12$$

The y-intercept is $(0, -12)$. The sketch of $f(x) = x^2 - 4x - 12$ is shown.

■ **Work Practice Problem 1**

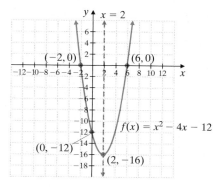

PRACTICE PROBLEM 1

Graph: $f(x) = x^2 - 4x - 5$. Find the vertex and any intercepts.

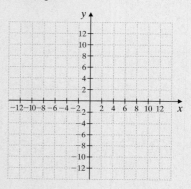

Answer

1. vertex: $(2, -9)$; x-intercepts: $(-1, 0)$, $(5, 0)$; y-intercept: $(0, -5)$

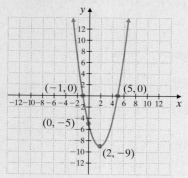

EXAMPLE 2 Graph: $f(x) = 3x^2 + 3x + 1$. Find the vertex and any intercepts.

Solution: We replace $f(x)$ with y and complete the square on x to write the equation in the form $y = a(x - h)^2 + k$.

$y = 3x^2 + 3x + 1$ Replace $f(x)$ with y.
$y - 1 = 3x^2 + 3x$ Get the x-variable terms alone.

Next we factor 3 from the terms $3x^2 + 3x$ so that the coefficient of x^2 is 1.

$y - 1 = 3(x^2 + x)$ Factor out 3.

The coefficient of x is 1. Then $\frac{1}{2}(1) = \frac{1}{2}$ and $\left(\frac{1}{2}\right)^2 = \frac{1}{4}$. Since we are adding $\frac{1}{4}$

inside the parentheses, we are really adding $3\left(\frac{1}{4}\right)$, so we *must* add $3\left(\frac{1}{4}\right)$ to the left side.

$$y - 1 + 3\left(\frac{1}{4}\right) = 3\left(x^2 + x + \frac{1}{4}\right)$$

$$y - \frac{1}{4} = 3\left(x + \frac{1}{2}\right)^2 \qquad \text{Simplify the left side and factor the right side.}$$

$$y = 3\left(x + \frac{1}{2}\right)^2 + \frac{1}{4} \qquad \text{Add } \frac{1}{4} \text{ to both sides.}$$

$$f(x) = 3\left(x + \frac{1}{2}\right)^2 + \frac{1}{4} \qquad \text{Replace } y \text{ with } f(x).$$

Then $a = 3$, $h = -\frac{1}{2}$, and $k = \frac{1}{4}$. This means that the parabola opens upward with

vertex $\left(-\frac{1}{2}, \frac{1}{4}\right)$ and that the axis of symmetry is the line $x = -\frac{1}{2}$. This parabola

has no x-intercepts since the vertex is in the second quadrant and it opens upward.
    To find the y-intercept, we let $x = 0$. Then

$$f(0) = 3(0)^2 + 3(0) + 1 = 1$$

We use the vertex, axis of symmetry, and y-intercept to graph the parabola.

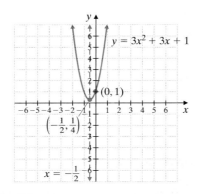

Work Practice Problem 2

PRACTICE PROBLEM 2

Graph: $f(x) = 2x^2 + 2x + 5$. Find the vertex and any intercepts.

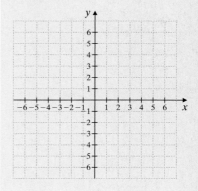

Answer

2. vertex: $\left(-\frac{1}{2}, \frac{9}{2}\right)$; y-intercept: $(0, 5)$

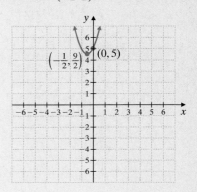

Helpful Hint

Parabola Opens Upward
Vertex in quadrant I or II: no x-intercepts
Vertex in quadrant III or IV: 2 x-intercepts

Parabola Opens Downward
Vertex in quadrant I or II: 2 x-intercepts
Vertex in quadrant III or IV: no x-intercepts

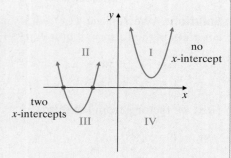

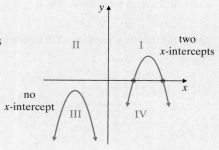

PRACTICE PROBLEM 3

Graph: $f(x) = -x^2 - 2x + 8$.
Find the vertex and any intercepts.

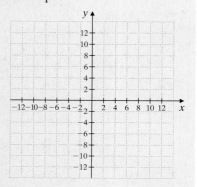

Helpful Hint

This can be written as $f(x) = -1[x - (-1)]^2 + 4$.
Notice that the vertex is $(-1, 4)$.

Answer

3. vertex: $(-1, 9)$; x-intercepts: $(-4, 0)$, $(2, 0)$; y-intercept: $(0, 8)$

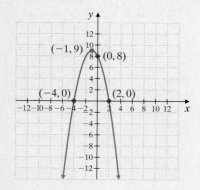

EXAMPLE 3 Graph: $f(x) = -x^2 - 2x + 3$. Find the vertex and any intercepts.

Solution: We write $f(x)$ in the form $a(x - h)^2 + k$ by completing the square. First we replace $f(x)$ with y.

$$f(x) = -x^2 - 2x + 3$$
$$y = -x^2 - 2x + 3$$
$$y - 3 = -x^2 - 2x \quad \text{Subtract 3 from both sides to get the } x\text{-variable terms alone.}$$
$$y - 3 = -1(x^2 + 2x) \quad \text{Factor } -1 \text{ from the terms } -x^2 - 2x.$$

The coefficient of x is 2. Then $\frac{1}{2}(2) = 1$ and $1^2 = 1$. We add 1 to the right side inside the parentheses and add $-1(1)$ to the left side.

$$y - 3 - 1(1) = -1(x^2 + 2x + 1)$$
$$y - 4 = -1(x + 1)^2 \quad \text{Simplify the left side and factor the right side.}$$
$$y = -1(x + 1)^2 + 4 \quad \text{Add 4 to both sides.}$$
$$f(x) = -1(x + 1)^2 + 4 \quad \text{Replace } y \text{ with } f(x).$$

Since $a = -1$, the parabola opens downward with vertex $(-1, 4)$ and axis of symmetry $x = -1$.

To find the x-intercepts, we let y or $f(x) = 0$ and solve for x.

$$f(x) = -x^2 - 2x + 3$$
$$0 = -x^2 - 2x + 3 \quad \text{Let } f(x) = 0.$$

Now we divide both sides by -1 so that the coefficient of x^2 is 1. (If you prefer, you may factor -1 from the trinomial on the right side.)

$$\frac{0}{-1} = \frac{-x^2}{-1} - \frac{2x}{-1} + \frac{3}{-1} \qquad \text{Divide both sides by } -1.$$

$$0 = x^2 + 2x - 3 \qquad \text{Simplify.}$$

$$0 = (x + 3)(x - 1) \qquad \text{Factor.}$$

$$x + 3 = 0 \quad \text{or} \quad x - 1 = 0 \qquad \text{Set each factor equal to 0.}$$

$$x = -3 \qquad\qquad x = 1 \qquad \text{Solve.}$$

The x-intercepts are $(-3, 0)$ and $(1, 0)$.

To find the y-intercept, we let $x = 0$ and solve for y. Then

$$f(0) = -0^2 - 2(0) + 3 = 3$$

Thus, $(0, 3)$ is the y-intercept. We use these points to graph the parabola.

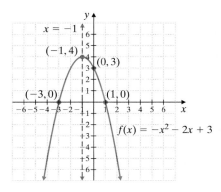

◼ Work Practice Problem 3

Objective **B** Deriving a Formula for Finding the Vertex

As you have seen in previous examples, it can sometimes be tedious to find the vertex of a parabola by completing the square. There is a formula for finding the vertex of a parabola. Now that we have practiced completing the square, we will show that the x-coordinate of the vertex of the graph of $f(x)$ or $y = ax^2 + bx + c$ can be found by the formula $x = \dfrac{-b}{2a}$. To do so, we complete the square on x and write the equation in the form $y = (x - h)^2 + k$.

First we get the x-variable terms alone by subtracting c from both sides.

$$y = ax^2 + bx + c$$

$$y - c = ax^2 + bx$$

$$y - c = a\left(x^2 + \frac{b}{a}x \right) \qquad \text{Factor } a \text{ from the terms } ax^2 + bx.$$

Now we add the square of half of $\dfrac{b}{a}$, or $\left(\dfrac{b}{2a} \right)^2 = \dfrac{b^2}{4a^2}$, to the right side inside the parentheses. Because of the factor a, what we really added is $a\left(\dfrac{b^2}{4a^2} \right)$ and this must be added to the left side as well.

$$y - c + a\left(\frac{b^2}{4a^2} \right) = a\left(x^2 + \frac{b}{a}x + \frac{b^2}{4a^2} \right)$$

$$y - c + \frac{b^2}{4a} = a\left(x + \frac{b}{2a} \right)^2 \qquad \text{Simplify the left side and factor the right}$$
$$\qquad\qquad\qquad\qquad\qquad\qquad \text{side. Add } c \text{ to both sides and subtract } \dfrac{b^2}{4a}$$
$$y = a\left(x + \frac{b}{2a} \right)^2 + c - \frac{b^2}{4a} \qquad \text{from both sides.}$$

Compare this form with $f(x)$ or $y = a(x - h)^2 + k$ and see that h is $\frac{-b}{2a}$, which means that the x-coordinate of the vertex of the graph of $f(x) = ax^2 + bx + c$ is $\frac{-b}{2a}$.

Let's use the vertex formula below to find the vertex of the parabola we graphed in Example 1.

Vertex Formula

The graph of $f(x) = ax^2 + bx + c$, when $a \neq 0$, is a parabola with vertex

$$\left(\frac{-b}{2a}, f\left(\frac{-b}{2a} \right) \right)$$

Find the vertex of the graph of $f(x) = x^2 - 4x - 5$. Compare your result with the result of Practice Problem 1.

EXAMPLE 4 Find the vertex of the graph of $f(x) = x^2 - 4x - 12$.

Solution: In the quadratic function $f(x) = x^2 - 4x - 12$, notice that $a = 1$, $b = -4$, and $c = -12$.

$$\frac{-b}{2a} = \frac{-(-4)}{2(1)} = 2$$

The x-value of the vertex is 2. To find the corresponding $f(x)$ or y-value, find $f(2)$. Then

$$f(2) = 2^2 - 4(2) - 12 = 4 - 8 - 12 = -16$$

The vertex is $(2, -16)$. These results agree with our findings in Example 1.

■ **Work Practice Problem 4**

Objective C Finding Minimum and Maximum Values

The quadratic function whose graph is a parabola that opens upward has a minimum value, and the quadratic function whose graph is a parabola that opens downward has a maximum value. The $f(x)$- or y-value of the vertex is the minimum or maximum value of the function.

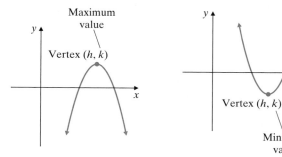

✔**Concept Check** Without making any calculations, tell whether the graph of $f(x) = 7 - x - 0.3x^2$ has a maximum value or a minimum value. Explain your reasoning.

Answer

4. $(2, -9)$

✔ **Concept Check Answer**

$f(x)$ has a maximum value since it opens downward.

EXAMPLE 5 **Finding Maximum Height**

A rock is thrown upward from the ground. Its height in feet above ground after t seconds is given by the function $f(t) = -16t^2 + 20t$. Find the maximum height of the rock and the number of seconds it took for the rock to reach its maximum height.

Solution:

1. UNDERSTAND. The maximum height of the rock is the largest value of $f(t)$. Since the function $f(t) = -16t^2 + 20t$ is a quadratic function, its graph is a parabola. It opens downward since $-16 < 0$. Thus, the maximum value of $f(t)$ is the $f(t)$- or y-value of the vertex of its graph.

2. TRANSLATE. To find the vertex (h, k), we notice that for $f(t) = -16t^2 + 20t$, $a = -16$, $b = 20$, and $c = 0$. We will use these values and the vertex formula

$$\left(\frac{-b}{2a}, f\left(\frac{-b}{2a} \right) \right)$$

3. SOLVE. $h = \dfrac{-b}{2a} = \dfrac{-20}{-32} = \dfrac{5}{8}$

$$f\left(\frac{5}{8} \right) = -16\left(\frac{5}{8} \right)^2 + 20\left(\frac{5}{8} \right) = -16\left(\frac{25}{64} \right) + \frac{25}{2} = -\frac{25}{4} + \frac{50}{4} = \frac{25}{4}$$

4. INTERPRET. The graph of $f(t)$ is a parabola opening downward with vertex $\left(\frac{5}{8}, \frac{25}{4} \right)$. This means that the rock's maximum height is $\dfrac{25}{4}$ feet, or $6\dfrac{1}{4}$ feet, which was reached in $\dfrac{5}{8}$ second.

■ **Work Practice Problem 5**

PRACTICE PROBLEM 5

An object is thrown upward from the top of a 100-foot cliff. Its height in feet above ground after t seconds is given by the function $f(t) = -16t^2 + 10t + 100$. Find the maximum height of the object and the number of seconds it took for the object to reach its maximum height.

Answer

5. maximum height: $101\dfrac{9}{16}$ ft in $\dfrac{5}{16}$ sec

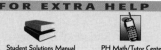
Objectives Ⓐ Ⓑ **Mixed Practice** *Find the vertex of the graph of each quadratic function by completing the square or using the vertex formula. See Examples 1 through 4.*

1. $f(x) = x^2 + 8x + 7$ **2.** $f(x) = x^2 + 6x + 5$ **3.** $f(x) = -x^2 + 10x + 5$ **4.** $f(x) = -x^2 - 8x + 2$

5. $f(x) = 5x^2 - 10x + 3$ **6.** $f(x) = -3x^2 + 6x + 4$ **7.** $f(x) = -x^2 + x + 1$ **8.** $f(x) = x^2 - 9x + 8$

Match each function with its graph. See Examples 1 through 4.

A.
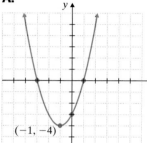
$(-1, -4)$

B.
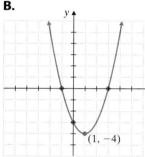
$(1, -4)$

C.
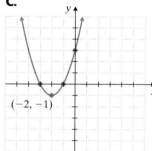
$(-2, -1)$

D.
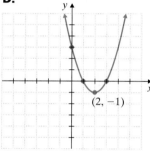
$(2, -1)$

9. $f(x) = x^2 - 4x + 3$ **10.** $f(x) = x^2 + 2x - 3$ **11.** $f(x) = x^2 - 2x - 3$ **12.** $f(x) = x^2 + 4x + 3$

Find the vertex of the graph of each quadratic function. Determine whether the graph opens upward or downward, find any intercepts, and graph the function. See Examples 1 through 4.

13. $f(x) = x^2 + 4x - 5$

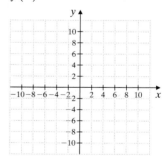

14. $f(x) = x^2 + 2x - 3$

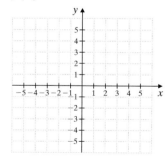

 15. $f(x) = -x^2 + 2x - 1$

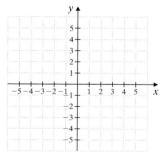

16. $f(x) = -x^2 + 4x - 4$

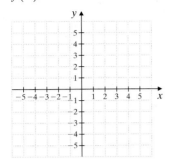

17. $f(x) = x^2 - 4$

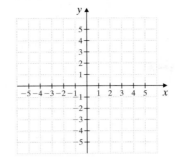

18. $f(x) = x^2 - 1$

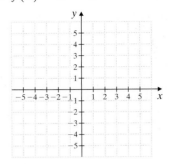

19. $f(x) = 4x^2 + 4x - 3$

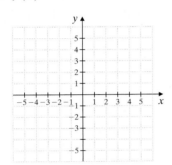

20. $f(x) = 2x^2 - x - 3$

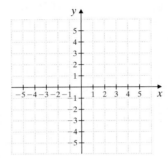

21. $f(x) = \frac{1}{2}x^2 + 4x + \frac{15}{2}$

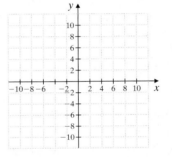

22. $f(x) = \frac{1}{5}x^2 + 2x + \frac{9}{5}$

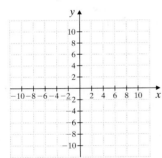

23. $f(x) = x^2 - 4x + 5$

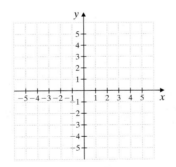

24. $f(x) = x^2 - 6x + 11$

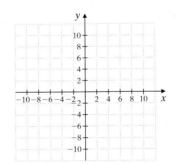

25. $f(x) = 2x^2 + 4x + 5$　　**26.** $f(x) = 3x^2 + 12x + 16$　**27.** $f(x) = -2x^2 + 12x$　　　**28.** $f(x) = -4x^2 + 8x$

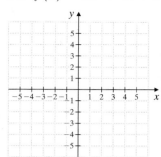　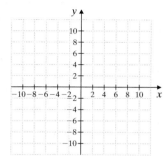　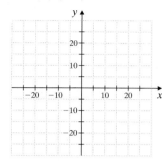　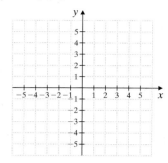

Objective **C** *Solve. See Example 5.*

29. If a projectile is fired straight upward from the ground with an initial speed of 96 feet per second, then its height h in feet after t seconds is given by the function $h(t) = -16t^2 + 96t$. Find the maximum height of the projectile.

30. If Rheam Gaspar throws a ball upward with an initial speed of 32 feet per second, then its height h in feet after t seconds is given by the function $h(t) = -16t^2 + 32t$. Find the maximum height of the ball.

31. The cost C in dollars of manufacturing x bicycles at Holladay's Production Plant is given by the function $C(x) = 2x^2 - 800x + 92,000$.

　a. Find the number of bicycles that must be manufactured to minimize the cost.

　b. Find the minimum cost.

32. The Utah Ski Club sells calendars to raise money. The profit P, in cents, from selling x calendars is given by the function $P(x) = 360x - x^2$.

　a. Find how many calendars must be sold to maximize profit.

　b. Find the maximum profit.

33. Find two numbers whose sum is 60 and whose product is as large as possible. [*Hint:* Let x and $60 - x$ be the two positive numbers. Their product can be described by the function $f(x) = x(60 - x)$.]

34. Find two numbers whose sum is 11 and whose product is as large as possible. (Use the hint for Exercise 33.)

35. Find two numbers whose difference is 10 and whose product is as small as possible. (Use the hint for Exercise 33.)

36. Find two numbers whose difference is 8 and whose product is as small as possible.

△ **37.** The length and width of a rectangle must have a sum of 40. Find the dimensions of the rectangle that will have the maximum area. (Use the hint for Exercise 33.)

△ **38.** The length and width of a rectangle must have a sum of 50. Find the dimensions of the rectangle that will have maximum area.

Review

Find the vertex of the graph of each function. See Section 8.5.

39. $f(x) = x^2 + 2$　　　**40.** $f(x) = (x - 3)^2$　　　**41.** $g(x) = (x + 2)^2$　　　**42.** $h(x) = x^2 - 3$

43. $f(x) = (x + 5)^2 + 2$　　**44.** $f(x) = 2(x - 3)^2 + 2$　　**45.** $f(x) = 3(x - 4)^2 + 1$　　**46.** $f(x) = (x + 1)^2 + 4$

Concept Extensions

Without calculating, tell whether each graph has a minimum value or a maximum value. See the Concept Check in the section.

47. $f(x) = 2x^2 - 5$ **48.** $g(x) = -7x^2 + x + 1$ **49.** $F(x) = 3 - \dfrac{1}{2}x^2$ **50.** $G(x) = 3 - \dfrac{1}{2}x + 0.8x^2$

Find the vertex of the graph of each quadratic function. Determine whether the graph opens upward or downward, find the y-intercept, approximate the x-intercepts to one decimal place, and graph the function.

51. $f(x) = x^2 + 10x + 15$

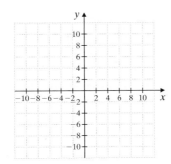

52. $f(x) = 2x^2 + 4x - 1$

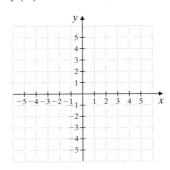

Use a graphing calculator to verify the graph of each exercise.

53. Exercise 21.

54. Exercise 22.

Find the maximum or minimum value of each function. Approximate to two decimal places.

55. $f(x) = 2.3x^2 - 6.1x + 3.2$

56. $f(x) = 7.6x^2 + 9.8x - 2.1$

57. The number of inmates in custody in U.S. prisons and jails can be modeled by the quadratic function $p(x) = -18x^2 + 298x + 988$, where $p(x)$ is the number of inmates in thousands and x is the number of years after 1995. (*Source:* Based on data from the Bureau of Justice Statistics, U.S. Department of Justice, 1995–2004.)

   a. Will this function have a maximum or minimum. How can you tell?

   b. According to this model, in what year will the number of prison and jail inmates in custody in the United States be at its maximum or minimum?

   c. What is the maximum/minimum number of inmates predicted?

58. Methane is a gas produced by landfills, natural gas systems, and coal mining that contributes to the greenhouse effect and global warming. Projected methane emissions in the United States can be modeled by the quadratic function

$$f(x) = -0.072x^2 + 1.93x + 173.9$$

where $f(x)$ is the amount of methane produced in million metric tons and x is the number of years after 2000. (*Source:* Based on data from the U.S. Environmental Protection Agency, 2000–2020)

   a. According to this model, what will U.S. emissions of methane be in 2009?

   b. Will this function have a maximum or a minimum? How can you tell?

   c. In what year will methane emissions in the United States be at their maximum/minimum? Round to the nearest whole year.

   d. What is the level of methane emissions for that year? (Use your rounded answer from part c.)

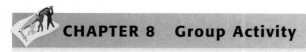

CHAPTER 8   Group Activity

Recognizing Linear and Quadratic Models

This activity may be completed by working in groups or individually.

We have seen in this and previous chapters that data can be modeled by both linear models and quadratic models. However, when we are given a set of data to model, how can we tell if a linear or quadratic model is appropriate? The best answer requires looking at a scatter diagram of the data. If the plotted data points fall roughly on a line, a linear model is usually the better choice. If the plotted data points seem to fall on a definite curve or if a maximum or minimum point is apparent, a quadratic model is usually the better choice.

One of the sets of data shown in the tables is best modeled by a linear function and one is best modeled by a quadratic function. In each case, the variable x represents the number of years after 2000.

Hummer Vehicle Sales				
Year	2001	2002	2003	2004
x	1	2	3	4
Number of Hummers Sold, y	768	19,581	35,259	29,346

(*Source:* General Motors)

Number of Domestic Wal-Mart Stores and Supercenters					
Year	2000	2001	2002	2003	2004
x	0	1	2	3	4
Number of Stores, y	2522	2624	2713	2826	2949

(*Source:* Wal-Mart Stores, Inc.)

1. Make a scatter diagram for each set of data. Which type of model should be used for each set of data?

2. For the set of data that you have determined to be linear, find a linear function that fits the data points. Explain the method that you used.

3. For the set of data that you have determined to be quadratic, identify the point on your scatter diagram that appears to be the vertex of the parabola. Use the coordinates of this vertex in the quadratic model $f(x) = a(x - h)^2 + k$.

4. Solve for the remaining unknown constant in the quadratic model by substituting the coordinates for another data point into the function. Write the final form of the quadratic model for this data set.

5. Use your models to estimate the number of Hummers sold and the number of domestic Wal-Mart stores and supercenters in 2006.

6. (Optional) For each set of data, enter the data from the table into a graphing calculator and use either the linear regression feature or the quadratic regression feature to find an appropriate function that models the data.* Compare these functions with the ones you found by hand. How are they alike or different?

*To find out more about using your graphing calculator to find a regression equation, consult your user's manual.

Chapter 8 Vocabulary Check

Fill in each blank with one of the words or phrases listed below.

quadratic formula	quadratic	discriminant	$\pm\sqrt{b}$
completing the square	quadratic inequality		

(h, k) $(0, k)$ $(h, 0)$ $\dfrac{-b}{2a}$

1. The _____ helps us know find the number and type of solutions of a quadratic equation.

2. If $a^2 = b$, then $a =$ _____.

3. The graph of $f(x) = ax^2 + bx + c$, where a is not 0, is a parabola whose vertex has an x-value of ____.

4. A(n) _____ is an inequality that can be written so that one side is a quadratic expression and the other side is 0.

5. The process of writing a quadratic equation so that one side is a perfect square trinomial is called _____.

6. The graph of $f(x) = x^2 + k$ has vertex ____.

7. The graph of $f(x) = (x - h)^2$ has vertex ____.

8. The graph of $f(x) = (x - h)^2 + k$ has vertex ____.

9. The formula $x = \dfrac{-b \pm \sqrt{b^2 - 4ac}}{2a}$ is called the _____.

10. A _____ equation is one that can be written in the form $ax^2 + bx + c = 0$, where $a, b,$ and c are real numbers and a is not 0.

> **Helpful Hint**
>
> Are you preparing for your test? Don't forget to take the Chapter 8 Test on page 629. Then check your answers at the back of the text and use the Chapter Test Prep Video CD to see the fully worked-out solutions to any of the exercises you want to review.

8 Chapter Highlights

DEFINITIONS AND CONCEPTS	EXAMPLES

Section 8.1   Solving Quadratic Equations by Completing the Square

SQUARE ROOT PROPERTY If b is a real number and if $a^2 = b$, then $a = \pm\sqrt{b}$.	Solve: $(x + 3)^2 = 14$ $\qquad x + 3 = \pm\sqrt{14}$ $\qquad\qquad x = -3 \pm \sqrt{14}$
SOLVING A QUADRATIC EQUATION IN x BY COMPLETING THE SQUARE **Step 1.** If the coefficient of x^2 is not 1, divide both sides of the equation by the coefficient of x^2. **Step 2.** Get the variable terms alone. **Step 3.** Complete the square by adding the square of half of the coefficient of x to both sides. **Step 4.** Write the resulting trinomial as the square of a binomial. **Step 5.** Use the square root property.	Solve: $3x^2 - 12x - 18 = 0$ **1.** $x^2 - 4x - 6 = 0$ **2.** $\qquad x^2 - 4x = 6$ **3.** $\dfrac{1}{2}(-4) = -2$ and $(-2)^2 = 4$ $\qquad x^2 - 4x + 4 = 6 + 4$ **4.** $(x - 2)^2 = 10$ **5.** $x - 2 = \pm\sqrt{10}$ $\qquad\qquad x = 2 \pm \sqrt{10}$

DEFINITIONS AND CONCEPTS	EXAMPLES

Section 8.2   Solving Quadratic Equations by Using the Quadratic Formula

QUADRATIC FORMULA

A quadratic equation written in the form $ax^2 + bx + c = 0$ has solutions

$$x = \frac{-b \pm \sqrt{b^2 - 4ac}}{2a}$$

Solve: $x^2 - x - 3 = 0$

$$a = 1, b = -1, c = -3$$

$$x = \frac{-(-1) \pm \sqrt{(-1)^2 - 4(1)(-3)}}{2 \cdot 1}$$

$$x = \frac{1 \pm \sqrt{13}}{2}$$

Section 8.3   Solving Equations by Using Quadratic Methods

Substitution is often helpful in solving an equation that contains a repeated variable expression.

Solve: $(2x + 1)^2 - 5(2x + 1) + 6 = 0$

Let $m = 2x + 1$. Then

$$\begin{aligned} m^2 - 5m + 6 &= 0 \\ (m - 3)(m - 2) &= 0 \end{aligned}$$ Let $m = 2x + 1$.

$$m = 3 \quad \text{or} \quad m = 2$$

$$2x + 1 = 3 \quad 2x + 1 = 2$$ Substitute back.

$$x = 1 \qquad x = \frac{1}{2}$$

Section 8.4   Nonlinear Inequalities in One Variable

SOLVING A POLYNOMIAL INEQUALITY

Step 1. Write the inequality in standard form and solve the related equation.

Step 2. Use solutions from Step 1 to separate the number line into regions.

Step 3. Use a test point to determine whether values in each region satisfy the original inequality.

Step 4. Write the solution set as the union of regions whose test point values are solutions.

Solve: $x^2 \geq 6x$

1. $x^2 - 6x \geq 0$

2. $x^2 - 6x = 0$

   $x(x - 6) = 0$

   $x = 0 \quad \text{or} \quad x = 6$

3.

4.

Region	Test Point Value	$x^2 \geq 6x$	Result
A	-2	$(-2)^2 \geq 6(-2)$	True
B	1	$1^2 \geq 6(1)$	False
C	7	$7^2 \geq 6(7)$	True

5.

The solution set is $(-\infty, 0] \cup [6, \infty)$.

SOLVING A RATIONAL INEQUALITY

Step 1. Solve for values that make all denominators 0.

Step 2. Solve the related equation.

Solve: $\dfrac{6}{x - 1} < -2$

1. $x - 1 = 0$ Set the denominator equal to 0.

   $x = 1$

2. $\dfrac{6}{x - 1} = -2$

$$\begin{aligned} 6 &= -2(x - 1) \quad \text{Multiply by } (x - 1). \\ 6 &= -2x + 2 \\ 4 &= -2x \\ -2 &= x \end{aligned}$$

| **DEFINITIONS AND CONCEPTS** | **EXAMPLES** |

Section 8.4   Nonlinear Inequalities in One Variable (*continued*)

Step 3. Use solutions from Steps 1 and 2 to separate the number line into regions.

Step 4. Use a test point to determine whether values in each region satisfy the original inequality.

Step 5. Write the solution set as the union of regions whose test point value is a solution.

3.
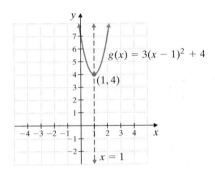

4. Only a test value from region B satisfies the original inequality.

5.

The solution set is $(-2, 1)$.

Section 8.5   Quadratic Functions and Their Graphs

GRAPHING A QUADRATIC FUNCTION

The graph of a quadratic function written in the form $f(x) = a(x - h)^2 + k$ is a parabola with vertex (h, k).
If $a > 0$, the parabola opens upward.
If $a < 0$, the parabola opens downward.
The axis of symmetry is the line whose equation is $x = h$.

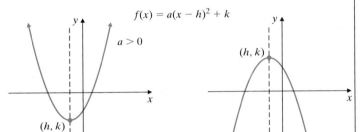

Graph: $g(x) = 3(x - 1)^2 + 4$

The graph is a parabola with vertex $(1, 4)$ and axis of symmetry $x = 1$. Since $a = 3$ is positive, the graph opens upward.

Section 8.6   Further Graphing of Quadratic Functions

The graph of $f(x) = ax^2 + bx + c, a \neq 0$, is a parabola with vertex

$$\left(\frac{-b}{2a}, f\left(\frac{-b}{2a}\right)\right)$$

Graph: $f(x) = x^2 - 2x - 8$. Find the vertex and x- and y-intercepts.

$$\frac{-b}{2a} = \frac{-(-2)}{2 \cdot 1} = 1$$
$$f(1) = 1^2 - 2(1) - 8 = -9$$

The vertex is $(1, -9)$.

$$0 = x^2 - 2x - 8$$
$$0 = (x - 4)(x + 2)$$
$$x = 4 \quad \text{or} \quad x = -2$$

continued

DEFINITIONS AND CONCEPTS	**EXAMPLES**

Section 8.6   Further Graphing of Quadratic Functions (*continued*)

The *x*-intercepts are $(4, 0)$ and $(-2, 0)$.

$$f(0) = 0^2 - 2 \cdot 0 - 8 = -8$$

The *y*-intercept is $(0, -8)$.

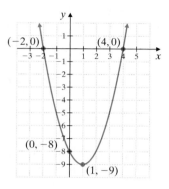

 STUDY SKILLS BUILDER

Are You Prepared for a Test on Chapter 8?

Below I have listed some common trouble areas for students in Chapter 8. After studying for your test—but before taking your test—read these.

- Don't forget that to solve a quadratic equation such as $x^2 + 6x = 1$, by completing the square, add the square of half of 6 to *both* sides.

$$x^2 + 6x = 1$$
$$x^2 + 6x + 9 = 1 + 9 \quad \text{Add 9 to both sides.}$$
$$(x + 3)^2 = 10 \qquad \left(\tfrac{1}{2}(6) = 3 \text{ and } 3^2 = 9\right)$$
$$x + 3 = \pm\sqrt{10}$$
$$x = -3 \pm \sqrt{10}$$

- Remember to write a quadratic equation in standard form $(ax^2 + bx + c = 0)$ before using the quadratic formula of solve.

$$x(4x - 1) = 1$$
$$4x^2 - x - 1 = 0 \quad \text{Write in standard form.}$$
$$x = \frac{-(-1) \pm \sqrt{(-1)^2 - 4(4)(-1)}}{2 \cdot 4} \quad \begin{array}{l}\text{Use the quadratic}\\ \text{formula with } a = 4,\\ b = -1, \text{ and } c = -1.\end{array}$$
$$x = \frac{1 \pm \sqrt{17}}{8} \qquad \text{Simplify.}$$

- Review the steps for solving a quadratic equation in general on page 578.

- Don't forget how to graph a quadratic function in the form $f(x) = a(x - h)^2 + k$. The graph of
$$f(x) = -2(x - 3)^2 - 1$$

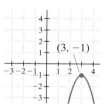

Remember: This is simply a checklist of common trouble areas. For a review of Chapter 8, see the Highlights and Chapter Review at the end of this chapter.

9

Exponential and Logarithmic Functions

Taken from:
Intermediate Algebra, Third Edition, by Elayn Martin-Gay

9.1 THE ALGEBRA OF FUNCTIONS

Objectives

A Add, Subtract, Multiply, and Divide Functions.

B Compose Functions.

Objective **A** Adding, Subtracting, Multiplying, and Dividing Functions

As we have seen in earlier chapters, it is possible to add, subtract, multiply, and divide functions. Although we have not stated them as such, the sums, differences, products, and quotients of functions are themselves functions. For example, if $f(x) = 3x$ and $g(x) = x + 1$, their product, $f(x) \cdot g(x) = 3x(x + 1) = 3x^2 + 3x$, is a new function. We can use the notation $(f \cdot g)(x)$ to denote this new function. Finding the sum, difference, product, and quotient of functions to generate new functions is called the **algebra of functions**.

Algebra of Functions

Let f and g be functions. New functions from f and g are defined as follows:

Sum	$(f + g)(x) = f(x) + g(x)$
Difference	$(f - g)(x) = f(x) - g(x)$
Product	$(f \cdot g)(x) = f(x) \cdot g(x)$
Quotient	$\left(\dfrac{f}{g}\right)(x) = \dfrac{f(x)}{g(x)}, \ g(x) \neq 0$

EXAMPLE 1 If $f(x) = x - 1$ and $g(x) = 2x - 3$, find the following.

a. $(f + g)(x)$

b. $(f - g)(x)$

c. $(f \cdot g)(x)$

d. $\left(\dfrac{f}{g}\right)(x)$

Solution: Use the algebra of functions and replace $f(x)$ by $x - 1$ and $g(x)$ by $2x - 3$. Then simplify.

a. $(f + g)(x) = f(x) + g(x)$
$$= (x - 1) + (2x - 3)$$
$$= 3x - 4$$

b. $(f - g)(x) = f(x) - g(x)$
$$= (x - 1) - (2x - 3)$$
$$= x - 1 - 2x + 3$$
$$= -x + 2$$

c. $(f \cdot g)(x) = f(x) \cdot g(x)$
$$= (x - 1)(2x - 3)$$
$$= 2x^2 - 5x + 3$$

d. $\left(\dfrac{f}{g}\right)(x) = \dfrac{f(x)}{g(x)} = \dfrac{x - 1}{2x - 3}$, where $x \neq \dfrac{3}{2}$

☐ **Work Practice Problem 1**

There is an interesting but not surprising relationship between the graphs of functions and the graphs of their sum, difference, product, and quotient. For example, the graph of $(f + g)$ can be found by adding the graph of f to the graph of g. We add two graphs by adding corresponding y-values.

PRACTICE PROBLEM 1

If $f(x) = x + 3$ and $g(x) = 3x - 1$, find

a. $(f + g)(x)$

b. $(f - g)(x)$

c. $(f \cdot g)(x)$

d. $\left(\dfrac{f}{g}\right)(x)$

Answers

1. a. $4x + 2$, **b.** $-2x + 4$,
c. $3x^2 + 8x - 3$,
d. $\dfrac{x + 3}{3x - 1}$ where $x \neq \dfrac{1}{3}$

535

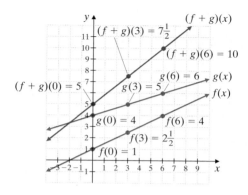

Objective B Composition of Functions

Another way to combine functions is called **function composition.** To understand this new way of combining functions, study the tables below. They show degrees Fahrenheit converted to equivalent degrees Celsius, and then degrees Celsius converted to equivalent degrees Kelvin. (The Kelvin scale is a temperature scale devised by Lord Kelvin in 1848.)

x = Degrees Fahrenheit (Input)	-31	-13	32	68	149	212
$C(x)$ = Degrees Celsius (Output)	-35	-25	0	20	65	100

$C(x)$ = Degrees Celsius (Input)	-35	-25	0	20	65	100
$K(C(x))$ = Kelvins (Output)	238.15	248.15	273.15	293.15	338.15	373.15

Suppose that we want a table that shows a direct conversion from degrees Fahrenheit to kelvins. In other words, suppose that a table is needed that shows kelvins as a function of degrees Fahrenheit. This can easily be done because in the tables, the output of the first table is the same as the input of the second table. The new table is as follows.

x = Degrees Fahrenheit (Input)	-31	-13	32	68	149	212
$K(C(x))$ = Kelvins (Output)	238.15	248.15	273.15	293.15	338.15	373.15

Since the output of the first table is used as the input of the second table, we write the new function as $K(C(x))$. The new function is formed from the composition of the other two functions. The mathematical symbol for this composition is $(K \circ C)(x)$. Thus, $(K \circ C)(x) = K(C(x))$.

It is possible to find an equation for the composition of the two functions $C(x)$ and $K(x)$. In other words, we can find a function that converts degrees Fahrenheit directly to kelvins. The function $C(x) = \dfrac{5}{9}(x - 32)$ converts degrees Fahrenheit to degrees Celsius, and the function $K(C(x)) = C(x) + 273.15$ converts degrees Celsius to kelvins. Thus,

$$(K \circ C)(x) = K(C(x)) = K\left(\frac{5}{9}(x - 32)\right) = \frac{5}{9}(x - 32) + 273.15$$

In general, the notation $f(g(x))$ means "f composed with g" and can be written as $(f \circ g)(x)$. Also $g(f(x))$, or $(g \circ f)(x)$, means "g composed with f."

Composite Functions

The composition of functions f and g is

$$(f \circ g)(x) = f(g(x))$$

Helpful Hint

$(f \circ g)(x)$ does not mean the same as $(f \cdot g)(x)$.

$(f \circ g)(x) = f(g(x))$ while $(f \cdot g)(x) = f(x) \cdot g(x)$

EXAMPLE 2 If $f(x) = x^2$ and $g(x) = x + 3$, find each composition.

a. $(f \circ g)(2)$ and $(g \circ f)(2)$
b. $(f \circ g)(x)$ and $(g \circ f)(x)$

Solution:

a. $(f \circ g)(2) = f(g(2))$

$\qquad\qquad = f(5)$ Since $g(x) = x + 3$, then $g(2) = 2 + 3 = 5$.

$\qquad\qquad = 5^2 = 25$

$\quad (g \circ f)(2) = g(f(2))$

$\qquad\qquad = g(4)$ Since $f(x) = x^2$, then $f(2) = 2^2 = 4$.

$\qquad\qquad = 4 + 3 = 7$

b. $(f \circ g)(x) = f(g(x))$

$\qquad\qquad = f(x + 3)$ Replace $g(x)$ with $x + 3$.

$\qquad\qquad = (x + 3)^2$ $f(x + 3) = (x + 3)^2$

$\qquad\qquad = x^2 + 6x + 9$ Square $(x + 3)$.

$\quad (g \circ f)(x) = g(f(x))$

$\qquad\qquad = g(x^2)$ Replace $f(x)$ with x^2.

$\qquad\qquad = x^2 + 3$ $g(x^2) = x^2 + 3$

■ **Work Practice Problem 2**

EXAMPLE 3 If $f(x) = |x|$ and $g(x) = x - 2$, find each composition.

a. $(f \circ g)(x)$
b. $(g \circ f)(x)$

Solution:

a. $(f \circ g)(x) = f(g(x)) = f(x - 2) = |x - 2|$
b. $(g \circ f)(x) = g(f(x)) = g(|x|) = |x| - 2$

■ **Work Practice Problem 3**

Helpful Hint

In Examples 2 and 3, notice that $(g \circ f)(x) \neq (f \circ g)(x)$. In general, $(g \circ f)(x)$ *may* or *may not* equal $(f \circ g)(x)$.

PRACTICE PROBLEM 2

If $f(x) = x^2$ and $g(x) = 2x + 1$, find each composition.

a. $(f \circ g)(3)$ and $(g \circ f)(3)$
b. $(f \circ g)(x)$ and $(g \circ f)(x)$

PRACTICE PROBLEM 3

If $f(x) = \sqrt{x}$ and $g(x) = x + 1$, find each composition.

a. $(f \circ g)(x)$
b. $(g \circ f)(x)$

Answers

2. a. $49; 19,$ **b.** $4x^2 + 4x + 1; 2x^2 + 1,$

3. a. $\sqrt{x + 1},$ **b.** $\sqrt{x} + 1$

Answer

PRACTICE PROBLEM 4

If $f(x) = 2x$, $g(x) = x + 5$, and $h(x) = |x|$, write each function as a composition of f, g, or h.

a. $F(x) = |x + 5|$

b. $G(x) = 2x + 5$

EXAMPLE 4 If $f(x) = 5x$, $g(x) = x - 2$, and $h(x) = \sqrt{x}$, write each function as a composition with f, g, or h.

a. $F(x) = \sqrt{x - 2}$

b. $G(x) = 5x - 2$

Solution:

a. Notice the order in which the function F operates on an input value x. First, 2 is subtracted from x, and then the square root of that result is taken. This means that $F(x) = (h \circ g)(x)$. To check, we find $(h \circ g)(x)$.

$$(h \circ g)(x) = h(g(x)) = h(x - 2) = \sqrt{x - 2}$$

b. Notice the order in which the function G operates on an input value x. First, x is multiplied by 5, and then 2 is subtracted from the result. This means that $G(x) = (g \circ f)(x)$. To check, we find $(g \circ f)(x)$.

$$(g \circ f)(x) = g(f(x)) = g(5x) = 5x - 2$$

■ **Work Practice Problem 4**

▦ CALCULATOR EXPLORATIONS Graphing

If $f(x) = \dfrac{1}{2}x + 2$ and $g(x) = \dfrac{1}{3}x^2 + 4$, then

$$(f + g)(x) = f(x) + g(x)$$

$$= \left(\frac{1}{2}x + 2\right) + \left(\frac{1}{3}x^2 + 4\right)$$

$$= \frac{1}{3}x^2 + \frac{1}{2}x + 6$$

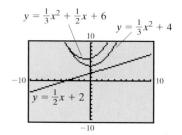

To visualize this addition of functions with a grapher, graph

$$Y_1 = \frac{1}{2}x + 2, \quad Y_2 = \frac{1}{3}x^2 + 4, \quad \text{and} \quad Y_3 = \frac{1}{3}x^2 + \frac{1}{2}x + 6$$

Use a TABLE feature to verify that for a given x value, $Y_1 + Y_2 = Y_3$. For example, verify that when $x = 0$, $Y_1 = 2$, $Y_2 = 4$ and $Y_3 = 2 + 4 = 6$.

---

4. a. $(h \circ g)(x)$, **b.** $(g \circ f)(x)$

Objective **A** *For the functions f and g, find* **a.** $(f + g)(x)$, **b.** $(f - g)(x)$, **c.** $(f \cdot g)(x)$, *and* **d.** $\left(\dfrac{f}{g}\right)(x)$. *See Example 1.*

1. $f(x) = x - 7; g(x) = 2x + 1$

2. $f(x) = x + 4; g(x) = 5x - 2$

3. $f(x) = x^2 + 1; g(x) = 5x$

4. $f(x) = x^2 - 2; g(x) = 3x$

5. $f(x) = \sqrt{x}; g(x) = x + 5$

6. $f(x) = \sqrt[3]{x}; g(x) = x - 3$

7. $f(x) = -3x; g(x) = 5x^2$

8. $f(x) = 4x^3; g(x) = -6x$

Objective **B** *If* $f(x) = x^2 - 6x + 2$, $g(x) = -2x$, *and* $h(x) = \sqrt{x}$, *find each composition. See Example 2.*

9. $(f \circ g)(2)$

10. $(h \circ f)(-2)$

11. $(g \circ f)(-1)$

12. $(f \circ h)(1)$

13. $(g \circ h)(0)$

14. $(h \circ g)(0)$

Find $(f \circ g)(x)$ *and* $(g \circ f)(x)$. *See Examples 2 and 3.*

15. $f(x) = x^2 + 1; g(x) = 5x$

16. $f(x) = x - 3; g(x) = x^2$

17. $f(x) = 2x - 3; g(x) = x + 7$

18. $f(x) = x + 10; g(x) = 3x + 1$

19. $f(x) = x^3 + x - 2; g(x) = -2x$

20. $f(x) = -4x; g(x) = x^3 + x^2 - 6$

21. $f(x) = |x|; g(x) = 10x - 3$

22. $f(x) = |x|; g(x) = 14x - 8$

23. $f(x) = \sqrt{x}; g(x) = -5x + 2$

24. $f(x) = 7x - 1; g(x) = \sqrt[3]{x}$

If $f(x) = 3x$, $g(x) = \sqrt{x}$, and $h(x) = x^2 + 2$, write each function as a composition with f, g, or h. See Example 4.

25. $H(x) = \sqrt{x^2 + 2}$

26. $G(x) = \sqrt{3x}$

27. $F(x) = 9x^2 + 2$

28. $H(x) = 3x^2 + 6$

29. $G(x) = 3\sqrt{x}$

30. $F(x) = x + 2$

Find $f(x)$ and $g(x)$ so that the given function $h(x) = (f \circ g)(x)$.

31. $h(x) = (x + 2)^2$

32. $h(x) = |x - 1|$

33. $h(x) = \sqrt{x + 5} + 2$

34. $h(x) = (3x + 4)^2 + 3$

35. $h(x) = \dfrac{1}{2x - 3}$

36. $h(x) = \dfrac{1}{x + 10}$

Review

Solve each equation for y. See Section 2.3.

37. $x = y + 2$

38. $x = y - 5$

39. $x = 3y$

40. $x = -6y$

41. $x = -2y - 7$

42. $x = 4y + 7$

Concept Extensions

43. Business people are concerned with cost functions, revenue functions, and profit functions. Recall that the profit $P(x)$ obtained from selling x units of a product is equal to the revenue $R(x)$ from selling the x units minus the cost $C(x)$ of manufacturing the x units. Write an equation expressing this relationship among $C(x)$, $R(x)$, and $P(x)$.

44. Suppose the revenue $R(x)$ for x units of a product can be described by $R(x) = 25x$, and the cost $C(x)$ can be described by $C(x) = 50 + x^2 + 4x$. Find the profit $P(x)$ for x units.

45. If you are given $f(x)$ and $g(x)$, explain in your own words how to find $(f \circ g)(x)$, and then how to find $(g \circ f)(x)$.

46. Given $f(x)$ and $g(x)$, describe in your own words the difference between $(f \circ g)(x)$ and $(f \cdot g)(x)$.

STUDY SKILLS BUILDER

Tips for Studying for an Exam

To prepare for an exam, try the following study techniques.

- Start the study process days before your exam.

- Make sure that you are up-to-date on your assignments.

- If there is a topic that you are unsure of, use one of the many resources that are available to you. For example,

   See your instructor.

   Visit a learning resource center on campus.

   Read the textbook material and examples on the topic.

   View a video on the topic.

- Reread your notes and carefully review the Chapter Highlights at the end of any chapter.

- Work the review exercises at the end of the chapter. Check your answers and correct any mistakes. If you have trouble, use a resource listed above.

- Find a quiet place to take the Chapter Test found at the end of the chapter. Do not use any resources when taking this sample test. This way, you will have a clear indication of how prepared you are for your exam.

Check your answers and make sure that you correct any missed exercises.

- Get lots of rest the night before the exam. It's hard to show how well you know the material if your brain is foggy from lack of sleep.

Good luck and keep a positive attitude.

Let's see how you did on your last exam.

1. How many days before your last exam did you start studying?

2. Were you up-to-date on your assignments at that time or did you need to catch up on assignments?

3. List the most helpful text supplement (if you used one).

4. List the most helpful campus supplement (if you used one).

5. List your process for preparing for a mathematics test.

6. Was this process helpful? In other words, were you satisfied with your performance on your exam?

7. If not, what changes can you make in your process that will make it more helpful to you?

9.2 INVERSE FUNCTIONS

In the next sections, we begin a study of two new functions: exponential and logarithmic functions. As we learn more about these functions, we will discover that they share a special relation to each other; they are inverses of each other.

Before we study these functions, we need to learn about inverses. We begin by defining one-to-one functions.

Objective Ⓐ Determining Whether a Function Is One-to-One

Study the following table.

Degrees Fahrenheit (Input)	−31	−13	32	68	149	212
Degrees Celsius (Output)	−35	−25	0	20	65	100

PRACTICE PROBLEMS 1–5

Determine whether each function described is one-to-one.
1. $f = \{(7, 3), (-1, 1), (5, 0), (4, -2)\}$
2. $g = \{(-3, 2), (6, 3), (2, 14), (-6, 2)\}$
3. $h = \{(0, 0), (1, 2), (3, 4), (5, 6)\}$

4.

State (Input)	Colorado	Mississippi	Nevada	New Mexico	Utah
Number of Colleges and Universities (Output)	16	7	4	10	7

Source: American Educational Guidance Center, 2005.

5.

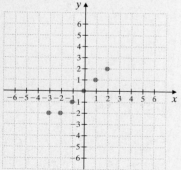

Recall that since each degrees Fahrenheit (input) corresponds to exactly one degrees Celsius (output), this table of inputs and outputs does describe a function. Also notice that each output corresponds to a different input. This type of function is given a special name—a *one-to-one function.*

Does the set $f = \{(0, 1), (2, 2), (-3, 5), (7, 6)\}$ describe a one-to-one function? It is a function since each x-value corresponds to a unique y-value. For this particular function f, each y-value corresponds to a unique x-value. Thus, this function is also a one-to-one function.

One-to-One Function

For a **one-to-one function,** each x-value (input) corresponds to only one y-value (output) and each y-value (output) corresponds to only one x-value (input).

EXAMPLES Determine whether each function described is one-to-one.

1. $f = \{(6, 2), (5, 4), (-1, 0), (7, 3)\}$

   The function f is one-to-one since each y-value corresponds to only one x-value.

2. $g = \{(3, 9), (-4, 2), (-3, 9), (0, 0)\}$

   The function g is not one-to-one because the y-value 9 in $(3, 9)$ and $(-3, 9)$ corresponds to two different x-values.

3. $h = \{(1, 1), (2, 2), (10, 10), (-5, -5)\}$

   The function h is one-to-one since each y-value corresponds to only one x-value.

4.

Mineral (Input)	Talc	Gypsum	Diamond	Topaz	Stibnite
Hardness on the Mohs Scale (Output)	1	2	10	8	2

This table does not describe a one-to-one function since the output 2 corresponds to two different inputs, gypsum and stibnite.

Answers
1. one-to-one, 2. not one-to-one,
3. one-to-one, 4. not one-to-one,
5. not one-to-one

5.

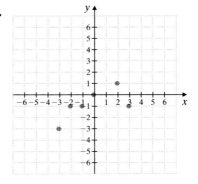

This graph does not describe a one-to-one function since the *y*-value −1 corresponds to three different *x*-values, −2, −1 and 3, as shown to the right.

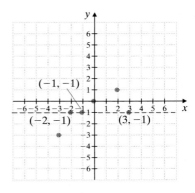

■ **Work Practice Problems 1–5**

Objective B Using the Horizontal Line Test

Recall that we recognize the graph of a function when it passes the vertical line test. Since every *x*-value of the function corresponds to exactly one *y*-value, each vertical line intersects the function's graph at most once. The graph shown next, for instance, is the graph of a function.

Is this function a *one-to-one* function? The answer is no. To see why not, notice that the *y*-value of the ordered pair (−3, 3), for example, is the same as the *y*-value of the ordered pair (3, 3). This function is therefore not one-to-one.

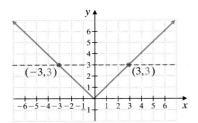

To test whether a graph is the graph of a one-to-one function, we can apply the vertical line test to see whether it is a function, and then apply a similar **horizontal line test** to see whether it is a one-to-one function.

Horizontal Line Test

If every horizontal line intersects the graph of a function at most once, then the function is a one-to-one function.

PRACTICE PROBLEM 6

Use the vertical and horizontal line tests to determine whether each graph is the graph of a one-to-one function.

a.

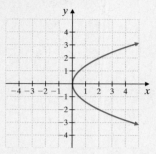

b.

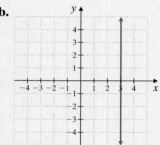

c.

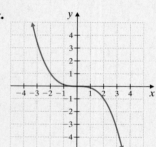

d.

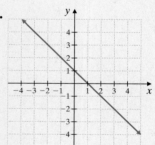

e.

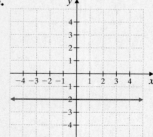

EXAMPLE 6 Use the vertical and horizontal line tests to determine whether each graph is the graph of a one-to-one function.

a.

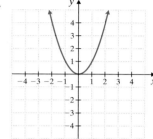

b.

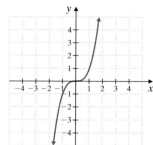

c.

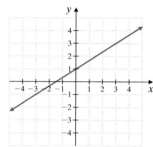

d.

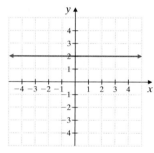

e.

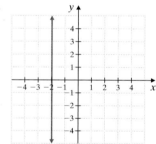

Solution: Graphs **a, b, c,** and **d** all pass the vertical line test, so only these graphs are graphs of functions. But, of these, only **b** and **c** pass the horizontal line test, so only **b** and **c** are graphs of one-to-one functions.

Work Practice Problem 6

Helpful Hint

All linear equations are one-to-one functions except those whose graphs are horizontal or vertical lines. A vertical line does not pass the vertical line test and hence is not the graph of a function. A horizontal line is the graph of a function but does not pass the horizontal line test and hence is not the graph of a one-to-one function.

Objective **C** Finding the Inverse of a Function

One-to-one functions are special in that their graphs pass the vertical and horizontal line tests. They are special, too, in another sense: We can find the **inverse function** for any one-to-one function by switching the coordinates of the ordered pairs of the function, or the inputs and the outputs. For example, the inverse of the one-to-one function

Degrees Fahrenheit (Input)	−31	−13	32	68	149	212
Degrees Celsius (Output)	−35	−25	0	20	65	100

is the function

Degrees Celsius (Input)	-35	-25	0	20	65	100
Degrees Fahrenheit (Output)	-31	-13	32	68	149	212

Notice that the ordered pair $(-31, -35)$ of the function, for example, becomes the ordered pair $(-35, -31)$ of its inverse.

Also, the inverse of the one-to-one function $f = \{(2, -3), (5, 10), (9, 1)\}$ is $\{(-3, 2), (10, 5), (1, 9)\}$. For a function f, we use the notation f^{-1}, read "f inverse," to denote its inverse function. Notice that since the coordinates of each ordered pair have been switched, the domain (set of inputs) of f is the range (set of outputs) of f^{-1}, and the range of f is the domain of f^{-1}.

Inverse Function

The inverse of a one-to-one function f is the one-to-one function f^{-1} that consists of the set of all ordered pairs (y, x) where (x, y) belongs to f.

EXAMPLE 7 Find the inverse of the one-to-one function:

$$f = \{(0, 1), (-2, 7), (3, -6), (4, 4)\}$$

Solution:

$$f^{-1} = \{(1, 0), (7, -2), (-6, 3), (4, 4)\}$$

Switch coordinates of each ordered pair.

■ **Work Practice Problem 7**

✔ **Concept Check** Suppose that f is a one-to-one function and that $f(1) = 5$.
a. Write the corresponding ordered pair.
b. Write one point that we know must belong to the inverse function f^{-1}.

Objective **D** **Finding the Equation of the Inverse of a Function**

If a one-to-one function f is defined as a set of ordered pairs, we can find f^{-1} by interchanging the x- and y-coordinates of the ordered pairs. If a one-to-one function f is given in the form of an equation, we can find the equation of f^{-1} by using a similar procedure.

Finding an Equation of the Inverse of a One-to-One Function f

Step 1: Replace $f(x)$ with y.

Step 2: Interchange x and y.

Step 3: Solve the equation for y.

Step 4: Replace y with the notation $f^{-1}(x)$.

Helpful Hint

The symbol f^{-1} is the single symbol used to denote the inverse of the function f. It is read as "f inverse." This symbol *does not mean* $\dfrac{1}{f}$.

PRACTICE PROBLEM 7

Find the inverse of the one-to-one function:
$f = \{(2, -4), (-1, 13), (0, 0), (-7, -8)\}$

Answer
7. $f^{-1} = \{(-4, 2), (13, -1), (0, 0), (-8, -7)\}$

✔ **Concept Check Answers**
a. $(1, 5)$, b. $(5, 1)$

PRACTICE PROBLEM 8

Find the equation of the inverse of $f(x) = x - 6$.

EXAMPLE 8 Find the equation of the inverse of $f(x) = x + 3$.

Solution: $f(x) = x + 3$

Step 1:	$y = x + 3$	Replace $f(x)$ with y.
Step 2:	$x = y + 3$	Interchange x and y.
Step 3:	$x - 3 = y$	Solve for y.
Step 4:	$f^{-1}(x) = x - 3$	Replace y with $f^{-1}(x)$.

The inverse of $f(x) = x + 3$ is $f^{-1}(x) = x - 3$. Notice that, for example,

$$f(1) = 1 + 3 = 4 \quad \text{and} \quad f^{-1}(4) = 4 - 3 = 1$$

Ordered pair: $(1, 4)$ Ordered pair: $(4, 1)$

The coordinates are switched, as expected.

■ **Work Practice Problem 8**

PRACTICE PROBLEM 9

Find the equation of the inverse of $f(x) = 2x + 3$. Graph f and f^{-1} on the same set of axes.

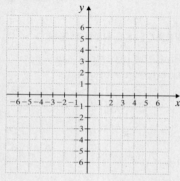

EXAMPLE 9 Find the equation of the inverse of $f(x) = 3x - 5$. Graph f and f^{-1} on the same set of axes.

Solution: $f(x) = 3x - 5$

Step 1:	$y = 3x - 5$	Replace $f(x)$ with y.
Step 2:	$x = 3y - 5$	Interchange x and y.
Step 3:	$x + 5 = 3y$	Solve for y.

$$\frac{x + 5}{3} = y \quad \text{or} \quad y = \frac{x + 5}{3}$$

Step 4: $f^{-1}(x) = \dfrac{x + 5}{3}$ Replace y with $f^{-1}(x)$.

Now we graph f and f^{-1} on the same set of axes. Both $f(x) = 3x - 5$ and $f^{-1}(x) = \dfrac{x + 5}{3}$ are linear functions, so each graph is a line.

8. $f^{-1}(x) = x + 6$,

9. $f^{-1}(x) = \dfrac{x - 3}{2}$

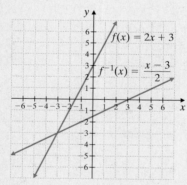

10. a.

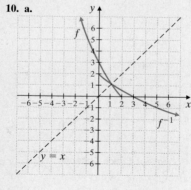

$f(x) = 3x - 5$	
x	$y = f(x)$
1	-2
0	-5
$\dfrac{5}{3}$	0

$f^{-1}(x) = \dfrac{x + 5}{3}$	
x	$y = f^{-1}(x)$
-2	1
-5	0
0	$\dfrac{5}{3}$

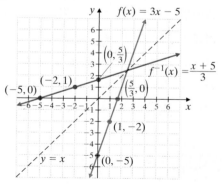

■ **Work Practice Problem 9**

Objective E Graphing Inverse Functions

Notice that the graphs of f and f^{-1} in Example 9 are mirror images of each other, and the "mirror" is the dashed line $y = x$. This is true for every function and its inverse. For this reason, we say that the *graphs of f and f⁻¹ are symmetric about the line* $y = x$.

To see why this happens, study the graph of a few ordered pairs and their switched coordinates.

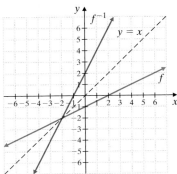

EXAMPLE 10 Graph the inverse of each function.

Solution: The function is graphed in blue and the inverse is graphed in red.

a.

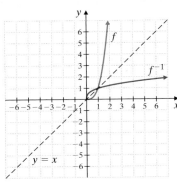

b.

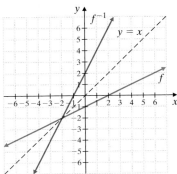

■ **Work Practice Problem 10**

PRACTICE PROBLEM 10

Graph the inverse of each function.

a.

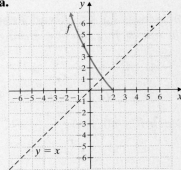

b.

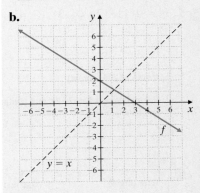

Answers

See page 646 for 10a.

10. b.

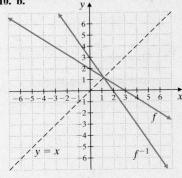

📟 **CALCULATOR EXPLORATIONS** Graphing

A grapher can be used to visualize functions and their inverses. Recall that the graph of a function f and its inverse f^{-1} are mirror images of each other across the line $y = x$. To see this for the function $f(x) = 3x + 2$, use a square window and graph

the given function: $Y_1 = 3x + 2$

its inverse: $Y_2 = \dfrac{x - 2}{3}$

and the line: $Y_3 = x$

Exercises will follow in Exercise Set 9.2.

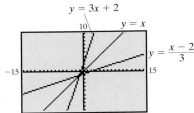

9.2 EXERCISE SET

FOR EXTRA HELP

Student Solutions Manual

PH Math/Tutor Center

CD/Video for Review

Math XL
MathXL®

MyMathLab
MyMathLab

Objectives A C **Mixed Practice** *Determine whether each function is a one-to-one function. If it is one-to-one, list the inverse function by switching coordinates, or inputs and outputs. See Examples 1 through 5, and 7.*

1. $g = \{(0, 3), (3, 7), (6, 7), (-2, -2)\}$

2. $g = \{(8, 6), (9, 6), (3, 4), (-4, 4)\}$

3. $h = \{(10, 10)\}$

4. $r = \{(1, 2), (3, 4), (5, 6), (6, 7)\}$

5. $f = \{(11, 12), (4, 3), (3, 4), (6, 6)\}$

6. $f = \{(-1, -1), (1, 1), (0, 2), (2, 0)\}$

7.

Month of 2004 (Input)	July	August	September	October	November	December
Unemployment Rate in Percent (Output)	5.5	5.4	5.4	5.5	5.4	5.4

(*Source:* U.S. Bureau of Labor Statistics)

8.

State (Input)	Wisconsin	Ohio	Georgia	Colorado	California	Arizona
Electoral Votes (Output)	10	20	15	9	55	10

(*Source:* National Archives and Records Administration, based on the 2000 Census)

9.

State (Input)	California	Alaska	Indiana	Louisiana	New Mexico
Rank in Population (Output)	1	47	14	24	36

(*Source:* U.S. Bureau of the Census)

10.

Shape (Input)	Triangle	Pentagon	Quadrilateral	Hexagon	Decagon
Number of Sides (Output)	3	5	4	6	10

Given the one-to-one function $f(x) = x^3 + 2$, *find the following. (Hint: You do not need to find the equation for* f^{-1}.)

11. a. $f(1)$
  b. $f^{-1}(3)$

12. a. $f(0)$
  b. $f^{-1}(2)$

13. a. $f(-1)$
  b. $f^{-1}(1)$

14. a. $f(-2)$
  b. $f^{-1}(-6)$

Objective **B** *Determine whether the graph of each function is the graph of a one-to-one function. See Example 6.*

15.

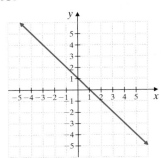

16.

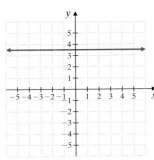

17.

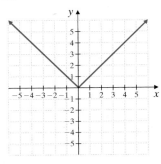

18.

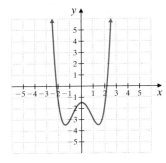

19.

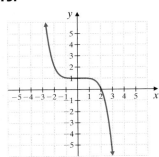

20.

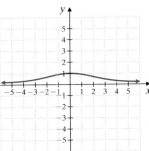

21.

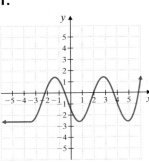

22.

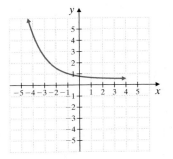

Objectives **D** **E** **Mixed Practice** *Each of the following functions is one-to-one. Find the inverse of each function and graph the function and its inverse on the same set of axes. See Examples 8 and 9.*

23. $f(x) = x + 4$

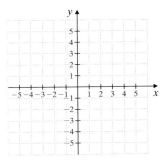

24. $f(x) = x - 5$

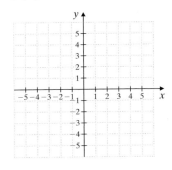

25. $f(x) = 2x - 3$

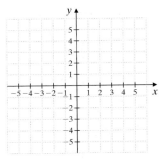

26. $f(x) = 4x + 9$

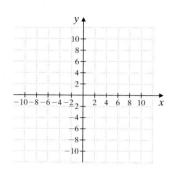

27. $f(x) = \frac{1}{2}x - 1$

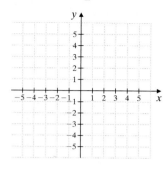

28. $f(x) = -\frac{1}{2}x + 2$

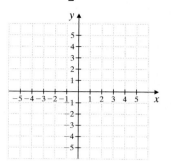

29. $f(x) = x^3$

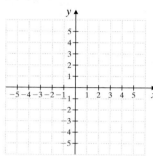

30. $f(x) = x^3 - 1$

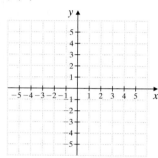

Find the inverse of each one-to-one function. See Examples 8 and 9.

31. $f(x) = \dfrac{x - 2}{5}$

32. $f(x) = \dfrac{4x - 3}{2}$

33. $f(x) = \sqrt[3]{x}$

34. $f(x) = \sqrt[3]{x + 1}$

35. $f(x) = \dfrac{5}{3x + 1}$

36. $f(x) = \dfrac{7}{2x + 4}$

37. $f(x) = (x + 2)^3$

38. $f(x) = (x - 5)^3$

Graph the inverse of each function on the same set of axes. See Example 10.

39.

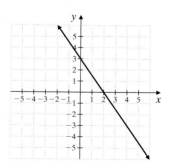

40.

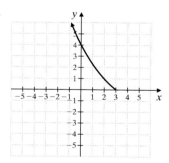

41.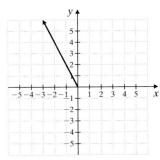

42.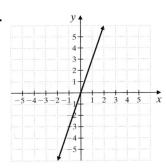

Review

Evaluate each exponential expression. See Section 7.2.

43. $25^{1/2}$

44. $49^{1/2}$

45. $16^{3/4}$

46. $27^{2/3}$

47. $9^{-3/2}$

48. $81^{-3/4}$

If $f(x) = 3^x$, find each value. In Exercises 51 and 52, give an exact answer and a two-decimal-place approximation. See Section 3.6.

49. $f(2)$

50. $f(0)$

📱 **51.** $f\left(\dfrac{1}{2}\right)$

📱 **52.** $f\left(\dfrac{2}{3}\right)$

Concept Extensions

Solve. See the Concept Check in this section.

53. Suppose that f is a one-to-one function and that $f(2) = 9$.
   a. Write the corresponding ordered pair.
   b. Name one ordered-pair that we know is a solution of the inverse of f, or f^{-1}.

54. Suppose that F is a one-to-one function and that $F\left(\dfrac{1}{2}\right) = -0.7$.
   a. Write the corresponding ordered pair.
   b. Name one ordered pair that we know is a solution of the inverse of F, or F^{-1}.

For Exercises 55 and 56.

   a. *Write the ordered pairs for f whose points are highlighted. (Include the points whose coordinates are given.)*
   b. *Write the corresponding ordered pairs for the inverse of f, f^{-1}.*
   c. *Graph the ordered pairs for f^{-1} found in part (b).*
   d. *Graph f^{-1} by drawing a smooth curve through the plotted points.*

55. a.

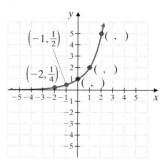

56. a.

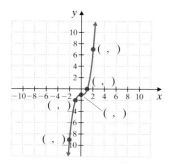

c. d.

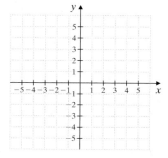

c. d.

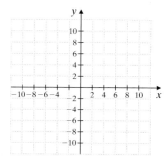

57. If you are given the graph of a function, describe how you can tell from the graph whether a function has an inverse.

58. Describe the appearance of the graphs of a function and its inverse.

Find the inverse of each one-to-one function. Then graph the function and its inverse in a square window.

59. $f(x) = 3x + 1$ **60.** $f(x) = -2x - 6$ **61.** $f(x) = \sqrt[3]{x + 3}$ **62.** $f(x) = x^3 - 3$

9.3 EXPONENTIAL FUNCTIONS

O b j e c t i v e s

A Graph Exponential Functions.

B Solve Equations of the Form $b^x = b^y$.

C Solve Problems Modeled by Exponential Equations.

In earlier chapters, we gave meaning to exponential expressions such as 2^x, where x is a rational number. Recall the following examples.

$$2^3 = 2 \cdot 2 \cdot 2 \qquad \text{Three factors; each factor is 2}$$
$$2^{3/2} = (2^{1/2})^3 = \sqrt{2} \cdot \sqrt{2} \cdot \sqrt{2} \qquad \text{Three factors; each factor is } \sqrt{2}$$

When x is an irrational number (for example, $\sqrt{3}$), what meaning can we give to $2^{\sqrt{3}}$?

It is beyond the scope of this book to give precise meaning to 2^x if x is irrational. We can confirm your intuition and say that $2^{\sqrt{3}}$ is a real number, and since $1 < \sqrt{3} < 2$, then $2^1 < 2^{\sqrt{3}} < 2^2$. We can also use a calculator and approximate $2^{\sqrt{3}} : 2^{\sqrt{3}} \approx 3.321997$. In fact, as long as the base b is positive, b^x is a real number for all real numbers x. Finally, the rules of exponents apply whether x is rational or irrational, as long as b is positive.

In this section, we are interested in functions of the form $f(x) = b^x$, or $y = b^x$, where $b > 0$. A function of this form is called an *exponential function*.

Exponential Function

A function of the form

$$f(x) = b^x$$

is called an **exponential function,** where $b > 0$, b is not 1, and x is a real number.

Objective **A** Graphing Exponential Functions

Now let's practice graphing exponential functions.

EXAMPLE 1 Graph the exponential functions $f(x) = 2^x$ and $g(x) = 3^x$ on the same set of axes.

Solution: To graph these functions, we find some ordered pair solutions, plot the points, and connect them with a smooth curve. Remember throughout that $y = f(x)$.

x	0	1	2	3	-1	-2
$f(x) = 2^x$ — $f(x)$	1	2	4	8	$\frac{1}{2}$	$\frac{1}{4}$

x	0	1	2	3	-1	-2
$g(x) = 3^x$ — $g(x)$	1	3	9	27	$\frac{1}{3}$	$\frac{1}{9}$

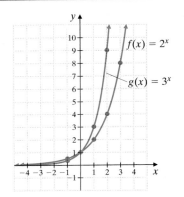

■ **Work Practice Problem 1**

PRACTICE PROBLEM 1

Graph the exponential function $f(x) = 6^x$.

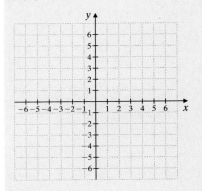

Answer

1.

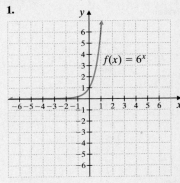

A number of things should be noted about the two graphs of exponential functions in Example 1. First, the graphs show that $f(x) = 2^x$ and $g(x) = 3^x$ are one-to-one functions since each graph passes the vertical and horizontal line tests. The y-intercept of each graph is $(0, 1)$, but neither graph has an x-intercept. From the graph, we can also see that the domain of each function is all real numbers and that the range is $(0, \infty)$. We can also see that as x-values are increasing, y-values are increasing also.

PRACTICE PROBLEM 2

Graph the exponential function $f(x) = \left(\dfrac{1}{5}\right)^x$.

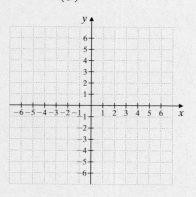

EXAMPLE 2 Graph the exponential functions $y = \left(\dfrac{1}{2}\right)^x$ and $y = \left(\dfrac{1}{3}\right)^x$ on the same set of axes.

Solution: As before, we find some ordered pair solutions, plot the points, and connect them with a smooth curve.

$y = \left(\dfrac{1}{2}\right)^x$	x	0	1	2	3	-1	-2
	y	1	$\dfrac{1}{2}$	$\dfrac{1}{4}$	$\dfrac{1}{8}$	2	4

$y = \left(\dfrac{1}{3}\right)^x$	x	0	1	2	3	-1	-2
	y	1	$\dfrac{1}{3}$	$\dfrac{1}{9}$	$\dfrac{1}{27}$	3	9

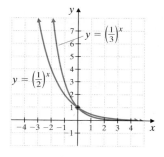

Work Practice Problem 2

Each function in Example 2 again is a one-to-one function. The y-intercept of both is $(0, 1)$. The domain is the set of all real numbers, and the range is $(0, \infty)$.

Notice the difference between the graphs of Example 1 and the graphs of Example 2. An exponential function is always increasing if the base is greater than 1. When the base is between 0 and 1, the graph is always decreasing. The following figures summarize these characteristics of exponential functions.

Answer

2.

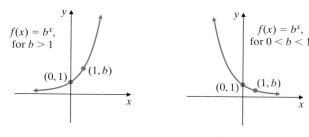

EXAMPLE 3 Graph the exponential function $f(x) = 3^{x+2}$.

Solution: As before, we find and plot a few ordered pair solutions. Then we connect the points with a smooth curve.

$f(x) = 3^{x+2}$	x	0	-1	-2	-3	-4
	y	9	3	1	$\frac{1}{3}$	$\frac{1}{9}$

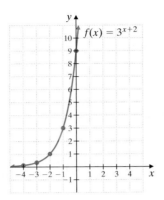

Work Practice Problem 3

✔ **Concept Check** Which functions are exponential functions?

a. $f(x) = x^3$ **b.** $g(x) = \left(\dfrac{2}{3}\right)^x$ **c.** $h(x) = 5^{x-2}$ **d.** $w(x) = (2x)^2$

Objective B Solving Equations of the Form $b^x = b^y$

We have seen that an exponential function $y = b^x$ is a one-to-one function. Another way of stating this fact is a property that we can use to solve exponential equations.

Uniqueness of b^x

Let $b > 0$ and $b \neq 1$. Then $b^x = b^y$ is equivalent to $x = y$.

Thus, one way to solve an exponential equation depends on whether it's possible to write each side of the equation with the same base; that is, $b^x = b^y$. We solve by this method first.

EXAMPLE 4 Solve: $2^x = 16$

Solution: We write 16 as a power of 2 so that each side of the equation has the same base. Then we use the uniqueness of b^x to solve.

$$2^x = 16$$
$$2^x = 2^4$$

Since the bases are the same and are nonnegative, by the uniqueness of b^x we then have that the exponents are equal. Thus,

$$x = 4$$

To check, we replace x with 4 in the original equation.
The solution set is {4}.

Work Practice Problem 4

PRACTICE PROBLEM 3

Graph the exponential function $f(x) = 2^{x-1}$.

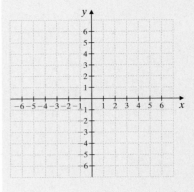

PRACTICE PROBLEM 4

Solve: $5^x = 125$

Answers

3.

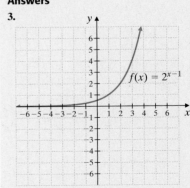

4. {3}

✔ **Concept Check Answer**

b and c

PRACTICE PROBLEM 5

Solve: $4^x = 8$

EXAMPLE 5 Solve: $25^x = 125$

Solution: Since both 25 and 125 are powers of 5, we can use the uniqueness of b^x.

$$25^x = 125$$
$$(5^2)^x = 5^3 \qquad \text{Write 25 and 125 as powers of 5.}$$
$$5^{2x} = 5^3$$
$$2x = 3 \qquad \text{Use the uniqueness of } b^x.$$
$$x = \frac{3}{2} \qquad \text{Divide both sides by 2.}$$

To check, we replace x with $\frac{3}{2}$ in the original equation.

The solution set is $\left\{\frac{3}{2}\right\}$.

🔲 **Work Practice Problem 5**

PRACTICE PROBLEM 6

Solve: $9^{x-1} = 27^x$

EXAMPLE 6 Solve: $4^{x+3} = 8^x$

Solution: We write both 4 and 8 as powers of 2, and then use the uniqueness of b^x.

$$4^{x+3} = 8^x$$
$$(2^2)^{x+3} = (2^3)^x$$
$$2^{2x+6} = 2^{3x}$$
$$2x + 6 = 3x \qquad \text{Use the uniqueness of } b^x.$$
$$6 = x \qquad \text{Subtract } 2x \text{ from both sides.}$$

Check to see that the solution set is $\{6\}$.

🔲 **Work Practice Problem 6**

There is one major problem with the preceding technique. Often the two sides of an equation, $4 = 3^x$ for example, cannot easily be written as powers of a common base. We explore how to solve such an equation with the help of *logarithms* later.

Objective C Solving Problems Modeled by Exponential Equations

The bar graph below shows the increase in the number of cellular phone users. Notice that the graph of the exponential function $y = 52.47(1.196)^x$ approximates the heights of the bars. This is just one example of how the world abounds with patterns that can be modeled by exponential functions. To make these applications realistic, we use numbers that warrant a calculator.

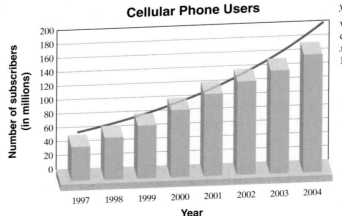

Cellular Phone Users

$y = 52.47(1.196)^x$
where $x = 0$ corresponds to 1997, $x = 1$ corresponds to 1998, and so on

Source: Cellular Telecommunications & Internet Association

Answers

5. $\left\{\frac{3}{2}\right\}$, 6. $\{-2\}$

Another application of an exponential function has to do with interest rates on loans. The exponential function defined by $A = P\left(1 + \dfrac{r}{n}\right)^{nt}$ models the pattern relating the dollars A accrued (or owed) after P dollars are invested (or loaned) at an annual rate of interest r compounded n times each year for t years. This function is known as the *compound interest formula*.

EXAMPLE 7 Using the Compound Interest Formula

Find the amount owed at the end of 5 years if $1600 is loaned at a rate of 9% compounded monthly.

Solution: Use the formula $A = P\left(1 + \dfrac{r}{n}\right)^{nt}$, with the following values:

$P = \$1600$ (the amount of the loan)
$r = 9\% = 0.09$ (the annual rate of interest)
$n = 12$ (the number of times interest is compounded each year)
$t = 5$ (the duration of the loan, in years)

$$A = P\left(1 + \frac{r}{n}\right)^{nt} \qquad \text{Compound interest formula}$$

$$= 1600\left(1 + \frac{0.09}{12}\right)^{12(5)} \qquad \text{Substitute known values.}$$

$$= 1600(1.0075)^{60}$$

To approximate A, use the $\boxed{y^x}$ or $\boxed{\wedge}$ key on your calculator.

$$\boxed{2505.0896}$$

Thus, the amount A owed is approximately $2505.09.

■ **Work Practice Problem 7**

PRACTICE PROBLEM 7

a. As a result of the Chernobyl nuclear accident, radioactive debris was carried through the atmosphere. One immediate concern was the impact that the debris had on the milk supply. The percent y of radioactive material in raw milk t days after the accident is estimated by $y = 100(2.7)^{-0.1t}$. Estimate the expected percent of radioactive material in the milk after 30 days.

b. Find the amount owed at the end of 6 years if $23,000 is loaned at a rate of 12% compounded quarterly. (4 times a year). Round your answer to the nearest cent.

Answers

7. a. approximately 5.08%,
   b. $46,754.26

CALCULATOR EXPLORATIONS Graphing

We can use a graphing calculator and its TRACE feature to solve Practice Problem 7a graphically.

To estimate the percent of radioactive material in the milk after 30 days, enter $Y_1 = 100(2.7)^{-0.1x}$. The graph does not appear on a standard viewing window, so we need to determine an appropriate viewing window. Because it doesn't make sense to look at radioactivity *before* the Chernobyl nuclear accident, we use Xmin = 0. We are interested in finding the percent of radioactive material in the milk when $x = 30$, so we choose Xmax = 35 to leave enough space to see the graph at $x = 30$. Because the values of y are percents, it seems appropriate that $0 \leq y \leq 100$. (We also use Xscl = 1 and Yscl = 10.) Now we graph the function.

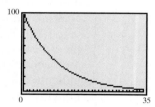

We can use the TRACE feature to obtain an approximation of the expected percent of radioactive material in the milk when $x = 30$. (A TABLE feature may also be used to approximate the percent.) To obtain a better approximation, let's use the ZOOM feature several times to zoom in near $x = 30$.

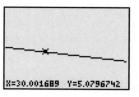

The percent of radioactive material in the milk 30 days after the Chernobyl accident was 5.08%, accurate to two decimal places.

Use a grapher to find each percent. Approximate your solutions so that they are accurate to two decimal places.

1. Estimate the percent of radioactive material in the milk 2 days after the Chernobyl nuclear accident.

2. Estimate the percent of radioactive material in the milk 10 days after the Chernobyl nuclear accident.

3. Estimate the percent of radioactive material in the milk 15 days after the Chernobyl nuclear accident.

4. Estimate the percent of radioactive material in the milk 25 days after the Chernobyl nuclear accident.

Objective **A** *Graph each exponential function. See Examples 1 through 3.*

1. $y = 5^x$

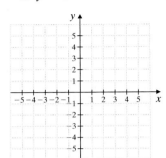

2. $y = 4^x$

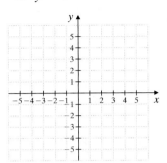

3. $y = 1 + 2^x$

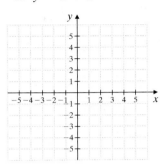

4. $y = 3^x - 1$

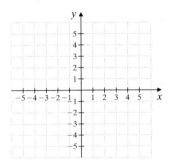

5. $y = \left(\dfrac{1}{4}\right)^x$

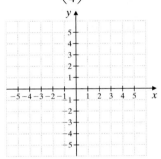

6. $y = \left(\dfrac{1}{5}\right)^x$

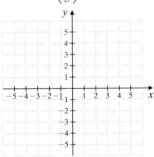

7. $y = \left(\dfrac{1}{2}\right)^x - 2$

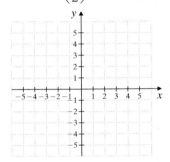

8. $y = \left(\dfrac{1}{3}\right)^x + 2$

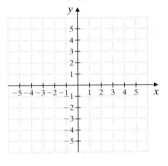

9. $y = -2^x$

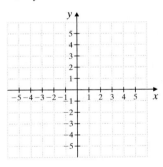

10. $y = -3^x$

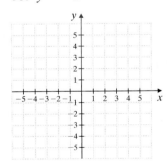

11. $y = 3^x - 2$

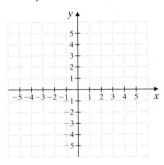

12. $y = 2^x - 3$

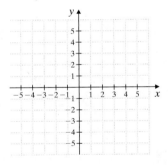

13. $y = -\left(\dfrac{1}{4}\right)^x$

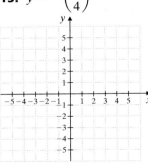

14. $y = -\left(\dfrac{1}{5}\right)^x$

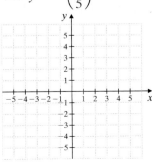

15. $y = \left(\dfrac{1}{3}\right)^x + 1$

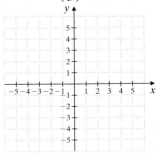

16. $y = \left(\dfrac{1}{2}\right)^x + 2$

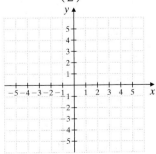

17. $f(x) = 2^{x-2}$

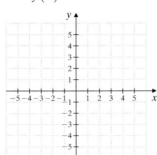

18. $g(x) = 2^{x+1}$

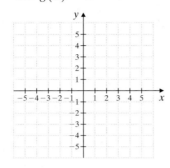

19. $F(x) = 5^{x+1}$

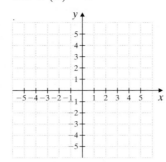

20. $G(x) = 3^{x-2}$

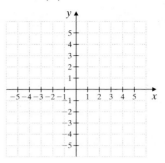

Objective **B** *Solve. See Examples 4 through 6.*

21. $3^x = 27$ **22.** $6^x = 36$ **23.** $16^x = 8$ **24.** $64^x = 16$ **25.** $32^{2x-3} = 2$

26. $9^{2x+1} = 81$ **27.** $\dfrac{1}{4} = 2^{3x}$ **28.** $\dfrac{1}{27} = 3^{2x}$ **29.** $9^x = 27$ **30.** $32^x = 4$

31. $27^{x+1} = 9$ **32.** $125^{x-2} = 25$ **33.** $81^{x-1} = 27^{2x}$ **34.** $4^{3x-7} = 32^{2x}$ **35.** $\left(\dfrac{1}{8}\right)^x = 16^{1-x}$

36. $\left(\dfrac{1}{9}\right)^x = 27^{2-x}$

Objective **C** *Solve. Unless otherwise indicated, round results to one decimal place. See Example 7.*

37. One type of uranium has a daily radioactive decay rate of 0.4%. If 30 pounds of this uranium is available today, how much will still remain after 50 days? Use $y = 30(2.7)^{-0.004t}$, and let t be 50.

38. The nuclear waste from an atomic energy plant decays at a rate of 3% each century. If 150 pounds of nuclear waste is disposed of, how much of it will still remain after 10 centuries? Use $y = 150(2.7)^{-0.03t}$, and let t be 10.

39. This atmospheric pressure p, in millibars, on a weather balloon decreases with increasing height. This pressure is related to the height in kilometers h above sea level and is given by the function $p(h) = 760(2.7)^{-0.145h}$. (*Source:* National Weather Service)

   a. Find the atmospheric pressure on a weather balloon at a height of 2 km.

   b. Find the atmospheric pressure on a weather balloon at its expected maximum altitude of 30.48 km.

   c. What causes the difference in atmospheric pressure at these two heights?

40. The equation $y = 158.97(1.012)^x$ models the population of the United States from 1950 through 2003. In this equation, y is the population in millions and x represents the number of years after 1950. Round answers to the nearest tenth of a million.

   (*Source:* Based on data from the U.S. Bureau of the Census)

   a. Estimate the population of the United States in 1970.

   b. Assuming this equation continues to be valid in the future, use the equation to predict the population of the United States in 2020.

41. Retail revenue from shopping on the Internet is currently growing at a rate of 29% per year. In 2002, a total of $44 billion in revenue was collected through Internet retail sales. Answer the following questions using $y = 44(1.29)^t$, where y is Internet revenues in billions of dollars and t is the number of years after 2002. Round answers to the nearest tenth of a billion dollars. (*Source:* U.S. Bureau of the Census)

   a. According to the model, what level of retail revenues from Internet shopping was expected in 2003?

   b. If the given model continues, predict the level of Internet shopping revenues in 2009.

42. Carbon dioxide (CO_2) is a greenhouse gas that contributes to global warming. Partially due to the combustion of fossil fuels, the amount of CO_2 in Earth's atmosphere has been increasing by 0.4% annually over the past century. In 2000, the concentration of CO_2 in the atmosphere was 369.4 parts per million by volume. To make the following predictions, use $y = 369.4(1.004)^t$ where y is the concentration of CO_2 in parts per million and t is the number of years after 2000. (*Sources:* Based on data from the United Nations Environment Programme and the Carbon Dioxide Information Analysis Center)

   a. Predict the concentration of CO_2 in the atmosphere in the year 2006.

   b. Predict the concentration of CO_2 in the atmosphere in the year 2030.

The equation $y = 52.47(1.196)^x$ gives the number of cellular phone users y (in millions) in the United States for the years 1997 through 2004. In this equation, $x = 0$ corresponds to 1997, $x = 1$ corresponds to 1998, and so on. Use this model to solve Exercises 43 and 44. Round answers to the nearest tenth of a million.

43. Predict the number of cellular phone users in the year 2010.

44. Predict the number of cellular phone users in the year 2017.

Solve. Use $A = P\left(1 + \dfrac{r}{n}\right)^{nt}$. Round answers to two decimal places. See Example 7.

45. Find the amount Erica Entada owes at the end of 3 years if $6000 is loaned to her at a rate of 8% compounded monthly.

46. Find the amount owed at the end of 5 years if $3000 is loaned at a rate of 10% compounded quarterly.

Review

Solve each equation. See Section 2.1.

47. $5x - 2 = 18$

48. $3x - 7 = 11$

49. $3x - 4 = 3(x + 1)$

50. $2 - 6x = 6(1 - x)$

Concept Extensions

Which functions are exponential functions? See the Concept Check in this section.

51. $f(x) = 1.5x^2$

52. $g(x) = 3^x$

53. $h(x) = \left(\frac{1}{2}x\right)^2$

54. $F(x) = 0.4^{x+1}$

Match each exponential function with its graph.

55. $f(x) = \left(\frac{1}{2}\right)^x$

56. $f(x) = 2^x$

57. $f(x) = \left(\frac{1}{4}\right)^x$

58. $f(x) = 3^x$

A
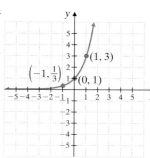

B
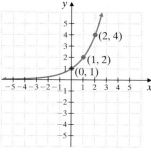

C
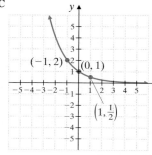

D
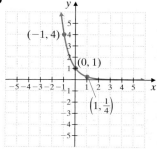

59. Explain why the graph of an exponential function $y = b^x$ contains the point $(1, b)$.

60. Explain why an exponential function $y = b^x$ has a y-intercept of $(0, 1)$.

Use a graphing calculator to solve. Estimate your results to two decimal places.

61. Verify the results of Exercise 37.

62. From Exercise 37, estimate the number of pounds of uranium that will be available after 100 days.

63. From Exercise 37, estimate the number of pounds of uranium that will be available after 120 days.

9.4 LOGARITHMIC FUNCTIONS

Objectives

A Write Exponential Equations with Logarithmic Notation and Write Logarithmic Equations with Exponential Notation.

B Solve Logarithmic Equations by Using Exponential Notation.

C Identify and Graph Logarithmic Functions.

Objective A Using Logarithmic Notation

Since the exponential function $f(x) = 2^x$ is a one-to-one function, it has an inverse. We can create a table of values for f^{-1} by switching the coordinates in the accompanying table of values for $f(x) = 2^x$.

x	y = f(x)
-3	$\frac{1}{8}$
-2	$\frac{1}{4}$
-1	$\frac{1}{2}$
0	1
1	2
2	4
3	8

x	y = f⁻¹(x)
$\frac{1}{8}$	-3
$\frac{1}{4}$	-2
$\frac{1}{2}$	-1
1	0
2	1
4	2
8	3

The graphs of f and its inverse are shown in the margin. Notice that the graphs of f and f^{-1} are symmetric about the line $y = x$, as expected.

Now we would like to be able to write an equation for f^{-1}. To do so, we follow the steps for finding the equation of an inverse.

$$f(x) = 2^x$$

Step 1: Replace $f(x)$ by y. $\qquad\qquad y = 2^x$

Step 2: Interchange x and y. $\qquad\quad x = 2^y$

Step 3: Solve for y.

At this point, we are stuck. To solve this equation for y, a new notation, **logarithmic notation,** is needed.

The symbol $\log_b x$ means "the power to which b is raised to produce a result of x." In other words,

$\log_b x = y$ means $b^y = x$

We say that $\log_b x$ is "the logarithm of x to the base b" or "the log of x to the base b."

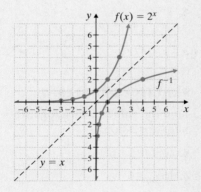

Logarithmic Definition

If $b > 0$, and $b \neq 1$, then

$$y = \log_b x \quad \text{means} \quad x = b^y$$

for every $x > 0$ and every real number y.

Before returning to the function $x = 2^y$ and solving it for y in terms of x, let's practice using the new notation $\log_b x$.

It is important to be able to write exponential equations with logarithmic notation, and vice versa. The following table shows examples of both forms.

Logarithmic Equation	Corresponding Exponential Equation
$\log_3 9 = 2$	$3^2 = 9$
$\log_6 1 = 0$	$6^0 = 1$
$\log_2 8 = 3$	$2^3 = 8$
$\log_4 \dfrac{1}{16} = -2$	$4^{-2} = \dfrac{1}{16}$
$\log_8 2 = \dfrac{1}{3}$	$8^{1/3} = 2$

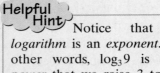

Notice that a *logarithm* is an *exponent*. In other words, $\log_3 9$ is the *power* that we raise 3 to in order to get 9.

PRACTICE PROBLEMS 1–3

Write as an exponential equation.

1. $\log_7 49 = 2$ **2.** $\log_8 \dfrac{1}{8} = -1$

3. $\log_3 \sqrt{3} = \dfrac{1}{2}$

EXAMPLES Write as an exponential equation.

1. $\log_5 25 = 2$ means $5^2 = 25$.

2. $\log_6 \dfrac{1}{6} = -1$ means $6^{-1} = \dfrac{1}{6}$.

3. $\log_2 \sqrt{2} = \dfrac{1}{2}$ means $2^{1/2} = \sqrt{2}$.

■ **Work Practice Problems 1–3**

PRACTICE PROBLEMS 4–6

Write as a logarithmic equation.

4. $3^4 = 81$ **5.** $2^{-3} = \dfrac{1}{8}$

6. $7^{1/3} = \sqrt[3]{7}$

EXAMPLES Write as a logarithmic equation.

4. $9^3 = 729$ means $\log_9 729 = 3$.

5. $6^{-2} = \dfrac{1}{36}$ means $\log_6 \dfrac{1}{36} = -2$.

6. $5^{1/3} = \sqrt[3]{5}$ means $\log_5 \sqrt[3]{5} = \dfrac{1}{3}$.

■ **Work Practice Problems 4–6**

PRACTICE PROBLEM 7

Find the value of each logarithmic expression.

a. $\log_5 125$ **b.** $\log_7 \dfrac{1}{49}$

c. $\log_{100} 10$

EXAMPLE 7 Find the value of each logarithmic expression.

a. $\log_4 16$ **b.** $\log_{10} \dfrac{1}{10}$ **c.** $\log_9 3$

Solution:

a. $\log_4 16 = 2$ because $4^2 = 16$.

b. $\log_{10} \dfrac{1}{10} = -1$ because $10^{-1} = \dfrac{1}{10}$.

c. $\log_9 3 = \dfrac{1}{2}$ because $9^{1/2} = \sqrt{9} = 3$.

■ **Work Practice Problem 7**

Objective B Solving Logarithmic Equations

The ability to interchange the logarithmic and exponential forms of a statement is often the key to solving logarithmic equations.

PRACTICE PROBLEM 8

Solve: $\log_2 x = 4$

EXAMPLE 8 Solve: $\log_5 x = 3$

Solution: $\log_5 x = 3$

$5^3 = x$ Write as an exponential equation.

$125 = x$

The solution set is $\{125\}$.

■ **Work Practice Problem 8**

Answers

1. $7^2 = 49$, **2.** $8^{-1} = \dfrac{1}{8}$,

3. $3^{1/2} = \sqrt{3}$, **4.** $\log_3 81 = 4$,

5. $\log_2 \dfrac{1}{8} = -3$, **6.** $\log_7 \sqrt[3]{7} = \dfrac{1}{3}$,

7. a. 3, **b.** −2, **c.** $\dfrac{1}{2}$, **8.** $\{16\}$

EXAMPLE 9 Solve: $\log_x 25 = 2$

Solution: $\log_x 25 = 2$

$$x^2 = 25 \quad \text{Write as an exponential equation.}$$
$$x = 5$$

Even though $(-5)^2 = 25$, the base b of a logarithm must be positive. The solution set is $\{5\}$.

🔲 **Work Practice Problem 9**

PRACTICE PROBLEM 9

Solve: $\log_x 9 = 2$

EXAMPLE 10 Solve: $\log_3 1 = x$

Solution: $\log_3 1 = x$

$$3^x = 1 \quad \text{Write as an exponential equation.}$$
$$3^x = 3^0 \quad \text{Write 1 as } 3^0.$$
$$x = 0 \quad \text{Use the uniqueness of } b^x.$$

The solution set is $\{0\}$.

🔲 **Work Practice Problem 10**

In Example 10, we illustrated an important property of logarithms. That is, $\log_b 1$ is always 0. This property as well as two important others are given below.

PRACTICE PROBLEM 10

Solve: $\log_2 1 = x$

Properties of Logarithms

If b is a real number, $b > 0$ and $b \neq 1$, then

1. $\log_b 1 = 0$

2. $\log_b b^x = x$

3. $b^{\log_b x} = x$

To see that $\log_b b^x = x$, we change the logarithmic form to exponential form. Then, $\log_b b^x = x$ means $b^x = b^x$. In exponential form, the statement is true, so in logarithmic form, the statement is also true.

EXAMPLE 11 Simplify.

a. $\log_3 3^2$ **b.** $\log_7 7^{-1}$

c. $5^{\log_5 3}$ **d.** $2^{\log_2 6}$

Solution:

a. From property 2, $\log_3 3^2 = 2$.

b. From property 2, $\log_7 7^{-1} = -1$.

c. From property 3, $5^{\log_5 3} = 3$.

d. From property 3, $2^{\log_2 6} = 6$.

🔲 **Work Practice Problem 11**

PRACTICE PROBLEM 11

Simplify.

a. $\log_6 6^3$ **b.** $\log_{11} 11^{-4}$

c. $7^{\log_7 13}$ **d.** $3^{\log_3 10}$

Objective ◉ Graphing Logarithmic Functions

Let us now return to the function $f(x) = 2^x$ and write an equation for its inverse, f^{-1}. Recall our earlier work.

$$f(x) = 2^x$$

Step 1: Replace $f(x)$ by y. $y = 2^x$

Step 2: Interchange x and y. $x = 2^y$

Answers

9. $\{3\}$,   **10.** $\{0\}$,   **11. a.** 3,   **b.** -4,
c. 13,   **d.** 10

PRACTICE PROBLEM 12

Graph the logarithmic function $y = \log_4 x$.

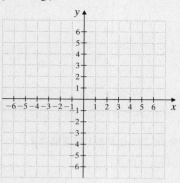

PRACTICE PROBLEM 13

Graph the logarithmic function $f(x) = \log_{1/2} x$.

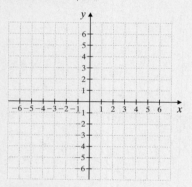

Answers

12.

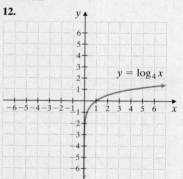

13.

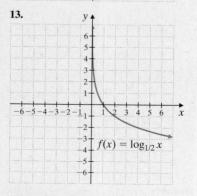

Having gained proficiency with the notation $\log_b x$, we can now complete the steps for writing the inverse equation.

Step 3: Solve for y. $\qquad\qquad y = \log_2 x$

Step 4: Replace y with $f^{-1}(x)$. $\quad f^{-1}(x) = \log_2 x$

Thus, $f^{-1}(x) = \log_2 x$ defines a function that is the inverse function of the function $f(x) = 2^x$. The function $f^{-1}(x)$ or $y = \log_2 x$ is called a *logarithmic function*.

Logarithmic Function

If x is a positive real number, b is a constant positive real number, and b is not 1, then a **logarithmic function** is a function that can be defined by

$$f(x) = \log_b x$$

The domain of f is the set of positive real numbers, and the range of f is the set of real numbers.

✔ **Concept Check** Let $f(x) = \log_3 x$ and $g(x) = 3^x$. These two functions are inverses of each other. Since $(2, 9)$ is an ordered pair solution of $g(x)$, what ordered pair do we know to be a solution of $f(x)$? Explain why.

We can explore logarithmic functions by graphing them.

EXAMPLE 12 Graph the logarithmic function $y = \log_2 x$.

Solution: First we write the equation with exponential notation as $2^y = x$. Then we find some ordered pair solutions that satisfy this equation. Finally, we plot the points and connect them with a smooth curve. The domain of this function is $(0, \infty)$, and the range is all real numbers.

Since $x = 2^y$ is solved for x, we choose y-values and compute corresponding x-values.

If $y = 0$, $x = 2^0 = 1$.
If $y = 1$, $x = 2^1 = 2$.
If $y = 2$, $x = 2^2 = 4$.
If $y = -1$, $x = 2^{-1} = \dfrac{1}{2}$.

$x = 2^y$	y
1	0
2	1
4	2
$\dfrac{1}{2}$	-1

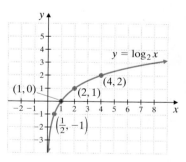

■ **Work Practice Problem 12**

EXAMPLE 13 Graph the logarithmic function $f(x) = \log_{1/3} x$.

Solution: We can replace $f(x)$ with y, and write the result with exponential notation.

$$f(x) = \log_{1/3} x$$

$$y = \log_{1/3} x \quad \text{Replace } f(x) \text{ with } y.$$

$$\left(\frac{1}{3}\right)^y = x \qquad \text{Write in exponential form.}$$

Now we can find ordered pair solutions that satisfy $\left(\dfrac{1}{3}\right)^{y} = x$, plot these points, and connect them with a smooth curve.

If $y = 0$, $x = \left(\dfrac{1}{3}\right)^{0} = 1$.

If $y = 1$, $x = \left(\dfrac{1}{3}\right)^{1} = \dfrac{1}{3}$.

If $y = -1$, $x = \left(\dfrac{1}{3}\right)^{-1} = 3$.

If $y = -2$, $x = \left(\dfrac{1}{3}\right)^{-2} = 9$.

$x = \left(\dfrac{1}{3}\right)^{y}$	y
1	0
$\dfrac{1}{3}$	1
3	-1
9	-2

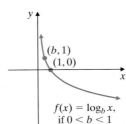

The domain of this function is $(0, \infty)$, and the range is the set of all real numbers.

■ **Work Practice Problem 13**

The following figures summarize characteristics of logarithmic functions.

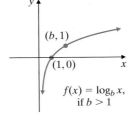

Objective **A** *Write each as an exponential equation. See Examples 1 through 3.*

1. $\log_6 36 = 2$

2. $\log_2 32 = 5$

3. $\log_3 \frac{1}{27} = -3$

4. $\log_5 \frac{1}{25} = -2$

5. $\log_{10} 1000 = 3$

6. $\log_{10} 10 = 1$

7. $\log_e x = 4$

8. $\log_e y = 7$

9. $\log_e \frac{1}{e^2} = -2$

10. $\log_e \frac{1}{e} = -1$

11. $\log_7 \sqrt{7} = \frac{1}{2}$

12. $\log_{11} \sqrt[4]{11} = \frac{1}{4}$

13. $\log_{0.7} 0.343 = 3$

14. $\log_{1.2} 1.44 = 2$

15. $\log_3 \frac{1}{81} = -4$

16. $\log_{1/4} 16 = -2$

Write each as a logarithmic equation. See Examples 4 through 6.

17. $2^4 = 16$

18. $5^3 = 125$

19. $10^2 = 100$

20. $10^4 = 10,000$

21. $e^3 = x$

22. $e^5 = y$

23. $10^{-1} = \frac{1}{10}$

24. $10^{-2} = \frac{1}{100}$

25. $4^{-2} = \frac{1}{16}$

26. $3^{-4} = \frac{1}{81}$

27. $5^{1/2} = \sqrt{5}$

28. $4^{1/3} = \sqrt[3]{4}$

Find the value of each logarithmic expression. See Example 7.

29. $\log_2 8$

30. $\log_3 9$

31. $\log_3 \frac{1}{9}$

32. $\log_2 \frac{1}{32}$

33. $\log_{25} 5$

34. $\log_8 \frac{1}{2}$

35. $\log_{1/2} 2$

36. $\log_{2/3} \frac{4}{9}$

37. $\log_6 1$

38. $\log_9 9$

39. $\log_{10} 100$

40. $\log_{10} \frac{1}{10}$ -1

41. $\log_3 81$

42. $\log_2 16$

43. $\log_4 \frac{1}{64}$

44. $\log_3 \frac{1}{9}$

Objective **B** *Solve. See Examples 8 through 10.*

45. $\log_3 9 = x$

46. $\log_2 8 = x$

47. $\log_3 x = 4$

48. $\log_2 x = 3$

49. $\log_x 49 = 2$

50. $\log_x 8 = 3$

51. $\log_2 \frac{1}{8} = x$

52. $\log_3 \frac{1}{81} = x$

53. $\log_3 \dfrac{1}{27} = x$

54. $\log_5 \dfrac{1}{125} = x$

55. $\log_8 x = \dfrac{1}{3}$

56. $\log_9 x = \dfrac{1}{2}$

57. $\log_4 16 = x$

58. $\log_2 16 = x$

59. $\log_{3/4} x = 3$

60. $\log_{2/3} x = 2$

61. $\log_x 100 = 2$

62. $\log_x 27 = 3$

63. $\log_2 2^4 = x$

64. $\log_6 6^{-2} = x$

65. $3^{\log_3 5} = x$

66. $5^{\log_5 7} = x$

67. $\log_x \dfrac{1}{7} = \dfrac{1}{2}$

68. $\log_x 2 = -\dfrac{1}{3}$

Simplify. See Example 11.

69. $\log_5 5^3$

70. $\log_6 6^2$

71. $2^{\log_2 3}$

72. $7^{\log_7 4}$

73. $\log_9 9$

74. $\log_8 (8)^{-1}$

Objective C *Graph each logarithmic function. See Examples 12 and 13.*

75. $y = \log_3 x$

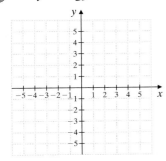

76. $y = \log_2 x$

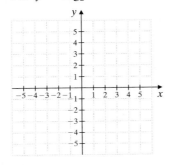

77. $f(x) = \log_{1/4} x$

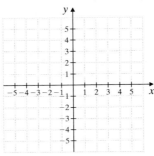

78. $f(x) = \log_{1/2} x$

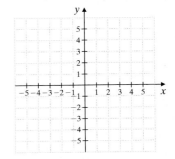

79. $f(x) = \log_5 x$

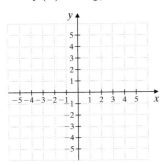

80. $f(x) = \log_6 x$

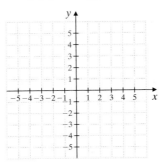

81. $f(x) = \log_{1/6} x$

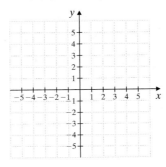

82. $f(x) = \log_{1/5} x$

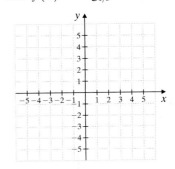

Review

Simplify each rational expression. See Section 6.1.

83. $\dfrac{x + 3}{3 + x}$

84. $\dfrac{x - 5}{5 - x}$

85. $\dfrac{x^2 - 8x + 16}{2x - 8}$

86. $\dfrac{x^2 - 3x - 10}{2 + x}$

Concept Extensions

Solve. See the Concept Check in this section.

87. Let $f(x) = \log_5 x$. Then $g(x) = 5^x$ is the inverse of $f(x)$. The ordered pair $(2, 25)$ is a solution of the function $g(x)$.

     a. Write this solution using function notation.

     b. Write an ordered pair that we know to be a solution of $f(x)$.

     c. Use the answer to part b and write the solution using function notation.

88. Let $f(x) = \log_{0.3} x$. Then $g(x) = 0.3^x$ is the inverse of $f(x)$. The ordered pair $(3, 0.027)$ is a solution of the function $g(x)$.

     a. Write this solution using function notation.

     b. Write an ordered pair that we know to be a solution of $f(x)$.

     c. Use the answer to part b and write the solution using function notation.

89. Explain why negative numbers are not included as logarithmic bases.

90. Explain why 1 is not included as a logarithmic base.

Graph each function and its inverse on the same set of axes.

91. $y = 4^x$; $y = \log_4 x$

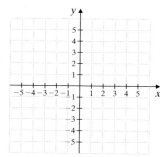

92. $y = 3^x$; $y = \log_3 x$

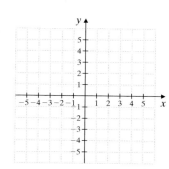

93. $y = \left(\dfrac{1}{3}\right)^x$; $y = \log_{1/3} x$

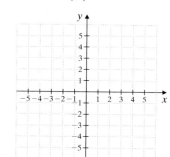

94. $y = \left(\dfrac{1}{2}\right)^x$; $y = \log_{1/2} x$

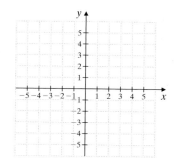

95. Explain why the graph of the function $y = \log_b x$ contains the point $(1, 0)$ no matter what b is.

96. $\log_3 10$ is between which two integers? Explain your answer.

97. The formula $\log_{10}(1 - k) = \dfrac{-0.3}{H}$ models the relationship between the half-life H of a radioactive material and its rate of decay k. Find the rate of decay of the iodine isotope I-131 if its half-life is 8 days. Round to four decimal places.

9.5 PROPERTIES OF LOGARITHMS

Objectives

A Use the Product Property of Logarithms.

B Use the Quotient Property of Logarithms.

C Use the Power Property of Logarithms.

D Use the Properties of Logarithms Together.

In the previous section we explored some basic properties of logarithms. We now introduce and study additional properties. Because a logarithm is an exponent, logarithmic properties are just restatements of exponential properties.

Objective **A** Using the Product Property

The first of these properties is called the **product property of logarithms** because it deals with the logarithm of a product.

Product Property of Logarithms

If x, y, and b are positive real numbers and $b \neq 1$, then

$$\log_b xy = \log_b x + \log_b y$$

To prove this, we let $\log_b x = M$ and $\log_b y = N$. Now we write each logarithm with exponential notation.

$\log_b x = M$ is equivalent to $b^M = x$

$\log_b y = N$ is equivalent to $b^N = y$

When we multiply the left sides and the right sides of the exponential equations, we have that

$$xy = (b^M)(b^N) = b^{M+N}$$

If we write the equation $xy = b^{M+N}$ in equivalent logarithmic form, we have

$$\log_b xy = M + N$$

But since $M = \log_b x$ and $N = \log_b y$, we can write

$$\log_b xy = \log_b x + \log_b y \quad \text{Let } M = \log_b x \text{ and } N = \log_b y.$$

In other words, the logarithm of a product is the sum of the logarithms of the factors. This property is sometimes used to simplify logarithmic expressions.

EXAMPLE 1 Write as a single logarithm: $\log_{11} 10 + \log_{11} 3$

Solution: $\log_{11} 10 + \log_{11} 3 = \log_{11}(10 \cdot 3)$ Use the product property.

$$= \log_{11} 30$$

■ **Work Practice Problem 1**

PRACTICE PROBLEM 1

Write as a single logarithm:
$\log_2 7 + \log_2 5$

EXAMPLE 2 Write as a single logarithm: $\log_2(x + 2) + \log_2 x$

Solution: $\log_2(x + 2) + \log_2 x = \log_2[(x + 2) \cdot x] = \log_2(x^2 + 2x)$

■ **Work Practice Problem 2**

PRACTICE PROBLEM 2

Write as a single logarithm:
$\log_3 x + \log_3(x - 9)$

Objective **B** Using the Quotient Property

The second property is the **quotient property of logarithms**.

Answers

1. $\log_2 35$,   **2.** $\log_3(x^2 - 9x)$

Quotient Property of Logarithms

If x, y, and b are positive real numbers and $b \neq 1$, then

$$\log_b \frac{x}{y} = \log_b x - \log_b y$$

The proof of the quotient property of logarithms is similar to the proof of the product property. Notice that the quotient property says that the logarithm of a quotient is the difference of the logarithms of the dividend and divisor.

✔ **Concept Check** Which of the following is the correct way to rewrite $\log_5 \frac{7}{2}$?

a. $\log_5 7 - \log_5 2$ **b.** $\log_5(7 - 2)$ **c.** $\dfrac{\log_5 7}{\log_5 2}$ **d.** $\log_5 14$

PRACTICE PROBLEM 3

Write as a single logarithm:
$\log_7 40 - \log_7 8$

EXAMPLE 3 Write as a single logarithm: $\log_{10} 27 - \log_{10} 3$

Solution: $\log_{10} 27 - \log_{10} 3 = \log_{10} \dfrac{27}{3}$ Use the quotient property.

$$= \log_{10} 9$$

▣ **Work Practice Problem 3**

PRACTICE PROBLEM 4

Write as a single logarithm:
$\log_3(x^3 + 4) - \log_3(x^2 + 2)$

EXAMPLE 4 Write as a single logarithm: $\log_3(x^2 + 5) - \log_3(x^2 + 1)$

Solution: $\log_3(x^2 + 5) - \log_3(x^2 + 1) = \log_3 \dfrac{x^2 + 5}{x^2 + 1}$ Use the quotient property.

▣ **Work Practice Problem 4**

Objective C Using the Power Property

The third and final property we introduce is the **power property of logarithms.**

Power Property of Logarithms

If x and b are positive real numbers, $b \neq 1$, and r is a real number, then

$$\log_b x^r = r \log_b x$$

PRACTICE PROBLEMS 5–6

Use the power property to rewrite each expression.
5. $\log_3 x^5$ **6.** $\log_7 \sqrt[3]{4}$

EXAMPLES Use the power property to rewrite each expression.

5. $\log_5 x^3 = 3 \log_5 x$

6. $\log_4 \sqrt{2} = \log_4 2^{1/2} = \dfrac{1}{2} \log_4 2$

▣ **Work Practice Problems 5–6**

Objective D Using More Than One Property

Many times we must use more than one property of logarithms to simplify logarithmic expressions.

Answers

3. $\log_7 5$,   **4.** $\log_3 \dfrac{x^3 + 4}{x^2 + 2}$,   **5.** $5 \log_3 x$,

6. $\dfrac{1}{3} \log_7 4$

✔ **Concept Check Answer**

a

EXAMPLES Write as a single logarithm.

7. $2\log_5 3 + 3\log_5 2 = \log_5 3^2 + \log_5 2^3$ Use the power property.

$\qquad\qquad\qquad = \log_5 9 + \log_5 8$

$\qquad\qquad\qquad = \log_5(9 \cdot 8)$ Use the product property.

$\qquad\qquad\qquad = \log_5 72$

8. $3\log_9 x - \log_9(x + 1) = \log_9 x^3 - \log_9(x + 1)$ Use the power property.

$\qquad\qquad\qquad\qquad = \log_9 \dfrac{x^3}{x + 1}$ Use the quotient property.

◾ **Work Practice Problems 7–8**

PRACTICE PROBLEMS 7–8

Write as a single logarithm.

7. $3\log_4 2 + 2\log_4 5$

8. $5\log_2(2x - 1) - \log_2 x$

EXAMPLES Write each expression as sums or differences of logarithms.

9. $\log_3 \dfrac{5 \cdot 7}{4} = \log_3(5 \cdot 7) - \log_3 4$ Use the quotient property.

$\qquad\qquad\quad = \log_3 5 + \log_3 7 - \log_3 4$ Use the product property.

10. $\log_2 \dfrac{x^5}{y^2} = \log_2(x^5) - \log_2(y^2)$ Use the quotient property.

$\qquad\qquad\quad = 5\log_2 x - 2\log_2 y$ Use the power property.

◾ **Work Practice Problems 9–10**

PRACTICE PROBLEMS 9–10

Write each expression as sums or differences of logarithms.

9. $\log_7 \dfrac{6 \cdot 2}{5}$ **10.** $\log_3 \dfrac{x^4}{y^3}$

Helpful Hint

Notice that we are not able to simplify further a logarithmic expression such as $\log_5(2x - 1)$. None of the basic properties gives a way to write the logarithm of a difference (or sum) in some equivalent form.

✔ **Concept Check** What is wrong with the following?

$\log_{10}(x^2 + 5) = \log_{10} x^2 + \log_{10} 5$
$\qquad\qquad\quad = 2\log_{10} x + \log_{10} 5$

Use a numerical example to demonstrate that the result is incorrect.

EXAMPLES If $\log_b 2 = 0.43$ and $\log_b 3 = 0.68$, use the properties of logarithms to evaluate each expression.

11. $\log_b 6 = \log_b(2 \cdot 3)$ Write 6 as $2 \cdot 3$.

$\qquad\quad = \log_b 2 + \log_b 3$ Use the product property.

$\qquad\quad = 0.43 + 0.68$ Substitute given values.

$\qquad\quad = 1.11$ Simplify.

12. $\log_b 9 = \log_b 3^2$ Write 9 as 3^2.

$\qquad\quad = 2\log_b 3$ Use the power property.

$\qquad\quad = 2(0.68)$ Substitute the given value.

$\qquad\quad = 1.36$ Simplify.

13. $\log_b \sqrt{2} = \log_b 2^{1/2}$ Write $\sqrt{2}$ as $2^{1/2}$.

$\qquad\quad = \dfrac{1}{2}\log_b 2$ Use the power property.

$\qquad\quad = \dfrac{1}{2}(0.43)$ Substitute the given value.

$\qquad\quad = 0.215$ Simplify.

◾ **Work Practice Problems 11–13**

PRACTICE PROBLEMS 11–13

If $\log_b 4 = 0.86$ and $\log_b 7 = 1.21$, use the properties of logarithms to evaluate each expression.

11. $\log_b 28$ **12.** $\log_b 49$

13. $\log_b \sqrt[3]{4}$

Answers

7. $\log_4 200$,   **8.** $\log_2 \dfrac{(2x - 1)^5}{x}$,

9. $\log_7 6 + \log_7 2 - \log_7 5$,

10. $4\log_3 x - 3\log_3 y$,   **11.** 2.07,

12. 2.42,   **13.** 0.286

✔ **Concept Check Answer**

The properties do not give any way to simplify the logarithm of a sum; answers may vary.

9.5 EXERCISE SET

Objective Ⓐ *Write each sum as a single logarithm. Assume that variables represent positive numbers. See Examples 1 and 2.*

1. $\log_5 2 + \log_5 7$

2. $\log_3 8 + \log_3 4$

3. $\log_4 9 + \log_4 x$

4. $\log_2 x + \log_2 y$

5. $\log_6 x + \log_6 (x + 1)$

6. $\log_5 y^3 + \log_5 (y - 7)$

7. $\log_{10} 5 + \log_{10} 2 + \log_{10} (x^2 + 2)$

8. $\log_6 3 + \log_6 (x + 4) + \log_6 5$

Objective Ⓑ *Write each difference as a single logarithm. Assume that variables represent positive numbers. See Examples 3 and 4.*

9. $\log_5 12 - \log_5 4$

10. $\log_7 20 - \log_7 4$

11. $\log_3 8 - \log_3 2$

12. $\log_5 12 - \log_5 3$

13. $\log_2 x - \log_2 y$

14. $\log_3 12 - \log_3 z$

15. $\log_2 (x^2 + 6) - \log_2 (x^2 + 1)$

16. $\log_7 (x + 9) - \log_7 (x^2 + 10)$

Objective Ⓒ *Use the power property to rewrite each expression. See Examples 5 and 6.*

17. $\log_3 x^2$

18. $\log_2 x^5$

19. $\log_4 5^{-1}$

20. $\log_6 7^{-2}$

21. $\log_5 \sqrt{y}$

22. $\log_5 \sqrt[3]{x}$

Objective Ⓓ **Mixed Practice** *Write each as a single logarithm. Assume that variables represent positive numbers. See Examples 7 and 8.*

23. $\log_2 5 + \log_2 x^3$

24. $\log_5 2 + \log_5 y^2$

25. $3 \log_4 2 + \log_4 6$

26. $2 \log_3 5 + \log_3 2$

27. $3 \log_5 x + 6 \log_5 z$

28. $2 \log_7 y + 6 \log_7 z$

29. $\log_4 2 + \log_4 10 - \log_4 5$

30. $\log_6 18 + \log_6 2 - \log_6 9$

31. $\log_7 6 + \log_7 3 - \log_7 4$

32. $\log_8 5 + \log_8 15 - \log_8 20$

33. $\log_{10} x - \log_{10} (x + 1) + \log_{10} (x^2 - 2)$

34. $\log_9 (4x) - \log_9 (x - 3) + \log_9 (x^3 + 1)$

35. $3 \log_2 x + \dfrac{1}{2} \log_2 x - 2 \log_2 (x + 1)$

36. $2 \log_5 x + \dfrac{1}{3} \log_5 x - 3 \log_5 (x + 5)$

37. $2 \log_8 x - \dfrac{2}{3} \log_8 x + 4 \log_8 x$

38. $5 \log_6 x - \dfrac{3}{4} \log_6 x + 3 \log_6 x$

Mixed Practice *Write each expression as a sum or difference of logarithms. Assume that variables represent positive numbers. See Examples 9 and 10.*

39. $\log_3 \dfrac{4y}{5}$

40. $\log_7 \dfrac{5x}{4}$

41. $\log_4 \dfrac{2}{9z}$

42. $\log_9 \dfrac{7}{8y}$

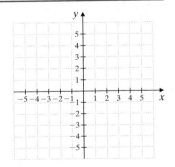 **43.** $\log_2 \dfrac{x^3}{y}$

44. $\log_5 \dfrac{x}{y^4}$

45. $\log_b \sqrt{7x}$

46. $\log_b \sqrt{\dfrac{3}{y}}$

47. $\log_6 x^4 y^5$

48. $\log_2 y^3 z$

49. $\log_5 x^3 (x + 1)$

50. $\log_3 x^2 (x - 9)$

51. $\log_6 \dfrac{x^2}{x + 3}$

52. $\log_3 \dfrac{(x + 5)^2}{x}$

If $\log_b 3 = 0.5$ and $\log_b 5 = 0.7$, evaluate each expression. See Examples 11 through 13.

53. $\log_b \dfrac{5}{3}$

54. $\log_b 25$

55. $\log_b 15$

56. $\log_b \dfrac{3}{5}$

57. $\log_b \sqrt{5}$

58. $\log_b \sqrt[4]{3}$

If $\log_b 2 = 0.43$ and $\log_b 3 = 0.68$, evaluate each expression. See Examples 11 through 13.

59. $\log_b 8$

60. $\log_b 81$

61. $\log_b \dfrac{3}{9}$

62. $\log_b \dfrac{4}{32}$

63. $\log_b \sqrt{\dfrac{2}{3}}$

64. $\log_b \sqrt{\dfrac{3}{2}}$

Review

65. Graph the functions $y = 10^x$ and $y = \log_{10} x$ on the same set of axes. See Section 9.4.

Evaluate each expression. See Section 9.4.

66. $\log_{10} 100$

67. $\log_{10} \dfrac{1}{10}$

68. $\log_7 7^2$

69. $\log_7 \sqrt{7}$

Concept Extensions

Solve. See the Concept Checks in this section.

70. Which of the following is the correct way to rewrite $\log_3 \dfrac{14}{11}$?

  a. $\dfrac{\log_3 14}{\log_3 11}$

  b. $\log_3 14 - \log_3 11$

  c. $\log_3 (14 - 11)$

  d. $\log_3 154$

71. Which of the following is the correct way to rewrite $\log_9 \dfrac{21}{3}$?

  a. $\log_9 7$

  b. $\log_9 (21 - 3)$

  c. $\dfrac{\log_9 21}{\log_9 3}$

  d. $\log_9 21 - \log_9 3$

Determine whether each statement is true or false.

72. $\log_2 x^3 = 3\log_2 x$

73. $\log_3 (x + y) = \log_3 x + \log_3 y$

74. $\dfrac{\log_7 10}{\log_7 5} = \log_7 2$

75. $\log_7 \dfrac{14}{8} = \log_7 14 - \log_7 8$

76. $\dfrac{\log_7 x}{\log_7 y} = \log_7 x - \log_7 y$

77. $(\log_3 6) \cdot (\log_3 4) = \log_3 24$

78. It is true that $\log_b 8 = \log_b (8 \cdot 1) = \log_b 8 + \log_b 1$. Explain how $\log_b 8$ can equal $\log_b 8 + \log_b 1$.

INTEGRATED REVIEW — Sections 9.1–9.5

Functions and Properties of Logarithms

If $f(x) = x - 6$ and $g(x) = x^2 + 1$, find each value.

1. $(f + g)(x)$ **2.** $(f - g)(x)$ **3.** $(f \cdot g)(x)$ **4.** $\left(\dfrac{f}{g}\right)(x)$

If $f(x) = \sqrt{x}$ and $g(x) = 3x - 1$, find each value.

5. $(f \circ g)(x)$ **6.** $(g \circ f)(x)$

Determine whether each is a one-to-one function. If it is, find its inverse.

7. $f = \{(-2, 6), (4, 8), (2, -6), (3, 3)\}$ **8.** $g = \{(4, 2), (-1, 3), (5, 3), (7, 1)\}$

Determine whether the graph of each function is one-to-one.

9.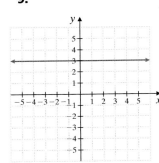

10.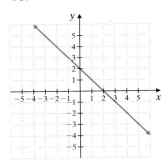

11.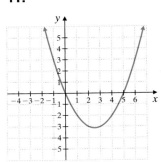

Each function listed is one-to-one. Find the inverse of each function.

12. $f(x) = 3x$ **13.** $f(x) = x + 4$

14. $f(x) = 5x - 1$ **15.** $f(x) = 3x + 2$

Graph each function.

16. $y = \left(\dfrac{1}{2}\right)^x$

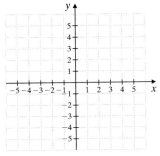

17. $y = 2^x + 1$

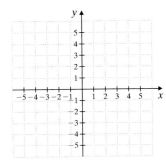

Answers

1.
2.
3.
4.
5.
6.
7.
8.
9.
10.
11.
12.
13.
14.
15.
16. see graph
17. see graph

18. see graph

19. see graph

20. _____

21. _____

22. _____

23. _____

24. _____

25. _____

26. _____

27. _____

28. _____

29. _____

30. _____

31. _____

32. _____

33. _____

34. _____

35. _____

36. _____

37. _____

18. $y = \log_3 x$

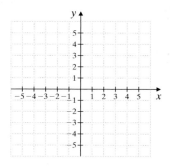

19. $y = \log_{1/3} x$

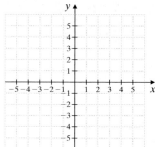

Solve.

20. $2^x = 8$

21. $9 = 3^{x-5}$

22. $4^{x-1} = 8^{x+2}$

23. $25^x = 125^{x-1}$

24. $\log_4 16 = x$

25. $\log_{49} 7 = x$

26. $\log_2 x = 5$

27. $\log_x 64 = 3$

28. $\log_x \dfrac{1}{125} = -3$

29. $\log_3 x = -2$

Write each as a single logarithm.

30. $\log_2 x + \log_2 14$

31. $x \log_2 5 + \log_2 8$

32. $3 \log_5 x - 5 \log_5 y$

33. $9 \log_5 x + 3 \log_5 y$

34. $\log_2 x + \log_2 (x - 3) - \log_2 (x^2 + 4)$

35. $\log_3 y - \log_3 (y + 2) + \log_3 (y^3 + 11)$

Write each expression as a sum or difference of logarithms.

36. $\log_7 \dfrac{9x^2}{y}$

37. $\log_6 \dfrac{5y}{z^2}$

9.6 COMMON LOGARITHMS, NATURAL LOGARITHMS, AND CHANGE OF BASE

In this section we look closely at two particular logarithmic bases. These two logarithmic bases are used so frequently that logarithms to their bases are given special names. **Common logarithms** are logarithms to base 10. **Natural logarithms** are logarithms to base e, which we introduce in this section. The work in this section is based on the use of a calculator that has both the "common log" $\boxed{\text{LOG}}$ and the "natural log" $\boxed{\text{LN}}$ keys.

Objective A Approximating Common Logarithms

Logarithms to base 10—**common logarithms**—are used frequently because our number system is a base 10 decimal system. The notation $\log x$ means the same as $\log_{10} x$.

Common Logarithm

$$\log x \quad \text{means} \quad \log_{10} x$$

EXAMPLE 1 Use a calculator to approximate $\log 7$ to four decimal places.

Solution: Press the following sequence of keys:

$$\boxed{7}\,\boxed{\text{LOG}} \quad \text{or} \quad \boxed{\text{LOG}}\,\boxed{7}\,\boxed{\text{ENTER}}$$

To four decimal places,

$$\log 7 \approx 0.8451$$

■ **Work Practice Problem 1**

Objective B Evaluating Common Logarithms of Powers of 10

To evaluate the common log of a power of 10, a calculator is not needed. According to the property of logarithms,

$$\log_b b^x = x$$

It follows that if b is replaced with 10, we have

$$\log 10^x = x$$

> **Helpful Hint**
> Remember that the base of this logarithm is understood to be 10.

EXAMPLES Find the exact value of each logarithm.

2. $\log 10 = \log 10^1 = 1$

3. $\log \dfrac{1}{10} = \log 10^{-1} = -1$

4. $\log 100,000 = \log 10^5 = 5$

5. $\log \sqrt[4]{10} = \log 10^{1/4} = \dfrac{1}{4}$

■ **Work Practice Problems 2–5**

O b j e c t i v e s

Ⓐ Identify Common Logarithms and Approximate Them with a Calculator.

Ⓑ Evaluate Common Logarithms of Powers of 10.

Ⓒ Identify Natural Logarithms and Approximate Them with a Calculator.

Ⓓ Evaluate Natural Logarithms of Powers of e.

Ⓔ Use the Change of Base Formula.

PRACTICE PROBLEM 1

Use a calculator to approximate $\log 21$ to four decimal places.

PRACTICE PROBLEMS 2–5

Find the exact value of each logarithm.

2. $\log 1000$

3. $\log \dfrac{1}{100}$

4. $\log 10,000$

5. $\log \sqrt[3]{10}$

Answers

1. 1.3222, **2.** 3, **3.** −2, **4.** 4, **5.** $\dfrac{1}{3}$

579

PRACTICE PROBLEM 6

Solve: $\log x = 2.9$. Give an exact solution and then approximate the solution to four decimal places.

Helpful Hint

The understood base is 10.

As we will soon see, equations containing common logs are useful models of many natural phenomena.

EXAMPLE 6 Solve: $\log x = 1.2$. Give an exact solution and then approximate the solution to four decimal places.

Solution: Remember that the base of a common log is understood to be 10.

$$\log x = 1.2$$
$$10^{1.2} = x \qquad \text{Write with exponential notation.}$$

The exact solution is $10^{1.2}$ or the solution set is $\{10^{1.2}\}$. To four decimal places, $x \approx 15.8489$.

🔲 **Work Practice Problem 6**

Objective C Approximating Natural Logarithms

Natural logarithms are also frequently used, especially to describe natural events; hence the label "natural logarithm." **Natural logarithms** are logarithms to the base e, which is a constant approximately equal to 2.7183. The number e is an irrational number, as is π. The notation $\log_e x$ is usually abbreviated to $\ln x$. (The abbreviation ln is read "el en.")

Natural Logarithm

$\ln x$ means $\log_e x$

PRACTICE PROBLEM 7

Use a calculator to approximate $\ln 11$ to four decimal places.

EXAMPLE 7 Use a calculator to approximate $\ln 8$ to four decimal places.

Solution: Press the following sequence of keys:

$\boxed{8}\,\boxed{\ln}$ or $\boxed{\ln}\,\boxed{8}\,\boxed{\text{ENTER}}$

To four decimal places,
  $\ln 8 \approx 2.0794$

🔲 **Work Practice Problem 7**

Objective D Evaluating Natural Logarithms of Powers of e

As a result of the property $\log_b b^x = x$, we know that $\log_e e^x = x$, or $\ln e^x = x$.

PRACTICE PROBLEMS 8–9

Find the exact value of each natural logarithm.
8. $\ln e^9$
9. $\ln \sqrt[3]{e}$

EXAMPLES Find the exact value of each natural logarithm.

8. $\ln e^3 = 3$
9. $\ln \sqrt[7]{e} = \ln e^{1/7} = \dfrac{1}{7}$

🔲 **Work Practice Problems 8–9**

Answers

6. $x = 10^{2.9}$; $x \approx 794.3282$, **7.** 2.3979,
8. 9, 9. $\dfrac{1}{3}$

EXAMPLE 10   Solve: $\ln 3x = 5$. Give an exact solution and then approximate the solution to four decimal places.

Solution: Remember that the base of a natural logarithm is understood to be e.

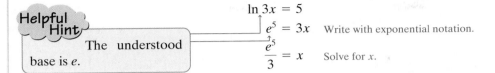

$$\ln 3x = 5$$
$$e^5 = 3x \qquad \text{Write with exponential notation.}$$
$$\frac{e^5}{3} = x \qquad \text{Solve for } x.$$

Helpful Hint: The understood base is e.

The exact solution is $\dfrac{e^5}{3}$. To four decimal places, $x \approx 49.4711$.

■ **Work Practice Problem 10**

PRACTICE PROBLEM 10

Solve: $\ln 7x = 10$. Give an exact solution and then approximate the solution to four decimal places.

Recall from Section 9.3 the formula $A = P\left(1 + \dfrac{r}{n}\right)^{nt}$ for compound interest, where n represents the number of compoundings per year. When interest is compounded continuously, we use the formula $A = Pe^{rt}$, where r is the annual interest rate and interest is compounded continuously for t years.

EXAMPLE 11   **Finding the Amount Owed on a Loan**

Find the amount owed at the end of 5 years if $1600 is loaned at a rate of 9% compounded continuously.

Solution: We use the formula $A = Pe^{rt}$ and the following values of the variables.

$\quad P = \$1600$ (the amount of the loan)
$\quad r = 9\% = 0.09$ (the rate of interest)
$\quad t = 5$ (the 5-year duration of the loan)
$\quad A = Pe^{rt}$
$\qquad = 1600e^{0.09(5)}$ Substitute known values.
$\qquad = 1600e^{0.45}$

Now we can use a calculator to approximate the solution.

$\quad A \approx 2509.30$

The total amount of money owed is approximately $2509.30.

■ **Work Practice Problem 11**

PRACTICE PROBLEM 11

Find the amount owed at the end of 3 years if $1200 is loaned at a rate of 8% compounded continuously.

Objective **E** Using the Change of Base Formula

Calculators are handy tools for approximating natural and common logarithms. Unfortunately, some calculators cannot be used to approximate logarithms to bases other than e or 10—at least not directly. In such cases, we use the **change of base formula.**

Answers

10. $x = \dfrac{e^{10}}{7}; x \approx 3146.6380,$

11. $\$1525.50$

Change of Base

If $a, b,$ and c are positive real numbers and neither b nor c is 1, then

$$\log_b a = \frac{\log_c a}{\log_c b}$$

PRACTICE PROBLEM 12

Approximate $\log_7 5$ to four decimal places.

EXAMPLE 12 Approximate $\log_5 3$ to four decimal places.

Solution: We use the change of base property to write $\log_5 3$ as a quotient of logarithms to base 10.

$$\log_5 3 = \frac{\log 3}{\log 5} \qquad \text{Use the change of base property.}$$

$$\approx \frac{0.4771213}{0.69897} \qquad \text{Approximate the logarithms by calculator.}$$

$$\approx 0.6826063 \qquad \text{Simplify by calculator.}$$

To four decimal places, $\log_5 3 \approx 0.6826$.

▢ **Work Practice Problem 12**

✔**Concept Check** If a graphing calculator cannot directly evaluate logarithms to base 5, describe how you could use the graphing calculator to graph the function $f(x) = \log_5 x$.

Answer

12. 0.8271

✔ **Concept Check Answer**

$f(x) = \dfrac{\log x}{\log 5}$

9.6 EXERCISE SET

Objectives Ⓐ Ⓒ **Mixed Practice** *Use a calculator to approximate each logarithm to four decimal places. See Examples 1 and 7.*

1. $\log 8$

2. $\log 6$

3. $\log 2.31$

4. $\log 4.86$

5. $\ln 2$

6. $\ln 3$

7. $\ln 0.0716$

8. $\ln 0.0032$

9. $\log 12.6$

10. $\log 25.9$

11. $\ln 5$

12. $\ln 7$

13. $\log 41.5$

14. $\ln 41.5$

Objectives Ⓑ Ⓓ **Mixed Practice** *Find the exact value of each logarithm. See Examples 2 through 5, 8, and 9.*

15. $\log 100$

16. $\log 10{,}000$

17. $\log \dfrac{1}{1000}$

18. $\log \dfrac{1}{10}$

19. $\ln e^2$

20. $\ln e^4$

21. $\ln \sqrt[4]{e}$

22. $\ln \sqrt[5]{e}$

23. $\log 10^3$

24. $\ln e^5$

25. $\ln e^{3.1}$

26. $\log 10^7$

27. $\log 0.0001$

28. $\log 0.001$

29. $\ln \sqrt{e}$

30. $\log \sqrt{10}$

Solve each equation. Give an exact solution and a four-decimal-place approximation. See Examples 6 and 10.

31. $\log x = 1.3$

32. $\log x = 2.1$

33. $\ln x = 1.4$

34. $\ln x = 2.1$

35. $\log x = 2.3$

36. $\log x = 3.1$

37. $\ln x = -2.3$

38. $\ln x = -3.7$

39. $\log 2x = 1.1$

40. $\log 3x = 1.3$

41. $\ln 4x = 0.18$

42. $\ln 3x = 0.76$

43. $\ln(3x - 4) = 2.3$

44. $\ln(2x + 5) = 3.4$

45. $\log(2x + 1) = -0.5$

46. $\log(3x - 2) = -0.8$

Use the formula $A = Pe^{rt}$ to solve. See Example 11.

47. How much money does Dana Jones have after 12 years if she invests $1400 at 8% interest compounded continuously?

48. Determine the size of an account in which $3500 earns 6% interest compounded continuously for 1 year.

49. How much money does Barbara Mack owe at the end of 4 years if 6% interest is compounded continuously on her $2000 debt?

50. Find the amount of money for which a $2500 certificate of deposit is redeemable if it has been paying 10% interest compounded continuously for 3 years.

Objective **E** *Approximate each logarithm to four decimal places. See Example 12.*

51. $\log_2 3$ **52.** $\log_3 2$ **53.** $\log_8 6$ **54.** $\log_6 8$ **55.** $\log_4 9$

56. $\log_9 4$ **57.** $\log_3 \dfrac{1}{6}$ **58.** $\log_6 \dfrac{2}{3}$ **59.** $\log_{1/2} 5$ **60.** $\log_{1/3} 2$

Review

Solve for x. See Sections 2.1, 2.3, and 5.7.

61. $6x - 3(2 - 5x) = 6$ **62.** $2x + 3 = 5 - 2(3x - 1)$

63. $2x + 3y = 6x$ **64.** $4x - 8y = 10x$

65. $x^2 + 7x = -6$ **66.** $x^2 + 4x = 12$

Concept Extensions

67. Use a calculator to try to approximate $\log 0$. Describe what happens and explain why.

68. Use a calculator to try to approximate $\ln 0$. Describe what happens and explain why.

Graph each function by finding ordered pair solutions, plotting the solutions, and then drawing a smooth curve through the plotted points.

69. $f(x) = e^x$ **70.** $f(x) = e^{2x}$ **71.** $f(x) = \ln x$ **72.** $f(x) = \log x$

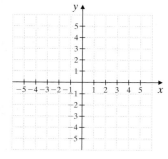 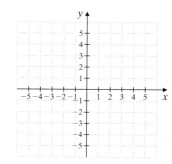 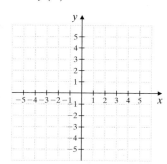 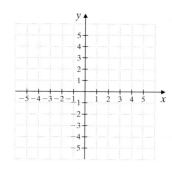

73. Without using a calculator, explain which of $\log 50$ or $\ln 50$ must be larger.

74. Without using a calculator, explain which of $\log 50^{-1}$ or $\ln 50^{-1}$ must be larger.

The Richter scale measures the intensity, or magnitude, of an earthquake. The formula for the magnitude R of an earthquake is $R = \log\left(\dfrac{a}{T}\right) + B$, where a is the amplitude in micrometers of the vertical motion of the ground at the recording station, T is the number of seconds between successive seismic waves, and B is an adjustment factor that takes into account the weakening of the seismic wave as the distance increases from the epicenter of the earthquake.

Use the Richter scale formula to find the magnitude R of the earthquake that fits the description given. Round answers to one decimal place.

75. Amplitude *a* is 200 micrometers, time *T* between waves is 1.6 seconds, and *B* is 2.1.

76. Amplitude *a* is 150 micrometers, time *T* between waves is 3.6 seconds, and *B* is 1.9.

77. Amplitude *a* is 400 micrometers, time *T* between waves is 2.6 seconds, and *B* is 3.1.

78. Amplitude *a* is 450 micrometers, time *T* between waves is 4.2 seconds, and *B* is 2.7.

 STUDY SKILLS BUILDER

What to Do the Day of an Exam?

On the day of an exam, don't forget to try the following:

- Allow yourself plenty of time to arrive.
- Read the directions on the test carefully.
- Read each problem carefully as you take your test. Make sure that you answer the question asked.
- Watch your time and pace yourself so that you may attempt each problem on your test.
- Check your work and answers.
- ***Do not turn your test in early.*** If you have extra time, spend it double-checking your work.

Good luck!

Answer the following questions based on your most recent mathematics exam, whenever that was.

1. How soon before class did you arrive?

2. Did you read the directions on the test carefully?

3. Did you make sure you answered the question asked for each problem on the exam?

4. Were you able to attempt each problem on your exam?

5. If your answer to Question 4 is no, list reasons why.

6. Did you have extra time on your exam?

7. If your answer to Question 6 is yes, describe how you spent that extra time.

A Solve Exponential Equations.

B Solve Logarithmic Equations.

C Solve Problems That Can Be Modeled by Exponential and Logarithmic Equations.

9.7 EXPONENTIAL AND LOGARITHMIC EQUATIONS AND PROBLEM SOLVING

Objective **A** Solving Exponential Equations

In Section 9.3 we solved exponential equations such as $2^x = 16$ by writing both sides in terms of the same base. Here, we write 16 as a power of 2 and using the uniqueness of b^x.

$$2^x = 16$$
$$2^x = 2^4 \quad \text{Write 16 as } 2^4.$$
$$x = 4 \quad \text{Use the uniqueness of } b^x.$$

How do we solve an exponential equation when the bases cannot easily be written the same? For example, how do we solve an equation such as $3^x = 7$? We use the fact that $f(x) = \log_b x$ is a one-to-one function. Another way of stating this fact is as a property of equality.

Logarithm Property of Equality

Let a, b, and c be real numbers such that $\log_b a$ and $\log_b c$ are real numbers and b is not 1. Then

$$\log_b a = \log_b c \quad \text{is equivalent to} \quad a = c$$

PRACTICE PROBLEM 1

Solve: $2^x = 5$. Give an exact answer and a four-decimal-place approximation.

EXAMPLE 1 Solve: $3^x = 7$. Give an exact answer and a four-decimal-place approximation.

Solution: We use the logarithm property of equality and take the logarithm of both sides. For this example, we use the common logarithm.

$$3^x = 7$$
$$\log 3^x = \log 7 \quad \text{Take the common log of both sides.}$$
$$x \log 3 = \log 7 \quad \text{Use the power property of logarithms.}$$
$$x = \frac{\log 7}{\log 3} \quad \text{Divide both sides by log 3.}$$

The exact solution is $\dfrac{\log 7}{\log 3}$. When we approximate to four decimal places, we have

$$\frac{\log 7}{\log 3} \approx \frac{0.845098}{0.4771213} \approx 1.7712$$

The solution set is $\left\{ \dfrac{\log 7}{\log 3} \right\}$, or approximately $\{1.7712\}$.

Work Practice Problem 1

Objective **B** Solving Logarithmic Equations

By applying the appropriate properties of logarithms, we can solve a broad variety of logarithmic equations.

Answer

1. $\left\{ \dfrac{\log 5}{\log 2} \right\}$; $\{2.3219\}$

EXAMPLE 2 Solve: $\log_4(x - 2) = 2$

Solution: Notice that $x - 2$ must be positive, so x must be greater than 2. With this in mind, we first write the equation with exponential notation.

$$\log_4(x - 2) = 2$$
$$4^2 = x - 2$$
$$16 = x - 2$$
$$18 = x \qquad \text{Add 2 to both sides.}$$

To check, we replace x with 18 in the original equation.

$$\log_4(x - 2) = 2$$
$$\log_4(18 - 2) \stackrel{?}{=} 2 \qquad \text{Let } x = 18.$$
$$\log_4 16 \stackrel{?}{=} 2$$
$$4^2 = 16 \qquad \text{True}$$

The solution set is $\{18\}$.

🔲 **Work Practice Problem 2**

PRACTICE PROBLEM 2
Solve: $\log_3(x + 5) = 2$

EXAMPLE 3 Solve: $\log_2 x + \log_2(x - 1) = 1$

Solution: Notice that $x - 1$ must be positive, so x must be greater than 1. We use the product property on the left side of the equation.

$$\log_2 x + \log_2(x - 1) = 1$$
$$\log_2[x(x - 1)] = 1 \qquad \text{Use the product property.}$$
$$\log_2(x^2 - x) = 1$$

Next we write the equation with exponential notation and solve for x.

$$2^1 = x^2 - x$$
$$0 = x^2 - x - 2 \qquad \text{Subtract 2 from both sides.}$$
$$0 = (x - 2)(x + 1) \qquad \text{Factor.}$$
$$0 = x - 2 \quad \text{or} \quad 0 = x + 1 \qquad \text{Set each factor equal to 0.}$$
$$2 = x \qquad\qquad -1 = x$$

Recall that -1 cannot be a solution because x must be greater than 1. If we forgot this, we would still reject -1 after checking. To see this, we replace x with -1 in the original equation.

$$\log_2 x + \log_2(x - 1) = 1$$
$$\log_2(-1) + \log_2(-1 - 1) \stackrel{?}{=} 1 \qquad \text{Let } x = -1.$$

Because the logarithm of a negative number is undefined, -1 is rejected. Check to see that the solution set is $\{2\}$.

🔲 **Work Practice Problem 3**

PRACTICE PROBLEM 3
Solve: $\log_6 x + \log_6(x + 1) = 1$

Answers
2. $\{4\}$, **3.** $\{2\}$

PRACTICE PROBLEM 4

Solve: $\log(x + 1) - \log x = 1$

EXAMPLE 4 Solve: $\log(x + 2) - \log x = 2$

Solution: We use the quotient property of logarithms on the left side of the equation.

$$\log(x + 2) - \log x = 2$$

$$\log\frac{x + 2}{x} = 2 \qquad \text{Use the quotient property.}$$

$$10^2 = \frac{x + 2}{x} \qquad \text{Write using exponential notation.}$$

$$100 = \frac{x + 2}{x}$$

$$100x = x + 2 \qquad \text{Multiply both sides by } x.$$

$$99x = 2 \qquad \text{Subtract } x \text{ from both sides.}$$

$$x = \frac{2}{99} \qquad \text{Divide both sides by 99.}$$

Check to see that the solution set is $\left\{\frac{2}{99}\right\}$.

■ **Work Practice Problem 4**

Objective C Solving Problems Modeled by Exponential and Logarithmic Equations

Logarithmic and exponential functions are used in a variety of scientific, technical, and business settings. A few examples follow.

PRACTICE PROBLEM 5

Use the equation in Example 5 to estimate the lemming population in 8 months.

EXAMPLE 5 Estimating Population Size

The population size y of a community of lemmings varies according to the relationship $y = y_0 e^{0.15t}$. In this formula, t is time in months, and y_0 is the initial population at time 0. Estimate the population after 6 months if there were originally 5000 lemmings.

Solution: We substitute 5000 for y_0 and 6 for t.

$$y = y_0 e^{0.15t}$$

$$= 5000 e^{0.15(6)} \qquad \text{Let } t = 6 \text{ and } y_0 = 5000.$$

$$= 5000 e^{0.9} \qquad \text{Multiply.}$$

Using a calculator, we find that $y \approx 12{,}298.016$. In 6 months the population will be approximately 12,300 lemmings.

■ **Work Practice Problem 5**

PRACTICE PROBLEM 6

How long does it take an investment of $1000 to double if it is invested at 6% interest compounded quarterly?

EXAMPLE 6 Doubling an Investment

How long does it take an investment of $2000 to double if it is invested at 5% interest compounded quarterly? The necessary formula is $A = P\left(1 + \frac{r}{n}\right)^{nt}$, where A is the accrued amount, P is the principal invested, r is the annual rate of interest, n is the number of compounding periods per year, and t is the number of years.

Answers

4. $\left\{\frac{1}{9}\right\}$,

5. approximately 16,600 lemmings,

6. $11\frac{3}{4}$ yr

Solution: We are given that $P = \$2000$ and $r = 5\% = 0.05$. Compounding quarterly means 4 times a year, so $n = 4$. The investment is to double, so A must be $\$4000$. We substitute these values and solve for t.

$$A = P\left(1 + \frac{r}{n}\right)^{nt}$$

$$4000 = 2000\left(1 + \frac{0.05}{4}\right)^{4t} \qquad \text{Substitute known values.}$$

$$4000 = 2000(1.0125)^{4t} \qquad \text{Simplify } 1 + \frac{0.05}{4}.$$

$$2 = (1.0125)^{4t} \qquad \text{Divide both sides by 2000.}$$

$$\log 2 = \log 1.0125^{4t} \qquad \text{Take the logarithm of both sides.}$$

$$\log 2 = 4t(\log 1.0125) \qquad \text{Use the power property.}$$

$$\frac{\log 2}{4\log 1.0125} = t \qquad \text{Divide both sides by 4 log 1.0125.}$$

$$13.949408 \approx t \qquad \text{Approximate by calculator.}$$

It takes approximately 14 years for the money to double in value.

⬛ **Work Practice Problem 6**

🖩 **CALCULATOR EXPLORATIONS**   Graphing

Use a grapher to find how long it takes an investment of $\$1500$ to triple if it is invested at 8% interest compounded monthly. First, let $P = \$1500$, $r = 0.08$, and $n = 12$ (for monthly compounding) in the formula

$$A = P\left(1 + \frac{r}{n}\right)^{nt}$$

Notice that when the investment has tripled, the accrued amount A is $\$4500$. Thus,

$$4500 = 1500\left(1 + \frac{0.08}{12}\right)^{12t}$$

Determine an appropriate viewing window and enter and graph the equations

$$Y_1 = 1500\left(1 + \frac{0.08}{12}\right)^{12x}$$

and

$$Y_2 = 4500$$

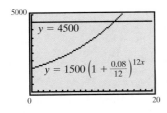

The point of intersection of the two curves is the solution. The x-coordinate tells how long it takes for the investment to triple.

Use a TRACE feature or an INTERSECT feature to approximate the coordinates of the point of intersection of the two curves. It takes approximately 13.78 years, or 13 years and 10 months, for the investment to triple in value to $\$4500$.

Use this graphical solution method to solve each problem. Round each answer to the nearest hundredth.

1. Find how long it takes an investment of $\$5000$ to grow to $\$6000$ if it is invested at 5% interest compounded quarterly.

2. Find how long it takes an investment of $\$1000$ to double if it is invested at 4.5% interest compounded daily. (Use 365 days in a year.)

3. Find how long it takes an investment of $\$10,000$ to quadruple if it is invested at 6% interest compounded monthly.

4. Find how long it takes $\$500$ to grow to $\$800$ if it is invested at 4% interest compounded semiannually.

Objective A *Solve each equation. Give an exact solution and a four-decimal-place approximation. See Example 1.*

1. $3^x = 6$ **2.** $4^x = 7$ **3.** $9^x = 5$ **4.** $3^x = 11$

5. $3^{2x} = 3.8$ **6.** $5^{3x} = 5.6$ **7.** $e^{6x} = 5$ **8.** $e^{2x} = 8$

9. $2^{x-3} = 5$ **10.** $8^{x-2} = 12$ **11.** $4^{x+7} = 3$

12. $6^{x+3} = 2$ **13.** $7^{3x-4} = 11$ **14.** $5^{2x-6} = 12$

Objective B *Solve each equation. See Examples 2 through 4.*

15. $\log_2(x + 5) = 4$ **16.** $\log_2(x - 5) = 3$ **17.** $\log_4 2 + \log_4 x = 0$ **18.** $\log_3 5 + \log_3 x = 1$

19. $\log_2 6 - \log_2 x = 3$ **20.** $\log_4 10 - \log_4 x = 2$ **21.** $\log_2(x^2 + x) = 1$ **22.** $\log_6(x^2 - x) = 1$

23. $\log_4 x + \log_4(x + 6) = 2$ **24.** $\log_3 x + \log_3(x + 6) = 3$ **25.** $\log_5(x + 3) - \log_5 x = 2$

26. $\log_6(x + 2) - \log_6 x = 2$ **27.** $\log_4(x^2 - 3x) = 1$ **28.** $\log_8(x^2 - 2x) = 1$

29. $\log_2 x + \log_2(3x + 1) = 1$ **30.** $\log_3 x + \log_3(x - 8) = 2$

Objective C *Solve. See Example 5.*

31. The size of the wolf population at Isle Royale National Park increases at a rate of 4.3% per year. If the size of the current population is 83 wolves, find how many there should be in 5 years. Use $y = y_0 e^{0.043t}$ and round to the nearest whole number.

32. The number of victims of a flu epidemic is increasing at a rate of 7.5% per week. If 20,000 people are currently infected, in how many days can we expect 45,000 people to have the flu? Use $y = y_0 e^{0.075t}$ and round to the nearest whole number.

33. The population of Paraguay is increasing at a rate of 2.5% per year. The population of Paraguay in 2004 was approximately 6,191,000. Use $y = y_0e^{0.025t}$ to estimate the population of Paraguay in 2010. Round to the nearest whole number. (*Source:* Population Reference Bureau)

34. In 2004, 184.1 million people lived in Brazil. The population of Brazil is growing at a rate of 1.3% per year. Find how long it will take the Brazilian population to reach a size of 200 million people. Use $y = y_0e^{0.013t}$ and round to the nearest tenth. (*Source:* Population Reference Bureau)

35. In 2004, Hungary had a population of about 10,032,000. At that time, Hungary's population was declining at a rate of 0.4% per year. At that rate, how long will it take for Hungary's population to decline to 9,000,000? Use $y = y_0e^{-0.004t}$ and round to the nearest tenth. (*Source:* Population Reference Bureau)

36. The population of Russia has been decreasing at the rate of 0.6% per year. There were about 143,800,000 people living in Russia in 2004. How many inhabitants will there be in 2016? Use $y = y_0e^{-0.006t}$. Round to the nearest whole number. (*Source:* Population Reference Bureau)

Use the formula $A = P\left(1 + \dfrac{r}{n}\right)^{nt}$ to solve these compound interest problems. Round to the nearest tenth. See Example 6.

37. How long does it take for $600 to double if it is invested at 7% interest compounded monthly?

38. How long does it take for $600 to double if it is invested at 12% interest compounded monthly?

39. How long does it take for a $1200 investment to earn $200 interest if it is invested at 9% interest compounded quarterly?

40. How long does it take for a $1500 investment to earn $200 interest if it is invested at 10% interest compounded semiannually?

41. How long does it take for $1000 to double if it is invested at 8% interest compounded semiannually?

42. How long does it take for $1000 to double if it is invested at 8% interest compounded monthly?

The formula $w = 0.00185h^{2.67}$ is used to estimate the normal weight w in pounds of a boy h inches tall. Use this formula to solve Exercises 43 and 44. Round to the nearest tenth.

43. Find the expected height of a boy who weighs 85 pounds.

44. Find the expected height of a boy who weighs 140 pounds.

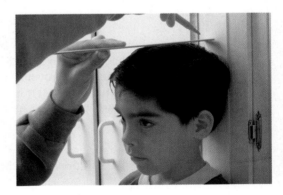

The formula $P = 14.7e^{-0.21x}$ gives the average atmospheric pressure P, in pounds per square inch, at an altitude x, in miles above sea level. Use this formula to solve Exercises 45 through 58. Round to the nearest tenth.

45. Find the average atmospheric pressure of Denver, which is 1 mile above sea level.

46. Find the average atmospheric pressure of Pikes Peak, which is 2.7 miles above sea level.

47. Find the elevation of a Delta jet if the atmospheric pressure outside the jet is 7.5 pounds per square inch.

48. Find the elevation of a remote Himalayan peak if the atmospheric pressure atop the peak is 6.5 pounds per square inch.

Psychologists call the graph of the formula $t = \dfrac{1}{c}\ln\left(\dfrac{A}{A-N}\right)$ *the learning curve since the formula relates time t passed, in weeks, to a measure N of learning achieved, to a measure A of maximum learning possible, and to a measure c of an individual's learning style. Use this formula to answer Exercises 49 through 52. Round to the nearest whole number.*

49. Norman Weidner is learning to type. If he wants to type at a rate of 50 words per minute ($N = 50$) and his expected maximum rate is 75 words per minute ($A = 75$), how many weeks should it take him to achieve his goal? Assume that c is 0.09.

50. An experiment of teaching chimpanzees sign language shows that a typical chimp can master a maximum of 65 signs. How many weeks should it take a chimpanzee to master 30 signs if c is 0.03?

51. Janine Jenkins is working on her dictation skills. She wants to take dictation at a rate of 150 words per minute and believes that the maximum rate she can hope for is 210 words per minute. How many weeks should it take her to achieve the 150-word level if c is 0.07?

52. A psychologist is measuring human capability to memorize nonsense syllables. How many weeks should it take a subject to learn 15 nonsense syllables if the maximum possible to learn is 24 syllables and c is 0.17?

Review

If $x = -2$, $y = 0$, and $z = 3$, find the value of each expression. See Section 1.5.

53. $\dfrac{x^2 - y + 2z}{3x}$

54. $\dfrac{x^3 - 2y + z}{2z}$

55. $\dfrac{3z - 4x + y}{x + 2z}$

56. $\dfrac{4y - 3x + z}{2x + y}$

Concept Extensions

The formula $y = y_0 e^{kt}$ gives the population size y of a population that experiences an annual rate of population growth k (given as a decimal). In this formula, t is time in years and y_0 is the initial population at time 0. Use this formula to solve Exercises 57 and 58.

57. In 2000, the population of Arizona was 5,130,632. By 2003, the population had grown to 5,880,811. Find the annual rate of population growth over this period. Round your answer to the nearest tenth of a percent. (*Source:* U.S. Census Bureau, State of Arizona)

58. In 2000, the population of Nevada was 1,998,257. By 2003, the population had grown to 2,241,154. Find the annual rate of population growth over this period. Round your answer to the nearest tenth of a percent. (*Source:* U.S. Census Bureau, State of Nevada)

59. When solving a logarithmic equation, explain why you must check possible solutions in the original equation.

60. Solve $5^x = 9$ by taking the common logarithm of both sides of the equation. Next, solve this equation by taking the natural logarithm of both sides. Compare your solutions. Are they the same? Why or why not?

Use a graphing calculator to solve. Round your answers to two decimal places.

61. $e^{0.3x} = 8$

62. $10^{0.5x} = 7$

THE BIGGER PICTURE   Solving Equations and Inequalities

Continue your outline from Sections 2.6, 5.7, 6.4, 7.6, and 8.4. Write how to recognize and how to solve exponential and logarithmic equations in your own words. For example:

Solving Equations and Inequalities

I. **Equations**

    A. **Linear equations** (Sec. 2.1)

    B. **Absolute value equations** (Sec. 2.6)

    C. **Quadratic and higher degree equations** (Sec. 5.7 and Chapter 8)

    D. **Equations with rational expressions** (Sec. 6.4)

    E. **Equations with radicals** (Sec. 7.6)

    F. **Exponential Equations—equations with variables in the exponent.**

1. If we can write both expressions with the same base, then set the exponents equal to each other and solve	**2.** If we can't write both expressions with the same base, then solve using logarithms
$9^x = 27^{x+1}$ $(3^2)^x = (3^3)^{x+1}$ $3^{2x} = 3^{3x+3}$ $2x = 3x + 3$ $-3 = x$	$5^x = 7$ $\log 5^x = \log 7$ $x \log 5 = \log 7$ $x = \dfrac{\log 7}{\log 5}$ $x \approx 1.2091$

    G. **Logarithmic Equations—equations with logarithms of variable expressions**

$\log 7 + \log(x + 3) = 2$ Write equation so that single logarithm on
$\quad\log 7(x + 3) = 2$ one side and constant on the other side.
$\qquad 10^2 = 7(x + 3)$ Use definition of logarithm.
$\qquad 100 = 7x + 21$ Multiply.
$\qquad 79 = 7x$
$\qquad \dfrac{79}{7} = x$ Solve.

II. **Inequalities**

    A. **Linear inequalities** (Sec. 2.4)

    B. **Compound inequalities** (Sec. 2.5)

    C. **Absolute value inequalities** (Sec. 2.6)

    D. **Nonlinear inequalities** (Sec. 8.4)

       1. Polynomial inequalities

       2. Rational inequalities

Solve. Write solutions to inequalities in interval notation.

1. $8^x = 2^{x-3}$

2. $11^x = 5$

3. $-7x + 3 \le -5x + 13$

4. $-7 \le 3x + 6 \le 0$

5. $|5y + 3| < 3$

6. $(x - 6)(5x + 1) = 0$

7. $\log_{13} 8 + \log_{13}(x - 1) = 1$

8. $\left|\dfrac{3x - 1}{4}\right| = 2$

9. $|7x + 1| > -2$

10. $x^2 = 4$

11. $(x + 5)^2 = 3$

12. $\log_7(4x^2 - 27x) = 1$

CHAPTER 9   Group Activity

Sound Intensity

The decibel (dB) measures sound intensity, or the relative loudness or strength of a sound. One decibel is the smallest difference in sound levels that is detectable by humans. The decibel is a logarithmic unit. This means that for approximately every 3-decibel increase in sound intensity, the relative loudness of the sound is doubled. For example, a 35 dB sound is twice as loud as a 32 dB sound.

In the modern world, noise pollution has increasingly become a concern. Sustained exposure to high sound intensities can lead to hearing loss. Regular exposure to 90 dB sounds can eventually lead to loss of hearing. Sounds of 130 dB and more can cause permanent loss of hearing instantaneously.

The relative loudness of a sound D in decibels is given by the equation

$$D = 10 \log_{10} \frac{I}{10^{-16}}$$

where I is the intensity of a sound given in watts per square centimeter. Some sound intensities of common noises are listed in the table in order of increasing sound intensity.

Group Activity

1. Work together to create a table of the relative loudness (in decibels) of the sounds listed in the table.

2. Research the loudness of other common noises. Add these sounds and their decibel levels to your table. Be sure to list the sounds in order of increasing sound intensity.

Some Sound Intensities of Common Noises	
Noise	**Intensity (watts/cm²)**
Whispering	10^{-15}
Rustling leaves	$10^{-14.2}$
Normal conversation	10^{-13}
Background noise in a quiet residence	$10^{-12.2}$
Typewriter	10^{-11}
Air conditioning	10^{-10}
Freight train at 50 feet	$10^{-8.5}$
Vacuum cleaner	10^{-8}
Nearby thunder	10^{-7}
Air hammer	$10^{-6.5}$
Jet plane at takeoff	10^{-6}
Threshold of pain	10^{-4}

STUDY SKILLS BUILDER

Are You Prepared for a Test on Chapter 9?

Below I have listed some common trouble areas for students in Chapter 9. After studying for your test—but before taking your test—read these.

- Don't forget how to find the composition of two functions.

    If $f(x) = x^2 + 5$ and $g(x) = 3x$,   then
    $$(f \circ g)(x) = f[g(x)] = f(3x)$$
    $$= (3x)^2 + 5 = 9x^2 + 5$$
    $$(g \circ f)(x) = g[f(x)] = g(x^2 + 5)$$
    $$= 3(x^2 + 5) = 3x^2 + 15$$

- Don't forget that f^{-1} is a special notation used to denote the inverse of a function.

    Let's find the inverse of the one-to-one function $f(x) = 3x - 5$.

$$f(x) = 3x - 5$$
$$y = 3x - 5 \quad \text{Replace } f(x) \text{ with } y.$$
$$x = 3y - 5 \quad \text{Interchange } x \text{ and } y.$$
$$x + 5 = 3y$$
$$\frac{x + 5}{3} = y \quad \text{Solve for } y.$$
$$f^{-1}(x) = \frac{x + 5}{3} \quad \text{Replace } y \text{ with } f^{-1}(x).$$

- Don't forget that $y = \log_b x$ means $b^y = x$.

    Thus, $3 = \log_5 125$ means $5^3 = 125$.

- Remember rules for logarithms.

    $\log_b 3x = \log_b 3 + \log_b x$
    $\log_b (3 + x)$ cannot be simplified in the same manner.

Remember: This is simply a checklist of common trouble areas. For a review of Chapter 9, see the Highlights and Chapter Review at the end of this chapter.

Chapter 9 Vocabulary Check

Fill in each blank with one of the words or phrases listed below.

    inverse   common   composition   symmetric   exponential

    vertical   logarithmic   natural   horizontal

1. For a one-to-one function, we can find its _____ function by switching the coordinates of the ordered pairs of the function.

2. The _____ of functions f and g is $(f \circ g)(x) = f(g(x))$.

3. A function of the form $f(x) = b^x$ is called an _____ function if $b > 0$, b is not 1, and x is a real number.

4. The graphs of f and f^{-1} are _____ about the line $y = x$.

5. _____ logarithms are logarithms to base e.

6. _____ logarithms are logarithms to base 10.

7. To see whether a graph is the graph of a one-to-one function, apply the _____ line test to see whether it is a function, and then apply the _____ line test to see whether it is a one-to-one function.

8. A _____ function is a function that can be defined by $f(x) = \log_b x$ where x is a positive real number, b is a constant positive real number, and b is not 1.

Helpful Hint

Are you preparing for your test? Don't forget to take the Chapter 9 Test on page 705. Then check your answers at the back of the text and use the Chapter Test Prep Video CD to see the fully worked-out solutions to any of the exercises you want to review.

9 Chapter Highlights

DEFINITIONS AND CONCEPTS	EXAMPLES
Section 9.1 The Algebra of Functions	

ALGEBRA OF FUNCTIONS Let f and g be functions. Sum $(f + g)(x) = f(x) + g(x)$ Difference $(f - g)(x) = f(x) - g(x)$ Product $(f \cdot g)(x) = f(x) \cdot g(x)$ Quotient $\left(\dfrac{f}{g}\right)(x) = \dfrac{f(x)}{g(x)}, g(x) \neq 0$	If $f(x) = 7x$ and $g(x) = x^2 + 1$, $(f + g)(x) = f(x) + g(x) = 7x + x^2 + 1$ $(f - g)(x) = f(x) - g(x) = 7x - (x^2 + 1)$ $\qquad\qquad\qquad\qquad\qquad = 7x - x^2 - 1$ $(f \cdot g)(x) = f(x) \cdot g(x) = 7x(x^2 + 1)$ $\qquad\qquad\qquad\qquad = 7x^3 + 7x^2$ $\left(\dfrac{f}{g}\right)(x) = \dfrac{f(x)}{g(x)} = \dfrac{7x}{x^2 + 1}$
COMPOSITE FUNCTIONS The notation $(f \circ g)(x)$ means "f composed with g." $(f \circ g)(x) = f(g(x))$ $(g \circ f)(x) = g(f(x))$	If $f(x) = x^2 + 1$ and $g(x) = x - 5$, find $(f \circ g)(x)$. $(f \circ g)(x) = f(g(x))$ $\qquad\qquad = f(x - 5)$ $\qquad\qquad = (x - 5)^2 + 1$ $\qquad\qquad = x^2 - 10x + 26$

DEFINITIONS AND CONCEPTS	EXAMPLES

Section 9.2   Inverse Functions

ONE-TO-ONE FUNCTION

If f is a function, then f is a **one-to-one function** only if each y-value (output) corresponds to only one x-value (input).

HORIZONTAL LINE TEST

If every horizontal line intersects the graph of a function at most once, then the function is a one-to-one function.

Determine whether each graph is a one-to-one function.

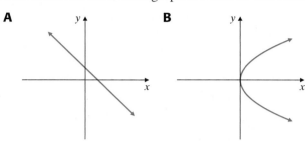

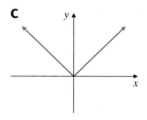

Graphs A and C pass the vertical line test, so only these are graphs of functions. Of graphs A and C, only graph A passes the horizontal line test, so only graph A is the graph of a one-to-one function.

The **inverse** of a one-to-one function f is the one-to-one function f^{-1} that is the set of all ordered pairs (b, a) such that (a, b) belongs to f.

FINDING THE INVERSE OF A ONE-TO-ONE FUNCTION f

Step 1. Replace $f(x)$ with y.

Step 2. Interchange x and y.

Step 3. Solve for the equation for y.

Step 4. Replace y with the notation $f^{-1}(x)$.

Find the inverse of $f(x) = 2x + 7$.

$$y = 2x + 7 \quad \text{Replace } f(x) \text{ with } y.$$
$$x = 2y + 7 \quad \text{Interchange } x \text{ and } y.$$
$$2y = x - 7 \quad \text{Solve for } y.$$
$$y = \frac{x - 7}{2}$$

$$f^{-1}(x) = \frac{x - 7}{2} \quad \text{Replace } y \text{ with } f^{-1}(x).$$

The inverse of $f(x) = 2x + 7$ is $f^{-1}(x) = \dfrac{x - 7}{2}$.

Section 9.3   Exponential Functions

EXPONENTIAL FUNCTION

A function of the form $f(x) = b^x$ is an **exponential function,** where $b > 0, b \neq 1$, and x is a real number.

Graph the exponential function $y = 4^x$.

x	y
−2	$\dfrac{1}{16}$
−1	$\dfrac{1}{4}$
0	1
1	4
2	16

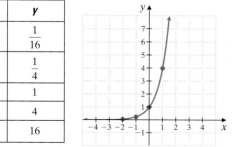

DEFINITIONS AND CONCEPTS	**EXAMPLES**

Section 9.3   Exponential Functions (*continued*)

UNIQUENESS OF b^x

If $b > 0$ and $b \neq 1$, then $b^x = b^y$ is equivalent to $x = y$.

Solve: $2^{x+5} = 8$

$\quad 2^{x+5} = 2^3$ Write 8 as 2^3.

$\quad\; x + 5 = 3$ Use the uniqueness of b^x.

$\quad\quad\quad x = -2$ Subtract 5 from both sides.

Section 9.4   Logarithmic Functions

LOGARITHMIC DEFINITION

If $b > 0$ and $b \neq 1$, then

$\quad y = \log_b x \quad$ means $\quad x = b^y$

for any positive number x and real number y.

LOGARITHMIC FORM	**CORRESPONDING EXPONENTIAL STATEMENT**
$\log_5 25 = 2$	$5^2 = 25$
$\log_9 3 = \dfrac{1}{2}$	$9^{1/2} = 3$

PROPERTIES OF LOGARITHMS

If b is a real number, $b > 0$ and $b \neq 1$, then

$\quad \log_b 1 = 0, \quad \log_b b^x = x, \quad$ and $\quad b^{\log_b x} = x$

$\log_5 1 = 0, \quad \log_7 7^2 = 2, \quad$ and $\quad 3^{\log_3 6} = 6$

LOGARITHMIC FUNCTION

If $b > 0$ and $b \neq 1$, then a **logarithmic function** is a function that can be defined as

$\quad f(x) = \log_b x$

The domain of f is the set of positive real numbers, and the range of f is the set of real numbers.

Graph: $y = \log_3 x$

Write $y = \log_3 x$ as $3^y = x$. Plot the ordered pair solutions listed in the table, and connect them with a smooth curve.

x	y
3	1
1	0
$\dfrac{1}{3}$	-1
$\dfrac{1}{9}$	-2

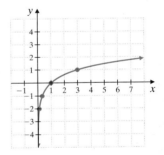

Section 9.5   Properties of Logarithms

Let x, y, and b be positive numbers, $b \neq 1$, and r is a real number.

PRODUCT PROPERTY

$\quad \log_b xy = \log_b x + \log_b y$

QUOTIENT PROPERTY

$\quad \log_b \dfrac{x}{y} = \log_b x - \log_b y$

POWER PROPERTY

$\quad \log_b x^r = r \log_b x$

Write as a single logarithm:

$\quad 2 \log_5 6 + \log_5 x - \log_5 (y + 2)$

$\quad = \log_5 6^2 + \log_5 x - \log_5 (y + 2)$ Power property

$\quad = \log_5 36 \cdot x - \log_5 (y + 2)$ Product property

$\quad = \log_5 \dfrac{36x}{y + 2}$ Quotient property

DEFINITIONS AND CONCEPTS	**EXAMPLES**

Section 9.6   Common Logarithms, Natural Logarithms, and Change of Base

COMMON LOGARITHMS

$\log x$ means $\log_{10} x$

NATURAL LOGARITHMS

$\ln x$ means $\log_e x$

CONTINUOUSLY COMPOUNDED INTEREST FORMULA

$A = Pe^{rt}$

where r is the annual interest rate for P dollars invested for t years.

CHANGE OF BASE FORMULA

If $a, b,$ and c are positive real numbers and neither b nor c is 1, then

$$\log_b a = \frac{\log_c a}{\log_c b}$$

$\log 5 = \log_{10} 5 \approx 0.6990$

$\ln 7 = \log_e 7 \approx 1.9459$

Find the amount in an account at the end of 3 years if $1000 is invested at an interest rate of 4% compounded continuously.

Here, $t = 3$ years, $P = \$1000,$ and $r = 0.04.$

$A = Pe^{rt}$

$\quad = 1000e^{0.04(3)}$

$\quad \approx \$1127.50$

Section 9.7   Exponential and Logarithmic Equations and Problem Solving

LOGARITHM PROPERTY OF EQUALITY

Let $\log_b a$ and $\log_b c$ be real numbers and $b \neq 1.$ Then

$\log_b a = \log_b c$ is equivalent to $a = c$

Solve: $2^x = 5$

$\log 2^x = \log 5$ Log property of equality

$x \log 2 = \log 5$ Power property

$x = \dfrac{\log 5}{\log 2}$ Divide both sides by log 2.

$x \approx 2.3219$ Use a calculator.

10

Conic Sections

Taken from:
Intermediate Algebra, Third Edition, by Elayn Martin-Gay

A Graph Parabolas of the Forms
$y = a(x - h)^2 + k$ and
$x = a(y - k)^2 + h$.

B Graph Circles of the Form
$(x - h)^2 + (y - k)^2 = r^2$.

C Write the Equation of a Circle,
Given Its Center and Radius.

D Find the Center and the Radius of
a Circle, Given Its Equation.

10.1 THE PARABOLA AND THE CIRCLE

Conic sections are called such because each conic section is the intersection of a right circular cone and a plane. The circle, parabola, ellipse, and hyperbola are the conic sections.

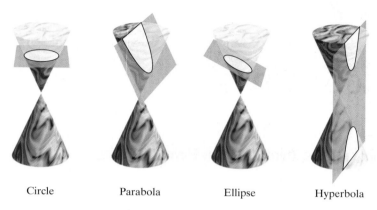

Circle   Parabola   Ellipse   Hyperbola

Objective **A** Graphing Parabolas

Thus far, we have seen that $f(x)$ or $y = a(x - h)^2 + k$ is the equation of a parabola that opens upward if $a > 0$ or downward if $a < 0$. Parabolas can also open left or right, or even on a slant. Equations of these parabolas are not functions of x, of course, since a parabola opening any way other than upward or downward fails the vertical line test. In this section, we introduce parabolas that open to the left and to the right. Parabolas opening on a slant will not be developed in this book.

Just as $y = a(x - h)^2 + k$ is the equation of a parabola that opens upward or downward, $x = a(y - k)^2 + h$ is the equation of a parabola that opens to the right or to the left. The parabola opens to the right if $a > 0$ and to the left if $a < 0$. The parabola has vertex (h, k), and its axis of symmetry is the line $y = k$.

Parabolas

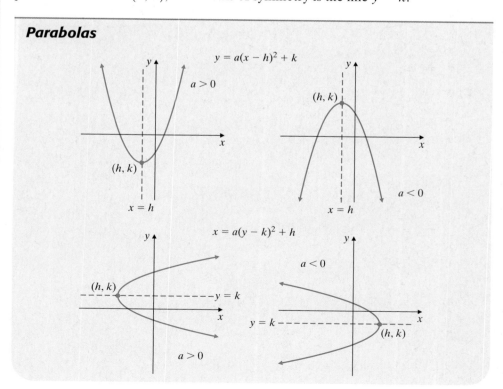

The forms $y = a(x - h)^2 + k$ and $x = a(y - k)^2 + h$ are called **standard forms.**

✔ **Concept Check** Does the graph of the parabola given by the equation $x = -3y^2$ open to the left, to the right, upward, or downward?

EXAMPLE 1 Graph: $x = 2y^2$

Solution: Written in standard form, the equation $x = 2y^2$ is $x = 2(y - 0)^2 + 0$ with $a = 2, h = 0$, and $k = 0$. Its graph is a parabola with vertex $(0, 0)$, and its axis of symmetry is the line $y = 0$. Since $a > 0$, this parabola opens to the right. We use a table to obtain a few more ordered pair solutions to help us graph $x = 2y^2$.

x	y
8	-2
2	-1
0	0
2	1
8	2

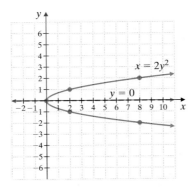

■ **Work Practice Problem 1**

EXAMPLE 2 Graph: $x = -3(y - 1)^2 + 2$

Solution: The equation $x = -3(y - 1)^2 + 2$ is in the form $x = a(y - k)^2 + h$ with $a = -3, k = 1$, and $h = 2$. Since $a < 0$, the parabola opens to the left. The vertex (h, k) is $(2, 1)$, and the axis of symmetry is the horizontal line $y = 1$. When $y = 0$, the x-value is -1, so the x-intercept is $(-1, 0)$.

Again, we use a table to obtain a few ordered pair solutions and then graph the parabola.

x	y
2	1
-1	0
-1	2

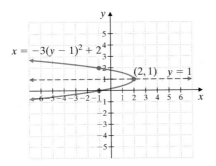

■ **Work Practice Problem 2**

PRACTICE PROBLEM 1

Graph: $x = 4y^2$

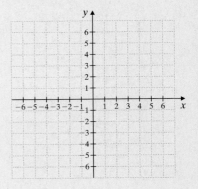

PRACTICE PROBLEM 2

Graph: $x = -2(y - 3)^2 + 1$

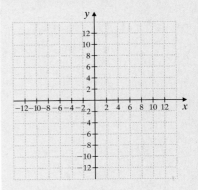

Answers

1.

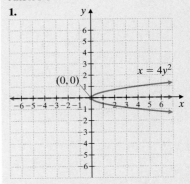

2.

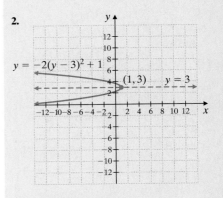

✔ **Concept Check Answer**

to the left

PRACTICE PROBLEM 3

Graph: $y = -x^2 - 4x + 12$

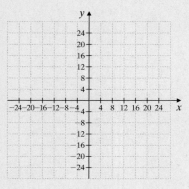

EXAMPLE 3 Graph: $y = -x^2 - 2x + 15$

Solution: Notice that this equation is not written in standard form, $y = a(x - h)^2 + k$. There are two methods that we can use to find the vertex. The first method is completing the square.

$$y - 15 = -x^2 - 2x \qquad \text{Subtract 15 from both sides.}$$

$$y - 15 = -1(x^2 + 2x) \qquad \text{Factor } -1 \text{ from the terms } -x^2 - 2x.$$

The coefficient of x is 2, so we find the square of half of 2.

$$\frac{1}{2}(2) = 1 \quad \text{and} \quad 1^2 = 1$$

$$y - 15 - 1(1) = -1(x^2 + 2x + 1) \qquad \text{Add } -1 \ (1) \text{ to both sides.}$$

$$y - 16 = -1(x + 1)^2 \qquad \text{Simplify the left side, and factor the right side.}$$

$$y = -(x + 1)^2 + 16 \qquad \text{Add 16 to both sides.}$$

The vertex is $(-1, 16)$.

The second method for finding the vertex is by using the expression $\frac{-b}{2a}$. Since the equation is quadratic in x, the expression gives us the x-value of the vertex.

$$x = \frac{-(-2)}{2(-1)} = \frac{2}{-2} = -1$$

To find the corresponding y-value of the vertex, replace x with -1 in the original equation.

$$y = -(-1)^2 - 2(-1) + 15 = -1 + 2 + 15 = 16$$

Again, we see that the vertex is $(-1, 16)$, and the axis of symmetry is the vertical line $x = -1$. The y-intercept is $(0, 15)$. Now we can use a few more ordered pair solutions to graph the parabola.

x	y
−5	0
−3	12
−2	15
−1	16
0	15
1	12
3	0

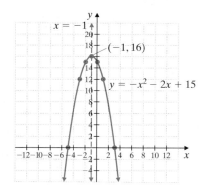

■ **Work Practice Problem 3**

Answer

3.

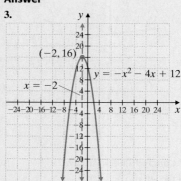

EXAMPLE 4 Graph: $x = 2y^2 + 4y + 5$

Solution: We notice that this equation is quadratic in y so its graph is a parabola that opens to the left or the right. We can complete the square on y or we can use the expression $\dfrac{-b}{2a}$ to find the vertex.

Since the equation is quadratic in y, the expression gives us the y-value of the vertex.

$$y = \frac{-4}{2 \cdot 2} = \frac{-4}{4} = -1$$

$$x = 2(-1)^2 + 4(-1) + 5 = 2 \cdot 1 - 4 + 5 = 3$$

The vertex is $(3, -1)$, and the axis of symmetry is the line $y = -1$. The parabola opens to the right since $a > 0$. The x-intercept is $(5, 0)$.

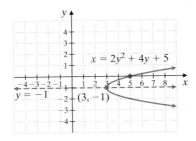

■ **Work Practice Problem 4**

Objective B **Graphing Circles**

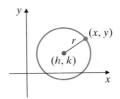

Another conic section is the **circle**. A circle is the set of all points in a plane that are the same distance from a fixed point called the **center**. The distance is called the **radius** of the circle. To find a standard equation for a circle, let (h, k) represent the center of the circle, and let (x, y) represent any point on the circle. The distance between (h, k) and (x, y) is defined to be the radius, r units. We can find this distance r by using the distance formula. (For a review of the distance formula, see Section 7.3.)

$r = \sqrt{(x - h)^2 + (y - k)^2}$ The distance formula.

$r^2 = (x - h)^2 + (y - k)^2$ Square both sides.

Circle

The graph of $(x - h)^2 + (y - k)^2 = r^2$ is a circle with center (h, k) and radius r.

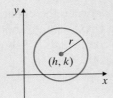

PRACTICE PROBLEM 4

Graph: $x = 3y^2 + 12y + 13$

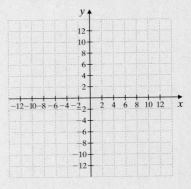

Answer

4.

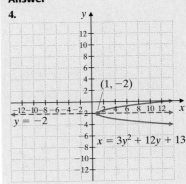

The form $(x - h)^2 + (y - k)^2 = r^2$ is called **standard form.**

If an equation can be written in the standard form

$$(x - h)^2 + (y - k)^2 = r^2$$

then its graph is a circle, which we can draw by graphing the center (h, k) and using the radius r.

Helpful Hint

Notice that the radius is the *distance* from the center of the circle to any point of the circle. Also notice that the *midpoint* of a diameter of a circle is the center of the circle.

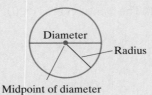

PRACTICE PROBLEM 5

Graph: $x^2 + y^2 = 36$

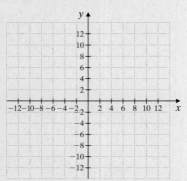

EXAMPLE 5 Graph: $x^2 + y^2 = 4$

Solution: The equation can be written in standard form as

$$(x - 0)^2 + (y - 0)^2 = 2^2$$

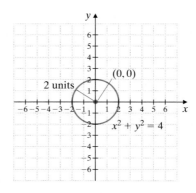

The center of the circle is $(0, 0)$, and the radius is 2. The graph of the circle is shown above.

📖 **Work Practice Problem 5**

Answer

5.

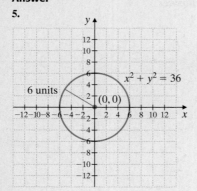

Helpful Hint

Notice the difference between the equation of a circle and the equation of a parabola. The equation of a circle contains both x^2- and y^2-terms on the same side of the equation with equal coefficients. The equation of a parabola has either an x^2-term or a y^2-term but not both.

EXAMPLE 6 Graph: $(x + 1)^2 + y^2 = 8$

Solution: The equation can be written as $(x - (-1))^2 + (y - 0)^2 = 8$ with $h = -1$, $k = 0$, and $r = \sqrt{8}$. The center is $(-1, 0)$, and the radius is $\sqrt{8} = 2\sqrt{2} \approx 2.8$. We use the decimal approximation to approximate the radius when graphing.

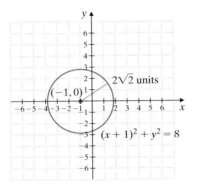

■ **Work Practice Problem 6**

✔**Concept Check** In the graph of the equation $(x - 3)^2 + (y - 2)^2 = 5$, what is the distance between the center of the circle and any point on the circle?

Objective C Writing Equations of Circles

Since a circle is determined entirely by its center and radius, this information is all we need to write the equation of a circle.

EXAMPLE 7 Write an equation of the circle with center $(-7, 3)$ and radius 10.

Solution: Using the given values $h = -7$, $k = 3$, and $r = 10$, we write the equation

$$(x - h)^2 + (y - k)^2 = r^2$$

or

$$(x - (-7))^2 + (y - 3)^2 = 10^2 \qquad \text{Substitute the given values.}$$

or

$$(x + 7)^2 + (y - 3)^2 = 100$$

■ **Work Practice Problem 7**

Objective D Finding the Center and the Radius of a Circle

To find the center and the radius of a circle from its equation, we write the equation in standard form. To write the equation of a circle in standard form, we complete the square on both x and y.

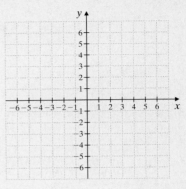
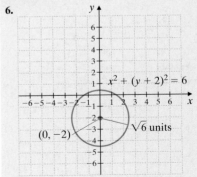

PRACTICE PROBLEM 8

Graph: $x^2 + y^2 - 2x + 6y = 6$

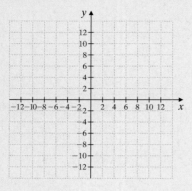

EXAMPLE 8 Graph: $x^2 + y^2 + 4x - 8y = 16$

Solution: Since this equation contains x^2- and y^2-terms on the same side of the equation with equal coefficients, its graph is a circle. To write the equation in standard form, we group the terms involving x and the terms involving y, and then complete the square on each variable.

$$(x^2 + 4x) + (y^2 - 8y) = 16$$

Now, $\frac{1}{2}(4) = 2$ and $2^2 = 4$. Also, $\frac{1}{2}(-8) = -4$ and $(-4)^2 = 16$. We add 4 and then 16 to both sides.

$$(x^2 + 4x + 4) + (y^2 - 8y + 16) = 16 + 4 + 16$$
$$(x + 2)^2 + (y - 4)^2 = 36 \qquad \text{Factor.}$$

This circle has the center $(-2, 4)$ and radius 6, as shown.

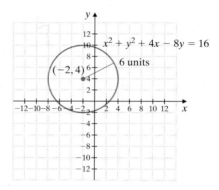

■ **Work Practice Problem 8**

Answer

8.

▨ CALCULATOR EXPLORATIONS Graphing

To graph an equation such as $x^2 + y^2 = 25$ with a graphing calculator, we first solve the equation for y.

$$x^2 + y^2 = 25$$
$$y^2 = 25 - x^2$$
$$y = \pm\sqrt{25 - x^2}$$

The graph of $y = \sqrt{25 - x^2}$ will be the top half of the circle, and the graph of $y = -\sqrt{25 - x^2}$ will be the bottom half of the circle.

To graph, we press ▢ Y= ▢ and enter $Y_1 = \sqrt{25 - x^2}$ and $Y_2 = -\sqrt{25 - x^2}$. We insert parentheses about $25 - x^2$ so that $\sqrt{25 - x^2}$ and not $\sqrt{25} - x^2$ is graphed.

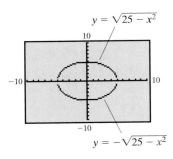

$$y = \sqrt{25 - x^2}$$
$$y = -\sqrt{25 - x^2}$$

The graph does not appear to be a circle because we are currently using a standard window and the screen is rectangular. This causes the tick marks on the x-axis to be farther apart than the tick marks on the y-axis and thus creates the distorted circle. If we want the graph to appear circular, we define a square window by using a feature of the graphing calculator or redefine the window to show the x-axis from -15 to 15 and the y-axis from -10 to 10. Using a square window, the graph appears as follows:

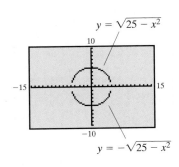

$$y = \sqrt{25 - x^2}$$
$$y = -\sqrt{25 - x^2}$$

Use a graphing calculator to graph each circle.

1. $x^2 + y^2 = 55$

2. $x^2 + y^2 = 20$

3. $7x^2 + 7y^2 - 89 = 0$

4. $3x^2 + 3y^2 - 35 = 0$

Mental Math

The graph of each equation is a parabola. Determine whether the parabola opens upward, downward, to the left, or to the right.

1. $y = x^2 - 7x + 5$

2. $y = -x^2 + 16$

3. $x = -y^2 - y + 2$

4. $x = 3y^2 + 2y - 5$

5. $y = -x^2 + 2x + 1$

6. $x = -y^2 + 2y - 6$

10.1 EXERCISE SET

Objective **A** *The graph of each equation is a parabola. Find the vertex of the parabola and then graph it. See Examples 1 through 4.*

1. $x = 3y^2$

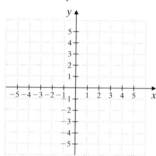

2. $x = 5y^2$

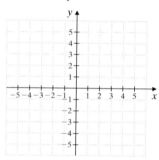

3. $x = -2y^2$

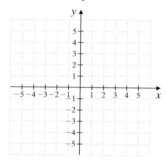

4. $x = -4y^2$

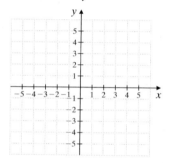

5. $y = -4x^2$

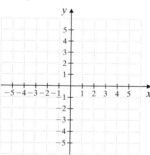

6. $y = -2x^2$

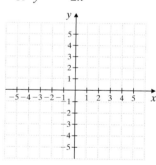

7. $x = (y - 2)^2 + 3$

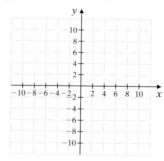

8. $x = (y - 4)^2 - 1$

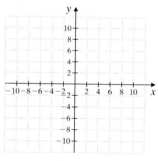

9. $y = -3(x - 1)^2 + 5$

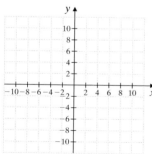

10. $x = -4(y - 2)^2 + 2$

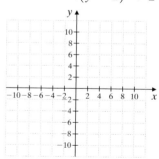

11. $x = y^2 + 6y + 8$

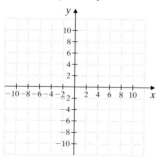

12. $x = y^2 - 6y + 6$

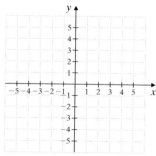

13. $y = x^2 + 10x + 20$

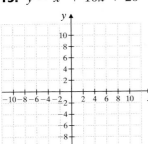

14. $y = x^2 + 4x - 5$

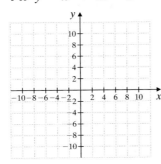

15. $x = -2y^2 + 4y + 6$

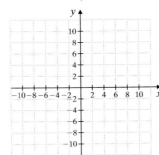

16. $x = 3y^2 + 6y + 7$

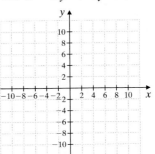

Objectives **B** **D** **Mixed Practice** *The graph of each equation is a circle. Find the center and the radius, and then graph the circle. See Examples 5, 6, and 8.*

17. $x^2 + y^2 = 9$

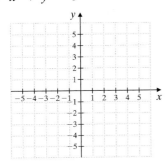

18. $x^2 + y^2 = 25$

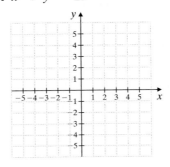

19. $x^2 + (y - 2)^2 = 1$

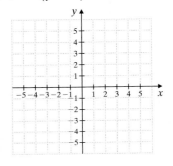

20. $(x - 3)^2 + y^2 = 9$

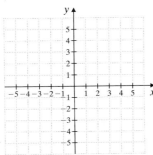

21. $(x - 5)^2 + (y + 2)^2 = 1$

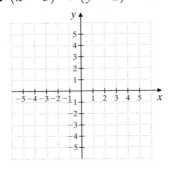

22. $(x + 3)^2 + (y + 3)^2 = 4$

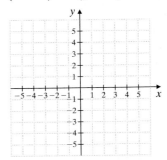

23. $x^2 + y^2 + 6y = 0$

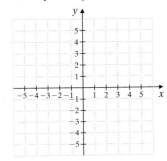

24. $x^2 + 10x + y^2 = 0$

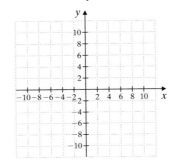

25. $x^2 + y^2 + 2x - 4y = 4$

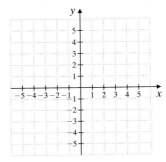

26. $x^2 + y^2 + 6x - 4y = 3$

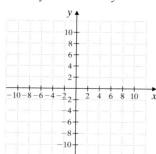

27. $x^2 + y^2 - 4x - 8y - 2 = 0$

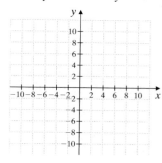

28. $x^2 + y^2 - 2x - 6y - 5 = 0$

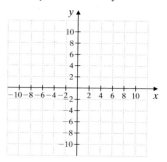

Hint: For Exercises 29 through 32, first divide the equation through by the coefficient of x^2 (or y^2).

29. $3x^2 + 3y^2 = 75$

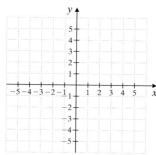

30. $2x^2 + 2y^2 = 18$

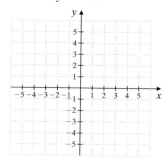

31. $4(x + 1)^2 + 4(y - 3)^2 = 12$

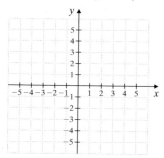

32. $5(x - 2)^2 + 5(y + 1) = 50$

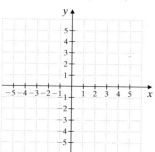

Objective C *Write an equation of the circle with the given center and radius. See Example 7.*

33. $(2, 3); 6$

34. $(-7, 6); 2$

35. $(0, 0); \sqrt{3}$

36. $(0, -6); \sqrt{2}$

37. $(-5, 4); 3\sqrt{5}$

38. The origin; $4\sqrt{7}$

10.2 THE ELLIPSE AND THE HYPERBOLA

Objective **A** Graphing Ellipses

An **ellipse** can be thought of as the set of points in a plane such that the sum of the distances of each of those points from two fixed points is constant. Each of the two fixed points is called a **focus**. The plural of focus is **foci**. The point midway between the foci is called the **center**.

An ellipse may be drawn by hand by using two tacks, a piece of string, and a pencil. Secure the two tacks into a piece of cardboard, for example, and tie each end of the string to a tack. Use your pencil to pull the string tight and draw the ellipse. The two tacks are the foci of the drawn ellipse.

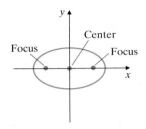

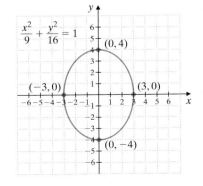

Ellipse with Center (0, 0)

The graph of an equation of the form $\dfrac{x^2}{a^2} + \dfrac{y^2}{b^2} = 1$ is an ellipse with center $(0, 0)$.

The x-intercepts are $(a, 0)$ and $(-a, 0)$ and the y-intercepts are $(0, b)$ and $(0, -b)$.

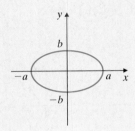

The **standard form** of an ellipse with center $(0, 0)$ is $\dfrac{x^2}{a^2} + \dfrac{y^2}{b^2} = 1$.

EXAMPLE 1 Graph: $\dfrac{x^2}{9} + \dfrac{y^2}{16} = 1$

Solution: The equation is of the form $\dfrac{x^2}{a^2} + \dfrac{y^2}{b^2} = 1$ with $a = 3$ and $b = 4$, so its graph is an ellipse with center $(0, 0)$, x-intercepts $(3, 0)$ and $(-3, 0)$, and y-intercepts $(0, 4)$ and $(0, -4)$.

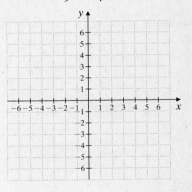

PRACTICE PROBLEM 1

Graph: $\dfrac{x^2}{9} + \dfrac{y^2}{4} = 1$

Answer

1.

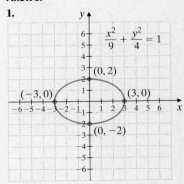

🔲 **Work Practice Problem 1**

PRACTICE PROBLEM 2

Graph: $4x^2 + 36y^2 = 144$

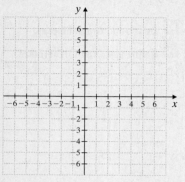

PRACTICE PROBLEM 3

Graph: $\dfrac{(x-1)^2}{9} + \dfrac{(y-3)^2}{16} = 1$

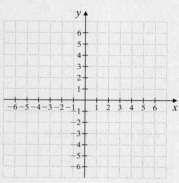

Answers

2.

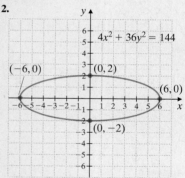

$4x^2 + 36y^2 = 144$

$(-6, 0)$ $(0, 2)$ $(6, 0)$ $(0, -2)$

3. $\dfrac{(x-1)^2}{9} + \dfrac{(y-3)^2}{16} = 1$

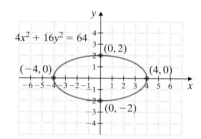

$(1, 3)$ 4 3

EXAMPLE 2 Graph: $4x^2 + 16y^2 = 64$

Solution: Although this equation contains a sum of squared terms in x and y on the same side of an equation, this is not the equation of a circle since the coefficients of x^2 and y^2 are not the same. When this happens, the graph is an ellipse. Since the standard form of the equation of an ellipse has 1 on one side, we divide both sides of this equation by 64 to get it in standard form.

$$4x^2 + 16y^2 = 64$$

$$\frac{4x^2}{64} + \frac{16y^2}{64} = \frac{64}{64} \qquad \text{Divide both sides by 64.}$$

$$\frac{x^2}{16} + \frac{y^2}{4} = 1 \qquad \text{Simplify.}$$

We now recognize the equation of an ellipse with center $(0, 0)$, x-intercepts $(4, 0)$ and $(-4, 0)$, and y-intercepts $(0, 2)$ and $(0, -2)$.

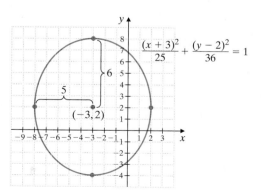

$4x^2 + 16y^2 = 64$ $(0, 2)$ $(-4, 0)$ $(4, 0)$ $(0, -2)$

🔲 **Work Practice Problem 2**

The center of an ellipse is not always $(0, 0)$, as shown in the next example. The standard form of an ellipse with center (h, k) is

$$\frac{(x-h)^2}{a^2} + \frac{(y-k)^2}{b^2} = 1$$

EXAMPLE 3 Graph: $\dfrac{(x+3)^2}{25} + \dfrac{(y-2)^2}{36} = 1$

Solution: This ellipse has center $(-3, 2)$. Notice that $a = 5$ and $b = 6$. To find four points on the graph of the ellipse, we first graph the center, $(-3, 2)$. Since $a = 5$, we count 5 units right and then 5 units left of the point with coordinates $(-3, 2)$. Next, since $b = 6$, we start at $(-3, 2)$ and count 6 units up and then 6 units down to find two more points on the ellipse.

$\dfrac{(x+3)^2}{25} + \dfrac{(y-2)^2}{36} = 1$

6 5 $(-3, 2)$

🔲 **Work Practice Problem 3**

✔ **Concept Check** In the graph of the equation $\dfrac{x^2}{64} + \dfrac{y^2}{36} = 1$, which distance is longer: the distance between the x-intercepts or the distance between the y-intercepts? How much longer? Explain.

Objective B Graphing Hyperbolas

The final conic section is the **hyperbola.** A hyperbola is the set of points in a plane such that for each point in the set, the absolute value of the difference of the distances from two fixed points is constant. Each of the two fixed points is called a **focus.** The point midway between the foci is called the **center.**

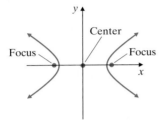

Using the distance formula, we can show that the graph of $\dfrac{x^2}{a^2} - \dfrac{y^2}{b^2} = 1$ is a hyperbola with center $(0, 0)$ and x-intercepts $(a, 0)$ and $(-a, 0)$. Also, the graph of $\dfrac{y^2}{b^2} - \dfrac{x^2}{a^2} = 1$ is a hyperbola with center $(0, 0)$ and y-intercepts $(0, b)$ and $(0, -b)$.

Hyperbola with Center (0, 0)

The graph of an equation of the form $\dfrac{x^2}{a^2} - \dfrac{y^2}{b^2} = 1$ is a hyperbola with center $(0, 0)$ and x-intercepts $(a, 0)$ and $(-a, 0)$.

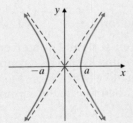

The graph of an equation of the form $\dfrac{y^2}{b^2} - \dfrac{x^2}{a^2} = 1$ is a hyperbola with center $(0, 0)$ and y-intercepts $(0, b)$ and $(0, -b)$.

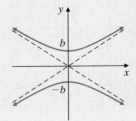

The equations $\dfrac{x^2}{a^2} - \dfrac{y^2}{b^2} = 1$ and $\dfrac{y^2}{b^2} - \dfrac{x^2}{a^2} = 1$ are the **standard forms** for the equation of a hyperbola.

Notice the difference between the equation of an ellipse and a hyperbola. The equation of the ellipse contains x^2- and y^2-terms on the same side of the equation with same-sign coefficients. For a hyperbola, the coefficients on the same side of the equation have different signs.

Graphing a hyperbola such as $\dfrac{y^2}{b^2} - \dfrac{x^2}{a^2} = 1$ is made easier by recognizing one of its important characteristics. Examining the figure below, notice how the sides of the branches of the hyperbola extend indefinitely and seem to approach, but not intersect, the dashed lines in the figure. These dashed lines are called the **asymptotes** of the hyperbola.

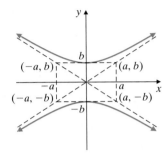

To sketch these lines, or asymptotes, draw a rectangle with vertices (a, b), $(-a, b)$, $(a, -b)$, and $(-a, -b)$. The asymptotes of the hyperbola are the extended diagonals of this rectangle.

PRACTICE PROBLEM 4

Graph: $\dfrac{x^2}{9} - \dfrac{y^2}{4} = 1$

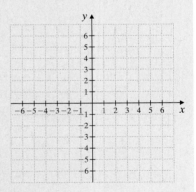

EXAMPLE 4 Graph: $\dfrac{x^2}{16} - \dfrac{y^2}{25} = 1$

Solution: This equation has the form $\dfrac{x^2}{a^2} - \dfrac{y^2}{b^2} = 1$, with $a = 4$ and $b = 5$. Thus, its graph is a hyperbola with center $(0, 0)$ and x-intercepts of $(4, 0)$ and $(-4, 0)$. To aid in graphing the hyperbola, we first sketch its asymptotes. The extended diagonals of the rectangle with coordinates $(4, 5)$, $(4, -5)$, $(-4, 5)$, and $(-4, -5)$ are the asymptotes of the hyperbola. Then we use the asymptotes to aid in graphing the hyperbola.

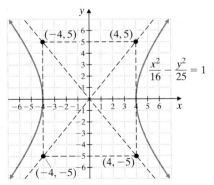

Answer
4.

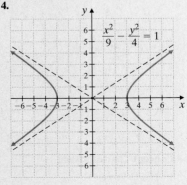

■ **Work Practice Problem 4**

EXAMPLE 5 Graph: $4y^2 - 9x^2 = 36$

Solution: Since this is a difference of squared terms in x and y on the same side of the equation, its graph is a hyperbola, as opposed to an ellipse or a circle. The standard form of the equation of a hyperbola has a 1 on one side, so we divide both sides of the equation by 36 to get it in standard form.

$$4y^2 - 9x^2 = 36$$

$$\frac{4y^2}{36} - \frac{9x^2}{36} = \frac{36}{36} \quad \text{Divide both sides by 36.}$$

$$\frac{y^2}{9} - \frac{x^2}{4} = 1 \quad \text{Simplify.}$$

The equation is of the form $\frac{y^2}{b^2} - \frac{x^2}{a^2} = 1$ with $a = 2$ and $b = 3$, so the hyperbola is centered at $(0, 0)$ with y-intercepts $(0, 3)$ and $(0, -3)$.

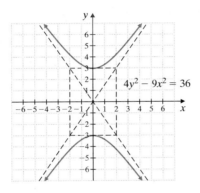

■ **Work Practice Problem 5**

PRACTICE PROBLEM 5

Graph: $9y^2 - 16x^2 = 144$

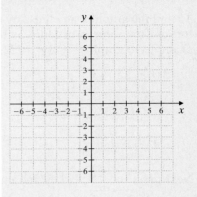

Answer

5.

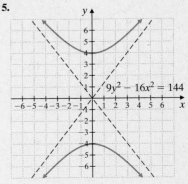

CALCULATOR EXPLORATIONS Graphing

To find the graph of an ellipse by using a graphing calculator, use the same procedure as for graphing a circle. For example, to graph $x^2 + 3y^2 = 22$, first solve for y.

$$3y^2 = 22 - x^2$$

$$y^2 = \frac{22 - x^2}{3}$$

$$y = \pm\sqrt{\frac{22 - x^2}{3}}$$

Next press the $\boxed{Y=}$ key and enter $Y_1 = \sqrt{\dfrac{22 - x^2}{3}}$ and $Y_2 = -\sqrt{\dfrac{22 - x^2}{3}}$. (Insert two sets of parentheses in the radicand as in $\sqrt{((22 - x^2)/3)}$ so that the desired graph is obtained.) The graph appears as follows:

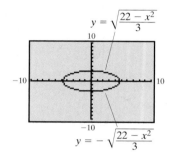

$$y = \sqrt{\frac{22 - x^2}{3}}$$

$$y = -\sqrt{\frac{22 - x^2}{3}}$$

Use a graphing calculator to graph each ellipse.

1. $10x^2 + y^2 = 32$

2. $20x^2 + 5y^2 = 100$

3. $7.3x^2 + 15.5y^2 = 95.2$

4. $18.8x^2 + 36.1y^2 = 205.8$

Mental Math

Identify the graph of each equation as an ellipse or a hyperbola.

1. $\dfrac{x^2}{16} + \dfrac{y^2}{4} = 1$

2. $\dfrac{x^2}{16} - \dfrac{y^2}{4} = 1$

3. $x^2 - 5y^2 = 3$

4. $-x^2 + 5y^2 = 3$

5. $-\dfrac{y^2}{25} + \dfrac{x^2}{36} = 1$

6. $\dfrac{y^2}{25} + \dfrac{x^2}{36} = 1$

10.2 EXERCISE SET

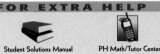

Objective Ⓐ *Graph each ellipse. See Examples 1 and 2.*

1. $\dfrac{x^2}{4} + \dfrac{y^2}{25} = 1$

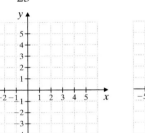

2. $\dfrac{x^2}{16} + \dfrac{y^2}{9} = 1$

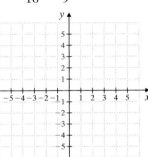

3. $\dfrac{x^2}{9} + y^2 = 1$

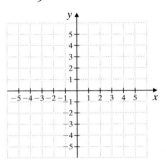

4. $x^2 + \dfrac{y^2}{4} = 1$

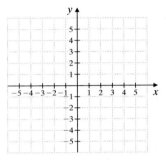

5. $9x^2 + 4y^2 = 36$

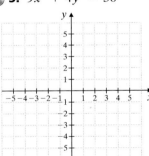

6. $x^2 + 4y^2 = 16$

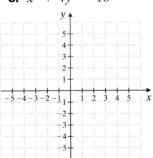

7. $4x^2 + 25y^2 = 100$

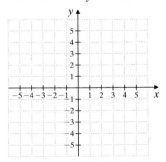

8. $36x^2 + y^2 = 36$

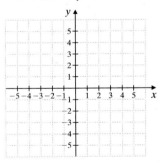

Graph each ellipse. See Example 3.

9. $\dfrac{(x+1)^2}{36} + \dfrac{(y-2)^2}{49} = 1$

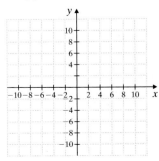

10. $\dfrac{(x-3)^2}{9} + \dfrac{(y+3)^2}{16} = 1$

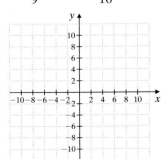

11. $\dfrac{(x-1)^2}{4} + \dfrac{(y-1)^2}{25} = 1$

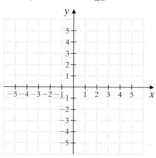

12. $\dfrac{(x+3)^2}{16} + \dfrac{(y+2)^2}{4} = 1$

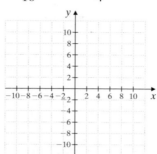

Objective **B** *Graph each hyperbola. See Examples 4 and 5.*

13. $\dfrac{x^2}{4} - \dfrac{y^2}{9} = 1$

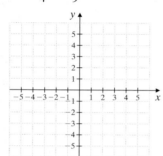

14. $\dfrac{x^2}{36} - \dfrac{y^2}{36} = 1$

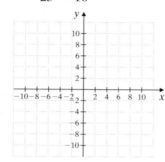

15. $\dfrac{y^2}{25} - \dfrac{x^2}{16} = 1$

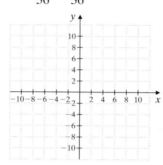

16. $\dfrac{y^2}{25} - \dfrac{x^2}{49} = 1$

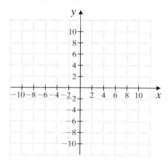

17. $x^2 - 4y^2 = 16$

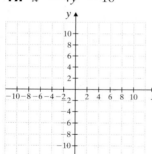

18. $4x^2 - y^2 = 36$

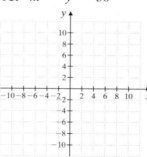

19. $16y^2 - x^2 = 16$

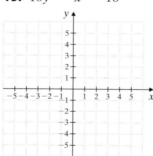

20. $4y^2 - 25x^2 = 100$

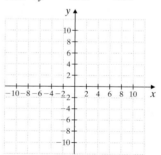

Objectives **A** **B** **Mixed Practice** *Graph each equation. See Examples 1 through 5.*

21. $\dfrac{y^2}{36} = 1 - x^2$

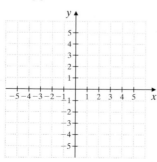

22. $\dfrac{x^2}{36} = 1 - y^2$

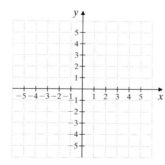

23. $4(x-1)^2 + 9(y+2)^2 = 36$

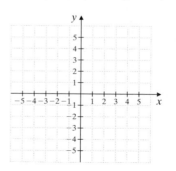

24. $25(x + 3)^2 + 4(y - 3)^2 = 100$ **25.** $8x^2 + 2y^2 = 32$ **26.** $3x^2 + 12y^2 = 48$

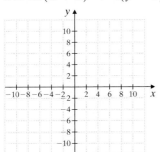   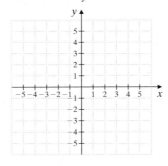   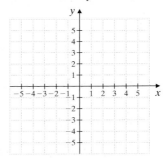

27. $25x^2 - y^2 = 25$ **28.** $x^2 - 9y^2 = 9$

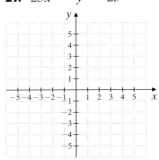   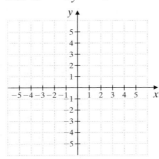

Review

Perform each indicated operation. See Sections 5.1 and 5.2.

29. $(2x^3)(-4x^2)$ **30.** $2x^3 - 4x^3$ **31.** $-5x^2 + x^2$ **32.** $(-5x^2)(x^2)$

Concept Extensions

The graph of each equation is an ellipse. Determine which distance is longer. The distance between the x-intercepts or the distance between the y-intercepts. How much longer? See the Concept Check in this section.

33. $\dfrac{x^2}{16} + \dfrac{y^2}{25} = 1$ **34.** $\dfrac{x^2}{100} + \dfrac{y^2}{49} = 1$ **35.** $4x^2 + y^2 = 16$ **36.** $x^2 + 4y^2 = 36$

37. We know that $x^2 + y^2 = 25$ is the equation of a circle. Rewrite the equation so that the right side is equal to 1. Which type of conic section does this equation form resemble? In fact, the circle is a special case of this type of conic section. Describe the conditions under which this type of conic section is a circle.

The orbits of stars, planets, comets, asteroids, and satellites all have the shape of one of the conic sections. Astronomers use a measure called eccentricity *to describe the shape and elongation of an orbital path. For the circle and ellipse, eccentricity e is calculated with the formula* $e = \dfrac{c}{d}$, *where* $c^2 = |a^2 - b^2|$ *and d is the larger value of a or b. For a hyperbola, eccentricity e is calculated with the formula* $e = \dfrac{c}{d}$, *where* $c^2 = a^2 + b^2$ *and the value of d is equal to a if the hyperbola has x-intercepts or equal to b if the hyperbola has y-intercepts. Use equations A–H to answer Exercises 38–47.*

A. $\dfrac{x^2}{36} - \dfrac{y^2}{13} = 1$ **B.** $\dfrac{x^2}{4} + \dfrac{y^2}{4} = 1$ **C.** $\dfrac{x^2}{25} + \dfrac{y^2}{16} = 1$ **D.** $\dfrac{y^2}{25} - \dfrac{x^2}{39} = 1$

Chapter 10 Vocabulary Check

Fill in each blank with one of the words or phrases listed below.

circle	ellipse	hyperbola
center	radius	nonlinear system of equations

1. A(n) _____ is the set of all points in a plane that are the same distance from a fixed point, called the _____.

2. A _____ is a system of equations at least one of which is not linear.

3. A(n) _____ is the set of points on a plane such that the sum of the distances of those points from two fixed points is a constant.

4. In a circle, the distance from the center to a point of the circle is called its _____.

5. A(n) _____ is the set of points in a plane such that the absolute value of the difference of the distance from two fixed points is constant.

> **Helpful Hint**
>
> Are you preparing for your test? Don't forget to take the Chapter 10 Test on page 760. Then check your answers at the back of the text and use the Chapter Test Prep Video CD to see the fully worked-out solutions to any of the exercises you want to review.

10 Chapter Highlights

DEFINITIONS AND CONCEPTS	**EXAMPLES**

Section 10.1   The Parabola and the Circle

PARABOLAS

$$y = a(x - h)^2 + k$$

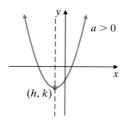
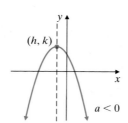

$$x = a(y - k)^2 + h$$

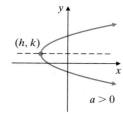
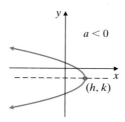

Graph: $x = 3y^2 - 12y + 13$

$$x - 13 = 3(y^2 - 4y)$$
$$x - 13 + 3(4) = 3(y^2 - 4y + 4)$$
$$x = 3(y - 2)^2 + 1$$

Since $a = 3$, this parabola opens to the right with vertex $(1, 2)$. Its axis of symmetry is $y = 2$. The x-intercept is $(13, 0)$.

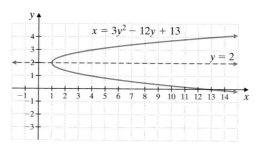

DEFINITIONS AND CONCEPTS	**EXAMPLES**

Section 10.1   The Parabola and the Circle (continued)

CIRCLE

The graph $(x - h)^2 + (y - k)^2 = r^2$ is a circle with center (h, k) and radius r.

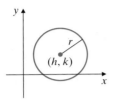

Graph: $x^2 + (y + 3)^2 = 5$

This equation can be written as

$$(x - 0)^2 + (y + 3)^2 = 5$$

with $h = 0$, $k = -3$, and $r = \sqrt{5}$. The center of this circle is $(0, -3)$, and the radius is $\sqrt{5}$.

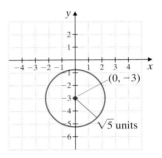

Section 10.2   The Ellipse and the Hyperbola

ELLIPSE WITH CENTER (0, 0)

The graph of an equation of the form $\dfrac{x^2}{a^2} + \dfrac{y^2}{b^2} = 1$ is an ellipse with center $(0, 0)$. The x-intercepts are $(a, 0)$ and $(-a, 0)$, and the y-intercepts are $(0, b)$ and $(0, -b)$.

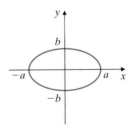

Graph: $4x^2 + 9y^2 = 36$

$$\frac{x^2}{9} + \frac{y^2}{4} = 1 \qquad \text{Divide both sides by 36.}$$

$$\frac{x^2}{3^2} + \frac{y^2}{2^2} = 1$$

The ellipse has center $(0, 0)$, x-intercepts $(3, 0)$ and $(-3, 0)$, and y-intercepts $(0, 2)$ and $(0, -2)$.

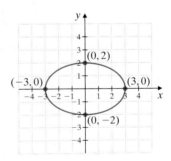

continued

DEFINITIONS AND CONCEPTS	EXAMPLES

Section 10.2 The Ellipse and the Hyperbola *(continued)*

HYPERBOLA WITH CENTER (0, 0)

The graph of an equation of the form $\dfrac{x^2}{a^2} - \dfrac{y^2}{b^2} = 1$ is a hyperbola with center $(0, 0)$ and x-intercepts $(a, 0)$ and $(-a, 0)$.

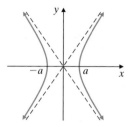

The graph of an equation of the form $\dfrac{y^2}{b^2} - \dfrac{x^2}{a^2} = 1$ is a hyperbola with center $(0, 0)$ and y-intercepts $(0, b)$ and $(0, -b)$.

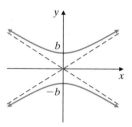

Graph: $\dfrac{x^2}{9} - \dfrac{y^2}{4} = 1$. Here $a = 3$ and $b = 2$.

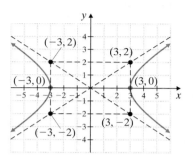

Section 10.3 Solving Nonlinear Systems of Equations

A **nonlinear system of equations** is a system of equations at least one of which is not linear. Both the substitution method and the elimination method may be used to solve a nonlinear system of equations.

Solve the nonlinear system: $\begin{cases} y = x + 2 \\ 2x^2 + y^2 = 3 \end{cases}$

Substitute $x + 2$ for y in the second equation:

$$2x^2 + y^2 = 3$$
$$2x^2 + (x + 2)^2 = 3$$
$$2x^2 + x^2 + 4x + 4 = 3$$
$$3x^2 + 4x + 1 = 0$$
$$(3x + 1)(x + 1) = 0$$
$$x = -\frac{1}{3} \quad \text{or} \quad x = -1$$

If $x = -\dfrac{1}{3}$, $y = x + 2 = -\dfrac{1}{3} + 2 = \dfrac{5}{3}$.

If $x = -1$, $y = x + 2 = -1 + 2 = 1$.

The solution set is $\left\{ \left(-\dfrac{1}{3}, \dfrac{5}{3} \right), (-1, 1) \right\}$

4

Trigonometric Functions

Taken from:
Precalculus, Third Edition, by Robert Blitzer

Trigonometric Functions

HAVE YOU HAD DAYS WHERE *your physical, intellectual, and emotional potentials were all at their peak? Then there are those other days when we feel we should not even bother getting out of bed. Do our potentials run in oscillating cycles like the tides? Can they be described mathematically? In this chapter, you will encounter functions that enable us to model phenomena that occur in cycles.*

WHAT A DAY! IT STARTED WHEN YOU added two miles to your morning run. You've experienced a feeling of peak physical well-being ever since. College was wonderful: You actually enjoyed two difficult lectures and breezed through a math test that had you worried. Now you're having dinner with a group of old friends. You experience the warmth from bonds of friendship filling the room.

Graphs of functions showing a person's *biorhythms*, the physical, intellectual, and emotional cycles we experience in life, are presented in Exercises 75–82 of Exercise Set 4.5.

SECTION 4.1 *Angles and Radian Measure*

Objectives

❶ Recognize and use the vocabulary of angles.

❷ Use degree measure.

❸ Use radian measure.

❹ Convert between degrees and radians.

❺ Draw angles in standard position.

❻ Find coterminal angles.

❼ Find the length of a circular arc.

❽ Use linear and angular speed to describe motion on a circular path.

The San Francisco Museum of Modern Art was constructed in 1995 to illustrate how art and architecture can enrich one another. The exterior involves geometric shapes, symmetry, and unusual facades. Although there are no windows, natural light streams in through a truncated cylindrical skylight that crowns the building. The architect worked with a scale model of the museum at the site and observed how light hit it during different times of the day. These observations were used to cut the cylindrical skylight at an angle that maximizes sunlight entering the interior.

Angles play a critical role in creating modern architecture. They are also fundamental in trigonometry. In this section, we begin our study of trigonometry by looking at angles and methods for measuring them.

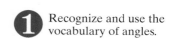

❶ Recognize and use the vocabulary of angles.

Figure 4.1 Clock with hands forming an angle

Angles

The hour hand of a clock suggests a **ray**, a part of a line that has only one endpoint and extends forever in the opposite direction. An **angle** is formed by two rays that have a common endpoint. One ray is called the **initial side** and the other the **terminal side**.

A rotating ray is often a useful way to think about angles. The ray in Figure 4.1 rotates from 12 to 2. The ray pointing to 12 is the **initial side** and the ray pointing to 2 is the **terminal side**. The common endpoint of an angle's initial side and terminal side is the **vertex** of the angle.

Figure 4.2 shows an angle. The arrow near the vertex shows the direction and the amount of rotation from the initial side to the terminal side. Several methods can be used to name an angle. Lowercase Greek letters, such as α (alpha), β (beta), γ (gamma), and θ (theta), are often used.

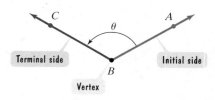

Figure 4.2 An angle; two rays with a common endpoint

An angle is in **standard position** if

• its vertex is at the origin of a rectangular coordinate system and

• its initial side lies along the positive x-axis.

The angles in Figure 4.3 at the top of the next page are both in standard position.

When we see an initial side and a terminal side in place, there are two kinds of rotation that could have generated the angle. The arrow in Figure 4.3(a) indicates that the rotation from the initial side to the terminal side is in the counterclockwise

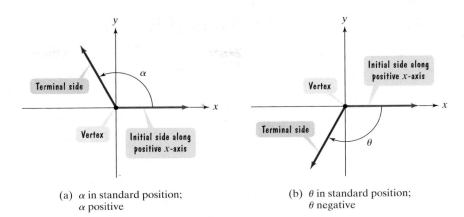

(a) α in standard position;
α positive

(b) θ in standard position;
θ negative

Figure 4.3 Two angles in standard position

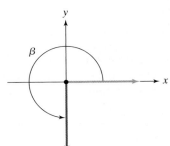

Figure 4.4 β is a quadrantal angle.

2 Use degree measure.

A complete 360° rotation

direction. **Positive angles** are generated by counterclockwise rotation. Thus, angle α is positive. By contrast, the arrow in Figure 4.3(b) shows that the rotation from the initial side to the terminal side is in the clockwise direction. **Negative angles** are generated by clockwise rotation. Thus, angle θ is negative.

When an angle is in standard position, its terminal side can lie in a quadrant. We say that the angle **lies in that quadrant**. For example, in Figure 4.3(a), the terminal side of angle α lies in quadrant II. Thus, angle α lies in quadrant II. By contrast, in Figure 4.3(b), the terminal side of angle θ lies in quadrant III. Thus, angle θ lies in quadrant III.

Must all angles in standard position lie in a quadrant? The answer is no. The terminal side can lie on the x-axis or the y-axis. For example, angle β in Figure 4.4 has a terminal side that lies on the negative y-axis. An angle is called a **quadrantal angle** if its terminal side lies on the x-axis or the y-axis. Angle β in Figure 4.4 is an example of a quadrantal angle.

Measuring Angles Using Degrees

Angles are measured by determining the amount of rotation from the initial side to the terminal side. One way to measure angles is in **degrees**, symbolized by a small, raised circle °. Think of the hour hand of a clock. From 12 noon to 12 midnight, the hour hand moves around in a complete circle. By definition, the ray has rotated through 360 degrees, or 360°. Using 360° as the amount of rotation of a ray back onto itself, a degree, 1°, is $\frac{1}{360}$ of a complete rotation.

Figure 4.5 shows that certain angles have special names. An **acute angle** measures less than 90° [see Figure 4.5(a)]. A **right angle**, one quarter of a complete rotation, measures 90° [Figure 4.5(b)]. Examine the right angle—do you see a small square at the vertex? This symbol is used to indicate a right angle. An **obtuse angle** measures more than 90°, but less than 180° [Figure 4.5(c)]. Finally, a **straight angle**, one-half a complete rotation, measures 180° [Figure 4.5(d)].

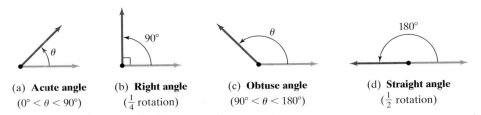

(a) **Acute angle**
$(0° < θ < 90°)$

(b) **Right angle**
($\frac{1}{4}$ rotation)

(c) **Obtuse angle**
$(90° < θ < 180°)$

(d) **Straight angle**
($\frac{1}{2}$ rotation)

Figure 4.5 Classifying angles by their degree measurement

We will be using notation such as $θ = 60°$ to refer to an angle θ whose measure is 60°. We also refer to *an angle of* 60° or a 60° *angle*, rather than using the more precise (but cumbersome) phrase *an angle whose measure is* 60°.

Technology

Fractional parts of degrees are measured in minutes and seconds. One minute, written $1'$, is $\frac{1}{60}$ degree: $1' = \frac{1}{60}°$.

One second, written $1''$, is $\frac{1}{3600}$ degree: $1'' = \frac{1}{3600}°$.

For example,

$$31°47'12''$$

$$= \left(31 + \frac{47}{60} + \frac{12}{3600}\right)°$$

$$\approx 31.787°.$$

Many calculators have keys for changing an angle from degree-minute-second notation ($D°M'S''$) to a decimal form and vice versa.

③ Use radian measure.

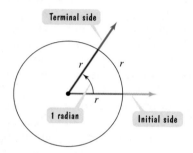

Figure 4.6 For a 1-radian angle, the intercepted arc and the radius are equal.

Measuring Angles Using Radians

Another way to measure angles is in *radians*. Let's first define an angle measuring **1 radian**. We use a circle of radius r. In Figure 4.6, we've constructed an angle whose vertex is at the center of the circle. Such an angle is called a **central angle**. Notice that this central angle intercepts an arc along the circle measuring r units. The radius of the circle is also r units. The measure of such an angle is 1 radian.

> ### Definition of a Radian
>
> **One radian** is the measure of the central angle of a circle that intercepts an arc equal in length to the radius of the circle.

The **radian measure** of any central angle is the length of the intercepted arc divided by the circle's radius. In Figure 4.7(a), the length of the arc intercepted by angle β is double the radius, r. We find the measure of angle β in radians by dividing the length of the intercepted arc by the radius.

$$\beta = \frac{\text{length of the intercepted arc}}{\text{radius}} = \frac{2r}{r} = 2$$

Thus, angle β measures 2 radians.

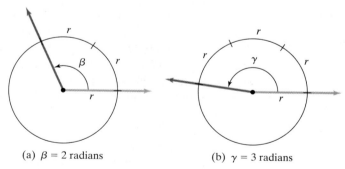

(a) $\beta = 2$ radians   (b) $\gamma = 3$ radians

Figure 4.7 Two central angles measured in radians

In Figure 4.7(b), the length of the intercepted arc is triple the radius, r. Let us find the measure of angle γ:

$$\gamma = \frac{\text{length of the intercepted arc}}{\text{radius}} = \frac{3r}{r} = 3.$$

Thus, angle γ measures 3 radians.

Radian Measure

Consider an arc of length s on a circle of radius r. The measure of the central angle, θ, that intercepts the arc is

$$\theta = \frac{s}{r} \text{ radians.}$$

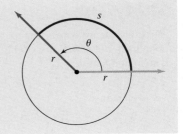

EXAMPLE 1   Computing Radian Measure

A central angle, θ, in a circle of radius 6 inches intercepts an arc of length 15 inches. What is the radian measure of θ?

Solution   Angle θ is shown in Figure 4.8. The radian measure of a central angle is the length of the intercepted arc, s, divided by the circle's radius, r. The length of the intercepted arc is 15 inches: $s = 15$ inches. The circle's radius is 6 inches: $r = 6$ inches. Now we use the formula for radian measure to find the radian measure of θ.

$$\theta = \frac{s}{r} = \frac{15 \; \cancel{\text{inches}}}{6 \; \cancel{\text{inches}}} = 2.5$$

Thus, the radian measure of θ is 2.5.

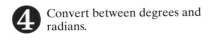

Figure 4.8

Study Tip

Before applying the formula for radian measure, be sure that the same unit of length is used for the intercepted arc, s, and the radius, r.

In Example 1, notice that the units (inches) cancel when we use the formula for radian measure. We are left with a number with no units. Thus, if an angle θ has a measure of 2.5 radians, we can write $\theta = 2.5$ radians or $\theta = 2.5$. We will often include the word *radians* simply for emphasis. There should be no confusion as to whether radian or degree measure is being used. Why is this so? If θ has a degree measure of, say, 2.5°, we must include the degree symbol and write $\theta = 2.5°$, and *not* $\theta = 2.5$.

Check Point 1   A central angle, θ, in a circle of radius 12 feet intercepts an arc of length 42 feet. What is the radian measure of θ?

④ Convert between degrees and radians.

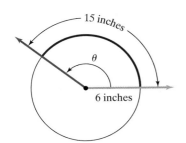

Figure 4.9 A complete rotation

Relationship between Degrees and Radians

How can we obtain a relationship between degrees and radians? We compare the number of degrees and the number of radians in one complete rotation, shown in Figure 4.9. We know that 360° is the amount of rotation of a ray back onto itself. The length of the intercepted arc is equal to the circumference of the circle. Thus, the radian measure of this central angle is the circumference of the circle divided by the circle's radius, r. The circumference of a circle of radius r is $2\pi r$. We use the formula for radian measure to find the radian measure of the 360° angle.

$$\theta = \frac{s}{r} = \frac{\text{the circle's circumference}}{r} = \frac{2\pi \cancel{r}}{\cancel{r}} = 2\pi$$

Because one complete rotation measures 360° and 2π radians,

$$360° = 2\pi \text{ radians.}$$

Dividing both sides by 2, we have

$$180° = \pi \text{ radians.}$$

Dividing this last equation by 180° or π gives the conversion rules in the box on the next page.

Study Tip

The unit you are converting *to* appears in the *numerator* of the conversion factor.

Conversion between Degrees and Radians

Using the basic relationship π radians $= 180°$,

1. To convert degrees to radians, multiply degrees by $\dfrac{\pi \text{ radians}}{180°}$.

2. To convert radians to degrees, multiply radians by $\dfrac{180°}{\pi \text{ radians}}$.

Angles that are fractions of a complete rotation are usually expressed in radian measure as fractional multiples of π, rather than as decimal approximations. For example, we write $\theta = \dfrac{\pi}{2}$ rather than using the decimal approximation $\theta \approx 1.57$.

EXAMPLE 2   Converting from Degrees to Radians

Convert each angle in degrees to radians:

    a. $30°$ **b.** $90°$ **c.** $-135°$.

Solution   To convert degrees to radians, multiply by $\dfrac{\pi \text{ radians}}{180°}$. Observe how the degree units cancel.

  a. $30° = 30° \cdot \dfrac{\pi \text{ radians}}{180°} = \dfrac{30\pi}{180} \text{ radians} = \dfrac{\pi}{6} \text{ radians}$

  b. $90° = 90° \cdot \dfrac{\pi \text{ radians}}{180°} = \dfrac{90\pi}{180} \text{ radians} = \dfrac{\pi}{2} \text{ radians}$

  c. $-135° = -135° \cdot \dfrac{\pi \text{ radians}}{180°} = -\dfrac{135\pi}{180} \text{ radians} = -\dfrac{3\pi}{4} \text{ radians}$

> Divide the numerator and denominator by 45.

Check Point 2   Convert each angle in degrees to radians:

    a. $60°$ **b.** $270°$ **c.** $-300°$.

EXAMPLE 3   Converting from Radians to Degrees

Convert each angle in radians to degrees:

    a. $\dfrac{\pi}{3}$ radians   **b.** $-\dfrac{5\pi}{3}$ radians   **c.** 1 radian.

Solution   To convert radians to degrees, multiply by $\dfrac{180°}{\pi \text{ radians}}$. Observe how the radian units cancel.

  a. $\dfrac{\pi}{3} \text{ radians} = \dfrac{\pi \text{ radians}}{3} \cdot \dfrac{180°}{\pi \text{ radians}} = \dfrac{180°}{3} = 60°$

  b. $-\dfrac{5\pi}{3} \text{ radians} = -\dfrac{5\pi \text{ radians}}{3} \cdot \dfrac{180°}{\pi \text{ radians}} = -\dfrac{5 \cdot 180°}{3} = -300°$

  c. $1 \text{ radian} = 1 \text{ radian} \cdot \dfrac{180°}{\pi \text{ radians}} = \dfrac{180°}{\pi} \approx 57.3°$

Study Tip

In Example 3(c), we see that 1 radian is approximately 57°. Keep in mind that a radian is much larger than a degree.

Check Point 3   Convert each angle in radians to degrees:

    a. $\dfrac{\pi}{4}$ radians   **b.** $-\dfrac{4\pi}{3}$ radians   **c.** 6 radians.

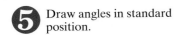

Draw angles in standard position.

Drawing Angles in Standard Position

Although we can convert angles in radians to degrees, it is helpful to "think in radians" without having to make this conversion. To become comfortable with radian measure, consider angles in standard position: Each vertex is at the origin and each initial side lies along the positive *x*-axis. Think of the terminal side of the angle revolving around the origin. Thinking in radians means determining what part of a complete revolution or how many full revolutions will produce an angle whose radian measure is known. And here's the thing: We want to do this without having to convert from radians to degrees.

Figure 4.10 is a starting point for learning to think in radians. The figure illustrates that when the terminal side makes one full revolution, it forms an angle whose radian measure is 2π. The figure shows the quadrantal angles formed by $\frac{3}{4}$ of a revolution, $\frac{1}{2}$ of a revolution, and $\frac{1}{4}$ of a revolution.

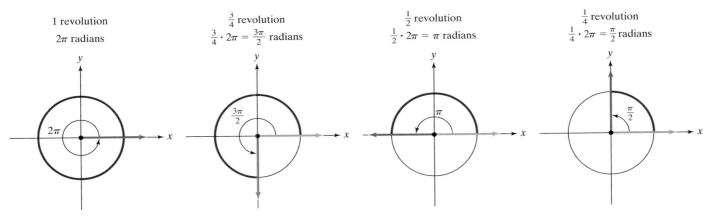

Figure 4.10 Angles formed by revolutions of terminal sides

EXAMPLE 4   Drawing Angles in Standard Position

Draw and label each angle in standard position:

a. $\theta = \dfrac{\pi}{4}$ **b.** $\alpha = \dfrac{5\pi}{4}$ **c.** $\beta = -\dfrac{3\pi}{4}$ **d.** $\gamma = \dfrac{9\pi}{4}$.

theta   alpha   beta   gamma

Solution   Because we are drawing angles in standard position, each vertex is at the origin and each initial side lies along the positive *x*-axis.

a. An angle of $\dfrac{\pi}{4}$ radians is a positive angle. It is obtained by rotating the terminal side counterclockwise. Because 2π is a full-circle revolution, we can express $\dfrac{\pi}{4}$ as a fractional part of 2π to determine the necessary rotation:

$$\frac{\pi}{4} = \frac{1}{8} \cdot 2\pi$$

$\dfrac{\pi}{4}$ is $\dfrac{1}{8}$ of a complete revolution of 2π radians.

We see that $\theta = \dfrac{\pi}{4}$ is obtained by rotating the terminal side counterclockwise for $\dfrac{1}{8}$ of a revolution. The angle lies in quadrant I and is shown in Figure 4.11.

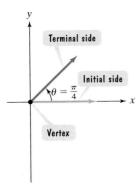

Figure 4.11

b. An angle of $\frac{5\pi}{4}$ radians is a positive angle. It is obtained by rotating the terminal side counterclockwise. Here are two ways to determine the necessary rotation:

Method 1

$$\frac{5\pi}{4} = \frac{5}{8} \cdot 2\pi$$

$\frac{5\pi}{4}$ is $\frac{5}{8}$ of a complete revolution of 2π radians.

Method 2

$$\frac{5\pi}{4} = \pi + \frac{\pi}{4}.$$

π is a half-circle revolution.

$\frac{\pi}{4}$ is $\frac{1}{8}$ of a complete revolution.

Method 1 shows that $\alpha = \frac{5\pi}{4}$ is obtained by rotating the terminal side counterclockwise for $\frac{5}{8}$ of a revolution. Method 2 shows that $\alpha = \frac{5\pi}{4}$ is obtained by rotating the terminal side counterclockwise for half of a revolution followed by a counterclockwise rotation of $\frac{1}{4}$ of a revolution. The angle lies in quadrant III and is shown in Figure 4.12.

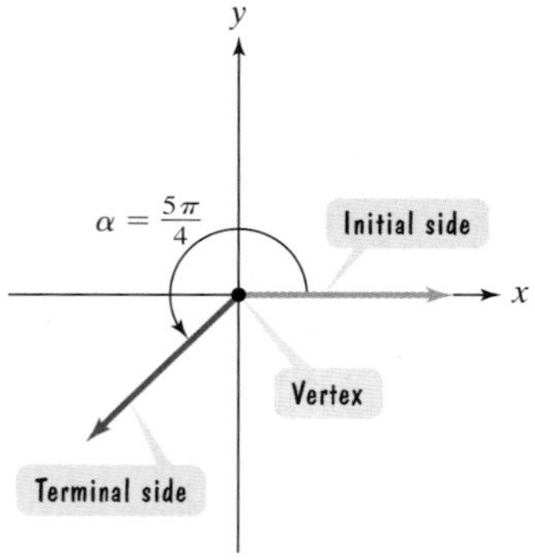
y
$\alpha = \frac{5\pi}{4}$
Initial side
x
Vertex
Terminal side

Figure 4.12

c. An angle of $-\frac{3\pi}{4}$ is a negative angle. It is obtained by rotating the terminal side clockwise. We use $\left|-\frac{3\pi}{4}\right|$, or $\frac{3\pi}{4}$, to determine the necessary rotation.

Method 1

$$\frac{3\pi}{4} = \frac{3}{8} \cdot 2\pi$$

$\frac{3\pi}{4}$ is $\frac{3}{8}$ of a complete revolution of 2π radians.

Method 2

$$\frac{3\pi}{4} = \frac{2\pi}{4} + \frac{\pi}{4} = \frac{\pi}{2} + \frac{\pi}{4}$$

$\frac{\pi}{2}$ is a quarter-circle revolution.

$\frac{\pi}{4}$ is $\frac{1}{8}$ of a complete revolution.

Method 1 shows that $\beta = -\frac{3\pi}{4}$ is obtained by rotating the terminal side clockwise for $\frac{3}{8}$ of a revolution. Method 2 shows that $\beta = -\frac{3\pi}{4}$ is obtained by rotating the terminal side clockwise for $\frac{1}{4}$ of a revolution followed by a clockwise rotation of $\frac{1}{8}$ of a revolution. The angle lies in quadrant III and is shown in Figure 4.13.

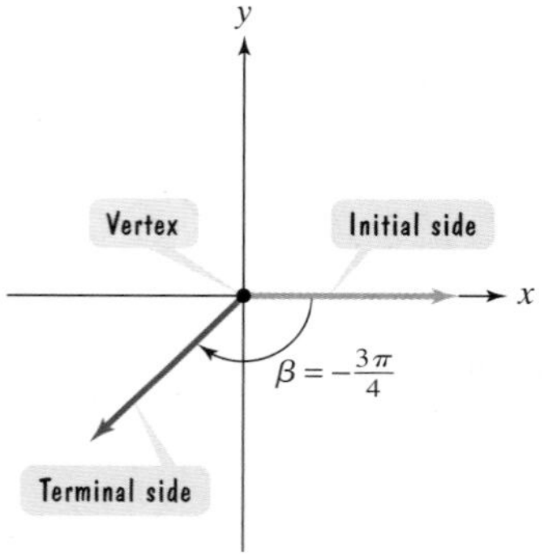
y
Vertex
Initial side
x
$\beta = -\frac{3\pi}{4}$
Terminal side

Figure 4.13

d. An angle of $\frac{9\pi}{4}$ radians is a positive angle. It is obtained by rotating the terminal side counterclockwise. Here are two methods to determine the necessary rotation:

Method 1

$$\frac{9\pi}{4} = \frac{9}{8} \cdot 2\pi$$

$\frac{9\pi}{4}$ is $\frac{9}{8}$, or $1\frac{1}{8}$, complete revolutions of 2π radians.

Method 2

$$\frac{9\pi}{4} = 2\pi + \frac{\pi}{4}.$$

2π is a full-circle revolution.

$\frac{\pi}{4}$ is $\frac{1}{8}$ of a complete revolution.

Method 1 shows that $\gamma = \frac{9\pi}{4}$ is obtained by rotating the terminal side counterclockwise for $1\frac{1}{8}$ revolutions. Method 2 shows that $\gamma = \frac{9\pi}{4}$ is obtained by rotating the terminal side counterclockwise for a full-circle revolution followed by a counterclockwise rotation of $\frac{1}{8}$ of a revolution. The angle lies in quadrant I and is shown in Figure 4.14.

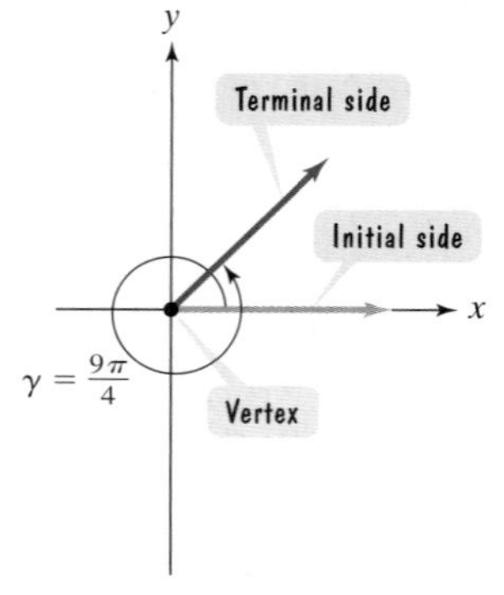
y
Terminal side
Initial side
x
$\gamma = \frac{9\pi}{4}$
Vertex

Figure 4.14

Check Point 4 Draw and label each angle in standard position:

a. $\theta = -\dfrac{\pi}{4}$ **b.** $\alpha = \dfrac{3\pi}{4}$ **c.** $\beta = -\dfrac{7\pi}{4}$ **d.** $\gamma = \dfrac{13\pi}{4}$.

Figure 4.15 illustrates the degree and radian measures of angles that you will commonly see in trigonometry. Each angle is in standard position, so that the initial side lies along the positive *x*-axis. We will be using both degree and radian measure for these angles.

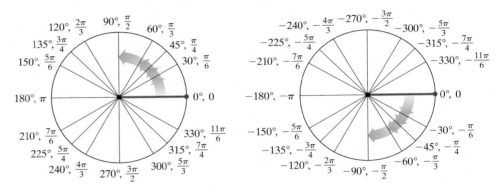

Figure 4.15 Degree and radian measures of selected positive and negative angles

Table 4.1 describes some of the positive angles in Figure 4.15 in terms of revolutions of the angle's terminal side around the origin.

Study Tip

When drawing the angles in Table 4.1 and Figure 4.15, it is helpful to first divide the rectangular coordinate system into eight equal sectors:

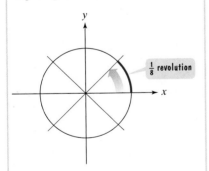

or 12 equal sectors:

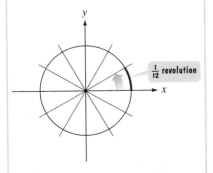

Perhaps we should call this study tip "Making a Clone of Arc."

Table 4.1

Terminal Side	Radian Measure of Angle	Degree Measure of Angle
$\dfrac{1}{12}$ revolution	$\dfrac{1}{12} \cdot 2\pi = \dfrac{\pi}{6}$	$\dfrac{1}{12} \cdot 360° = 30°$
$\dfrac{1}{8}$ revolution	$\dfrac{1}{8} \cdot 2\pi = \dfrac{\pi}{4}$	$\dfrac{1}{8} \cdot 360° = 45°$
$\dfrac{1}{6}$ revolution	$\dfrac{1}{6} \cdot 2\pi = \dfrac{\pi}{3}$	$\dfrac{1}{6} \cdot 360° = 60°$
$\dfrac{1}{4}$ revolution	$\dfrac{1}{4} \cdot 2\pi = \dfrac{\pi}{2}$	$\dfrac{1}{4} \cdot 360° = 90°$
$\dfrac{1}{3}$ revolution	$\dfrac{1}{3} \cdot 2\pi = \dfrac{2\pi}{3}$	$\dfrac{1}{3} \cdot 360° = 120°$
$\dfrac{1}{2}$ revolution	$\dfrac{1}{2} \cdot 2\pi = \pi$	$\dfrac{1}{2} \cdot 360° = 180°$
$\dfrac{2}{3}$ revolution	$\dfrac{2}{3} \cdot 2\pi = \dfrac{4\pi}{3}$	$\dfrac{2}{3} \cdot 360° = 240°$
$\dfrac{3}{4}$ revolution	$\dfrac{3}{4} \cdot 2\pi = \dfrac{3\pi}{2}$	$\dfrac{3}{4} \cdot 360° = 270°$
$\dfrac{7}{8}$ revolution	$\dfrac{7}{8} \cdot 2\pi = \dfrac{7\pi}{4}$	$\dfrac{7}{8} \cdot 360° = 315°$
1 revolution	$1 \cdot 2\pi = 2\pi$	$1 \cdot 360° = 360°$

6 Find coterminal angles.

Coterminal Angles

Two angles with the same initial and terminal sides but possibly different rotations are called **coterminal angles**.

Every angle has infinitely many coterminal angles. Why? Think of an angle in standard position. If the rotation of the angle is extended by one or more complete rotations of 360° or 2π, clockwise or counterclockwise, the result is an angle with the same initial and terminal sides as the original angle.

Coterminal Angles

Increasing or decreasing the degree measure of an angle in standard position by an integer multiple of 360° results in a coterminal angle. Thus, an angle of $\theta°$ is coterminal with angles of $\theta° \pm 360°k$, where k is an integer.

Increasing or decreasing the radian measure of an angle by an integer multiple of 2π results in a coterminal angle. Thus, an angle of θ radians is coterminal with angles of $\theta \pm 2\pi k$, where k is an integer.

Two coterminal angles for an angle of $\theta°$ can be found by adding 360° to $\theta°$ and subtracting 360° from $\theta°$.

EXAMPLE 5 Finding Coterminal Angles

Assume the following angles are in standard position. Find a positive angle less than 360° that is coterminal with each of the following:

    a. a 420° angle   **b.** a −120° angle.

Solution We obtain the coterminal angle by adding or subtracting 360°. The requirement to obtain a positive angle less than 360° determines whether we should add or subtract.

  a. For a 420° angle, subtract 360° to find a positive coterminal angle.

$$420° - 360° = 60°$$

A 60° angle is coterminal with a 420° angle. Figure 4.16(a) illustrates that these angles have the same initial and terminal sides.

  b. For a −120° angle, add 360° to find a positive coterminal angle.

$$-120° + 360° = 240°$$

A 240° angle is coterminal with a −120° angle. Figure 4.16(b) illustrates that these angles have the same initial and terminal sides.

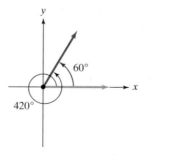

(a) Angles of 420° and 60° are coterminal.

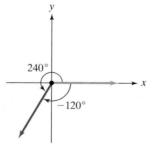

(b) Angles of −120° and 240° are coterminal.

Figure 4.16 Pairs of coterminal angles

Check Point 5 Find a positive angle less than 360° that is coterminal with each of the following:

    a. a 400° angle   **b.** a −135° angle.

Two coterminal angles for an angle of θ radians can be found by adding 2π to θ and subtracting 2π from θ.

EXAMPLE 6   Finding Coterminal Angles

Assume the following angles are in standard position. Find a positive angle less than 2π that is coterminal with each of the following:

a. a $\dfrac{17\pi}{6}$ angle   **b.** a $-\dfrac{\pi}{12}$ angle.

Solution   We obtain the coterminal angle by adding or subtracting 2π. The requirement to obtain a positive angle less than 2π determines whether we should add or subtract.

a. For a $\dfrac{17\pi}{6}$, or $2\dfrac{5}{6}\pi$, angle, subtract 2π to find a positive coterminal angle.

$$\frac{17\pi}{6} - 2\pi = \frac{17\pi}{6} - \frac{12\pi}{6} = \frac{5\pi}{6}$$

A $\dfrac{5\pi}{6}$ angle is coterminal with a $\dfrac{17\pi}{6}$ angle. Figure 4.17(a) illustrates that these angles have the same initial and terminal sides.

b. For a $-\dfrac{\pi}{12}$ angle, add 2π to find a positive coterminal angle.

$$-\frac{\pi}{12} + 2\pi = -\frac{\pi}{12} + \frac{24\pi}{12} = \frac{23\pi}{12}$$

A $\dfrac{23\pi}{12}$ angle is coterminal with a $-\dfrac{\pi}{12}$ angle. Figure 4.17(b) illustrates that these angles have the same initial and terminal sides.

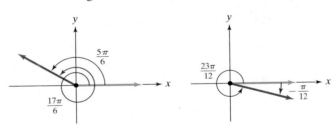

(a) Angles of $\frac{17\pi}{6}$ and $\frac{5\pi}{6}$ are coterminal.

(b) Angles of $-\frac{\pi}{12}$ and $\frac{23\pi}{12}$ are coterminal.

Figure 4.17 Pairs of coterminal angles

Check Point 6   Find a positive angle less than 2π that is coterminal with each of the following:

a. a $\dfrac{13\pi}{5}$ angle   **b.** a $-\dfrac{\pi}{15}$ angle.

To find a positive coterminal angle less than $360°$ or 2π, it is sometimes necessary to add or subtract more than one multiple of $360°$ or 2π.

EXAMPLE 7   Finding Coterminal Angles

Find a positive angle less than $360°$ or 2π that is coterminal with each of the following:

a. a $750°$ angle   **b.** a $\dfrac{22\pi}{3}$ angle   **c.** a $-\dfrac{17\pi}{6}$ angle.

Solution

a. For a 750° angle, subtract two multiples of 360°, or 720°, to find a positive coterminal angle less than 360°.

$$750° - 360° \cdot 2 = 750° - 720° = 30°$$

A 30° angle is coterminal with a 750° angle.

b. For a $\dfrac{22\pi}{3}$, or $7\dfrac{1}{3}\pi$, angle, subtract three multiples of 2π, or 6π, to find a positive coterminal angle less than 2π.

$$\frac{22\pi}{3} - 2\pi \cdot 3 = \frac{22\pi}{3} - 6\pi = \frac{22\pi}{3} - \frac{18\pi}{3} = \frac{4\pi}{3}$$

A $\dfrac{4\pi}{3}$ angle is coterminal with a $\dfrac{22\pi}{3}$ angle.

c. For a $-\dfrac{17\pi}{6}$, or $-2\dfrac{5}{6}\pi$ angle, add two multiples of 2π, or 4π, to find a positive coterminal angle less than 2π.

$$-\frac{17\pi}{6} + 2\pi \cdot 2 = -\frac{17\pi}{6} + 4\pi = -\frac{17\pi}{6} + \frac{24\pi}{6} = \frac{7\pi}{6}$$

A $\dfrac{7\pi}{6}$ angle is coterminal with a $-\dfrac{17\pi}{6}$ angle.

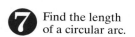

Discovery

Make a sketch for each part of Example 7 illustrating that the coterminal angle we found and the given angle have the same initial and terminal sides.

Check Point 7 Find a positive angle less than 360° or 2π that is coterminal with each of the following:

a. an 855° angle   **b.** a $\dfrac{17\pi}{3}$ angle   **c.** a $-\dfrac{25\pi}{6}$ angle.

⑦ Find the length of a circular arc.

The Length of a Circular Arc

We can use the radian measure formula, $\theta = \dfrac{s}{r}$, to find the length of the arc of a circle. How do we do this? Remember that s represents the length of the arc intercepted by the central angle θ. Thus, by solving the formula for s, we have an equation for arc length.

The Length of a Circular Arc

Let r be the radius of a circle and θ the nonnegative radian measure of a central angle of the circle. The length of the arc intercepted by the central angle is

$$s = r\theta.$$

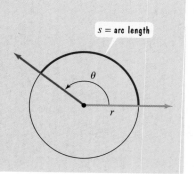

EXAMPLE 8   Finding the Length of a Circular Arc

A circle has a radius of 10 inches. Find the length of the arc intercepted by a central angle of 120°.

Solution   The formula $s = r\theta$ can be used only when θ is expressed in radians. Thus, we begin by converting 120° to radians. Multiply by $\dfrac{\pi \text{ radians}}{180°}$.

$$120° = 120° \cdot \frac{\pi \text{ radians}}{180°} = \frac{120\pi}{180}\text{ radians} = \frac{2\pi}{3}\text{ radians}$$

Now we can use the formula $s = r\theta$ to find the length of the arc. The circle's radius is 10 inches: $r = 10$ inches. The measure of the central angle, in radians, is $\dfrac{2\pi}{3}$: $\theta = \dfrac{2\pi}{3}$. The length of the arc intercepted by this central angle is

$$s = r\theta = (10 \text{ inches})\left(\frac{2\pi}{3}\right) = \frac{20\pi}{3} \text{ inches} \approx 20.94 \text{ inches.}$$

Check Point 8 A circle has a radius of 6 inches. Find the length of the arc intercepted by a central angle of 45°. Express arc length in terms of π. Then round your answer to two decimal places.

⑧ Use linear and angular speed to describe motion on a circular path.

Linear and Angular Speed

A carousel contains four circular rows of animals. As the carousel revolves, the animals in the outer row travel a greater distance per unit of time than those in the inner rows. These animals have a greater *linear speed* than those in the inner rows. By contrast, all animals, regardless of the row, complete the same number of revolutions per unit of time. All animals in the four circular rows travel at the same *angular speed*.

Using v for linear speed and ω (omega) for angular speed, we define these two kinds of speeds along a circular path as follows:

Definitions of Linear and Angular Speed
If a point is in motion on a circle of radius r through an angle of θ radians in time t, then its **linear speed** is
$$v = \frac{s}{t},$$
where s is the arc length given by $s = r\theta$, and its **angular speed** is
$$\omega = \frac{\theta}{t}.$$

The hard drive in a computer rotates at 3600 revolutions per minute. This angular speed, expressed in revolutions per minute, can also be expressed in revolutions per second, radians per minute, and radians per second. Using 2π radians = 1 revolution, we express the angular speed of a hard drive in radians per minute as follows:

3600 revolutions per minute

$$= \frac{3600 \text{ revolutions}}{1 \text{ minute}} \cdot \frac{2\pi \text{ radians}}{1 \text{ revolution}} = \frac{7200\pi \text{ radians}}{1 \text{ minute}}$$

$$= 7200\pi \text{ radians per minute.}$$

We can establish a relationship between the two kinds of speed by dividing both sides of the arc length formula, $s = r\theta$, by t:

$$\frac{s}{t} = \frac{r\theta}{t} = r\frac{\theta}{t}.$$

This expression defines linear speed.   This expression defines angular speed.

Thus, linear speed is the product of the radius and the angular speed.

Linear Speed in Terms of Angular Speed
The linear speed, v, of a point a distance r from the center of rotation is given by
$$v = r\omega,$$
where ω is the angular speed in radians per unit of time.

EXAMPLE 9 Finding Linear Speed

A wind machine used to generate electricity has blades that are 10 feet in length (see Figure 4.18). The propeller is rotating at four revolutions per second. Find the linear speed, in feet per second, of the tips of the blades.

Solution We are given ω, the angular speed.

$\omega = 4$ revolutions per second

We use the formula $v = r\omega$ to find v, the linear speed. Before applying the formula, we must express ω in radians per second.

Figure 4.18

$$\omega = \frac{4 \text{ revolutions}}{1 \text{ second}} \cdot \frac{2\pi \text{ radians}}{1 \text{ revolution}} = \frac{8\pi \text{ radians}}{1 \text{ second}} \quad \text{or} \quad \frac{8\pi}{1 \text{ second}}$$

The angular speed of the propeller is 8π radians per second. The linear speed is

$$v = r\omega = 10 \text{ feet} \cdot \frac{8\pi}{1 \text{ second}} = \frac{80\pi \text{ feet}}{\text{second}}.$$

The linear speed of the tips of the blades is 80π feet per second, which is approximately 251 feet per second.

 9 Long before iPods that hold thousands of songs and play them with superb audio quality, individual songs were delivered on 75-rpm and 45-rpm circular records. A 45-rpm record has an angular speed of 45 revolutions per minute. Find the linear speed, in inches per minute, at the point where the needle is 1.5 inches from the record's center.

EXERCISE SET 4.1

 Practice Exercises

In Exercises 1–6, the measure of an angle is given. Classify the angle as acute, right, obtuse, or straight.

1. 135°   **2.** 177°   **3.** 83.135°

4. 87.177°   **5.** π **6.** $\frac{\pi}{2}$

In Exercises 7–12, find the radian measure of the central angle of a circle of radius r that intercepts an arc of length s.

Radius, r	Arc length, s
7. 10 inches	40 inches
8. 5 feet	30 feet
9. 6 yards	8 yards
10. 8 yards	18 yards
11. 1 meter	400 centimeters
12. 1 meter	600 centimeters

In Exercises 13–20, convert each angle in degrees to radians. Express your answer as a multiple of π.

13. 45°   **14.** 18°   **15.** 135°

16. 150°   **17.** 300°   **18.** 330°

19. −225°   **20.** −270°

In Exercises 21–28, convert each angle in radians to degrees.

21. $\frac{\pi}{2}$ **22.** $\frac{\pi}{9}$ **23.** $\frac{2\pi}{3}$

24. $\frac{3\pi}{4}$ **25.** $\frac{7\pi}{6}$ **26.** $\frac{11\pi}{6}$

27. -3π **28.** -4π

In Exercises 29–34, convert each angle in degrees to radians. Round to two decimal places.

29. 18°   **30.** 76°   **31.** −40°

32. −50°   **33.** 200°   **34.** 250°

In Exercises 35–40, convert each angle in radians to degrees. Round to two decimal places.

35. 2 radians   **36.** 3 radians

37. $\frac{\pi}{13}$ radians   **38.** $\frac{\pi}{17}$ radians

39. −4.8 radians   **40.** −5.2 radians

In Exercises 41–56, use the circle shown in the rectangular coordinate system to draw each angle in standard position. State the quadrant in which the angle lies. When an angle's measure is given in radians, work the exercise without converting to degrees.

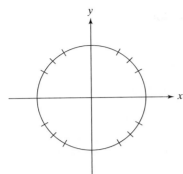

41. $\dfrac{7\pi}{6}$ **42.** $\dfrac{4\pi}{3}$ **43.** $\dfrac{3\pi}{4}$

44. $\dfrac{7\pi}{4}$ **45.** $-\dfrac{2\pi}{3}$ **46.** $-\dfrac{5\pi}{6}$

47. $-\dfrac{5\pi}{4}$ **48.** $-\dfrac{7\pi}{4}$ **49.** $\dfrac{16\pi}{3}$

50. $\dfrac{14\pi}{3}$ **51.** $120°$ **52.** $150°$

53. $-210°$ **54.** $-240°$ **55.** $420°$

56. $405°$

In Exercises 57–70, find a positive angle less than 360° or 2π that is coterminal with the given angle.

57. $395°$ **58.** $415°$ **59.** $-150°$

60. $-160°$ **61.** $-765°$ **62.** $-760°$

63. $\dfrac{19\pi}{6}$ **64.** $\dfrac{17\pi}{5}$ **65.** $\dfrac{23\pi}{5}$

66. $\dfrac{25\pi}{6}$ **67.** $-\dfrac{\pi}{50}$ **68.** $-\dfrac{\pi}{40}$

69. $-\dfrac{31\pi}{7}$ **70.** $-\dfrac{38\pi}{9}$

In Exercises 71–74, find the length of the arc on a circle of radius r intercepted by a central angle θ. Express arc length in terms of π. Then round your answer to two decimal places.

Radius, r	Central angle, θ
71. 12 inches	$\theta = 45°$
72. 16 inches	$\theta = 60°$
73. 8 feet	$\theta = 225°$
74. 9 yards	$\theta = 315°$

In Exercises 75–76, express each angular speed in radians per second.

75. 6 revolutions per second   **76.** 20 revolutions per second

Practice Plus

Use the circle shown in the rectangular coordinate system to solve Exercises 77–82. Find two angles, in radians, between −2π and 2π such that each angle's terminal side passes through the origin and the given point.

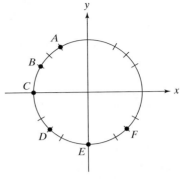

77. A **78.** B
79. D **80.** F
81. E **82.** C

In Exercises 83–86, find the positive radian measure of the angle that the second hand of a clock moves through in the given time.

83. 55 seconds   **84.** 35 seconds
85. 3 minutes and 40 seconds
86. 4 minutes and 25 seconds

 ### Application Exercises

87. The minute hand of a clock moves from 12 to 2 o'clock, or $\frac{1}{6}$ of a complete revolution. Through how many degrees does it move? Through how many radians does it move?

88. The minute hand of a clock moves from 12 to 4 o'clock, or $\frac{1}{3}$ of a complete revolution. Through how many degrees does it move? Through how many radians does it move?

89. The minute hand of a clock is 8 inches long and moves from 12 to 2 o'clock. How far does the tip of the minute hand move? Express your answer in terms of π and then round to two decimal places.

90. The minute hand of a clock is 6 inches long and moves from 12 to 4 o'clock. How far does the tip of the minute hand move? Express your answer in terms of π and then round to two decimal places.

91. The figure shows a highway sign that warns of a railway crossing. The lines that form the cross pass through the circle's center and intersect at right angles. If the radius of the circle is 24 inches, find the length of each of the four arcs formed by the cross. Express your answer in terms of π and then round to two decimal places.

92. The radius of a wheel rolling on the ground is 80 centimeters. If the wheel rotates through an angle of 60°, how many centimeters does it move? Express your answer in terms of π and then round to two decimal places.

How do we measure the distance between two points, A and B, on Earth? We measure along a circle with a center, C, at the center of Earth. The radius of the circle is equal to the distance from C to the surface. Use the fact that Earth is a sphere of radius equal to approximately 4000 miles to solve Exercises 93–96.

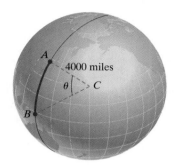

93. If two points, A and B, are 8000 miles apart, express angle θ in radians and in degrees.

94. If two points, A and B, are 10,000 miles apart, express angle θ in radians and in degrees.

95. If $\theta = 30°$, find the distance between A and B to the nearest mile.

96. If $\theta = 10°$, find the distance between A and B to the nearest mile.

97. The angular speed of a point on Earth is $\frac{\pi}{12}$ radians per hour. The Equator lies on a circle of radius approximately 4000 miles. Find the linear velocity, in miles per hour, of a point on the Equator.

98. A Ferris wheel has a radius of 25 feet. The wheel is rotating at two revolutions per minute. Find the linear speed, in feet per minute, of a seat on this Ferris wheel.

99. A water wheel has a radius of 12 feet. The wheel is rotating at 20 revolutions per minute. Find the linear speed, in feet per minute, of the water.

100. On a carousel, the outer row of animals is 20 feet from the center. The inner row of animals is 10 feet from the center. The carousel is rotating at 2.5 revolutions per minute. What is the difference, in feet per minute, in the linear speeds of the animals in the outer and inner rows? Round to the nearest foot per minute.

Writing in Mathematics

101. What is an angle?

102. What determines the size of an angle?

103. Describe an angle in standard position.

104. Explain the difference between positive and negative angles. What are coterminal angles?

105. Explain what is meant by one radian.

106. Explain how to find the radian measure of a central angle.

107. Describe how to convert an angle in degrees to radians.

108. Explain how to convert an angle in radians to degrees.

109. Explain how to find the length of a circular arc.

110. If a carousel is rotating at 2.5 revolutions per minute, explain how to find the linear speed of a child seated on one of the animals.

111. The angular velocity of a point on Earth is $\frac{\pi}{12}$ radians per hour. Describe what happens every 24 hours.

112. Have you ever noticed that we use the vocabulary of angles in everyday speech? Here is an example:

> My opinion about art museums took a 180° turn after visiting the San Francisco Museum of Modern Art.

Explain what this means. Then give another example of the vocabulary of angles in everyday use.

Technology Exercises

In Exercises 113–116, use the keys on your calculator or graphing utility for converting an angle in degrees, minutes, and seconds (D°M'S") into decimal form, and vice versa.

In Exercises 113–114, convert each angle to a decimal in degrees. Round your answer to two decimal places.

113. 30°15'10"   **114.** 65°45'20"

In Exercises 115–116, convert each angle to D°M'S" form. Round your answer to the nearest second.

115. 30.42°   **116.** 50.42°

Critical Thinking Exercises

117. If $\theta = \frac{3}{2}$, is this angle larger or smaller than a right angle?

118. A railroad curve is laid out on a circle. What radius should be used if the track is to change direction by 20° in a distance of 100 miles? Round your answer to the nearest mile.

119. Assuming Earth to be a sphere of radius 4000 miles, how many miles north of the Equator is Miami, Florida, if it is 26° north from the Equator? Round your answer to the nearest mile.

SECTION 4.2 Trigonometric Functions: The Unit Circle

Objectives

❶ Use a unit circle to define trigonometric functions of real numbers.

❷ Recognize the domain and range of sine and cosine functions.

❸ Find exact values of the trigonometric functions at $\frac{\pi}{4}$.

❹ Use even and odd trigonometric functions.

❺ Recognize and use fundamental identities.

❻ Use periodic properties.

❼ Evaluate trigonometric functions with a calculator.

There is something comforting in the repetition of some of nature's patterns. The ocean level at a beach varies between high and low tide approximately every 12 hours. The number of hours of daylight oscillates from a maximum on the summer solstice, June 21, to a minimum on the winter solstice, December 21. Then it increases to the same maximum the following June 21. Some believe that cycles, called biorhythms, represent physical, emotional, and intellectual aspects of our lives. In this chapter, we study six functions, the six *trigonometric functions*, that are used to model phenomena that occur again and again.

Calculus and the Unit Circle

The word *trigonometry* means measurement of triangles. Trigonometric functions, with domains consisting of sets of angles, were first defined using right triangles. By contrast, problems in calculus are solved using functions whose domains are sets of real numbers. Therefore, we introduce the trigonometric functions using unit circles and radians, rather than right triangles and degrees.

A **unit circle** is a circle of radius 1, with its center at the origin of a rectangular coordinate system. The equation of this unit circle is $x^2 + y^2 = 1$. Figure 4.19 shows a unit circle in which the central angle measures t radians.

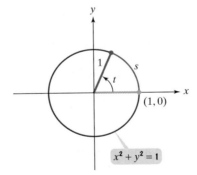

Figure 4.19 Unit circle with a central angle measuring t radians

We can use the formula for the length of a circular arc, $s = r\theta$, to find the length of the intercepted arc.

$$s = r\theta = 1 \cdot t = t$$

| The radius of a unit circle is 1. | The radian measure of the central angle is t. |

Thus, the length of the intercepted arc is t. This is also the radian measure of the central angle. Thus, **in a unit circle, the radian measure of the central angle is equal to the length of the intercepted arc.** Both are given by the same *real number t*.

In Figure 4.20, the radian measure of the angle and the length of the intercepted arc are both shown by t. Let $P = (x, y)$ denote the point on the unit circle that has arc length t from $(1, 0)$. Figure 4.20(a) shows that if t is positive, point P is reached by moving counterclockwise along the unit circle from $(1, 0)$. Figure 4.20(b) shows that if t is negative, point P is reached by moving clockwise along the unit circle from $(1, 0)$. For each real number t, there corresponds a point $P = (x, y)$ on the unit circle.

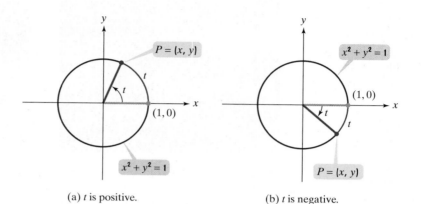

Figure 4.20 (a) t is positive. (b) t is negative.

❶ Use a unit circle to define trigonometric functions of real numbers.

The Six Trigonometric Functions

We begin the study of trigonometry by defining the six trigonometric functions. The inputs of these functions are real numbers, represented by t in Figure 4.20. The outputs involve the point $P = (x, y)$ on the unit circle that corresponds to t and the coordinates of this point.

The trigonometric functions have names that are words, rather than single letters such as f, g, and h. For example, the **sine of t** is the y-coordinate of point P on the unit circle:

$$\sin t = y.$$

| Input is the real number t. | Output is the y-coordinate of a point on the unit circle. |

The value of y depends on the real number t and thus is a function of t. The expression $\sin t$ really means $\sin(t)$, where sine is the name of the function and t, a real number, is an input.

For example, a point $P = (x, y)$ on the unit circle corresponding to a real number t is shown in Figure 4.21 for $\pi < t < \dfrac{3\pi}{2}$. We see that the coordinates of $P = (x, y)$ are $x = -\dfrac{3}{5}$ and $y = -\dfrac{4}{5}$. Because the sine function is the y-coordinate of P, the value of this trigonometric function at the real number t is

$$\sin t = -\frac{4}{5}.$$

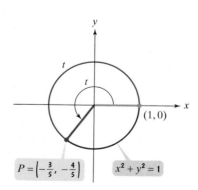

Figure 4.21

Here are the names of the six trigonometric functions, along with their abbreviations.

Name	Abbreviation	Name	Abbreviation
sine	sin	cosecant	csc
cosine	cos	secant	sec
tangent	tan	cotangent	cot

Definitions of the Trigonometric Functions in Terms of a Unit Circle

If t is a real number and $P = (x, y)$ is a point on the unit circle that corresponds to t, then

$$\sin t = y \qquad\qquad \csc t = \frac{1}{y}, y \neq 0$$

$$\cos t = x \qquad\qquad \sec t = \frac{1}{x}, x \neq 0$$

$$\tan t = \frac{y}{x}, x \neq 0 \qquad \cot t = \frac{x}{y}, y \neq 0.$$

Because this definition expresses function values in terms of coordinates of a point on a unit circle, the trigonometric functions are sometimes called the **circular functions**. Observe that the function values in the second column in the box are the reciprocals of the corresponding function values in the first column.

EXAMPLE 1   Finding Values of the Trigonometric Functions

In Figure 4.22, t is a real number equal to the length of the intercepted arc of an angle that measures t radians and $P = \left(-\dfrac{1}{2}, \dfrac{\sqrt{3}}{2}\right)$ is the point on the unit circle that corresponds to t. Use the figure to find the values of the trigonometric functions at t.

Solution   The point P on the unit circle that corresponds to t has coordinates $\left(-\dfrac{1}{2}, \dfrac{\sqrt{3}}{2}\right)$. We use $x = -\dfrac{1}{2}$ and $y = \dfrac{\sqrt{3}}{2}$ to find the values of the trigonometric functions. Because radical expressions are usually written without radicals in the denominators, we simplify by rationalizing denominators where appropriate.

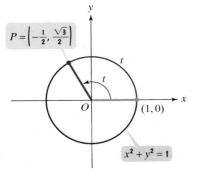

Figure 4.22

$$\sin t = y = \frac{\sqrt{3}}{2}$$

$$\csc t = \frac{1}{y} = \frac{1}{\frac{\sqrt{3}}{2}} = \frac{2}{\sqrt{3}} = \frac{2}{\sqrt{3}} \cdot \frac{\sqrt{3}}{\sqrt{3}} = \frac{2\sqrt{3}}{3}$$

$$\cos t = x = -\frac{1}{2}$$

$$\sec t = \frac{1}{x} = \frac{1}{-\frac{1}{2}} = -2$$

> Rationalize denominators. We are multiplying by 1 and not changing function values.

$$\tan t = \frac{y}{x} = \frac{\frac{\sqrt{3}}{2}}{-\frac{1}{2}} = -\sqrt{3}$$

$$\cot t = \frac{x}{y} = \frac{-\frac{1}{2}}{\frac{\sqrt{3}}{2}} = -\frac{1}{\sqrt{3}} = -\frac{1}{\sqrt{3}} \cdot \frac{\sqrt{3}}{\sqrt{3}} = -\frac{\sqrt{3}}{3}$$

Check Point 1   Use the figure on the right to find the values of the trigonometric functions at t.

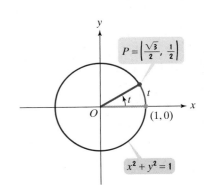

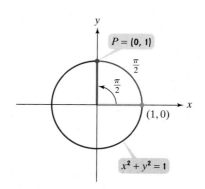

Figure 4.23

EXAMPLE 2   Finding Values of the Trigonometric Functions

Use Figure 4.23 to find the values of the trigonometric functions at $t = \dfrac{\pi}{2}$.

Solution   The point P on the unit circle that corresponds to $t = \dfrac{\pi}{2}$ has coordinates $(0, 1)$. We use $x = 0$ and $y = 1$ to find the values of the trigonometric functions at $\dfrac{\pi}{2}$.

$$\sin \frac{\pi}{2} = y = 1 \qquad\qquad \csc \frac{\pi}{2} = \frac{1}{y} = \frac{1}{1} = 1$$

$$\cos \frac{\pi}{2} = x = 0 \qquad\qquad \sec \frac{\pi}{2} = \frac{1}{x} = \frac{1}{0}$$

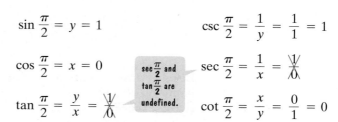

$$\tan \frac{\pi}{2} = \frac{y}{x} = \frac{1}{0} \qquad\qquad \cot \frac{\pi}{2} = \frac{x}{y} = \frac{0}{1} = 0$$

sec $\dfrac{\pi}{2}$ and tan $\dfrac{\pi}{2}$ are undefined.

Check Point 2   Use the figure on the right to find the values of the trigonometric functions at $t = \pi$.

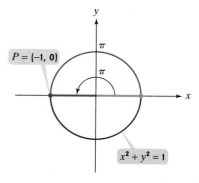

② Recognize the domain and range of sine and cosine functions.

Domain and Range of Sine and Cosine Functions

The domain and range of each trigonometric function can be found from the unit circle definition. At this point, let's look only at the sine and cosine functions,

$$\sin t = y \quad \text{and} \quad \cos t = x.$$

Figure 4.24 shows the sine function at t as the y-coordinate of a point along the unit circle:

$y = \sin t$.

The domain is associated with t, the angle's radian measure and the intercepted arc's length.

The range is associated with y, the point's second coordinate.

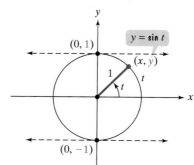

Figure 4.24

Because t can be any real number, the domain of the sine function is $(-\infty, \infty)$, the set of all real numbers. The radius of the unit circle is 1 and the dashed horizontal lines in Figure 4.24 show that y cannot be less than -1 or greater than 1. Thus, the range of the sine function is $[-1, 1]$, the set of all real numbers from -1 to 1, inclusive.

Figure 4.25 shows the cosine function at t as the x-coordinate of a point along the unit circle:

$$x = \cos t.$$

> The domain is associated with t, the angle's radian measure and the intercepted arc's length.

> The range is associated with x, the point's first coordinate.

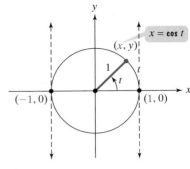

Figure 4.25

Because t can be any real number, the domain of the cosine function is $(-\infty, \infty)$. The radius of the unit circle is 1 and the dashed vertical lines in Figure 4.25 show that x cannot be less than -1 or greater than 1. Thus, the range of the cosine function is $[-1, 1]$.

The Domain and Range of the Sine and Cosine Functions

The domain of the sine function and the cosine function is $(-\infty, \infty)$, the set of all real numbers. The range of these functions is $[-1, 1]$, the set of all real numbers from -1 to 1, inclusive.

---

③ Find exact values of the trigonometric functions at $\dfrac{\pi}{4}$.

Exact Values of Trigonometric Functions at $t = \dfrac{\pi}{4}$

Trigonometric functions at $t = \dfrac{\pi}{4}$ occur frequently. How do we use the unit circle to find values of the trigonometric functions at $t = \dfrac{\pi}{4}$? Look at Figure 4.26. We must find the coordinates of point $P = (a, b)$ on the unit circle that correspond to $t = \dfrac{\pi}{4}$. Can you see that P lies on the line $y = x$? Thus, point P has equal x- and y-coordinates: $a = b$. We find these coordinates as follows:

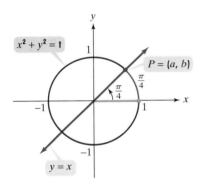

Figure 4.26

$x^2 + y^2 = 1$	This is the equation of the unit circle.
$a^2 + b^2 = 1$	Point $P = (a, b)$ lies on the unit circle. Thus, its coordinates satisfy the circle's equation.
$a^2 + a^2 = 1$	Because $a = b$, substitute a for b in the previous equation.
$2a^2 = 1$	Add like terms.
$a^2 = \frac{1}{2}$	Divide both sides of the equation by 2.
$a = \sqrt{\frac{1}{2}}$	Because $a > 0$, take the positive square root of both sides.

We see that $a = \sqrt{\dfrac{1}{2}} = \dfrac{1}{\sqrt{2}}$. Because $a = b$, we also have $b = \dfrac{1}{\sqrt{2}}$. Thus, if $t = \dfrac{\pi}{4}$, point $P = \left(\dfrac{1}{\sqrt{2}}, \dfrac{1}{\sqrt{2}}\right)$ is the point on the unit circle that corresponds to t. Let's rationalize the denominator on each coordinate:

$$\frac{1}{\sqrt{2}} = \frac{1}{\sqrt{2}} \cdot \frac{\sqrt{2}}{\sqrt{2}} = \frac{\sqrt{2}}{2}.$$

> We are multiplying by 1 and not changing the value of $\dfrac{1}{\sqrt{2}}$.

We use $\left(\dfrac{\sqrt{2}}{2}, \dfrac{\sqrt{2}}{2}\right)$ to find the values of the trigonometric functions at $t = \dfrac{\pi}{4}$.

EXAMPLE 3 Finding Values of the Trigonometric Functions at $t = \dfrac{\pi}{4}$

Find $\sin \dfrac{\pi}{4}$, $\cos \dfrac{\pi}{4}$, and $\tan \dfrac{\pi}{4}$.

Solution The point P on the unit circle that corresponds to $t = \dfrac{\pi}{4}$ has coordinates $\left(\dfrac{\sqrt{2}}{2}, \dfrac{\sqrt{2}}{2}\right)$. We use $x = \dfrac{\sqrt{2}}{2}$ and $y = \dfrac{\sqrt{2}}{2}$ to find the values of the three trigonometric functions at $\dfrac{\pi}{4}$.

$$\sin \frac{\pi}{4} = y = \frac{\sqrt{2}}{2} \qquad \cos \frac{\pi}{4} = x = \frac{\sqrt{2}}{2} \qquad \tan \frac{\pi}{4} = \frac{y}{x} = \frac{\dfrac{\sqrt{2}}{2}}{\dfrac{\sqrt{2}}{2}} = 1$$

Check Point 3 Find $\csc \dfrac{\pi}{4}$, $\sec \dfrac{\pi}{4}$, and $\cot \dfrac{\pi}{4}$.

Because you will often see the trigonometric functions at $\dfrac{\pi}{4}$, it is a good idea to memorize the values shown in the following box. In the next section, you will learn to use a right triangle to obtain these values.

Trigonometric Functions at $\dfrac{\pi}{4}$	
$\sin \dfrac{\pi}{4} = \dfrac{\sqrt{2}}{2}$	$\csc \dfrac{\pi}{4} = \sqrt{2}$
$\cos \dfrac{\pi}{4} = \dfrac{\sqrt{2}}{2}$	$\sec \dfrac{\pi}{4} = \sqrt{2}$
$\tan \dfrac{\pi}{4} = 1$	$\cot \dfrac{\pi}{4} = 1$

④ Use even and odd trigonometric functions.

Even and Odd Trigonometric Functions

We have seen that a function is even if $f(-t) = f(t)$ and odd if $f(-t) = -f(t)$. We can use Figure 4.27 to show that the cosine function is an even function and the sine function is an odd function. By definition, the coordinates of the points P and Q in Figure 4.27 are as follows:

$$P: (\cos t, \sin t)$$
$$Q: (\cos(-t), \sin(-t)).$$

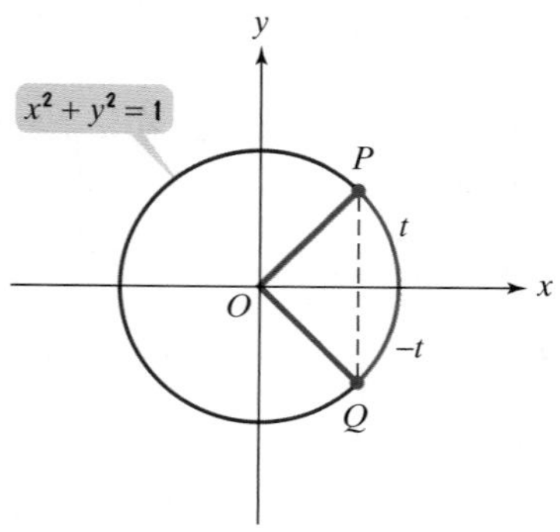

In Figure 4.27, the x-coordinates of P and Q are the same. Thus,

$$\cos(-t) = \cos t.$$

This shows that the cosine function is an even function. By contrast, the y-coordinates of P and Q are negatives of each other. Thus,

$$\sin(-t) = -\sin t.$$

This shows that the sine function is an odd function.

Figure 4.27

This argument is valid regardless of the length of t. Thus, the arc may terminate in any of the four quadrants or on any axis. Using the unit circle definition of the trigonometric functions, we obtain the following results:

Even and Odd Trigonometric Functions

The cosine and secant functions are *even*.

$$\cos(-t) = \cos t \qquad\qquad \sec(-t) = \sec t$$

The sine, cosecant, tangent, and cotangent functions are *odd*.

$$\sin(-t) = -\sin t \qquad\qquad \csc(-t) = -\csc t$$
$$\tan(-t) = -\tan t \qquad\qquad \cot(-t) = -\cot t$$

**EXAMPLE 4   Using Even and Odd Functions
to Find Values of Trigonometric Functions**

Find the value of each trigonometric function:

a. $\cos\left(-\dfrac{\pi}{4}\right)$ **b.** $\tan\left(-\dfrac{\pi}{4}\right)$.

Solution

a. $\cos\left(-\dfrac{\pi}{4}\right) = \cos\dfrac{\pi}{4} = \dfrac{\sqrt{2}}{2}$ **b.** $\tan\left(-\dfrac{\pi}{4}\right) = -\tan\dfrac{\pi}{4} = -1$

 Check Point 4 Find the value of each trigonometric function:

a. $\sec\left(-\dfrac{\pi}{4}\right)$ **b.** $\sin\left(-\dfrac{\pi}{4}\right)$.

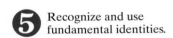 **⑤** Recognize and use fundamental identities.

Fundamental Identities

Many relationships exist among the six trigonometric functions. These relationships are described using **trigonometric identities**. Trigonometric identities are equations that are true for all real numbers for which the trigonometric expressions in the equations are defined. For example, the definitions of the cosine and secant functions are given by

$$\cos t = x \quad \text{and} \quad \sec t = \dfrac{1}{x}, x \neq 0.$$

Substituting $\cos t$ for x in the equation on the right, we see that

$$\sec t = \dfrac{1}{\cos t}, \cos t \neq 0.$$

This identity is one of six **reciprocal identities**.

Reciprocal Identities

$$\sin t = \dfrac{1}{\csc t} \qquad\qquad \csc t = \dfrac{1}{\sin t}$$
$$\cos t = \dfrac{1}{\sec t} \qquad\qquad \sec t = \dfrac{1}{\cos t}$$
$$\tan t = \dfrac{1}{\cot t} \qquad\qquad \cot t = \dfrac{1}{\tan t}$$

Two other relationships that follow from the definitions of the trigonometric functions are called the **quotient identities**.

Quotient Identities

$$\tan t = \frac{\sin t}{\cos t} \qquad\qquad \cot t = \frac{\cos t}{\sin t}$$

If $\sin t$ and $\cos t$ are known, a quotient identity and three reciprocal identities make it possible to find the value of each of the four remaining trigonometric functions.

EXAMPLE 5 Using Quotient and Reciprocal Identities

Given $\sin t = \frac{2}{5}$ and $\cos t = \frac{\sqrt{21}}{5}$, find the value of each of the four remaining trigonometric functions.

Solution We can find $\tan t$ by using the quotient identity that describes $\tan t$ as the quotient of $\sin t$ and $\cos t$.

$$\tan t = \frac{\sin t}{\cos t} = \frac{\frac{2}{5}}{\frac{\sqrt{21}}{5}} = \frac{2}{5} \cdot \frac{5}{\sqrt{21}} = \frac{2}{\sqrt{21}} = \frac{2}{\sqrt{21}} \cdot \frac{\sqrt{21}}{\sqrt{21}} = \frac{2\sqrt{21}}{21}$$

Rationalize the denominator.

We use the reciprocal identities to find the value of each of the remaining three functions.

$$\csc t = \frac{1}{\sin t} = \frac{1}{\frac{2}{5}} = \frac{5}{2}$$

$$\sec t = \frac{1}{\cos t} = \frac{1}{\frac{\sqrt{21}}{5}} = \frac{5}{\sqrt{21}} = \frac{5}{\sqrt{21}} \cdot \frac{\sqrt{21}}{\sqrt{21}} = \frac{5\sqrt{21}}{21}$$

Rationalize the denominator.

$$\cot t = \frac{1}{\tan t} = \frac{1}{\frac{2}{\sqrt{21}}} = \frac{\sqrt{21}}{2}$$

We found $\tan t = \frac{2}{\sqrt{21}}$. We could use $\tan t = \frac{2\sqrt{21}}{21}$, but then we would have to rationalize the denominator.

Check Point 5 Given $\sin t = \frac{2}{3}$ and $\cos t = \frac{\sqrt{5}}{3}$, find the value of each of the four remaining trigonometric functions.

Other relationships among trigonometric functions follow from the equation of the unit circle

$$x^2 + y^2 = 1.$$

Because $\cos t = x$ and $\sin t = y$, we see that

$$(\cos t)^2 + (\sin t)^2 = 1.$$

We will eliminate the parentheses in this identity by writing $\cos^2 t$ instead of $(\cos t)^2$ and $\sin^2 t$ instead of $(\sin t)^2$. With this notation, we can write the identity as

$$\cos^2 t + \sin^2 t = 1$$

or

$$\sin^2 t + \cos^2 t = 1. \qquad \text{The identity usually appears in this form.}$$

Two additional identities can be obtained from $x^2 + y^2 = 1$ by dividing both sides by x^2 and y^2, respectively. The three identities are called the **Pythagorean identities**.

Pythagorean Identities

$$\sin^2 t + \cos^2 t = 1 \qquad 1 + \tan^2 t = \sec^2 t \qquad 1 + \cot^2 t = \csc^2 t$$

EXAMPLE 6   Using a Pythagorean Identity

Given that $\sin t = \dfrac{3}{5}$ and $0 \le t < \dfrac{\pi}{2}$, find the value of $\cos t$ using a trigonometric identity.

Solution   We can find the value of $\cos t$ by using the Pythagorean identity

$$\sin^2 t + \cos^2 t = 1.$$

$$\left(\frac{3}{5}\right)^2 + \cos^2 t = 1 \qquad \text{We are given that } \sin t = \frac{3}{5}.$$

$$\frac{9}{25} + \cos^2 t = 1 \qquad \text{Square } \frac{3}{5}\!: \left(\frac{3}{5}\right)^2 = \frac{3^2}{5^2} = \frac{9}{25}.$$

$$\cos^2 t = 1 - \frac{9}{25} \qquad \text{Subtract } \frac{9}{25} \text{ from both sides.}$$

$$\cos^2 t = \frac{16}{25} \qquad \text{Simplify: } 1 - \frac{9}{25} = \frac{25}{25} - \frac{9}{25} = \frac{16}{25}.$$

$$\cos t = \sqrt{\frac{16}{25}} = \frac{4}{5} \qquad \text{Because } 0 \le t < \frac{\pi}{2}, \cos t, \text{ the x-coordinate of}$$

a point on the unit circle, is positive.

Thus, $\cos t = \dfrac{4}{5}.$

Check Point 6   Given that $\sin t = \dfrac{1}{2}$ and $0 \le t < \dfrac{\pi}{2}$, find the value of $\cos t$ using a trigonometric identity.

   Use periodic properties.

Periodic Functions

Certain patterns in nature repeat again and again. For example, the ocean level at a beach varies from low tide to high tide and then back to low tide approximately every 12 hours. If low tide occurs at noon, then high tide will be around 6 P.M. and low tide will occur again around midnight, and so on infinitely. If $f(t)$ represents the ocean level at the beach at any time t, then the level is the same 12 hours later. Thus,

$$f(t + 12) = f(t).$$

The word *periodic* means that this tidal behavior repeats infinitely. The *period*, 12 hours, is the time it takes to complete one full cycle.

Definition of a Periodic Function

A function f is **periodic** if there exists a positive number p such that

$$f(t + p) = f(t)$$

for all t in the domain of f. The smallest positive number p for which f is periodic is called the **period** of f.

The trigonometric functions are used to model periodic phenomena. Why? If we begin at any point P on the unit circle and travel a distance of 2π units along the perimeter, we will return to the same point P. Because the trigonometric functions are defined in terms of the coordinates of that point P, we obtain the following results:

Periodic Properties of the Sine and Cosine Functions

$$\sin(t + 2\pi) = \sin t \quad \text{and} \quad \cos(t + 2\pi) = \cos t$$

The sine and cosine functions are periodic functions and have period 2π.

Like the sine and cosine functions, the secant and cosecant functions have period 2π. However, the tangent and cotangent functions have a smaller period. Figure 4.28 shows that if we begin at any point $P(x, y)$ on the unit circle and travel a distance of π units along the perimeter, we arrive at the point $Q(-x, -y)$. The tangent function, defined in terms of the coordinates of a point, is the same at (x, y) and $(-x, -y)$.

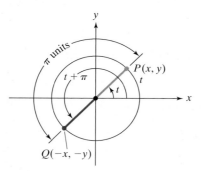

Figure 4.28 tan at P = tan at Q

| Tangent function at (x, y) | $\dfrac{y}{x} = \dfrac{-y}{-x}$ | Tangent function π radians later |

We see that $\tan(t + \pi) = \tan t$. The same observations apply to the cotangent function.

Periodic Properties of the Tangent and Cotangent Functions

$$\tan(t + \pi) = \tan t \quad \text{and} \quad \cot(t + \pi) = \cot t$$

The tangent and cotangent functions are periodic functions and have period π.

EXAMPLE 7   Using Periodic Properties

Find the value of each trigonometric function:

a. $\sin \dfrac{9\pi}{4}$ **b.** $\tan\left(-\dfrac{5\pi}{4}\right)$.

Solution

a. $\sin \dfrac{9\pi}{4} = \sin\left(\dfrac{\pi}{4} + 2\pi\right) = \sin \dfrac{\pi}{4} = \dfrac{\sqrt{2}}{2}$

$\sin(t + 2\pi) = \sin t$

b. $\tan\left(-\dfrac{5\pi}{4}\right) = -\tan \dfrac{5\pi}{4} = -\tan\left(\dfrac{\pi}{4} + \pi\right) = -\tan \dfrac{\pi}{4} = -1$

The tangent function is odd: $\tan(-t) = -\tan t$. $\tan(t + \pi) = \tan t$

Check Point 7 Find the value of each trigonometric function:

a. $\cot \dfrac{5\pi}{4}$ **b.** $\cos\left(-\dfrac{9\pi}{4}\right)$.

Why do the trigonometric functions model phenomena that repeat *indefinitely*? By starting at point P on the unit circle and traveling a distance of 2π units, 4π units, 6π units, and so on, we return to the starting point P. Because the trigonometric functions are defined in terms of the coordinates of that point P, if we add (or subtract) multiples of 2π to t, the values of the trigonometric functions of t do not change. Furthermore, the values for the tangent and cotangent functions of t do not change if we add (or subtract) multiples of π to t.

> **Repetitive Behavior of the Sine, Cosine, and Tangent Functions**
>
> For any integer n and real number t,
> $$\sin(t + 2\pi n) = \sin t, \quad \cos(t + 2\pi n) = \cos t, \quad \text{and} \quad \tan(t + \pi n) = \tan t.$$

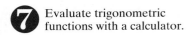

7 Evaluate trigonometric functions with a calculator.

Using a Calculator to Evaluate Trigonometric Functions

We used a unit circle to find values of the trigonometric functions at $\dfrac{\pi}{4}$. These are exact values. We can find approximate values of the trigonometric functions using a calculator.

The first step in using a calculator to evaluate trigonometric functions is to set the calculator to the correct *mode*, degrees or radians. The domains of the trigonometric functions in the unit circle are sets of real numbers. Therefore, we use the radian mode.

Most calculators have keys marked $\boxed{\text{SIN}}$, $\boxed{\text{COS}}$, and $\boxed{\text{TAN}}$. For example, to find the value of sin 1.2, set the calculator to the radian mode and enter 1.2 $\boxed{\text{SIN}}$ on most scientific calculators and $\boxed{\text{SIN}}$ 1.2 $\boxed{\text{ENTER}}$ on most graphing calculators. Consult the manual for your calculator.

To evaluate the cosecant, secant, and cotangent functions, use the key for the respective reciprocal function, $\boxed{\text{SIN}}$, $\boxed{\text{COS}}$, or $\boxed{\text{TAN}}$, and then use the reciprocal key. The reciprocal key is $\boxed{1/x}$ on many scientific calculators and $\boxed{x^{-1}}$ on many graphing calculators. For example, we can evaluate $\sec\dfrac{\pi}{12}$ using the following reciprocal relationship:

$$\sec\frac{\pi}{12} = \frac{1}{\cos\dfrac{\pi}{12}}.$$

Using the radian mode, enter one of the following keystroke sequences:

Many Scientific Calculators

$$\boxed{\pi}\ \boxed{\div}\ 12\ \boxed{=}\ \boxed{\text{COS}}\ \boxed{1/x}$$

Many Graphing Calculators

$$\boxed{(}\ \boxed{\text{COS}}\ \boxed{(}\ \boxed{\pi}\ \boxed{\div}\ 12\ \boxed{)}\ \boxed{)}\ \boxed{x^{-1}}\ \boxed{\text{ENTER}}.$$

Rounding the display to four decimal places, we obtain $\sec\dfrac{\pi}{12} \approx 1.0353$.

EXAMPLE 8   Evaluating Trigonometric Functions with a Calculator

Use a calculator to find the value to four decimal places:

   a. $\cos\dfrac{\pi}{4}$ **b.** cot 1.2.

Solution

Scientific Calculator Solution

Function	Mode	Keystrokes	Display, rounded to four decimal places
a. $\cos\dfrac{\pi}{4}$	Radian	$\boxed{\pi}\ \boxed{\div}\ 4\ \boxed{=}\ \boxed{\text{COS}}$	0.7071
b. cot 1.2	Radian	1.2 $\boxed{\text{TAN}}$ $\boxed{1/x}$	0.3888

Graphing Calculator Solution

Function	Mode	Keystrokes	Display, rounded to four decimal places
a. $\cos\dfrac{\pi}{4}$	Radian	$\boxed{\text{COS}}\ \boxed{(}\ \boxed{\pi}\ \boxed{\div}\ \boxed{4}\ \boxed{)}\ \boxed{\text{ENTER}}$	0.7071
b. $\cot 1.2$	Radian	$\boxed{(}\ \boxed{\text{TAN}}\ 1.2\ \boxed{)}\ \boxed{x^{-1}}\ \boxed{\text{ENTER}}$	0.3888

Check Point 8 Use a calculator to find the value to four decimal places:

a. $\sin\dfrac{\pi}{4}$ b. $\csc 1.5$.

EXERCISE SET 4.2

Practice Exercises

In Exercises 1–4, a point $P(x, y)$ is shown on the unit circle corresponding to a real number t. Find the values of the trigonometric functions at t.

1.

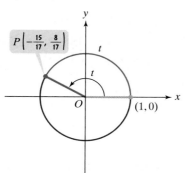

2.

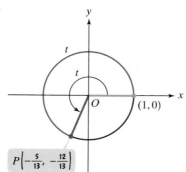

3.

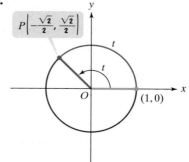

4.

In Exercises 5–18, the unit circle has been divided into twelve equal arcs, corresponding to t-values of

$$0, \frac{\pi}{6}, \frac{\pi}{3}, \frac{\pi}{2}, \frac{2\pi}{3}, \frac{5\pi}{6}, \pi, \frac{7\pi}{6}, \frac{4\pi}{3}, \frac{3\pi}{2}, \frac{5\pi}{3}, \frac{11\pi}{6}, \text{ and } 2\pi.$$

Use the (x, y) coordinates in the figure to find the value of each trigonometric function at the indicated real number, t, or state that the expression is undefined.

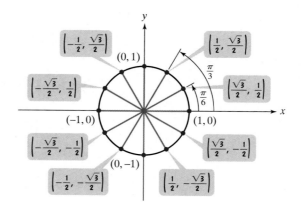

5. $\sin\dfrac{\pi}{6}$ **6.** $\sin\dfrac{\pi}{3}$ **7.** $\cos\dfrac{5\pi}{6}$

8. $\cos\dfrac{2\pi}{3}$ **9.** $\tan\pi$ **10.** $\tan 0$

11. $\csc\dfrac{7\pi}{6}$ **12.** $\csc\dfrac{4\pi}{3}$ **13.** $\sec\dfrac{11\pi}{6}$

14. $\sec \dfrac{5\pi}{3}$ **15.** $\sin \dfrac{3\pi}{2}$ **16.** $\cos \dfrac{3\pi}{2}$

17. $\sec \dfrac{3\pi}{2}$ **18.** $\tan \dfrac{3\pi}{2}$

In Exercises 19–24,

   a. *Use the unit circle shown for Exercises 5–18 to find the value of the trigonometric function.*

   b. *Use even and odd properties of trigonometric functions and your answer from part (a) to find the value of the same trigonometric function at the indicated real number.*

19. a. $\cos \dfrac{\pi}{6}$ **20. a.** $\cos \dfrac{\pi}{3}$

   b. $\cos\left(-\dfrac{\pi}{6}\right)$ **b.** $\cos\left(-\dfrac{\pi}{3}\right)$

21. a. $\sin \dfrac{5\pi}{6}$ **22. a.** $\sin \dfrac{2\pi}{3}$

   b. $\sin\left(-\dfrac{5\pi}{6}\right)$ **b.** $\sin\left(-\dfrac{2\pi}{3}\right)$

23. a. $\tan \dfrac{5\pi}{3}$ **24. a.** $\tan \dfrac{11\pi}{6}$

   b. $\tan\left(-\dfrac{5\pi}{3}\right)$ **b.** $\tan\left(-\dfrac{11\pi}{6}\right)$

In Exercises 25–28, $\sin t$ and $\cos t$ are given. Use identities to find $\tan t$, $\csc t$, $\sec t$, and $\cot t$. Where necessary, rationalize denominators.

25. $\sin t = \dfrac{8}{17}$, $\cos t = \dfrac{15}{17}$ **26.** $\sin t = \dfrac{3}{5}$, $\cos t = \dfrac{4}{5}$

27. $\sin t = \dfrac{1}{3}$, $\cos t = \dfrac{2\sqrt{2}}{3}$ **28.** $\sin t = \dfrac{2}{3}$, $\cos t = \dfrac{\sqrt{5}}{3}$

In Exercises 29–32, $0 \le t < \dfrac{\pi}{2}$ and $\sin t$ is given. Use the Pythagorean identity $\sin^2 t + \cos^2 t = 1$ to find $\cos t$.

29. $\sin t = \dfrac{6}{7}$ **30.** $\sin t = \dfrac{7}{8}$

31. $\sin t = \dfrac{\sqrt{39}}{8}$ **32.** $\sin t = \dfrac{\sqrt{21}}{5}$

In Exercises 33–38, use an identity to find the value of each expression. Do not use a calculator.

33. $\sin 1.7 \csc 1.7$ **34.** $\cos 2.3 \sec 2.3$

35. $\sin^2 \dfrac{\pi}{6} + \cos^2 \dfrac{\pi}{6}$ **36.** $\sin^2 \dfrac{\pi}{3} + \cos^2 \dfrac{\pi}{3}$

37. $\sec^2 \dfrac{\pi}{3} - \tan^2 \dfrac{\pi}{3}$ **38.** $\csc^2 \dfrac{\pi}{6} - \cot^2 \dfrac{\pi}{6}$

In Exercises 39–52, find the exact value of each trigonometric function. Do not use a calculator.

39. $\cos \dfrac{9\pi}{4}$ **40.** $\csc \dfrac{9\pi}{4}$

41. $\sin\left(-\dfrac{9\pi}{4}\right)$ **42.** $\sec\left(-\dfrac{9\pi}{4}\right)$

43. $\tan \dfrac{5\pi}{4}$ **44.** $\cot \dfrac{5\pi}{4}$

45. $\cot\left(-\dfrac{5\pi}{4}\right)$ **46.** $\tan\left(-\dfrac{9\pi}{4}\right)$

47. $-\tan\left(\dfrac{\pi}{4} + 15\pi\right)$ **48.** $-\cot\left(\dfrac{\pi}{4} + 17\pi\right)$

49. $\sin\left(-\dfrac{\pi}{4} - 1000\pi\right)$ **50.** $\sin\left(-\dfrac{\pi}{4} - 2000\pi\right)$

51. $\cos\left(-\dfrac{\pi}{4} - 1000\pi\right)$ **52.** $\cos\left(-\dfrac{\pi}{4} - 2000\pi\right)$

In Exercises 53–60, the unit circle has been divided into eight equal arcs, corresponding to t-values of

$$0, \dfrac{\pi}{4}, \dfrac{\pi}{2}, \dfrac{3\pi}{4}, \pi, \dfrac{5\pi}{4}, \dfrac{3\pi}{2}, \dfrac{7\pi}{4}, \text{ and } 2\pi.$$

   a. *Use the (x, y) coordinates in the figure to find the value of the trigonometric function.*

   b. *Use periodic properties and your answer from part (a) to find the value of the same trigonometric function at the indicated real number.*

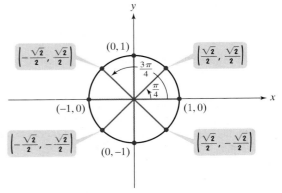

53. a. $\sin \dfrac{3\pi}{4}$ **54. a.** $\cos \dfrac{3\pi}{4}$

   b. $\sin \dfrac{11\pi}{4}$ **b.** $\cos \dfrac{11\pi}{4}$

55. a. $\cos \dfrac{\pi}{2}$ **56. a.** $\sin \dfrac{\pi}{2}$

   b. $\cos \dfrac{9\pi}{2}$ **b.** $\sin \dfrac{9\pi}{2}$

57. a. $\tan \pi$ **58. a.** $\cot \dfrac{\pi}{2}$

   b. $\tan 17\pi$ **b.** $\cot \dfrac{15\pi}{2}$

59. a. $\sin \dfrac{7\pi}{4}$ **60. a.** $\cos \dfrac{7\pi}{4}$

   b. $\sin \dfrac{47\pi}{4}$ **b.** $\cos \dfrac{47\pi}{4}$

In Exercises 61–70, use a calculator to find the value of the trigonometric function to four decimal places.

61. $\sin 0.8$ **62.** $\cos 0.6$

63. $\tan 3.4$ **64.** $\tan 3.7$

65. $\csc 1$ **66.** $\sec 1$

67. $\cos \dfrac{\pi}{10}$ **68.** $\sin \dfrac{3\pi}{10}$

69. $\cot \dfrac{\pi}{12}$ **70.** $\cot \dfrac{\pi}{18}$

Practice Plus

In Exercises 71–80, let
$$\sin t = a, \; \cos t = b, \; \text{and} \; \tan t = c.$$
Write each expression in terms of a, b, and c.

71. $\sin(-t) - \sin t$
72. $\tan(-t) - \tan t$
73. $4\cos(-t) - \cos t$
74. $3\cos(-t) - \cos t$
75. $\sin(t + 2\pi) - \cos(t + 4\pi) + \tan(t + \pi)$
76. $\sin(t + 2\pi) + \cos(t + 4\pi) - \tan(t + \pi)$
77. $\sin(-t - 2\pi) - \cos(-t - 4\pi) - \tan(-t - \pi)$
78. $\sin(-t - 2\pi) + \cos(-t - 4\pi) - \tan(-t - \pi)$
79. $\cos t + \cos(t + 1000\pi) - \tan t - \tan(t + 999\pi) - \sin t + 4\sin(t - 1000\pi)$
80. $-\cos t + 7\cos(t + 1000\pi) + \tan t + \tan(t + 999\pi) + \sin t + \sin(t - 1000\pi)$

Application Exercises

81. The number of hours of daylight, H, on day t of any given year (on January 1, $t = 1$) in Fairbanks, Alaska, can be modeled by the function
$$H(t) = 12 + 8.3\sin\left[\frac{2\pi}{365}(t - 80)\right].$$

    a. March 21, the 80th day of the year, is the spring equinox. Find the number of hours of daylight in Fairbanks on this day.

    b. June 21, the 172nd day of the year, is the summer solstice, the day with the maximum number of hours of daylight. To the nearest tenth of an hour, find the number of hours of daylight in Fairbanks on this day.

    c. December 21, the 355th day of the year, is the winter solstice, the day with the minimum number of hours of daylight. Find, to the nearest tenth of an hour, the number of hours of daylight in Fairbanks on this day.

82. The number of hours of daylight, H, on day t of any given year (on January 1, $t = 1$) in San Diego, California, can be modeled by the function
$$H(t) = 12 + 2.4\sin\left[\frac{2\pi}{365}(t - 80)\right].$$

    a. March 21, the 80th day of the year, is the spring equinox. Find the number of hours of daylight in San Diego on this day.

    b. June 21, the 172nd day of the year, is the summer solstice, the day with the maximum number of hours of daylight. Find, to the nearest tenth of an hour, the number of hours of daylight in San Diego on this day.

    c. December 21, the 355th day of the year, is the winter solstice, the day with the minimum number of hours of daylight. To the nearest tenth of an hour, find the number of hours of daylight in San Diego on this day.

83. People who believe in biorhythms claim that there are three cycles that rule our behavior—the physical, emotional, and mental. Each is a sine function of a certain period. The function for our emotional fluctuations is
$$E = \sin\frac{\pi}{14}t,$$
where t is measured in days starting at birth. Emotional fluctuations, E, are measured from -1 to 1, inclusive, with 1 representing peak emotional well-being, -1 representing the

low for emotional well-being, and 0 representing feeling neither emotionally high nor low.

    a. Find E corresponding to $t = 7, 14, 21, 28,$ and 35. Describe what you observe.

    b. What is the period of the emotional cycle?

84. The height of the water, H, in feet, at a boat dock t hours after 6 A.M. is given by
$$H = 10 + 4\sin\frac{\pi}{6}t.$$

    a. Find the height of the water at the dock at 6 A.M., 9 A.M., noon, 6 P.M., midnight, and 3 A.M.

    b. When is low tide and when is high tide?

    c. What is the period of this function and what does this mean about the tides?

Writing in Mathematics

85. Why are the trigonometric functions sometimes called circular functions?

86. Define the sine of t.

87. Given a point on the unit circle that corresponds to t, explain how to find $\tan t$.

88. What is the range of the sine function? Use the unit circle to explain where this range comes from.

89. Explain how to use the unit circle to find values of the trigonometric functions at $\frac{\pi}{4}$.

90. What do we mean by even trigonometric functions? Which of the six functions fall into this category?

91. Use words (not an equation) to describe one of the reciprocal identities.

92. Use words (not an equation) to describe one of the quotient identities.

93. Use words (not an equation) to describe one of the Pythagorean identities

94. What is a periodic function? Why are the sine and cosine functions periodic?

95. Explain how you can use the function for emotional fluctuations in Exercise 83 to determine good days for having dinner with your moody boss.

96. Describe a phenomenon that repeats infinitely. What is its period?

Critical Thinking Exercises

97. If $\pi < t < \frac{3\pi}{2}$, which of the following is true?

    a. $\sin t > 0$ and $\tan t > 0$.
    b. $\sin t < 0$ and $\tan t < 0$.
    c. $\tan t > 0$ and $\cot t > 0$.
    d. $\tan t < 0$ and $\cot t < 0$.

98. If $f(x) = \sin x$ and $f(a) = \frac{1}{4}$, find the value of
$$f(a) + f(a + 2\pi) + f(a + 4\pi) + f(a + 6\pi).$$

99. If $f(x) = \sin x$ and $f(a) = \frac{1}{4}$, find the value of $f(a) + 2f(-a)$.

100. The seats of a Ferris wheel are 40 feet from the wheel's center. When you get on the ride, your seat is 5 feet above the ground. How far above the ground are you after rotating through an angle of $\frac{17\pi}{4}$ radians? Round to the nearest foot.

SECTION 4.3 *Right Triangle Trigonometry*

Objectives

❶ Use right triangles to evaluate trigonometric functions.

❷ Find function values for $30° \left(\dfrac{\pi}{6} \right)$, $45° \left(\dfrac{\pi}{4} \right)$, and $60° \left(\dfrac{\pi}{3} \right)$.

❸ Use equal cofunctions of complements.

❹ Use right triangle trigonometry to solve applied problems.

In the last century, Ang Rita Sherpa climbed Mount Everest ten times, all without the use of bottled oxygen.

Mountain climbers have forever been fascinated by reaching the top of Mount Everest, sometimes with tragic results. The mountain, on Asia's Tibet-Nepal border, is Earth's highest, peaking at an incredible 29,035 feet. The heights of mountains can be found using trigonometric functions. Remember that the word *trigonometry* means *measurement of triangles.* Trigonometry is used in navigation, building, and engineering. For centuries, Muslims used trigonometry and the stars to navigate across the Arabian desert to Mecca, the birthplace of the prophet Muhammad, the founder of Islam. The ancient Greeks used trigonometry to record the locations of thousands of stars and worked out the motion of the Moon relative to Earth. Today, trigonometry is used to study the structure of DNA, the master molecule that determines how we grow from a single cell to a complex, fully developed adult.

❶ Use right triangles to evaluate trigonometric functions.

Right Triangle Definitions of Trigonometric Functions

We have seen that in a unit circle, the radian measure of a central angle is equal to the measure of the intercepted arc. Thus, the value of a trigonometric function at the real number t is its value at an angle of t radians

Figure 4.29(a) shows a central angle that measures $\dfrac{\pi}{3}$ radians and an intercepted arc of length $\dfrac{\pi}{3}$. Interpret $\dfrac{\pi}{3}$ as the measure of the central angle. In Figure 4.29(b), we construct a right triangle by dropping a line segment from point P perpendicular to the x-axis.

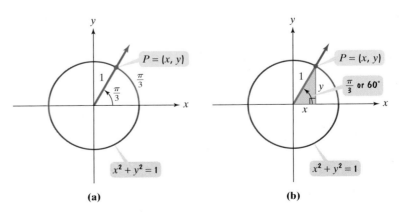

(a)   (b)

Figure 4.29 Interpreting trigonometric functions using a unit circle and a right triangle

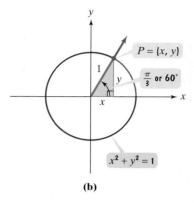

(b)

Figure 4.29(b) (repeated)

Now we can think of $\frac{\pi}{3}$, or 60°, as the measure of an acute angle in the right triangle in Figure 4.29(b). Because sin t is the second coordinate of point P and cos t is the first coordinate of point P, we see that

$$\sin\frac{\pi}{3} = \sin 60° = y = \frac{y}{1}$$

> This is the length of the side opposite the 60° angle in the right triangle.

> This is the length of the hypotenuse in the right triangle.

$$\cos\frac{\pi}{3} = \cos 60° = x = \frac{x}{1}.$$

> This is the length of the side adjacent to the 60° angle in the right triangle.

> This is the length of the hypotenuse in the right triangle.

In solving certain kinds of problems, it is helpful to interpret trigonometric functions in right triangles, where angles are limited to acute angles. Figure 4.30 shows a right triangle with one of its acute angles labeled θ. The side opposite the right angle, the hypotenuse, has length c. The other sides of the triangle are described by their position relative to the acute angle θ. One side is opposite θ. The length of this side is a. One side is adjacent to θ. The length of this side is b.

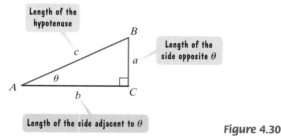

Figure 4.30

Right Triangle Definitions of Trigonometric Functions

See Figure 4.30. The six **trigonometric functions of the acute angle θ** are defined as follows:

$$\sin\theta = \frac{\text{length of side opposite angle } \theta}{\text{length of hypotenuse}} = \frac{a}{c} \qquad \csc\theta = \frac{\text{length of hypotenuse}}{\text{length of side opposite angle } \theta} = \frac{c}{a}$$

$$\cos\theta = \frac{\text{length of side adjacent to angle } \theta}{\text{length of hypotenuse}} = \frac{b}{c} \qquad \sec\theta = \frac{\text{length of hypotenuse}}{\text{length of side adjacent to angle } \theta} = \frac{c}{b}$$

$$\tan\theta = \frac{\text{length of side opposite angle } \theta}{\text{length of side adjacent to angle } \theta} = \frac{a}{b} \qquad \cot\theta = \frac{\text{length of side adjacent to angle } \theta}{\text{length of side opposite angle } \theta} = \frac{b}{a}$$

Each of the trigonometric functions of the acute angle θ is positive. Observe that the ratios in the second column in the box are the reciprocals of the corresponding ratios in the first column.

Study Tip

The word

SOHCAHTOA (pronounced: so-cah-tow-ah)

is a way to remember the right triangle definitions of the three basic trigonometric functions, sine, cosine, and tangent.

S	O H	C	A H	T	O A
↑	opp	↑	adj	↑	opp
	hyp		hyp		adj
Sine		Cosine		Tangent	

"<u>S</u>ome <u>O</u>ld <u>H</u>og <u>C</u>ame <u>A</u>round <u>H</u>ere and <u>T</u>ook <u>O</u>ur <u>A</u>pples."

Figure 4.31 shows four right triangles of varying sizes. In each of the triangles, θ is the same acute angle, measuring approximately 56.3°. All four of these similar triangles have the same shape and the lengths of corresponding sides are in the same ratio. In each triangle, the tangent function has the same value for the angle θ: $\tan \theta = \frac{3}{2}$.

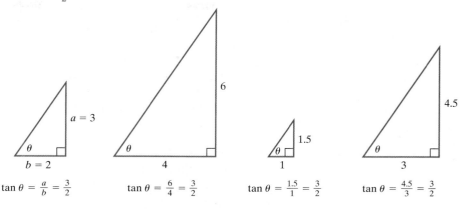

$$\tan \theta = \frac{a}{b} = \frac{3}{2} \qquad \tan \theta = \frac{6}{4} = \frac{3}{2} \qquad \tan \theta = \frac{1.5}{1} = \frac{3}{2} \qquad \tan \theta = \frac{4.5}{3} = \frac{3}{2}$$

Figure 4.31 A particular acute angle always gives the same ratio of opposite to adjacent sides.

In general, **the trigonometric function values of θ depend only on the size of angle θ and not on the size of the triangle.**

EXAMPLE 1   Evaluating Trigonometric Functions

Find the value of each of the six trigonometric functions of θ in Figure 4.32.

Solution   We need to find the values of the six trigonometric functions of θ. However, we must know the lengths of all three sides of the triangle (a, b, and c) to evaluate all six functions. The values of a and b are given. We can use the Pythagorean Theorem, $c^2 = a^2 + b^2$, to find c.

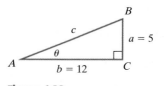

Figure 4.32

$$\boxed{a = 5} \quad \boxed{b = 12}$$

$$c^2 = a^2 + b^2 = 5^2 + 12^2 = 25 + 144 = 169$$

$$c = \sqrt{169} = 13$$

Now that we know the lengths of the three sides of the triangle, we apply the definitions of the six trigonometric functions of θ. Referring to these lengths as opposite, adjacent, and hypotenuse, we have

$$\sin \theta = \frac{\text{opposite}}{\text{hypotenuse}} = \frac{5}{13} \qquad\qquad \csc \theta = \frac{\text{hypotenuse}}{\text{opposite}} = \frac{13}{5}$$

$$\cos \theta = \frac{\text{adjacent}}{\text{hypotenuse}} = \frac{12}{13} \qquad\qquad \sec \theta = \frac{\text{hypotenuse}}{\text{adjacent}} = \frac{13}{12}$$

$$\tan \theta = \frac{\text{opposite}}{\text{adjacent}} = \frac{5}{12} \qquad\qquad \cot \theta = \frac{\text{adjacent}}{\text{opposite}} = \frac{12}{5}.$$

Study Tip

The function values in the second column are reciprocals of those in the first column. You can obtain these values by exchanging the numerator and denominator of the corresponding ratios in the first column.

Check Point 1   Find the value of each of the six trigonometric functions of θ in the figure.

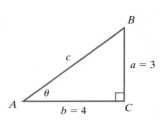

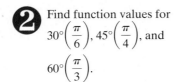

Figure 4.33

EXAMPLE 2   Evaluating Trigonometric Functions

Find the value of each of the six trigonometric functions of θ in Figure 4.33.

Solution   We begin by finding b.

$a^2 + b^2 = c^2$	Use the Pythagorean Theorem.
$1^2 + b^2 = 3^2$	Figure 4.33 shows that $a = 1$ and $c = 3$.
$1 + b^2 = 9$	$1^2 = 1$ and $3^2 = 9$.
$b^2 = 8$	Subtract 1 from both sides.
$b = \sqrt{8} = 2\sqrt{2}$	Take the principal square root and simplify: $\sqrt{8} = \sqrt{4 \cdot 2} = \sqrt{4}\sqrt{2} = 2\sqrt{2}$.

Now that we know the lengths of the three sides of the triangle, we apply the definitions of the six trigonometric functions of θ.

$$\sin \theta = \frac{\text{opposite}}{\text{hypotenuse}} = \frac{1}{3} \qquad \csc \theta = \frac{\text{hypotenuse}}{\text{opposite}} = \frac{3}{1} = 3$$

$$\cos \theta = \frac{\text{adjacent}}{\text{hypotenuse}} = \frac{2\sqrt{2}}{3} \qquad \sec \theta = \frac{\text{hypotenuse}}{\text{adjacent}} = \frac{3}{2\sqrt{2}}$$

$$\tan \theta = \frac{\text{opposite}}{\text{adjacent}} = \frac{1}{2\sqrt{2}} \qquad \cot \theta = \frac{\text{adjacent}}{\text{opposite}} = \frac{2\sqrt{2}}{1} = 2\sqrt{2}$$

We can simplify the values of $\tan \theta$ and $\sec \theta$ by rationalizing the denominators:

$$\tan \theta = \frac{1}{2\sqrt{2}} = \frac{1}{2\sqrt{2}} \cdot \frac{\sqrt{2}}{\sqrt{2}} = \frac{\sqrt{2}}{2 \cdot 2} = \frac{\sqrt{2}}{4} \qquad \sec \theta = \frac{3}{2\sqrt{2}} = \frac{3}{2\sqrt{2}} \cdot \frac{\sqrt{2}}{\sqrt{2}} = \frac{3\sqrt{2}}{2 \cdot 2} = \frac{3\sqrt{2}}{4}.$$

We are multiplying by 1 and not changing the value of $\dfrac{1}{2\sqrt{2}}$.

We are multiplying by 1 and not changing the value of $\dfrac{3}{2\sqrt{2}}$.

Check Point 2   Find the value of each of the six trigonometric functions of θ in the figure. Express each value in simplified form.

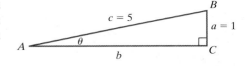

2 Find function values for $30° \left(\dfrac{\pi}{6}\right)$, $45° \left(\dfrac{\pi}{4}\right)$, and $60° \left(\dfrac{\pi}{3}\right)$.

Function Values for Some Special Angles

In Section 4.2, we used the unit circle to find values of the trigonometric functions at $\dfrac{\pi}{4}$. How can we find the values of the trigonometric functions at $\dfrac{\pi}{4}$, or 45°, using a right triangle? We construct a right triangle with a 45° angle, as shown in Figure 4.34 at the top of the next page. The triangle actually has two 45° angles. Thus, the triangle is isosceles—that is, it has two sides of the same length. Assume that each leg of the triangle has a length equal to 1. We can find the length of the hypotenuse using the Pythagorean Theorem.

$$(\text{length of hypotenuse})^2 = 1^2 + 1^2 = 2$$

$$\text{length of hypotenuse} = \sqrt{2}$$

With Figure 4.34, we can determine the trigonometric function values for 45°.

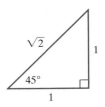

Figure 4.34 An isosceles right triangle

EXAMPLE 3 Evaluating Trigonometric Functions of 45°

Use Figure 4.34 to find sin 45°, cos 45°, and tan 45°.

Solution   We apply the definitions of these three trigonometric functions. Where appropriate, we simplify by rationalizing denominators.

$$\sin 45° = \frac{\text{length of side opposite } 45°}{\text{length of hypotenuse}} = \frac{1}{\sqrt{2}} = \frac{1}{\sqrt{2}} \cdot \frac{\sqrt{2}}{\sqrt{2}} = \frac{\sqrt{2}}{2}$$

> Rationalize denominators

$$\cos 45° = \frac{\text{length of side adjacent to } 45°}{\text{length of hypotenuse}} = \frac{1}{\sqrt{2}} = \frac{1}{\sqrt{2}} \cdot \frac{\sqrt{2}}{\sqrt{2}} = \frac{\sqrt{2}}{2}$$

$$\tan 45° = \frac{\text{length of side opposite } 45°}{\text{length of side adjacent to } 45°} = \frac{1}{1} = 1$$

Check Point 3   Use Figure 4.34 to find csc 45°, sec 45°, and cot 45°.

When you worked Check Point 3, did you actually use Figure 4.34 or did you use reciprocals to find the values?

$$\csc 45° = \sqrt{2} \qquad\qquad \sec 45° = \sqrt{2} \qquad\qquad \cot 45° = 1$$

> Take the reciprocal of sin 45° $= \frac{1}{\sqrt{2}}$.

> Take the reciprocal of cos 45° $= \frac{1}{\sqrt{2}}$.

> Take the reciprocal of tan 45° $= \frac{1}{1}$.

Notice that if you use reciprocals, you should take the reciprocal of a function value before the denominator is rationalized. In this way, the reciprocal value will not contain a radical in the denominator.

Two other angles that occur frequently in trigonometry are 30°, or $\frac{\pi}{6}$ radian, and 60°, or $\frac{\pi}{3}$ radian, angles. We can find the values of the trigonometric functions of 30° and 60° by using a right triangle. To form this right triangle, draw an equilateral triangle—that is a triangle with all sides the same length. Assume that each side has a length equal to 2. Now take half of the equilateral triangle. We obtain the right triangle in Figure 4.35. This right triangle has a hypotenuse of length 2 and a leg of length 1. The other leg has length a, which can be found using the Pythagorean Theorem.

$$a^2 + 1^2 = 2^2$$
$$a^2 + 1 = 4$$
$$a^2 = 3$$
$$a = \sqrt{3}$$

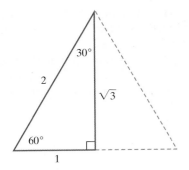

Figure 4.35 30°–60°–90° triangle

With the right triangle in Figure 4.35, we can determine the trigonometric functions for 30° and 60°.

EXAMPLE 4 Evaluating Trigonometric Functions of 30° and 60°

Use Figure 4.35 to find sin 60°, cos 60°, sin 30°, and cos 30°.

Solution   We begin with 60°. Use the angle on the lower left in Figure 4.35.

$$\sin 60° = \frac{\text{length of side opposite } 60°}{\text{length of hypotenuse}} = \frac{\sqrt{3}}{2}$$

$$\cos 60° = \frac{\text{length of side adjacent to } 60°}{\text{length of hypotenuse}} = \frac{1}{2}$$

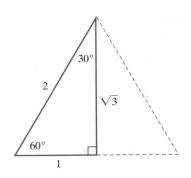

Figure 4.35 (repeated)

To find sin 30° and cos 30°, use the angle on the upper right in Figure 4.35.

$$\sin 30° = \frac{\text{length of side opposite } 30°}{\text{length of hypotenuse}} = \frac{1}{2}$$

$$\cos 30° = \frac{\text{length of side adjacent to } 30°}{\text{length of hypotenuse}} = \frac{\sqrt{3}}{2}$$

Check Point 4 Use Figure 4.35 to find tan 60° and tan 30°. If a radical appears in a denominator, rationalize the denominator.

Because we will often use the function values of 30°, 45°, and 60°, you should learn to construct the right triangles shown in Figures 4.34 and 4.35. With sufficient practice, you will memorize the values in Table 4.2.

Table 4.2   Trigonometric Functions of Special Angles

θ	$30° = \dfrac{\pi}{6}$	$45° = \dfrac{\pi}{4}$	$60° = \dfrac{\pi}{3}$
$\sin \theta$	$\dfrac{1}{2}$	$\dfrac{\sqrt{2}}{2}$	$\dfrac{\sqrt{3}}{2}$
$\cos \theta$	$\dfrac{\sqrt{3}}{2}$	$\dfrac{\sqrt{2}}{2}$	$\dfrac{1}{2}$
$\tan \theta$	$\dfrac{\sqrt{3}}{3}$	1	$\sqrt{3}$

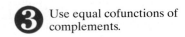

❸ Use equal cofunctions of complements.

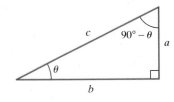

Figure 4.36

Trigonometric Functions and Complements

Two positive angles are **complements** if their sum is 90° or $\dfrac{\pi}{2}$. For example, angles of 70° and 20° are complements because 70° + 20° = 90°.

In Section 4.2, we used the unit circle to establish fundamental trigonometric identities. Another relationship among trigonometric functions is based on angles that are complements. Refer to Figure 4.36. Because the sum of the angles of any triangle is 180°, in a right triangle the sum of the acute angles is 90°. Thus, the acute angles are complements. If the degree measure of one acute angle is θ, then the degree measure of the other acute angle is $(90° - \theta)$. This angle is shown on the upper right in Figure 4.36.

Let's use Figure 4.36 to compare sin θ and cos(90° − θ).

$$\sin \theta = \frac{\text{length of side opposite } \theta}{\text{length of hypotenuse}} = \frac{a}{c}$$

$$\cos(90° - \theta) = \frac{\text{length of side adjacent to } (90° - \theta)}{\text{length of hypotenuse}} = \frac{a}{c}$$

Thus, sin θ = cos(90° − θ). If two angles are complements, the sine of one equals the cosine of the other. Because of this relationship, the sine and cosine are called *cofunctions* of each other. The name *cosine* is a shortened form of the phrase *complement's sine*.

Any pair of trigonometric functions f and g for which

$$f(\theta) = g(90° - \theta) \quad \text{and} \quad g(\theta) = f(90° - \theta)$$

are called **cofunctions**. Using Figure 4.36, we can show that the tangent and cotangent are also cofunctions of each other. So are the secant and cosecant.

Cofunction Identities

The value of a trigonometric function of θ is equal to the cofunction of the complement of θ. Cofunctions of complementary angles are equal.

$$\sin \theta = \cos(90° - \theta) \qquad \cos \theta = \sin(90° - \theta)$$
$$\tan \theta = \cot(90° - \theta) \qquad \cot \theta = \tan(90° - \theta)$$
$$\sec \theta = \csc(90° - \theta) \qquad \csc \theta = \sec(90° - \theta)$$

If θ is in radians, replace $90°$ with $\dfrac{\pi}{2}$.

EXAMPLE 5   Using Cofunction Identities

Find a cofunction with the same value as the given expression:

    a. $\sin 72°$ **b.** $\csc \dfrac{\pi}{3}$.

Solution Because the value of a trigonometric function of θ is equal to the cofunction of the complement of θ, we need to find the complement of each angle. We do this by subtracting the angle's measure from $90°$ or its radian equivalent, $\dfrac{\pi}{2}$.

    a. $\sin 72° = \cos(90° - 72°) = \cos 18°$

> We have a function and its cofunction.

    b. $\csc \dfrac{\pi}{3} = \sec\left(\dfrac{\pi}{2} - \dfrac{\pi}{3}\right) = \sec\left(\dfrac{3\pi}{6} - \dfrac{2\pi}{6}\right) = \sec\dfrac{\pi}{6}$

> We have a cofunction and its function.

> Perform the subtraction using the least common denominator, 6.

Check Point 5 Find a cofunction with the same value as the given expression:

    a. $\sin 46°$ **b.** $\cot \dfrac{\pi}{12}$.

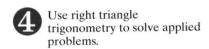

    Use right triangle trigonometry to solve applied problems.

Applications

Many applications of right triangle trigonometry involve the angle made with an imaginary horizontal line. As shown in Figure 4.37, an angle formed by a horizontal line and the line of sight to an object that is above the horizontal line is called the **angle of elevation**. The angle formed by a horizontal line and the line of sight to an object that is below the horizontal line is called the **angle of depression**. Transits and sextants are instruments used to measure such angles.

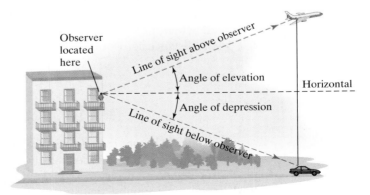

Figure 4.37

EXAMPLE 6   Problem Solving Using an Angle of Elevation

Sighting the top of a building, a surveyor measured the angle of elevation to be 22°. The transit is 5 feet above the ground and 300 feet from the building. Find the building's height.

Solution   The situation is illustrated in Figure 4.38. Let a be the height of the portion of the building that lies above the transit. The height of the building is the transit's height, 5 feet, plus a. Thus, we need to identify a trigonometric function that will make it possible to find a. In terms of the 22° angle, we are looking for the side

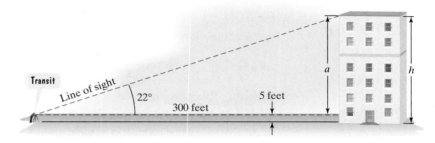

Figure 4.38

opposite the angle. The transit is 300 feet from the building, so the side adjacent to the 22° angle is 300 feet. Because we have a known angle, an unknown opposite side, and a known adjacent side, we select the tangent function.

$$\tan 22° = \frac{a}{300} \quad \begin{array}{l} \boxed{\text{Length of side opposite the 22° angle}} \\ \boxed{\text{Length of side adjacent to the 22° angle}} \end{array}$$

$$a = 300 \tan 22° \qquad \text{Multiply both sides of the equation by 300.}$$

$$a \approx 121 \qquad \text{Use a calculator in the degree mode.}$$

The height of the part of the building above the transit is approximately 121 feet. Thus, the height of the building is determined by adding the transit's height, 5 feet, to 121 feet.

$$h \approx 5 + 121 = 126$$

The building's height is approximately 126 feet.

Check Point 6   The irregular blue shape in Figure 4.39 represents a lake. The distance across the lake, a, is unknown. To find this distance, a surveyor took the measurements shown in the figure. What is the distance across the lake?

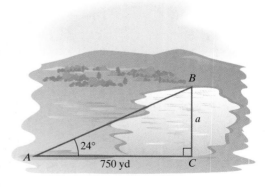

Figure 4.39

If two sides of a right triangle are known, an appropriate trigonometric function can be used to find an acute angle θ in the triangle. You will also need to use an inverse trigonometric key on a calculator. These keys use a function value to display the acute angle θ. For example, suppose that $\sin \theta = 0.866$. We can find θ in the degree mode by using the secondary *inverse sine* key, usually labeled $\boxed{\text{SIN}^{-1}}$. The key $\boxed{\text{SIN}^{-1}}$ is not a button you will actually press. It is the secondary function for the button labeled $\boxed{\text{SIN}}$.

Many Scientific Calculators:

.866 $\boxed{\text{2nd}}$ $\boxed{\text{SIN}}$

Pressing $\boxed{\text{2nd}}$ $\boxed{\text{SIN}}$ accesses the inverse sine key, $\boxed{\text{SIN}^{-1}}$.

Many Graphing Calculators:

$\boxed{\text{2nd}}$ $\boxed{\text{SIN}}$ .866 $\boxed{\text{ENTER}}$

The display should show approximately 59.99, which can be rounded to 60. Thus, if sin θ = 0.866, then $\theta \approx 60°$.

EXAMPLE 7   Determining the Angle of Elevation

A building that is 21 meters tall casts a shadow 25 meters long. Find the angle of elevation of the sun to the nearest degree.

Solution   The situation is illustrated in Figure 4.40. We are asked to find θ. We begin with the tangent function.

$$\tan \theta = \frac{\text{side opposite } \theta}{\text{side adjacent to } \theta} = \frac{21}{25}$$

We use a calculator in the degree mode to find θ.

Many Scientific Calculators:

$\boxed{(}$ 21 $\boxed{\div}$ 25 $\boxed{)}$ $\boxed{\text{2nd}}$ $\boxed{\text{TAN}}$

Pressing $\boxed{\text{2nd}}$ $\boxed{\text{TAN}}$ accesses the inverse tangent key, $\boxed{\text{TAN}^{-1}}$.

Many Graphing Calculators:

$\boxed{\text{2nd}}$ $\boxed{\text{TAN}}$ $\boxed{(}$ 21 $\boxed{\div}$ 25 $\boxed{)}$ $\boxed{\text{ENTER}}$

The display should show approximately 40. Thus, the angle of elevation of the sun is approximately 40°.

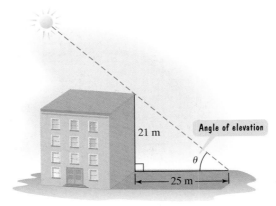

Figure 4.40

Check Point 7   A flagpole that is 14 meters tall casts a shadow 10 meters long. Find the angle of elevation of the sun to the nearest degree.

The Mountain Man

In the 1930s, a *National Geographic* team headed by Brad Washburn used trigonometry to create a map of the 5000-square-mile region of the Yukon, near the Canadian border. The team started with aerial photography. By drawing a network of angles on the photographs, the approximate locations of the major mountains and their rough heights were determined. The expedition then spent three months on foot to find the exact heights. Team members established two base points a known distance apart, one directly under the mountain's peak. By measuring the angle of elevation from one of the base points to the peak, the tangent function was used to determine the peak's height. The Yukon expedition was a major advance in the way maps are made.

EXERCISE SET 4.3

Practice Exercises

In Exercises 1–8, use the Pythagorean Theorem to find the length of the missing side of each right triangle. Then find the value of each of the six trigonometric functions of θ.

1.

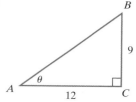

2.

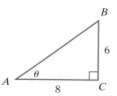

3.

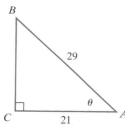

4.

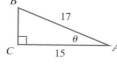

5.

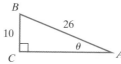

6.

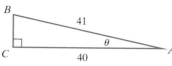

7.

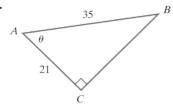

8.

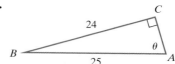

In Exercises 9–20, use the given triangles to evaluate each expression. If necessary, express the value without a square root in the denominator by rationalizing the denominator.

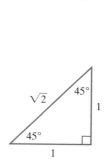 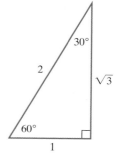

9. cos 30°   **10.** tan 30°

11. sec 45°   **12.** csc 45°

13. $\tan \dfrac{\pi}{3}$ **14.** $\cot \dfrac{\pi}{3}$

15. $\sin \dfrac{\pi}{4} - \cos \dfrac{\pi}{4}$ **16.** $\tan \dfrac{\pi}{4} + \csc \dfrac{\pi}{6}$

17. $\sin \dfrac{\pi}{3} \cos \dfrac{\pi}{4} - \tan \dfrac{\pi}{4}$ **18.** $\cos \dfrac{\pi}{3} \sec \dfrac{\pi}{3} - \cot \dfrac{\pi}{3}$

19. $2 \tan \dfrac{\pi}{3} + \cos \dfrac{\pi}{4} \tan \dfrac{\pi}{6}$ **20.** $6 \tan \dfrac{\pi}{4} + \sin \dfrac{\pi}{3} \sec \dfrac{\pi}{6}$

In Exercises 21–28, find a cofunction with the same value as the given expression.

21. sin 7°   **22.** sin 19°

23. csc 25°   **24.** csc 35°

25. $\tan \dfrac{\pi}{9}$ **26.** $\tan \dfrac{\pi}{7}$

27. $\cos \dfrac{2\pi}{5}$

28. $\cos \dfrac{3\pi}{8}$

In Exercises 29–34, find the measure of the side of the right triangle whose length is designated by a lowercase letter. Round answers to the nearest whole number.

29.

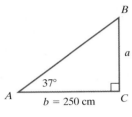

30.

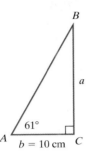

31.

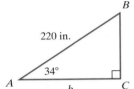

32.

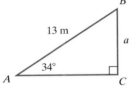

33.

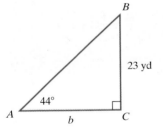

34.

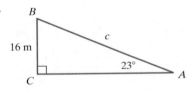

In Exercises 35–38, use a calculator to find the value of the acute angle θ to the nearest degree.

35. $\sin \theta = 0.2974$

36. $\cos \theta = 0.8771$

37. $\tan \theta = 4.6252$

38. $\tan \theta = 26.0307$

In Exercises 39–42, use a calculator to find the value of the acute angle θ in radians, rounded to three decimal places.

39. $\cos \theta = 0.4112$

40. $\sin \theta = 0.9499$

41. $\tan \theta = 0.4169$

42. $\tan \theta = 0.5117$

Practice Plus

In Exercises 43–48, find the exact value of each expression. Do not use a calculator.

43. $\dfrac{\tan \dfrac{\pi}{3}}{2} - \dfrac{1}{\sec \dfrac{\pi}{6}}$

44. $\dfrac{1}{\cot \dfrac{\pi}{4}} - \dfrac{2}{\csc \dfrac{\pi}{6}}$

45. $1 + \sin^2 40° + \sin^2 50°$

46. $1 - \tan^2 10° + \csc^2 80°$

47. $\csc 37° \sec 53° - \tan 53° \cot 37°$

48. $\cos 12° \sin 78° + \cos 78° \sin 12°$

In Exercises 49–50, express each exact value as a single fraction. Do not use a calculator.

49. If $f(\theta) = 2 \cos \theta - \cos 2\theta$, find $f\left(\dfrac{\pi}{6}\right)$.

50. If $f(\theta) = 2 \sin \theta - \sin \dfrac{\theta}{2}$, find $f\left(\dfrac{\pi}{3}\right)$.

51. If θ is an acute angle and $\cot \theta = \dfrac{1}{4}$, find $\tan\left(\dfrac{\pi}{2} - \theta\right)$.

52. If θ is an acute angle and $\cos \theta = \dfrac{1}{3}$, find $\csc\left(\dfrac{\pi}{2} - \theta\right)$.

 Application Exercises

53. To find the distance across a lake, a surveyor took the measurements shown in the figure. Use these measurements to determine how far it is across the lake. Round to the nearest yard.

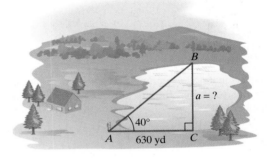

54. At a certain time of day, the angle of elevation of the sun is 40°. To the nearest foot, find the height of a tree whose shadow is 35 feet long.

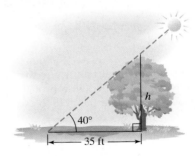

55. A tower that is 125 feet tall casts a shadow 172 feet long. Find the angle of elevation of the sun to the nearest degree.

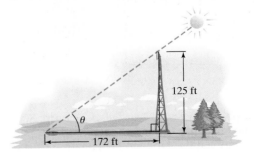

56. The Washington Monument is 555 feet high. If you stand one quarter of a mile, or 1320 feet, from the base of the monument and look to the top, find the angle of elevation to the nearest degree.

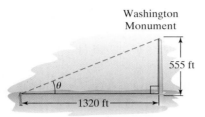

Washington
Monument

555 ft

1320 ft

57. A plane rises from take-off and flies at an angle of 10° with the horizontal runway. When it has gained 500 feet, find the distance, to the nearest foot, the plane has flown.

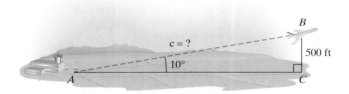

B

c = ?

500 ft

10°

A   C

58. A road is inclined at an angle of 5°. After driving 5000 feet along this road, find the driver's increase in altitude. Round to the nearest foot.

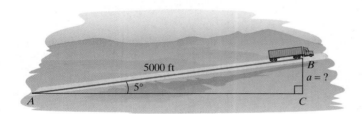

5000 ft

B

a = ?

5°

A   C

59. A telephone pole is 60 feet tall. A guy wire 75 feet long is attached from the ground to the top of the pole. Find the angle between the wire and the pole to the nearest degree.

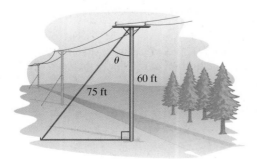

θ

60 ft

75 ft

60. A telephone pole is 55 feet tall. A guy wire 80 feet long is attached from the ground to the top of the pole. Find the angle between the wire and the pole to the nearest degree.

Writing in Mathematics

61. If you are given the lengths of the sides of a right triangle, describe how to find the sine of either acute angle.

62. Describe one similarity and one difference between the definitions of $\sin \theta$ and $\cos \theta$, where θ is an acute angle of a right triangle.

63. Describe the triangle used to find the trigonometric functions of 45°.

64. Describe the triangle used to find the trigonometric functions of 30° and 60°.

65. Describe a relationship among trigonometric functions that is based on angles that are complements.

66. Describe what is meant by an angle of elevation and an angle of depression.

67. Stonehenge, the famous "stone circle" in England, was built between 2750 B.C. and 1300 B.C. using solid stone blocks weighing over 99,000 pounds each. It required 550 people to pull a single stone up a ramp inclined at a 9° angle. Describe how right triangle trigonometry can be used to determine the distance the 550 workers had to drag a stone in order to raise it to a height of 30 feet.

Technology Exercises

68. Use a calculator in the radian mode to fill in the values in the following table. Then draw a conclusion about $\dfrac{\sin \theta}{\theta}$ as θ approaches 0.

θ	0.4	0.3	0.2	0.1	0.01	0.001	0.0001	0.00001
$\sin \theta$								
$\dfrac{\sin \theta}{\theta}$								

69. Use a calculator in the radian mode to fill in the values in the following table. Then draw a conclusion about $\dfrac{\cos \theta - 1}{\theta}$ as θ approaches 0.

θ	0.4	0.3	0.2	0.1	0.01	0.001	0.0001	0.00001
$\cos \theta$								
$\dfrac{\cos \theta - 1}{\theta}$								

Critical Thinking Exercises

70. Which one of the following is true?

a. $\dfrac{\tan 45°}{\tan 15°} = \tan 3°$

b. $\tan^2 15° - \sec^2 15° = -1$

c. $\sin 45° + \cos 45° = 1$

d. $\tan^2 5° = \tan 25°$

71. Explain why the sine or cosine of an acute angle cannot be greater than or equal to 1.

72. Describe what happens to the tangent of an acute angle as the angle gets close to 90°. What happens at 90°?

73. From the top of a 250-foot lighthouse, a plane is sighted overhead and a ship is observed directly below the plane. The angle of elevation of the plane is 22° and the angle of depression of the ship is 35°. Find **a.** the distance of the ship from the lighthouse; **b.** the plane's height above the water. Round to the nearest foot.

SECTION 4.4 Trigonometric Functions of Any Angle

Objectives
1 Use the definitions of trigonometric functions of any angle.
2 Use the signs of the trigonometric functions.
3 Find reference angles.
4 Use reference angles to evaluate trigonometric functions.

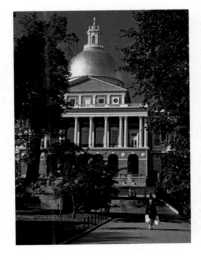

Cycles govern many aspects of life—heartbeats, sleep patterns, seasons, and tides all follow regular, predictable cycles. Because of their periodic nature, trigonometric functions are used to model phenomena that occur in cycles. It is helpful to apply these models regardless of whether we think of the domains of trigonometric functions as sets of real numbers or sets of angles. In order to understand and use models for cyclic phenomena from an angle perspective, we need to move beyond right triangles.

Use the definitions of trigonometric functions of any angle.

Trigonometric Functions of Any Angle

In the last section, we evaluated trigonometric functions of acute angles, such as that shown in Figure 4.41(a). Note that this angle is in standard position. The point $P = (x, y)$ is a point r units from the origin on the terminal side of θ. A right triangle is formed by drawing a line segment from $P = (x, y)$ perpendicular to the x-axis. Note that y is the length of the side opposite θ and x is the length of the side adjacent to θ.

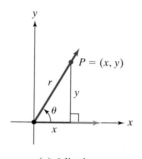

(a) θ lies in quadrant I.

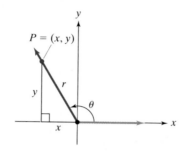

(b) θ lies in quadrant II.

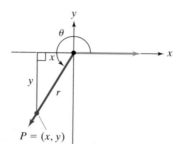

(c) θ lies in quadrant III.

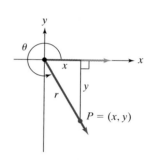

(d) θ lies in quadrant IV.

Figure 4.41

Figures 4.41(b), (c), and (d) show angles in standard position, but they are not acute. We can extend our definitions of the six trigonometric functions to include such angles, as well as quadrantal angles. (Recall that a quadrantal angle has its terminal side on the x-axis or y-axis; such angles are *not* shown in Figure 4.41.) The point $P = (x, y)$ may be any point on the terminal side of the angle θ other than the origin, $(0, 0)$.

If θ is acute, we have the right triangle shown in Figure 4.41(a). In this situation, the definitions in the box are the right triangle definitions of the trigonometric functions. This should make it easier for you to remember the six definitions.

Definitions of Trigonometric Functions of Any Angle

Let θ be any angle in standard position and let $P = (x, y)$ be a point on the terminal side of θ. If $r = \sqrt{x^2 + y^2}$ is the distance from $(0, 0)$ to (x, y), as shown in Figure 4.41, the **six trigonometric functions of θ** are defined by the following ratios:

$$\sin \theta = \frac{y}{r} \qquad \csc \theta = \frac{r}{y}, y \neq 0$$

$$\cos \theta = \frac{x}{r} \qquad \sec \theta = \frac{r}{x}, x \neq 0$$

$$\tan \theta = \frac{y}{x}, x \neq 0 \qquad \cot \theta = \frac{x}{y}, y \neq 0.$$

The ratios in the second column are the reciprocals of the corresponding ratios in the first column.

Because the point $P = (x, y)$ is any point on the terminal side of θ other than the origin, $(0, 0)$, $r = \sqrt{x^2 + y^2}$ cannot be zero. Examine the six trigonometric functions defined above. Note that the denominator of the sine and cosine functions is r. Because $r \neq 0$, the sine and cosine functions are defined for any real value of the angle θ. This is not true for the other four trigonometric functions. Note that the denominator of the tangent and secant functions is x: $\tan \theta = \frac{y}{x}$ and $\sec \theta = \frac{r}{x}$. These functions are not defined if $x = 0$. If the point $P = (x, y)$ is on the y-axis, then $x = 0$. Thus, the tangent and secant functions are undefined for all quadrantal angles with terminal sides on the positive or negative y-axis. Likewise, if $P = (x, y)$ is on the x-axis, then $y = 0$, and the cotangent and cosecant functions are undefined: $\cot \theta = \frac{x}{y}$ and $\csc \theta = \frac{r}{y}$. The cotangent and cosecant functions are undefined for all quadrantal angles with terminal sides on the positive or negative x-axis.

EXAMPLE 1   Evaluating Trigonometric Functions

Let $P = (-3, -5)$ be a point on the terminal side of θ. Find each of the six trigonometric functions of θ.

Solution   The situation is shown in Figure 4.42. We need values for x, y, and r to evaluate all six trigonometric functions. We are given the values of x and y. Because $P = (-3, -5)$ is a point on the terminal side of θ, $x = -3$ and $y = -5$. Furthermore,

$$r = \sqrt{x^2 + y^2} = \sqrt{(-3)^2 + (-5)^2} = \sqrt{9 + 25} = \sqrt{34}.$$

Now that we know x, y, and r, we can find the six trigonometric functions of θ. Where appropriate, we will rationalize denominators.

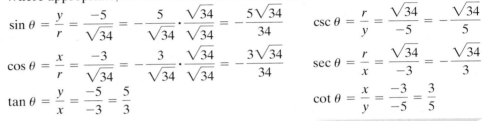

$$\sin \theta = \frac{y}{r} = \frac{-5}{\sqrt{34}} = -\frac{5}{\sqrt{34}} \cdot \frac{\sqrt{34}}{\sqrt{34}} = -\frac{5\sqrt{34}}{34} \qquad \csc \theta = \frac{r}{y} = \frac{\sqrt{34}}{-5} = -\frac{\sqrt{34}}{5}$$

$$\cos \theta = \frac{x}{r} = \frac{-3}{\sqrt{34}} = -\frac{3}{\sqrt{34}} \cdot \frac{\sqrt{34}}{\sqrt{34}} = -\frac{3\sqrt{34}}{34} \qquad \sec \theta = \frac{r}{x} = \frac{\sqrt{34}}{-3} = -\frac{\sqrt{34}}{3}$$

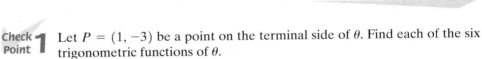

$$\tan \theta = \frac{y}{x} = \frac{-5}{-3} = \frac{5}{3} \qquad \cot \theta = \frac{x}{y} = \frac{-3}{-5} = \frac{3}{5}$$

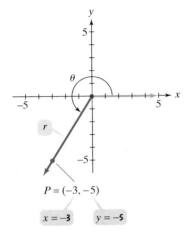

Figure 4.42

Check Point 1   Let $P = (1, -3)$ be a point on the terminal side of θ. Find each of the six trigonometric functions of θ.

How do we find the values of the trigonometric functions for a quadrantal angle? First, draw the angle in standard position. Second, choose a point P on the angle's terminal side. The trigonometric function values of θ depend only on the size of θ and not on the distance of point P from the origin. Thus, we will choose a point that is 1 unit from the origin. Finally, apply the definitions of the appropriate trigonometric functions.

EXAMPLE 2   Trigonometric Functions of Quadrantal Angles

Evaluate, if possible, the sine function and the tangent function at the following four quadrantal angles:

a. $\theta = 0° = 0$ **b.** $\theta = 90° = \dfrac{\pi}{2}$ **c.** $\theta = 180° = \pi$ **d.** $\theta = 270° = \dfrac{3\pi}{2}$.

Solution

a. If $\theta = 0° = 0$ radians, then the terminal side of the angle is on the positive x-axis. Let us select the point $P = (1, 0)$ with $x = 1$ and $y = 0$. This point is 1 unit from the origin, so $r = 1$. Figure 4.43 shows values of x, y, and r corresponding to $\theta = 0°$ or 0 radians. Now that we know x, y, and r, we can apply the definitions of the sine and tangent functions.

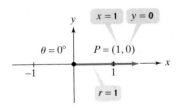

Figure 4.43

$$\sin 0° = \sin 0 = \frac{y}{r} = \frac{0}{1} = 0$$

$$\tan 0° = \tan 0 = \frac{y}{x} = \frac{0}{1} = 0$$

b. If $\theta = 90° = \dfrac{\pi}{2}$ radians, then the terminal side of the angle is on the positive y-axis. Let us select the point $P = (0, 1)$ with $x = 0$ and $y = 1$. This point is 1 unit from the origin, so $r = 1$. Figure 4.44 shows values of x, y, and r corresponding to $\theta = 90°$ or $\dfrac{\pi}{2}$. Now that we know x, y, and r, we can apply the definitions of the sine and tangent functions.

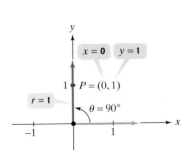

Figure 4.44

$$\sin 90° = \sin \frac{\pi}{2} = \frac{y}{r} = \frac{1}{1} = 1$$

$$\tan 90° = \tan \frac{\pi}{2} = \frac{y}{x} = \frac{1}{0}$$

Because division by 0 is undefined, $\tan 90°$ is undefined.

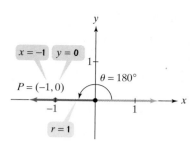

Figure 4.45

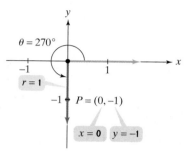

Figure 4.46

Discovery

Try finding tan 90° and tan 270° with your calculator. Describe what occurs.

c. If $\theta = 180° = \pi$ radians, then the terminal side of the angle is on the negative x-axis. Let us select the point $P = (-1, 0)$ with $x = -1$ and $y = 0$. This point is 1 unit from the origin, so $r = 1$. Figure 4.45 shows values of x, y, and r corresponding to $\theta = 180°$ or π. Now that we know x, y, and r, we can apply the definitions of the sine and tangent functions.

$$\sin 180° = \sin \pi = \frac{y}{r} = \frac{0}{1} = 0$$

$$\tan 180° = \tan \pi = \frac{y}{x} = \frac{0}{-1} = 0$$

d. If $\theta = 270° = \frac{3\pi}{2}$ radians, then the terminal side of the angle is on the negative y-axis. Let us select the point $P = (0, -1)$ with $x = 0$ and $y = -1$. This point is 1 unit from the origin, so $r = 1$. Figure 4.46 shows values of x, y, and r corresponding to $\theta = 270°$ or $\frac{3\pi}{2}$. Now that we know x, y, and r, we can apply the definitions of the sine and tangent functions.

$$\sin 270° = \sin \frac{3\pi}{2} = \frac{y}{r} = \frac{-1}{1} = -1$$

$$\tan 270° = \tan \frac{3\pi}{2} = \frac{y}{x} = \frac{-1}{0}$$

Because division by 0 is undefined, tan 270° is undefined.

Check Point 2 Evaluate, if possible, the cosine function and the cosecant function at the following four quadrantal angles:

a. $\theta = 0° = 0$ **b.** $\theta = 90° = \frac{\pi}{2}$

c. $\theta = 180° = \pi$ **d.** $\theta = 270° = \frac{3\pi}{2}$.

② Use the signs of the trigonometric functions.

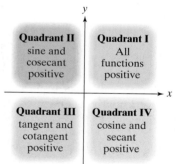

Figure 4.47 The signs of the trigonometric functions

The Signs of the Trigonometric Functions

In Example 2, we evaluated trigonometric functions of quadrantal angles. However, we will now return to the trigonometric functions of nonquadrantal angles. **If θ is not a quadrantal angle, the sign of a trigonometric function depends on the quadrant in which θ lies.** In all four quadrants, r is positive. However, x and y can be positive or negative. For example, if θ lies in quadrant II, x is negative and y is positive. Thus, the only positive ratios in this quadrant are $\frac{y}{r}$ and its reciprocal, $\frac{r}{y}$. These ratios are the function values for the sine and cosecant, respectively. In short, if θ lies in quadrant II, $\sin \theta$ and $\csc \theta$ are positive. The other four trigonometric functions are negative.

Figure 4.47 summarizes the signs of the trigonometric functions. If θ lies in quadrant I, all six functions are positive. If θ lies in quadrant II, only $\sin \theta$ and $\csc \theta$ are positive. If θ lies in quadrant III, only $\tan \theta$ and $\cot \theta$ are positive. Finally, if θ lies in quadrant IV, only $\cos \theta$ and $\sec \theta$ are positive. Observe that the positive functions in each quadrant occur in reciprocal pairs.

Study Tip

Your author's high school trig teacher showed him this sentence to remember the signs of the trig functions:

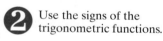

All   **Students**   **Take**   **Calculus.**

| All trig functions are positive in QI. | Sine and its reciprocal, cosecant, are positive in QII. | Tangent and its reciprocal, cotangent, are positive in QIII. | Cosine and its reciprocal, secant, are positive in QIV. |

The sentence isn't true anymore, so you may prefer these memory devices:

All Snakes **T**ease **C**hickens.
A Smart **T**rig **C**lass.

EXAMPLE 3   Finding the Quadrant in Which an Angle Lies

If $\tan \theta < 0$ and $\cos \theta > 0$, name the quadrant in which angle θ lies.

Solution   When $\tan \theta < 0$, θ lies in quadrant II or IV. When $\cos \theta > 0$, θ lies in quadrant I or IV. When both conditions are met ($\tan \theta < 0$ and $\cos \theta > 0$), θ must lie in quadrant IV.

Check Point 3   If $\sin \theta < 0$ and $\cos \theta < 0$, name the quadrant in which angle θ lies.

EXAMPLE 4   Evaluating Trigonometric Functions

Given $\tan \theta = -\frac{2}{3}$ and $\cos \theta > 0$, find $\cos \theta$ and $\csc \theta$.

Solution   Because the tangent is negative and the cosine is positive, θ lies in quadrant IV. This will help us to determine whether the negative sign in $\tan \theta = -\frac{2}{3}$ should be associated with the numerator or the denominator. Keep in mind that in quadrant IV, x is positive and y is negative. Thus,

In quadrant IV, y is negative.

$$\tan \theta = -\frac{2}{3} = \frac{y}{x} = \frac{-2}{3}.$$

(See Figure 4.48.) Thus, $x = 3$ and $y = -2$. Furthermore,

$$r = \sqrt{x^2 + y^2} = \sqrt{3^2 + (-2)^2} = \sqrt{9 + 4} = \sqrt{13}.$$

Now that we know x, y, and r, we can find $\cos \theta$ and $\csc \theta$.

$$\cos \theta = \frac{x}{r} = \frac{3}{\sqrt{13}} = \frac{3}{\sqrt{13}} \cdot \frac{\sqrt{13}}{\sqrt{13}} = \frac{3\sqrt{13}}{13} \qquad \csc \theta = \frac{r}{y} = \frac{\sqrt{13}}{-2} = -\frac{\sqrt{13}}{2}$$

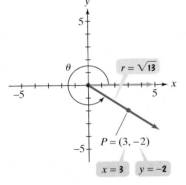

Figure 4.48 $\tan \theta = -\frac{2}{3}$ and $\cos \theta > 0$

Check Point 4   Given $\tan \theta = -\frac{1}{3}$ and $\cos \theta < 0$, find $\sin \theta$ and $\sec \theta$.

In Example 4, we used the quadrant in which θ lies to determine whether a negative sign should be associated with the numerator or the denominator. Here's a situation, similar to Example 4, where negative signs should be associated with *both* the numerator and the denominator:

$$\tan \theta = \frac{3}{5} \quad \text{and} \quad \cos \theta < 0.$$

Because the tangent is positive and the cosine is negative, θ lies in quadrant III. In quadrant III, x is negative and y is negative. Thus,

$$\tan \theta = \frac{3}{5} = \frac{y}{x} = \frac{-3}{-5}.$$

We see that $x = -5$ and $y = -3$.

3 Find reference angles.

Reference Angles

We will often evaluate trigonometric functions of positive angles greater than $90°$ and all negative angles by making use of a positive acute angle. This positive acute angle is called a *reference angle*.

Definition of a Reference Angle

Let θ be a nonacute angle in standard position that lies in a quadrant. Its **reference angle** is the positive acute angle θ' formed by the terminal side of θ and the x-axis.

Figure 4.49 shows the reference angle for θ lying in quadrants II, III, and IV. Notice that the formula used to find θ', the reference angle, varies according to the quadrant in which θ lies. You may find it easier to find the reference angle for a given angle by making a figure that shows the angle in standard position. The acute angle formed by the terminal side of this angle and the x-axis is the reference angle.

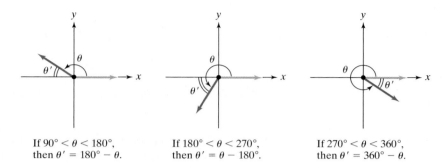

Figure 4.49 Reference angles, θ', for positive angles, θ, in quadrants II, III, and IV

If $90° < \theta < 180°$, then $\theta' = 180° - \theta$.

If $180° < \theta < 270°$, then $\theta' = \theta - 180°$.

If $270° < \theta < 360°$, then $\theta' = 360° - \theta$.

EXAMPLE 5 Finding Reference Angles

Find the reference angle, θ', for each of the following angles:

a. $\theta = 345°$ **b.** $\theta = \dfrac{5\pi}{6}$ **c.** $\theta = -135°$ **d.** $\theta = 2.5$.

Solution

a. A 345° angle in standard position is shown in Figure 4.50. Because 345° lies in quadrant IV, the reference angle is

$$\theta' = 360° - 345° = 15°.$$

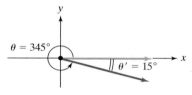

Figure 4.50

b. Because $\dfrac{5\pi}{6}$ lies between $\dfrac{\pi}{2} = \dfrac{3\pi}{6}$ and

$\pi = \dfrac{6\pi}{6}, \theta = \dfrac{5\pi}{6}$ lies in quadrant II. The angle is shown in Figure 4.51. The reference angle is

$$\theta' = \pi - \dfrac{5\pi}{6} = \dfrac{6\pi}{6} - \dfrac{5\pi}{6} = \dfrac{\pi}{6}.$$

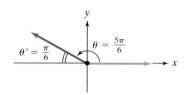

Figure 4.51

c. A $-135°$ angle in standard position is shown in Figure 4.52. The figure indicates that the positive acute angle formed by the terminal side of θ and the x-axis is 45°. The reference angle is

$$\theta' = 45°.$$

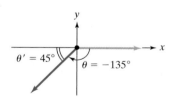

Figure 4.52

d. The angle $\theta = 2.5$ lies between $\dfrac{\pi}{2} \approx 1.57$ and $\pi \approx 3.14$. This means that $\theta = 2.5$ is in quadrant II, shown in Figure 4.53. The reference angle is

$$\theta' = \pi - 2.5 \approx 0.64.$$

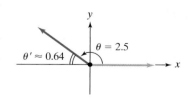

Figure 4.53

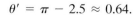

Check Point 5 Find the reference angle, θ', for each of the following angles:

a. $\theta = 210°$ **b.** $\theta = \dfrac{7\pi}{4}$ **c.** $\theta = -240°$ **d.** $\theta = 3.6$.

Finding reference angles for angles that are greater than $360°\ (2\pi)$ or less than $-360°\ (-2\pi)$ involves using coterminal angles. We have seen that coterminal angles have the same initial and terminal sides. Recall that coterminal angles can be obtained by increasing or decreasing an angle's measure by an integer multiple of $360°$ or 2π.

Finding Reference Angles for Angles Greater Than $360°\ (2\pi)$ or Less Than $-360°\ (-2\pi)$

1. Find a positive angle α less than $360°$ or 2π that is coterminal with the given angle.
2. Draw α in standard position.
3. Use the drawing to find the reference angle for the given angle. The positive acute angle formed by the terminal side of α and the x-axis is the reference angle.

EXAMPLE 6   Finding Reference Angles

Find the reference angle for each of the following angles:

a. $\theta = 580°$ **b.** $\theta = \dfrac{8\pi}{3}$ **c.** $\theta = -\dfrac{13\pi}{6}$.

Solution

a. For a $580°$ angle, subtract $360°$ to find a positive coterminal angle less than $360°$.

$$580° - 360° = 220°$$

Figure 4.54 shows $\alpha = 220°$ in standard position. Because $220°$ lies in quadrant III, the reference angle is

$$\alpha' = 220° - 180° = 40°.$$

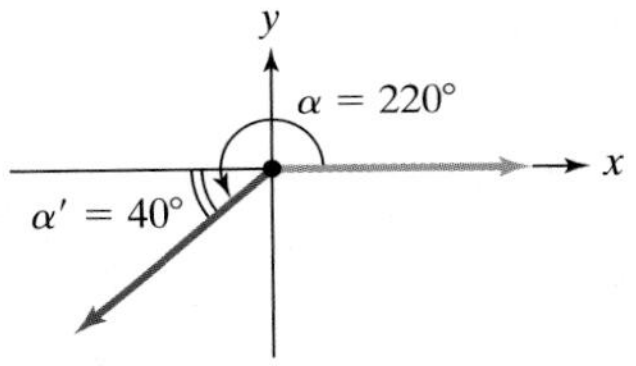

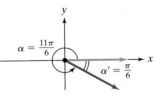

Figure 4.54

b. For an $\dfrac{8\pi}{3}$, or $2\dfrac{2}{3}\pi$ angle, subtract 2π to find a positive coterminal angle less than 2π.

$$\frac{8\pi}{3} - 2\pi = \frac{8\pi}{3} - \frac{6\pi}{3} = \frac{2\pi}{3}$$

Figure 4.55 shows $\alpha = \dfrac{2\pi}{3}$ in standard position. Because $\dfrac{2\pi}{3}$ lies in quadrant II, the reference angle is

$$\alpha' = \pi - \frac{2\pi}{3} = \frac{3\pi}{3} - \frac{2\pi}{3} = \frac{\pi}{3}.$$

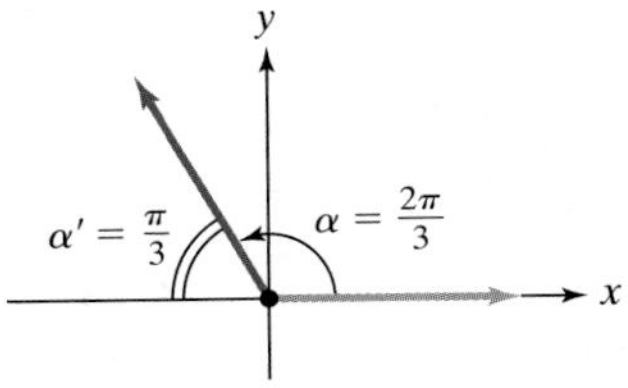

Figure 4.55

c. For a $-\dfrac{13\pi}{6}$, or $-2\dfrac{1}{6}\pi$ angle, add 4π to find a positive coterminal angle less than 2π.

$$-\frac{13\pi}{6} + 4\pi = -\frac{13\pi}{6} + \frac{24\pi}{6} = \frac{11\pi}{6}$$

Figure 4.56 shows $\alpha = \dfrac{11\pi}{6}$ in standard position.

Because $\dfrac{11\pi}{6}$ lies in quadrant IV, the reference angle is

$$\alpha' = 2\pi - \frac{11\pi}{6} = \frac{12\pi}{6} - \frac{11\pi}{6} = \frac{\pi}{6}.$$

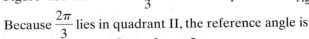

Figure 4.56

Discovery

Solve part (c) using the coterminal angle formed by adding 2π, rather than 4π, to the given angle.

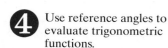

Check Point 6 Find the reference angle for each of the following angles:

    a. $\theta = 665°$ **b.** $\theta = \dfrac{15\pi}{4}$ **c.** $\theta = -\dfrac{11\pi}{3}$.

④ Use reference angles to evaluate trigonometric functions.

Evaluating Trigonometric Functions Using Reference Angles

The way that reference angles are defined makes them useful in evaluating trigonometric functions.

> ### Using Reference Angles to Evaluate Trigonometric Functions
>
> The values of the trigonometric functions of a given angle, θ, are the same as the values of the trigonometric functions of the reference angle, θ', except possibly for the sign. A function value of the acute reference angle, θ', is always positive. However, the same function value for θ may be positive or negative.

For example, we can use a reference angle, θ', to obtain an exact value for $\tan 120°$. The reference angle for $\theta = 120°$ is $\theta' = 180° - 120° = 60°$. We know the exact value of the tangent function of the reference angle: $\tan 60° = \sqrt{3}$. We also know that the value of a trigonometric function of a given angle, θ, is the same as that of its reference angle, θ', except possibly for the sign. Thus, we can conclude that $\tan 120°$ equals $-\sqrt{3}$ or $\sqrt{3}$.

What sign should we attach to $\sqrt{3}$? A $120°$ angle lies in quadrant II, where only the sine and cosecant are positive. Thus, the tangent function is negative for a $120°$ angle. Therefore,

> Prefix by a negative sign to show tangent is negative in quadrant II.

$$\tan 120° = -\tan 60° = -\sqrt{3}.$$

> The reference angle for 120° is 60°.

In the previous section, we used two right triangles to find exact trigonometric values of $30°, 45°$, and $60°$. Using a procedure similar to finding $\tan 120°$, we can now find the exact function values of all angles for which $30°, 45°$, or $60°$ are reference angles.

> ### A Procedure for Using Reference Angles to Evaluate Trigonometric Functions
>
> The value of a trigonometric function of any angle θ is found as follows:
>
> **1.** Find the associated reference angle, θ', and the function value for θ'.
> **2.** Use the quadrant in which θ lies to prefix the appropriate sign to the function value in step 1.

Discovery

Draw the two right triangles involving $30°, 45°$, and $60°$. Indicate the length of each side. Use these lengths to verify the function values for the reference angles in the solution to Example 7.

EXAMPLE 7 **Using Reference Angles to Evaluate Trigonometric Functions**

Use reference angles to find the exact value of each of the following trigonometric functions:

    a. $\sin 135°$ **b.** $\cos \dfrac{4\pi}{3}$ **c.** $\cot\left(-\dfrac{\pi}{3}\right)$.

Solution

a. We use our two-step procedure to find sin 135°.

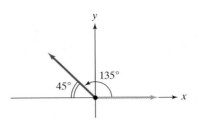

Figure 4.57 Reference angle for 135°

Step 1   Find the reference angle, θ', and sin θ'. Figure 4.57 shows 135° lies in quadrant II. The reference angle is

$$\theta' = 180° - 135° = 45°.$$

The function value for the reference angle is $\sin 45° = \dfrac{\sqrt{2}}{2}$.

Step 2   Use the quadrant in which θ lies to prefix the appropriate sign to the function value in step 1. The angle $\theta = 135°$ lies in quadrant II. Because the sine is positive in quadrant II, we put a $+$ sign before the function value of the reference angle. Thus,

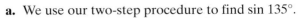

The sine is positive in quadrant II.

$$\sin 135° = +\sin 45° = \dfrac{\sqrt{2}}{2}.$$

The reference angle for 135° is 45°.

b. We use our two-step procedure to find $\cos \dfrac{4\pi}{3}$.

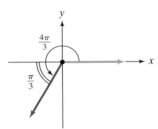

Figure 4.58 Reference angle for $\dfrac{4\pi}{3}$

Step 1   Find the reference angle, θ', and cos θ'. Figure 4.58 shows that $\theta = \dfrac{4\pi}{3}$ lies in quadrant III. The reference angle is

$$\theta' = \dfrac{4\pi}{3} - \pi = \dfrac{4\pi}{3} - \dfrac{3\pi}{3} = \dfrac{\pi}{3}.$$

The function value for the reference angle is

$$\cos \dfrac{\pi}{3} = \dfrac{1}{2}.$$

Step 2   Use the quadrant in which θ lies to prefix the appropriate sign to the function value in step 1. The angle $\theta = \dfrac{4\pi}{3}$ lies in quadrant III. Because only the tangent and cotangent are positive in quadrant III, the cosine is negative in this quadrant. We put a $-$ sign before the function value of the reference angle. Thus,

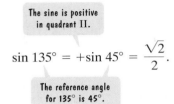

The cosine is negative in quadrant III.

$$\cos \dfrac{4\pi}{3} = -\cos \dfrac{\pi}{3} = -\dfrac{1}{2}.$$

The reference angle for $\dfrac{4\pi}{3}$ is $\dfrac{\pi}{3}$.

c. We use our two-step procedure to find $\cot\left(-\dfrac{\pi}{3}\right)$.

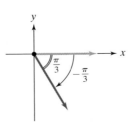

Figure 4.59 Reference angle for $-\dfrac{\pi}{3}$

Step 1   Find the reference angle, θ', and cot θ'. Figure 4.59 shows that $\theta = -\dfrac{\pi}{3}$ lies in quadrant IV. The reference angle is $\theta' = \dfrac{\pi}{3}$. The function value for the reference angle is $\cot \dfrac{\pi}{3} = \dfrac{\sqrt{3}}{3}$.

Step 2   Use the quadrant in which θ lies to prefix the appropriate sign to the function value in step 1. The angle $\theta = -\dfrac{\pi}{3}$ lies in quadrant IV. Because only the cosine and secant are positive in quadrant IV, the cotangent is negative in this quadrant. We put a $-$ sign before the function value of the reference angle. Thus,

> The cotangent is negative in quadrant IV.

$$\cot\left(-\frac{\pi}{3}\right) = -\cot\frac{\pi}{3} = -\frac{\sqrt{3}}{3}.$$

> The reference angle for $-\frac{\pi}{3}$ is $\frac{\pi}{3}$.

Check Point 7 Use reference angles to find the exact value of the following trigonometric functions:

    a. $\sin 300°$ **b.** $\tan\dfrac{5\pi}{4}$ **c.** $\sec\left(-\dfrac{\pi}{6}\right)$.

In our final example, we use positive coterminal angles less than 2π to find the reference angles.

EXAMPLE 8   Using Reference Angles to Evaluate Trigonometric Functions

Use reference angles to find the exact value of each of the following trigonometric functions:

    a. $\tan\dfrac{14\pi}{3}$ **b.** $\sec\left(-\dfrac{17\pi}{4}\right)$.

Solution

    a. We use our two-step procedure to find $\tan\dfrac{14\pi}{3}$.

    Step 1   Find the reference angle, θ', and $\tan \theta'$. Because the given angle, $\dfrac{14\pi}{3}$ or $4\dfrac{2}{3}\pi$, exceeds 2π, subtract 4π to find a positive coterminal angle less than 2π.

$$\theta = \frac{14\pi}{3} - 4\pi = \frac{14\pi}{3} - \frac{12\pi}{3} = \frac{2\pi}{3}$$

Figure 4.60 shows $\theta = \dfrac{2\pi}{3}$ in standard position. The angle lies in quadrant II. The reference angle is

$$\theta' = \pi - \frac{2\pi}{3} = \frac{3\pi}{3} - \frac{2\pi}{3} = \frac{\pi}{3}.$$

The function value for the reference angle is $\tan\dfrac{\pi}{3} = \sqrt{3}$.

Step 2   Use the quadrant in which θ lies to prefix the appropriate sign to the function value in step 1. The coterminal angle $\theta = \dfrac{2\pi}{3}$ lies in quadrant II.

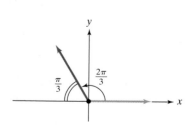

Figure 4.60 Reference angle for $\dfrac{2\pi}{3}$

Because the tangent is negative in quadrant II, we put a − sign before the function value of the reference angle. Thus,

> The tangent is negative
> in quadrant II.

$$\tan \frac{14\pi}{3} = \tan \frac{2\pi}{3} = -\tan \frac{\pi}{3} = -\sqrt{3}.$$

> The reference angle
> for $\frac{2\pi}{3}$ is $\frac{\pi}{3}$.

b. We use our two-step procedure to find $\sec\left(-\frac{17\pi}{4}\right)$.

Step 1   Find the reference angle, θ', and $\sec \theta'$. Because the given angle, $-\frac{17\pi}{4}$ or $-4\frac{1}{4}\pi$, is less than -2π, add 6π (three multiples of 2π) to find a positive coterminal angle less than 2π.

$$\theta = -\frac{17\pi}{4} + 6\pi = -\frac{17\pi}{4} + \frac{24\pi}{4} = \frac{7\pi}{4}$$

Figure 4.61 shows $\theta = \frac{7\pi}{4}$ in standard position. The angle lies in quadrant IV. The reference angle is

$$\theta' = 2\pi - \frac{7\pi}{4} = \frac{8\pi}{4} - \frac{7\pi}{4} = \frac{\pi}{4}.$$

The function value for the reference angle is $\sec \frac{\pi}{4} = \sqrt{2}$.

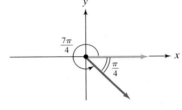

Figure 4.61 Reference angle for $\frac{7\pi}{4}$

Step 2   Use the quadrant in which θ lies to prefix the appropriate sign to the function value in step 1. The coterminal angle $\theta = \frac{7\pi}{4}$ lies in quadrant IV. Because the secant is positive in quadrant IV, we put a + sign before the function value of the reference angle. Thus,

> The secant is
> positive in quadrant IV.

$$\sec\left(-\frac{17\pi}{4}\right) = \sec \frac{7\pi}{4} = +\sec \frac{\pi}{4} = \sqrt{2}.$$

> The reference angle
> for $\frac{7\pi}{4}$ is $\frac{\pi}{4}$.

Check Point 8   Use reference angles to find the exact value of each of the following trigonometric functions:

a. $\cos \frac{17\pi}{6}$ **b.** $\sin\left(-\frac{22\pi}{3}\right)$.

Study Tip

Evaluating trigonometric functions like those in Example 8 and Check Point 8 involves using a number of concepts, including finding coterminal angles and reference angles, locating special angles, determining the signs of trigonometric functions in specific quadrants, and finding the trigonometric functions of special angles $\left(30° = \dfrac{\pi}{6}, 45° = \dfrac{\pi}{4}, \text{ and } 60° = \dfrac{\pi}{3} \right)$. To be successful in trigonometry, it is often necessary to connect concepts. Here's an early reference sheet showing some of the concepts you should have at your fingertips (or memorized).

Degree and Radian Measures of Special and Quadrantal Angles

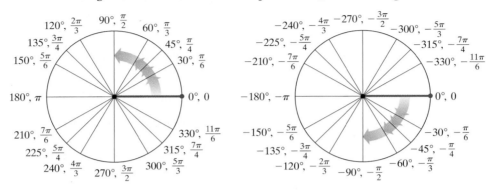

Special Right Triangles and Trigonometric Functions of Special Angles

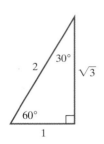

θ	$30° = \dfrac{\pi}{6}$	$45° = \dfrac{\pi}{4}$	$60° = \dfrac{\pi}{3}$
$\sin \theta$	$\dfrac{1}{2}$	$\dfrac{\sqrt{2}}{2}$	$\dfrac{\sqrt{3}}{2}$
$\cos \theta$	$\dfrac{\sqrt{3}}{2}$	$\dfrac{\sqrt{2}}{2}$	$\dfrac{1}{2}$
$\tan \theta$	$\dfrac{\sqrt{3}}{3}$	1	$\sqrt{3}$

Signs of the Trigonometric Functions

y

Quadrant II
sine and cosecant positive

Quadrant I
All functions positive

x

Quadrant III
tangent and cotangent positive

Quadrant IV
cosine and secant positive

Trigonometric Functions of Quadrantal Angles

θ	$0° = 0$	$90° = \dfrac{\pi}{2}$	$180° = \pi$	$270° = \dfrac{3\pi}{2}$
$\sin \theta$	0	1	0	-1
$\cos \theta$	1	0	-1	0
$\tan \theta$	0	undefined	0	undefined

Using Reference Angles to Evaluate Trigonometric Functions

$\sin \theta = \boxed{}\, \sin \theta'$
$\cos \theta = \boxed{}\, \cos \theta'$
$\tan \theta = \boxed{}\, \tan \theta'$

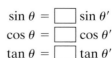

+ or − in ☐ determined by the quadrant in which θ lies and the sign of the function in that quadrant.

EXERCISE SET 4.4

Practice Exercises

In Exercises 1–8, a point on the terminal side of angle θ is given. Find the exact value of each of the six trigonometric functions of θ.

1. $(-4, 3)$ **2.** $(-12, 5)$ **3.** $(2, 3)$

4. $(3, 7)$ **5.** $(3, -3)$ **6.** $(5, -5)$

7. $(-2, -5)$ **8.** $(-1, -3)$

In Exercises 9–16, evaluate the trigonometric function at the quadrantal angle, or state that the expression is undefined.

9. $\cos \pi$ **10.** $\tan \pi$ **11.** $\sec \pi$

12. $\csc \pi$ **13.** $\tan \dfrac{3\pi}{2}$ **14.** $\cos \dfrac{3\pi}{2}$

15. $\cot \dfrac{\pi}{2}$ **16.** $\tan \dfrac{\pi}{2}$

In Exercises 17–22, let θ be an angle in standard position. Name the quadrant in which θ lies.

17. $\sin \theta > 0, \quad \cos \theta > 0$ **18.** $\sin \theta < 0, \quad \cos \theta > 0$

19. $\sin \theta < 0, \quad \cos \theta < 0$ **20.** $\tan \theta < 0, \quad \sin \theta < 0$

21. $\tan \theta < 0, \quad \cos \theta < 0$ **22.** $\cot \theta > 0, \quad \sec \theta < 0$

In Exercises 23–34, find the exact value of each of the remaining trigonometric functions of θ.

23. $\cos \theta = -\frac{3}{5}, \quad \theta$ in quadrant III

24. $\sin \theta = -\frac{12}{13}, \quad \theta$ in quadrant III

25. $\sin \theta = \frac{5}{13}, \quad \theta$ in quadrant II

26. $\cos \theta = \frac{4}{5}, \quad \theta$ in quadrant IV

27. $\cos \theta = \frac{8}{17}, \quad 270° < \theta < 360°$

28. $\cos \theta = \frac{1}{3}, \quad 270° < \theta < 360°$

29. $\tan \theta = -\frac{2}{3}, \quad \sin \theta > 0$ **30.** $\tan \theta = -\frac{1}{3}, \quad \sin \theta > 0$

31. $\tan \theta = \frac{4}{3}, \quad \cos \theta < 0$ **32.** $\tan \theta = \frac{5}{12}, \quad \cos \theta < 0$

33. $\sec \theta = -3, \quad \tan \theta > 0$ **34.** $\csc \theta = -4, \quad \tan \theta > 0$

In Exercises 35–60, find the reference angle for each angle.

35. $160°$ **36.** $170°$ **37.** $205°$

38. $210°$ **39.** $355°$ **40.** $351°$

41. $\dfrac{7\pi}{4}$ **42.** $\dfrac{5\pi}{4}$ **43.** $\dfrac{5\pi}{6}$

44. $\dfrac{5\pi}{7}$ **45.** $-150°$ **46.** $-250°$

47. $-335°$ **48.** $-359°$ **49.** 4.7

50. 5.5 **51.** $565°$ **52.** $553°$

53. $\dfrac{17\pi}{6}$ **54.** $\dfrac{11\pi}{4}$ **55.** $\dfrac{23\pi}{4}$

56. $\dfrac{17\pi}{3}$ **57.** $-\dfrac{11\pi}{4}$ **58.** $-\dfrac{17\pi}{6}$

59. $-\dfrac{25\pi}{6}$ **60.** $-\dfrac{13\pi}{3}$

In Exercises 61–86, use reference angles to find the exact value of each expression. Do not use a calculator.

61. $\cos 225°$ **62.** $\sin 300°$ **63.** $\tan 210°$

64. $\sec 240°$ **65.** $\tan 420°$ **66.** $\tan 405°$

67. $\sin \dfrac{2\pi}{3}$ **68.** $\cos \dfrac{3\pi}{4}$ **69.** $\csc \dfrac{7\pi}{6}$

70. $\cot \dfrac{7\pi}{4}$ **71.** $\tan \dfrac{9\pi}{4}$ **72.** $\tan \dfrac{9\pi}{2}$

73. $\sin(-240°)$ **74.** $\sin(-225°)$ **75.** $\tan\left(-\dfrac{\pi}{4}\right)$

76. $\tan\left(-\dfrac{\pi}{6}\right)$ **77.** $\sec 495°$ **78.** $\sec 510°$

79. $\cot \dfrac{19\pi}{6}$ **80.** $\cot \dfrac{13\pi}{3}$ **81.** $\cos \dfrac{23\pi}{4}$

82. $\cos \dfrac{35\pi}{6}$ **83.** $\tan\left(-\dfrac{17\pi}{6}\right)$ **84.** $\tan\left(-\dfrac{11\pi}{4}\right)$

85. $\sin\left(-\dfrac{17\pi}{3}\right)$ **86.** $\sin\left(-\dfrac{35\pi}{6}\right)$

Practice Plus

In Exercises 87–92, find the exact value of each expression. Write the answer as a single fraction. Do not use a calculator.

87. $\sin \dfrac{\pi}{3} \cos \pi - \cos \dfrac{\pi}{3} \sin \dfrac{3\pi}{2}$

88. $\sin \dfrac{\pi}{4} \cos 0 - \sin \dfrac{\pi}{6} \cos \pi$

89. $\sin \dfrac{11\pi}{4} \cos \dfrac{5\pi}{6} + \cos \dfrac{11\pi}{4} \sin \dfrac{5\pi}{6}$

90. $\sin \dfrac{17\pi}{3} \cos \dfrac{5\pi}{4} + \cos \dfrac{17\pi}{3} \sin \dfrac{5\pi}{4}$

91. $\sin \dfrac{3\pi}{2} \tan\left(-\dfrac{15\pi}{4}\right) - \cos\left(-\dfrac{5\pi}{3}\right)$

92. $\sin \dfrac{3\pi}{2} \tan\left(-\dfrac{8\pi}{3}\right) + \cos\left(-\dfrac{5\pi}{6}\right)$

In Exercises 93–98, let
$$f(x) = \sin x, g(x) = \cos x, \text{ and } h(x) = 2x.$$
Find the exact value of each expression. Do not use a calculator.

93. $f\left(\dfrac{4\pi}{3} + \dfrac{\pi}{6}\right) + f\left(\dfrac{4\pi}{3}\right) + f\left(\dfrac{\pi}{6}\right)$

94. $g\left(\dfrac{5\pi}{6} + \dfrac{\pi}{6}\right) + g\left(\dfrac{5\pi}{6}\right) + g\left(\dfrac{\pi}{6}\right)$

95. $(h \circ g)\left(\dfrac{17\pi}{3}\right)$ **96.** $(h \circ f)\left(\dfrac{11\pi}{4}\right)$

97. the average rate of change of f from $x_1 = \dfrac{5\pi}{4}$ to $x_2 = \dfrac{3\pi}{2}$

98. the average rate of change of g from $x_1 = \dfrac{3\pi}{4}$ to $x_2 = \pi$

In Exercises 99–104, find two values of θ, 0 ≤ θ < 2π, that satisfy each equation.

99. $\sin \theta = \dfrac{\sqrt{2}}{2}$

100. $\cos \theta = \dfrac{1}{2}$

101. $\sin \theta = -\dfrac{\sqrt{2}}{2}$

102. $\cos \theta = -\dfrac{1}{2}$

103. $\tan \theta = -\sqrt{3}$

104. $\tan \theta = -\dfrac{\sqrt{3}}{3}$

 Writing in Mathematics

105. If you are given a point on the terminal side of angle θ, explain how to find sin θ.

106. Explain why tan 90° is undefined.

107. If cos θ > 0 and tan θ < 0, explain how to find the quadrant in which θ lies.

108. What is a reference angle? Give an example with your description.

109. Explain how reference angles are used to evaluate trigonometric functions. Give an example with your description.

CHAPTER 4
MID-CHAPTER CHECK POINT

What You Know: We learned to use radians to measure angles: One radian (approximately 57°) is the measure of the central angle that intercepts an arc equal in length to the radius of the circle. Using 180° = π radians, we converted degrees to radians (multiply by $\dfrac{\pi}{180°}$) and radians to degrees (multiply by $\dfrac{180°}{\pi}$). We defined the six trigonometric functions using coordinates of points along the unit circle, right triangles, and angles in standard position. Evaluating trigonometric functions using reference angles involved connecting a number of concepts, including finding coterminal and reference angles, locating special angles, determining the signs of the trigonometric functions in specific quadrants, and finding the function values at special angles. Use the important Study Tip on page 498 as a reference sheet to help connect these concepts.

In Exercises 1–2, convert each angle in degrees to radians. Express your answer as a multiple of π.

1. 10°

2. −105°

In Exercises 3–4, convert each angle in radians to degrees.

3. $\dfrac{5\pi}{12}$

4. $-\dfrac{13\pi}{20}$

In Exercises 5–7,

a. *Find a positive angle less than 360° or 2π that is coterminal with the given angle.*

b. *Draw the given angle in standard position.*

c. *Find the reference angle for the given angle.*

5. $\dfrac{11\pi}{3}$

6. $-\dfrac{19\pi}{4}$

7. 510°

8. Use the point shown on the unit circle to find each of the six trigonometric functions at *t*.

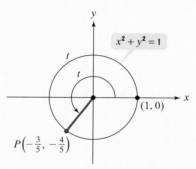

9. Use the triangle to find each of the six trigonometric functions of θ.

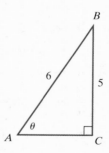

10. Use the point on the terminal side of θ to find each of the six trigonometric functions of θ.

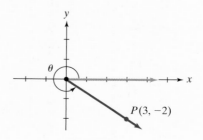

In Exercises 11–12, find the exact value of the remaining trigonometric functions of θ.

11. $\tan \theta = -\dfrac{3}{4}$, $\cos \theta < 0$ **12.** $\cos \theta = \dfrac{3}{7}$, $\sin \theta < 0$

In Exercises 13–14, find the measure of the side of the right triangle whose length is designated by a lowercase letter. Round the answer to the nearest whole number.

13.

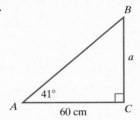

14.

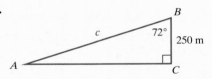

15. If $\cos \theta = \dfrac{1}{6}$ and θ is acute, find $\cot\left(\dfrac{\pi}{2} - \theta\right)$.

In Exercises 16–26, find the exact value of each expression. Do not use a calculator.

16. $\tan 30°$ **17.** $\cot 120°$

18. $\cos 240°$ **19.** $\sec \dfrac{11\pi}{6}$

20. $\sin^2 \dfrac{\pi}{7} + \cos^2 \dfrac{\pi}{7}$ **21.** $\sin\left(-\dfrac{2\pi}{3}\right)$

22. $\csc\left(\dfrac{22\pi}{3}\right)$ **23.** $\cos 495°$

24. $\tan\left(-\dfrac{17\pi}{6}\right)$ **25.** $\sin^2 \dfrac{\pi}{2} - \cos \pi$

26. $\cos\left(\dfrac{5\pi}{6} + 2\pi n\right) + \tan\left(\dfrac{5\pi}{6} + n\pi\right)$, n is an integer.

27. A circle has a radius of 40 centimeters. Find the length of the arc intercepted by a central angle of 36°. Express the answer in terms of π. Then round to two decimal places.

28. A merry-go-round makes 8 revolutions per minute. Find the linear speed, in feet per minute, of a horse 10 feet from the center. Express the answer in terms of π. Then round to one decimal place.

29. A plane takes off at an angle of 6°. After traveling for one mile, or 5280 feet, along this flight path, find the plane's height, to the nearest tenth of a foot, above the ground.

30. A tree that is 50 feet tall casts a shadow that is 60 feet long. Find the angle of elevation, to the nearest degree, of the sun.

SECTION 4.5   *Graphs of Sine and Cosine Functions*

Objectives

❶ Understand the graph of $y = \sin x$.

❷ Graph variations of $y = \sin x$.

❸ Understand the graph of $y = \cos x$.

❹ Graph variations of $y = \cos x$.

❺ Use vertical shifts of sine and cosine curves.

❻ Model periodic behavior.

Take a deep breath and relax. Many relaxation exercises involve slowing down our breathing. Some people suggest that the way we breathe affects every part of our lives. Did you know that graphs of trigonometric functions can be used to analyze the breathing cycle, which is our closest link to both life and death?

In this section, we use graphs of sine and cosine functions to visualize their properties. We use the traditional symbol x, rather than θ or t, to represent the independent variable. We use the symbol y for the dependent variable, or the function's value at x. Thus, we will be graphing $y = \sin x$ and $y = \cos x$ in rectangular coordinates. In all graphs of trigonometric functions, the independent variable, x, is measured in radians.

❶ Understand the graph of $y = \sin x$.

The Graph of $y = \sin x$

The trigonometric functions can be graphed in a rectangular coordinate system by plotting points whose coordinates satisfy the function. Thus, we graph $y = \sin x$ by listing some points on the graph. Because the period of the sine function is 2π, we will graph the function on the interval $[0, 2\pi]$. The rest of the graph is made up of repetitions of this portion.

Table 4.3 lists some values of (x, y) on the graph of $y = \sin x, 0 \leq x \leq 2\pi$.

Table 4.3   Values of (x, y) on the graph of $y = \sin x$

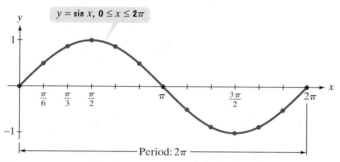

x	0	$\frac{\pi}{6}$	$\frac{\pi}{3}$	$\frac{\pi}{2}$	$\frac{2\pi}{3}$	$\frac{5\pi}{6}$	π	$\frac{7\pi}{6}$	$\frac{4\pi}{3}$	$\frac{3\pi}{2}$	$\frac{5\pi}{3}$	$\frac{11\pi}{6}$	2π
$y = \sin x$	0	$\frac{1}{2}$	$\frac{\sqrt{3}}{2}$	1	$\frac{\sqrt{3}}{2}$	$\frac{1}{2}$	0	$-\frac{1}{2}$	$-\frac{\sqrt{3}}{2}$	-1	$-\frac{\sqrt{3}}{2}$	$-\frac{1}{2}$	0

As x increases from 0 to $\frac{\pi}{2}$, y increases from 0 to 1.

As x increases from $\frac{\pi}{2}$ to π, y decreases from 1 to 0.

As x increases from π to $\frac{3\pi}{2}$, y decreases from 0 to -1.

As x increases from $\frac{3\pi}{2}$ to 2π, y increases from -1 to 0.

In plotting the points obtained in Table 4.3, we will use the approximation $\frac{\sqrt{3}}{2} \approx 0.87$. Rather than approximating π, we will mark off units on the x-axis in terms of π. If we connect these points with a smooth curve, we obtain the graph shown in Figure 4.62. The figure shows one period of the graph of $y = \sin x$.

$y = \sin x, 0 \leq x \leq 2\pi$

Figure 4.62 One period of the graph of $y = \sin x$

We can obtain a more complete graph of $y = \sin x$ by continuing the portion shown in Figure 4.62 to the left and to the right. The graph of the sine function, called a **sine curve**, is shown in Figure 4.63. Any part of the graph that corresponds to one period (2π) is one cycle of the graph of $y = \sin x$.

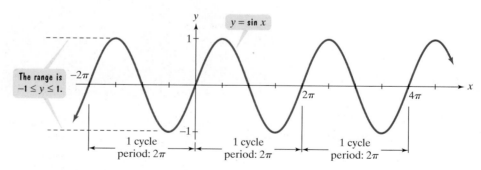

The range is $-1 \leq y \leq 1$.

$y = \sin x$

1 cycle period: 2π

Figure 4.63 The graph of $y = \sin x$

The graph of $y = \sin x$ allows us to visualize some of the properties of the sine function.

- The domain is $(-\infty, \infty)$, the set of all real numbers. The graph extends indefinitely to the left and to the right with no gaps or holes.
- The range is $[-1, 1]$, the set of all real numbers between -1 and 1, inclusive. The graph never rises above 1 or falls below -1.
- The period is 2π. The graph's pattern repeats in every interval of length 2π.
- The function is an odd function: $\sin(-x) = -\sin x$. This can be seen by observing that the graph is symmetric with respect to the origin.

Graphing Variations of $y = \sin x$

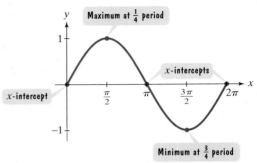

To graph variations of $y = \sin x$ by hand, it is helpful to find x-intercepts, maximum points, and minimum points. One complete cycle of the sine curve includes three x-intercepts, one maximum point, and one minimum point. The graph of $y = \sin x$ has x-intercepts at the beginning, middle, and end of its full period, shown in Figure 4.64. The curve reaches its maximum point $\frac{1}{4}$ of the way through the period. It reaches its minimum point $\frac{3}{4}$ of the

Figure 4.64 Key points in graphing the sine function

way through the period. Thus, key points in graphing sine functions are obtained by dividing the period into four equal parts. The x-coordinates of the five key points are as follows:

$$x_1 = \text{value of } x \text{ where the cycle begins}$$

$$x_2 = x_1 + \frac{\text{period}}{4}$$

$$x_3 = x_2 + \frac{\text{period}}{4}$$

$$x_4 = x_3 + \frac{\text{period}}{4}$$

$$x_5 = x_4 + \frac{\text{period}}{4}.$$

> Add "quarter-periods" to find successive values of x.

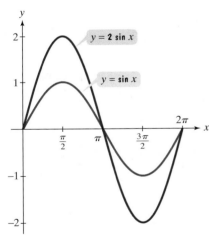

Figure 4.65 Comparing the graphs of $y = \sin x$ and $y = 2 \sin x$

The y-coordinates of the five key points are obtained by evaluating the given function at each of these values of x.

The graph of $y = \sin x$ forms the basis for graphing functions of the form

$$y = A \sin x.$$

For example, consider $y = 2 \sin x$, in which $A = 2$. We can obtain the graph of $y = 2 \sin x$ from that of $y = \sin x$ if we multiply each y-coordinate on the graph of $y = \sin x$ by 2. Figure 4.65 shows the graphs. The basic sine curve is *stretched* and ranges between -2 and 2, rather than between -1 and 1. However, both $y = \sin x$ and $y = 2 \sin x$ have a period of 2π.

In general, the graph of $y = A \sin x$ ranges between $-|A|$ and $|A|$. Thus, the range of the function is $-|A| \le y \le |A|$. If $|A| > 1$, the basic sine curve is *stretched*, as in Figure 4.65. If $|A| < 1$, the basic sine curve is *shrunk*. We call $|A|$ the **amplitude** of $y = A \sin x$. The maximum value of y on the graph of $y = A \sin x$ is $|A|$, the amplitude.

Graphing Variations of $y = \sin x$

1. Identify the amplitude and the period.
2. Find the values of x for the five key points—the three x-intercepts, the maximum point, and the minimum point. Start with the value of x where the cycle begins and add quarter-periods—that is, $\dfrac{\text{period}}{4}$—to find successive values of x.
3. Find the values of y for the five key points by evaluating the function at each value of x from step 2.
4. Connect the five key points with a smooth curve and graph one complete cycle of the given function.
5. Extend the graph in step 4 to the left or right as desired.

2 Graph variations of $y = \sin x$.

EXAMPLE 1   Graphing a Variation of $y = \sin x$

Determine the amplitude of $y = \frac{1}{2}\sin x$. Then graph $y = \sin x$ and $y = \frac{1}{2}\sin x$ for $0 \le x \le 2\pi$.

Solution

Step 1   Identify the amplitude and the period. The equation $y = \frac{1}{2}\sin x$ is of the form $y = A \sin x$ with $A = \frac{1}{2}$. Thus, the amplitude is $|A| = \frac{1}{2}$. This means that the maximum value of y is $\frac{1}{2}$ and the minimum value of y is $-\frac{1}{2}$. The period for both $y = \frac{1}{2}\sin x$ and $y = \sin x$ is 2π.

Step 2   Find the values of x for the five key points. We need to find the three x-intercepts, the maximum point, and the minimum point on the interval $[0, 2\pi]$. To do so, we begin by dividing the period, 2π, by 4.

$$\frac{\text{period}}{4} = \frac{2\pi}{4} = \frac{\pi}{2}$$

We start with the value of x where the cycle begins: $x_1 = 0$. Now we add quarter-periods, $\dfrac{\pi}{2}$, to generate x-values for each of the key points. The five x-values are

$$x_1 = 0, \quad x_2 = 0 + \frac{\pi}{2} = \frac{\pi}{2}, \quad x_3 = \frac{\pi}{2} + \frac{\pi}{2} = \pi,$$

$$x_4 = \pi + \frac{\pi}{2} = \frac{3\pi}{2}, \quad x_5 = \frac{3\pi}{2} + \frac{\pi}{2} = 2\pi.$$

Step 3   Find the values of y for the five key points. We evaluate the function at each value of x from step 2.

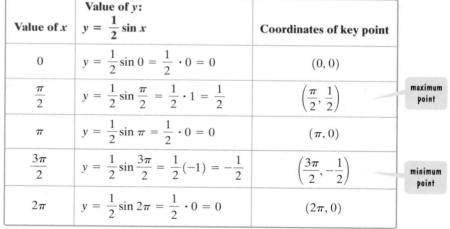

Value of x	Value of y: $y = \dfrac{1}{2}\sin x$	Coordinates of key point	
0	$y = \dfrac{1}{2}\sin 0 = \dfrac{1}{2}\cdot 0 = 0$	$(0, 0)$	
$\dfrac{\pi}{2}$	$y = \dfrac{1}{2}\sin\dfrac{\pi}{2} = \dfrac{1}{2}\cdot 1 = \dfrac{1}{2}$	$\left(\dfrac{\pi}{2}, \dfrac{1}{2}\right)$	maximum point
π	$y = \dfrac{1}{2}\sin \pi = \dfrac{1}{2}\cdot 0 = 0$	$(\pi, 0)$	
$\dfrac{3\pi}{2}$	$y = \dfrac{1}{2}\sin\dfrac{3\pi}{2} = \dfrac{1}{2}(-1) = -\dfrac{1}{2}$	$\left(\dfrac{3\pi}{2}, -\dfrac{1}{2}\right)$	minimum point
2π	$y = \dfrac{1}{2}\sin 2\pi = \dfrac{1}{2}\cdot 0 = 0$	$(2\pi, 0)$	

There are x-intercepts at 0, π, and 2π. The maximum and minimum points are indicated by the voice balloons.

Step 4   Connect the five key points with a smooth curve and graph one complete cycle of the given function. The five key points for $y = \frac{1}{2}\sin x$ are shown in Figure 4.66. By connecting the points with a smooth curve, the figure shows one complete cycle of $y = \frac{1}{2}\sin x$. Also shown is the graph of $y = \sin x$. The graph of $y = \frac{1}{2}\sin x$ is the graph of $y = \sin x$ vertically shrunk by a factor of $\frac{1}{2}$.

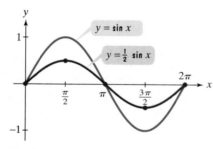

Figure 4.66 The graphs of $y = \sin x$ and $y = \frac{1}{2}\sin x$, $0 \le x \le 2\pi$

Check Point 1   Determine the amplitude of $y = 3 \sin x$. Then graph $y = \sin x$ and $y = 3 \sin x$ for $0 \le x \le 2\pi$.

EXAMPLE 2   **Graphing a Variation of $y = \sin x$**

Determine the amplitude of $y = -2 \sin x$. Then graph $y = \sin x$ and $y = -2 \sin x$ for $-\pi \leq x \leq 3\pi$.

Solution

Step 1   Identify the amplitude and the period. The equation $y = -2 \sin x$ is of the form $y = A \sin x$ with $A = -2$. Thus, the amplitude is $|A| = |-2| = 2$. This means that the maximum value of y is 2 and the minimum value of y is -2. Both $y = \sin x$ and $y = -2 \sin x$ have a period of 2π.

Step 2   Find the x-values for the five key points. Begin by dividing the period, 2π, by 4.

$$\frac{\text{period}}{4} = \frac{2\pi}{4} = \frac{\pi}{2}$$

Start with the value of x where the cycle begins: $x_1 = 0$. Adding quarter-periods, $\frac{\pi}{2}$, the five x-values for the key points are

$$x_1 = 0, \quad x_2 = 0 + \frac{\pi}{2} = \frac{\pi}{2}, \quad x_3 = \frac{\pi}{2} + \frac{\pi}{2} = \pi,$$

$$x_4 = \pi + \frac{\pi}{2} = \frac{3\pi}{2}, \quad x_5 = \frac{3\pi}{2} + \frac{\pi}{2} = 2\pi.$$

Although we will be graphing on $[-\pi, 3\pi]$, we select $x_1 = 0$ rather than $x_1 = -\pi$. Knowing the graph's shape on $[0, 2\pi]$ will enable us to continue the pattern and extend it to the left to $-\pi$ and to the right to 3π.

Step 3   Find the values of y for the five key points. We evaluate the function at each value of x from step 2.

Value of x	Value of y: $y = -2 \sin x$	Coordinates of key point	
0	$y = -2 \sin 0 = -2 \cdot 0 = 0$	$(0, 0)$	
$\dfrac{\pi}{2}$	$y = -2 \sin \dfrac{\pi}{2} = -2 \cdot 1 = -2$	$\left(\dfrac{\pi}{2}, -2\right)$	minimum point
π	$y = -2 \sin \pi = -2 \cdot 0 = 0$	$(\pi, 0)$	
$\dfrac{3\pi}{2}$	$y = -2 \sin \dfrac{3\pi}{2} = -2(-1) = 2$	$\left(\dfrac{3\pi}{2}, 2\right)$	maximum point
2π	$y = -2 \sin 2\pi = -2 \cdot 0 = 0$	$(2\pi, 0)$	

There are x-intercepts at 0, π, and 2π. The minimum and maximum points are indicated by the voice balloons.

Step 4   Connect the five key points with a smooth curve and graph one complete cycle of the given function. The five key points for $y = -2 \sin x$ are shown in Figure 4.67. By connecting the points with a smooth curve, the dark red portion shows one complete cycle of $y = -2 \sin x$. Also shown in dark blue is one complete cycle of the graph of $y = \sin x$. The graph of $y = -2 \sin x$ is the graph of $y = \sin x$ reflected about the x-axis and vertically stretched by a factor of 2.

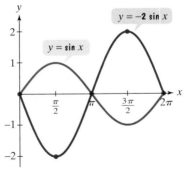

Figure 4.67 The graphs of $y = \sin x$ and $y = -2 \sin x, 0 \leq x \leq 2\pi$

Step 5   Extend the graph in step 4 to the left or right as desired. The dark red and dark blue portions of the graphs in Figure 4.67 are from 0 to 2π. In order to graph for $-\pi \leq x \leq 3\pi$, continue the pattern of each graph to the left and to the right. These extensions are shown by the lighter colors in Figure 4.68 at the top of the next page.

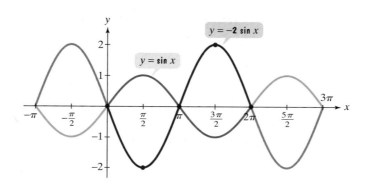

Figure 4.68 The graphs of $y = \sin x$ and $y = -2 \sin x$, $-\pi \le x \le 3\pi$

Check Point 2 Determine the amplitude of $y = -\frac{1}{2} \sin x$. Then graph $y = \sin x$ and $y = -\frac{1}{2} \sin x$ for $-\pi \le x \le 3\pi$.

Now let us examine the graphs of functions of the form $y = A \sin Bx$, where B is the coefficient of x and $B > 0$. How do such graphs compare to those of functions of the form $y = A \sin x$? We know that $y = A \sin x$ completes one cycle from $x = 0$ to $x = 2\pi$. Thus, $y = A \sin Bx$ completes one cycle as Bx increases from 0 to 2π. Set up an inequality to represent this and solve for x to determine the values of x for which $y = \sin Bx$ completes one cycle.

$$0 \le Bx \le 2\pi \qquad \text{$y = \sin Bx$ completes one cycle as Bx}$$
increases from 0 to 2π.

$$0 \le x \le \frac{2\pi}{B} \qquad \text{Divide by B, where $B > 0$, and solve for x.}$$

This means that $y = A \sin Bx$ completes one cycle from 0 to $\frac{2\pi}{B}$. The period is $\frac{2\pi}{B}$.

The graph of $y = A \sin Bx$ is the graph of $y = A \sin x$ horizontally shrunk by a factor of $\frac{1}{B}$ if $B > 1$ and horizontally stretched by a factor of $\frac{1}{B}$ if $0 < B < 1$.

Amplitudes and Periods

The graph of $y = A \sin Bx$ has

amplitude $= |A|$

period $= \dfrac{2\pi}{B}$.

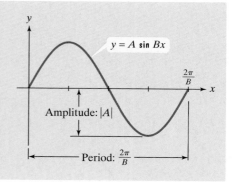

EXAMPLE 3   Graphing a Function of the Form $y = A \sin Bx$

Determine the amplitude and period of $y = 3 \sin 2x$. Then graph the function for $0 \le x \le 2\pi$.

Solution

Step 1   Identify the amplitude and the period. The equation $y = 3 \sin 2x$ is of the form $y = A \sin Bx$ with $A = 3$ and $B = 2$.

amplitude: $|A| = |3| = 3$

period: $\dfrac{2\pi}{B} = \dfrac{2\pi}{2} = \pi$

The amplitude, 3, tells us that the maximum value of y is 3 and the minimum value of y is -3. The period, π, tells us that the graph completes one cycle from 0 to π.

Step 2   Find the x-values for the five key points. Begin by dividing the period of $y = 3 \sin 2x$, π, by 4.

$$\frac{\text{period}}{4} = \frac{\pi}{4}$$

Start with the value of x where the cycle begins: $x_1 = 0$. Adding quarter-periods, $\frac{\pi}{4}$, the five x-values for the key points are

$$x_1 = 0, \quad x_2 = 0 + \frac{\pi}{4} = \frac{\pi}{4}, \quad x_3 = \frac{\pi}{4} + \frac{\pi}{4} = \frac{\pi}{2},$$

$$x_4 = \frac{\pi}{2} + \frac{\pi}{4} = \frac{3\pi}{4}, \quad x_5 = \frac{3\pi}{4} + \frac{\pi}{4} = \pi.$$

Step 3   Find the values of y for the five key points. We evaluate the function at each value of x from step 2.

Value of x	Value of y: $y = 3 \sin 2x$	Coordinates of key point	
0	$y = 3 \sin(2 \cdot 0)$ $= 3 \sin 0 = 3 \cdot 0 = 0$	$(0, 0)$	
$\frac{\pi}{4}$	$y = 3 \sin\left(2 \cdot \frac{\pi}{4}\right)$ $= 3 \sin \frac{\pi}{2} = 3 \cdot 1 = 3$	$\left(\frac{\pi}{4}, 3\right)$	maximum point
$\frac{\pi}{2}$	$y = 3 \sin\left(2 \cdot \frac{\pi}{2}\right)$ $= 3 \sin \pi = 3 \cdot 0 = 0$	$\left(\frac{\pi}{2}, 0\right)$	
$\frac{3\pi}{4}$	$y = 3 \sin\left(2 \cdot \frac{3\pi}{4}\right)$ $= 3 \sin \frac{3\pi}{2} = 3(-1) = -3$	$\left(\frac{3\pi}{4}, -3\right)$	minimum point
π	$y = 3 \sin(2 \cdot \pi)$ $= 3 \sin 2\pi = 3 \cdot 0 = 0$	$(\pi, 0)$	

In the interval $[0, \pi]$, there are x-intercepts at $0, \frac{\pi}{2}$, and π. The maximum and minimum points are indicated by the voice balloons.

Step 4   Connect the five key points with a smooth curve and graph one complete cycle of the given function. The five key points for $y = 3 \sin 2x$ are shown in Figure 4.69. By connecting the points with a smooth curve, the blue portion shows one complete cycle of $y = 3 \sin 2x$ from 0 to π. The graph of $y = 3 \sin 2x$ is the graph of $y = \sin x$ vertically stretched by a factor of 3 and horizontally shrunk by a factor of $\frac{1}{2}$.

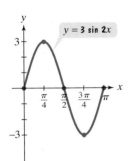

y = 3 sin 2x

Figure 4.69 The graph of $y = 3 \sin 2x$, $0 \le x \le \pi$

Step 5   Extend the graph in step 4 to the left or right as desired. The blue portion of the graph in Figure 4.69 is from 0 to π. In order to graph for $0 \le x \le 2\pi$, we continue this portion and extend the graph another full period to the right. This extension is shown in black in Figure 4.70.

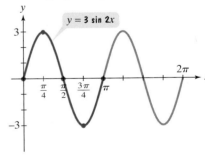

y = 3 sin 2x

Figure 4.70

Technology

The graph of $y = 3 \sin 2x$ in a $\left[0, 2\pi, \frac{\pi}{2}\right]$ by $[-4, 4, 1]$ viewing rectangle verifies our hand-drawn graph in Figure 4.70.

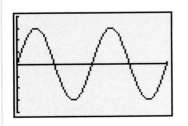

Check Point 3   Determine the amplitude and period of $y = 2 \sin \frac{1}{2}x$. Then graph the function for $0 \le x \le 8\pi$.

Now let us examine the graphs of functions of the form $y = A \sin(Bx - C)$, where $B > 0$. How do such graphs compare to those of functions of the form $y = A \sin Bx$? In both cases, the amplitude is $|A|$ and the period is $\frac{2\pi}{B}$. One complete cycle occurs if $Bx - C$ increases from 0 to 2π. This means that we can find an interval containing one cycle by solving the following inequality:

$$0 \leq Bx - C \leq 2\pi. \qquad \text{$y = A \sin(Bx - C)$ completes one cycle as $Bx - C$ increases from 0 to 2π.}$$

$$C \leq Bx \leq C + 2\pi \qquad \text{Add C to all three parts.}$$

$$\frac{C}{B} \leq x \leq \frac{C}{B} + \frac{2\pi}{B} \qquad \text{Divide by B, where $B > 0$, and solve for x.}$$

This is the x-coordinate on the left where the cycle begins.

This is the x-coordinate on the right where the cycle ends. $\frac{2\pi}{B}$ is the period.

The voice balloon on the left indicates that the graph of $y = A \sin(Bx - C)$ is the graph of $y = A \sin Bx$ shifted horizontally by $\frac{C}{B}$. Thus, the number $\frac{C}{B}$ is the **phase shift** associated with the graph.

The Graph of $y = A \sin(Bx - C)$

The graph of $y = A \sin(Bx - C)$ is obtained by horizontally shifting the graph of $y = A \sin Bx$ so that the starting point of the cycle is shifted from $x = 0$ to $x = \frac{C}{B}$. If $\frac{C}{B} > 0$, the shift is to the right. If $\frac{C}{B} < 0$, the shift is to the left. The number $\frac{C}{B}$ is called the **phase shift**.

$$\text{amplitude} = |A|$$

$$\text{period} = \frac{2\pi}{B}$$

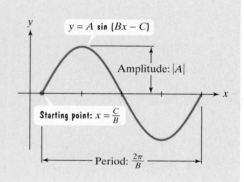

EXAMPLE 4 Graphing a Function of the Form $y = A \sin(Bx - C)$

Determine the amplitude, period, and phase shift of $y = 4 \sin\left(2x - \frac{2\pi}{3}\right)$. Then graph one period of the function.

Solution

Step 1 Identify the amplitude, the period, and the phase shift. We must first identify values for A, B, and C.

The equation is of the form $y = A \sin(Bx - C)$.

$$y = 4 \sin\left(2x - \frac{2\pi}{3}\right)$$

Using the voice balloon, we see that $A = 4$, $B = 2$, and $C = \frac{2\pi}{3}$.

$$\text{amplitude:} \quad |A| = |4| = 4 \qquad \text{The maximum y is 4 and the minimum is -4.}$$

$$\text{period:} \quad \frac{2\pi}{B} = \frac{2\pi}{2} = \pi \qquad \text{Each cycle is of length π.}$$

$$\text{phase shift:} \quad \frac{C}{B} = \frac{\frac{2\pi}{3}}{2} = \frac{2\pi}{3} \cdot \frac{1}{2} = \frac{\pi}{3} \qquad \text{A cycle starts at $x = \frac{\pi}{3}$.}$$

Step 2   Find the x-values for the five key points. Begin by dividing the period, π, by 4.

$$\frac{\text{period}}{4} = \frac{\pi}{4}$$

Start with the value of x where the cycle begins: $x_1 = \frac{\pi}{3}$. Adding quarter-periods, $\frac{\pi}{4}$, the five x-values for the key points are

$$x_1 = \frac{\pi}{3}, \quad x_2 = \frac{\pi}{3} + \frac{\pi}{4} = \frac{4\pi}{12} + \frac{3\pi}{12} = \frac{7\pi}{12},$$

$$x_3 = \frac{7\pi}{12} + \frac{\pi}{4} = \frac{7\pi}{12} + \frac{3\pi}{12} = \frac{10\pi}{12} = \frac{5\pi}{6},$$

$$x_4 = \frac{5\pi}{6} + \frac{\pi}{4} = \frac{10\pi}{12} + \frac{3\pi}{12} = \frac{13\pi}{12},$$

$$x_5 = \frac{13\pi}{12} + \frac{\pi}{4} = \frac{13\pi}{12} + \frac{3\pi}{12} = \frac{16\pi}{12} = \frac{4\pi}{3}.$$

Study Tip

You can speed up the additions on the right by first writing the starting point, $\frac{\pi}{3}$, and the quarter-period, $\frac{\pi}{4}$, with a common denominator, 12.

starting point
$$= \frac{\pi}{3} = \frac{4\pi}{12}$$

quarter-period
$$= \frac{\pi}{4} = \frac{3\pi}{12}$$

Study Tip

You can check your computations for the x-values for the five key points. The difference between x_5 and x_1, or $x_5 - x_1$, should equal the period.

$$x_5 - x_1 = \frac{4\pi}{3} - \frac{\pi}{3} = \frac{3\pi}{3} = \pi$$

Because the period is π, this verifies that our five x-values are correct.

Step 3   Find the values of y for the five key points. We evaluate the function at each value of x from step 2.

Value of x	Value of y: $y = 4 \sin\left(2x - \frac{2\pi}{3}\right)$	Coordinates of key point
$\dfrac{\pi}{3}$	$y = 4 \sin\left(2 \cdot \dfrac{\pi}{3} - \dfrac{2\pi}{3}\right)$ $= 4 \sin 0 = 4 \cdot 0 = 0$	$\left(\dfrac{\pi}{3}, 0\right)$
$\dfrac{7\pi}{12}$	$y = 4 \sin\left(2 \cdot \dfrac{7\pi}{12} - \dfrac{2\pi}{3}\right)$ $= 4 \sin\left(\dfrac{7\pi}{6} - \dfrac{2\pi}{3}\right)$ $= 4 \sin \dfrac{3\pi}{6} = 4 \sin \dfrac{\pi}{2} = 4 \cdot 1 = 4$	$\left(\dfrac{7\pi}{12}, 4\right)$ maximum point
$\dfrac{5\pi}{6}$	$y = 4 \sin\left(2 \cdot \dfrac{5\pi}{6} - \dfrac{2\pi}{3}\right)$ $= 4 \sin\left(\dfrac{5\pi}{3} - \dfrac{2\pi}{3}\right)$ $= 4 \sin \dfrac{3\pi}{3} = 4 \sin \pi = 4 \cdot 0 = 0$	$\left(\dfrac{5\pi}{6}, 0\right)$
$\dfrac{13\pi}{12}$	$y = 4 \sin\left(2 \cdot \dfrac{13\pi}{12} - \dfrac{2\pi}{3}\right)$ $= 4 \sin\left(\dfrac{13\pi}{6} - \dfrac{4\pi}{6}\right)$ $= 4 \sin \dfrac{9\pi}{6} = 4 \sin \dfrac{3\pi}{2} = 4(-1) = -4$	$\left(\dfrac{13\pi}{12}, -4\right)$ minimum point
$\dfrac{4\pi}{3}$	$y = 4 \sin\left(2 \cdot \dfrac{4\pi}{3} - \dfrac{2\pi}{3}\right)$ $= 4 \sin \dfrac{6\pi}{3} = 4 \sin 2\pi = 4 \cdot 0 = 0$	$\left(\dfrac{4\pi}{3}, 0\right)$

The key points $\left(\dfrac{\pi}{3}, 0\right)$, $\left(\dfrac{5\pi}{6}, 0\right)$, and $\left(\dfrac{4\pi}{3}, 0\right)$ indicate that in the interval $\left[\dfrac{\pi}{3}, \dfrac{4\pi}{3}\right]$, there are x-intercepts at $\dfrac{\pi}{3}, \dfrac{5\pi}{6}$, and $\dfrac{4\pi}{3}$. The voice balloons on the previous page indicate that $\left(\dfrac{7\pi}{12}, 4\right)$ is a maximum point and $\left(\dfrac{13\pi}{12}, -4\right)$ is a minimum point.

Step 4 Connect the five key points with a smooth curve and graph one complete cycle of the given function. The key points, $\left(\dfrac{\pi}{3}, 0\right)$, $\left(\dfrac{7\pi}{12}, 4\right)$, $\left(\dfrac{5\pi}{6}, 0\right)$, $\left(\dfrac{13\pi}{12}, -4\right)$, and $\left(\dfrac{4\pi}{3}, 0\right)$, and the graph of $y = 4\sin\left(2x - \dfrac{2\pi}{3}\right)$ are shown in Figure 4.71.

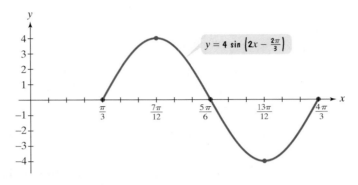

Figure 4.71

Check Point 4 Determine the amplitude, period, and phase shift of $y = 3\sin\left(2x - \dfrac{\pi}{3}\right)$. Then graph one period of the function.

③ Understand the graph of $y = \cos x$.

The Graph of $y = \cos x$

We graph $y = \cos x$ by listing some points on the graph. Because the period of the cosine function is 2π, we will concentrate on the graph of the basic cosine curve on the interval $[0, 2\pi]$. The rest of the graph is made up of repetitions of this portion. Table 4.4 lists some values of (x, y) on the graph of $y = \cos x$.

Table 4.4 Values of (x, y) on the graph of $y = \cos x$

x	0	$\dfrac{\pi}{6}$	$\dfrac{\pi}{3}$	$\dfrac{\pi}{2}$	$\dfrac{2\pi}{3}$	$\dfrac{5\pi}{6}$	π	$\dfrac{7\pi}{6}$	$\dfrac{4\pi}{3}$	$\dfrac{3\pi}{2}$	$\dfrac{5\pi}{3}$	$\dfrac{11\pi}{6}$	2π
$y = \cos x$	1	$\dfrac{\sqrt{3}}{2}$	$\dfrac{1}{2}$	0	$-\dfrac{1}{2}$	$-\dfrac{\sqrt{3}}{2}$	-1	$-\dfrac{\sqrt{3}}{2}$	$-\dfrac{1}{2}$	0	$\dfrac{1}{2}$	$\dfrac{\sqrt{3}}{2}$	1

As x increases from 0 to $\dfrac{\pi}{2}$, y decreases from 1 to 0.

As x increases from $\dfrac{\pi}{2}$ to π, y decreases from 0 to -1.

As x increases from π to $\dfrac{3\pi}{2}$, y increases from -1 to 0.

As x increases from $\dfrac{3\pi}{2}$ to 2π, y increases from 0 to 1.

Plotting the points in Table 4.4 and connecting them with a smooth curve, we obtain the graph shown in Figure 4.72. The portion of the graph in dark blue shows one complete period. We can obtain a more complete graph of $y = \cos x$ by extending this dark blue portion to the left and to the right.

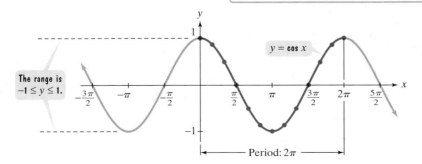

The range is $-1 \le y \le 1$.

Period: 2π

Figure 4.72 The graph of $y = \cos x$

The graph of $y = \cos x$ allows us to visualize some of the properties of the cosine function.

- The domain is $(-\infty, \infty)$, the set of all real numbers. The graph extends indefinitely to the left and to the right with no gaps or holes.
- The range is $[-1, 1]$, the set of all real numbers between -1 and 1, inclusive. The graph never rises above 1 or falls below -1.
- The period is 2π. The graph's pattern repeats in every interval of length 2π.
- The function is an even function: $\cos(-x) = \cos x$. This can be seen by observing that the graph is symmetric with respect to the y-axis.

Take a second look at Figure 4.72. Can you see that the graph of $y = \cos x$ is the graph of $y = \sin x$ with a phase shift of $-\dfrac{\pi}{2}$? If you trace along the curve from $x = -\dfrac{\pi}{2}$ to $x = \dfrac{3\pi}{2}$, you are tracing one complete cycle of the sine curve. This can be expressed as an identity:

$$\cos x = \sin\left(x + \frac{\pi}{2}\right).$$

Because of this similarity, the graphs of sine functions and cosine functions are called **sinusoidal graphs**.

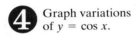 Graph variations of $y = \cos x$.

Graphing Variations of $y = \cos x$

We use the same steps to graph variations of $y = \cos x$ as we did for graphing variations of $y = \sin x$. We will continue finding key points by dividing the period into four equal parts. Amplitudes, periods, and phase shifts play an important role when graphing by hand.

The Graph of $y = A \cos Bx$

The graph of $y = A \cos Bx$ has

$$\text{amplitude} = |A|$$
$$\text{period} = \frac{2\pi}{B}.$$

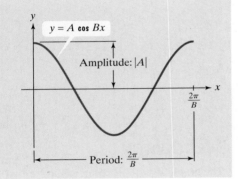

EXAMPLE 5   Graphing a Function of the Form $y = A \cos Bx$

Determine the amplitude and period of $y = -3 \cos \dfrac{\pi}{2} x$. Then graph the function for $-4 \le x \le 4$.

Solution

Step 1   Identify the amplitude and the period. The equation $y = -3 \cos \dfrac{\pi}{2} x$ is of the form $y = A \cos Bx$ with $A = -3$ and $B = \dfrac{\pi}{2}$.

amplitude: $|A| = |-3| = 3$ The maximum y is 3 and the minimum is -3.

period: $\dfrac{2\pi}{B} = \dfrac{2\pi}{\dfrac{\pi}{2}} = 2\pi \cdot \dfrac{2}{\pi} = 4$ Each cycle is of length 4.

Step 2   Find the x-values for the five key points. Begin by dividing the period, 4, by 4.

$$\frac{\text{period}}{4} = \frac{4}{4} = 1$$

Start with the value of x where the cycle begins: $x_1 = 0$. Adding quarter-periods, 1, the five x-values for the key points are

$$x_1 = 0, \quad x_2 = 0 + 1 = 1, \quad x_3 = 1 + 1 = 2, \quad x_4 = 2 + 1 = 3, \quad x_5 = 3 + 1 = 4.$$

Step 3   Find the values of y for the five key points. We evaluate the function at each value of x from step 2.

Value of x	Value of y: $y = -3\cos\frac{\pi}{2}x$	Coordinates of key point	
0	$y = -3\cos\left(\frac{\pi}{2}\cdot 0\right)$ $= -3\cos 0 = -3\cdot 1 = -3$	$(0, -3)$	minimum point
1	$y = -3\cos\left(\frac{\pi}{2}\cdot 1\right)$ $= -3\cos\frac{\pi}{2} = -3\cdot 0 = 0$	$(1, 0)$	
2	$y = -3\cos\left(\frac{\pi}{2}\cdot 2\right)$ $= -3\cos\pi = -3(-1) = 3$	$(2, 3)$	maximum point
3	$y = -3\cos\left(\frac{\pi}{2}\cdot 3\right)$ $= -3\cos\frac{3\pi}{2} = -3\cdot 0 = 0$	$(3, 0)$	
4	$y = -3\cos\left(\frac{\pi}{2}\cdot 4\right)$ $= -3\cos 2\pi = -3\cdot 1 = -3$	$(4, -3)$	minimum point

In the interval $[0, 4]$, there are x-intercepts at 1 and 3. The minimum and maximum points are indicated by the voice balloons.

Technology

The graph of $y = -3\cos\frac{\pi}{2}x$ in a $[-4, 4, 1]$ by $[-4, 4, 1]$ viewing rectangle verifies our hand-drawn graph in Figure 4.73.

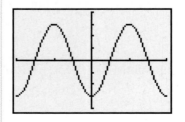

Step 4   Connect the five key points with a smooth curve and graph one complete cycle of the given function. The five key points for $y = -3\cos\frac{\pi}{2}x$ are shown in Figure 4.73. By connecting the points with a smooth curve, the blue portion shows one complete cycle of $y = -3\cos\frac{\pi}{2}x$ from 0 to 4.

Step 5   Extend the graph in step 4 to the left or right as desired. The blue portion of the graph in Figure 4.73 is for x from 0 to 4. In order to graph for $-4 \le x \le 4$, we continue this portion and extend the graph another full period to the left. This extension is shown in black in Figure 4.73.

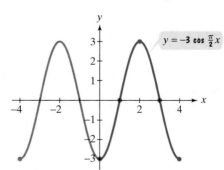

Figure 4.73

Check Point 5   Determine the amplitude and period of $y = -4\cos\pi x$. Then graph the function for $-2 \le x \le 2$.

Finally, let us examine the graphs of functions of the form $y = A\cos(Bx - C)$. Graphs of these functions shift the graph of $y = A\cos Bx$ horizontally by $\dfrac{C}{B}$.

The Graph of $y = A\cos(Bx - C)$

The graph of $y = A\cos(Bx - C)$ is obtained by horizontally shifting the graph of $y = A\cos Bx$ so that the starting point of the cycle is shifted from $x = 0$ to $x = \dfrac{C}{B}$. If $\dfrac{C}{B} > 0$, the shift is to the right. If $\dfrac{C}{B} < 0$, the shift is to the left.

The number $\dfrac{C}{B}$ is called the **phase shift**.

$$\text{amplitude} = |A|$$

$$\text{period} = \frac{2\pi}{B}.$$

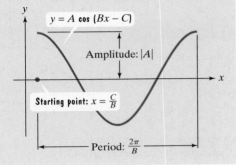

EXAMPLE 6   Graphing a Function of the Form $y = A\cos(Bx - C)$

Determine the amplitude, period, and phase shift of $y = \frac{1}{2}\cos(4x + \pi)$. Then graph one period of the function.

Solution

Step 1   Identify the amplitude, the period, and the phase shift. We must first identify values for A, B, and C. To do this, we need to express the equation in the form $y = A\cos(Bx - C)$. Thus, we write $y = \frac{1}{2}\cos(4x + \pi)$ as $y = \frac{1}{2}\cos[4x - (-\pi)]$. Now we can identify values for A, B, and C.

The equation is of the form
$y = A\cos(Bx - C)$.

$$y = \frac{1}{2}\cos[4x - (-\pi)]$$

Using the voice balloon, we see that $A = \frac{1}{2}$, $B = 4$, and $C = -\pi$.

amplitude: $|A| = \left|\dfrac{1}{2}\right| = \dfrac{1}{2}$ The maximum y is $\frac{1}{2}$ and the minimum is $-\frac{1}{2}$.

period: $\dfrac{2\pi}{B} = \dfrac{2\pi}{4} = \dfrac{\pi}{2}$ Each cycle is of length $\frac{\pi}{2}$.

phase shift: $\dfrac{C}{B} = -\dfrac{\pi}{4}$ A cycle starts at $x = -\frac{\pi}{4}$.

Step 2   Find the x-values for the five key points. Begin by dividing the period, $\dfrac{\pi}{2}$, by 4.

$$\frac{\text{period}}{4} = \frac{\dfrac{\pi}{2}}{4} = \frac{\pi}{8}$$

Start with the value of x where the cycle begins: $x_1 = -\dfrac{\pi}{4}$. Adding quarter-periods, $\dfrac{\pi}{8}$, the five x-values for the key points are

$$x_1 = -\frac{\pi}{4}, \quad x_2 = -\frac{\pi}{4} + \frac{\pi}{8} = -\frac{2\pi}{8} + \frac{\pi}{8} = -\frac{\pi}{8}, \quad x_3 = -\frac{\pi}{8} + \frac{\pi}{8} = 0,$$

$$x_4 = 0 + \frac{\pi}{8} = \frac{\pi}{8}, \quad x_5 = \frac{\pi}{8} + \frac{\pi}{8} = \frac{2\pi}{8} = \frac{\pi}{4}.$$

Step 3 Find the values of y for the five key points. Take a few minutes and use your calculator to evaluate the function at each value of x from step 2. Show that the key points are

$$\left(-\frac{\pi}{4}, \frac{1}{2}\right), \quad \left(-\frac{\pi}{8}, 0\right), \quad \left(0, -\frac{1}{2}\right), \quad \left(\frac{\pi}{8}, 0\right), \text{ and } \left(\frac{\pi}{4}, \frac{1}{2}\right).$$

| maximum point | x-intercept at $-\dfrac{\pi}{8}$ | minimum point | x-intercept at $\dfrac{\pi}{8}$ | maximum point |

Step 4 Connect the five key points with a smooth curve and graph one complete cycle of the given function. The key points and the graph of $y = \frac{1}{2}\cos(4x + \pi)$ are shown in Figure 4.74.

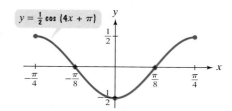

Figure 4.74

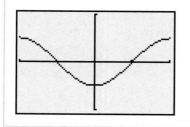

Check Point 6 Determine the amplitude, period, and phase shift of $y = \frac{3}{2}\cos(2x + \pi)$. Then graph one period of the function.

⑤ Use vertical shifts of sine and cosine curves.

Vertical Shifts of Sinusoidal Graphs

We now look at sinusoidal graphs of

$$y = A\sin(Bx - C) + D \quad \text{and} \quad y = A\cos(Bx - C) + D.$$

The constant D causes vertical shifts in the graphs of $y = A\sin(Bx - C)$ and $y = A\cos(Bx - C)$. If D is positive, the shift is D units upward. If D is negative, the shift is D units downward. These vertical shifts result in sinusoidal graphs oscillating about the horizontal line $y = D$ rather than about the x-axis. Thus, the maximum y is $D + |A|$ and the minimum y is $D - |A|$.

EXAMPLE 7 A Vertical Shift

Graph one period of the function $y = \frac{1}{2}\cos x - 1$.

Solution The graph of $y = \frac{1}{2}\cos x - 1$ is the graph of $y = \frac{1}{2}\cos x$ shifted one unit downward. The period of $y = \frac{1}{2}\cos x$ is 2π, which is also the period for the vertically shifted graph. The key points on the interval $[0, 2\pi]$ for $y = \frac{1}{2}\cos x - 1$ are found by first determining their x-coordinates. The quarter-period is $\dfrac{2\pi}{4}$, or $\dfrac{\pi}{2}$. The cycle begins at $x = 0$. As always, we add quarter-periods to generate x-values for each of the key points. The five x-values are

$$x_1 = 0, \quad x_2 = 0 + \frac{\pi}{2} = \frac{\pi}{2}, \quad x_3 = \frac{\pi}{2} + \frac{\pi}{2} = \pi,$$

$$x_4 = \pi + \frac{\pi}{2} = \frac{3\pi}{2}, \quad x_5 = \frac{3\pi}{2} + \frac{\pi}{2} = 2\pi.$$

The values of y for the five key points and their coordinates are determined as follows.

Value of x	Value of y: $y = \dfrac{1}{2}\cos x - 1$	Coordinates of key point
0	$y = \dfrac{1}{2}\cos 0 - 1$ $= \dfrac{1}{2}\cdot 1 - 1 = -\dfrac{1}{2}$	$\left(0, -\dfrac{1}{2}\right)$
$\dfrac{\pi}{2}$	$y = \dfrac{1}{2}\cos\dfrac{\pi}{2} - 1$ $= \dfrac{1}{2}\cdot 0 - 1 = -1$	$\left(\dfrac{\pi}{2}, -1\right)$
π	$y = \dfrac{1}{2}\cos\pi - 1$ $= \dfrac{1}{2}(-1) - 1 = -\dfrac{3}{2}$	$\left(\pi, -\dfrac{3}{2}\right)$
$\dfrac{3\pi}{2}$	$y = \dfrac{1}{2}\cos\dfrac{3\pi}{2} - 1$ $= \dfrac{1}{2}\cdot 0 - 1 = -1$	$\left(\dfrac{3\pi}{2}, -1\right)$
2π	$y = \dfrac{1}{2}\cos 2\pi - 1$ $= \dfrac{1}{2}\cdot 1 - 1 = -\dfrac{1}{2}$	$\left(2\pi, -\dfrac{1}{2}\right)$

The five key points for $y = \frac{1}{2}\cos x - 1$ are shown in Figure 4.75. By connecting the points with a smooth curve, we obtain one period of the graph.

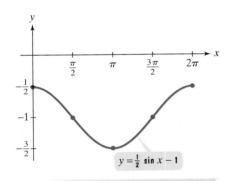

$y = \frac{1}{2}\sin x - 1$

Figure 4.75

Check Point 7 Graph one period of the function $y = 2\cos x + 1$.

6 Model periodic behavior.

Modeling Periodic Behavior

Our breathing consists of alternating periods of inhaling and exhaling. Each complete pumping cycle of the human heart can be described using a sine function. Our brain waves during deep sleep are sinusoidal. Viewed in this way, trigonometry becomes an intimate experience.

Some graphing utilities have a SINe REGression feature. This feature gives the sine function in the form $y = A\sin(Bx + C) + D$ of best fit for wavelike data. At least four data points must be used. However, it is not always necessary to use technology. In our next example, we use our understanding of sinusoidal graphs to model the process of breathing.

EXAMPLE 8 A Trigonometric Breath of Life

The graph in Figure 4.76 shows one complete normal breathing cycle. The cycle consists of inhaling and exhaling. It takes place every 5 seconds. Velocity of air flow is positive when we inhale and negative when we exhale. It is measured in liters per second. If y represents velocity of air flow after x seconds, find a function of the form $y = A \sin Bx$ that models air flow in a normal breathing cycle.

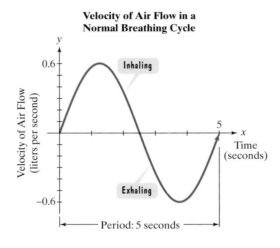

Velocity of Air Flow in a Normal Breathing Cycle

Figure 4.76

Solution We need to determine values for A and B in the equation $y = A \sin Bx$. A, the amplitude, is the maximum value of y. Figure 4.76 shows that this maximum value is 0.6. Thus, $A = 0.6$.

The value of B in $y = A \sin Bx$ can be found using the formula for the period: period $= \dfrac{2\pi}{B}$. The period of our breathing cycle is 5 seconds. Thus,

$$5 = \frac{2\pi}{B} \qquad \textit{Our goal is to solve this equation for B.}$$

$$5B = 2\pi \qquad \textit{Multiply both sides of the equation by B.}$$

$$B = \frac{2\pi}{5}. \qquad \textit{Divide both sides of the equation by 5.}$$

We see that $A = 0.6$ and $B = \dfrac{2\pi}{5}$. Substitute these values into $y = A \sin Bx$. The breathing cycle is modeled by

$$y = 0.6 \sin \frac{2\pi}{5} x.$$

Check Point 8 Find an equation of the form $y = A \sin Bx$ that produces the graph shown in the figure on the right.

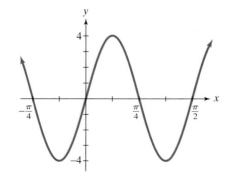

EXAMPLE 9   Modeling a Tidal Cycle

Figure 4.77 shows that the depth of water at a boat dock varies with the tides. The depth is 5 feet at low tide and 13 feet at high tide. On a certain day, low tide occurs at 4 A.M. and high tide at 10 A.M. If y represents the depth of the water, in feet, x hours after midnight, use a sine function of the form $y = A \sin(Bx - C) + D$ to model the water's depth.

Solution   We need to determine values for A, B, C, and D in the equation $y = A \sin(Bx - C) + D$. We can find these values using Figure 4.77. We begin with D.

To find D, we use the vertical shift. Because the water's depth ranges from a minimum of 5 feet to a maximum of 13 feet, the curve oscillates about the middle value, 9 feet. Thus, $D = 9$, which is the vertical shift.

At maximum depth, the water is 4 feet above 9 feet. Thus, A, the amplitude, is 4: $A = 4$.

To find B, we use the period. The blue portion of the graph shows that one complete tidal cycle occurs in $19 - 7$, or 12 hours. The period is 12. Thus,

$$12 = \frac{2\pi}{B}$$ *Our goal is to solve this equation for B.*

$$12B = 2\pi$$ *Multiply both sides by B.*

$$B = \frac{2\pi}{12} = \frac{\pi}{6}.$$ *Divide both sides by 12.*

To find C, we use the phase shift. The blue portion of the graph shows that the starting point of the cycle is shifted from 0 to 7. The phase shift, $\frac{C}{B}$, is 7.

$$7 = \frac{C}{B}$$ *The phase shift of $y = A \sin(Bx - C)$ is $\frac{C}{B}$.*

$$7 = \frac{C}{\frac{\pi}{6}}$$ *From above, we have $B = \frac{\pi}{6}$.*

$$\frac{7\pi}{6} = C$$ *Multiply both sides of the equation by $\frac{\pi}{6}$.*

We see that $A = 4$, $B = \frac{\pi}{6}$, $C = \frac{7\pi}{6}$, and $D = 9$. Substitute these values into $y = A \sin(Bx - C) + D$. The water's depth, in feet, x hours after midnight is modeled by

$$y = 4 \sin\left(\frac{\pi}{6}x - \frac{7\pi}{6}\right) + 9.$$

Technology

We can use a graphing utility to verify that the model in Example 9

$$y = 4 \sin\left(\frac{\pi}{6}x - \frac{7\pi}{6}\right) + 9$$

is correct. The graph of the function is shown in a $[0, 28, 4]$ by $[0, 15, 5]$ viewing rectangle.

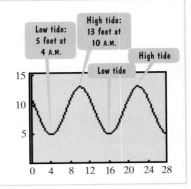

Check Point 9   A region that is 30° north of the Equator averages a minimum of 10 hours of daylight in December. Hours of daylight are at a maximum of 14 hours in June. Let x represent the month of the year, with 1 for January, 2 for February, 3 for March, and 12 for December. If y represents the number of hours of daylight in month x, use a sine function of the form $y = A \sin(Bx - C) + D$ to model the hours of daylight.

Figure 4.77
Depth of Water / The Number of Hours after Midnight

EXERCISE SET 4.5

Practice Exercises

In Exercises 1–6, determine the amplitude of each function. Then graph the function and $y = \sin x$ in the same rectangular coordinate system for $0 \le x \le 2\pi$.

1. $y = 4 \sin x$
2. $y = 5 \sin x$
3. $y = \frac{1}{3} \sin x$
4. $y = \frac{1}{4} \sin x$
5. $y = -3 \sin x$
6. $y = -4 \sin x$

In Exercises 7–16, determine the amplitude and period of each function. Then graph one period of the function.

7. $y = \sin 2x$
8. $y = \sin 4x$
9. $y = 3 \sin \frac{1}{2} x$
10. $y = 2 \sin \frac{1}{4} x$
11. $y = 4 \sin \pi x$
12. $y = 3 \sin 2\pi x$
13. $y = -3 \sin 2\pi x$
14. $y = -2 \sin \pi x$
15. $y = -\sin \frac{2}{3} x$
16. $y = -\sin \frac{4}{3} x$

In Exercises 17–30, determine the amplitude, period, and phase shift of each function. Then graph one period of the function.

17. $y = \sin(x - \pi)$
18. $y = \sin\left(x - \frac{\pi}{2}\right)$
19. $y = \sin(2x - \pi)$
20. $y = \sin\left(2x - \frac{\pi}{2}\right)$
21. $y = 3 \sin(2x - \pi)$
22. $y = 3 \sin\left(2x - \frac{\pi}{2}\right)$
23. $y = \frac{1}{2} \sin\left(x + \frac{\pi}{2}\right)$
24. $y = \frac{1}{2} \sin(x + \pi)$
25. $y = -2 \sin\left(2x + \frac{\pi}{2}\right)$
26. $y = -3 \sin\left(2x + \frac{\pi}{2}\right)$
27. $y = 3 \sin(\pi x + 2)$
28. $y = 3 \sin(2\pi x + 4)$
29. $y = -2 \sin(2\pi x + 4\pi)$
30. $y = -3 \sin(2\pi x + 4\pi)$

In Exercises 31–34, determine the amplitude of each function. Then graph the function and $y = \cos x$ in the same rectangular coordinate system for $0 \le x \le 2\pi$.

31. $y = 2 \cos x$
32. $y = 3 \cos x$
33. $y = -2 \cos x$
34. $y = -3 \cos x$

In Exercises 35–42, determine the amplitude and period of each function. Then graph one period of the function.

35. $y = \cos 2x$
36. $y = \cos 4x$
37. $y = 4 \cos 2\pi x$
38. $y = 5 \cos 2\pi x$
39. $y = -4 \cos \frac{1}{2} x$
40. $y = -3 \cos \frac{1}{3} x$
41. $y = -\frac{1}{2} \cos \frac{\pi}{3} x$
42. $y = -\frac{1}{2} \cos \frac{\pi}{4} x$

In Exercises 43–52, determine the amplitude, period, and phase shift of each function. Then graph one period of the function.

43. $y = \cos\left(x - \frac{\pi}{2}\right)$
44. $y = \cos\left(x + \frac{\pi}{2}\right)$
45. $y = 3 \cos(2x - \pi)$
46. $y = 4 \cos(2x - \pi)$
47. $y = \frac{1}{2} \cos\left(3x + \frac{\pi}{2}\right)$
48. $y = \frac{1}{2} \cos(2x + \pi)$
49. $y = -3 \cos\left(2x - \frac{\pi}{2}\right)$
50. $y = -4 \cos\left(2x - \frac{\pi}{2}\right)$
51. $y = 2 \cos(2\pi x + 8\pi)$
52. $y = 3 \cos(2\pi x + 4\pi)$

In Exercises 53–60, use a vertical shift to graph one period of the function.

53. $y = \sin x + 2$
54. $y = \sin x - 2$
55. $y = \cos x - 3$
56. $y = \cos x + 3$
57. $y = 2 \sin \frac{1}{2} x + 1$
58. $y = 2 \cos \frac{1}{2} x + 1$
59. $y = -3 \cos 2\pi x + 2$
60. $y = -3 \sin 2\pi x + 2$

Practice Plus

In Exercises 61–66, find an equation for each graph.

61.

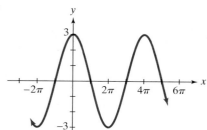

62.

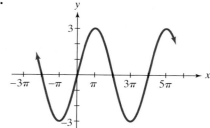

63.

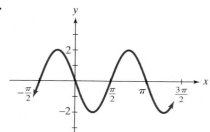

64.

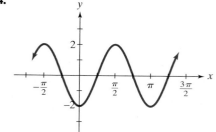

65.

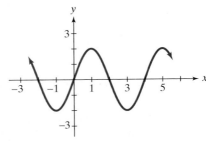

66.

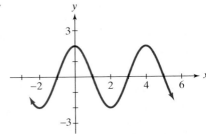

In Exercises 67–70, graph one period of each function.

67. $y = \left| 2 \cos \dfrac{x}{2} \right|$ **68.** $y = \left| 3 \cos \dfrac{2x}{3} \right|$

69. $y = -\left| 3 \sin \pi x \right|$ **70.** $y = -\left| 2 \sin \dfrac{\pi x}{2} \right|$

In Exercises 71–74, graph f, g, and h in the same rectangular coordinate system for $0 \le x \le 2\pi$. Obtain the graph of h by adding or subtracting the corresponding y-coordinates on the graphs of f and g.

71. $f(x) = -2 \sin x$, $g(x) = \sin 2x$, $h(x) = (f + g)(x)$

72. $f(x) = 2 \cos x$, $g(x) = \cos 2x$, $h(x) = (f + g)(x)$

73. $f(x) = \sin x$, $g(x) = \cos 2x$, $h(x) = (f - g)(x)$

74. $f(x) = \cos x$, $g(x) = \sin 2x$, $h(x) = (f - g)(x)$

Application Exercises

In the theory of biorhythms, sine functions are used to measure a person's potential. You can obtain your biorhythm chart online by simply entering your date of birth, the date you want your biorhythm chart to begin, and the number of months you wish to be included in the plot. Shown below is your author's chart, beginning January 25, 2006, when he was 22,188 days old. We all have cycles with the same amplitudes and periods as those shown here. Each of our three basic cycles begins at birth. Use the biorhythm chart shown to solve Exercises 75–82. The longer tick marks correspond to the dates shown.

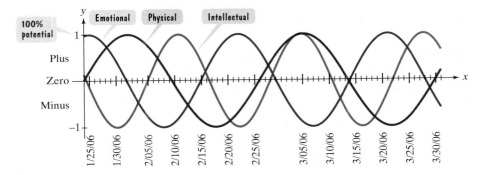

75. What is the period of the physical cycle?

76. What is the period of the emotional cycle?

77. What is the period of the intellectual cycle?

78. For the period shown, what is the worst day in February for your author to run in a marathon?

79. For the period shown, what is the best day in March for your author to meet an online friend for the first time?

80. For the period shown, what is the best day in February for your author to begin writing this trigonometry chapter?

81. If you extend these sinusoidal graphs to the end of the year, is there a day when your author should not even bother getting out of bed?

82. If you extend these sinusoidal graphs to the end of the year, are there any days where your author is at near-peak physical, emotional, and intellectual potential?

83. Rounded to the nearest hour, Los Angeles averages 14 hours of daylight in June, 10 hours in December, and 12 hours in March and September. Let x represent the number of months after June and let y represent the number of hours of daylight in month x. Make a graph that displays the information from June of one year to June of the following year.

84. A clock with an hour hand that is 15 inches long is hanging on a wall. At noon, the distance between the tip of the hour hand and the ceiling is 23 inches. At 3 P.M., the distance is 38 inches; at 6 P.M., 53 inches; at 9 P.M., 38 inches; and at midnight the distance is again 23 inches. If y represents distance between the tip of the hour hand and the ceiling x hours after noon, make a graph that displays the information for $0 \le x \le 24$.

85. The number of hours of daylight in Boston is given by

$$y = 3 \sin \frac{2\pi}{365}(x - 79) + 12,$$

where x is the number of days after January 1.

a. What is the amplitude of this function?

b. What is the period of this function?

c. How many hours of daylight are there on the longest day of the year?

d. How many hours of daylight are there on the shortest day of the year?

e. Graph the function for one period, starting on January 1.

86. The average monthly temperature, y, in degrees Fahrenheit, for Juneau, Alaska, can be modeled by $y = 16 \sin\left(\dfrac{\pi}{6}x - \dfrac{2\pi}{3}\right) + 40$, where x is the month of the year (January $= 1$, February $= 2, \ldots$ December $= 12$). Graph the function for $1 \le x \le 12$. What is the highest average monthly temperature? In which month does this occur?

87. The figure shows the depth of water at the end of a boat dock. The depth is 6 feet at low tide and 12 feet at high tide. On a certain day, low tide occurs at 6 A.M. and high tide at noon. If y represents the depth of the water x hours after midnight, use a cosine function of the form $y = A \cos Bx + D$ to model the water's depth.

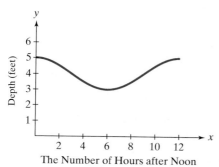

The Number of Hours after Midnight

88. The figure shows the depth of water at the end of a boat dock. The depth is 5 feet at high tide and 3 feet at low tide. On a certain day, high tide occurs at noon and low tide at 6 P.M. If y represents the depth of the water x hours after noon, use a cosine function of the form $y = A \cos Bx + D$ to model the water's depth.

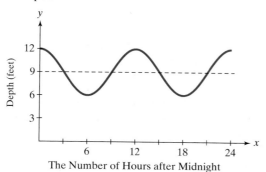

The Number of Hours after Noon

Writing in Mathematics

89. Without drawing a graph, describe the behavior of the basic sine curve.

90. What is the amplitude of the sine function? What does this tell you about the graph?

91. If you are given the equation of a sine function, how do you determine the period?

92. What does a phase shift indicate about the graph of a sine function? How do you determine the phase shift from the function's equation?

93. Describe a general procedure for obtaining the graph of $y = A \sin(Bx - C)$.

94. Without drawing a graph, describe the behavior of the basic cosine curve.

95. Describe a relationship between the graphs of $y = \sin x$ and $y = \cos x$.

96. Describe the relationship between the graphs of $y = A \cos(Bx - C)$ and $y = A \cos(Bx - C) + D$.

97. Biorhythm cycles provide interesting applications of sinusoidal graphs. But do you believe in the validity of biorhythms? Write a few sentences explaining why or why not.

Technology Exercises

98. Use a graphing utility to verify any five of the sine curves that you drew by hand in Exercises 7–30. The amplitude, period, and phase shift should help you to determine appropriate range settings.

99. Use a graphing utility to verify any five of the cosine curves that you drew by hand in Exercises 35–52.

100. Use a graphing utility to verify any two of the sinusoidal curves with vertical shifts that you drew in Exercises 53–60.

In Exercises 101–104, use a graphing utility to graph two periods of the function.

101. $y = 3 \sin(2x + \pi)$ **102.** $y = -2 \cos\left(2\pi x - \dfrac{\pi}{2}\right)$

103. $y = 0.2 \sin\left(\dfrac{\pi}{10}x + \pi\right)$ **104.** $y = 3 \sin(2x - \pi) + 5$

105. Use a graphing utility to graph $y = \sin x$ and $y = x - \dfrac{x^3}{6} + \dfrac{x^5}{120}$ in a $\left[-\pi, \pi, \dfrac{\pi}{2}\right]$ by $[-2, 2, 1]$ viewing rectangle. How do the graphs compare?

106. Use a graphing utility to graph $y = \cos x$ and $y = 1 - \dfrac{x^2}{2} + \dfrac{x^4}{24}$ in a $\left[-\pi, \pi, \dfrac{\pi}{2}\right]$ by $[-2, 2, 1]$ viewing rectangle. How do the graphs compare?

107. Use a graphing utility to graph

$$y = \sin x + \dfrac{\sin 2x}{2} + \dfrac{\sin 3x}{3} + \dfrac{\sin 4x}{4}$$

in a $\left[-2\pi, 2\pi, \dfrac{\pi}{2}\right]$ by $[-2, 2, 1]$ viewing rectangle. How do these waves compare to the smooth rolling waves of the basic sine curve?

108. Use a graphing utility to graph

$$y = \sin x - \dfrac{\sin 3x}{9} + \dfrac{\sin 5x}{25}$$

in a $\left[-2\pi, 2\pi, \dfrac{\pi}{2}\right]$ by $[-2, 2, 1]$ viewing rectangle. How do these waves compare to the smooth rolling waves of the basic sine curve?

109. The data show the average monthly temperatures for Washington, D.C.

    a. Use your graphing utility to draw a scatter plot of the data from $x = 1$ through $x = 12$.

    b. Use the SINe REGression feature to find the sinusoidal function of the form $y = A \sin(Bx + C) + D$ that best fits the data.

    c. Use your graphing utility to draw the sinusoidal function of best fit on the scatter plot.

x Month	Average Monthly Temperature, °F
1 (January)	34.6
2 (February)	37.5
3 (March)	47.2
4 (April)	56.5
5 (May)	66.4
6 (June)	75.6
7 (July)	80.0
8 (August)	78.5
9 (September)	71.3
10 (October)	59.7
11 (November)	49.8
12 (December)	39.4

Source: U.S. National Oceanic and Atmospheric Administration

110. Repeat Exercise 109 for data of your choice. The data can involve the average monthly temperatures for the region where you live or any data whose scatter plot takes the form of a sinusoidal function.

Critical Thinking Exercises

111. Determine the range of each of the following functions. Then give a viewing rectangle, or window, that shows two periods of the function's graph.

    a. $f(x) = 3 \sin\left(x + \dfrac{\pi}{6}\right) - 2$

    b. $g(x) = \sin 3\left(x + \dfrac{\pi}{6}\right) - 2$

112. Write the equation for a cosine function with amplitude π, period 1, and phase shift -2.

In Chapter 5, we will prove the following identities:

$$\sin^2 x = \frac{1}{2} - \frac{1}{2}\cos 2x$$

$$\cos^2 x = \frac{1}{2} + \frac{1}{2}\cos 2x.$$

Use these identities to solve Exercises 113–114.

113. Use the identity for $\sin^2 x$ to graph one period of $y = \sin^2 x$.

114. Use the identity for $\cos^2 x$ to graph one period of $y = \cos^2 x$.

Group Exercise

115. This exercise is intended to provide some fun with biorhythms, regardless of whether you believe they have any validity. We will use each member's chart to determine biorhythmic compatibility. Before meeting, each group member should go online and obtain his or her biorhythm chart. The date of the group meeting is the date on which your chart should begin. Include 12 months in the plot. At the meeting, compare differences and similarities among the intellectual sinusoidal curves. Using these comparisons, each person should find the one other person with whom he or she would be most intellectually compatible.

SECTION 4.6   *Graphs of Other Trigonometric Functions*

Objectives

❶ Understand the graph of $y = \tan x$.

❷ Graph variations of $y = \tan x$.

❸ Understand the graph of $y = \cot x$.

❹ Graph variations of $y = \cot x$.

❺ Understand the graphs of $y = \csc x$ and $y = \sec x$.

❻ Graph variations of $y = \csc x$ and $y = \sec x$.

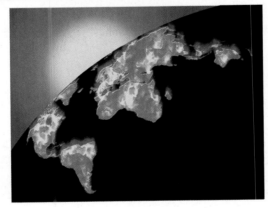

Recent advances in our understanding of climate have changed global warming from a subject for a disaster movie (the Statue of Liberty up to its chin in water) to a serious scientific and policy issue. Global warming is related to the burning of fossil fuels, which adds carbon dioxide to the atmosphere. In the 21st century, we will see whether our use of fossil fuels will add enough carbon dioxide to the atmosphere to change it (and our climate) in significant ways. In this section's exercise set, you will see how trigonometric graphs reveal interesting patterns in carbon dioxide concentration from 1990 through 2005. In the section itself, trigonometric graphs will reveal patterns involving the tangent, cotangent, secant, and cosecant functions.

① Understand the graph of $y = \tan x$.

The Graph of $y = \tan x$

The properties of the tangent function discussed in Section 4.2 will help us determine its graph. Because the tangent function has properties that are different from sinusoidal functions, its graph differs significantly from those of sine and cosine. Properties of the tangent function include the following:

- The period is π. It is only necessary to graph $y = \tan x$ over an interval of length π. The remainder of the graph consists of repetitions of that graph at intervals of π.
- The tangent function is an odd function: $\tan(-x) = -\tan x$. The graph is symmetric with respect to the origin.
- The tangent function is undefined at $\frac{\pi}{2}$. The graph of $y = \tan x$ has a vertical asymptote at $x = \frac{\pi}{2}$.

We obtain the graph of $y = \tan x$ using some points on the graph and origin symmetry. Table 4.5 lists some values of (x, y) on the graph of $y = \tan x$ on the interval $\left[0, \frac{\pi}{2}\right)$.

Table 4.5   Values of (x, y) on the graph of $y = \tan x$

x	0	$\frac{\pi}{6}$	$\frac{\pi}{4}$	$\frac{\pi}{3}$	$\frac{5\pi}{12}$ (75°)	$\frac{17\pi}{36}$ (85°)	$\frac{89\pi}{180}$ (89°)	1.57	$\frac{\pi}{2}$
$y = \tan x$	0	$\frac{\sqrt{3}}{3} \approx 0.6$	1	$\sqrt{3} \approx 1.7$	3.7	11.4	57.3	1255.8	undefined

As x increases from 0 to $\frac{\pi}{2}$, y increases slowly at first, then more and more rapidly.

The graph in Figure 4.78(a) is based on our observation that as x increases from 0 to $\frac{\pi}{2}$, y increases slowly at first, then more and more rapidly. Notice that y increases without bound as x approaches $\frac{\pi}{2}$. As the figure shows, the graph of $y = \tan x$ has a vertical asymptote at $x = \frac{\pi}{2}$.

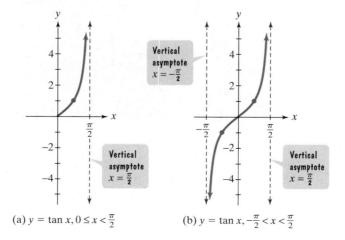

Figure 4.78 Graphing the tangent function

(a) $y = \tan x, 0 \le x < \frac{\pi}{2}$

(b) $y = \tan x, -\frac{\pi}{2} < x < \frac{\pi}{2}$

The graph of $y = \tan x$ can be completed on the interval $\left(-\dfrac{\pi}{2}, \dfrac{\pi}{2}\right)$ by using origin symmetry. Figure 4.78(b) shows the result of reflecting the graph in Figure 4.78(a) about the origin. The graph of $y = \tan x$ has another vertical asymptote at $x = -\dfrac{\pi}{2}$. Notice that y decreases without bound as x approaches $-\dfrac{\pi}{2}$.

Because the period of the tangent function is π, the graph in Figure 4.78(b) shows one complete period of $y = \tan x$. We obtain the complete graph of $y = \tan x$ by repeating the graph in Figure 4.78(b) to the left and right over intervals of π. The resulting graph and its main characteristics are shown in the following box:

The Tangent Curve: The Graph of $y = \tan x$ and Its Characteristics

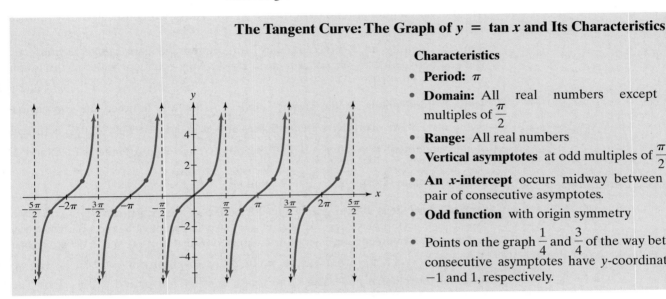

Characteristics

- **Period:** π
- **Domain:** All real numbers except odd multiples of $\dfrac{\pi}{2}$
- **Range:** All real numbers
- **Vertical asymptotes** at odd multiples of $\dfrac{\pi}{2}$
- **An x-intercept** occurs midway between each pair of consecutive asymptotes.
- **Odd function** with origin symmetry
- Points on the graph $\dfrac{1}{4}$ and $\dfrac{3}{4}$ of the way between consecutive asymptotes have y-coordinates of -1 and 1, respectively.

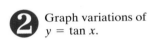

② Graph variations of $y = \tan x$.

Graphing Variations of $y = \tan x$

We use the characteristics of the tangent curve to graph tangent functions of the form $y = A \tan(Bx - C)$.

Graphing $y = A\tan(Bx - C)$

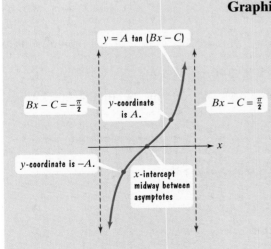

$y = A \tan (Bx - C)$

$Bx - C = -\dfrac{\pi}{2}$ y-coordinate is A. $Bx - C = \dfrac{\pi}{2}$

y-coordinate is $-A$.

x-intercept midway between asymptotes

1. Find two consecutive asymptotes by finding an interval containing one period:

$$-\dfrac{\pi}{2} < Bx - C < \dfrac{\pi}{2}.$$

A pair of consecutive asymptotes occur at

$$Bx - C = -\dfrac{\pi}{2} \text{ and } Bx - C = \dfrac{\pi}{2}.$$

2. Identify an x-intercept, midway between the consecutive asymptotes.

3. Find the points on the graph $\dfrac{1}{4}$ and $\dfrac{3}{4}$ of the way between the consecutive asymptotes. These points have y-coordinates of $-A$ and A, respectively.

4. Use steps 1–3 to graph one full period of the function. Add additional cycles to the left or right as needed.

EXAMPLE 1   Graphing a Tangent Function

Graph $y = 2 \tan \dfrac{x}{2}$ for $-\pi < x < 3\pi$.

Solution   Refer to Figure 4.79 as you read each step.

Step 1   Find two consecutive asymptotes. We do this by finding an interval containing one period.

$$-\frac{\pi}{2} < \frac{x}{2} < \frac{\pi}{2}$$ Set up the inequality $-\dfrac{\pi}{2} <$ variable expression in tangent $< \dfrac{\pi}{2}$.

$$-\pi < x < \pi$$ Multiply all parts by 2 and solve for x.

An interval containing one period is $(-\pi, \pi)$. Thus, two consecutive asymptotes occur at $x = -\pi$ and $x = \pi$.

Step 2   Identify an x-intercept, midway between the consecutive asymptotes. Midway between $x = -\pi$ and $x = \pi$ is $x = 0$. An x-intercept is 0 and the graph passes through $(0, 0)$.

Step 3   Find points on the graph $\dfrac{1}{4}$ and $\dfrac{3}{4}$ of the way between the consecutive asymptotes. These points have y-coordinates of $-A$ and A. Because A, the coefficient of the tangent in $y = 2 \tan \dfrac{x}{2}$ is 2, these points have y-coordinates of -2 and 2. The graph passes through $\left(-\dfrac{\pi}{2}, -2\right)$ and $\left(\dfrac{\pi}{2}, 2\right)$.

Step 4   Use steps 1–3 to graph one full period of the function. We use the two consecutive asymptotes, $x = -\pi$ and $x = \pi$, an x-intercept of 0, and points midway between the x-intercept and asymptotes with y-coordinates of -2 and 2. We graph one period of $y = 2 \tan \dfrac{x}{2}$ from $-\pi$ to π. In order to graph for $-\pi < x < 3\pi$, we continue the pattern and extend the graph another full period to the right. The graph is shown in Figure 4.79.

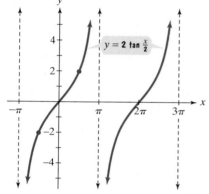

Figure 4.79 The graph is shown for two full periods.

Check Point 1   Graph $y = 3 \tan 2x$ for $-\dfrac{\pi}{4} < x < \dfrac{3\pi}{4}$.

EXAMPLE 2   Graphing a Tangent Function

Graph two full periods of $y = \tan\left(x + \dfrac{\pi}{4}\right)$.

Solution   The graph of $y = \tan\left(x + \dfrac{\pi}{4}\right)$ is the graph of $y = \tan x$ shifted horizontally to the left $\dfrac{\pi}{4}$ units. Refer to Figure 4.80 as you read each step.

Step 1   Find two consecutive asymptotes. We do this by finding an interval containing one period.

$$-\frac{\pi}{2} < x + \frac{\pi}{4} < \frac{\pi}{2}$$ Set up the inequality $-\dfrac{\pi}{2} <$ variable expression in tangent $< \dfrac{\pi}{2}$.

$$-\frac{\pi}{2} - \frac{\pi}{4} < x < \frac{\pi}{2} - \frac{\pi}{4}$$ Subtract $\dfrac{\pi}{4}$ from all parts and solve for x.

$$-\frac{3\pi}{4} < x < \frac{\pi}{4}$$ Simplify: $-\dfrac{\pi}{2} - \dfrac{\pi}{4} = -\dfrac{2\pi}{4} - \dfrac{\pi}{4} = -\dfrac{3\pi}{4}$

and $\dfrac{\pi}{2} - \dfrac{\pi}{4} = \dfrac{2\pi}{4} - \dfrac{\pi}{4} = \dfrac{\pi}{4}$.

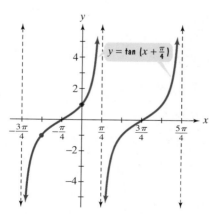

Figure 4.80 The graph is shown for two full periods.

An interval containing one period is $\left(-\dfrac{3\pi}{4}, \dfrac{\pi}{4}\right)$. Thus, two consecutive asymptotes occur at $x = -\dfrac{3\pi}{4}$ and $x = \dfrac{\pi}{4}$.

Step 2   Identify an *x*-intercept, midway between the consecutive asymptotes.

$$x\text{-intercept} = \frac{-\dfrac{3\pi}{4} + \dfrac{\pi}{4}}{2} = \frac{-\dfrac{2\pi}{4}}{2} = -\frac{2\pi}{8} = -\frac{\pi}{4}$$

An *x*-intercept is $-\dfrac{\pi}{4}$ and the graph passes through $\left(-\dfrac{\pi}{4}, 0\right)$.

Step 3   Find points on the graph $\dfrac{1}{4}$ and $\dfrac{3}{4}$ of the way between the consecutive asymptotes. These points have *y*-coordinates of $-A$ and A. Because *A*, the coefficient of the tangent in $y = \tan\left(x + \dfrac{\pi}{4}\right)$ is 1, these points have *y*-coordinates of -1 and 1. They are shown as blue dots in Figure 4.80.

Step 4   Use steps 1–3 to graph one full period of the function. We use the two consecutive asymptotes, $x = -\dfrac{3\pi}{4}$ and $x = \dfrac{\pi}{4}$, to graph one full period of $y = \tan\left(x + \dfrac{\pi}{4}\right)$ from $-\dfrac{3\pi}{4}$ to $\dfrac{\pi}{4}$. We graph two full periods by continuing the pattern and extending the graph another full period to the right. The graph is shown in Figure 4.80.

Check Point 2 Graph two full periods of $y = \tan\left(x - \dfrac{\pi}{2}\right)$.

❸ Understand the graph of $y = \cot x$.

The Graph of $y = \cot x$

Like the tangent function, the cotangent function, $y = \cot x$, has a period of π. The graph and its main characteristics are shown in the following box:

The Cotangent Curve: The Graph of $y = \cot x$ and Its Characteristics

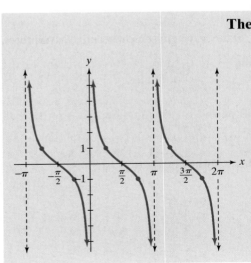

Characteristics

- **Period:** π
- **Domain:** All real numbers except integral multiples of π
- **Range:** All real numbers
- **Vertical asymptotes** at integral multiples of π
- **An *x*-intercept** occurs midway between each pair of consecutive asymptotes.
- **Odd function** with origin symmetry
- Points on the graph $\dfrac{1}{4}$ and $\dfrac{3}{4}$ of the way between consecutive asymptotes have *y*-coordinates of 1 and -1, respectively.

---

❹ Graph variations of $y = \cot x$.

Graphing Variations of $y = \cot x$

We use the characteristics of the cotangent curve to graph cotangent functions of the form $y = A \cot(Bx - C)$.

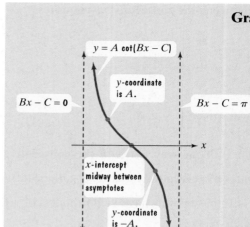

Graphing $y = A \cot(Bx - C)$

1. Find two consecutive asymptotes by finding an interval containing one full period:
$$0 < Bx - C < \pi.$$
   A pair of consecutive asymptotes occur at
$$Bx - C = 0 \text{ and } Bx - C = \pi.$$

2. Identify an x-intercept, midway between the consecutive asymptotes.

3. Find the points on the graph $\frac{1}{4}$ and $\frac{3}{4}$ of the way between the consecutive asymptotes. These points have y-coordinates of A and $-A$, respectively.

4. Use steps 1–3 to graph one full period of the function. Add additional cycles to the left or right as needed.

EXAMPLE 3 Graphing a Cotangent Function

Graph $y = 3 \cot 2x$.

Solution Refer to Figure 4.81 as you read each step.

Step 1 Find two consecutive asymptotes. We do this by finding an interval containing one period.

$$0 < 2x < \pi \qquad \text{Set up the inequality } 0 < \text{variable expression in cotangent} < \pi.$$

$$0 < x < \frac{\pi}{2} \qquad \text{Divide all parts by 2 and solve for x.}$$

An interval containing one period is $\left(0, \frac{\pi}{2}\right)$. Thus, two consecutive asymptotes occur at $x = 0$ and $x = \frac{\pi}{2}$.

Step 2 Identify an x-intercept, midway between the consecutive asymptotes. Midway between $x = 0$ and $x = \frac{\pi}{2}$ is $x = \frac{\pi}{4}$. An x-intercept is $\frac{\pi}{4}$ and the graph passes through $\left(\frac{\pi}{4}, 0\right)$.

Step 3 Find points on the graph $\frac{1}{4}$ and $\frac{3}{4}$ of the way between consecutive asymptotes. These points have y-coordinates of A and $-A$. Because A, the coefficient of the cotangent in $y = 3 \cot 2x$ is 3, these points have y-coordinates of 3 and -3. They are shown as blue dots in Figure 4.81.

Step 4 Use steps 1–3 to graph one full period of the function. We use the two consecutive asymptotes, $x = 0$ and $x = \frac{\pi}{2}$, to graph one full period of $y = 3 \cot 2x$. This curve is repeated to the left and right, as shown in Figure 4.81.

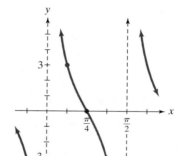

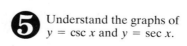
Figure 4.81 The graph of $y = 3 \cot 2x$

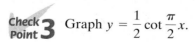
Check Point 3 Graph $y = \frac{1}{2} \cot \frac{\pi}{2} x$.

❺ Understand the graphs of $y = \csc x$ and $y = \sec x$.

The Graphs of $y = \csc x$ and $y = \sec x$

We obtain the graphs of the cosecant and secant curves by using the reciprocal identities

$$\csc x = \frac{1}{\sin x} \quad \text{and} \quad \sec x = \frac{1}{\cos x}.$$

The identity $\csc x = \dfrac{1}{\sin x}$ tells us that the value of the cosecant function $y = \csc x$ at a given value of x equals the reciprocal of the corresponding value of the sine function, provided that the value of the sine function is not 0. If the value of $\sin x$ is 0, then at each of these values of x, the cosecant function is not defined. A vertical asymptote is associated with each of these values on the graph of $y = \csc x$.

We obtain the graph of $y = \csc x$ by taking reciprocals of the y-values in the graph of $y = \sin x$. Vertical asymptotes of $y = \csc x$ occur at the x-intercepts of $y = \sin x$. Likewise, we obtain the graph of $y = \sec x$ by taking the reciprocal of $y = \cos x$. Vertical asymptotes of $y = \sec x$ occur at the x-intercepts of $y = \cos x$. The graphs of $y = \csc x$ and $y = \sec x$ and their key characteristics are shown in the following boxes. We have used dashed red lines to graph $y = \sin x$ and $y = \cos x$ first, drawing vertical asymptotes through the x-intercepts.

The Cosecant Curve: The Graph of $y = \csc x$ and Its Characteristics

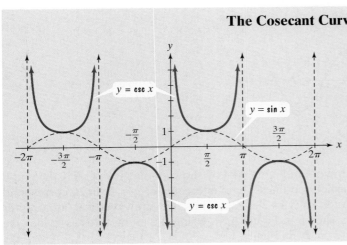

Characteristics

- **Period:** 2π

- **Domain:** All real numbers except integral multiples of π

- **Range:** All real numbers y such that $y \le -1$ or $y \ge 1 : (-\infty, -1] \cup [1, \infty)$

- **Vertical asymptotes** at integral multiples of π

- **Odd function,** $\csc(-x) = -\csc x$, with origin symmetry

The Secant Curve: The Graph of $y = \sec x$ and Its Characteristics

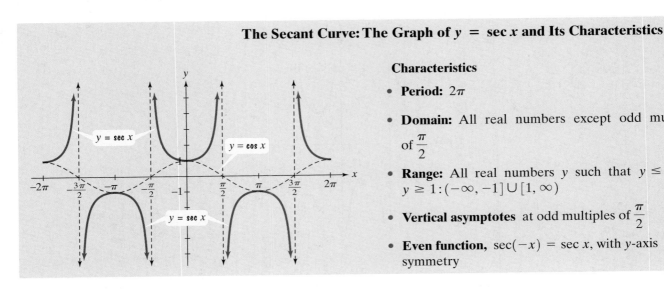

Characteristics

- **Period:** 2π

- **Domain:** All real numbers except odd multiples of $\dfrac{\pi}{2}$

- **Range:** All real numbers y such that $y \le -1$ or $y \ge 1 : (-\infty, -1] \cup [1, \infty)$

- **Vertical asymptotes** at odd multiples of $\dfrac{\pi}{2}$

- **Even function,** $\sec(-x) = \sec x$, with y-axis symmetry

⑥ Graph variations of $y = \csc x$ and $y = \sec x$.

Graphing Variations of $y = \csc x$ and $y = \sec x$

We use graphs of functions involving the corresponding reciprocal functions to obtain graphs of cosecant and secant functions. To graph a cosecant or secant curve, begin by graphing the function where cosecant or secant is replaced by its reciprocal function. For example, to graph $y = 2 \csc 2x$, we use the graph of $y = 2 \sin 2x$. Likewise, to graph $y = -3 \sec \dfrac{x}{2}$, we use the graph of $y = -3 \cos \dfrac{x}{2}$.

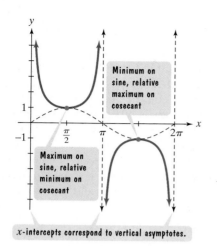

Minimum on sine, relative maximum on cosecant

Maximum on sine, relative minimum on cosecant

x-intercepts correspond to vertical asymptotes.

Figure 4.82

Figure 4.82 illustrates how we use a sine curve to obtain a cosecant curve. Notice that

- *x*-intercepts on the red sine curve correspond to vertical asymptotes of the blue cosecant curve.
- A maximum point on the red sine curve corresponds to a minimum point on a continuous portion of the blue cosecant curve.
- A minimum point on the red sine curve corresponds to a maximum point on a continuous portion of the blue cosecant curve.

EXAMPLE 4   Using a Sine Curve to Obtain a Cosecant Curve

Use the graph of $y = 2 \sin 2x$ in Figure 4.83 to obtain the graph of $y = 2 \csc 2x$.

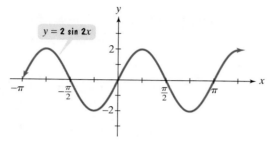

$y = 2 \sin 2x$

Figure 4.83

Solution   We begin our work in Figure 4.84 by showing the given graph, the graph of $y = 2 \sin 2x$, using dashed red lines. The *x*-intercepts of $y = 2 \sin 2x$ correspond to the vertical asymptotes of $y = 2 \csc 2x$. Thus, we draw vertical asymptotes through the *x*-intercepts, shown in Figure 4.84. Using the asymptotes as guides, we sketch the graph of $y = 2 \csc 2x$ in Figure 4.84.

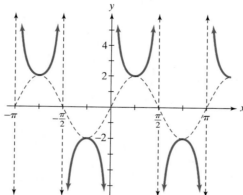

Figure 4.84 Using a sine curve to graph $y = 2 \csc 2x$

Check Point 4   Use the graph of $y = \sin\left(x + \dfrac{\pi}{4}\right)$, shown on the right, to obtain the graph of $y = \csc\left(x + \dfrac{\pi}{4}\right)$.

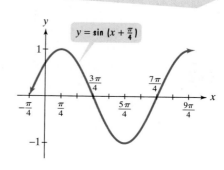

$y = \sin\left(x + \frac{\pi}{4}\right)$

We use a cosine curve to obtain a secant curve in exactly the same way we used a sine curve to obtain a cosecant curve. Thus,

- *x*-intercepts on the cosine curve correspond to vertical asymptotes on the secant curve.
- A maximum point on the cosine curve corresponds to a minimum point on a continuous portion of the secant curve.
- A minimum point on the cosine curve corresponds to a maximum point on a continuous portion of the secant curve.

EXAMPLE 5   Graphing a Secant Function

Graph $y = -3 \sec \dfrac{x}{2}$ for $-\pi < x < 5\pi$.

Solution   We begin by graphing the function $y = -3 \cos \dfrac{x}{2}$, where secant has been replaced by cosine, its reciprocal function. This equation is of the form $y = A \cos Bx$ with $A = -3$ and $B = \frac{1}{2}$.

$$\text{amplitude:} \quad |A| = |-3| = 3$$

> The maximum y is 3 and the minimum is -3.

$$\text{period:} \quad \frac{2\pi}{B} = \frac{2\pi}{\frac{1}{2}} = 4\pi$$

> Each cycle, including asymptotes, is of length 4π.

We use quarter-periods, $\dfrac{4\pi}{4}$, or π, to find the *x*-values for the five key points. Starting with $x = 0$, the *x*-values are $0, \pi, 2\pi, 3\pi,$ and 4π. Evaluating the function at each of these values of x, the key points are

$$(0, -3), (\pi, 0), (2\pi, 3), (3\pi, 0), \text{ and } (4\pi, -3).$$

We use these key points to graph $y = -3 \cos \dfrac{x}{2}$ from 0 to 4π, shown using a dashed red line in Figure 4.85. In order to graph for $-\pi \le x \le 5\pi$, extend the dashed red graph π units to the left and π units to the right. Now use this dashed red graph to obtain the graph of the corresponding secant function, its reciprocal function. Draw vertical asymptotes through the *x*-intercepts. Using these asymptotes as guides, the graph of $y = -3 \sec \dfrac{x}{2}$ is shown in blue in Figure 4.85.

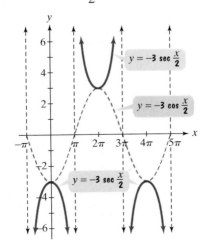

Figure 4.85 Using a cosine curve to graph $y = -3 \sec \dfrac{x}{2}$

Check Point 5 Graph $y = 2 \sec 2x$ for $-\dfrac{3\pi}{4} < x < \dfrac{3\pi}{4}$.

The Six Curves of Trigonometry

Table 4.6 summarizes the graphs of the six trigonometric functions. Below each of the graphs is a description of the domain, range, and period of the function.

Table 4.6   Graphs of the Six Trigonometric Functions

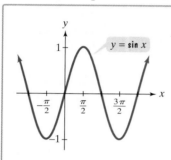

Domain: all real numbers: $(-\infty, \infty)$

Range: $[-1, 1]$

Period: 2π

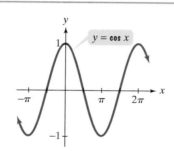

Domain: all real numbers: $(-\infty, \infty)$

Range: $[-1, 1]$

Period: 2π

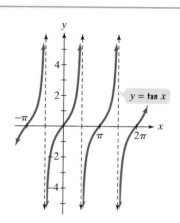

Domain: all real numbers except odd multiples of $\dfrac{\pi}{2}$

Range: all real numbers

Period: π

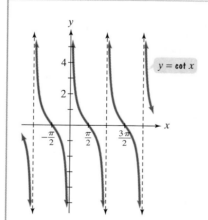

Domain: all real numbers except integral multiples of π

Range: all real numbers

Period: π

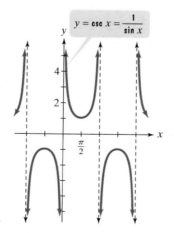

Domain: all real numbers except integral multiples of π

Range: $(-\infty, -1] \cup [1, \infty)$

Period: 2π

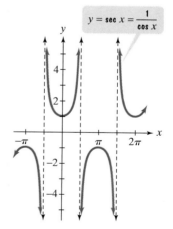

Domain: all real numbers except odd multiples of $\dfrac{\pi}{2}$

Range: $(-\infty, -1] \cup [1, \infty)$

Period: 2π

EXERCISE SET 4.6

Practice Exercises

In Exercises 1–4, the graph of a tangent function is given.
Select the equation for each graph from the following options:

$$y = \tan\left(x + \frac{\pi}{2}\right), \quad y = \tan(x + \pi), \quad y = -\tan x, \quad y = -\tan\left(x - \frac{\pi}{2}\right).$$

1.

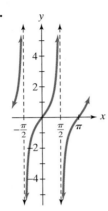

2.

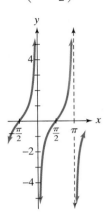

3.

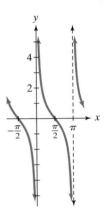

4.

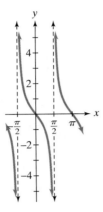

In Exercises 5–12, graph two periods of the given tangent function.

5. $y = 3 \tan \dfrac{x}{4}$

6. $y = 2 \tan \dfrac{x}{4}$

7. $y = \dfrac{1}{2} \tan 2x$

8. $y = 2 \tan 2x$

9. $y = -2 \tan \dfrac{1}{2}x$

10. $y = -3 \tan \dfrac{1}{2}x$

11. $y = \tan(x - \pi)$

12. $y = \tan\left(x - \dfrac{\pi}{4}\right)$

In Exercises 13–16, the graph of a cotangent function is given. Select the equation for each graph from the following options:

$$y = \cot\left(x + \frac{\pi}{2}\right), \quad y = \cot(x + \pi), \quad y = -\cot x, \quad y = -\cot\left(x - \frac{\pi}{2}\right).$$

13.

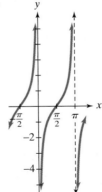

14.

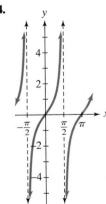

15.

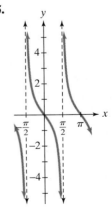

16.

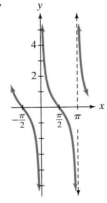

In Exercises 17–24, graph two periods of the given cotangent function.

17. $y = 2 \cot x$

18. $y = \dfrac{1}{2} \cot x$

19. $y = \dfrac{1}{2} \cot 2x$

20. $y = 2 \cot 2x$

21. $y = -3 \cot \dfrac{\pi}{2}x$

22. $y = -2 \cot \dfrac{\pi}{4}x$

23. $y = 3 \cot\left(x + \dfrac{\pi}{2}\right)$

24. $y = 3 \cot\left(x + \dfrac{\pi}{4}\right)$

In Exercises 25–28, use each graph to obtain the graph of the corresponding reciprocal function, cosecant or secant. Give the equation of the function for the graph that you obtain.

25.

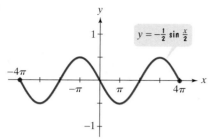
$y = -\frac{1}{2} \sin \frac{x}{2}$

26.

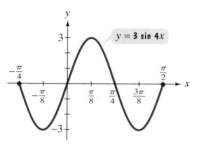
$y = 3 \sin 4x$

27.

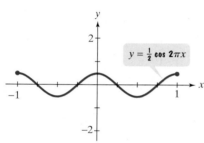
$y = \frac{1}{2} \cos 2\pi x$

28.

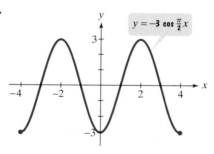
$y = -3 \cos \frac{\pi}{2} x$

In Exercises 29–44, graph two periods of the given cosecant or secant function.

29. $y = 3 \csc x$ **30.** $y = 2 \csc x$

31. $y = \frac{1}{2} \csc \frac{x}{2}$ **32.** $y = \frac{3}{2} \csc \frac{x}{4}$

33. $y = 2 \sec x$ **34.** $y = 3 \sec x$

35. $y = \sec \frac{x}{3}$ **36.** $y = \sec \frac{x}{2}$

37. $y = -2 \csc \pi x$ **38.** $y = -\frac{1}{2} \csc \pi x$

39. $y = -\frac{1}{2} \sec \pi x$ **40.** $y = -\frac{3}{2} \sec \pi x$

41. $y = \csc(x - \pi)$ **42.** $y = \csc\left(x - \frac{\pi}{2} \right)$

43. $y = 2 \sec(x + \pi)$ **44.** $y = 2 \sec\left(x + \frac{\pi}{2} \right)$

 Practice Plus

In Exercises 45–52, graph two periods of each function.

45. $y = 2 \tan\left(x - \frac{\pi}{6} \right) + 1$ **46.** $y = 2 \cot\left(x + \frac{\pi}{6} \right) - 1$

47. $y = \sec\left(2x + \frac{\pi}{2} \right) - 1$ **48.** $y = \csc\left(2x - \frac{\pi}{2} \right) + 1$

49. $y = \csc|x|$ **50.** $y = \sec|x|$

51. $y = \left|\cot \frac{1}{2} x\right|$ **52.** $y = \left|\tan \frac{1}{2} x\right|$

In Exercises 53–54, let $f(x) = 2 \sec x$, $g(x) = -2 \tan x$, *and* $h(x) = 2x - \frac{\pi}{2}$.

53. Graph two periods of
$$y = (f \circ h)(x).$$

54. Graph two periods of
$$y = (g \circ h)(x).$$

In Exercises 55–58, use a graph to solve each equation for $-2\pi \le x \le 2\pi$.

55. $\tan x = -1$ **56.** $\cot x = -1$

57. $\csc x = 1$ **58.** $\sec x = 1$

⭐ **Application Exercises**

59. An ambulance with a rotating beam of light is parked 12 feet from a building. The function

$$d = 12 \tan 2\pi t$$

describes the distance, d, in feet, of the rotating beam of light from point C after t seconds.

a. Graph the function on the interval $[0, 2]$.

b. For what values of t in $[0, 2]$ is the function undefined? What does this mean in terms of the rotating beam of light in the figure shown?

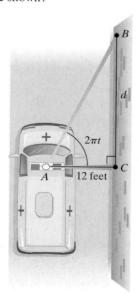

60. The angle of elevation from the top of a house to a jet flying 2 miles above the house is x radians. If d represents the horizontal distance, in miles, of the jet from the house, express d in terms of a trigonometric function of x. Then graph the function for $0 < x < \pi$.

61. Your best friend is marching with a band and has asked you to film him. The figure below shows that you have set yourself up 10 feet from the street where your friend will be passing from left to right. If d represents your distance, in feet, from your friend and x is the radian measure of the angle shown, express d in terms of a trigonometric function of x. Then graph the function for $-\dfrac{\pi}{2} < x < \dfrac{\pi}{2}$. Negative angles indicate that your marching buddy is on your left.

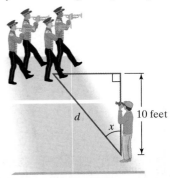

d x 10 feet

In Exercises 62–64, sketch a reasonable graph that models the given situation.

62. The number of hours of daylight per day in your hometown over a two-year period

63. The motion of a diving board vibrating 10 inches in each direction per second just after someone has dived off

64. The distance of a rotating beam of light from a point on a wall (See the figure for Exercise 59.)

Writing in Mathematics

65. Without drawing a graph, describe the behavior of the basic tangent curve.

66. If you are given the equation of a tangent function, how do you find a pair of consecutive asymptotes?

67. If you are given the equation of a tangent function, how do you identify an x-intercept?

68. Without drawing a graph, describe the behavior of the basic cotangent curve.

69. If you are given the equation of a cotangent function, how do you find a pair of consecutive asymptotes?

70. Explain how to determine the range of $y = \csc x$ from the graph. What is the range?

71. Explain how to use a sine curve to obtain a cosecant curve. Why can the same procedure be used to obtain a secant curve from a cosine curve?

72. Scientists record brain activity by attaching electrodes to the scalp and then connecting these electrodes to a machine. The brain activity recorded with this machine is shown in the three graphs at the top of the next column. Which trigonometric functions would be most appropriate for describing the oscillations in brain activity? Describe similarities and differences among these functions when modeling brain

activity when awake, during dreaming sleep, and during non-dreaming sleep.

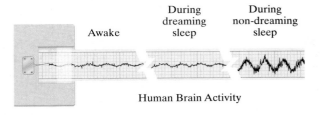

During dreaming sleep   During non-dreaming sleep

Awake

Human Brain Activity

Technology Exercises

In working Exercises 73–76, describe what happens at the asymptotes on the graphing utility. Compare the graphs in the connected and dot modes.

73. Use a graphing utility to verify any two of the tangent curves that you drew by hand in Exercises 5–12.

74. Use a graphing utility to verify any two of the cotangent curves that you drew by hand in Exercises 17–24.

75. Use a graphing utility to verify any two of the cosecant curves that you drew by hand in Exercises 29–44.

76. Use a graphing utility to verify any two of the secant curves that you drew by hand in Exercises 29–44.

In Exercises 77–82, use a graphing utility to graph each function. Use a range setting so that the graph is shown for at least two periods.

77. $y = \tan \dfrac{x}{4}$ **78.** $y = \tan 4x$

79. $y = \cot 2x$ **80.** $y = \cot \dfrac{x}{2}$

81. $y = \dfrac{1}{2}\tan \pi x$ **82.** $y = \dfrac{1}{2}\tan(\pi x + 1)$

In Exercises 83–86, use a graphing utility to graph each pair of functions in the same viewing rectangle. Use a range setting so that the graphs are shown for at least two periods.

83. $y = 0.8 \sin \dfrac{x}{2}$ and $y = 0.8 \csc \dfrac{x}{2}$

84. $y = -2.5 \sin \dfrac{\pi}{3}x$ and $y = -2.5 \csc \dfrac{\pi}{3}x$

85. $y = 4 \cos\left(2x - \dfrac{\pi}{6}\right)$ and $y = 4 \sec\left(2x - \dfrac{\pi}{6}\right)$

86. $y = -3.5 \cos\left(\pi x - \dfrac{\pi}{6}\right)$ and $y = -3.5 \sec\left(\pi x - \dfrac{\pi}{6}\right)$

87. Carbon dioxide particles in our atmosphere trap heat and raise the planet's temperature. The resultant gradually increasing temperature is called the greenhouse effect. Carbon dioxide accounts for about half of global warming. The function

$$y = 2.5 \sin 2\pi x + 0.0216x^2 + 0.654x + 316$$

models carbon dioxide concentration, y, in parts per million, where $x = 0$ represents January 1960; $x = \frac{1}{12}$, February 1960; $x = \frac{2}{12}$, March 1960; ..., $x = 1$, January 1961; $x = \frac{13}{12}$, February 1961; and so on. Use a graphing utility to graph the function in a $[30, 45, 5]$ by $[310, 420, 5]$ viewing rectangle. Describe what the graph reveals about carbon dioxide concentration from 1990 through 2005.

88. Graph $y = \sin \dfrac{1}{x}$ in a $[-0.2, 0.2, 0.01]$ by $[-1.2, 1.2, 0.01]$ viewing rectangle. What is happening as x approaches 0 from the left or the right? Explain this behavior.

Critical Thinking Exercises

In Exercises 89–90, write an equation for each blue graph.

89.

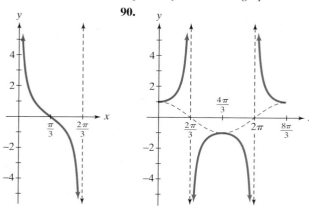

90.

In Exercises 91–92, write the equation for a cosecant function satisfying the given conditions.

91. period: 3π; range: $(-\infty, -2] \cup [2, \infty)$

92. period: 2; range: $(-\infty, -\pi] \cup [\pi, \infty)$

93. Determine the range of the following functions. Then give a viewing rectangle, or window, that shows two periods of the function's graph.

a. $f(x) = \sec\left(3x + \dfrac{\pi}{2}\right)$ **b.** $g(x) = 3 \sec \pi\left(x + \dfrac{1}{2}\right)$

94. For $x > 0$, what effect does 2^{-x} in $y = 2^{-x} \sin x$ have on the graph of $y = \sin x$? What kind of behavior can be modeled by a function such as $y = 2^{-x} \sin x$?

SECTION 4.7 *Inverse Trigonometric Functions*

Objectives

❶ Understand and use the inverse sine function.

❷ Understand and use the inverse cosine function.

❸ Understand and use the inverse tangent function.

❹ Use a calculator to evaluate inverse trigonometric functions.

❺ Find exact values of composite functions with inverse trigonometric functions.

In 2005, director George Lucas pulled out all the stops and completed the epic *Star Wars* odyssey with *Revenge of the Sith*. The movie is being shown at a local theater, where you can experience the stunning force of its 2151 visual-effect shots (*Source: Time*) on a large screen. Where in the theater should you sit to maximize the visual impact of the director's fantastic galactic visions? In this section's exercise set, you will see how an inverse trigonometric function can enhance your movie-going experiences.

Study Tip

Here are some helpful things to remember from our earlier discussion of inverse functions.

* If no horizontal line intersects the graph of a function more than once, the function is one-to-one and has an inverse function.

* If the point (a, b) is on the graph of f, then the point (b, a) is on the graph of the inverse function, denoted f^{-1}. The graph of f^{-1} is a reflection of the graph of f about the line $y = x$.

1 Understand and use the inverse sine function.

The Inverse Sine Function

Figure 4.86 shows the graph of $y = \sin x$. Can you see that every horizontal line that can be drawn between -1 and 1 intersects the graph infinitely many times? Thus, the sine function is not one-to-one and has no inverse function.

In Figure 4.87, we have taken a portion of the sine curve, restricting the domain of the sine function to $-\dfrac{\pi}{2} \leq x \leq \dfrac{\pi}{2}$. With this restricted domain, every horizontal line that can be drawn between -1 and 1 intersects the graph exactly once. Thus, the restricted function passes the horizontal line test and is one-to-one.

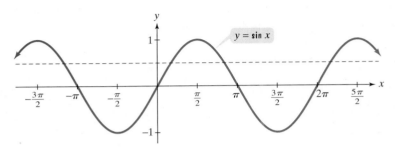

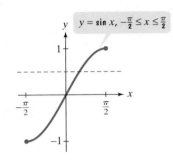

Figure 4.86 The horizontal line test shows that the sine function is not one-to-one and has no inverse function.

Figure 4.87 The restricted sine function passes the horizontal line test. It is one-to-one and has an inverse function.

On the restricted domain $-\dfrac{\pi}{2} \leq x \leq \dfrac{\pi}{2}$, $y = \sin x$ has an inverse function.

The inverse of the restricted sine function is called the **inverse sine function**. Two notations are commonly used to denote the inverse sine function:

$$y = \sin^{-1} x \quad \text{or} \quad y = \arcsin x.$$

In this book, we will use $y = \sin^{-1} x$. This notation has the same symbol as the inverse function notation $f^{-1}(x)$.

The Inverse Sine Function

The **inverse sine function**, denoted by $\sin^{-1}$, is the inverse of the restricted sine function $y = \sin x$, $-\dfrac{\pi}{2} \leq x \leq \dfrac{\pi}{2}$. Thus,

$$y = \sin^{-1} x \quad \text{means} \quad \sin y = x,$$

where $-\dfrac{\pi}{2} \leq y \leq \dfrac{\pi}{2}$ and $-1 \leq x \leq 1$. We read $y = \sin^{-1} x$ as "y equals the inverse sine at x."

Study Tip

The notation $y = \sin^{-1} x$ does not mean $y = \dfrac{1}{\sin x}$. The notation $y = \dfrac{1}{\sin x}$, or the reciprocal of the sine function, is written $y = (\sin x)^{-1}$ and means $y = \csc x$.

Inverse sine function

Reciprocal of sine function

$$y = \sin^{-1} x \qquad y = (\sin x)^{-1} = \dfrac{1}{\sin x} = \csc x$$

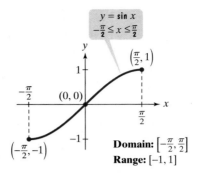

Figure 4.88 The restricted sine function

One way to graph $y = \sin^{-1} x$ is to take points on the graph of the restricted sine function and reverse the order of the coordinates. For example, Figure 4.88 shows that $\left(-\dfrac{\pi}{2}, -1\right)$, $(0, 0)$, and $\left(\dfrac{\pi}{2}, 1\right)$ are on the graph of the restricted sine function. Reversing the order of the coordinates gives $\left(-1, -\dfrac{\pi}{2}\right)$, $(0, 0)$, and $\left(1, \dfrac{\pi}{2}\right)$. We now use these three points to sketch the inverse sine function. The graph of $y = \sin^{-1} x$ is shown in Figure 4.89.

Another way to obtain the graph of $y = \sin^{-1} x$ is to reflect the graph of the restricted sine function about the line $y = x$, shown in Figure 4.90. The red graph is the restricted sine function and the blue graph is the graph of $y = \sin^{-1} x$.

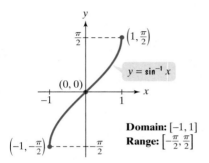

Figure 4.89 The graph of the inverse sine function

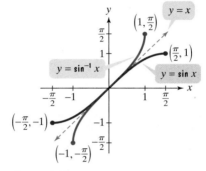

Figure 4.90 Using a reflection to obtain the graph of the inverse sine function

Exact values of $\sin^{-1} x$ can be found by thinking of **$\sin^{-1} x$ as the angle in the interval $\left[-\dfrac{\pi}{2}, \dfrac{\pi}{2}\right]$ whose sine is x**. For example, we can use the two points on the blue graph of the inverse sine function in Figure 4.90 and write

$$\sin^{-1}(-1) = -\dfrac{\pi}{2} \quad \text{and} \quad \sin^{-1} 1 = \dfrac{\pi}{2}.$$

The angle whose sine is -1 is $-\dfrac{\pi}{2}$. The angle whose sine is 1 is $\dfrac{\pi}{2}$.

Because we are thinking of $\sin^{-1} x$ in terms of an angle, we will represent such an angle by θ.

Finding Exact Values of $\sin^{-1} x$

1. Let $\theta = \sin^{-1} x$.

2. Rewrite $\theta = \sin^{-1} x$ as $\sin \theta = x$, where $-\dfrac{\pi}{2} \le \theta \le \dfrac{\pi}{2}$.

3. Use the exact values in Table 4.7 to find the value of θ in $\left[-\dfrac{\pi}{2}, \dfrac{\pi}{2}\right]$ that satisfies $\sin \theta = x$.

Table 4.7   Exact Values for $\sin \theta$, $-\dfrac{\pi}{2} \le \theta \le \dfrac{\pi}{2}$

θ	$-\dfrac{\pi}{2}$	$-\dfrac{\pi}{3}$	$-\dfrac{\pi}{4}$	$-\dfrac{\pi}{6}$	0	$\dfrac{\pi}{6}$	$\dfrac{\pi}{4}$	$\dfrac{\pi}{3}$	$\dfrac{\pi}{2}$
$\sin \theta$	-1	$-\dfrac{\sqrt{3}}{2}$	$-\dfrac{\sqrt{2}}{2}$	$-\dfrac{1}{2}$	0	$\dfrac{1}{2}$	$\dfrac{\sqrt{2}}{2}$	$\dfrac{\sqrt{3}}{2}$	1

EXAMPLE 1   Finding the Exact Value of an Inverse Sine Function

Find the exact value of $\sin^{-1}\dfrac{\sqrt{2}}{2}$.

Solution

Step 1   Let $\theta = \sin^{-1}x$. Thus,

$$\theta = \sin^{-1}\frac{\sqrt{2}}{2}.$$

We must find the angle θ, $-\dfrac{\pi}{2} \le \theta \le \dfrac{\pi}{2}$, whose sine equals $\dfrac{\sqrt{2}}{2}$.

Step 2   Rewrite $\theta = \sin^{-1}x$ as $\sin\theta = x$, where $-\dfrac{\pi}{2} \le \theta \le \dfrac{\pi}{2}$. Using the

definition of the inverse sine function, we rewrite $\theta = \sin^{-1}\dfrac{\sqrt{2}}{2}$ as

$$\sin\theta = \frac{\sqrt{2}}{2}, \text{ where } -\frac{\pi}{2} \le \theta \le \frac{\pi}{2}.$$

Step 3   Use the exact values in Table 4.7 to find the value of θ in $\left[-\dfrac{\pi}{2}, \dfrac{\pi}{2}\right]$ that

satisfies $\sin\theta = x$. Table 4.7 on the previous page shows that the only angle in the

interval $\left[-\dfrac{\pi}{2}, \dfrac{\pi}{2}\right]$ that satisfies $\sin\theta = \dfrac{\sqrt{2}}{2}$ is $\dfrac{\pi}{4}$. Thus, $\theta = \dfrac{\pi}{4}$. Because θ, in step 1,

represents $\sin^{-1}\dfrac{\sqrt{2}}{2}$, we conclude that

$$\sin^{-1}\frac{\sqrt{2}}{2} = \frac{\pi}{4}. \qquad \text{The angle in } \left[-\frac{\pi}{2}, \frac{\pi}{2}\right] \text{ whose sine is } \frac{\sqrt{2}}{2} \text{ is } \frac{\pi}{4}.$$

Check Point 1   Find the exact value of $\sin^{-1}\dfrac{\sqrt{3}}{2}$.

EXAMPLE 2   Finding the Exact Value of an Inverse Sine Function

Find the exact value of $\sin^{-1}\left(-\dfrac{1}{2}\right)$.

Solution

Step 1   Let $\theta = \sin^{-1}x$. Thus,

$$\theta = \sin^{-1}\left(-\frac{1}{2}\right).$$

We must find the angle θ, $-\dfrac{\pi}{2} \le \theta \le \dfrac{\pi}{2}$, whose sine equals $-\dfrac{1}{2}$.

Step 2   Rewrite $\theta = \sin^{-1}x$ as $\sin\theta = x$, where $-\dfrac{\pi}{2} \le \theta \le \dfrac{\pi}{2}$. We rewrite

$\theta = \sin^{-1}\left(-\dfrac{1}{2}\right)$ and obtain

$$\sin\theta = -\frac{1}{2}, \text{ where } -\frac{\pi}{2} \le \theta \le \frac{\pi}{2}.$$

Step 3   Use the exact values in Table 4.7 to find the value of θ in $\left[-\dfrac{\pi}{2}, \dfrac{\pi}{2}\right]$ that satisfies $\sin\theta = x$. Table 4.7 on page 536 shows that the only angle in the interval $\left[-\dfrac{\pi}{2}, \dfrac{\pi}{2}\right]$ that satisfies $\sin\theta = -\dfrac{1}{2}$ is $-\dfrac{\pi}{6}$. Thus,

$$\sin^{-1}\left(-\frac{1}{2}\right) = -\frac{\pi}{6}$$

Check Point 2 Find the exact value of $\sin^{-1}\left(-\dfrac{\sqrt{2}}{2}\right)$.

Some inverse sine expressions cannot be evaluated. Because the domain of the inverse sine function is $[-1, 1]$, it is only possible to evaluate $\sin^{-1} x$ for values of x in this domain. Thus, $\sin^{-1} 3$ cannot be evaluated. There is no angle whose sine is 3.

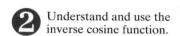 Understand and use the inverse cosine function.

The Inverse Cosine Function

Figure 4.91 shows how we restrict the domain of the cosine function so that it becomes one-to-one and has an inverse function. Restrict the domain to the interval $[0, \pi]$, shown by the dark blue graph. Over this interval, the restricted cosine function passes the horizontal line test and has an inverse function.

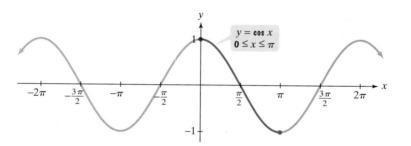

Figure 4.91 $y = \cos x$ is one-to-one on the interval $[0, \pi]$.

> **The Inverse Cosine Function**
> The **inverse cosine function**, denoted by $\cos^{-1}$, is the inverse of the restricted cosine function $y = \cos x$, $0 \le x \le \pi$. Thus,
> $$y = \cos^{-1} x \quad \text{means} \quad \cos y = x,$$
> where $0 \le y \le \pi$ and $-1 \le x \le 1$.

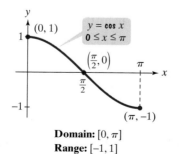

Domain: $[0, \pi]$
Range: $[-1, 1]$

Figure 4.92 The restricted cosine function

One way to graph $y = \cos^{-1} x$ is to take points on the graph of the restricted cosine function and reverse the order of the coordinates. For example, Figure 4.92 shows that $(0, 1)$, $\left(\dfrac{\pi}{2}, 0\right)$, and $(\pi, -1)$ are on the graph of the restricted cosine function. Reversing the order of the coordinates gives $(1, 0)$, $\left(0, \dfrac{\pi}{2}\right)$, and $(-1, \pi)$.

We now use these three points to sketch the inverse cosine function. The graph of $y = \cos^{-1} x$ is shown in Figure 4.93. You can also obtain this graph by reflecting the graph of the restricted cosine function about the line $y = x$.

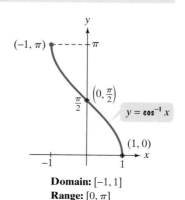

Domain: $[-1, 1]$
Range: $[0, \pi]$

Figure 4.93 The graph of the inverse cosine function

Exact values of $\cos^{-1} x$ can be found by thinking of $\cos^{-1} x$ **as the angle in the interval $[0, \pi]$ whose cosine is x.**

Finding Exact Values of $\cos^{-1} x$

1. Let $\theta = \cos^{-1} x$.
2. Rewrite $\theta = \cos^{-1} x$ as $\cos \theta = x$, where $0 \leq \theta \leq \pi$.
3. Use the exact values in Table 4.8 to find the value of θ in $[0, \pi]$ that satisfies $\cos \theta = x$.

Table 4.8   Exact Values for $\cos \theta, 0 \leq \theta \leq \pi$

θ	0	$\dfrac{\pi}{6}$	$\dfrac{\pi}{4}$	$\dfrac{\pi}{3}$	$\dfrac{\pi}{2}$	$\dfrac{2\pi}{3}$	$\dfrac{3\pi}{4}$	$\dfrac{5\pi}{6}$	π
$\cos \theta$	1	$\dfrac{\sqrt{3}}{2}$	$\dfrac{\sqrt{2}}{2}$	$\dfrac{1}{2}$	0	$-\dfrac{1}{2}$	$-\dfrac{\sqrt{2}}{2}$	$-\dfrac{\sqrt{3}}{2}$	-1

EXAMPLE 3   Finding the Exact Value of an Inverse Cosine Function

Find the exact value of $\cos^{-1}\left(-\dfrac{\sqrt{3}}{2}\right)$.

Solution

Step 1   Let $\theta = \cos^{-1} x$. Thus,

$$\theta = \cos^{-1}\left(-\frac{\sqrt{3}}{2}\right).$$

We must find the angle $\theta, 0 \leq \theta \leq \pi$, whose cosine equals $-\dfrac{\sqrt{3}}{2}$.

Step 2   Rewrite $\theta = \cos^{-1} x$ as $\cos \theta = x$, where $0 \leq \theta \leq \pi$. We obtain

$$\cos \theta = -\frac{\sqrt{3}}{2}, \text{ where } 0 \leq \theta \leq \pi.$$

Step 3   Use the exact values in Table 4.8 to find the value of θ in $[0, \pi]$ that satisfies $\cos \theta = x$. The table shows that the only angle in the interval $[0, \pi]$ that satisfies $\cos \theta = -\dfrac{\sqrt{3}}{2}$ is $\dfrac{5\pi}{6}$. Thus, $\theta = \dfrac{5\pi}{6}$ and

$$\cos^{-1}\left(-\frac{\sqrt{3}}{2}\right) = \frac{5\pi}{6}. \qquad \text{\small The angle in } [0, \pi] \text{ whose cosine is } -\frac{\sqrt{3}}{2} \text{ is } \frac{5\pi}{6}.$$

Check Point 3   Find the exact value of $\cos^{-1}\left(-\dfrac{1}{2}\right)$.

3   Understand and use the inverse tangent function.

The Inverse Tangent Function

Figure 4.94 at the top of the next page shows how we restrict the domain of the tangent function so that it becomes one-to-one and has an inverse function. Restrict the domain to the interval $\left(-\dfrac{\pi}{2}, \dfrac{\pi}{2}\right)$, shown by the solid blue graph. Over this interval, the restricted tangent function passes the horizontal line test and has an inverse function.

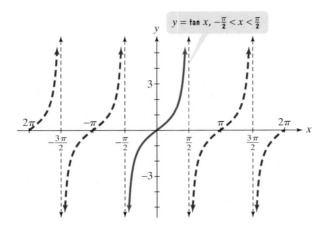

Figure 4.94 $y = \tan x$ is one-to-one on the interval $\left(-\dfrac{\pi}{2}, \dfrac{\pi}{2}\right)$.

The Inverse Tangent Function

The **inverse tangent function**, denoted by $\tan^{-1}$, is the inverse of the restricted tangent function $y = \tan x$, $-\dfrac{\pi}{2} < x < \dfrac{\pi}{2}$. Thus,

$$y = \tan^{-1} x \quad \text{means} \quad \tan y = x,$$

where $-\dfrac{\pi}{2} < y < \dfrac{\pi}{2}$ and $-\infty < x < \infty$.

We graph $y = \tan^{-1} x$ by taking points on the graph of the restricted function and reversing the order of the coordinates. Figure 4.95 shows that $\left(-\dfrac{\pi}{4}, -1\right)$, $(0, 0)$, and $\left(\dfrac{\pi}{4}, 1\right)$ are on the graph of the restricted tangent function. Reversing the order gives $\left(-1, -\dfrac{\pi}{4}\right)$, $(0, 0)$, and $\left(1, \dfrac{\pi}{4}\right)$. We now use these three points to graph the inverse tangent function. The graph of $y = \tan^{-1} x$ is shown in Figure 4.96. Notice that the vertical asymptotes become horizontal asymptotes for the graph of the inverse function.

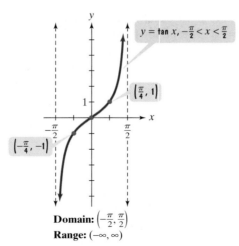

Domain: $\left(-\dfrac{\pi}{2}, \dfrac{\pi}{2}\right)$
Range: $(-\infty, \infty)$

Figure 4.95 The restricted tangent function

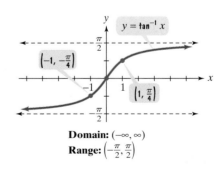

Domain: $(-\infty, \infty)$
Range: $\left(-\dfrac{\pi}{2}, \dfrac{\pi}{2}\right)$

Figure 4.96 The graph of the inverse tangent function

Exact values of $\tan^{-1} x$ can be found by thinking of **$\tan^{-1} x$ as the angle in the interval** $\left(-\dfrac{\pi}{2}, \dfrac{\pi}{2}\right)$ **whose tangent is x.**

Finding Exact Values of $\tan^{-1} x$

1. Let $\theta = \tan^{-1} x$.
2. Rewrite $\theta = \tan^{-1} x$ as $\tan \theta = x$, where $-\dfrac{\pi}{2} < \theta < \dfrac{\pi}{2}$.

3. Use the exact values in Table 4.9 to find the value of θ in $\left(-\dfrac{\pi}{2}, \dfrac{\pi}{2} \right)$ that satisfies $\tan \theta = x$.

Table 4.9   Exact Values for $\tan \theta$, $-\dfrac{\pi}{2} < \theta < \dfrac{\pi}{2}$

θ	$-\dfrac{\pi}{2}$	$-\dfrac{\pi}{3}$	$-\dfrac{\pi}{4}$	$-\dfrac{\pi}{6}$	0	$\dfrac{\pi}{6}$	$\dfrac{\pi}{4}$	$\dfrac{\pi}{3}$	$\dfrac{\pi}{2}$
$\tan \theta$	undef.	$-\sqrt{3}$	-1	$-\dfrac{\sqrt{3}}{3}$	0	$\dfrac{\sqrt{3}}{3}$	1	$\sqrt{3}$	undef.

EXAMPLE 4   Finding the Exact Value of an Inverse Tangent Function

Find the exact value of $\tan^{-1}\sqrt{3}$.

Solution

Step 1   Let $\theta = \tan^{-1} x$. Thus,

$$\theta = \tan^{-1}\sqrt{3}.$$

We must find the angle θ, $-\dfrac{\pi}{2} < \theta < \dfrac{\pi}{2}$, whose tangent equals $\sqrt{3}$.

Step 2   Rewrite $\theta = \tan^{-1} x$ as $\tan \theta = x$, where $-\dfrac{\pi}{2} < \theta < \dfrac{\pi}{2}$. We obtain

$$\tan \theta = \sqrt{3}, \text{ where } -\dfrac{\pi}{2} < \theta < \dfrac{\pi}{2}.$$

Step 3   Use the exact values in Table 4.9 to find the value of θ in $\left(-\dfrac{\pi}{2}, \dfrac{\pi}{2} \right)$ that satisfies $\tan \theta = x$. The table shows that the only angle in the interval $\left(-\dfrac{\pi}{2}, \dfrac{\pi}{2} \right)$ that satisfies $\tan \theta = \sqrt{3}$ is $\dfrac{\pi}{3}$. Thus, $\theta = \dfrac{\pi}{3}$ and

$$\tan^{-1}\sqrt{3} = \dfrac{\pi}{3}. \qquad \text{The angle in } \left(-\dfrac{\pi}{2}, \dfrac{\pi}{2} \right) \text{ whose tangent is } \sqrt{3} \text{ is } \dfrac{\pi}{3}.$$

Study Tip

Do not confuse the domains of the restricted trigonometric functions with the intervals on which the nonrestricted functions complete one cycle.

Trigonometric Function	Domain of Restricted Function	Interval on Which Nonrestricted Function's Graph Completes One Period	
$y = \sin x$	$\left[-\dfrac{\pi}{2}, \dfrac{\pi}{2} \right]$	$[0, 2\pi]$	Period: 2π
$y = \cos x$	$[0, \pi]$	$[0, 2\pi]$	Period: 2π
$y = \tan x$	$\left(-\dfrac{\pi}{2}, \dfrac{\pi}{2} \right)$	$\left(-\dfrac{\pi}{2}, \dfrac{\pi}{2} \right)$	Period: π

These domain restrictions are the range for $y = \sin^{-1} x$, $y = \cos^{-1} x$, and $y = \tan^{-1} x$, respectively.

Check Point 4 Find the exact value of $\tan^{-1}(-1)$.

Table 4.10 summarizes the graphs of the three basic inverse trigonometric functions. Below each of the graphs is a description of the function's domain and range.

Table 4.10 Graphs of the Three Basic Inverse Trigonometric Functions

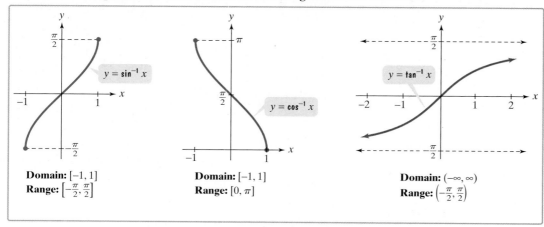

Domain: $[-1, 1]$	**Domain:** $[-1, 1]$	**Domain:** $(-\infty, \infty)$
Range: $\left[-\frac{\pi}{2}, \frac{\pi}{2}\right]$	**Range:** $[0, \pi]$	**Range:** $\left(-\frac{\pi}{2}, \frac{\pi}{2}\right)$

④ Use a calculator to evaluate inverse trigonometric functions.

Using a Calculator to Evaluate Inverse Trigonometric Functions

Calculators give approximate values of inverse trigonometric functions. Use the secondary keys marked $\boxed{\text{SIN}^{-1}}$, $\boxed{\text{COS}^{-1}}$, and $\boxed{\text{TAN}^{-1}}$. These keys are not buttons that you actually press. They are the secondary functions for the buttons labeled $\boxed{\text{SIN}}$, $\boxed{\text{COS}}$, and $\boxed{\text{TAN}}$, respectively. Consult your manual for the location of this feature.

EXAMPLE 5   Calculators and Inverse Trigonometric Functions

Use a calculator to find the value to four decimal places of each function:

a. $\sin^{-1}\dfrac{1}{4}$ **b.** $\tan^{-1}(-9.65)$.

Solution

Scientific Calculator Solution

Function	Mode	Keystrokes	Display, rounded to four places
a. $\sin^{-1}\dfrac{1}{4}$	Radian	1 $\boxed{\div}$ 4 $\boxed{=}$ $\boxed{\text{2nd}}$ $\boxed{\text{SIN}}$	0.2527
b. $\tan^{-1}(-9.65)$	Radian	9.65 $\boxed{+/-}$ $\boxed{\text{2nd}}$ $\boxed{\text{TAN}}$	-1.4675

Graphing Calculator Solution

Function	Mode	Keystrokes	Display, rounded to four places
a. $\sin^{-1}\dfrac{1}{4}$	Radian	$\boxed{\text{2nd}}$ $\boxed{\text{SIN}}$ $\boxed{(}$ 1 $\boxed{\div}$ 4 $\boxed{)}$ $\boxed{\text{ENTER}}$	0.2527
b. $\tan^{-1}(-9.65)$	Radian	$\boxed{\text{2nd}}$ $\boxed{\text{TAN}}$ $\boxed{(-)}$ 9.65 $\boxed{\text{ENTER}}$	-1.4675

Check Point 5 Use a calculator to find the value to four decimal places of each function:
a. $\cos^{-1}\dfrac{1}{3}$ **b.** $\tan^{-1}(-35.85)$.

What happens if you attempt to evaluate an inverse trigomometric function at a value that is not in its domain? In real number mode, most calculators will display an error message. For example, an error message can result if you attempt to approximate $\cos^{-1} 3$. There is no angle whose cosine is 3. The domain of the inverse cosine function is $[-1, 1]$ and 3 does not belong to this domain.

⑤ Find exact values of composite functions with inverse trigonometric functions.

Composition of Functions Involving Inverse Trigonometric Functions

In our earlier discussion of functions and their inverses, we saw that

$$f(f^{-1}(x)) = x \quad \text{and} \quad f^{-1}(f(x)) = x.$$

x must be in the domain of f^{-1}.

x must be in the domain of f.

We apply these properties to the sine, cosine, tangent, and their inverse functions to obtain the following properties:

Inverse Properties

The Sine Function and Its Inverse

$$\sin(\sin^{-1} x) = x \qquad \text{for every } x \text{ in the interval } [-1, 1]$$
$$\sin^{-1}(\sin x) = x \qquad \text{for every } x \text{ in the interval } \left[-\frac{\pi}{2}, \frac{\pi}{2}\right]$$

The Cosine Function and Its Inverse

$$\cos(\cos^{-1} x) = x \qquad \text{for every } x \text{ in the interval } [-1, 1]$$
$$\cos^{-1}(\cos x) = x \qquad \text{for every } x \text{ in the interval } [0, \pi]$$

The Tangent Function and Its Inverse

$$\tan(\tan^{-1} x) = x \qquad \text{for every real number } x$$
$$\tan^{-1}(\tan x) = x \qquad \text{for every } x \text{ in the interval } \left(-\frac{\pi}{2}, \frac{\pi}{2}\right)$$

The restrictions on x in the inverse properties are a bit tricky. For example,

$$\sin^{-1}\left(\sin \frac{\pi}{4}\right) = \frac{\pi}{4}.$$

$\sin^{-1}(\sin x) = x$ for x in $\left[-\frac{\pi}{2}, \frac{\pi}{2}\right]$.
Observe that $\frac{\pi}{4}$ is in this interval.

Can we use $\sin^{-1}(\sin x) = x$ to find the exact value of $\sin^{-1}\left(\sin \frac{5\pi}{4}\right)$? Is $\frac{5\pi}{4}$ in the interval $\left[-\frac{\pi}{2}, \frac{\pi}{2}\right]$? No. Thus, to evaluate $\sin^{-1}\left(\sin \frac{5\pi}{4}\right)$, we must first find $\sin \frac{5\pi}{4}$.

$\frac{5\pi}{4}$ is in quadrant III, where the sine is negative.

$$\sin \frac{5\pi}{4} = -\sin \frac{\pi}{4} = -\frac{\sqrt{2}}{2}$$

The reference angle for $\frac{5\pi}{4}$ is $\frac{\pi}{4}$.

We evaluate $\sin^{-1}\left(\sin \frac{5\pi}{4}\right)$ as follows:

$$\sin^{-1}\left(\sin \frac{5\pi}{4}\right) = \sin^{-1}\left(-\frac{\sqrt{2}}{2}\right) = -\frac{\pi}{4} \qquad \text{If necessary, see Table 4.7 on page 536.}$$

To determine how to evaluate the composition of functions involving inverse trigonometric functions, first examine the value of x. You can use the inverse properties in the box shown on the previous page only if x is in the specified interval.

EXAMPLE 6   Evaluating Compositions of Functions and Their Inverses

Find the exact value, if possible:

a. $\cos(\cos^{-1} 0.6)$ **b.** $\sin^{-1}\left(\sin \dfrac{3\pi}{2}\right)$ **c.** $\cos(\cos^{-1} 1.5)$.

Solution

a. The inverse property $\cos(\cos^{-1} x) = x$ applies for every x in $[-1, 1]$. To evaluate $\cos(\cos^{-1} 0.6)$, observe that $x = 0.6$. This value of x lies in $[-1, 1]$, which is the domain of the inverse cosine function. This means that we can use the inverse property $\cos(\cos^{-1} x) = x$. Thus,

$$\cos(\cos^{-1} 0.6) = 0.6.$$

b. The inverse property $\sin^{-1}(\sin x) = x$ applies for every x in $\left[-\dfrac{\pi}{2}, \dfrac{\pi}{2}\right]$. To evaluate $\sin^{-1}\left(\sin \dfrac{3\pi}{2}\right)$, observe that $x = \dfrac{3\pi}{2}$. This value of x does not lie in $\left[-\dfrac{\pi}{2}, \dfrac{\pi}{2}\right]$. To evaluate this expression, we first find $\sin \dfrac{3\pi}{2}$.

$$\sin^{-1}\left(\sin \dfrac{3\pi}{2}\right) = \sin^{-1}(-1) = -\dfrac{\pi}{2} \quad \text{The angle in } \left[-\dfrac{\pi}{2}, \dfrac{\pi}{2}\right] \text{ whose sine is } -1 \text{ is } -\dfrac{\pi}{2}.$$

c. The inverse property $\cos(\cos^{-1} x) = x$ applies for every x in $[-1, 1]$. To attempt to evaluate $\cos(\cos^{-1} 1.5)$, observe that $x = 1.5$. This value of x does not lie in $[-1, 1]$, which is the domain of the inverse cosine function. Thus, the expression $\cos(\cos^{-1} 1.5)$ is not defined because $\cos^{-1} 1.5$ is not defined.

Check Point 6 Find the exact value, if possible:

a. $\cos(\cos^{-1} 0.7)$ **b.** $\sin^{-1}(\sin \pi)$ **c.** $\cos[\cos^{-1}(-1.2)]$.

We can use points on terminal sides of angles in standard position to find exact values of expressions involving the composition of a function and a different inverse function. Here are two examples:

$$\cos\left(\tan^{-1} \dfrac{5}{12}\right) \qquad \cot\left[\sin^{-1}\left(-\dfrac{1}{3}\right)\right].$$

Inner part involves the angle in $\left(-\dfrac{\pi}{2}, \dfrac{\pi}{2}\right)$ whose tangent is $\dfrac{5}{12}$.

Inner part involves the angle in $\left[-\dfrac{\pi}{2}, \dfrac{\pi}{2}\right]$ whose sine is $-\dfrac{1}{3}$.

The inner part of each expression involves an angle. To evaluate such expressions, we represent such angles by θ. Then we use a sketch that illustrates our representation. Examples 7 and 8 show how to carry out such evaluations.

EXAMPLE 7   Evaluating a Composite Trigonometric Expression

Find the exact value of $\cos\left(\tan^{-1}\dfrac{5}{12}\right)$.

Solution   We let θ represent the angle in $\left(-\dfrac{\pi}{2}, \dfrac{\pi}{2}\right)$ whose tangent is $\dfrac{5}{12}$. Thus,

$$\theta = \tan^{-1}\frac{5}{12}.$$

Using the definition of the inverse tangent function, we can rewrite this as

$$\tan\theta = \frac{5}{12}, \quad \text{where} \quad -\frac{\pi}{2} < \theta < \frac{\pi}{2}.$$

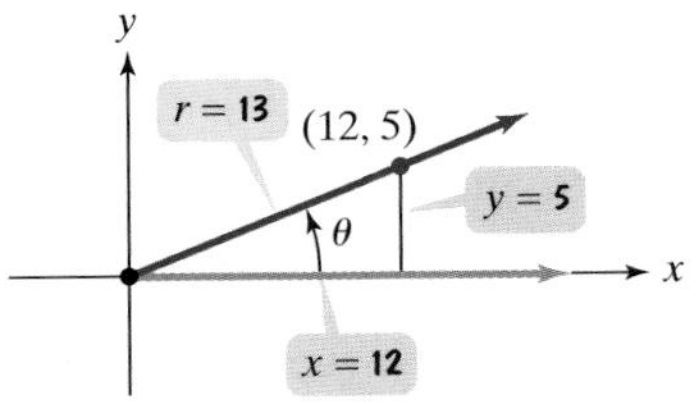

Because $\tan\theta$ is positive, θ must be an angle in $\left(0, \dfrac{\pi}{2}\right)$. Thus, θ is a first-quadrant angle. Figure 4.97 shows a right triangle in quadrant I with

$$\tan\theta = \frac{5}{12}. \quad \boxed{\text{Side opposite } \theta, \text{ or } y} \quad \boxed{\text{Side adjacent to } \theta, \text{ or } x}$$

The hypotenuse of the triangle, r, or the distance from the origin to $(12, 5)$, is found using $r = \sqrt{x^2 + y^2}$.

$$r = \sqrt{x^2 + y^2} = \sqrt{12^2 + 5^2} = \sqrt{144 + 25} = \sqrt{169} = 13$$

We use the values for x and r to find the exact value of $\cos\left(\tan^{-1}\dfrac{5}{12}\right)$.

$$\cos\left(\tan^{-1}\frac{5}{12}\right) = \cos\theta = \frac{\text{side adjacent to } \theta, \text{ or } x}{\text{hypotenuse, or } r} = \frac{12}{13}$$

Check Point 7   Find the exact value of $\sin\left(\tan^{-1}\dfrac{3}{4}\right)$.

EXAMPLE 8   Evaluating a Composite Trigonometric Expression

Find the exact value of $\cot\left[\sin^{-1}\left(-\dfrac{1}{3}\right)\right]$.

Solution   We let θ represent the angle in $\left[-\dfrac{\pi}{2}, \dfrac{\pi}{2}\right]$ whose sine is $-\dfrac{1}{3}$. Thus,

$$\theta = \sin^{-1}\left(-\frac{1}{3}\right) \quad \text{and} \quad \sin\theta = -\frac{1}{3}, \quad \text{where} \quad -\frac{\pi}{2} \le \theta \le \frac{\pi}{2}.$$

Because $\sin\theta$ is negative in $\sin\theta = -\dfrac{1}{3}$, θ must be an angle in $\left[-\dfrac{\pi}{2}, 0\right)$. Thus, θ is a negative angle that lies in quadrant IV. Figure 4.98 shows angle θ in quadrant IV with

$$\boxed{\text{In quadrant IV, } y \text{ is negative.}}$$

$$\sin\theta = -\frac{1}{3} = \frac{y}{r} = \frac{-1}{3}.$$

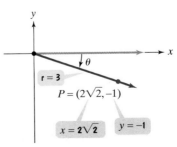

Figure 4.97 Representing $\tan\theta = \frac{5}{12}$

Figure 4.98 Representing $\sin\theta = -\frac{1}{3}$

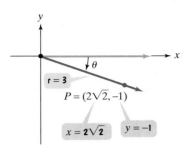

Figure 4.98 (repeated)

Thus, $y = -1$ and $r = 3$. The value of x can be found using $r = \sqrt{x^2 + y^2}$ or $x^2 + y^2 = r^2$.

$$x^2 + (-1)^2 = 3^2 \qquad \text{Use } x^2 + y^2 = r^2 \text{ with } y = -1 \text{ and } r = 3.$$

$$x^2 + 1 = 9 \qquad \text{Square } -1 \text{ and square } 3.$$

$$x^2 = 8 \qquad \text{Subtract 1 from both sides.}$$

$$x = \sqrt{8} = \sqrt{4 \cdot 2} = 2\sqrt{2} \qquad \text{Use the square root property. Remember that } x \text{ is positive in quadrant IV.}$$

We use values for x and y to find the exact value of $\cot\left[\sin^{-1}\left(-\dfrac{1}{3}\right)\right]$.

$$\cot\left[\sin^{-1}\left(-\frac{1}{3}\right)\right] = \cot\theta = \frac{x}{y} = \frac{2\sqrt{2}}{-1} = -2\sqrt{2}$$

Check Point 8 Find the exact value of $\cos\left[\sin^{-1}\left(-\dfrac{1}{2}\right)\right]$.

Some composite functions with inverse trigonometric functions can be simplified to algebraic expressions. To simplify such an expression, we represent the inverse trigonometric function in the expression by θ. Then we use a right triangle.

EXAMPLE 9   Simplifying an Expression Involving $\sin^{-1} x$

If $0 < x \le 1$, write $\cos(\sin^{-1} x)$ as an algebraic expression in x.

Solution   We let θ represent the angle in $\left[-\dfrac{\pi}{2}, \dfrac{\pi}{2}\right]$ whose sine is x. Thus,

$$\theta = \sin^{-1} x \quad \text{and} \quad \sin\theta = x, \quad \text{where} \quad -\frac{\pi}{2} \le \theta \le \frac{\pi}{2}.$$

Because $0 < x \le 1$, $\sin\theta$ is positive. Thus, θ is a first-quadrant angle and can be represented as an acute angle of a right triangle. Figure 4.99 shows a right triangle with

$$\sin\theta = x = \frac{x}{1}. \qquad \begin{array}{l}\text{Side opposite } \theta \\ \text{Hypotenuse}\end{array}$$

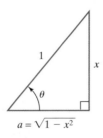

Figure 4.99
Representing
$\sin\theta = x$

The third side, a in Figure 4.99, can be found using the Pythagorean Theorem.

$$a^2 + x^2 = 1^2 \qquad \text{Apply the Pythagorean Theorem to the right triangle in Figure 4.99.}$$

$$a^2 = 1 - x^2 \qquad \text{Subtract } x^2 \text{ from both sides.}$$

$$a = \sqrt{1 - x^2} \qquad \text{Use the square root property and solve for } a. \text{ Remember that side } a \text{ is positive}$$

We use the right triangle in Figure 4.99 to write $\cos(\sin^{-1} x)$ as an algebraic expression.

$$\cos(\sin^{-1} x) = \cos\theta = \frac{\text{side adjacent to } \theta}{\text{hypotenuse}} = \frac{\sqrt{1 - x^2}}{1} = \sqrt{1 - x^2}$$

Check Point 9 If $x > 0$, write $\sec(\tan^{-1} x)$ as an algebraic expression in x.

The inverse secant function, $y = \sec^{-1} x$, is used in calculus. However, inverse cotangent and inverse cosecant functions are rarely used. Two of these remaining inverse trigonometric functions are briefly developed in the exercise set that follows.

EXERCISE SET 4.7

Practice Exercises

In Exercises 1–18, find the exact value of each expression.

1. $\sin^{-1}\dfrac{1}{2}$

2. $\sin^{-1}0$

3. $\sin^{-1}\dfrac{\sqrt{2}}{2}$

4. $\sin^{-1}\dfrac{\sqrt{3}}{2}$

5. $\sin^{-1}\left(-\dfrac{1}{2}\right)$

6. $\sin^{-1}\left(-\dfrac{\sqrt{3}}{2}\right)$

7. $\cos^{-1}\dfrac{\sqrt{3}}{2}$

8. $\cos^{-1}\dfrac{\sqrt{2}}{2}$

9. $\cos^{-1}\left(-\dfrac{\sqrt{2}}{2}\right)$

10. $\cos^{-1}\left(-\dfrac{\sqrt{3}}{2}\right)$

11. $\cos^{-1}0$

12. $\cos^{-1}1$

13. $\tan^{-1}\dfrac{\sqrt{3}}{3}$

14. $\tan^{-1}1$

15. $\tan^{-1}0$

16. $\tan^{-1}(-1)$

17. $\tan^{-1}\left(-\sqrt{3}\right)$

18. $\tan^{-1}\left(-\dfrac{\sqrt{3}}{3}\right)$

In Exercises 19–30, use a calculator to find the value of each expression rounded to two decimal places.

19. $\sin^{-1}0.3$

20. $\sin^{-1}0.47$

21. $\sin^{-1}(-0.32)$

22. $\sin^{-1}(-0.625)$

23. $\cos^{-1}\dfrac{3}{8}$

24. $\cos^{-1}\dfrac{4}{9}$

25. $\cos^{-1}\dfrac{\sqrt{5}}{7}$

26. $\cos^{-1}\dfrac{\sqrt{7}}{10}$

27. $\tan^{-1}(-20)$

28. $\tan^{-1}(-30)$

29. $\tan^{-1}\left(-\sqrt{473}\right)$

30. $\tan^{-1}\left(-\sqrt{5061}\right)$

In Exercises 31–46, find the exact value of each expression, if possible. Do not use a calculator.

31. $\sin(\sin^{-1}0.9)$

32. $\cos(\cos^{-1}0.57)$

33. $\sin^{-1}\left(\sin\dfrac{\pi}{3}\right)$

34. $\cos^{-1}\left(\cos\dfrac{2\pi}{3}\right)$

35. $\sin^{-1}\left(\sin\dfrac{5\pi}{6}\right)$

36. $\cos^{-1}\left(\cos\dfrac{4\pi}{3}\right)$

37. $\tan(\tan^{-1}125)$

38. $\tan(\tan^{-1}380)$

39. $\tan^{-1}\left[\tan\left(-\dfrac{\pi}{6}\right)\right]$

40. $\tan^{-1}\left[\tan\left(-\dfrac{\pi}{3}\right)\right]$

41. $\tan^{-1}\left(\tan\dfrac{2\pi}{3}\right)$

42. $\tan^{-1}\left(\tan\dfrac{3\pi}{4}\right)$

43. $\sin^{-1}(\sin\pi)$

44. $\cos^{-1}(\cos2\pi)$

45. $\sin(\sin^{-1}\pi)$

46. $\cos(\cos^{-1}3\pi)$

In Exercises 47–62, use a sketch to find the exact value of each expression.

47. $\cos\left(\sin^{-1}\dfrac{4}{5}\right)$

48. $\sin\left(\tan^{-1}\dfrac{7}{24}\right)$

49. $\tan\left(\cos^{-1}\dfrac{5}{13}\right)$

50. $\cot\left(\sin^{-1}\dfrac{5}{13}\right)$

51. $\tan\left[\sin^{-1}\left(-\dfrac{3}{5}\right)\right]$

52. $\cos\left[\sin^{-1}\left(-\dfrac{4}{5}\right)\right]$

53. $\sin\left(\cos^{-1}\dfrac{\sqrt{2}}{2}\right)$

54. $\cos\left(\sin^{-1}\dfrac{1}{2}\right)$

55. $\sec\left[\sin^{-1}\left(-\dfrac{1}{4}\right)\right]$

56. $\sec\left[\sin^{-1}\left(-\dfrac{1}{2}\right)\right]$

57. $\tan\left[\cos^{-1}\left(-\dfrac{1}{3}\right)\right]$

58. $\tan\left[\cos^{-1}\left(-\dfrac{1}{4}\right)\right]$

59. $\csc\left[\cos^{-1}\left(-\dfrac{\sqrt{3}}{2}\right)\right]$

60. $\sec\left[\sin^{-1}\left(-\dfrac{\sqrt{2}}{2}\right)\right]$

61. $\cos\left[\tan^{-1}\left(-\dfrac{2}{3}\right)\right]$

62. $\sin\left[\tan^{-1}\left(-\dfrac{3}{4}\right)\right]$

In Exercises 63–72, use a right triangle to write each expression as an algebraic expression. Assume that x is positive and that the given inverse trigonometric function is defined for the expression in x.

63. $\tan(\cos^{-1}x)$

64. $\sin(\tan^{-1}x)$

65. $\cos(\sin^{-1}2x)$

66. $\sin(\cos^{-1}2x)$

67. $\cos\left(\sin^{-1}\dfrac{1}{x}\right)$

68. $\sec\left(\cos^{-1}\dfrac{1}{x}\right)$

69. $\cot\left(\tan^{-1}\dfrac{x}{\sqrt{3}}\right)$

70. $\cot\left(\tan^{-1}\dfrac{x}{\sqrt{2}}\right)$

71. $\sec\left(\sin^{-1}\dfrac{x}{\sqrt{x^2+4}}\right)$

72. $\cot\left(\sin^{-1}\dfrac{\sqrt{x^2-9}}{x}\right)$

73. a. Graph the restricted secant function, $y = \sec x$, by restricting x to the intervals $\left[0, \dfrac{\pi}{2}\right)$ and $\left(\dfrac{\pi}{2}, \pi\right]$.

   b. Use the horizontal line test to explain why the restricted secant function has an inverse function.

   c. Use the graph of the restricted secant function to graph $y = \sec^{-1}x$.

74. a. Graph the restricted cotangent function, $y = \cot x$, by restricting x to the interval $(0, \pi)$.

   b. Use the horizontal line test to explain why the restricted cotangent function has an inverse function.

   c. Use the graph of the restricted cotangent function to graph $y = \cot^{-1}x$.

Practice Plus

The graphs of $y = \sin^{-1}x$, $y = \cos^{-1}x$, and $y = \tan^{-1}x$ are shown in Table 4.10 on page 542. In Exercises 75–84, use transformations (vertical shifts, horizontal shifts, reflections, stretching, or shrinking) of these graphs to graph each function. Then use interval notation to give the function's domain and range.

75. $f(x) = \sin^{-1}x + \dfrac{\pi}{2}$

76. $f(x) = \cos^{-1}x + \dfrac{\pi}{2}$

77. $g(x) = \cos^{-1}(x + 1)$

78. $g(x) = \sin^{-1}(x + 1)$

79. $h(x) = -2 \tan^{-1} x$ **80.** $h(x) = -3 \tan^{-1} x$

81. $f(x) = \sin^{-1}(x - 2) - \dfrac{\pi}{2}$ **82.** $f(x) = \cos^{-1}(x - 2) - \dfrac{\pi}{2}$

83. $g(x) = \cos^{-1}\dfrac{x}{2}$ **84.** $g(x) = \sin^{-1}\dfrac{x}{2}$

In Exercises 85–92, determine the domain and the range of each function.

85. $f(x) = \sin(\sin^{-1} x)$ **86.** $f(x) = \cos(\cos^{-1} x)$
87. $f(x) = \cos^{-1}(\cos x)$ **88.** $f(x) = \sin^{-1}(\sin x)$
89. $f(x) = \sin^{-1}(\cos x)$ **90.** $f(x) = \cos^{-1}(\sin x)$
91. $f(x) = \sin^{-1} x + \cos^{-1} x$ **92.** $f(x) = \cos^{-1} x - \sin^{-1} x$

 Application Exercises

93. Your neighborhood movie theater has a 25-foot-high screen located 8 feet above your eye level. If you sit too close to the screen, your viewing angle is too small, resulting in a distorted picture. By contrast, if you sit too far back, the image is quite small, diminishing the movie's visual impact. If you sit x feet back from the screen, your viewing angle, θ, is given by

$$\theta = \tan^{-1}\frac{33}{x} - \tan^{-1}\frac{8}{x}.$$

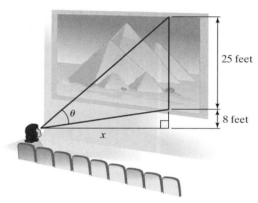

25 feet

8 feet

x

Find the viewing angle, in radians, at distances of 5 feet, 10 feet, 15 feet, 20 feet, and 25 feet.

94. The function $\theta = \tan^{-1}\dfrac{33}{x} - \tan^{-1}\dfrac{8}{x}$, described in Exercise 93,

is graphed below in a $[0, 50, 10]$ by $[0, 1, 0.1]$ viewing rectangle. Use the graph to describe what happens to your viewing angle as you move farther back from the screen. How far back from the screen, to the nearest foot, should you sit to maximize your viewing angle? Verify this observation by finding the viewing angle one foot closer to the screen and one foot farther from the screen for this ideal viewing distance.

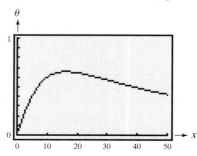

The formula

$$\theta = 2 \tan^{-1}\frac{21.634}{x}$$

gives the viewing angle, θ, in radians, for a camera whose lens is x millimeters wide. Use this formula to solve Exercises 95–96.

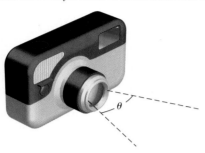

θ

95. Find the viewing angle, in radians and in degrees (to the nearest tenth of a degree), of a 28-millimeter lens.

96. Find the viewing angle, in radians and in degrees (to the nearest tenth of a degree), of a 300-millimeter telephoto lens.

For years, mathematicians were challenged by the following problem: What is the area of a region under a curve between two values of x? The problem was solved in the seventeenth century with the development of integral calculus. Using calculus, the area of the region under $y = \dfrac{1}{x^2 + 1}$, above the x-axis, and between $x = a$ and $x = b$ is $\tan^{-1} b - \tan^{-1} a$. Use this result, shown in the figure, to find the area of the region under $y = \dfrac{1}{x^2 + 1}$, above the x-axis, and between the values of a and b given in Exercises 97–98.

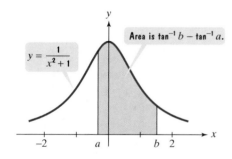

$y = \dfrac{1}{x^2 + 1}$

Area is $\tan^{-1} b - \tan^{-1} a$.

97. $a = 0$ and $b = 2$ **98.** $a = -2$ and $b = 1$

 Writing in Mathematics

99. Explain why, without restrictions, no trigonometric function has an inverse function.

100. Describe the restriction on the sine function so that it has an inverse function.

101. How can the graph of $y = \sin^{-1} x$ be obtained from the graph of the restricted sine function?

102. Without drawing a graph, describe the behavior of the graph of $y = \sin^{-1} x$. Mention the function's domain and range in your description.

103. Describe the restriction on the cosine function so that it has an inverse function.

104. Without drawing a graph, describe the behavior of the graph of $y = \cos^{-1} x$. Mention the function's domain and range in your description.

105. Describe the restriction on the tangent function so that it has an inverse function.

106. Without drawing a graph, describe the behavior of the graph of $y = \tan^{-1} x$. Mention the function's domain and range in your description.

107. If $\sin^{-1}\left(\sin \dfrac{\pi}{3}\right) = \dfrac{\pi}{3}$, is $\sin^{-1}\left(\sin \dfrac{5\pi}{6}\right) = \dfrac{5\pi}{6}$? Explain your answer.

108. Explain how a right triangle can be used to find the exact value of $\sec\left(\sin^{-1}\dfrac{4}{5}\right)$.

109. Find the height of the screen and the number of feet that it is located above eye level in your favorite movie theater. Modify the formula given in Exercise 93 so that it applies to your theater. Then describe where in the theater you should sit so that a movie creates the greatest visual impact.

 Technology Exercises

In Exercises 110–113, graph each pair of functions in the same viewing rectangle. Use your knowledge of the domain and range for the inverse trigonometric functions to select an appropriate viewing rectangle. How is the graph of the second equation in each exercise related to the graph of the first equation?

110. $y = \sin^{-1} x$ and $y = \sin^{-1} x + 2$

111. $y = \cos^{-1} x$ and $y = \cos^{-1}(x - 1)$

112. $y = \tan^{-1} x$ and $y = -2 \tan^{-1} x$

113. $y = \sin^{-1} x$ and $y = \sin^{-1}(x + 2) + 1$

114. Graph $y = \tan^{-1} x$ and its two horizontal asymptotes in a $[-3, 3, 1]$ by $\left[-\pi, \pi, \dfrac{\pi}{2}\right]$ viewing rectangle. Then change the range setting to $[-50, 50, 5]$ by $\left[-\pi, \pi, \dfrac{\pi}{2}\right]$. What do you observe?

115. Graph $y = \sin^{-1} x + \cos^{-1} x$ in a $[-2, 2, 1]$ by $[0, 3, 1]$ viewing rectangle. What appears to be true about the sum of the inverse sine and inverse cosine for values between -1 and 1, inclusive?

Critical Thinking Exercises

116. Solve $y = 2 \sin^{-1}(x - 5)$ for x in terms of y.

117. Solve for x: $2 \sin^{-1} x = \dfrac{\pi}{4}$.

118. Prove that if $x > 0$, $\tan^{-1} x + \tan^{-1}\dfrac{1}{x} = \dfrac{\pi}{2}$.

119. Derive the formula for θ, your viewing angle at the movie theater, in Exercise 93. *Hint*: Use the figure shown and represent the acute angle on the left in the smaller right triangle by α. Find expressions for $\tan \alpha$ and $\tan (\alpha + \theta)$.

SECTION 4.8 Applications of Trigonometric Functions

Objectives

❶ Solve a right triangle.

❷ Solve problems involving bearings.

❸ Model simple harmonic motion.

In the late 1960s, popular musicians were searching for new sounds. Film composers were looking for ways to create unique sounds as well. From these efforts, synthesizers that electronically reproduce musical sounds were born. From providing the backbone of today's most popular music to providing the strange sounds for the most experimental music, synthesizers are at the forefront of music technology.

If we did not understand the periodic nature of sinusoidal functions, the synthesizers used in almost all forms of music would not exist. In this section, we look at applications of trigonometric functions in solving right triangles and in modeling periodic phenomena such as sound.

Solve a right triangle.

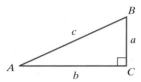

Figure 4.100 Labeling right triangles

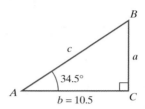

Figure 4.101 Find B, a, and c.

Solving Right Triangles

Solving a right triangle means finding the missing lengths of its sides and the measurements of its angles. We will label right triangles so that side a is opposite angle A, side b is opposite angle B, and side c, the hypotenuse, is opposite right angle C. Figure 4.100 illustrates this labeling.

When solving a right triangle, we will use the sine, cosine, and tangent functions, rather than their reciprocals. Example 1 shows how to solve a right triangle when we know the length of a side and the measure of an acute angle.

EXAMPLE 1   Solving a Right Triangle

Solve the right triangle shown in Figure 4.101, rounding lengths to two decimal places.

Solution   We begin by finding the measure of angle B. We do not need a trigonometric function to do so. Because $C = 90°$ and the sum of a triangle's angles is $180°$, we see that $A + B = 90°$. Thus,

$$B = 90° - A = 90° - 34.5° = 55.5°.$$

Now we need to find a. Because we have a known angle, an unknown opposite side, and a known adjacent side, we use the tangent function.

$$\tan 34.5° = \frac{a}{10.5}$$

Side opposite the 34.5° angle

Side adjacent to the 34.5° angle

Now we multiply both sides of this equation by 10.5 and solve for a.

$$a = 10.5 \tan 34.5° \approx 7.22$$

Finally, we need to find c. Because we have a known angle, a known adjacent side, and an unknown hypotenuse, we use the cosine function.

$$\cos 34.5° = \frac{10.5}{c}$$

Side adjacent to the 34.5° angle

Hypotenuse

Now we multiply both sides of this equation by c and then solve for c.

$$c \cos 34.5° = 10.5 \qquad \text{Multiply both sides by } c.$$

$$c = \frac{10.5}{\cos 34.5°} \approx 12.74 \qquad \text{Divide both sides by } \cos 34.5° \text{ and solve for } c.$$

In summary, $B = 55.5°$, $a \approx 7.22$, and $c \approx 12.74$.

Discovery

There is often more than one correct way to solve a right triangle. In Example 1, find a using angle $B = 55.5°$. Find c using the Pythagorean Theorem.

Check Point 1   In Figure 4.100, let $A = 62.7°$ and $a = 8.4$. Solve the right triangle, rounding lengths to two decimal places.

Trigonometry was first developed to measure heights and distances that were inconvenient or impossible to measure directly. In solving application problems, begin by making a sketch involving a right triangle that illustrates the problem's conditions. Then put your knowledge of solving right triangles to work and find the required distance or height.

EXAMPLE 2   Finding a Side of a Right Triangle

From a point on level ground 125 feet from the base of a tower, the angle of elevation is 57.2°. Approximate the height of the tower to the nearest foot.

Solution   A sketch is shown in Figure 4.102, where *a* represents the height of the tower. In the right triangle, we have a known angle, an unknown opposite side, and a known adjacent side. Therefore, we use the tangent function.

$$\tan 57.2° = \frac{a}{125}$$

Side opposite the 57.2° angle

Side adjacent to the 57.2° angle

Now we multiply both sides of this equation by 125 and solve for *a*.

$$a = 125 \tan 57.2° \approx 194$$

The tower is approximately 194 feet high.

Figure 4.102 Determining height without using direct measurement

Check Point 2 From a point on level ground 80 feet from the base of the Eiffel Tower, the angle of elevation is 85.4°. Approximate the height of the Eiffel Tower to the nearest foot.

Example 3 illustrates how to find the measure of an acute angle of a right triangle if the lengths of two sides are known.

EXAMPLE 3   Finding an Angle of a Right Triangle

A kite flies at a height of 30 feet when 65 feet of string is out. If the string is in a straight line, find the angle that it makes with the ground. Round to the nearest tenth of a degree.

Solution   A sketch is shown in Figure 4.103, where *A* represents the angle the string makes with the ground. In the right triangle, we have an unknown angle, a known opposite side, and a known hypotenuse. Therefore, we use the sine function.

$$\sin A = \frac{30}{65}$$

Side opposite A

Hypotenuse

$$A = \sin^{-1}\frac{30}{65} \approx 27.5°$$

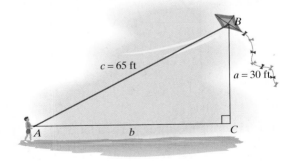

Figure 4.103 Flying a kite

The string makes an angle of approximately 27.5° with the ground.

Check Point 3 A guy wire is 13.8 yards long and is attached from the ground to a pole 6.7 yards above the ground. Find the angle, to the nearest tenth of a degree, that the wire makes with the ground.

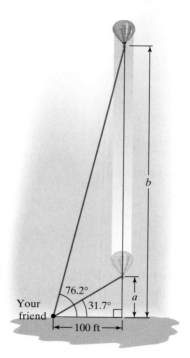

Figure 4.104 Ascending in a hot-air balloon

EXAMPLE 4   Using Two Right Triangles to Solve a Problem

You are taking your first hot-air balloon ride. Your friend is standing on level ground, 100 feet away from your point of launch, making a video of the terrified look on your rapidly ascending face. How rapidly? At one instant, the angle of elevation from the video camera to your face is 31.7°. One minute later, the angle of elevation is 76.2°. How far did you travel, to the nearest tenth of a foot, during that minute?

Solution   A sketch that illustrates the problem is shown in Figure 4.104. We need to determine $b - a$, the distance traveled during the one-minute period. We find a using the small right triangle. Because we have a known angle, an unknown opposite side, and a known adjacent side, we use the tangent function.

$$\tan 31.7° = \frac{a}{100}$$

    Side opposite the 31.7° angle

    Side adjacent to the 31.7° angle

$$a = 100 \tan 31.7° \approx 61.8$$

We find b using the tangent function in the large right triangle.

$$\tan 76.2° = \frac{b}{100}$$

    Side opposite the 76.2° angle

    Side adjacent to the 76.2° angle

$$b = 100 \tan 76.2° \approx 407.1$$

The balloon traveled $407.1 - 61.8$, or approximately 345.3 feet, during the minute.

Check Point 4 You are standing on level ground 800 feet from Mt. Rushmore, looking at the sculpture of Abraham Lincoln's face. The angle of elevation to the bottom of the sculpture is 32° and the angle of elevation to the top is 35°. Find the height of the sculpture of Lincoln's face to the nearest tenth of a foot.

Trigonometry and Bearings

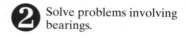
Solve problems involving bearings.

In navigation and surveying problems, the term *bearing* is used to specify the location of one point relative to another. The **bearing** from point O to point P is the acute angle, measured in degrees, between ray OP and a north-south line. Figure 4.105 illustrates some examples of bearings. The north-south line and the east-west line intersect at right angles.

Study Tip

The bearing from O to P can also be described using the phrase "the bearing of P from O."

Figure 4.105 An illustration of three bearings

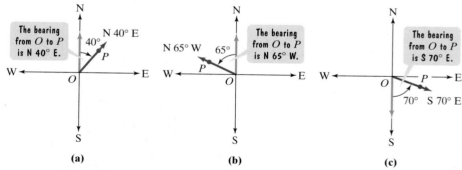

(a)   (b)   (c)

Each bearing has three parts: a letter (N or S), the measure of an acute angle, and a letter (E or W). Here's how we write a bearing:

- If the acute angle is measured from the *north side* of the north-south line, then we write N first. [See Figure 4.105(a).] If the acute angle is measured from the *south side* of the north-south line, then we write S first. [See Figure 4.105(c).]
- Second, we write the measure of the acute angle.
- If the acute angle is measured on the *east side* of the north-south line, then we write E last. [See Figure 4.105(a)]. If the acute angle is measured on the *west side* of the north-south line, then we write W last. [See Figure 4.105(b).]

EXAMPLE 5   Understanding Bearings

Use Figure 4.106 to find each of the following:

    a. the bearing from O to B

    b. the bearing from O to A.

Solution

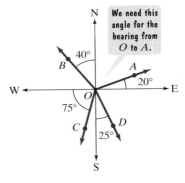

a. To find the bearing from O to B, we need the acute angle between the ray OB and the north-south line through O. The measurement of this angle is given to be 40°. Figure 4.106 shows that the angle is measured from the north side of the north-south line and lies west of the north-south line. Thus, the bearing from O to B is N 40° W.

b. To find the bearing from O to A, we need the acute angle between the ray OA and the north-south line through O. This angle is specified by the voice balloon in Figure 4.106. Because of the given 20° angle, this angle measures 90° − 20°, or 70°. This angle is measured from the north side of the north-south line. This angle is also east of the north-south line. Thus, the bearing from O to A is N 70° E.

Figure 4.106 Finding bearings

Check Point 5 Use Figure 4.106 to find each of the following:

    a. the bearing from O to D

    b. the bearing from O to C.

EXAMPLE 6   Finding the Bearing of a Boat

A boat leaves the entrance to a harbor and travels 25 miles on a bearing of N 42° E. Figure 4.107 shows that the captain then turns the boat 90° clockwise and travels 18 miles on a bearing of S 48° E. At that time:

    a. How far is the boat, to the nearest tenth of a mile, from the harbor entrance?

    b. What is the bearing, to the nearest tenth of a degree, of the boat from the harbor entrance?

Solution

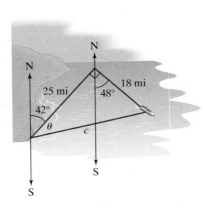

a. The boat's distance from the harbor entrance is represented by c in Figure 4.107. Because we know the length of two sides of the right triangle, we find c using the Pythagorean Theorem. We have

$$c^2 = a^2 + b^2 = 25^2 + 18^2 = 949$$
$$c = \sqrt{949} \approx 30.8.$$

The boat is approximately 30.8 miles from the harbor entrance.

Figure 4.107 Finding a boat's bearing from the harbor entrance

b. The bearing of the boat from the harbor entrance means the bearing from the entrance to the boat. Look at the north-south line passing through the harbor entrance on the left in Figure 4.107. The acute angle from this line to the ray on which the boat lies is $42° + \theta$. Because we are measuring the angle from the north side of the line and the boat is east of the harbor, its bearing from the harbor entrance is N$(42° + \theta)$E. To find θ, we use the right triangle shown in Figure 4.107 and the tangent function.

$$\tan \theta = \frac{\text{side opposite } \theta}{\text{side adjacent to } \theta} = \frac{18}{25}$$

$$\theta = \tan^{-1}\frac{18}{25}$$

We can use a calculator in degree mode to find the value of θ: $\theta \approx 35.8°$. Thus, $42° + \theta = 42° + 35.8° = 77.8°$. The bearing of the boat from the harbor entrance is N 77.8° E.

Study Tip

When making a diagram showing bearings, draw a north-south line through each point at which a change in course occurs. The north side of the line lies above each point. The south side of the line lies below each point.

You leave the entrance to a system of hiking trails and hike 2.3 miles on a bearing of S 31° W. Then the trail turns 90° clockwise and you hike 3.5 miles on a bearing of N 59° W. At that time:

a. How far are you, to the nearest tenth of a mile, from the entrance to the trail system?

b. What is your bearing, to the nearest tenth of a degree, from the entrance to the trail system?

Simple Harmonic Motion

Because of their periodic nature, trigonometric functions are used to model phenomena that occur again and again. This includes vibratory or oscillatory motion, such as the motion of a vibrating guitar string, the swinging of a pendulum, or the bobbing of an object attached to a spring. Trigonometric functions are also used to describe radio waves from your favorite FM station, television waves from your not-to-be-missed weekly sitcom, and sound waves from your most-prized CDs.

To see how trigonometric functions are used to model vibratory motion, consider this: A ball is attached to a spring hung from the ceiling. You pull the ball down 4 inches and then release it. If we neglect the effects of friction and air resistance, the ball will continue bobbing up and down on the end of the spring. These up-and-down oscillations are called **simple harmonic motion**.

To better understand this motion, we use a *d*-axis, where *d* represents distance. This axis is shown in Figure 4.108. On this axis, the position of the ball before you pull it down is $d = 0$. This rest position is called the **equilibrium position**. Now you pull the ball down 4 inches to $d = -4$ and release it. Figure 4.109 shows a sequence of "photographs" taken at one-second time intervals illustrating the distance of the ball from its rest position, *d*.

The curve in Figure 4.109 shows how the ball's distance from its rest position changes over time. The curve is sinusoidal and the motion can be described using a cosine or a sine function.

③ Model simple harmonic motion.

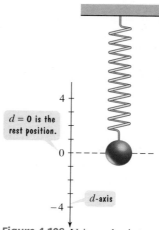

Figure 4.108 Using a *d*-axis to describe a ball's distance from its rest position

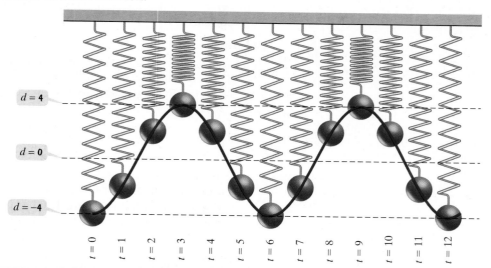

Figure 4.109 A sequence of "photographs" showing the bobbing ball's distance from the rest position, taken at one-second intervals

Simple Harmonic Motion

An object that moves on a coordinate axis is in **simple harmonic motion** if its distance from the origin, *d*, at time *t* is given by either

$$d = a \cos \omega t \quad \text{or} \quad d = a \sin \omega t.$$

The motion has **amplitude** $|a|$, the maximum displacement of the object from its rest position. The **period** of the motion is $\dfrac{2\pi}{\omega}$, where $\omega > 0$. The period gives the time it takes for the motion to go through one complete cycle.

Diminishing Motion with Increasing Time

Due to friction and other resistive forces, the motion of an oscillating object decreases over time. The function

$$d = 3e^{-0.1t} \cos 2t$$

models this type of motion. The graph of the function is shown in a $t = [0, 10, 1]$ by $d = [-3, 3, 1]$ viewing rectangle. Notice how the amplitude is decreasing with time as the moving object loses energy.

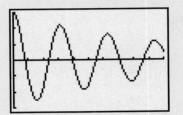

In describing simple harmonic motion, the equation with the cosine function, $d = a \cos \omega t$, is used if the object is at its greatest distance from rest position, the origin, at $t = 0$. By contrast, the equation with the sine function, $d = a \sin \omega t$, is used if the object is at its rest position, the origin, at $t = 0$.

EXAMPLE 7   Finding an Equation for an Object in Simple Harmonic Motion

A ball on a spring is pulled 4 inches below its rest position and then released. The period of the motion is 6 seconds. Write the equation for the ball's simple harmonic motion.

Solution   We need to write an equation that describes d, the distance of the ball from its rest position, after t seconds. (The motion is illustrated by the "photo" sequence in Figure 4.109 on page 554.) When the object is released ($t = 0$), the ball's distance from its rest position is 4 inches down. Because it is *down* 4 inches, d is negative: When $t = 0$, $d = -4$. Notice that the greatest distance from rest position occurs at $t = 0$. Thus, we will use the equation with the cosine function,

$$d = a \cos \omega t,$$

to model the ball's simple harmonic motion.

Now we determine values for a and ω. Recall that $|a|$ is the maximum displacement. Because the ball is initially below rest position, $a = -4$.

The value of ω in $d = a \cos \omega t$ can be found using the formula for the period.

$$\text{period} = \frac{2\pi}{\omega} = 6 \qquad \text{\small We are given that the period of the motion is 6 seconds.}$$

$$2\pi = 6\omega \qquad \text{\small Multiply both sides by } \omega.$$

$$\omega = \frac{2\pi}{6} = \frac{\pi}{3} \qquad \text{\small Divide both sides by 6 and solve for } \omega.$$

We see that $a = -4$ and $\omega = \dfrac{\pi}{3}$. Substitute these values into $d = a \cos \omega t$. The equation for the ball's simple harmonic motion is

$$d = -4 \cos \frac{\pi}{3} t.$$

Modeling Music

Sounds are caused by vibrating objects that result in variations in pressure in the surrounding air. Areas of high and low pressure moving through the air are modeled by the harmonic motion formulas. When these vibrations reach our eardrums, the eardrums' vibrations send signals to our brains which create the sensation of hearing.

French mathematician John Fourier (1768–1830) proved that all musical sounds—instrumental and vocal—could be modeled by sums involving sine functions. Modeling musical sounds with sinusoidal functions is used by synthesizers to electronically produce sounds unobtainable from ordinary musical instruments.

Check Point 7   A ball on a spring is pulled 6 inches below its rest position and then released. The period for the motion is 4 seconds. Write the equation for the ball's simple harmonic motion.

The period of the harmonic motion in Example 7 was 6 seconds. It takes 6 seconds for the moving object to complete one cycle. Thus, $\frac{1}{6}$ of a cycle is completed every second. We call $\frac{1}{6}$ the *frequency* of the moving object. **Frequency** describes the number of complete cycles per unit time and is the reciprocal of the period.

Frequency of an Object in Simple Harmonic Motion

An object in simple harmonic motion given by

$$d = a \cos \omega t \quad \text{or} \quad d = a \sin \omega t$$

has **frequency** f given by

$$f = \frac{\omega}{2\pi}, \omega > 0.$$

Equivalently,

$$f = \frac{1}{\text{period}}.$$

EXAMPLE 8   Analyzing Simple Harmonic Motion

Figure 4.110 shows a mass on a smooth table attached to a spring. The mass moves in simple harmonic motion described by

$$d = 10 \cos \frac{\pi}{6} t,$$

with t measured in seconds and d in centimeters. Find **a.** the maximum displacement, **b.** the frequency, and **c.** the time required for one cycle.

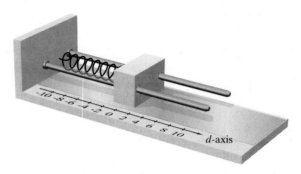

Figure 4.110 A mass attached to a spring, moving in simple harmonic motion

Solution   We begin by identifying values for a and ω.

$$d = 10 \cos \frac{\pi}{6} t$$

The form of this equation is
$d = a \cos \omega t$
with $a = 10$ and $\omega = \frac{\pi}{6}$.

a. The maximum displacement from the rest position is the amplitude. Because $a = 10$, the maximum displacement is 10 centimeters.

b. The frequency, f, is

$$f = \frac{\omega}{2\pi} = \frac{\frac{\pi}{6}}{2\pi} = \frac{\pi}{6} \cdot \frac{1}{2\pi} = \frac{1}{12}.$$

The frequency is $\frac{1}{12}$ cycle (or oscillation) per second.

c. The time required for one cycle is the period.

$$\text{period} = \frac{2\pi}{\omega} = \frac{2\pi}{\frac{\pi}{6}} = 2\pi \cdot \frac{6}{\pi} = 12$$

The time required for one cycle is 12 seconds. This value can also be obtained by taking the reciprocal of the frequency in part (b).

Check Point 8   An object moves in simple harmonic motion described by $d = 12 \cos \frac{\pi}{4} t$, where t is measured in seconds and d in centimeters. Find **a.** the maximum displacement, **b.** the frequency, and **c.** the time required for one cycle.

Resisting Damage of Simple Harmonic Motion

Simple harmonic motion from an earthquake caused this highway in Oakland, California, to collapse. By studying the harmonic motion of the soil under the highway, engineers learn to build structures that can resist damage.

EXERCISE SET 4.8

Practice Exercises

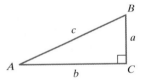

In Exercises 1–12, solve the right triangle shown in the figure. Round lengths to two decimal places and express angles to the nearest tenth of a degree.

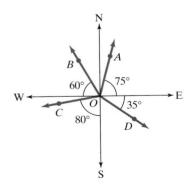

1. $A = 23.5°, b = 10$ **2.** $A = 41.5°, b = 20$

3. $A = 52.6°, c = 54$ **4.** $A = 54.8°, c = 80$

5. $B = 16.8°, b = 30.5$ **6.** $B = 23.8°, b = 40.5$

7. $a = 30.4, c = 50.2$ **8.** $a = 11.2, c = 65.8$

9. $a = 10.8, b = 24.7$ **10.** $a = 15.3, b = 17.6$

11. $b = 2, c = 7$ **12.** $b = 4, c = 9$

Use the figure shown to solve Exercises 13–16.

13. Find the bearing from O to A.

14. Find the bearing from O to B.

15. Find the bearing from O to C.

16. Find the bearing from O to D.

In Exercises 17–20, an object is attached to a coiled spring. In Exercises 17–18, the object is pulled down (negative direction from the rest position) and then released. In Exercises 19–20, the object is initially at its rest position. After that, it is pulled down and then released. Write an equation for the distance of the object from its rest position after t seconds.

Distance from rest position at $t = 0$	Amplitude	Period
17. 6 centimeters	6 centimeters	4 seconds
18. 8 inches	8 inches	2 seconds
19. 0	3 inches	1.5 seconds
20. 0	5 centimeters	2.5 seconds

In Exercises 21–28, an object moves in simple harmonic motion described by the given equation, where t is measured in seconds and d in inches. In each exercise, find the following:

  a. *the maximum displacement*

  b. *the frequency*

  c. *the time required for one cycle.*

21. $d = 5 \cos \dfrac{\pi}{2} t$ **22.** $d = 10 \cos 2\pi t$

23. $d = -6 \cos 2\pi t$ **24.** $d = -8 \cos \dfrac{\pi}{2} t$

25. $d = \tfrac{1}{2} \sin 2t$ **26.** $d = \tfrac{1}{3} \sin 2t$

27. $d = -5 \sin \dfrac{2\pi}{3} t$ **28.** $d = -4 \sin \dfrac{3\pi}{2} t$

Practice Plus

In Exercises 29–36, find the length x to the nearest whole number.

29.

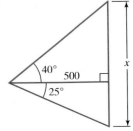

30.

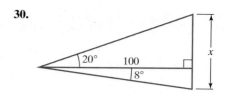

31.

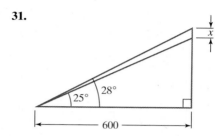

32.

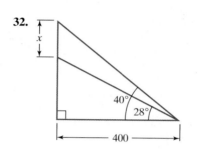

33.

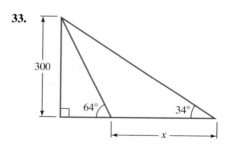

34.

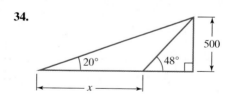

35.

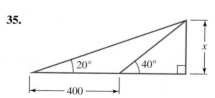

36.

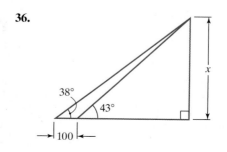

In Exercises 37–40, an object moves in simple harmonic motion described by the given equation, where t is measured in seconds and d in inches. In each exercise, graph one period of the equation. Then find the following:

    a. *the maximum displacement*
    b. *the frequency*
    c. *the time required for one cycle*
    d. *the phase shift of the motion.*

Describe how (a) through (d) are illustrated by your graph.

37. $d = 4 \cos\left(\pi t - \dfrac{\pi}{2}\right)$ **38.** $d = 3 \cos\left(\pi t + \dfrac{\pi}{2}\right)$

39. $d = -2 \sin\left(\dfrac{\pi t}{4} + \dfrac{\pi}{2}\right)$ **40.** $d = -\dfrac{1}{2} \sin\left(\dfrac{\pi t}{4} - \dfrac{\pi}{2}\right)$

Application Exercises

41. The tallest television transmitting tower in the world is in North Dakota. From a point on level ground 5280 feet (one mile) from the base of the tower, the angle of elevation is 21.3°. Approximate the height of the tower to the nearest foot.

42. From a point on level ground 30 yards from the base of a building, the angle of elevation is 38.7°. Approximate the height of the building to the nearest foot.

43. The Statue of Liberty is approximately 305 feet tall. If the angle of elevation from a ship to the top of the statue is 23.7°, how far, to the nearest foot, is the ship from the statue's base?

44. A 200-foot cliff drops vertically into the ocean. If the angle of elevation from a ship to the top of the cliff is 22.3°, how far off shore, to the nearest foot, is the ship?

45. A helicopter hovers 1000 feet above a small island. The figure shows that the angle of depression from the helicopter to point *P* on the coast is 36°. How far off the coast, to the nearest foot, is the island?

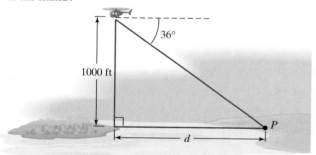

46. A police helicopter is flying at 800 feet. A stolen car is sighted at an angle of depression of 72°. Find the distance of the stolen car, to the nearest foot, from a point directly below the helicopter.

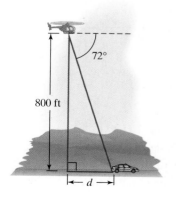

47. A wheelchair ramp is to be built beside the steps to the campus library. Find the angle of elevation of the 23-foot ramp, to the nearest tenth of a degree, if its final height is 6 feet.

48. A building that is 250 feet high casts a shadow 40 feet long. Find the angle of elevation, to the nearest tenth of a degree, of the sun at this time.

49. A hot-air balloon is rising vertically. From a point on level ground 125 feet from the point directly under the passenger compartment, the angle of elevation to the ballon changes from 19.2° to 31.7°. How far, to the nearest tenth of a foot, does the balloon rise during this period?

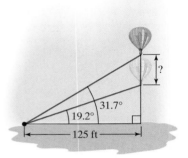

50. A flagpole is situated on top of a building. The angle of elevation from a point on level ground 330 feet from the building to the top of the flagpole is 63°. The angle of elevation from the same point to the bottom of the flagpole is 53°. Find the height of the flagpole to the nearest tenth of a foot.

51. A boat leaves the entrance to a harbor and travels 150 miles on a bearing of N53°E. How many miles north and how many miles east from the harbor has the boat traveled?

52. A boat leaves the entrance to a harbor and travels 40 miles on a bearing of S64°E. How many miles south and how many miles east from the harbor has the boat traveled?

53. A forest ranger sights a fire directly to the south. A second ranger, 7 miles east of the first ranger, also sights the fire. The bearing from the second ranger to the fire is S 28° W. How far, to the nearest tenth of a mile, is the first ranger from the fire?

54. A ship sights a lighthouse directly to the south. A second ship, 9 miles east of the first ship, also sights the lighthouse. The bearing from the second ship to the lighthouse is S 34° W. How far, to the nearest tenth of a mile, is the first ship from the lighthouse?

55. You leave your house and run 2 miles due west followed by 1.5 miles due north. At that time, what is your bearing from your house?

56. A ship is 9 miles east and 6 miles south of a harbor. What bearing should be taken to sail directly to the harbor?

57. A jet leaves a runway whose bearing is N 35° E from the control tower. After flying 5 miles, the jet turns 90° and flies on a bearing of S 55° E for 7 miles. At that time, what is the bearing of the jet from the control tower?

58. A ship leaves port with a bearing of S 40° W. After traveling 7 miles, the ship turns 90° and travels on a bearing of N 50° W for 11 miles. At that time, what is the bearing of the ship from port?

59. An object in simple harmonic motion has a frequency of $\frac{1}{2}$ oscillation per minute and an amplitude of 6 feet. Write an equation in the form $d = a \sin \omega t$ for the object's simple harmonic motion.

60. An object in simple harmonic motion has a frequency of $\frac{1}{4}$ oscillation per minute and an amplitude of 8 feet. Write an equation in the form $d = a \sin \omega t$ for the object's simple harmonic motion.

61. A piano tuner uses a tuning fork. If middle C has a frequency of 264 vibrations per second, write an equation in the form $d = \sin \omega t$ for the simple harmonic motion.

62. A radio station, 98.1 on the FM dial, has radio waves with a frequency of 98.1 million cycles per second. Write an equation in the form $d = \sin \omega t$ for the simple harmonic motion of the radio waves.

Writing in Mathematics

63. What does it mean to solve a right triangle?

64. Explain how to find one of the acute angles of a right triangle if two sides are known.

65. Describe a situation in which a right triangle and a trigonometric function are used to measure a height or distance that would otherwise be inconvenient or impossible to measure.

66. What is meant by the bearing from point O to point P? Give an example with your description.

67. What is simple harmonic motion? Give an example with your description.

68. Explain the period and the frequency of simple harmonic motion. How are they related?

69. Explain how the photograph of the damaged highway on page 557 illustrates simple harmonic motion.

Technology Exercises

The functions in Exercises 70–71 model motion in which the amplitude decreases with time due to friction or other resistive forces. Graph each function in the given viewing rectangle. How many complete oscillations occur on the time interval $0 \le x \le 10$?

70. $y = 4e^{-0.1x} \cos 2x$ $[0, 10, 1]$ by $[-4, 4, 1]$

71. $y = -6e^{-0.09x} \cos 2\pi x$ $[0, 10, 1]$ by $[-6, 6, 1]$

Critical Thinking Exercises

72. The figure shows a satellite circling 112 miles above Earth. When the satellite is directly above point *B*, angle *A* measures 76.6°. Find Earth's radius to the nearest mile.

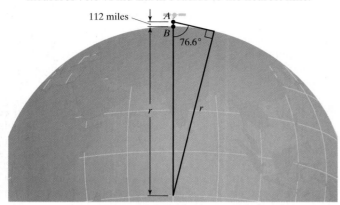

73. The angle of elevation to the top of a building changes from 20° to 40° as an observer advances 75 feet toward the building. Find the height of the building to the nearest foot.

Group Exercise

74. Music and mathematics have been linked over the centuries. Group members should research and present a seminar to the class on music and mathematics. Be sure to include the role of trigonometric functions in the music-mathematics link.

Chapter 4
Summary

Summary

DEFINITIONS AND CONCEPTS	**EXAMPLES**
4.1 Angles and Radian Measure	
a. An angle consists of two rays with a common endpoint, the vertex.	
b. An angle is in standard position if its vertex is at the origin and its initial side lies along the positive *x*-axis. Figure 4.3 on page 447 shows positive and negative angles in standard position.	
c. A quadrantal angle is an angle with its terminal side on the *x*-axis or the *y*-axis.	
d. Angles can be measured in degrees. 1° is $\frac{1}{360}$ of a complete rotation.	
e. Acute angles measure more than 0° but less than 90°, right angles 90°, obtuse angles more than 90° but less than 180°, and straight angles 180°.	Figure 4.5, p. 447
f. Angles can be measured in radians. One radian is the measure of the central angle when the intercepted arc and radius have the same length. In general, the radian measure of a central angle is the length of the intercepted arc divided by the circle's radius: $\theta = \frac{s}{r}$.	Ex. 1, p. 449
g. To convert from degrees to radians, multiply degrees by $\frac{\pi \text{ radians}}{180°}$. To convert from radians to degrees, multiply radians by $\frac{180°}{\pi \text{ radians}}$.	Ex. 2, p. 450; Ex. 3, p. 450
h. To draw angles measured in radians in standard position, it is helpful to "think in radians" without having to convert to degrees. See Figure 4.15 on page 453.	Ex. 4, p. 451
i. Two angles with the same initial and terminal sides are called coterminal angles. Increasing or decreasing an angle's measure by integer multiples of 360° or 2π produces coterminal angles.	Ex. 5, p. 454; Ex. 6, p. 455; Ex. 7, p. 455
j. The arc length formula, $s = r\theta$, is described in the box on page 456.	Ex. 8, p. 456

DEFINITIONS AND CONCEPTS	**EXAMPLES**

k. The definitions of linear speed, $v = \dfrac{s}{t}$, and angular speed, $\omega = \dfrac{\theta}{t}$, are given in the box on page 457.

l. Linear speed is expressed in terms of angular speed by $v = r\omega$, where v is the linear speed of a point a distance r from the center of rotation and ω is the angular speed in radians per unit of time.

Ex. 9, p. 458

4.2 Trigonometric Functions: The Unit Circle

a. Definitions of the trigonometric functions in terms of a unit circle are given in the box on page 463.

Ex. 1, p. 463;
Ex. 2, p. 464

b. The cosine and secant functions are even:

$$\cos(-t) = \cos t, \quad \sec(-t) = \sec t.$$

The other trigonometric functions are odd:

$$\sin(-t) = -\sin t, \quad \csc(-t) = -\csc t,$$
$$\tan(-t) = -\tan t, \quad \cot(-t) = -\cot t.$$

Ex. 4, p. 467

c. Fundamental Identities

  1. Reciprocal Identities

$$\sin t = \frac{1}{\csc t} \text{ and } \csc t = \frac{1}{\sin t}; \cos t = \frac{1}{\sec t} \text{ and } \sec t = \frac{1}{\cos t}; \tan t = \frac{1}{\cot t} \text{ and } \cot t = \frac{1}{\tan t}$$

  2. Quotient Identities

$$\tan t = \frac{\sin t}{\cos t}; \cot t = \frac{\cos t}{\sin t}$$

  3. Pythagorean Identities

$$\sin^2 t + \cos^2 t = 1; 1 + \tan^2 t = \sec^2 t; 1 + \cot^2 t = \csc^2 t$$

Ex. 5, p. 468;
Ex. 6, p. 469

d. If $f(t + p) = f(t)$, the function f is periodic. The smallest p for which $f(t + p) = f(t)$ is the period of f. The tangent and cotangent functions have period π. The other four trigonometric functions have period 2π.

Ex. 7, p. 470

4.3 Right Triangle Trigonometry

a. The right triangle definitions of the six trigonometric functions are given in the box on page 476.

Ex. 1, p. 477;
Ex. 2, p. 478

b. Function values for $30°, 45°,$ and $60°$ can be obtained using these special triangles.

Ex. 3, p. 479;
Ex. 4, p. 479

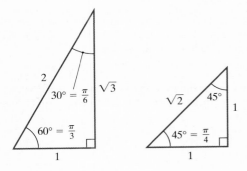

c. Two angles are complements if their sum is $90°$ or $\dfrac{\pi}{2}$. The value of a trigonometric function of θ is equal to the cofunction of the complement of θ. Cofunction identities are listed in the box on page 481.

Ex. 5, p. 481

DEFINITIONS AND CONCEPTS	EXAMPLES

4.4 Trigonometric Functions of Any Angle

a. Definitions of the trigonometric functions of any angle are given in the box on page 488.

Ex. 1, p. 489;
Ex. 2, p. 489

b. Signs of the trigonometric functions: All functions are positive in quadrant I. If θ lies in quadrant II, $\sin \theta$ and $\csc \theta$ are positive. If θ lies in quadrant III, $\tan \theta$ and $\cot \theta$ are positive. If θ lies in quadrant IV, $\cos \theta$ and $\sec \theta$ are positive.

Ex. 3, p. 491;
Ex. 4, p. 491

c. If θ is a nonacute angle in standard position that lies in a quadrant, its reference angle is the positive acute angle θ' formed by the terminal side of θ and the x-axis. The reference angle for a given angle can be found by making a sketch that shows the angle in standard position. Figure 4.49 on page 492 shows reference angles for θ in quadrants II, III, and IV.

Ex. 5, p. 492;
Ex. 6, p. 493

d. The values of the trigonometric functions of a given angle are the same as the values of the functions of the reference angle, except possibly for the sign. A procedure for using reference angles to evaluate trigonometric functions is given in the lower box on page 494.

Ex. 7, p. 494;
Ex. 8, p. 496

4.5 and 4.6 Graphs of the Trigonometric Functions

a. Graphs of the six trigonometric functions, with a description of the domain, range, and period of each function, are given in Table 4.6 on page 530.

b. The graph of $y = A \sin(Bx - C)$ can be obtained using amplitude $= |A|$, period $= \dfrac{2\pi}{B}$, and phase shift $= \dfrac{C}{B}$. See the illustration in the box on page 508.

Ex. 1, p. 504;
Ex. 2, p. 505;
Ex. 3, p. 506;
Ex. 4, p. 508

c. The graph of $y = A \cos(Bx - C)$ can be obtained using amplitude $= |A|$, period $= \dfrac{2\pi}{B}$, and phase shift $= \dfrac{C}{B}$. See the illustration in the box on page 513.

Ex. 5, p. 511;
Ex. 6, p. 513

d. The constant D in $y = A \sin(Bx - C) + D$ and $y = A \cos(Bx - C) + D$ causes vertical shifts in the graphs in the preceding items (b) and (c). If $D > 0$, the shift is D units upward and if $D < 0$, the shift is D units downward. Oscillation is about the horizontal line $y = D$.

Ex. 7, p. 514

e. The graph of $y = A \tan(Bx - C)$ is obtained using the procedure in the box on page 523. Consecutive asymptotes $\left(\text{solve } -\dfrac{\pi}{2} < Bx - C < \dfrac{\pi}{2}; \text{ consecutive asymptotes occur at } Bx - C = -\dfrac{\pi}{2} \text{ and } Bx - C = \dfrac{\pi}{2} \right)$ and an x-intercept midway between them play a key role in the graphing process.

Ex. 1, p. 524;
Ex. 2, p. 524

f. The graph of $y = A \cot(Bx - C)$ is obtained using the procedure in the box on page 526. Consecutive asymptotes (solve $0 < Bx - C < \pi$; consecutive asymptotes occur at $Bx - C = 0$ and $Bx - C = \pi$) and an x-intercept midway between them play a key role in the graphing process.

Ex. 3, p. 526

g. To graph a cosecant curve, begin by graphing the corresponding sine curve. Draw vertical asymptotes through x-intercepts, using asymptotes as guides to sketch the graph. To graph a secant curve, first graph the corresponding cosine curve and use the same procedure.

Ex. 4, p. 528;
Ex. 5, p. 529

4.7 Inverse Trigonometric Functions

a. On the restricted domain $-\dfrac{\pi}{2} \leq x \leq \dfrac{\pi}{2}$, $y = \sin x$ has an inverse function, defined in the box on page 535. Think of $\sin^{-1} x$ as the angle in $\left[-\dfrac{\pi}{2}, \dfrac{\pi}{2} \right]$ whose sine is x. A procedure for finding exact values of $\sin^{-1} x$ is given in the box on page 536.

Ex. 1, p. 537;
Ex. 2, p. 537

DEFINITIONS AND CONCEPTS	**EXAMPLES**
b. On the restricted domain $0 \le x \le \pi$, $y = \cos x$ has an inverse function, defined in the box on page 538. Think of $\cos^{-1} x$ as the angle in $[0, \pi]$ whose cosine is x. A procedure for finding exact values of $\cos^{-1} x$ is given in the box on page 539.	Ex. 3, p. 539
c. On the restricted domain $-\dfrac{\pi}{2} < x < \dfrac{\pi}{2}$, $y = \tan x$ has an inverse function, defined in the box on page 540. Think of $\tan^{-1} x$ as the angle in $\left(-\dfrac{\pi}{2}, \dfrac{\pi}{2}\right)$ whose tangent is x. A procedure for finding exact values of $\tan^{-1} x$ is given in the box on page 541.	Ex. 4, p. 541
d. Graphs of the three basic inverse trigonometric functions, with a description of the domain and range of each function, are given in Table 4.10 on page 542.	
e. Inverse properties are given in the box on page 543. Points on terminal sides of angles in standard position and right triangles are used to find exact values of the composition of a function and a different inverse function.	Ex. 6, p. 544; Ex. 7, p. 545; Ex. 8, p. 545; Ex. 9, p. 546

4.8 Applications of Trigonometric Functions

a. Solving a right triangle means finding the missing lengths of its sides and the measurements of its angles. The Pythagorean Theorem, two acute angles whose sum is $90°$, and appropriate trigonometric functions are used in this process.	Ex. 1, p. 550; Ex. 2, p. 551; Ex. 3, p. 551; Ex. 4, p. 552
b. The bearing from point O to point P is the acute angle between ray OP and a north-south line, shown in Figure 4.105 on page 552.	Ex. 5, p. 553; Ex. 6, p. 553
c. Simple harmonic motion, described in the box on page 554, is modeled by $d = a \cos \omega t$ or $d = a \sin \omega t$, with amplitude $= |a|$, period $= \dfrac{2\pi}{\omega}$, and frequency $= \dfrac{\omega}{2\pi} = \dfrac{1}{\text{period}}$.	Ex. 7, p. 555; Ex. 8, p. 556

Study Tip

Much of the essential information in this chapter can be found in three places:

- Study Tip on page 498, showing special angles and how to obtain exact values of trigonometric functions at these angles
- Table 4.6 on page 530, showing the graphs of the six trigonometric functions, with their domains, ranges, and periods
- Table 4.10 on page 542, showing graphs of the three basic inverse trigonometric functions, with their domains and ranges.

Make copies of these pages and mount them on cardstock. Use this reference sheet as you work the review exercises until you have all the information on the reference sheet memorized for the chapter test.

5

Analytic Trigonometry

Taken from:
Precalculus, Third Edition, by Robert Blitzer

Analytic Trigonometry

T HIS CHAPTER EMPHASIZES THE *algebraic aspects of trigonometry. We derive important categories of identities involving trigonometric functions. These identities are used to simplify and analyze expressions that model phenomena as diverse as the distance achieved when throwing an object and musical sounds on a touch-tone phone. For*

example, we can find out critical information about an athlete's performance by using an identity to analyze an expression involving throwing distance. You will learn how to use trigonometric identities to better understand your periodic world.

YOU ENJOY WATCHING YOUR FRIEND participate in the shot put at college track and field events. After a few full turns in a circle, he throws ("puts") an 8-pound, 13-ounce shot from the shoulder. The range of his throwing distance continues to improve. Knowing that you are studying trigonometry, he asks if there is some way that a trigonometric expression might help achieve his best possible distance in the event.

This problem appears as Exercise 79 in Exercise Set 5.3.

SECTION 5.1 Verifying Trigonometric Identities

Objective
1 Use the fundamental trigonometric identities to verify identities.

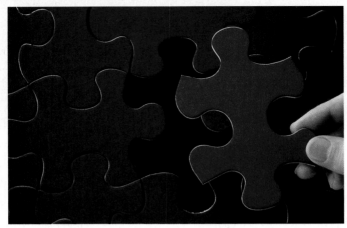

Do you enjoy solving puzzles? The process is a natural way to develop problem-solving skills that are important in every area of our lives. Engaging in problem solving for sheer pleasure releases chemicals in the brain that enhance our feeling of well-being. Perhaps this is why puzzles have fascinated people for over 12,000 years.

Thousands of relationships exist among the six trigonometric functions. Verifying these relationships is like solving a puzzle. Why? There are no rigid rules for the process. Thus, proving a trigonometric relationship requires you to be creative in your approach to problem solving. By learning to establish these relationships, you will become a better, more confident problem solver. Furthermore, you may enjoy the feeling of satisfaction that accompanies solving each "puzzle."

The Fundamental Identities

In Chapter 4, we used right triangles to establish relationships among the trigonometric functions. Although we limited domains to acute angles, the fundamental identities listed in the following box are true for all values of x for which the expressions are defined.

Fundamental Trigonometric Identities

Reciprocal Identities

$$\sin x = \frac{1}{\csc x} \quad \cos x = \frac{1}{\sec x} \quad \tan x = \frac{1}{\cot x}$$

$$\csc x = \frac{1}{\sin x} \quad \sec x = \frac{1}{\cos x} \quad \cot x = \frac{1}{\tan x}$$

Quotient Identities

$$\tan x = \frac{\sin x}{\cos x} \quad \cot x = \frac{\cos x}{\sin x}$$

Pythagorean Identities

$$\sin^2 x + \cos^2 x = 1 \quad 1 + \tan^2 x = \sec^2 x \quad 1 + \cot^2 x = \csc^2 x$$

Even-Odd Identities

$$\sin(-x) = -\sin x \quad \cos(-x) = \cos x \quad \tan(-x) = -\tan x$$

$$\csc(-x) = -\csc x \quad \sec(-x) = \sec x \quad \cot(-x) = -\cot x$$

Study Tip

Memorize the identities in the box. You may need to use variations of these fundamental identities. For example, instead of

$$\sin^2 x + \cos^2 x = 1,$$

you might want to use

$$\sin^2 x = 1 - \cos^2 x$$

or

$$\cos^2 x = 1 - \sin^2 x.$$

Therefore, it is important to know each relationship well so that mental algebraic manipulation is possible.

 Use the fundamental trigonometric identities to verify identities.

Using Fundamental Identities to Verify Other Identities

The fundamental trigonometric identities are used to establish other relationships among trigonometric functions. To **verify an identity**, we show that one side of the identity can be simplified so that it is identical to the other side. Each side of the equation is manipulated independently of the other side of the equation. Start with the side containing the more complicated expression. If you substitute one or more fundamental identities on the more complicated side, you will often be able to rewrite it in a form identical to that of the other side.

No one method or technique can be used to verify every identity. Some identities can be verified by rewriting the more complicated side so that it contains only sines and cosines.

EXAMPLE 1   Changing to Sines and Cosines to Verify an Identity

Verify the identity: $\sec x \cot x = \csc x$.

Solution   The left side of the equation contains the more complicated expression. Thus, we work with the left side. Let us express this side of the identity in terms of sines and cosines. Perhaps this strategy will enable us to transform the left side into $\csc x$, the expression on the right.

$$\sec x \cot x = \frac{1}{\cos x} \cdot \frac{\cos x}{\sin x}$$

Apply a reciprocal identity: $\sec x = \dfrac{1}{\cos x}$ and a quotient identity: $\cot x = \dfrac{\cos x}{\sin x}$.

$$= \frac{1}{\overset{1}{\underset{1}{\cancel{\cos x}}}} \cdot \frac{\overset{1}{\cancel{\cos x}}}{\sin x}$$

Divide both the numerator and the denominator by cos x, the common factor.

$$= \frac{1}{\sin x}$$

Multiply the remaining factors in the numerator and denominator.

$$= \csc x$$

Apply a reciprocal identity: $\csc x = \dfrac{1}{\sin x}$.

By working with the left side and simplifying it so that it is identical to the right side, we have verified the given identity.

Technology

You can use a graphing utility to provide evidence of an identity. Enter each side of the identity separately under y_1 and y_2. Then use the $\boxed{\text{TABLE}}$ feature or the graphs. The table should show that the function values are the same except for those values of x for which y_1, y_2, or both, are undefined. The graphs should appear to be identical.

Let's check the identity in Example 1:

$$\sec x \cot x = \csc x.$$

$y_1 = \sec x \cot x$
Enter sec x as $\dfrac{1}{\cos x}$
and cot x as $\dfrac{1}{\tan x}$.

$y_2 = \csc x$
Enter csc x as $\dfrac{1}{\sin x}$.

Numeric Check
Display a table for y_1 and y_2. We started our table at $-\pi$ and used $\Delta Tbl = \dfrac{\pi}{8}$.

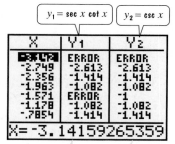

Function values are the same except for values of x for which y_1, y_2, or both, are undefined.

Graphic Check
Display graphs for y_1 and y_2.

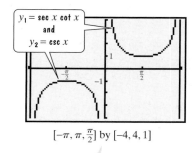

$[-\pi, \pi, \frac{\pi}{2}]$ by $[-4, 4, 1]$

The graphs appear to be identical.

Check Point 1 Verify the identity: $\csc x \tan x = \sec x.$

In verifying an identity, stay focused on your goal. When manipulating one side of the equation, continue to look at the other side to keep the desired form of the result in mind.

Study Tip

Verifying that an equation is an identity is different from solving an equation. You do not verify an identity by adding, subtracting, multiplying, or dividing each side by the same expression. If you do this, you have already assumed that the given statement is true. You do not know that it is true until after you have verified it.

EXAMPLE 2   Changing to Sines and Cosines to Verify an Identity

Verify the identity: $\sin x \tan x + \cos x = \sec x.$

Solution   The left side is more complicated, so we start with it. Notice that the left side contains the sum of two terms, but the right side contains only one term. This means that somewhere during the verification process, the two terms on the left side must be added to form one term.

Let's begin by expressing the left side of the identity so that it contains only sines and cosines. Thus, we apply a quotient identity and replace $\tan x$ by $\dfrac{\sin x}{\cos x}$. Perhaps this strategy will enable us to transform the left side into $\sec x$, the expression on the right.

Study Tip

When proving identities, be sure to write the variable associated with each trigonometric function. Do not get lazy and write

$$\sin \tan + \cos$$

for

$$\sin x \tan x + \cos x$$

because sin, tan, and cos are meaningless without specified variables.

$$\sin x \tan x + \cos x = \sin x \left(\frac{\sin x}{\cos x} \right) + \cos x$$

Apply a quotient identity: $\tan x = \dfrac{\sin x}{\cos x}.$

$$= \frac{\sin^2 x}{\cos x} + \cos x.$$

Multiply.

$$= \frac{\sin^2 x}{\cos x} + \cos x \cdot \frac{\cos x}{\cos x}$$

The least common denominator is cos x. Write the second expression with a denominator of cos x.

$$= \frac{\sin^2 x}{\cos x} + \frac{\cos^2 x}{\cos x}$$

Multiply.

$$= \frac{\sin^2 x + \cos^2 x}{\cos x}$$

Add numerators and place this sum over the least common denominator.

$$= \frac{1}{\cos x}$$

Apply a Pythagorean identity: $\sin^2 x + \cos^2 x = 1.$

$$= \sec x$$

Apply a reciprocal identity: $\sec x = \dfrac{1}{\cos x}.$

By working with the left side and arriving at the right side, the identity is verified.

Check Point 2 Verify the identity: $\cos x \cot x + \sin x = \csc x.$

Some identities are verified using factoring to simplify a trigonometric expression.

EXAMPLE 3   Using Factoring to Verify an Identity

Verify the identity: $\cos x - \cos x \sin^2 x = \cos^3 x$.

Solution We start with the more complicated side, the left side. Factor out the greatest common factor, $\cos x$, from each of the two terms.

$$\cos x - \cos x \sin^2 x = \cos x(1 - \sin^2 x) \qquad \text{Factor cos x from the two terms.}$$

$$= \cos x \cdot \cos^2 x \qquad \text{Use a variation of sin}^2 \text{ x + cos}^2 \text{ x = 1.}$$
Solving for cos² x, we obtain
cos² x = 1 − sin² x.

$$= \cos^3 x \qquad \text{Multiply.}$$

We worked with the left side and arrived at the right side. Thus, the identity is verified.

Check Point 3 Verify the identity: $\sin x - \sin x \cos^2 x = \sin^3 x$.

There is often more than one technique that can be used to verify an identity.

EXAMPLE 4   Using Two Techniques to Verify an Identity

Verify the identity: $\dfrac{1 + \sin \theta}{\cos \theta} = \sec \theta + \tan \theta$.

Solution

Method 1.   Separating a Single-Term Quotient into Two Terms
Let's separate the quotient on the left side into two terms using

$$\frac{a + b}{c} = \frac{a}{c} + \frac{b}{c}.$$

Perhaps this strategy will enable us to transform the left side into $\sec \theta + \tan \theta$, the sum on the right.

$$\frac{1 + \sin \theta}{\cos \theta} = \frac{1}{\cos \theta} + \frac{\sin \theta}{\cos \theta} \qquad \text{Divide each term in the numerator by cos } \theta.$$

$$= \sec \theta + \tan \theta \qquad \text{Apply a reciprocal identity and a quotient identity:}$$
$$\sec \theta = \frac{1}{\cos \theta} \text{ and } \tan \theta = \frac{\sin \theta}{\cos \theta}.$$

We worked with the left side and arrived at the right side. Thus, the identity is verified.

Method 2.   Changing to Sines and Cosines
Let's work with the right side of the identity and express it so that it contains only sines and cosines.

$$\sec \theta + \tan \theta = \frac{1}{\cos \theta} + \frac{\sin \theta}{\cos \theta} \qquad \text{Apply a reciprocal identity and a quotient identity:}$$
$$\sec \theta = \frac{1}{\cos \theta} \text{ and } \tan \theta = \frac{\sin \theta}{\cos \theta}.$$

$$= \frac{1 + \sin \theta}{\cos \theta} \qquad \text{Add numerators. Put this sum over the common denominator.}$$

We worked with the right side and arrived at the left side. Thus, the identity is verified.

Check Point 4 Verify the identity: $\dfrac{1 + \cos \theta}{\sin \theta} = \csc \theta + \cot \theta$.

How do we verify identities in which sums or differences of fractions with trigonometric functions appear on one side? Use the least common denominator and combine the fractions. This technique is especially useful when the other side of the identity contains only one term.

EXAMPLE 5   Combining Fractional Expressions to Verify an Identity

Verify the identity: $\dfrac{\cos x}{1 + \sin x} + \dfrac{1 + \sin x}{\cos x} = 2 \sec x.$

Solution   We start with the more complicated side, the left side. The least common denominator of the fractions is $(1 + \sin x)(\cos x)$. We express each fraction in terms of this least common denominator by multiplying the numerator and denominator by the extra factor needed to form $(1 + \sin x)(\cos x)$.

<table>
<tr>
<td>

$\dfrac{\cos x}{1 + \sin x} + \dfrac{1 + \sin x}{\cos x}$

</td>
<td>

The least common denominator is $(1 + \sin x)(\cos x)$.

</td>
</tr>
<tr>
<td>

$= \dfrac{\cos x(\cos x)}{(1 + \sin x)(\cos x)} + \dfrac{(1 + \sin x)(1 + \sin x)}{(1 + \sin x)(\cos x)}$

</td>
<td>

Rewrite each fraction with the least common denominator.

</td>
</tr>
<tr>
<td>

$= \dfrac{\cos^2 x}{(1 + \sin x)(\cos x)} + \dfrac{1 + 2 \sin x + \sin^2 x}{(1 + \sin x)(\cos x)}$

</td>
<td>

Use the FOIL method to multiply $(1 + \sin x)(1 + \sin x)$.

</td>
</tr>
<tr>
<td>

$= \dfrac{\cos^2 x + 1 + 2 \sin x + \sin^2 x}{(1 + \sin x)(\cos x)}$

</td>
<td>

Add numerators. Put this sum over the least common denominator.

</td>
</tr>
<tr>
<td>

$= \dfrac{(\sin^2 x + \cos^2 x) + 1 + 2 \sin x}{(1 + \sin x)(\cos x)}$

</td>
<td>

Regroup terms to apply a Pythagorean identity.

</td>
</tr>
<tr>
<td>

$= \dfrac{1 + 1 + 2 \sin x}{(1 + \sin x)(\cos x)}$

</td>
<td>

Apply a Pythagorean identity: $\sin^2 x + \cos^2 x = 1.$

</td>
</tr>
<tr>
<td>

$= \dfrac{2 + 2 \sin x}{(1 + \sin x)(\cos x)}$

</td>
<td>

Add constant terms in the numerator: $1 + 1 = 2.$

</td>
</tr>
<tr>
<td>

$= \dfrac{2\,\cancel{(1 + \sin x)}}{\cancel{(1 + \sin x)}(\cos x)}$

</td>
<td>

Factor and simplify.

</td>
</tr>
<tr>
<td>

$= \dfrac{2}{\cos x}$

</td>
<td></td>
</tr>
<tr>
<td>

$= 2 \sec x$

</td>
<td>

Apply a reciprocal identity: $\sec x = \dfrac{1}{\cos x}.$

</td>
</tr>
</table>

We worked with the left side and arrived at the right side. Thus, the identity is verified.

Check Point 5   Verify the identity: $\dfrac{\sin x}{1 + \cos x} + \dfrac{1 + \cos x}{\sin x} = 2 \csc x.$

Some identities are verified using a technique that may remind you of rationalizing a denominator.

EXAMPLE 6   Multiplying the Numerator and Denominator by the Same Factor to Verify an Identity

Verify the identity: $\dfrac{\sin x}{1 + \cos x} = \dfrac{1 - \cos x}{\sin x}.$

Solution   The suggestions given in the previous examples do not apply here. Everything is already expressed in terms of sines and cosines. Furthermore, there are no fractions to combine and neither side looks more complicated than the other. Let's solve the puzzle by working with the left side and making it look like the expression on the right. The expression on the right contains $1 - \cos x$ in the numerator. This suggests multiplying the numerator and denominator of the left side by $1 - \cos x$. By doing this, we obtain a factor of $1 - \cos x$ in the numerator, as in the numerator on the right.

$$\frac{\sin x}{1 + \cos x} = \frac{\sin x}{1 + \cos x} \cdot \frac{1 - \cos x}{1 - \cos x} \qquad \text{Multiply numerator and denominator by } 1 - \cos x.$$

$$= \frac{\sin x(1 - \cos x)}{1 - \cos^2 x} \qquad \begin{array}{l}\text{Multiply. Use } (A + B)(A - B) = A^2 - B^2, \text{ with} \\ A = 1 \text{ and } B = \cos x, \text{ to multiply denominators.}\end{array}$$

$$= \frac{\sin x(1 - \cos x)}{\sin^2 x} \qquad \begin{array}{l}\text{Use a variation of } \sin^2 x + \cos^2 x = 1. \text{ Solving for} \\ \sin^2 x, \text{ we obtain } \sin^2 x = 1 - \cos^2 x.\end{array}$$

$$= \frac{1 - \cos x}{\sin x} \qquad \text{Simplify: } \frac{\sin x}{\sin^2 x} = \frac{\cancel{\sin x}}{\cancel{\sin x} \cdot \sin x} = \frac{1}{\sin x}.$$

We worked with the left side and arrived at the right side. Thus, the identity is verified.

Check Point 6   Verify the identity: $\dfrac{\cos x}{1 + \sin x} = \dfrac{1 - \sin x}{\cos x}$.

EXAMPLE 7   Changing to Sines and Cosines to Verify an Identity

Verify the identity: $\dfrac{\tan x - \sin(-x)}{1 + \cos x} = \tan x$.

Solution   We begin with the left side. Our goal is to obtain $\tan x$, the expression on the right.

$$\frac{\tan x - \sin(-x)}{1 + \cos x} = \frac{\tan x - (-\sin x)}{1 + \cos x} \qquad \begin{array}{l}\text{The sine function is odd:} \\ \sin(-x) = -\sin x.\end{array}$$

$$= \frac{\tan x + \sin x}{1 + \cos x} \qquad \text{Simplify.}$$

$$= \frac{\dfrac{\sin x}{\cos x} + \sin x}{1 + \cos x} \qquad \begin{array}{l}\text{Apply a quotient identity:} \\ \tan x = \dfrac{\sin x}{\cos x}.\end{array}$$

$$= \frac{\dfrac{\sin x}{\cos x} + \dfrac{\sin x \cos x}{\cos x}}{1 + \cos x} \qquad \begin{array}{l}\text{Express the terms in the} \\ \text{numerator with the least} \\ \text{common denominator, } \cos x.\end{array}$$

$$= \frac{\dfrac{\sin x + \sin x \cos x}{\cos x}}{1 + \cos x} \qquad \text{Add in the numerator.}$$

$$= \frac{\sin x + \sin x \cos x}{\cos x} \div \frac{1 + \cos x}{1} \qquad \begin{array}{l}\text{Rewrite the main fraction bar} \\ \text{as } \div.\end{array}$$

$$= \frac{\sin x + \sin x \cos x}{\cos x} \cdot \frac{1}{1 + \cos x} \qquad \text{Invert the divisor and multiply.}$$

$$= \frac{\sin x \cancel{(1 + \cos x)}^{1}}{\cos x} \cdot \frac{1}{\cancel{1 + \cos x}_{1}} \qquad \text{Factor and simplify.}$$

$$= \frac{\sin x}{\cos x} \qquad \begin{array}{l}\text{Multiply the remaining factors} \\ \text{in the numerator and in the} \\ \text{denominator.}\end{array}$$

$$= \tan x \qquad \text{Apply a quotient identity.}$$

The left side simplifies to $\tan x$, the right side. Thus, the identity is verified.

Discovery

Verify the identity in Example 6 by making the right side look like the left side. Start with the expression on the right. Multiply the numerator and denominator by $1 + \cos x$.

Discovery

Try simplifying

$$\frac{\dfrac{\sin x}{\cos x} + \sin x}{1 + \cos x}$$

by multiplying the two terms in the numerator and the two terms in the denominator by $\cos x$. This method for simplifying the complex fraction involves multiplying the numerator and the denominator by the least common denominator of all fractions in the expression. Do you prefer this simplification procedure over the method used on the right?

Check Point 7 Verify the identity: $\dfrac{\sec x + \csc(-x)}{\sec x \csc x} = \sin x - \cos x.$

Is every identity verified by working with only one side? No. You can sometimes work with each side separately and show that both sides are equal to the same trigonometric expression. This is illustrated in Example 8.

EXAMPLE 8 Working with Both Sides Separately to Verify an Identity

Verify the identity: $\dfrac{1}{1 + \cos \theta} + \dfrac{1}{1 - \cos \theta} = 2 + 2 \cot^2 \theta.$

Solution We begin by working with the left side.

$$\dfrac{1}{1 + \cos \theta} + \dfrac{1}{1 - \cos \theta}$$

The least common denominator is $(1 + \cos \theta)(1 - \cos \theta)$.

$$= \dfrac{1(1 - \cos \theta)}{(1 + \cos \theta)(1 - \cos \theta)} + \dfrac{1(1 + \cos \theta)}{(1 + \cos \theta)(1 - \cos \theta)}$$

Rewrite each fraction with the least common denominator.

$$= \dfrac{1 - \cos \theta + 1 + \cos \theta}{(1 + \cos \theta)(1 - \cos \theta)}$$

Add numerators. Put this sum over the least common denominator.

$$= \dfrac{2}{(1 + \cos \theta)(1 - \cos \theta)}$$

Simplify the numerator: $-\cos \theta + \cos \theta = 0$ and $1 + 1 = 2$.

$$= \dfrac{2}{1 - \cos^2 \theta}$$

Multiply the factors in the denominator.

Now we work with the right side. Our goal is to transform this side into the simplified form attained for the left side, $\dfrac{2}{1 - \cos^2 \theta}$.

$$2 + 2 \cot^2 \theta = 2 + 2 \left(\dfrac{\cos^2 \theta}{\sin^2 \theta} \right)$$

Use a quotient identity: $\cot \theta = \dfrac{\cos \theta}{\sin \theta}$.

$$= \dfrac{2 \sin^2 \theta}{\sin^2 \theta} + \dfrac{2 \cos^2 \theta}{\sin^2 \theta}$$

Rewrite each fraction with the least common denominator, $\sin^2 \theta$.

$$= \dfrac{2 \sin^2 \theta + 2 \cos^2 \theta}{\sin^2 \theta}$$

Add numerators. Put this sum over the least common denominator.

$$= \dfrac{2(\sin^2 \theta + \cos^2 \theta)}{\sin^2 \theta}$$

Factor out the greatest common factor, 2.

$$= \dfrac{2}{\sin^2 \theta}$$

Apply a Pythagorean identity: $\sin^2 \theta + \cos^2 \theta = 1$.

$$= \dfrac{2}{1 - \cos^2 \theta}$$

Use a variation of $\sin^2 \theta + \cos^2 \theta = 1$ and solve for $\sin^2 \theta$: $\sin^2 \theta = 1 - \cos^2 \theta$.

The identity is verified because both sides are equal to $\dfrac{2}{1 - \cos^2 \theta}$.

Check Point 8 Verify the identity: $\dfrac{1}{1 + \sin \theta} + \dfrac{1}{1 - \sin \theta} = 2 + 2 \tan^2 \theta.$

Guidelines for Verifying Trigonometric Identities

There is often more than one correct way to solve a puzzle, although one method may be shorter and more efficient than another. The same is true for verifying an identity. For example, how would you verify

$$\frac{\csc^2 x - 1}{\csc^2 x} = \cos^2 x?$$

One approach is to use a Pythagorean identity, $1 + \cot^2 x = \csc^2 x$, on the left side. Then change the resulting expression to sines and cosines.

$$\frac{\csc^2 x - 1}{\csc^2 x} = \frac{(1 + \cot^2 x) - 1}{\csc^2 x} = \frac{\cot^2 x}{\csc^2 x} = \frac{\dfrac{\cos^2 x}{\sin^2 x}}{\dfrac{1}{\sin^2 x}} = \frac{\cos^2 x}{\sin^2 x} \cdot \frac{\sin^2 x}{1} = \cos^2 x$$

Apply a Pythagorean identity: $1 + \cot^2 x = \csc^2 x$.

Use $\cot x = \dfrac{\cos x}{\sin x}$ and $\csc x = \dfrac{1}{\sin x}$ to change to sines and cosines.

Invert the divsor and multiply.

A more efficient strategy for verifying this identity may not be apparent at first glance. Work with the left side and divide each term in the numerator by the denominator, $\csc^2 x$.

$$\frac{\csc^2 x - 1}{\csc^2 x} = \frac{\csc^2 x}{\csc^2 x} - \frac{1}{\csc^2 x} = 1 - \sin^2 x = \cos^2 x$$

Apply a reciprocal identity: $\sin x = \dfrac{1}{\csc x}$.

Use $\sin^2 x + \cos^2 x = 1$ and solve for $\cos^2 x$.

With this strategy, we again obtain $\cos^2 x$, the expression on the right side, and it takes fewer steps than the first approach.

An even longer strategy, but one that works, is to replace each of the two occurrences of $\csc^2 x$ on the left side by $\dfrac{1}{\sin^2 x}$. This may be the approach that you first consider, particularly if you become accustomed to rewriting the more complicated side in terms of sines and cosines. The selection of an appropriate fundamental identity to solve the puzzle most efficiently is learned through lots of practice.

The more identities you prove, the more confident and efficient you will become. Although practice is the only way to learn how to verify identities, there are some guidelines developed throughout the section that should help you get started.

Guidelines for Verifying Trigonometric Identities

- Work with each side of the equation independently of the other side. Start with the more complicated side and transform it in a step-by-step fashion until it looks exactly like the other side.
- Analyze the identity and look for opportunities to apply the fundamental identities.
- Try using one or more of the following techniques:
  1. Rewrite the more complicated side in terms of sines and cosines.
  2. Factor out the greatest common factor.
  3. Separate a single-term quotient into two terms:
  $$\frac{a + b}{c} = \frac{a}{c} + \frac{b}{c} \quad \text{and} \quad \frac{a - b}{c} = \frac{a}{c} - \frac{b}{c}.$$
  4. Combine fractional expressions using the least common denominator.
  5. Multiply the numerator and the denominator by a binomial factor that appears on the other side of the identity.
- Don't be afraid to stop and start over again if you are not getting anywhere. Creative puzzle solvers know that strategies leading to dead ends often provide good problem-solving ideas.

EXERCISE SET 5.1

Practice Exercises

In Exercises 1–60, verify each identity.

1. $\sin x \sec x = \tan x$
2. $\cos x \csc x = \cot x$
3. $\tan(-x) \cos x = -\sin x$
4. $\cot(-x) \sin x = -\cos x$
5. $\tan x \csc x \cos x = 1$
6. $\cot x \sec x \sin x = 1$
7. $\sec x - \sec x \sin^2 x = \cos x$
8. $\csc x - \csc x \cos^2 x = \sin x$
9. $\cos^2 x - \sin^2 x = 1 - 2 \sin^2 x$
10. $\cos^2 x - \sin^2 x = 2 \cos^2 x - 1$
11. $\csc \theta - \sin \theta = \cot \theta \cos \theta$
12. $\tan \theta + \cot \theta = \sec \theta \csc \theta$
13. $\dfrac{\tan \theta \cot \theta}{\csc \theta} = \sin \theta$
14. $\dfrac{\cos \theta \sec \theta}{\cot \theta} = \tan \theta$
15. $\sin^2 \theta (1 + \cot^2 \theta) = 1$
16. $\cos^2 \theta (1 + \tan^2 \theta) = 1$
17. $\sin t \tan t = \dfrac{1 - \cos^2 t}{\cos t}$
18. $\cos t \cot t = \dfrac{1 - \sin^2 t}{\sin t}$
19. $\dfrac{\csc^2 t}{\cot t} = \csc t \sec t$
20. $\dfrac{\sec^2 t}{\tan t} = \sec t \csc t$
21. $\dfrac{\tan^2 t}{\sec t} = \sec t - \cos t$
22. $\dfrac{\cot^2 t}{\csc t} = \csc t - \sin t$
23. $\dfrac{1 - \cos \theta}{\sin \theta} = \csc \theta - \cot \theta$
24. $\dfrac{1 - \sin \theta}{\cos \theta} = \sec \theta - \tan \theta$
25. $\dfrac{\sin t}{\csc t} + \dfrac{\cos t}{\sec t} = 1$
26. $\dfrac{\sin t}{\tan t} + \dfrac{\cos t}{\cot t} = \sin t + \cos t$
27. $\tan t + \dfrac{\cos t}{1 + \sin t} = \sec t$
28. $\cot t + \dfrac{\sin t}{1 + \cos t} = \csc t$
29. $1 - \dfrac{\sin^2 x}{1 + \cos x} = \cos x$
30. $1 - \dfrac{\cos^2 x}{1 + \sin x} = \sin x$
31. $\dfrac{\cos x}{1 - \sin x} + \dfrac{1 - \sin x}{\cos x} = 2 \sec x$
32. $\dfrac{\sin x}{\cos x + 1} + \dfrac{\cos x - 1}{\sin x} = 0$
33. $\sec^2 x \csc^2 x = \sec^2 x + \csc^2 x$
34. $\csc^2 x \sec x = \sec x + \csc x \cot x$
35. $\dfrac{\sec x - \csc x}{\sec x + \csc x} = \dfrac{\tan x - 1}{\tan x + 1}$
36. $\dfrac{\csc x - \sec x}{\csc x + \sec x} = \dfrac{\cot x - 1}{\cot x + 1}$
37. $\dfrac{\sin^2 x - \cos^2 x}{\sin x + \cos x} = \sin x - \cos x$
38. $\dfrac{\tan^2 x - \cot^2 x}{\tan x + \cot x} = \tan x - \cot x$
39. $\tan^2 2x + \sin^2 2x + \cos^2 2x = \sec^2 2x$
40. $\cot^2 2x + \cos^2 2x + \sin^2 2x = \csc^2 2x$
41. $\dfrac{\tan 2\theta + \cot 2\theta}{\csc 2\theta} = \sec 2\theta$
42. $\dfrac{\tan 2\theta + \cot 2\theta}{\sec 2\theta} = \csc 2\theta$

43. $\dfrac{\tan x + \tan y}{1 - \tan x \tan y} = \dfrac{\sin x \cos y + \cos x \sin y}{\cos x \cos y - \sin x \sin y}$
44. $\dfrac{\cot x + \cot y}{1 - \cot x \cot y} = \dfrac{\cos x \sin y + \sin x \cos y}{\sin x \sin y - \cos x \cos y}$
45. $(\sec x - \tan x)^2 = \dfrac{1 - \sin x}{1 + \sin x}$
46. $(\csc x - \cot x)^2 = \dfrac{1 - \cos x}{1 + \cos x}$
47. $\dfrac{\sec t + 1}{\tan t} = \dfrac{\tan t}{\sec t - 1}$
48. $\dfrac{\csc t - 1}{\cot t} = \dfrac{\cot t}{\csc t + 1}$
49. $\dfrac{1 + \cos t}{1 - \cos t} = (\csc t + \cot t)^2$
50. $\dfrac{\cos^2 t + 4 \cos t + 4}{\cos t + 2} = \dfrac{2 \sec t + 1}{\sec t}$
51. $\cos^4 t - \sin^4 t = 1 - 2 \sin^2 t$
52. $\sin^4 t - \cos^4 t = 1 - 2 \cos^2 t$
53. $\dfrac{\sin \theta - \cos \theta}{\sin \theta} + \dfrac{\cos \theta - \sin \theta}{\cos \theta} = 2 - \sec \theta \csc \theta$
54. $\dfrac{\sin \theta}{1 - \cot \theta} - \dfrac{\cos \theta}{\tan \theta - 1} = \sin \theta + \cos \theta$
55. $(\tan^2 \theta + 1)(\cos^2 \theta + 1) = \tan^2 \theta + 2$
56. $(\cot^2 \theta + 1)(\sin^2 \theta + 1) = \cot^2 \theta + 2$
57. $(\cos \theta - \sin \theta)^2 + (\cos \theta + \sin \theta)^2 = 2$
58. $(3 \cos \theta - 4 \sin \theta)^2 + (4 \cos \theta + 3 \sin \theta)^2 = 25$
59. $\dfrac{\cos^2 x - \sin^2 x}{1 - \tan^2 x} = \cos^2 x$
60. $\dfrac{\sin x + \cos x}{\sin x} - \dfrac{\cos x - \sin x}{\cos x} = \sec x \csc x$

Practice Plus

In Exercises 61–66, half of an identity and the graph of this half are given. Use the graph to make a conjecture as to what the right side of the identity should be. Then prove your conjecture.

61. $\dfrac{(\sec x + \tan x)(\sec x - \tan x)}{\sec x} = ?$

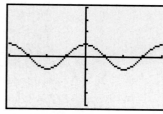

$[-2\pi, 2\pi, \frac{\pi}{2}]$ by $[-4, 4, 1]$

62. $\dfrac{\sec^2 x \csc x}{\sec^2 x + \csc^2 x} = ?$

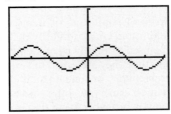

$[-2\pi, 2\pi, \frac{\pi}{2}]$ by $[-4, 4, 1]$

63. $\dfrac{\cos x + \cot x \sin x}{\cot x} = ?$

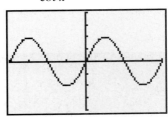

$[-2\pi, 2\pi, \frac{\pi}{2}]$ by $[-4, 4, 1]$

64. $\dfrac{\cos x \tan x - \tan x + 2 \cos x - 2}{\tan x + 2} = ?$

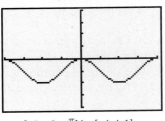

$[-2\pi, 2\pi, \frac{\pi}{2}]$ by $[-4, 4, 1]$

65. $\dfrac{1}{\sec x + \tan x} + \dfrac{1}{\sec x - \tan x} = ?$

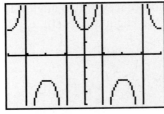

$[-2\pi, 2\pi, \frac{\pi}{2}]$ by $[-4, 4, 1]$

66. $\dfrac{1 + \cos x}{\sin x} + \dfrac{\sin x}{1 + \cos x} = ?$

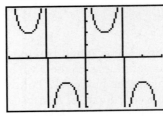

$[-2\pi, 2\pi, \frac{\pi}{2}]$ by $[-4, 4, 1]$

In Exercises 67–74, rewrite each expression in terms of the given function or functions.

67. $\dfrac{\tan x + \cot x}{\csc x}; \cos x$ **68.** $\dfrac{\sec x + \csc x}{1 + \tan x}; \sin x$

69. $\dfrac{\cos x}{1 + \sin x} + \tan x; \cos x$ **70.** $\dfrac{1}{\sin x \cos x} - \cot x; \cot x$

71. $\dfrac{1}{1 - \cos x} - \dfrac{\cos x}{1 + \cos x}; \csc x$

72. $(\sec x + \csc x)(\sin x + \cos x) - 2 - \cot x; \tan x$

73. $\dfrac{1}{\csc x - \sin x}; \sec x$ and $\tan x$

74. $\dfrac{1 - \sin x}{1 + \sin x} - \dfrac{1 + \sin x}{1 - \sin x}; \sec x$ and $\tan x$

Writing in Mathematics

75. Explain how to verify an identity.

76. Describe two strategies that can be used to verify identities.

77. Describe how you feel when you successfully verify a difficult identity. What other activities do you engage in that evoke the same feelings?

78. A 10-point question on a quiz asks students to verify the identity

$$\frac{\sin^2 x - \cos^2 x}{\sin x + \cos x} = \sin x - \cos x.$$

One student begins with the left side and obtains the right side as follows:

$$\frac{\sin^2 x - \cos^2 x}{\sin x + \cos x} = \frac{\sin^2 x}{\sin x} - \frac{\cos^2 x}{\cos x} = \sin x - \cos x.$$

How many points (out of 10) would you give this student? Explain your answer.

Technology Exercises

In Exercises 79–87, graph each side of the equation in the same viewing rectangle. If the graphs appear to coincide, verify that the equation is an identity. If the graphs do not appear to coincide, this indicates the equation is not an identity. In these exercises, find a value of x for which both sides are defined but not equal.

79. $\tan x = \sec x(\sin x - \cos x) + 1$

80. $\sin x = -\cos x \tan(-x)$

81. $\sin\left(x + \dfrac{\pi}{4}\right) = \sin x + \sin\dfrac{\pi}{4}$

82. $\cos\left(x + \dfrac{\pi}{4}\right) = \cos x + \cos\dfrac{\pi}{4}$

83. $\cos(x + \pi) = \cos x$

84. $\sin(x + \pi) = \sin x$

85. $\dfrac{\sin x}{1 - \cos^2 x} = \csc x$

86. $\sin x - \sin x \cos^2 x = \sin^3 x$

87. $\sqrt{\sin^2 x + \cos^2 x} = \sin x + \cos x$

Critical Thinking Exercises

In Exercises 88–91, verify each identity.

88. $\dfrac{\sin^3 x - \cos^3 x}{\sin x - \cos x} = 1 + \sin x \cos x$

89. $\dfrac{\sin x - \cos x + 1}{\sin x + \cos x - 1} = \dfrac{\sin x + 1}{\cos x}$

90. $\ln|\sec x| = -\ln|\cos x|$ **91.** $\ln e^{\tan^2 x - \sec^2 x} = -1$

92. Use one of the fundamental identities in the box on page 570 to create an original identity.

Group Exercise

93. Group members are to write a helpful list of items for a pamphlet called "The Underground Guide to Verifying Identities." The pamphlet will be used primarily by students who sit, stare, and freak out every time they are asked to verify an identity. List easy ways to remember the fundamental identities. What helpful guidelines can you offer from the perspective of a student that you probably won't find in math books? If you have your own strategies that work particularly well, include them in the pamphlet.

SECTION 5.2 *Sum and Difference Formulas*

Objectives

1 Use the formula for the cosine of the difference of two angles.

2 Use sum and difference formulas for cosines and sines.

3 Use sum and difference formulas for tangents.

Listen to the same note played on a piano and a violin. The notes have a different quality or "tone." Tone depends on the way an instrument vibrates. However, the less than 1% of the population with amusia, or true tone deafness, cannot tell the two sounds apart. Even simple, familiar tunes such as *Happy Birthday* and *Jingle Bells* are mystifying to amusics.

When a note is played, it vibrates at a specific fundamental frequency and has a particular amplitude. Amusics cannot tell the difference between two sounds from tuning forks modeled by $p = 3 \sin 2t$ and $p = 2 \sin(2t + \pi)$, respectively. However, they can recognize the difference between the two equations. Notice that the second equation contains the sine of the sum of two angles. In this section, we will be developing identities involving the sums or differences of two angles. These formulas are called the **sum and difference formulas**. We begin with $\cos(\alpha - \beta)$, the cosine of the difference of two angles.

The Cosine of the Difference of Two Angles

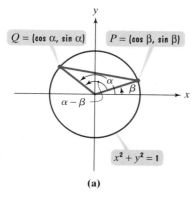

The Cosine of the Difference of Two Angles

$$\cos(\alpha - \beta) = \cos \alpha \cos \beta + \sin \alpha \sin \beta$$

The cosine of the difference of two angles equals the cosine of the first angle times the cosine of the second angle plus the sine of the first angle times the sine of the second angle.

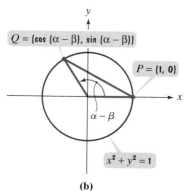

Figure 5.1 Using the unit circle and QP to develop a formula for $\cos(\alpha - \beta)$

We use Figure 5.1 to prove the identity in the box. The graph in Figure 5.1(a) shows a unit circle, $x^2 + y^2 = 1$. The figure uses the definitions of the cosine and sine functions as the x- and y-coordinates of points along the unit circle. For example, point P corresponds to angle β. By definition, the x-coordinate of P is $\cos \beta$ and the y-coordinate is $\sin \beta$. Similarly, point Q corresponds to angle α. By definition, the x-coordinate of Q is $\cos \alpha$ and the y-coordinate is $\sin \alpha$.

Note that if we draw a line segment between points P and Q, a triangle is formed. Angle $\alpha - \beta$ is one of the angles of this triangle. What happens if we rotate this triangle so that point P falls on the x-axis at $(1, 0)$? The result is shown in Figure 5.1(b). This rotation changes the coordinates of points P and Q. However, it has no effect on the length of line segment PQ.

We can use the distance formula, $d = \sqrt{(x_2 - x_1)^2 + (y_2 - y_1)^2}$, to find an expression for PQ in Figure 5.1(a) and in Figure 5.1(b). By equating the two expressions for PQ, we will obtain the identity for the cosine of the difference of two angles, $\alpha - \beta$. We first apply the distance formula in Figure 5.1(a).

$$PQ = \sqrt{(\cos \alpha - \cos \beta)^2 + (\sin \alpha - \sin \beta)^2}$$

Apply the distance formula, $d = \sqrt{(x_2 - x_1)^2 + (y_2 - y_1)^2}$, to find the distance between $(\cos \beta, \sin \beta)$ and $(\cos \alpha, \sin \alpha)$.

$$= \sqrt{\cos^2 \alpha - 2\cos \alpha \cos \beta + \cos^2 \beta + \sin^2 \alpha - 2\sin \alpha \sin \beta + \sin^2 \beta}$$

Square each expression using $(A - B)^2 = A^2 - 2AB + B^2$.

$$= \sqrt{(\sin^2 \alpha + \cos^2 \alpha) + (\sin^2 \beta + \cos^2 \beta) - 2\cos \alpha \cos \beta - 2\sin \alpha \sin \beta}$$

Regroup terms to apply a Pythagorean identity.

$$= \sqrt{1 + 1 - 2\cos \alpha \cos \beta - 2\sin \alpha \sin \beta}$$

Because $\sin^2 x + \cos^2 x = 1$, each expression in parentheses equals 1.

$$= \sqrt{2 - 2\cos \alpha \cos \beta - 2\sin \alpha \sin \beta}$$

Simplify.

Next, we apply the distance formula in Figure 5.1(b) to obtain a second expression for PQ. We let $(x_1, y_1) = (1, 0)$ and $(x_2, y_2) = (\cos(\alpha - \beta), \sin(\alpha - \beta))$.

$$PQ = \sqrt{[\cos(\alpha - \beta) - 1]^2 + [\sin(\alpha - \beta) - 0]^2}$$

Apply the distance formula to find the distance between $(1, 0)$ and $(\cos(\alpha - \beta), \sin(\alpha - \beta))$.

$$= \sqrt{\cos^2(\alpha - \beta) - 2\cos(\alpha - \beta) + 1 + \sin^2(\alpha - \beta)}$$

Square each expression.

$$= \sqrt{\cos^2(\alpha - \beta) - 2\cos(\alpha - \beta) + 1 + \sin^2(\alpha - \beta)}$$

Using a Pythagorean identity, $\sin^2(\alpha - \beta) + \cos^2(\alpha - \beta) = 1$.

$$= \sqrt{1 - 2\cos(\alpha - \beta) + 1}$$

Use a Pythagorean identity.

$$= \sqrt{2 - 2\cos(\alpha - \beta)}$$

Simplify.

Now we equate the two expressions for PQ.

$$\sqrt{2 - 2\cos(\alpha - \beta)} = \sqrt{2 - 2\cos \alpha \cos \beta - 2\sin \alpha \sin \beta}$$

The rotation does not change the length of PQ.

$$2 - 2\cos(\alpha - \beta) = 2 - 2\cos \alpha \cos \beta - 2\sin \alpha \sin \beta$$

Square both sides to eliminate radicals.

$$-2\cos(\alpha - \beta) = -2\cos \alpha \cos \beta - 2\sin \alpha \sin \beta$$

Subtract 2 from both sides of the equation.

$$\cos(\alpha - \beta) = \cos \alpha \cos \beta + \sin \alpha \sin \beta$$

Divide both sides of the equation by -2.

This proves the identity for the cosine of the difference of two angles.

Now that we see where the identity for the cosine of the difference of two angles comes from, let's look at some applications of this result.

① Use the formula for the cosine of the difference of two angles.

Sound Quality and Amusia

People with true tone deafness cannot hear the difference among tones produced by a tuning fork, a flute, an oboe, and a violin. They cannot dance or tell the difference between harmony and dissonance. People with amusia appear to have been born without the wiring necessary to process music. Intriguingly, they show no overt signs of brain damage and their brain scans appear normal. Thus, they can visually recognize the difference among sound waves that produce varying sound qualities.

Varying Sound Qualities

- Tuning fork: Sound waves are rounded and regular, giving a pure and gentle tone.

- Flute: Sound waves are smooth and give a fluid tone.

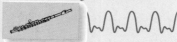

- Oboe: Rapid wave changes give a richer tone.

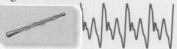

- Violin: Jagged waves give a brighter harsher tone.

EXAMPLE 1   Using the Difference Formula for Cosines to Find Exact Values

Find the exact value of cos 15°.

Solution   We know exact values for trigonometric functions of 60° and 45°. Thus, we write 15° as 60° − 45° and use the difference formula for cosines.

$$\cos 15° = \cos(60° - 45°)$$

$$= \cos 60° \cos 45° + \sin 60° \sin 45°$$ $\cos(\alpha - \beta) = \cos\alpha\cos\beta + \sin\alpha\sin\beta$
Substitute exact values from memory or use special right triangles.

$$= \frac{1}{2} \cdot \frac{\sqrt{2}}{2} + \frac{\sqrt{3}}{2} \cdot \frac{\sqrt{2}}{2}$$

$$= \frac{\sqrt{2}}{4} + \frac{\sqrt{6}}{4}$$ Multiply.

$$= \frac{\sqrt{2} + \sqrt{6}}{4}$$ Add.

Check Point 1   We know that $\cos 30° = \dfrac{\sqrt{3}}{2}$. Obtain this exact value using $\cos 30° = \cos(90° - 60°)$ and the difference formula for cosines.

EXAMPLE 2   Using the Difference Formula for Cosines to Find Exact Values

Find the exact value of $\cos 80° \cos 20° + \sin 80° \sin 20°$.

Solution   The given expression is the right side of the formula for $\cos(\alpha - \beta)$ with $\alpha = 80°$ and $\beta = 20°$.

$$\cos(\alpha - \beta) = \cos\alpha\cos\beta + \sin\alpha\sin\beta$$

$$\cos 80° \cos 20° + \sin 80° \sin 20° = \cos(80° - 20°) = \cos 60° = \frac{1}{2}$$

Check Point 2   Find the exact value of

$$\cos 70° \cos 40° + \sin 70° \sin 40°.$$

EXAMPLE 3   Verifying an Identity

Verify the identity: $\dfrac{\cos(\alpha - \beta)}{\sin\alpha\cos\beta} = \cot\alpha + \tan\beta$.

Solution   We work with the left side.

$$\frac{\cos(\alpha - \beta)}{\sin\alpha\cos\beta} = \frac{\cos\alpha\cos\beta + \sin\alpha\sin\beta}{\sin\alpha\cos\beta}$$ Use the formula for $\cos(\alpha - \beta)$.

$$= \frac{\cos\alpha\cos\beta}{\sin\alpha\cos\beta} + \frac{\sin\alpha\sin\beta}{\sin\alpha\cos\beta}$$ Divide each term in the numerator by $\sin\alpha\cos\beta$.

$$= \frac{\cos\alpha}{\sin\alpha} \cdot \frac{\cos\beta}{\cos\beta} + \frac{\sin\alpha}{\sin\alpha} \cdot \frac{\sin\beta}{\cos\beta}$$ This step can be done mentally. We wanted you to see the substitutions that follow.

$$= \cot\alpha \cdot 1 + 1 \cdot \tan\beta$$ Use quotient identities.

$$= \cot\alpha + \tan\beta$$ Simplify.

We worked with the left side and arrived at the right side. Thus, the identity is verified.

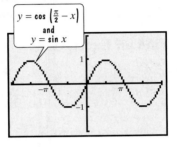
Check Point 3 Verify the identity: $\dfrac{\cos(\alpha - \beta)}{\cos \alpha \cos \beta} = 1 + \tan \alpha \tan \beta$.

The difference formula for cosines is used to establish other identities. For example, in our work with right triangles, we noted that cofunctions of complements are equal. Thus, because $\dfrac{\pi}{2} - \theta$ and θ are complements,

$$\cos\left(\frac{\pi}{2} - \theta\right) = \sin \theta.$$

We can use the formula for $\cos(\alpha - \beta)$ to prove this cofunction identity for all angles.

> Apply $\cos(\alpha - \beta)$ with $\alpha = \frac{\pi}{2}$ and $\theta = \beta$.
> $\cos(\alpha - \beta) = \cos \alpha \cos \beta + \sin \alpha \sin \beta$

$$\cos\left(\frac{\pi}{2} - \theta\right) = \cos\frac{\pi}{2} \cos \theta + \sin\frac{\pi}{2} \sin \theta$$
$$= 0 \cdot \cos \theta + 1 \cdot \sin \theta$$
$$= \sin \theta$$

Sum and Difference Formulas for Cosines and Sines

 Use sum and difference formulas for cosines and sines.

Our formula for $\cos(\alpha - \beta)$ can be used to verify an identity for a sum involving cosines, as well as identities for a sum and a difference for sines.

> ### Sum and Difference Formulas for Cosines and Sines
>
> **1.** $\cos(\alpha + \beta) = \cos \alpha \cos \beta - \sin \alpha \sin \beta$
> **2.** $\cos(\alpha - \beta) = \cos \alpha \cos \beta + \sin \alpha \sin \beta$
> **3.** $\sin(\alpha + \beta) = \sin \alpha \cos \beta + \cos \alpha \sin \beta$
> **4.** $\sin(\alpha - \beta) = \sin \alpha \cos \beta - \cos \alpha \sin \beta$

Up to now, we have concentrated on the second formula in the box. The first identity gives a formula for the cosine of the sum of two angles. It is proved as follows:

$$\cos(\alpha + \beta) = \cos[\alpha - (-\beta)]$$ Express addition as subtraction of an additive inverse.

$$= \cos \alpha \cos(-\beta) + \sin \alpha \sin(-\beta)$$ Use the difference formula for cosines.

$$= \cos \alpha \cos \beta + \sin \alpha(-\sin \beta)$$ Cosine is even: $\cos(-\beta) = \cos \beta$. Sine is odd: $\sin(-\beta) = -\sin \beta$.

$$= \cos \alpha \cos \beta - \sin \alpha \sin \beta.$$ Simplify.

Thus, the cosine of the sum of two angles equals the cosine of the first angle times the cosine of the second angle minus the sine of the first angle times the sine of the second angle.

The third identity in the box gives a formula for $\sin(\alpha + \beta)$, the sine of the sum of two angles. It is proved as follows:

$$\sin(\alpha + \beta) = \cos\left[\frac{\pi}{2} - (\alpha + \beta)\right]$$

Use a cofunction identity:
$\sin\theta = \cos\left(\frac{\pi}{2} - \theta\right)$.

$$= \cos\left[\left(\frac{\pi}{2} - \alpha\right) - \beta\right]$$

Regroup.

$$= \cos\left(\frac{\pi}{2} - \alpha\right)\cos\beta + \sin\left(\frac{\pi}{2} - \alpha\right)\sin\beta$$

Use the difference formula for cosines.

$$= \sin\alpha\cos\beta + \cos\alpha\sin\beta.$$

Use cofunction identities.

Thus, the sine of the sum of two angles equals the sine of the first angle times the cosine of the second angle plus the cosine of the first angle times the sine of the second angle.

The final identity in the box, $\sin(\alpha - \beta) = \sin\alpha\cos\beta - \cos\alpha\sin\beta$, gives a formula for $\sin(\alpha - \beta)$, the sine of the difference of two angles. It is proved by writing $\sin(\alpha - \beta)$ as $\sin[\alpha + (-\beta)]$ and then using the formula for the sine of a sum.

EXAMPLE 4   Using the Sine of a Sum to Find an Exact Value

Find the exact value of $\sin\dfrac{7\pi}{12}$ using the fact that $\dfrac{7\pi}{12} = \dfrac{\pi}{3} + \dfrac{\pi}{4}$.

Solution   We apply the formula for the sine of a sum.

$$\sin\frac{7\pi}{12} = \sin\left(\frac{\pi}{3} + \frac{\pi}{4}\right)$$

$$= \sin\frac{\pi}{3}\cos\frac{\pi}{4} + \cos\frac{\pi}{3}\sin\frac{\pi}{4} \qquad \sin(\alpha + \beta) = \sin\alpha\cos\beta + \cos\alpha\sin\beta$$

$$= \frac{\sqrt{3}}{2}\cdot\frac{\sqrt{2}}{2} + \frac{1}{2}\cdot\frac{\sqrt{2}}{2} \qquad \text{Substitute exact values.}$$

$$= \frac{\sqrt{6} + \sqrt{2}}{4} \qquad \text{Simplify.}$$

Check Point 4   Find the exact value of $\sin\dfrac{5\pi}{12}$ using the fact that

$$\frac{5\pi}{12} = \frac{\pi}{6} + \frac{\pi}{4}.$$

EXAMPLE 5   Finding Exact Values

Suppose that $\sin\alpha = \frac{12}{13}$ for a quadrant II angle α and $\sin\beta = \frac{3}{5}$ for a quadrant I angle β. Find the exact value of each of the following:

a. $\cos\alpha$ **b.** $\cos\beta$ **c.** $\cos(\alpha + \beta)$ **d.** $\sin(\alpha + \beta)$.

Solution

a. We find $\cos\alpha$ using a sketch that illustrates

$$\sin\alpha = \frac{12}{13} = \frac{y}{r}.$$

Figure 5.2 shows a quadrant II angle α with $\sin\alpha = \frac{12}{13}$. We find x using $x^2 + y^2 = r^2$. Because α lies in quadrant II, x is negative.

$$x^2 + 12^2 = 13^2 \qquad x^2 + y^2 = r^2$$

$$x^2 + 144 = 169 \qquad \text{Square 12 and 13, respectively.}$$

$$x^2 = 25 \qquad \text{Subtract 144 from both sides.}$$

$$x = -\sqrt{25} = -5 \qquad \text{If } x^2 = 25, \text{ then } x = \pm\sqrt{25} = \pm 5.$$

Choose $x = -\sqrt{25}$ because in quadrant II, x is negative.

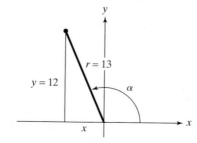

Figure 5.2 $\sin\alpha = \frac{12}{13}$: α lies in quadrant II.

Thus,

$$\cos \alpha = \frac{x}{r} = \frac{-5}{13} = -\frac{5}{13}.$$

b. We find $\cos \beta$ using a sketch that illustrates

$$\sin \beta = \frac{3}{5} = \frac{y}{r}.$$

Figure 5.3 shows a quadrant I angle β with $\sin \beta = \frac{3}{5}$. We find x using $x^2 + y^2 = r^2$.

$x^2 + 3^2 = 5^2$	$x^2 + y^2 = r^2$
$x^2 + 9 = 25$	Square 3 and 5, respectively.
$x^2 = 16$	Subtract 9 from both sides.
$x = \sqrt{16} = 4$	If $x^2 = 16$, then $x = \pm\sqrt{16} = \pm 4$. Choose $x = \sqrt{16}$ because in quadrant I, x is positive.

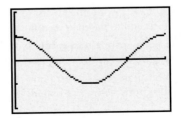

Figure 5.3 $\sin \beta = \frac{3}{5}$: β lies in quadrant I.

Thus,

$$\cos \beta = \frac{x}{r} = \frac{4}{5}.$$

We use the given values and the exact values that we determined to find exact values for $\cos(\alpha + \beta)$ and $\sin(\alpha + \beta)$.

These values are given.

These are the values we found.

$$\sin \alpha = \frac{12}{13}, \ \sin \beta = \frac{3}{5} \qquad \cos \alpha = -\frac{5}{13}, \ \cos \beta = \frac{4}{5}$$

c. We use the formula for the cosine of a sum.

$$\cos(\alpha + \beta) = \cos \alpha \cos \beta - \sin \alpha \sin \beta$$
$$= \left(-\frac{5}{13}\right)\left(\frac{4}{5}\right) - \frac{12}{13}\left(\frac{3}{5}\right) = -\frac{56}{65}$$

d. We use the formula for the sine of a sum.

$$\sin(\alpha + \beta) = \sin \alpha \cos \beta + \cos \alpha \sin \beta$$
$$= \frac{12}{13} \cdot \frac{4}{5} + \left(-\frac{5}{13}\right) \cdot \frac{3}{5} = \frac{33}{65}$$

Check Point 5 Suppose that $\sin \alpha = \frac{4}{5}$ for a quadrant II angle α and $\sin \beta = \frac{1}{2}$ for a quadrant I angle β. Find the exact value of each of the following:

a. $\cos \alpha$ **b.** $\cos \beta$ **c.** $\cos(\alpha + \beta)$ **d.** $\sin(\alpha + \beta)$.

EXAMPLE 6   Verifying Observations on a Graphing Utility

Figure 5.4 shows the graph of $y = \sin\left(x - \frac{3\pi}{2}\right)$ in a $\left[0, 2\pi, \frac{\pi}{2}\right]$ by $[-2, 2, 1]$ viewing rectangle.

a. Describe the graph using another equation.

b. Verify that the two equations are equivalent.

Figure 5.4 The graph of $y = \sin\left(x - \frac{3\pi}{2}\right)$ in a $\left[0, 2\pi, \frac{\pi}{2}\right]$ by $[-2, 2, 1]$ viewing rectangle

Solution

a. The graph appears to be the cosine curve $y = \cos x$. It cycles through maximum, intercept, minimum, intercept, and back to maximum. Thus, $y = \cos x$ also describes the graph.

b. We must show that

$$\sin\left(x - \frac{3\pi}{2}\right) = \cos x.$$

We apply the formula for the sine of a difference on the left side.

$$\sin\left(x - \frac{3\pi}{2}\right) = \sin x \cos\frac{3\pi}{2} - \cos x \sin\frac{3\pi}{2} \qquad \begin{array}{l} \sin(\alpha - \beta) = \\ \sin \alpha \cos \beta - \cos \alpha \sin \beta \end{array}$$

$$= \sin x \cdot 0 - \cos x(-1) \qquad \cos\frac{3\pi}{2} = 0 \text{ and } \sin\frac{3\pi}{2} = -1$$

$$= \cos x \qquad \text{Simplify.}$$

This verifies our observation that $y = \sin\left(x - \frac{3\pi}{2}\right)$ and $y = \cos x$ describe the same graph.

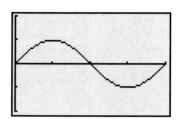

Figure 5.5

Check Point 6 Figure 5.5 shows the graph of $y = \cos\left(x + \frac{3\pi}{2}\right)$ in a $\left[0, 2\pi, \frac{\pi}{2}\right]$ by $[-2, 2, 1]$ viewing rectangle.

    a. Describe the graph using another equation.

    b. Verify that the two equations are equivalent.

③ Use sum and difference formulas for tangents.

Sum and Difference Formulas for Tangents

By writing $\tan(\alpha + \beta)$ as the quotient of $\sin(\alpha + \beta)$ and $\cos(\alpha + \beta)$, we can develop a formula for the tangent of a sum. Writing subtraction as addition of an inverse leads to a formula for the tangent of a difference.

Discovery

Derive the sum and difference formulas for tangents by working Exercises 55 and 56 in Exercise Set 5.2.

> **Sum and Difference Formulas for Tangents**
>
> $$\tan(\alpha + \beta) = \frac{\tan \alpha + \tan \beta}{1 - \tan \alpha \tan \beta}$$
>
> The tangent of the sum of two angles equals the tangent of the first angle plus the tangent of the second angle divided by 1 minus their product.
>
> $$\tan(\alpha - \beta) = \frac{\tan \alpha - \tan \beta}{1 + \tan \alpha \tan \beta}$$
>
> The tangent of the difference of two angles equals the tangent of the first angle minus the tangent of the second angle divided by 1 plus their product.

EXAMPLE 7   Verifying an Identity

Verify the identity: $\tan\left(x - \frac{\pi}{4}\right) = \frac{\tan x - 1}{\tan x + 1}$.

Solution   We work with the left side.

$$\tan\left(x - \frac{\pi}{4}\right) = \frac{\tan x - \tan\frac{\pi}{4}}{1 + \tan x \tan\frac{\pi}{4}} \qquad \tan(\alpha - \beta) = \frac{\tan \alpha - \tan \beta}{1 + \tan \alpha \tan \beta}$$

$$= \frac{\tan x - 1}{1 + \tan x \cdot 1} \qquad \tan\frac{\pi}{4} = 1$$

$$= \frac{\tan x - 1}{\tan x + 1}$$

Check Point 7 Verify the identity: $\tan(x + \pi) = \tan x$.

EXERCISE SET 5.2

 Practice Exercises

Use the formula for the cosine of the difference of two angles to solve Exercises 1–12.

In Exercises 1–4, find the exact value of each expression.

1. $\cos(45° - 30°)$

2. $\cos(120° - 45°)$

3. $\cos\left(\dfrac{3\pi}{4} - \dfrac{\pi}{6}\right)$

4. $\cos\left(\dfrac{2\pi}{3} - \dfrac{\pi}{6}\right)$

In Exercises 5–8, each expression is the right side of the formula for $\cos(\alpha - \beta)$ with particular values for α and β.

  a. *Identify α and β in each expression.*

  b. *Write the expression as the cosine of an angle.*

  c. *Find the exact value of the expression.*

5. $\cos 50° \cos 20° + \sin 50° \sin 20°$

6. $\cos 50° \cos 5° + \sin 50° \sin 5°$

7. $\cos\dfrac{5\pi}{12}\cos\dfrac{\pi}{12} + \sin\dfrac{5\pi}{12}\sin\dfrac{\pi}{12}$ **8.** $\cos\dfrac{5\pi}{18}\cos\dfrac{\pi}{9} + \sin\dfrac{5\pi}{18}\sin\dfrac{\pi}{9}$

In Exercises 9–12, verify each identity.

9. $\dfrac{\cos(\alpha - \beta)}{\cos \alpha \sin \beta} = \tan \alpha + \cot \beta$

10. $\dfrac{\cos(\alpha - \beta)}{\sin \alpha \sin \beta} = \cot \alpha \cot \beta + 1$

11. $\cos\left(x - \dfrac{\pi}{4}\right) = \dfrac{\sqrt{2}}{2}(\cos x + \sin x)$

12. $\cos\left(x - \dfrac{5\pi}{4}\right) = -\dfrac{\sqrt{2}}{2}(\cos x + \sin x)$

Use one or more of the six sum and difference identities to solve Exercises 13–54.

In Exercises 13–24, find the exact value of each expression.

13. $\sin(45° - 30°)$

14. $\sin(60° - 45°)$

15. $\sin 105°$

16. $\sin 75°$

17. $\cos(135° + 30°)$

18. $\cos(240° + 45°)$

19. $\cos 75°$

20. $\cos 105°$

21. $\tan\left(\dfrac{\pi}{6} + \dfrac{\pi}{4}\right)$

22. $\tan\left(\dfrac{\pi}{3} + \dfrac{\pi}{4}\right)$

23. $\tan\left(\dfrac{4\pi}{3} - \dfrac{\pi}{4}\right)$

24. $\tan\left(\dfrac{5\pi}{3} - \dfrac{\pi}{4}\right)$

In Exercises 25–32, write each expression as the sine, cosine, or tangent of an angle. Then find the exact value of the expression.

25. $\sin 25° \cos 5° + \cos 25° \sin 5°$

26. $\sin 40° \cos 20° + \cos 40° \sin 20°$

27. $\dfrac{\tan 10° + \tan 35°}{1 - \tan 10° \tan 35°}$

28. $\dfrac{\tan 50° - \tan 20°}{1 + \tan 50° \tan 20°}$

29. $\sin\dfrac{5\pi}{12}\cos\dfrac{\pi}{4} - \cos\dfrac{5\pi}{12}\sin\dfrac{\pi}{4}$ **30.** $\sin\dfrac{7\pi}{12}\cos\dfrac{\pi}{12} - \cos\dfrac{7\pi}{12}\sin\dfrac{\pi}{12}$

31. $\dfrac{\tan\dfrac{\pi}{5} - \tan\dfrac{\pi}{30}}{1 + \tan\dfrac{\pi}{5}\tan\dfrac{\pi}{30}}$ **32.** $\dfrac{\tan\dfrac{\pi}{5} + \tan\dfrac{4\pi}{5}}{1 - \tan\dfrac{\pi}{5}\tan\dfrac{4\pi}{5}}$

In Exercises 33–54, verify each identity.

33. $\sin\left(x + \dfrac{\pi}{2}\right) = \cos x$ **34.** $\sin\left(x + \dfrac{3\pi}{2}\right) = -\cos x$

35. $\cos\left(x - \dfrac{\pi}{2}\right) = \sin x$ **36.** $\cos(\pi - x) = -\cos x$

37. $\tan(2\pi - x) = -\tan x$ **38.** $\tan(\pi - x) = -\tan x$

39. $\sin(\alpha + \beta) + \sin(\alpha - \beta) = 2 \sin \alpha \cos \beta$

40. $\cos(\alpha + \beta) + \cos(\alpha - \beta) = 2 \cos \alpha \cos \beta$

41. $\dfrac{\sin(\alpha - \beta)}{\cos \alpha \cos \beta} = \tan \alpha - \tan \beta$

42. $\dfrac{\sin(\alpha + \beta)}{\cos \alpha \cos \beta} = \tan \alpha + \tan \beta$

43. $\tan\left(\theta + \dfrac{\pi}{4}\right) = \dfrac{\cos \theta + \sin \theta}{\cos \theta - \sin \theta}$

44. $\tan\left(\dfrac{\pi}{4} - \theta\right) = \dfrac{\cos \theta - \sin \theta}{\cos \theta + \sin \theta}$

45. $\cos(\alpha + \beta) \cos(\alpha - \beta) = \cos^2 \beta - \sin^2 \alpha$

46. $\sin(\alpha + \beta) \sin(\alpha - \beta) = \cos^2 \beta - \cos^2 \alpha$

47. $\dfrac{\sin(\alpha + \beta)}{\sin(\alpha - \beta)} = \dfrac{\tan \alpha + \tan \beta}{\tan \alpha - \tan \beta}$

48. $\dfrac{\cos(\alpha + \beta)}{\cos(\alpha - \beta)} = \dfrac{1 - \tan \alpha \tan \beta}{1 + \tan \alpha \tan \beta}$

49. $\dfrac{\cos(x + h) - \cos x}{h} = \cos x \dfrac{\cos h - 1}{h} - \sin x \dfrac{\sin h}{h}$

50. $\dfrac{\sin(x + h) - \sin x}{h} = \cos x \dfrac{\sin h}{h} + \sin x \dfrac{\cos h - 1}{h}$

51. $\sin 2\alpha = 2 \sin \alpha \cos \alpha$

   Hint: Write $\sin 2\alpha$ as $\sin(\alpha + \alpha)$.

52. $\cos 2\alpha = \cos^2 \alpha - \sin^2 \alpha$

   Hint: Write $\cos 2\alpha$ as $\cos(\alpha + \alpha)$.

53. $\tan 2\alpha = \dfrac{2 \tan \alpha}{1 - \tan^2 \alpha}$

   Hint: Write $\tan 2\alpha$ as $\tan(\alpha + \alpha)$.

54. $\tan\left(\dfrac{\pi}{4} + \alpha\right) - \tan\left(\dfrac{\pi}{4} - \alpha\right) = 2 \tan 2\alpha$

   Hint: Use the result in Exercise 53.

55. Derive the identity for $\tan(\alpha + \beta)$ using

$$\tan(\alpha + \beta) = \frac{\sin(\alpha + \beta)}{\cos(\alpha + \beta)}.$$

After applying the formulas for sums of sines and cosines, divide the numerator and denominator by $\cos \alpha \cos \beta$.

56. Derive the identity for $\tan(\alpha - \beta)$ using

$$\tan(\alpha - \beta) = \tan[\alpha + (-\beta)].$$

After applying the formula for the tangent of the sum of two angles, use the fact that the tangent is an odd function.

In Exercises 57–64, find the exact value of the following under the given conditions:

 a. $\cos(\alpha + \beta)$ **b.** $\sin(\alpha + \beta)$ **c.** $\tan(\alpha + \beta)$

57. $\sin \alpha = \frac{3}{5}, \alpha$ lies in quadrant I, and $\sin \beta = \frac{5}{13}, \beta$ lies in quadrant II.

58. $\sin \alpha = \frac{4}{5}, \alpha$ lies in quadrant I, and $\sin \beta = \frac{7}{25}, \beta$ lies in quadrant II.

59. $\tan \alpha = -\frac{3}{4}, \alpha$ lies in quadrant II, and $\cos \beta = \frac{1}{3}, \beta$ lies in quadrant I.

60. $\tan \alpha = -\frac{4}{3}, \alpha$ lies in quadrant II, and $\cos \beta = \frac{2}{3}, \beta$ lies in quadrant I.

61. $\cos \alpha = \frac{8}{17}, \alpha$ lies in quadrant IV, and $\sin \beta = -\frac{1}{2}, \beta$ lies in quadrant III.

62. $\cos \alpha = \frac{1}{2}, \alpha$ lies in quadrant IV, and $\sin \beta = -\frac{1}{3}, \beta$ lies in quadrant III.

63. $\tan \alpha = \frac{3}{4}, \pi < \alpha < \frac{3\pi}{2}$, and $\cos \beta = \frac{1}{4}, \frac{3\pi}{2} < \beta < 2\pi$.

64. $\sin \alpha = \frac{5}{6}, \frac{\pi}{2} < \alpha < \pi$, and $\tan \beta = \frac{3}{7}, \pi < \beta < \frac{3\pi}{2}$.

In Exercises 65–68, the graph with the given equation is shown in a $\left[0, 2\pi, \frac{\pi}{2}\right]$ by $[-2, 2, 1]$ viewing rectangle.

 a. *Describe the graph using another equation.*
 b. *Verify that the two equations are equivalent.*

65. $y = \sin(\pi - x)$

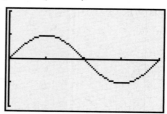

66. $y = \cos(x - 2\pi)$

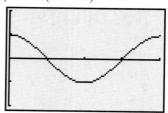

67. $y = \sin\left(x + \frac{\pi}{2}\right) + \sin\left(\frac{\pi}{2} - x\right)$

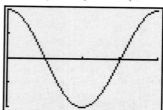

68. $y = \cos\left(x - \frac{\pi}{2}\right) - \cos\left(x + \frac{\pi}{2}\right)$

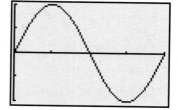

Practice Plus

In Exercises 69–74, rewrite each expression as a simplified expression containing one term.

69. $\cos(\alpha + \beta) \cos \beta + \sin(\alpha + \beta) \sin \beta$

70. $\sin(\alpha - \beta) \cos \beta + \cos(\alpha - \beta) \sin \beta$

71. $\dfrac{\sin(\alpha + \beta) - \sin(\alpha - \beta)}{\cos(\alpha + \beta) + \cos(\alpha - \beta)}$ **72.** $\dfrac{\cos(\alpha - \beta) + \cos(\alpha + \beta)}{-\sin(\alpha - \beta) + \sin(\alpha + \beta)}$

73. $\cos\left(\frac{\pi}{6} + \alpha\right) \cos\left(\frac{\pi}{6} - \alpha\right) - \sin\left(\frac{\pi}{6} + \alpha\right) \sin\left(\frac{\pi}{6} - \alpha\right)$
 (Do not use four different identities to solve this exercise.)

74. $\sin\left(\frac{\pi}{3} - \alpha\right) \cos\left(\frac{\pi}{3} + \alpha\right) + \cos\left(\frac{\pi}{3} - \alpha\right) \sin\left(\frac{\pi}{3} + \alpha\right)$
 (Do not use four different identities to solve this exercise.)

In Exercises 75–78, half of an identity and the graph of this half are given. Use the graph to make a conjecture as to what the right side of the identity should be. Then prove your conjecture.

75. $\cos 2x \cos 5x + \sin 2x \sin 5x = ?$

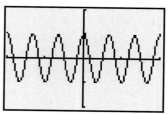

$[-2\pi, 2\pi, \frac{\pi}{2}]$ by $[-2, 2, 1]$

76. $\sin 5x \cos 2x - \cos 5x \sin 2x = ?$

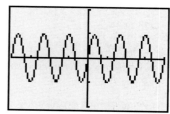

$[-2\pi, 2\pi, \frac{\pi}{2}]$ by $[-2, 2, 1]$

77. $\sin \dfrac{5x}{2} \cos 2x - \cos \dfrac{5x}{2} \sin 2x = ?$

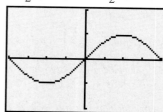

$[-2\pi, 2\pi, \frac{\pi}{2}]$ by $[-2, 2, 1]$

78. $\cos \dfrac{5x}{2} \cos 2x + \sin \dfrac{5x}{2} \sin 2x = ?$

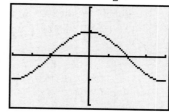

$[-2\pi, 2\pi, \frac{\pi}{2}]$ by $[-2, 2, 1]$

Application Exercises

79. A ball attached to a spring is raised 2 feet and released with an initial vertical velocity of 3 feet per second. The distance of the ball from its rest position after t seconds is given by $d = 2 \cos t + 3 \sin t$. Show that
$$2 \cos t + 3 \sin t = \sqrt{13} \cos(t - \theta),$$
where θ lies in quadrant I and $\tan \theta = \frac{3}{2}$. Use the identity to find the amplitude and the period of the ball's motion.

80. A tuning fork is held a certain distance from your ears and struck. Your eardrums' vibrations after t seconds are given by $p = 3 \sin 2t$. When a second tuning fork is struck, the formula $p = 2 \sin(2t + \pi)$ describes the effects of the sound on the eardrums' vibrations. The total vibrations are given by $p = 3 \sin 2t + 2 \sin(2t + \pi)$.

  a. Simplify p to a single term containing the sine.

  b. If the amplitude of p is zero, no sound is heard. Based on your equation in part (a), does this occur with the two tuning forks in this exercise? Explain your answer.

Writing in Mathematics

In Exercises 81–87, use words to describe the formula for each of the following:

81. the cosine of the difference of two angles.

82. the cosine of the sum of two angles.

83. the sine of the sum of two angles.

84. the sine of the difference of two angles.

85. the tangent of the difference of two angles.

86. the tangent of the sum of two angles.

87. The distance formula and the definitions for cosine and sine are used to prove the formula for the cosine of the difference of two angles. This formula logically leads the way to the other sum and difference identities. Using this development of ideas and formulas, describe a characteristic of mathematical logic.

Technology Exercises

In Exercises 88–93, graph each side of the equation in the same viewing rectangle. If the graphs appear to coincide, verify that the equation is an identity. If the graphs do not appear to coincide, this indicates that the equation is not an identity. In these exercises, find a value of x for which both sides are defined but not equal.

88. $\cos\left(\frac{3\pi}{2} - x\right) = -\sin x$

89. $\tan(\pi - x) = -\tan x$

90. $\sin\left(x + \frac{\pi}{2}\right) = \sin x + \sin \frac{\pi}{2}$

91. $\cos\left(x + \frac{\pi}{2}\right) = \cos x + \cos \frac{\pi}{2}$

92. $\cos 1.2x \cos 0.8x - \sin 1.2x \sin 0.8x = \cos 2x$

93. $\sin 1.2x \cos 0.8x + \cos 1.2x \sin 0.8x = \sin 2x$

Critical Thinking Exercises

94. Verify the identity:
$$\frac{\sin(x - y)}{\cos x \cos y} + \frac{\sin(y - z)}{\cos y \cos z} + \frac{\sin(z - x)}{\cos z \cos x} = 0.$$

In Exercises 95–98, find the exact value of each expression. Do not use a calculator.

95. $\sin\left(\cos^{-1}\frac{1}{2} + \sin^{-1}\frac{3}{5}\right)$

96. $\sin\left[\sin^{-1}\frac{3}{5} - \cos^{-1}\left(-\frac{4}{5}\right)\right]$

97. $\cos\left(\tan^{-1}\frac{4}{3} + \cos^{-1}\frac{5}{13}\right)$

98. $\cos\left[\cos^{-1}\left(-\frac{\sqrt{3}}{2}\right) - \sin^{-1}\left(-\frac{1}{2}\right)\right]$

In Exercises 99–101, write each trigonometric expression as an algebraic expression (that is, without any trigonometric functions). Assume that x and y are positive and in the domain of the given inverse trigonometric function.

99. $\cos(\sin^{-1} x - \cos^{-1} y)$

100. $\sin(\tan^{-1} x - \sin^{-1} y)$

101. $\tan(\sin^{-1} x + \cos^{-1} y)$

Group Exercise

102. Remembering the six sum and difference identities can be difficult. Did you have problems with some exercises because the identity you were using in your head turned out to be an incorrect formula? Are there easy ways to remember the six new identities presented in this section? Group members should address this question, considering one identity at a time. For each formula, list ways to make it easier to remember.

SECTION 5.5 Trigonometric Equations

Objectives

❶ Find all solutions of a trigonometric equation.

❷ Solve equations with multiple angles.

❸ Solve trigonometric equations quadratic in form.

❹ Use factoring to separate different functions in trigonometric equations.

❺ Use identities to solve trigonometric equations.

❻ Use a calculator to solve trigonometric equations.

Exponential functions display the manic energies of uncontrolled growth. By contrast, trigonometric functions repeat their behavior. Do they embody in their regularity some basic rhythm of the universe? The cycles of periodic phenomena provide events that we can comfortably count on. When will the moon look just as it does at this moment? When can I count on 13.5 hours of daylight? When will my breathing be exactly as it is right now? Models with trigonometric functions embrace the periodic rhythms of our world. Equations containing trigonometric functions are used to answer questions about these models.

❶ Find all solutions of a trigonometric equation.

Trigonometric Equations and Their Solutions

A **trigonometric equation** is an equation that contains a trigonometric expression with a variable, such as $\sin x$. We have seen that some trigonometric equations are identities, such as $\sin^2 x + \cos^2 x = 1$. These equations are true for every value of the variable for which the expressions are defined. In this section, we consider trigonometric equations that are true for only some values of the variable. The values that satisfy such an equation are its **solutions**. (There are trigonometric equations that have no solution.)

An example of a trigonometric equation is

$$\sin x = \tfrac{1}{2}.$$

A solution of this equation is $\frac{\pi}{6}$ because $\sin\frac{\pi}{6} = \frac{1}{2}$. By contrast, π is not a solution because $\sin \pi = 0 \neq \frac{1}{2}$.

Is $\frac{\pi}{6}$ the only solution of $\sin x = \frac{1}{2}$? The answer is no. Because of the periodic nature of the sine function, there are infinitely many values of x for which $\sin x = \frac{1}{2}$. Figure 5.7 shows five of the solutions, including $\frac{\pi}{6}$, for $-\frac{3\pi}{2} \leq x \leq \frac{7\pi}{2}$. Notice that the x-coordinates of the points where the graph of $y = \sin x$ intersects the line $y = \frac{1}{2}$ are the solutions of the equation $\sin x = \frac{1}{2}$.

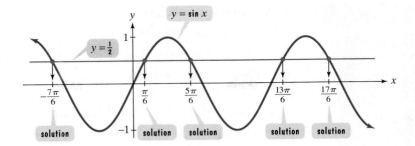

Figure 5.7 The equation $\sin x = \frac{1}{2}$ has five solutions when x is restricted to the interval $\left[-\frac{3\pi}{2}, \frac{7\pi}{2}\right]$.

How do we represent all solutions of $\sin x = \frac{1}{2}$? Because the period of the sine function is 2π, first find all solutions in $[0, 2\pi)$. The solutions are

$$x = \frac{\pi}{6} \quad \text{and} \quad x = \pi - \frac{\pi}{6} = \frac{5\pi}{6}.$$

> The sine is positive in quadrants I and II.

Any multiple of 2π can be added to these values and the sine is still $\frac{1}{2}$. Thus, all solutions of $\sin x = \frac{1}{2}$ are given by

$$x = \frac{\pi}{6} + 2n\pi \quad \text{or} \quad x = \frac{5\pi}{6} + 2n\pi$$

where n is any integer. By choosing any two integers, such as $n = 0$ and $n = 1$, we can find some solutions of $\sin x = \frac{1}{2}$. Thus, four of the solutions are determined as follows:

> Let $n = 0$.

$$x = \frac{\pi}{6} + 2 \cdot 0\pi \qquad x = \frac{5\pi}{6} + 2 \cdot 0\pi$$

$$= \frac{\pi}{6} \qquad\qquad = \frac{5\pi}{6}$$

> Let $n = 1$.

$$x = \frac{\pi}{6} + 2 \cdot 1\pi \qquad\qquad x = \frac{5\pi}{6} + 2 \cdot 1\pi$$

$$= \frac{\pi}{6} + 2\pi \qquad\qquad x = \frac{5\pi}{6} + 2\pi$$

$$= \frac{\pi}{6} + \frac{12\pi}{6} = \frac{13\pi}{6} \qquad = \frac{5\pi}{6} + \frac{12\pi}{6} = \frac{17\pi}{6}.$$

These four solutions are shown among the five solutions in Figure 5.7.

A city's tall buildings and narrow streets reduce the amount of sunlight. If h is the average height of the buildings and w is the width of the street, the angle of elevation from the street to the top of the buildings is given by the trigonometric equation

$$\tan \theta = \frac{h}{w}.$$

A value of $\theta = 63°$ can result in an 85% loss of illumination.

Equations Involving a Single Trigonometric Function

To solve an equation containing a single trigonometric function:

- Isolate the function on one side of the equation.
- Solve for the variable.

EXAMPLE 1 Finding All Solutions of a Trigonometric Equation

Solve the equation: $3 \sin x - 2 = 5 \sin x - 1$.

Solution   The equation contains a single trigonometric function, $\sin x$.

Step 1   Isolate the function on one side of the equation. We can solve for $\sin x$ by collecting terms with $\sin x$ on the left side and constant terms on the right side.

$3 \sin x - 2 = 5 \sin x - 1$	This is the given equation.
$3 \sin x - 5 \sin x - 2 = 5 \sin x - 5 \sin x - 1$	Subtract 5 sin x from both sides.
$-2 \sin x - 2 = -1$	Simplify.
$-2 \sin x = 1$	Add 2 to both sides.
$\sin x = -\frac{1}{2}$	Divide both sides by -2 and solve for sin x.

Step 2   Solve for the variable. We must solve for x in $\sin x = -\frac{1}{2}$. Because $\sin \frac{\pi}{6} = \frac{1}{2}$, the solutions of $\sin x = -\frac{1}{2}$ in $[0, 2\pi)$ are

$$x = \pi + \frac{\pi}{6} = \frac{6\pi}{6} + \frac{\pi}{6} = \frac{7\pi}{6} \qquad x = 2\pi - \frac{\pi}{6} = \frac{12\pi}{6} - \frac{\pi}{6} = \frac{11\pi}{6}.$$

The sine is negative in quadrant III.

The sine is negative in quadrant IV.

Because the period of the sine function is 2π, the solutions of the equation are given by

$$x = \frac{7\pi}{6} + 2n\pi \quad \text{and} \quad x = \frac{11\pi}{6} + 2n\pi,$$

where n is any integer.

Check Point 1   Solve the equation: $5 \sin x = 3 \sin x + \sqrt{3}$.

Now we will concentrate on finding solutions of trigonometric equations for $0 \le x < 2\pi$. You can use a graphing utility to check the solutions of these equations. Graph the left side and graph the right side. The solutions are the x-coordinates of the points where the graphs intersect.

② Solve equations with multiple angles.

Equations Involving Multiple Angles

Here are examples of two equations that include multiple angles:

$$\tan 3x = 1 \qquad \sin \frac{x}{2} = \frac{\sqrt{3}}{2}.$$

The angle is a multiple of 3.

The angle is a multiple of $\frac{1}{2}$.

We will solve each equation for $0 \le x < 2\pi$. The period of the function plays an important role in ensuring that we do not leave out any solutions.

EXAMPLE 2   Solving an Equation with a Multiple Angle

Solve the equation: $\tan 3x = 1, \quad 0 \le x < 2\pi$.

Solution   The period of the tangent function is π. In the interval $[0, \pi)$, the only value for which the tangent function is 1 is $\dfrac{\pi}{4}$. This means that $3x = \dfrac{\pi}{4}$. Because the period is π, all the solutions to $\tan 3x = 1$ are given by

$$3x = \frac{\pi}{4} + n\pi \qquad \textit{n is any integer.}$$

$$x = \frac{\pi}{12} + \frac{n\pi}{3} \qquad \textit{Divide both sides by 3 and solve for x.}$$

In the interval $[0, 2\pi)$, we obtain the solutions of $\tan 3x = 1$ as follows:

Let n = 0.
$$x = \frac{\pi}{12} + \frac{0\pi}{3}$$
$$= \frac{\pi}{12}$$

Let n = 1.
$$x = \frac{\pi}{12} + \frac{1\pi}{3}$$
$$= \frac{\pi}{12} + \frac{4\pi}{12} = \frac{5\pi}{12}$$

Let n = 2.
$$x = \frac{\pi}{12} + \frac{2\pi}{3}$$
$$= \frac{\pi}{12} + \frac{8\pi}{12} = \frac{9\pi}{12} = \frac{3\pi}{4}$$

Let n = 3.
$$x = \frac{\pi}{12} + \frac{3\pi}{3}$$
$$= \frac{\pi}{12} + \frac{12\pi}{12} = \frac{13\pi}{12}$$

Let n = 4.
$$x = \frac{\pi}{12} + \frac{4\pi}{3}$$
$$= \frac{\pi}{12} + \frac{16\pi}{12} = \frac{17\pi}{12}$$

Let n = 5.
$$x = \frac{\pi}{12} + \frac{5\pi}{3}$$
$$= \frac{\pi}{12} + \frac{20\pi}{12} = \frac{21\pi}{12} = \frac{7\pi}{4}.$$

If you let $n = 6$, you will obtain $x = \dfrac{25\pi}{12}$. This value exceeds 2π. In the interval $[0, 2\pi)$, the solutions of $\tan 3x = 1$ are $\dfrac{\pi}{12}, \dfrac{5\pi}{12}, \dfrac{3\pi}{4}, \dfrac{13\pi}{12}, \dfrac{17\pi}{12}$, and $\dfrac{7\pi}{4}$. These solutions are illustrated by the six intersection points in the technology box.

Technology

Shown below are the graphs of
$$y = \tan 3x$$
and
$$y = 1$$
in a $\left[0, 2\pi, \dfrac{\pi}{2}\right]$ by $[-3, 3, 1]$ viewing rectangle. The solutions of
$$\tan 3x = 1$$
in $[0, 2\pi)$ are shown by the x-coordinates of the six intersection points.

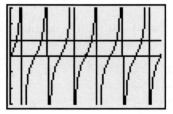

Check Point 2   Solve the equation: $\tan 2x = \sqrt{3}, 0 \le x < 2\pi$.

EXAMPLE 3   Solving an Equation with a Multiple Angle

Solve the equation: $\sin \dfrac{x}{2} = \dfrac{\sqrt{3}}{2}, 0 \le x < 2\pi$.

Solution   The period of the sine function is 2π. In the interval $[0, 2\pi)$, there are two values at which the sine function is $\dfrac{\sqrt{3}}{2}$. One of these values is $\dfrac{\pi}{3}$. The sine is positive in quadrant II; thus, the other value is $\pi - \dfrac{\pi}{3}$, or $\dfrac{2\pi}{3}$. This means that $\dfrac{x}{2} = \dfrac{\pi}{3}$ or $\dfrac{x}{2} = \dfrac{2\pi}{3}$. Because the period is 2π, all the solutions of $\sin \dfrac{x}{2} = \dfrac{\sqrt{3}}{2}$ are given by

$$\frac{x}{2} = \frac{\pi}{3} + 2n\pi \qquad \text{or} \qquad \frac{x}{2} = \frac{2\pi}{3} + 2n\pi. \qquad \textit{n is any integer.}$$

$$x = \frac{2\pi}{3} + 4n\pi \qquad\qquad x = \frac{4\pi}{3} + 4n\pi. \qquad \textit{Multiply both sides by 2 and solve for x.}$$

We see that $x = \dfrac{2\pi}{3} + 4n\pi$ or $x = \dfrac{4\pi}{3} + 4n\pi$. If $n = 0$, we obtain $x = \dfrac{2\pi}{3}$ from the first equation and $x = \dfrac{4\pi}{3}$ from the second equation. If we let $n = 1$, we are adding $4 \cdot 1 \cdot \pi$, or 4π, to $\dfrac{2\pi}{3}$ and $\dfrac{4\pi}{3}$. These values of x exceed 2π. Thus, in the interval $[0, 2\pi)$, the only solutions of $\sin\dfrac{x}{2} = \dfrac{\sqrt{3}}{2}$ are $\dfrac{2\pi}{3}$ and $\dfrac{4\pi}{3}$.

Check Point 3 Solve the equation: $\sin\dfrac{x}{3} = \dfrac{1}{2}, 0 \le x < 2\pi$.

③ Solve trigonometric equations quadratic in form.

Trigonometric Equations Quadratic in Form

Some trigonometric equations are in the form of a quadratic equation $au^2 + bu + c = 0$, where u is a trigonometric function and $a \ne 0$. Here are two examples of trigonometric equations that are quadratic in form:

$$2\cos^2 x + \cos x - 1 = 0 \qquad 2\sin^2 x - 3\sin x + 1 = 0.$$

The form of this equation is $2u^2 + u - 1 = 0$ with $u = \cos x$.

The form of this equation is $2u^2 - 3u + 1 = 0$ with $u = \sin x$.

To solve this kind of equation, try using factoring. If the trigonometric expression does not factor, use another method, such as the quadratic formula or the square root property.

Technology

The graph of
$$y = 2\cos^2 x + \cos x - 1$$
is shown in a
$$\left[0, 2\pi, \dfrac{\pi}{2}\right] \text{ by } [-3, 3, 1]$$
viewing rectangle. The x-intercepts,
$$\dfrac{\pi}{3}, \pi, \text{ and } \dfrac{5\pi}{3},$$
verify the three solutions of
$$2\cos^2 x + \cos x - 1 = 0$$
in $[0, 2\pi)$.

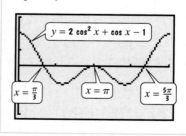

$y = 2\cos^2 x + \cos x - 1$

$x = \dfrac{\pi}{3}$ $x = \pi$ $x = \dfrac{5\pi}{3}$

EXAMPLE 4   Solving a Trigonometric Equation Quadratic in Form

Solve the equation: $2\cos^2 x + \cos x - 1 = 0, \quad 0 \le x < 2\pi$.

Solution The given equation is in quadratic form $2u^2 + u - 1 = 0$ with $u = \cos x$. Let us attempt to solve the equation by factoring.

$2\cos^2 x + \cos x - 1 = 0$ *This is the given equation.*

$(2\cos x - 1)(\cos x + 1) = 0$ *Factor. Notice that $2u^2 + u - 1$ factors as $(2u - 1)(u + 1)$.*

$2\cos x - 1 = 0$ or $\cos x + 1 = 0$ *Set each factor equal to 0.*

$2\cos x = 1$ $\cos x = -1$ *Solve for cos x.*

$\cos x = \dfrac{1}{2}$

$x = \dfrac{\pi}{3}$ $x = 2\pi - \dfrac{\pi}{3} = \dfrac{5\pi}{3}$ $x = \pi$ *Solve each equation for x, $0 \le x < 2\pi$.*

The cosine is positive in quadrants I and IV.

The solutions in the interval $[0, 2\pi)$ are $\dfrac{\pi}{3}, \pi,$ and $\dfrac{5\pi}{3}$.

Check Point 4 Solve the equation: $2\sin^2 x - 3\sin x + 1 = 0, \quad 0 \le x < 2\pi$.

EXAMPLE 5   Solving a Trigonometric Equation Quadratic in Form

Solve the equation: $4\sin^2 x - 1 = 0, \quad 0 \le x < 2\pi$.

Solution The given equation is in quadratic form $4u^2 - 1 = 0$ with $u = \sin x$. We can solve this equation by the square root property: If $u^2 = c$, then $u = \pm\sqrt{c}$.

$$4 \sin^2 x - 1 = 0 \qquad \text{This is the given equation.}$$

$$4 \sin^2 x = 1 \qquad \text{Add 1 to both sides.}$$

$$\sin^2 x = \frac{1}{4} \qquad \text{Divide both sides by 4 and solve for } \sin^2 x.$$

$$\sin x = \sqrt{\frac{1}{4}} = \frac{1}{2} \quad \text{or} \quad \sin x = -\sqrt{\frac{1}{4}} = -\frac{1}{2} \qquad \begin{array}{l} \text{Apply the square root property: If } u^2 = c, \\ \text{then } u = \sqrt{c} \text{ or } u = -\sqrt{c}. \end{array}$$

$$x = \frac{\pi}{6} \qquad x = \pi - \frac{\pi}{6} = \frac{5\pi}{6} \qquad x = \pi + \frac{\pi}{6} = \frac{7\pi}{6} \qquad x = 2\pi - \frac{\pi}{6} = \frac{11\pi}{6} \qquad \text{Solve each equation for } x, 0 \le x < 2\pi.$$

The sine is positive in quadrants I and II.

The sine is negative in quadrants III and IV.

The solutions in the interval $[0, 2\pi)$ are $\frac{\pi}{6}, \frac{5\pi}{6}, \frac{7\pi}{6},$ and $\frac{11\pi}{6}$.

Technology

You can use a graphing utility's $\boxed{\text{TABLE}}$ feature to verify that the solutions of $4 \sin^2 x - 1 = 0$ in $[0, 2\pi)$ are $\frac{\pi}{6}, \frac{5\pi}{6}, \frac{7\pi}{6},$ and $\frac{11\pi}{6}$. The table for $y = 4 \sin^2 x - 1$, shown on the right, verifies that $\frac{\pi}{6}$ and $\frac{5\pi}{6}$ are solutions. Scroll through the table to verify the other two solutions.

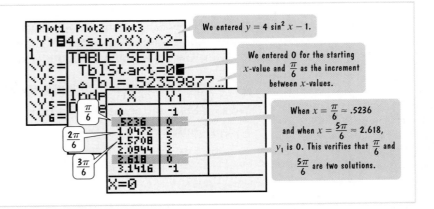

Check Point 5 Solve the equation: $4 \cos^2 x - 3 = 0, \quad 0 \le x < 2\pi$.

④ Use factoring to separate different functions in trigonometric equations.

Using Factoring to Separate Two Different Trigonometric Functions in an Equation

We have seen that factoring is used to solve some trigonometric equations that are quadratic in form. Factoring can also be used to solve some trigonometric equations that contain two different functions such as

$$\tan x \sin^2 x = 3 \tan x.$$

In such a case, move all terms to one side and obtain zero on the other side. Then try to use factoring to separate the different functions. Example 6 shows how this is done.

Study Tip

In solving
$$\tan x \sin^2 x = 3 \tan x,$$
do not begin by dividing both sides by $\tan x$. Division by zero is undefined. If you divide by $\tan x$, you lose the two solutions for which $\tan x = 0$, namely 0 and π.

EXAMPLE 6   Using Factoring to Separate Different Functions

Solve the equation: $\tan x \sin^2 x = 3 \tan x, \quad 0 \le x < 2\pi$.

Solution Move all terms to one side and obtain zero on the other side.

$$\tan x \sin^2 x = 3 \tan x \qquad \text{This is the given equation.}$$

$$\tan x \sin^2 x - 3 \tan x = 0 \qquad \text{Subtract 3 tan } x \text{ from both sides.}$$

We now have $\tan x \sin^2 x - 3 \tan x = 0$, which contains both tangent and sine functions. Use factoring to separate the two functions.

$$\tan x(\sin^2 x - 3) = 0 \quad \text{Factor out tan } x \text{ from the two terms on the left side.}$$

$$\tan x = 0 \quad \text{or} \quad \sin^2 x - 3 = 0 \quad \text{Set each factor equal to 0.}$$

$$x = 0 \quad x = \pi \qquad\qquad \sin^2 x = 3 \quad \text{Solve for x.}$$

$$\sin x = \pm\sqrt{3}$$

> This equation has no solution because $\sin x$ cannot be greater than 1 or less than -1.

The solutions in the interval $[0, 2\pi)$ are 0 and π.

Check Point 6 Solve the equation: $\sin x \tan x = \sin x, \quad 0 \le x < 2\pi.$

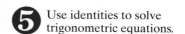 Use identities to solve trigonometric equations.

Using Identities to Solve Trigonometric Equations

Some trigonometric equations contain more than one function on the same side and these functions cannot be separated by factoring. For example, consider the equation

$$2 \cos^2 x + 3 \sin x = 0.$$

How can we obtain an equivalent equation that has only one trigonometric function? We use the identity $\sin^2 x + \cos^2 x = 1$ and substitute $1 - \sin^2 x$ for $\cos^2 x$. This forms the basis of our next example.

EXAMPLE 7   Using an Identity to Solve a Trigonometric Equation

Solve the equation: $2 \cos^2 x + 3 \sin x = 0, \quad 0 \le x < 2\pi.$

Solution

$$2 \cos^2 x + 3 \sin x = 0 \quad \text{This is the given equation.}$$

$$2(1 - \sin^2 x) + 3 \sin x = 0 \quad \cos^2 x = 1 - \sin^2 x$$

$$2 - 2 \sin^2 x + 3 \sin x = 0 \quad \text{Use the distributive property.}$$

> It's easier to factor with a positive leading coefficient.

$$-2 \sin^2 x + 3 \sin x + 2 = 0 \quad \text{Write the equation in descending powers of sin x.}$$

$$2 \sin^2 x - 3 \sin x - 2 = 0 \quad \text{Multiply both sides by } -1. \text{ The equation is in quadratic form } 2u^2 - 3u - 2 = 0 \text{ with } u = \sin x.$$

$$(2 \sin x + 1)(\sin x - 2) = 0 \quad \text{Factor. Notice that } 2u^2 - 3u - 2 \text{ factors as } (2u + 1)(u - 2).$$

$$2 \sin x + 1 = 0 \quad \text{or} \quad \sin x - 2 = 0 \quad \text{Set each factor equal to 0.}$$

$$2 \sin x = -1 \qquad\qquad \sin x = 2 \quad \text{Solve for sin x.}$$

> This equation has no solution because $\sin x$ cannot be greater than 1.

$$\sin x = -\frac{1}{2}$$

$$x = \pi + \frac{\pi}{6} = \frac{7\pi}{6} \qquad x = 2\pi - \frac{\pi}{6} = \frac{11\pi}{6} \quad \text{Solve for x.}$$

> $\sin \frac{\pi}{6} = \frac{1}{2}$. The sine is negative in quadrants III and IV.

The solutions in the interval $[0, 2\pi)$ are $\dfrac{7\pi}{6}$ and $\dfrac{11\pi}{6}$.

Check Point 7 Solve the equation: $2 \sin^2 x - 3 \cos x = 0, \quad 0 \le x < 2\pi.$

EXAMPLE 8   Using an Identity to Solve a Trigonometric Equation

Solve the equation: $\cos 2x + 3 \sin x - 2 = 0, \quad 0 \le x < 2\pi.$

Solution   The given equation contains a cosine function and a sine function. The cosine is a function of $2x$ and the sine is a function of x. We want one trigonometric function of the same angle. This can be accomplished by using the double-angle identity $\cos 2x = 1 - 2 \sin^2 x$ to obtain an equivalent equation involving $\sin x$ only.

$$\cos 2x + 3 \sin x - 2 = 0 \qquad \text{This is the given equation.}$$
$$1 - 2 \sin^2 x + 3 \sin x - 2 = 0 \qquad \cos 2x = 1 - 2 \sin^2 x$$
$$-2 \sin^2 x + 3 \sin x - 1 = 0 \qquad \text{Combine like terms.}$$
$$2 \sin^2 x - 3 \sin x + 1 = 0 \qquad \begin{array}{l}\text{Multiply both sides by } -1. \text{ The}\\ \text{equation is in quadratic form}\\ 2u^2 - 3u + 1 = 0 \text{ with}\\ u = \sin x.\end{array}$$

$$(2 \sin x - 1)(\sin x - 1) = 0 \qquad \begin{array}{l}\text{Factor. Notice that}\\ 2u^2 - 3u + 1 \text{ factors as}\\ (2u - 1)(u - 1).\end{array}$$

$$2 \sin x - 1 = 0 \quad \text{or} \quad \sin x - 1 = 0 \qquad \text{Set each factor equal to 0.}$$
$$\sin x = \tfrac{1}{2} \qquad\qquad \sin x = 1 \qquad \text{Solve for } \sin x.$$
$$x = \frac{\pi}{6} \qquad x = \pi - \frac{\pi}{6} = \frac{5\pi}{6} \qquad x = \frac{\pi}{2} \qquad \begin{array}{l}\text{Solve each equation for } x,\\ 0 \le x < 2\pi.\end{array}$$

> The sine is positive in quadrants I and II.

The solutions in the interval $[0, 2\pi)$ are $\dfrac{\pi}{6}, \dfrac{\pi}{2}$, and $\dfrac{5\pi}{6}$.

Check Point 8 Solve the equation: $\cos 2x + \sin x = 0, \quad 0 \le x < 2\pi.$

Sometimes it is necessary to do something to both sides of a trigonometric equation before using an identity. For example, consider the equation

$$\sin x \cos x = \tfrac{1}{2}.$$

This equation contains both a sine and a cosine function. How can we obtain a single function? Multiply both sides by 2. In this way, we can use the double-angle identity $\sin 2x = 2 \sin x \cos x$ and obtain $\sin 2x$, a single function, on the left side.

EXAMPLE 9   Using an Identity to Solve a Trigonometric Equation

Solve the equation: $\sin x \cos x = \tfrac{1}{2}, \quad 0 \le x < 2\pi.$

Solution

$$\sin x \cos x = \tfrac{1}{2} \qquad \text{This is the given equation.}$$
$$2 \sin x \cos x = 1 \qquad \begin{array}{l}\text{Multiply both sides by 2 in anticipation of}\\ \text{using } \sin 2x = 2 \sin x \cos x.\end{array}$$
$$\sin 2x = 1 \qquad \text{Use a double-angle identity.}$$

Technology

Shown below are the graphs of
$$y = \sin x \cos x$$
and
$$y = \frac{1}{2}$$
in a $\left[0, 2\pi, \frac{\pi}{2}\right]$ by $[-1, 1, 1]$
viewing rectangle.

The solutions of
$$\sin x \cos x = \frac{1}{2}$$
are shown by the x-coordinates of the two intersection points.

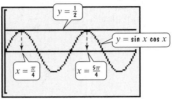

Notice that we have an equation, $\sin 2x = 1$, with $2x$, a multiple angle. The period of the sine function is 2π. In the interval $[0, 2\pi)$, the only value for which the sine function is 1 is $\frac{\pi}{2}$. This means that $2x = \frac{\pi}{2}$. Because the period is 2π, all the solutions of $\sin 2x = 1$ are given by

$$2x = \frac{\pi}{2} + 2n\pi \qquad \textit{n is any integer.}$$

$$x = \frac{\pi}{4} + n\pi \qquad \textit{Divide both sides by 2 and solve for x.}$$

The solutions of $\sin x \cos x = \frac{1}{2}$ in the interval $[0, 2\pi)$ are obtained by letting $n = 0$ and $n = 1$. The solutions are $\frac{\pi}{4}$ and $\frac{5\pi}{4}$.

Check Point 9 Solve the equation: $\sin x \cos x = -\frac{1}{2}, \quad 0 \leq x < 2\pi$.

Let's look at another equation that contains two different functions, $\sin x - \cos x = 1$. Can you think of an identity that can be used to produce only one function? Perhaps $\sin^2 x + \cos^2 x = 1$ might be helpful. The next example shows how we can use this identity after squaring both sides of the given equation. Remember that if we raise both sides of an equation to an even power, we have the possibility of introducing extraneous solutions. Thus, we must check each proposed solution in the given equation. Alternatively, we can use a graphing utility to verify actual solutions.

Technology

A graphing utility can be used instead of the algebraic check on the next page. Shown are the graphs of
$$y = \sin x - \cos x$$
and
$$y = 1$$
in a $\left[0, 2\pi, \frac{\pi}{2}\right]$ by $[-2, 2, 1]$
viewing rectangle. The actual solutions of
$$\sin x - \cos x = 1$$
are shown by the x-coordinates of the two intersection points, $\frac{\pi}{2}$ and π.

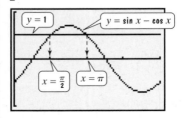

EXAMPLE 10   Using an Identity to Solve a Trigonometric Equation

Solve the equation: $\sin x - \cos x = 1, \quad 0 \leq x < 2\pi$.

Solution We square both sides of the equation in anticipation of using $\sin^2 x + \cos^2 x = 1$.

$\sin x - \cos x = 1$	This is the given equation.
$(\sin x - \cos x)^2 = 1^2$	Square both sides.
$\sin^2 x - 2 \sin x \cos x + \cos^2 x = 1$	Square the left side using $(A - B)^2 = A^2 - 2AB + B^2$.
$\sin^2 x + \cos^2 x - 2 \sin x \cos x = 1$	Rearrange terms.
$1 - 2 \sin x \cos x = 1$	Apply a Pythagorean identity: $\sin^2 x + \cos^2 x = 1$.
$-2 \sin x \cos x = 0$	Subtract 1 from both sides of the equation.
$\sin x \cos x = 0$	Divide both sides of the equation by -2.
$\sin x = 0 \quad \text{or} \quad \cos x = 0$	Set each factor equal to 0.
$x = 0 \quad x = \pi \quad x = \frac{\pi}{2} \quad x = \frac{3\pi}{2}$	Solve for x in $[0, 2\pi)$.

We check these proposed solutions to see if any are extraneous.

Check 0:

$$\sin x - \cos x = 1$$

$$\sin 0 - \cos 0 \overset{?}{=} 1$$

$$0 - 1 \overset{?}{=} 1$$

$$-1 = 1, \text{ false}$$

Check $\frac{\pi}{2}$:

$$\sin x - \cos x = 1$$

$$\sin \frac{\pi}{2} - \cos \frac{\pi}{2} \overset{?}{=} 1$$

$$1 - 0 \overset{?}{=} 1$$

$$1 = 1, \text{ true}$$

Check π:

$$\sin x - \cos x = 1$$

$$\sin \pi - \cos \pi \overset{?}{=} 1$$

$$0 - (-1) \overset{?}{=} 1$$

$$1 = 1, \text{ true}$$

Check $\frac{3\pi}{2}$:

$$\sin x - \cos x = 1$$

$$\sin \frac{3\pi}{2} - \cos \frac{3\pi}{2} \overset{?}{=} 1$$

$$-1 - 0 \overset{?}{=} 1$$

$$-1 = 1, \text{ false}$$

0 is extraneous.

$\frac{3\pi}{2}$ is extraneous.

The actual solutions in the interval $[0, 2\pi)$ are $\frac{\pi}{2}$ and π.

Check Point 10 Solve the equation: $\cos x - \sin x = -1$, $0 \le x < 2\pi$.

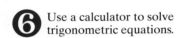 Use a calculator to solve trigonometric equations.

Using a Calculator to Solve Trigonometric Equations

In all our previous examples, the equations had solutions that were found by knowing the exact values of trigonometric functions of special angles, such as $\frac{\pi}{6}, \frac{\pi}{4}$, and $\frac{\pi}{3}$. However, not all trigonometric equations involve these special angles. For those that do not, we will use the secondary keys marked $\boxed{\text{SIN}^{-1}}$, $\boxed{\text{COS}^{-1}}$, and $\boxed{\text{TAN}^{-1}}$ on a calculator. Recall that on most calculators, the inverse trigonometric function keys are the secondary functions for the buttons labeled $\boxed{\text{SIN}}$, $\boxed{\text{COS}}$, and $\boxed{\text{TAN}}$, respectively.

EXAMPLE 11 Solving Trigonometric Equations with a Calculator

Solve each equation, correct to four decimal places, for $0 \le x < 2\pi$:

a. $\tan x = 12.8044$ **b.** $\cos x = -0.4317$.

Solution We begin by using a calculator to find $\theta, 0 \le \theta < \frac{\pi}{2}$ satisfying the following equations:

$$\tan \theta = 12.8044 \qquad \cos \theta = 0.4317.$$

These numbers are the absolute values of the given range values.

Once θ is determined, we use our knowledge of the signs of the trigonometric functions to find x in $[0, 2\pi)$ satisfying $\tan x = 12.8044$ and $\cos x = -0.4317$.

a. $\tan x = 12.8044$ This is the given equation.

$\tan \theta = 12.8044$ Use a calculator to solve this equation for $\theta, 0 \le \theta < \frac{\pi}{2}$.

$\theta = \tan^{-1}(12.8044) \approx 1.4929$ 12.8044 $\boxed{\text{2nd}}$ $\boxed{\text{TAN}}$ or
$\boxed{\text{2nd}}$ $\boxed{\text{TAN}}$ 12.8044 $\boxed{\text{ENTER}}$

$\tan x = 12.8044$ Return to the given equation. Because the tangent is positive, x lies in quadrant I or III.

$x \approx 1.4929$ $x \approx \pi + 1.4929 \approx 4.6345$ Solve for x, $0 \le x < 2\pi$.

The tangent is positive in quadrant I.

The tangent is positive in quadrant III.

Correct to four decimal places, the solutions of $\tan x = 12.8044$ in the interval $[0, 2\pi)$ are 1.4929 and 4.6345.

Study Tip

To find solutions in $[0, 2\pi)$, your calculator must be in radian mode. Most scientific calculators revert to degree mode every time they are cleared.

b. $\cos x = -0.4317$ *This is the given equation.*

$\cos \theta = 0.4317$ *Use a calculator to solve this equation for $\theta, 0 \leq \theta < \dfrac{\pi}{2}$.*

$\theta = \cos^{-1}(0.4317) \approx 1.1244$ *.4317* 2nd COS *or* 2nd COS *.4317* ENTER

$\cos x = -0.4317$ *Return to the given equation. Because the cosine is negative, x lies in quadrant II or III.*

$x \approx \pi - 1.1244 \approx 2.0172$ $x \approx \pi + 1.1244 \approx 4.2660$ *Solve for x, $0 \leq x < 2\pi$.*

| The cosine is negative in quadrant II. | The cosine is negative in quadrant III. |

Correct to four decimal places, the solutions of $\cos x = -0.4317$ in the interval $[0, 2\pi)$ are 2.0172 and 4.2660.

Check Point 11 Solve each equation, correct to four decimal places, for $0 \leq x < 2\pi$:
a. $\tan x = 3.1044$ **b.** $\sin x = -0.2315$.

EXAMPLE 12   Solving a Trigonometric Equation Using the Quadratic Formula and a Calculator

Solve the equation, correct to four decimal places, for $0 \leq x < 2\pi$:

$$\sin^2 x - \sin x - 1 = 0.$$

Solution The given equation is in quadratic form $u^2 - u - 1 = 0$ with $u = \sin x$. We use the quadratic formula to solve for $\sin x$ because $u^2 - u - 1$ cannot be factored. Begin by identifying the values for $a, b,$ and c.

$$\sin^2 x - \sin x - 1 = 0$$

$a = 1 \qquad b = -1 \qquad c = -1$

Substituting these values into the quadratic formula and simplifying gives the values for $\sin x$. Once we obtain these values, we will solve for x.

$$\sin x = \frac{-b \pm \sqrt{b^2 - 4ac}}{2a} = \frac{-(-1) \pm \sqrt{(-1)^2 - 4(1)(-1)}}{2(1)} = \frac{1 \pm \sqrt{1 - (-4)}}{2} = \frac{1 \pm \sqrt{5}}{2}$$

$$\sin x = \frac{1 + \sqrt{5}}{2} \approx 1.6180 \qquad \text{or} \qquad \sin x = \frac{1 - \sqrt{5}}{2} \approx -0.6180$$

| This equation has no solution because sin x cannot be greater than 1. | The sine is negative in quadrants III and IV. Use a calculator to solve $\sin \theta = 0.6180, 0 \leq \theta < \frac{\pi}{2}$. |

Using a calculator to solve $\sin \theta = 0.6180$, we have

$$\theta = \sin^{-1}(0.6180) \approx 0.6662.$$

We use 0.6662 to solve $\sin x = -0.6180, 0 \leq x < 2\pi$.

$$x \approx \pi + 0.6662 \approx 3.8078 \qquad x \approx 2\pi - 0.6662 \approx 5.6170$$

| The sine is negative in quadrant III. | The sine is negative in quadrant IV. |

Correct to four decimal places, the solutions of $\sin^2 x - \sin x - 1 = 0$ in the interval $[0, 2\pi)$ are 3.8078 and 5.6170.

Check Point 12 Solve the equation, correct to four decimal places, for $0 \le x < 2\pi$:

$$\cos^2 x + 5 \cos x + 3 = 0.$$

EXERCISE SET 5.5

Practice Exercises

In Exercises 1–10, use substitution to determine whether the given x-value is a solution of the equation.

1. $\cos x = \dfrac{\sqrt{2}}{2}, \quad x = \dfrac{\pi}{4}$ **2.** $\tan x = \sqrt{3}, \quad x = \dfrac{\pi}{3}$

3. $\sin x = \dfrac{\sqrt{3}}{2}, \quad x = \dfrac{\pi}{6}$ **4.** $\sin x = \dfrac{\sqrt{2}}{2}, \quad x = \dfrac{\pi}{3}$

5. $\cos x = -\dfrac{1}{2}, \quad x = \dfrac{2\pi}{3}$ **6.** $\cos x = -\dfrac{1}{2}, \quad x = \dfrac{4\pi}{3}$

7. $\tan 2x = -\dfrac{\sqrt{3}}{3}, \quad x = \dfrac{5\pi}{12}$

8. $\cos \dfrac{2x}{3} = -\dfrac{1}{2}, \quad x = \pi$

9. $\cos x = \sin 2x, \quad x = \dfrac{\pi}{3}$

10. $\cos x + 2 = \sqrt{3} \sin x, \quad x = \dfrac{\pi}{6}$

In Exercises 11–24, find all solutions of each equation.

11. $\sin x = \dfrac{\sqrt{3}}{2}$ **12.** $\cos x = \dfrac{\sqrt{3}}{2}$

13. $\tan x = 1$ **14.** $\tan x = \sqrt{3}$

15. $\cos x = -\dfrac{1}{2}$ **16.** $\sin x = -\dfrac{\sqrt{2}}{2}$

17. $\tan x = 0$ **18.** $\sin x = 0$

19. $2 \cos x + \sqrt{3} = 0$ **20.** $2 \sin x + \sqrt{3} = 0$

21. $4 \sin \theta - 1 = 2 \sin \theta$ **22.** $5 \sin \theta + 1 = 3 \sin \theta$

23. $3 \sin \theta + 5 = -2 \sin \theta$ **24.** $7 \cos \theta + 9 = -2 \cos \theta$

Exercises 25–38 involve equations with multiple angles. Solve each equation on the interval $[0, 2\pi)$.

25. $\sin 2x = \dfrac{\sqrt{3}}{2}$ **26.** $\cos 2x = \dfrac{\sqrt{2}}{2}$

27. $\cos 4x = -\dfrac{\sqrt{3}}{2}$ **28.** $\sin 4x = -\dfrac{\sqrt{2}}{2}$

29. $\tan 3x = \dfrac{\sqrt{3}}{3}$ **30.** $\tan 3x = \sqrt{3}$

31. $\tan \dfrac{x}{2} = \sqrt{3}$ **32.** $\tan \dfrac{x}{2} = \dfrac{\sqrt{3}}{3}$

33. $\sin \dfrac{2\theta}{3} = -1$ **34.** $\cos \dfrac{2\theta}{3} = -1$

35. $\sec \dfrac{3\theta}{2} = -2$ **36.** $\cot \dfrac{3\theta}{2} = -\sqrt{3}$

37. $\sin\left(2x + \dfrac{\pi}{6}\right) = \dfrac{1}{2}$ **38.** $\sin\left(2x - \dfrac{\pi}{4}\right) = \dfrac{\sqrt{2}}{2}$

Exercises 39–52 involve trigonometric equations quadratic in form. Solve each equation on the interval $[0, 2\pi)$.

39. $2 \sin^2 x - \sin x - 1 = 0$

40. $2 \sin^2 x + \sin x - 1 = 0$

41. $2 \cos^2 x + 3 \cos x + 1 = 0$

42. $\cos^2 x + 2 \cos x - 3 = 0$

43. $2 \sin^2 x = \sin x + 3$ **44.** $2 \sin^2 x = 4 \sin x + 6$

45. $\sin^2 \theta - 1 = 0$ **46.** $\cos^2 \theta - 1 = 0$

47. $4 \cos^2 x - 1 = 0$ **48.** $4 \sin^2 x - 3 = 0$

49. $9 \tan^2 x - 3 = 0$ **50.** $3 \tan^2 x - 9 = 0$

51. $\sec^2 x - 2 = 0$ **52.** $4 \sec^2 x - 2 = 0$

In Exercises 53–62, solve each equation on the interval $[0, 2\pi)$.

53. $(\tan x - 1)(\cos x + 1) = 0$

54. $(\tan x + 1)(\sin x - 1) = 0$

55. $(2 \cos x + \sqrt{3})(2 \sin x + 1) = 0$

56. $(2 \cos x - \sqrt{3})(2 \sin x - 1) = 0$

57. $\cot x(\tan x - 1) = 0$ **58.** $\cot x(\tan x + 1) = 0$

59. $\sin x + 2 \sin x \cos x = 0$ **60.** $\cos x - 2 \sin x \cos x = 0$

61. $\tan^2 x \cos x = \tan^2 x$ **62.** $\cot^2 x \sin x = \cot^2 x$

In Exercises 63–84, use an identity to solve each equation on the interval $[0, 2\pi)$.

63. $2 \cos^2 x + \sin x - 1 = 0$ **64.** $2 \cos^2 x - \sin x - 1 = 0$

65. $\sin^2 x - 2 \cos x - 2 = 0$ **66.** $4 \sin^2 x + 4 \cos x - 5 = 0$

67. $4 \cos^2 x = 5 - 4 \sin x$ **68.** $3 \cos^2 x = \sin^2 x$

69. $\sin 2x = \cos x$ **70.** $\sin 2x = \sin x$

71. $\cos 2x = \cos x$ **72.** $\cos 2x = \sin x$

73. $\cos 2x + 5 \cos x + 3 = 0$ **74.** $\cos 2x + \cos x + 1 = 0$

75. $\sin x \cos x = \dfrac{\sqrt{2}}{4}$ **76.** $\sin x \cos x = \dfrac{\sqrt{3}}{4}$

77. $\sin x + \cos x = 1$ **78.** $\sin x + \cos x = -1$

79. $\sin\left(x + \dfrac{\pi}{4}\right) + \sin\left(x - \dfrac{\pi}{4}\right) = 1$

80. $\sin\left(x + \dfrac{\pi}{3}\right) + \sin\left(x - \dfrac{\pi}{3}\right) = 1$

81. $\sin 2x \cos x + \cos 2x \sin x = \dfrac{\sqrt{2}}{2}$

82. $\sin 3x \cos 2x + \cos 3x \sin 2x = 1$

83. $\tan x + \sec x = 1$ **84.** $\tan x - \sec x = 1$

In Exercises 85–96, use a calculator to solve each equation, correct to four decimal places, on the interval $[0, 2\pi)$.

85. $\sin x = 0.8246$ **86.** $\sin x = 0.7392$

87. $\cos x = -\dfrac{2}{5}$ **88.** $\cos x = -\dfrac{4}{7}$

89. $\tan x = -3$ **90.** $\tan x = -5$

91. $\cos^2 x - \cos x - 1 = 0$

92. $3\cos^2 x - 8\cos x - 3 = 0$

93. $4\tan^2 x - 8\tan x + 3 = 0$

94. $\tan^2 x - 3\tan x + 1 = 0$

95. $7\sin^2 x - 1 = 0$ **96.** $5\sin^2 x - 1 = 0$

In Exercises 97–116, use the most appropriate method to solve each equation on the interval $[0, 2\pi)$. Use exact values where possible or give approximate solutions correct to four decimal places.

97. $2\cos 2x + 1 = 0$ **98.** $2\sin 3x + \sqrt{3} = 0$

99. $\sin 2x + \sin x = 0$ **100.** $\sin 2x + \cos x = 0$

101. $3\cos x - 6\sqrt{3} = \cos x - 5\sqrt{3}$

102. $\cos x - 5 = 3\cos x + 6$

103. $\tan x = -4.7143$ **104.** $\tan x = -6.2154$

105. $2\sin^2 x = 3 - \sin x$ **106.** $2\sin^2 x = 2 - 3\sin x$

107. $\cos x \csc x = 2\cos x$ **108.** $\tan x \sec x = 2\tan x$

109. $5\cot^2 x - 15 = 0$ **110.** $5\sec^2 x - 10 = 0$

111. $\cos^2 x + 2\cos x - 2 = 0$

112. $\cos^2 x + 5\cos x - 1 = 0$

113. $5\sin x = 2\cos^2 x - 4$ **114.** $7\cos x = 4 - 2\sin^2 x$

115. $2\tan^2 x + 5\tan x + 3 = 0$

116. $3\tan^2 x - \tan x - 2 = 0$

Practice Plus

In Exercises 117–120, graph f and g in the same rectangular coordinate system for $0 \le x \le 2\pi$. Then solve a trigonometric equation to determine points of intersection and identify these points on your graphs.

117. $f(x) = 3\cos x, g(x) = \cos x - 1$

118. $f(x) = 3\sin x, g(x) = \sin x - 1$

119. $f(x) = \cos 2x, g(x) = -2\sin x$

120. $f(x) = \cos 2x, g(x) = 1 - \sin x$

In Exercises 121–126, solve each equation on the interval $[0, 2\pi)$.

121. $|\cos x| = \dfrac{\sqrt{3}}{2}$ **122.** $|\sin x| = \dfrac{1}{2}$

123. $10\cos^2 x + 3\sin x - 9 = 0$

124. $3\cos^2 x - \sin x = \cos^2 x$

125. $2\cos^3 x + \cos^2 x - 2\cos x - 1 = 0$ (*Hint*: Use factoring by grouping.)

126. $2\sin^3 x - \sin^2 x - 2\sin x + 1 = 0$ (*Hint*: Use factoring by grouping.)

In Exercises 127–128, find the x-intercepts, correct to four decimal places, of the graph of each function. Then use the x-intercepts to match the function with its graph. The graphs are labeled (a) and (b).

127. $f(x) = \tan^2 x - 3\tan x + 1$

128. $g(x) = 4\tan^2 x - 8\tan x + 3$

a.

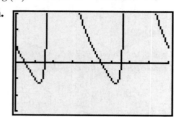

$[0, 2\pi, \frac{\pi}{4}]$ by $[-3, 3, 1]$

b.

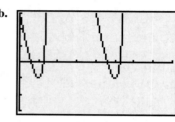

$[0, 2\pi, \frac{\pi}{4}]$ by $[-3, 3, 1]$

Application Exercises

Use this information to solve Exercises 129–130. Our cycle of normal breathing takes place every 5 seconds. Velocity of air flow, y, measured in liters per second, after x seconds is modeled by

$$y = 0.6 \sin \frac{2\pi}{5}x.$$

Velocity of air flow is positive when we inhale and negative when we exhale.

129. Within each breathing cycle, when are we inhaling at a rate of 0.3 liter per second? Round to the nearest tenth of a second.

130. Within each breathing cycle, when are we exhaling at a rate of 0.3 liter per second? Round to the nearest tenth of a second.

Use this information to solve Exercises 131–132. The number of hours of daylight in Boston is given by

$$y = 3\sin\left[\frac{2\pi}{365}(x - 79)\right] + 12,$$

where x is the number of days after January 1.

131. Within a year, when does Boston have 10.5 hours of daylight? Give your answer in days after January 1 and round to the nearest day.

132. Within a year, when does Boston have 13.5 hours of daylight? Give your answer in days after January 1 and round to the nearest day.

Use this information to solve Exercises 133–134. A ball on a spring is pulled 4 inches below its rest position and then released. After t seconds, the ball's distance, d, in inches from its rest position is given by

$$d = -4 \cos \frac{\pi}{3} t.$$

133. Find all values of t for which the ball is 2 inches above its rest position.

134. Find all values of t for which the ball is 2 inches below its rest position.

Use this information to solve Exercises 135–136. When throwing an object, the distance achieved depends on its initial velocity, v_0, and the angle above the horizontal at which the object is thrown, θ. The distance, d, in feet, that describes the range covered is given by

$$d = \frac{v_0^2}{16} \sin \theta \cos \theta,$$

where v_0 is measured in feet per second.

135. You and your friend are throwing a baseball back and forth. If you throw the ball with an initial velocity of $v_0 = 90$ feet per second, at what angle of elevation, θ, to the nearest degree, should you direct your throw so that it can be easily caught by your friend located 170 feet away?

136. In Exercise 135, you increase the distance between you and your friend to 200 feet. With this increase, at what angle of elevation, θ, to the nearest degree, should you direct your throw?

Writing in Mathematics

137. What are the solutions of a trigonometric equation?

138. Describe the difference between verifying a trigonometric identity and solving a trigonometric equation.

139. Without actually solving the equation, describe how to solve

$$3 \tan x - 2 = 5 \tan x - 1.$$

140. In the interval $[0, 2\pi)$, the solutions of $\sin x = \cos 2x$ are $\frac{\pi}{6}, \frac{5\pi}{6}$, and $\frac{3\pi}{2}$. Explain how to use graphs generated by a graphing utility to check these solutions.

141. Suppose you are solving equations in the interval $[0, 2\pi)$. Without actually solving equations, what is the difference between the number of solutions of $\sin x = \frac{1}{2}$ and $\sin 2x = \frac{1}{2}$? How do you account for this difference?

In Exercises 142–143, describe a general strategy for solving each equation. Do not solve the equation.

142. $2 \sin^2 x + 5 \sin x + 3 = 0$

143. $\sin 2x = \sin x$

144. Describe a natural periodic phenomenon. Give an example of a question that can be answered by a trigonometric equation in the study of this phenomenon.

145. Some people experience depression with loss of sunlight. Use the essay on page 610 to determine whether such a person should live on a city street that is 80 feet wide with buildings whose heights average 400 feet. Explain your answer and include θ, to the nearest degree, in your argument.

Technology Exercises

146. Use a graphing utility to verify the solutions of any five equations that you solved in Exercises 63–84.

In Exercises 147–151, use a graphing utility to approximate the solutions of each equation in the interval $[0, 2\pi)$. Round to the nearest hundredth of a radian.

147. $15 \cos^2 x + 7 \cos x - 2 = 0$

148. $\cos x = x$

149. $2 \sin^2 x = 1 - 2 \sin x$

150. $\sin 2x = 2 - x^2$

151. $\sin x + \sin 2x + \sin 3x = 0$

Critical Thinking Exercises

152. Which one of the following is true?
  a. The equation $(\sin x - 3)(\cos x + 2) = 0$ has no solution.
  b. The equation $\tan x = \dfrac{\pi}{2}$ has no solution.
  c. A trigonometric equation with an infinite number of solutions is an identity.
  d. The equations $\sin 2x = 1$ and $\sin 2x = \frac{1}{2}$ have the same number of solutions on the interval $[0, 2\pi)$.

In Exercises 153–155, solve each equation on the interval $[0, 2\pi)$. Do not use a calculator.

153. $2 \cos x - 1 + 3 \sec x = 0$

154. $\sin 3x + \sin x + \cos x = 0$

155. $\sin x + 2 \sin \dfrac{x}{2} = \cos \dfrac{x}{2} + 1$

Chapter 5
Summary

Summary

DEFINITIONS AND CONCEPTS	EXAMPLES

5.1 Verifying Trigonometric Identities

a. Identities are trigonometric equations that are true for all values of the variable for which the expressions are defined.

b. Fundamental trigonometric identities are given in the box on page 570.

c. Guidelines for verifying trigonometric identities are given in the box on page 577.

Ex. 1, p. 571;
Ex. 2, p. 572;
Ex. 3, p. 573;
Ex. 4, p. 573;
Ex. 5, p. 574;
Ex. 6, p. 574;
Ex. 7, p. 575;
Ex. 8, p. 576

5.2 Sum and Difference Formulas

a. Sum and difference formulas are given in the box on page 583 and the box on page 586.

b. Sum and difference formulas can be used to find exact values of trigonometric functions.

Ex. 1, p. 582;
Ex. 2, p. 582;
Ex. 4, p. 584;
Ex. 5, p. 584

c. Sum and difference formulas can be used to verify trigonometric identities.

Ex. 3, p. 582;
Ex. 6, p. 585;
Ex. 7, p. 586

5.3 Double-Angle, Power-Reducing, and Half-Angle Formulas

a. Double-angle, power-reducing, and half-angle formulas are given in the box on page 596.

b. Double-angle and half-angle formulas can be used to find exact values of trigonometric functions.

Ex. 1, p. 591;
Ex. 2, p. 591;
Ex. 5, p. 594

c. Double-angle and half-angle formulas can be used to verify trigonometric identities.

Ex. 3, p. 592;
Ex. 6, p. 595;
Ex. 7, p. 596

d. Power-reducing formulas can be used to reduce the powers of trigonometric functions.

Ex. 4, p. 593

5.4 Product-to-Sum and Sum-to-Product Formulas

a. The product-to-sum formulas are given in the box on page 601.

Ex. 1, p. 602

b. The sum-to-product formulas are given in the box on page 603. These formulas are useful to verify identities with fractions that contain sums and differences of sines and/or cosines.

Ex. 2, p. 603;
Ex. 3, p. 604

5.5 Trigonometric Equations

a. The values that satisfy a trigonometric equation are its solutions.

b. To solve an equation containing a single trigonometric function, isolate the function on one side and solve for the variable.

Ex. 1, p. 610

c. When solving equations involving multiple angles, the period plays an important role in ensuring that we do not leave out any solutions.

Ex. 2, p. 611;
Ex. 3, p. 611

DEFINITIONS AND CONCEPTS	**EXAMPLES**
d. Trigonometric equations quadratic in form can be expressed as $au^2 + bu + c = 0$, where u is a trigonometric function and $a \neq 0$. Such equations can be solved by factoring, the square root property, or the quadratic formula.	Ex. 4, p. 612; Ex. 5, p. 612; Ex. 12, p. 618
e. Factoring can be used to separate two different trigonometric functions in an equation.	Ex. 6, p. 613
f. Identities are used to solve some trigonometric equations.	Ex. 7, p. 614; Ex. 8, p. 615; Ex. 9, p. 615; Ex. 10, p. 616
g. Some trigonometric equations have solutions that cannot be determined by knowing the exact values of trigonometric functions of special angles. Such equations are solved using a calculator's inverse trigonometric function feature.	Ex. 11, p. 617; Ex. 12, p. 618

6

Additional Topics in Trigonometry

Taken from:
Precalculus, Third Edition, by Robert Blitzer

Additional Topics in Trigonometry

HESE DAYS, COMPUTERS AND trigonometric functions are everywhere. Trigonometry plays a critical role in analyzing the forces that surround your every move. Using trigonometry to understand how forces are measured is one of the topics in this chapter that focuses on additional applications of trigonometry.

YOU ENJOY RUNNING, ALTHOUGH LATELY you experience discomfort at various points of impact. Your doctor suggests a computer analysis. By attaching sensors to your running shoes as you jog along a treadmill, the computer provides a printout of the magnitude and direction of the forces as your feet hit the ground. Based on this analysis, customized orthotics can be made to fit inside your shoes to minimize the impact.

From running to standing still, our bodies are surrounded by forces, illustrated in the Section 6.6 opener and analyzed in the boxed essay on page 682.

SECTION 6.1   *The Law of Sines*

Objectives

❶ Use the Law of Sines to solve oblique triangles.

❷ Use the Law of Sines to solve, if possible, the triangle or triangles in the ambiguous case.

❸ Find the area of an oblique triangle using the sine function.

❹ Solve applied problems using the Law of Sines.

Point Reyes National Seashore, 40 miles north of San Francisco, consists of 75,000 acres with miles of pristine surf-pummeled beaches, forested ridges, and bays flanked by white cliffs. A few people, inspired by nature in the raw, live on private property adjoining the National Seashore. In 1995, a fire in the park burned 12,350 acres and destroyed 45 homes.

Fire is a necessary part of the life cycle in many wilderness areas. It is also an ongoing threat to those who choose to live surrounded by nature's unspoiled beauty. In this section, we see how trigonometry can be used to locate small wilderness fires before they become raging infernos. To do this, we begin by considering triangles other than right triangles.

The Law of Sines and Its Derivation

An **oblique triangle** is a triangle that does not contain a right angle. Figure 6.1 shows that an oblique triangle has either three acute angles or two acute angles and one obtuse angle. Notice that the angles are labeled A, B, and C. The sides opposite each angle are labeled as a, b, and c, respectively.

Study Tip

Up until now, our work with triangles has involved right triangles. **Do not apply relationships that are valid for right triangles to oblique triangles**. Avoid the error of using the Pythagorean Theorem, $a^2 + b^2 = c^2$, to find a missing side of an oblique triangle. This relationship among the three sides applies only to right triangles.

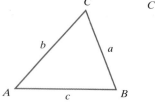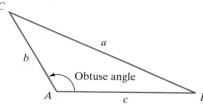

Figure 6.1 Oblique triangles

The relationships among the sides and angles of right triangles defined by the trigonometric functions are not valid for oblique triangles. Thus, we must observe and develop new relationships in order to work with oblique triangles.

Many relationships exist among the sides and angles in oblique triangles. One such relationship is called the **Law of Sines**.

Study Tip

The Law of Sines can be expressed with the sines in the numerator:

$$\frac{\sin A}{a} = \frac{\sin B}{b} = \frac{\sin C}{c}.$$

The Law of Sines

If A, B, and C are the measures of the angles of a triangle, and a, b, and c are the lengths of the sides opposite these angles, then

$$\frac{a}{\sin A} = \frac{b}{\sin B} = \frac{c}{\sin C}.$$

The ratio of the length of the side of any triangle to the sine of the angle opposite that side is the same for all three sides of the triangle.

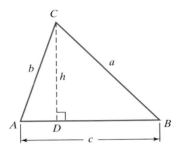

Figure 6.2 Drawing an altitude to prove the Law of Sines

To prove the Law of Sines, we draw an altitude of length h from one of the vertices of the triangle. In Figure 6.2, the altitude is drawn from vertex C. Two smaller triangles are formed, triangles ACD and BCD. Note that both are right triangles. Thus, we can use the definition of the sine of an angle of a right triangle.

$$\sin B = \frac{h}{a} \qquad \sin A = \frac{h}{b} \qquad \sin \theta = \frac{\text{opposite}}{\text{hypotenuse}}$$

$$h = a \sin B \qquad h = b \sin A \qquad \text{Solve each equation for } h.$$

Because we have found two expressions for h, we can set these expressions equal to each other.

$$a \sin B = b \sin A \qquad \text{Equate the expressions for } h.$$

$$\frac{a \sin B}{\sin A \sin B} = \frac{b \sin A}{\sin A \sin B} \qquad \text{Divide both sides by } \sin A \sin B.$$

$$\frac{a}{\sin A} = \frac{b}{\sin B} \qquad \text{Simplify.}$$

This proves part of the Law of Sines. If we use the same process and draw an altitude of length h from vertex A, we obtain the following result:

$$\frac{b}{\sin B} = \frac{c}{\sin C}.$$

When this equation is combined with the previous equation, we obtain the Law of Sines. Because the sine of an angle is equal to the sine of 180° minus that angle, the Law of Sines is derived in a similar manner if the oblique triangle contains an obtuse angle.

Solving Oblique Triangles

Use the Law of Sines to solve oblique triangles.

Solving an oblique triangle means finding the lengths of its sides and the measurements of its angles. The Law of Sines can be used to solve a triangle in which one side and two angles are known. The three known measurements can be abbreviated using SAA (a side and two angles are known) or ASA (two angles and the side between them are known).

EXAMPLE 1   Solving an SAA Triangle Using the Law of Sines

Solve the triangle shown in Figure 6.3 with $A = 46°$, $C = 63°$, and $c = 56$ inches. Round lengths of sides to the nearest tenth.

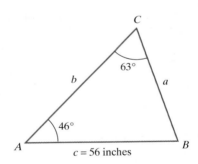

Figure 6.3 Solving an oblique SAA triangle

Solution   We begin by finding B, the third angle of the triangle. We do not need the Law of Sines to do this. Instead, we use the fact that the sum of the measures of the interior angles of a triangle is 180°.

$$A + B + C = 180°$$
$$46° + B + 63° = 180° \qquad \text{Substitute the given values:} \\ A = 46° \text{ and } C = 63°.$$
$$109° + B = 180° \qquad \text{Add.}$$
$$B = 71° \qquad \text{Subtract 109° from both sides.}$$

When we use the Law of Sines, we must be given one of the three ratios. In this example, we are given c and C: $c = 56$ and $C = 63°$. Thus, we use the ratio $\dfrac{c}{\sin C}$, or $\dfrac{56}{\sin 63°}$, to find the other two sides. Use the Law of Sines to find a.

$$\frac{a}{\sin A} = \frac{c}{\sin C} \qquad \text{The ratio of any side to the sine of its opposite angle equals} \\ \text{the ratio of any other side to the sine of its opposite angle.}$$

$$\frac{a}{\sin 46°} = \frac{56}{\sin 63°} \qquad A = 46°, c = 56, \text{ and } C = 63°.$$

$$a = \frac{56 \sin 46°}{\sin 63°} \qquad \text{Multiply both sides by } \sin 46° \text{ and solve for } a.$$

$$a \approx 45.2 \text{ inches} \qquad \text{Use a calculator.}$$

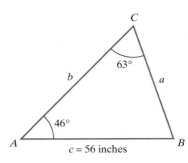

Figure 6.3 (repeated)

Use the Law of Sines again, this time to find b.

$$\frac{b}{\sin B} = \frac{c}{\sin C}$$ We use the given ratio, $\frac{c}{\sin C}$, to find b.

$$\frac{b}{\sin 71°} = \frac{56}{\sin 63°}$$ We found that $B = 71°$. We are given $c = 56$ and $C = 63°$.

$$b = \frac{56 \sin 71°}{\sin 63°}$$ Multiply both sides by $\sin 71°$ and solve for b.

$$b \approx 59.4 \text{ inches}$$ Use a calculator.

The solution is $B = 71°$, $a \approx 45.2$ inches, and $b \approx 59.4$ inches.

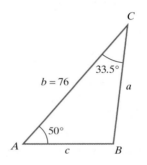

Figure 6.4

Check Point 1   Solve the triangle shown in Figure 6.4 with $A = 64°$, $C = 82°$, and $c = 14$ centimeters. Round as in Example 1.

EXAMPLE 2   Solving an ASA Triangle Using the Law of Sines

Solve triangle ABC if $A = 50°$, $C = 33.5°$, and $b = 76$. Round measures to the nearest tenth.

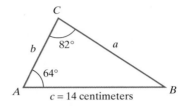

Figure 6.5 Solving an ASA triangle

Solution   We begin by drawing a picture of triangle ABC and labeling it with the given information. Figure 6.5 shows the triangle that we must solve. We begin by finding B.

$$A + B + C = 180°$$ The sum of the measures of a triangle's interior angles is 180°.

$$50° + B + 33.5° = 180°$$ $A = 50°$ and $C = 33.5°$.

$$83.5° + B = 180°$$ Add.

$$B = 96.5°$$ Subtract 83.5° from both sides.

Keep in mind that we must be given one of the three ratios to apply the Law of Sines. In this example, we are given that $b = 76$ and we found that $B = 96.5°$. Thus, we use the ratio $\dfrac{b}{\sin B}$, or $\dfrac{76}{\sin 96.5°}$, to find the other two sides. Use the Law of Sines to find a and c.

Find a: **Find c:**

This is the known ratio.

$$\frac{a}{\sin A} = \frac{b}{\sin B}$$ $$\frac{c}{\sin C} = \frac{b}{\sin B}$$

$$\frac{a}{\sin 50°} = \frac{76}{\sin 96.5°}$$ $$\frac{c}{\sin 33.5°} = \frac{76}{\sin 96.5°}$$

$$a = \frac{76 \sin 50°}{\sin 96.5°} \approx 58.6$$ $$c = \frac{76 \sin 33.5°}{\sin 96.5°} \approx 42.2$$

The solution is $B = 96.5°$, $a \approx 58.6$, and $c \approx 42.2$.

Check Point 2   Solve triangle ABC if $A = 40°$, $C = 22.5°$, and $b = 12$. Round as in Example 2.

Use the Law of Sines to solve, if possible, the triangle or triangles in the ambiguous case.

The Ambiguous Case (SSA)

If we are given two sides and an angle opposite one of them (SSA), does this determine a unique triangle? Can we solve this case using the Law of Sines? Such a case is called the **ambiguous case** because the given information may result in one triangle, two triangles, or no triangle at all. For example, in Figure 6.6, we are given a, b, and A. Because a is shorter than h, it is not long enough to form a triangle. The number of possible triangles, if any, that can be formed in the SSA case depends on h, the length of the altitude, where $h = b \sin A$.

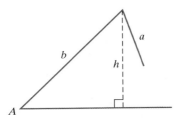

Figure 6.6 Given SSA, no triangle may result.

The Ambiguous Case (SSA)

Consider a triangle in which a, b, and A are given. This information may result in

One Triangle	One Right Triangle	No Triangle	Two Triangles

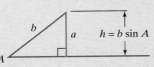

a is greater than h and a is greater than b. One triangle is formed.

$a = h$ and is just the right length to form a right triangle.

a is less than h and is not long enough to form a triangle.

a is greater than h and a is less than b. Two distinct triangles are formed.

In an SSA situation, it is not necessary to draw an accurate sketch like those shown in the box. The Law of Sines determines the number of triangles, if any, and gives the solution for each triangle.

EXAMPLE 3   Solving an SSA Triangle Using the Law of Sines (One Solution)

Solve triangle ABC if $A = 43°$, $a = 81$, and $b = 62$. Round lengths of sides to the nearest tenth and angle measures to the nearest degree.

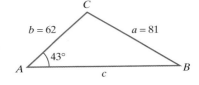

Figure 6.7 Solving an SSA triangle; the ambiguous case

Solution   We begin with the sketch in Figure 6.7. The known ratio is $\dfrac{a}{\sin A}$, or $\dfrac{81}{\sin 43°}$. Because side b is given, we use the Law of Sines to find angle B.

$$\frac{a}{\sin A} = \frac{b}{\sin B} \qquad \text{Apply the Law of Sines.}$$

$$\frac{81}{\sin 43°} = \frac{62}{\sin B} \qquad a = 81, b = 62, \text{ and } A = 43°.$$

$$81 \sin B = 62 \sin 43° \qquad \text{Cross multiply: If } \frac{a}{b} = \frac{c}{d}, \text{ then } ad = bc.$$

$$\sin B = \frac{62 \sin 43°}{81} \qquad \text{Divide both sides by 81 and solve for sin B.}$$

$$\sin B \approx 0.5220 \qquad \text{Use a calculator.}$$

There are two angles B between $0°$ and $180°$ for which $\sin B \approx 0.5220$.

$$B_1 \approx 31° \qquad\qquad B_2 \approx 180° - 31° = 149°$$

Obtain the acute angle with your calculator in degree mode: $\sin^{-1} 0.5220$.

The sine is positive in quadrant II.

Look at Figure 6.7. Given that $A = 43°$, can you see that $B_2 \approx 149°$ is impossible? By adding $149°$ to the given angle, $43°$, we exceed a $180°$ sum:

$$43° + 149° = 192°.$$

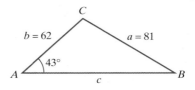

Figure 6.7 (repeated)

Thus, the only possibility is that $B_1 \approx 31°$. We find C using this approximation for B_1 and the measure that was given for A: $A = 43°$.

$$C = 180° - B_1 - A \approx 180° - 31° - 43° = 106°$$

Side c that lies opposite this 106° angle can now be found using the Law of Sines.

$\dfrac{c}{\sin C} = \dfrac{a}{\sin A}$	Apply the Law of Sines.
$\dfrac{c}{\sin 106°} = \dfrac{81}{\sin 43°}$	$a = 81, C \approx 106°,$ and $A = 43°.$
$c = \dfrac{81 \sin 106°}{\sin 43°} \approx 114.2$	Multiply both sides by sin 106° and solve for c.

There is one triangle and the solution is B_1(or B) $\approx 31°$, $C \approx 106°$, and $c \approx 114.2$.

Check Point 3 Solve triangle ABC if $A = 57°$, $a = 33$, and $b = 26$. Round as in Example 3.

EXAMPLE 4   Solving an SSA Triangle Using the Law of Sines (No Solution)

Solve triangle ABC if $A = 75°$, $a = 51$, and $b = 71$.

Solution   The known ratio is $\dfrac{a}{\sin A}$, or $\dfrac{51}{\sin 75°}$. Because side b is given, we use the Law of Sines to find angle B.

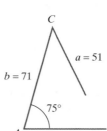

Figure 6.8 a is not long enough to form a triangle.

$\dfrac{a}{\sin A} = \dfrac{b}{\sin B}$	Use the Law of Sines.
$\dfrac{51}{\sin 75°} = \dfrac{71}{\sin B}$	Substitute the given values.
$51 \sin B = 71 \sin 75°$	Cross multiply: If $\dfrac{a}{b} = \dfrac{c}{d}$, then $ad = bc$.
$\sin B = \dfrac{71 \sin 75°}{51} \approx 1.34$	Divide by 51 and solve for sin B.

Because the sine can never exceed 1, there is no angle B for which $\sin B \approx 1.34$. There is no triangle with the given measurements, as illustrated in Figure 6.8.

Check Point 4 Solve triangle ABC if $A = 50°$, $a = 10$, and $b = 20$.

EXAMPLE 5   Solving an SSA Triangle Using the Law of Sines (Two Solutions)

Solve triangle ABC if $A = 40°$, $a = 54$, and $b = 62$. Round lengths of sides to the nearest tenth and angle measures to the nearest degree.

Solution   The known ratio is $\dfrac{a}{\sin A}$, or $\dfrac{54}{\sin 40°}$. We use the Law of Sines to find angle B.

$\dfrac{a}{\sin A} = \dfrac{b}{\sin B}$	Use the Law of Sines.
$\dfrac{54}{\sin 40°} = \dfrac{62}{\sin B}$	Substitute the given values.
$54 \sin B = 62 \sin 40°$	Cross multiply: If $\dfrac{a}{b} = \dfrac{c}{d}$, then $ad = bc$.
$\sin B = \dfrac{62 \sin 40°}{54} \approx 0.7380$	Divide by 54 and solve for sin B.

There are two angles B between $0°$ and $180°$ for which $\sin B \approx 0.7380$.

$$B_1 \approx 48° \qquad\qquad B_2 \approx 180° - 48° = 132°$$

Find $\sin^{-1} 0.7380$
with your calculator.

The sine is positive in
quadrant II.

If you add either angle to the given angle, $40°$, the sum does not exceed $180°$. Thus, there are two triangles with the given conditions, shown in Figure 6.9(a). The triangles, AB_1C_1 and AB_2C_2, are shown separately in Figure 6.9(b) and 6.9(c).

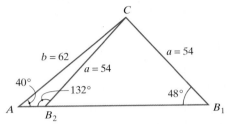

(a) Two triangles are possible with $A = 40°$, $a = 54$, and $b = 62$.

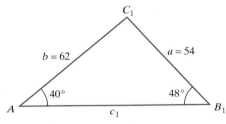

(b) In one possible triangle, $B_1 = 48°$.

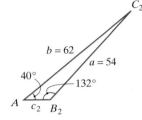

(c) In the second possible triangle, $B_2 = 132°$.

Figure 6.9

Study Tip

The two triangles shown in Figure 6.9 are helpful in organizing the solutions. However, if you keep track of the two triangles, one with the given information and $B_1 = 48°$, and the other with the given information and $B_2 = 132°$, you do not have to draw the figure to solve the triangles.

We find angles C_1 and C_2 using a $180°$ angle sum in each of the two triangles.

$$
\begin{aligned}
C_1 &= 180° - A - B_1 \\
&\approx 180° - 40° - 48° \\
&= 92°
\end{aligned}
\qquad\qquad
\begin{aligned}
C_2 &= 180° - A - B_2 \\
&\approx 180° - 40° - 132° \\
&= 8°
\end{aligned}
$$

We use the Law of Sines to find c_1 and c_2.

$$\frac{c_1}{\sin C_1} = \frac{a}{\sin A} \qquad\qquad \frac{c_2}{\sin C_2} = \frac{a}{\sin A}$$

$$\frac{c_1}{\sin 92°} = \frac{54}{\sin 40°} \qquad\qquad \frac{c_2}{\sin 8°} = \frac{54}{\sin 40°}$$

$$c_1 = \frac{54 \sin 92°}{\sin 40°} \approx 84.0 \qquad\qquad c_2 = \frac{54 \sin 8°}{\sin 40°} \approx 11.7$$

There are two triangles. In one triangle, the solution is $B_1 \approx 48°$, $C_1 \approx 92°$, and $c_1 \approx 84.0$. In the other triangle, $B_2 \approx 132°$, $C_2 \approx 8°$, and $c_2 \approx 11.7$.

Check Point 5 Solve triangle ABC if $A = 35°$, $a = 12$, and $b = 16$. Round as in Example 5.

The Area of an Oblique Triangle

3 Find the area of an oblique triangle using the sine function.

A formula for the area of an oblique triangle can be obtained using the procedure for proving the Law of Sines. We draw an altitude of length h from one of the vertices of the triangle, as shown in Figure 6.10. We apply the definition of the sine of angle A, $\dfrac{\text{opposite}}{\text{hypotenuse}}$, in right triangle ACD:

$$\sin A = \frac{h}{b}, \quad \text{so} \quad h = b \sin A.$$

The area of a triangle is $\frac{1}{2}$ the product of any side and the altitude drawn to that side. Using the altitude h in Figure 6.10, we have

$$\text{Area} = \frac{1}{2} ch = \frac{1}{2} cb \sin A.$$

Use the result from
above: $h = b \sin A$.

Figure 6.10

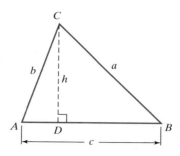

Figure 6.10 (repeated)

This result, Area $= \frac{1}{2} cb \sin A$, or $\frac{1}{2} bc \sin A$, indicates that the area of the triangle is one-half the product of b and c times the sine of their included angle. If we draw altitudes from the other two vertices, we can use any two sides to compute the area.

> ### Area of An Oblique Triangle
> The area of a triangle equals one-half the product of the lengths of two sides times the sine of their included angle. In Figure 6.10, this wording can be expressed by the formulas
> $$\text{Area} = \tfrac{1}{2} bc \sin A = \tfrac{1}{2} ab \sin C = \tfrac{1}{2} ac \sin B.$$

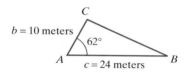

Figure 6.11 Finding the area of an SAS triangle

EXAMPLE 6   Finding the Area of an Oblique Triangle

Find the area of a triangle having two sides of lengths 24 meters and 10 meters and an included angle of 62°. Round to the nearest square meter.

Solution   The triangle is shown in Figure 6.11. Its area is half the product of the lengths of the two sides times the sine of the included angle.

$$\text{Area} = \tfrac{1}{2}(24)(10)(\sin 62°) \approx 106$$

The area of the triangle is approximately 106 square meters.

Check Point 6   Find the area of a triangle having two sides of lengths 8 meters and 12 meters and an included angle of 135°. Round to the nearest square meter.

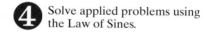

Solve applied problems using the Law of Sines.

Applications of the Law of Sines

We have seen how the trigonometry of right triangles can be used to solve many different kinds of applied problems. The Law of Sines enables us to work with triangles that are not right triangles. As a result, this law can be used to solve problems involving surveying, engineering, astronomy, navigation, and the environment. Example 7 illustrates the use of the Law of Sines in detecting potentially devastating fires.

EXAMPLE 7   An Application of the Law of Sines

Two fire-lookout stations are 20 miles apart, with station B directly east of station A. Both stations spot a fire on a mountain to the north. The bearing from station A to the fire is N50°E (50° east of north). The bearing from station B to the fire is N36°W (36° west of north). How far, to the nearest tenth of a mile, is the fire from station A?

Solution   Figure 6.12 shows the information given in the problem. The distance from station A to the fire is represented by b. Notice that the angles describing the bearing from each station to the fire, 50° and 36°, are not interior angles of triangle ABC. Using a north-south line, the interior angles are found as follows:

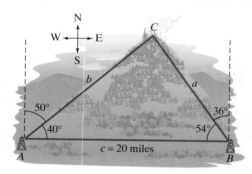

Figure 6.12

$$A = 90° - 50° = 40° \qquad B = 90° - 36° = 54°.$$

To find b using the Law of Sines, we need a known side and an angle opposite that side. Because $c = 20$ miles, we find angle C using a 180° angle sum in the triangle. Thus,

$$C = 180° - A - B = 180° - 40° - 54° = 86°.$$

The ratio $\frac{c}{\sin C}$, or $\frac{20}{\sin 86°}$, is now known. We use this ratio and the Law of Sines to find b.

$$\frac{b}{\sin B} = \frac{c}{\sin C} \qquad \text{Use the Law of Sines.}$$

$$\frac{b}{\sin 54°} = \frac{20}{\sin 86°} \qquad c = 20, B = 54°, \text{ and } C = 86°.$$

$$b = \frac{20 \sin 54°}{\sin 86°} \approx 16.2 \qquad \text{Multiply both sides by } \sin 54° \text{ and solve for } b.$$

The fire is approximately 16.2 miles from station A.

Check Point 7 Two fire-lookout stations are 13 miles apart, with station B directly east of station A. Both stations spot a fire. The bearing of the fire from station A is N35°E and the bearing of the fire from station B is N49°W. How far, to the nearest tenth of a mile, is the fire from station B?

EXERCISE SET 6.1

Practice Exercises

In Exercises 1–8, solve each triangle. Round lengths of sides to the nearest tenth and angle measures to the nearest degree.

1.
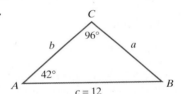

2.
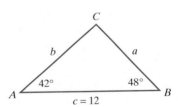

3.
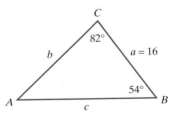

4.
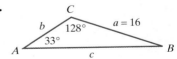

5.
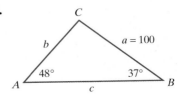

6.
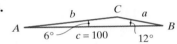

7.
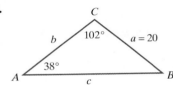

8.
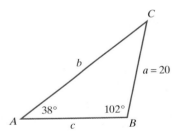

In Exercises 9–16, solve each triangle. Round lengths to the nearest tenth and angle measures to the nearest degree.

9. $A = 44°, B = 25°, a = 12$

10. $A = 56°, C = 24°, a = 22$

11. $B = 85°, C = 15°, b = 40$

12. $A = 85°, B = 35°, c = 30$

13. $A = 115°, C = 35°, c = 200$

14. $B = 5°, C = 125°, b = 200$

15. $A = 65°, B = 65°, c = 6$

16. $B = 80°, C = 10°, a = 8$

In Exercises 17–32, two sides and an angle (SSA) of a triangle are given. Determine whether the given measurements produce one triangle, two triangles, or no triangle at all. Solve each triangle that results. Round to the nearest tenth and the nearest degree for sides and angles, respectively.

17. $a = 20, b = 15, A = 40°$ **18.** $a = 30, b = 20, A = 50°$

19. $a = 10, c = 8.9, A = 63°$ **20.** $a = 57.5, c = 49.8, A = 136°$

21. $a = 42.1, c = 37, A = 112°$

22. $a = 6.1, b = 4, A = 162°$

23. $a = 10, b = 40, A = 30°$

24. $a = 10, b = 30, A = 150°$

25. $a = 16, b = 18, A = 60°$

26. $a = 30, b = 40, A = 20°$

27. $a = 12, b = 16.1, A = 37°$

28. $a = 7, b = 28, A = 12°$

29. $a = 22, c = 24.1, A = 58°$

30. $a = 95, c = 125, A = 49°$

31. $a = 9.3, b = 41, A = 18°$

32. $a = 1.4, b = 2.9, A = 142°$

In Exercises 33–38, find the area of the triangle having the given measurements. Round to the nearest square unit.

33. $A = 48°, b = 20$ feet, $c = 40$ feet

34. $A = 22°, b = 20$ feet, $c = 50$ feet

35. $B = 36°, a = 3$ yards, $c = 6$ yards

36. $B = 125°, a = 8$ yards, $c = 5$ yards

37. $C = 124°, a = 4$ meters, $b = 6$ meters

38. $C = 102°, a = 16$ meters, $b = 20$ meters

 Practice Plus

In Exercises 39–40, find h to the nearest tenth.

39.

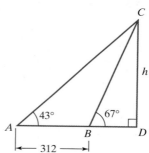

40.

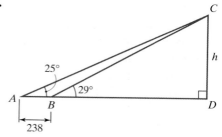

In Exercises 41–42, find a to the nearest tenth.

41.

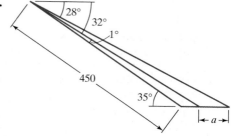

42.

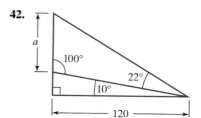

In Exercises 43–44, use the given measurements to solve the following triangle. Round lengths of sides to the nearest tenth and angle measures to the nearest degree.

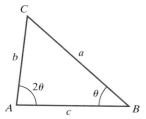

43. $a = 300, b = 200$ **44.** $a = 400, b = 300$

In Exercises 45–46, find the area of the triangle with the given vertices. Round to the nearest square unit.

45. $(-3, -2), (2, -2), (1, 2)$ **46.** $(-2, -3), (-2, 2), (2, 1)$

 Application Exercises

47. Two fire-lookout stations are 10 miles apart, with station B directly east of station A. Both stations spot a fire. The bearing of the fire from station A is N25°E and the bearing of the fire from station B is N56°W. How far, to the nearest tenth of a mile, is the fire from each lookout station?

48. The Federal Communications Commission is attempting to locate an illegal radio station. It sets up two monitoring stations, A and B, with station B 40 miles east of station A. Station A measures the illegal signal from the radio station as coming from a direction of 48° east of north. Station B measures the signal as coming from a point 34° west of north. How far is the illegal radio station from monitoring stations A and B? Round to the nearest tenth of a mile.

49. The figure shows a 1200-yard-long sand beach and an oil platform in the ocean. The angle made with the platform from one end of the beach is 85° and from the other end is 76°. Find the distance of the oil platform, to the nearest tenth of a yard, from each end of the beach.

50. A surveyor needs to determine the distance between two points that lie on opposite banks of a river. The figure shows that 300 yards are measured along one bank. The angles from each end of this line segment to a point on the opposite bank are 62° and 53°. Find the distance between A and B to the nearest tenth of a yard.

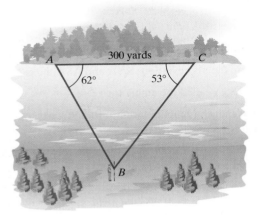

51. Closed to tourists since 1990, the Leaning Tower of Pisa in Italy leans at an angle of about 84.7°. The figure shows that 171 feet from the base of the tower, the angle of elevation to the top is 50°. Find the distance, to the nearest tenth of a foot, from the base to the top of the tower.

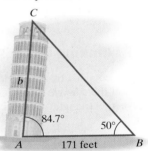

52. A pine tree growing on a hillside makes a 75° angle with the hill. From a point 80 feet up the hill, the angle of elevation to the top of the tree is 62° and the angle of depression to the bottom is 23°. Find, to the nearest tenth of a foot, the height of the tree.

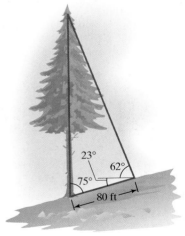

53. The figure shows a shot-put ring. The shot is tossed from A and lands at B. Using modern electronic equipment, the distance of the toss can be measured without the use of measuring tapes. When the shot lands at B, an electronic transmitter

placed at B sends a signal to a device in the official's booth above the track. The device determines the angles at B and C. At a track meet, the distance from the official's booth to the shot-put ring is 562 feet. If $B = 85.3°$ and $C = 5.7°$, determine the length of the toss to the nearest tenth of a foot.

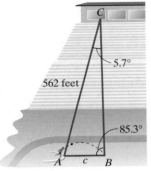

54. A pier forms an 85° angle with a straight shore. At a distance of 100 feet from the pier, the line of sight to the tip forms a 37° angle. Find the length of the pier to the nearest tenth of a foot.

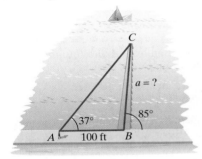

55. When the angle of elevation of the sun is 62°, a telephone pole that is tilted at an angle of 8° directly away from the sun casts a shadow 20 feet long. Determine the length of the pole to the nearest tenth of a foot.

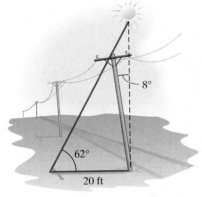

56. A leaning wall is inclined 6° from the vertical. At a distance of 40 feet from the wall, the angle of elevation to the top is 22°. Find the height of the wall to the nearest tenth of a foot.

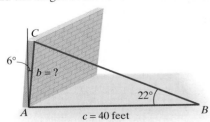

57. Redwood trees in California's Redwood National Park are hundreds of feet tall. The height of one of these trees is represented by *h* in the figure shown.

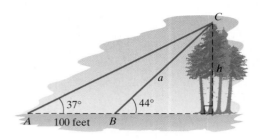

a. Use the measurements shown to find *a*, to the nearest tenth of a foot, in oblique triangle *ABC*.

b. Use the right triangle shown to find the height, to the nearest tenth of a foot, of a typical redwood tree in the park.

58. The figure shows a cable car that carries passengers from *A* to *C*. Point *A* is 1.6 miles from the base of the mountain. The angles of elevation from *A* and *B* to the mountain's peak are 22° and 66°, respectively.

a. Determine, to the nearest tenth of a foot, the distance covered by the cable car.

b. Find *a*, to the nearest tenth of a foot, in oblique triangle *ABC*.

c. Use the right triangle to find the height of the mountain to the nearest tenth of a foot.

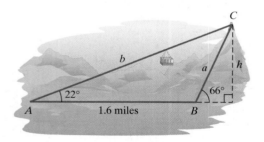

59. Lighthouse B is 7 miles west of lighthouse A. A boat leaves A and sails 5 miles. At this time, it is sighted from B. If the bearing of the boat from B is N62°E, how far from B is the boat? Round to the nearest tenth of a mile.

60. After a wind storm, you notice that your 16-foot flagpole may be leaning, but you are not sure. From a point on the ground 15 feet from the base of the flagpole, you find that the angle of elevation to the top is 48°. Is the flagpole leaning? If so, find the acute angle, to the nearest degree, that the flagpole makes with the ground.

Writing in Mathematics

61. What is an oblique triangle?

62. Without using symbols, state the Law of Sines in your own words.

63. Briefly describe how the Law of Sines is proved.

64. What does it mean to solve an oblique triangle?

65. What do the abbreviations SAA and ASA mean?

66. Why is SSA called the ambiguous case?

67. How is the sine function used to find the area of an oblique triangle?

68. Write an original problem that can be solved using the Law of Sines. Then solve the problem.

69. Use Exercise 53 to describe how the Law of Sines is used for throwing events at track and field meets. Why aren't tape measures used to determine tossing distance?

70. You are cruising in your boat parallel to the coast, looking at a lighthouse. Explain how you can use your boat's speed and a device for measuring angles to determine the distance at any instant from your boat to the lighthouse.

Critical Thinking Exercises

71. If you are given two sides of a triangle and their included angle, you can find the triangle's area. Can the Law of Sines be used to solve the triangle with this given information? Explain your answer.

72. Two buildings of equal height are 800 feet apart. An observer on the street between the buildings measures the angles of elevation to the tops of the buildings as 27° and 41°, respectively. How high, to the nearest foot, are the buildings?

73. The figure shows the design for the top of the wing of a jet fighter. The fuselage is 5 feet wide. Find the wing span *CC'* to the nearest tenth of a foot.

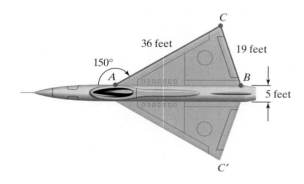

SECTION 6.2   The Law of Cosines

Objectives

❶ Use the Law of Cosines to solve oblique triangles.

❷ Solve applied problems using the Law of Cosines.

❸ Use Heron's formula to find the area of a triangle.

Paleontologists use trigonometry to study the movements made by dinosaurs millions of years ago. Figure 6.13, based on data collected at Dinosaur Valley State Park in Glen Rose, Texas, shows footprints made by a two-footed carnivorous (meat-eating) dinosaur and the hindfeet of a herbivorous (plant-eating) dinosaur.

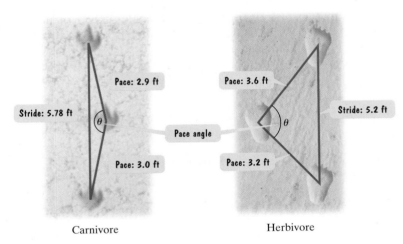

Carnivore   Herbivore

Figure 6.13 Dinosaur Footprints

Source: Glen J. Kuban, *An Overview of Dinosaur Tracking*

For each dinosaur, the figure indicates the *pace* and the *stride*. The pace is the distance from the left footprint to the right footprint, and vice versa. The stride is the distance from the left footprint to the next left footprint or from the right footprint to the next right footprint. Also shown in Figure 6.13 is the pace angle, designated by θ. Notice that neither dinosaur moves with a pace angle of $180°$, meaning that the footprints are directly in line. The footprints show a "zig-zig" pattern that is numerically described by the pace angle. A dinosaur that is an efficient walker has a pace angle close to $180°$, minimizing zig-zag motion and maximizing forward motion.

How can we determine the pace angles for the carnivore and the herbivore in Figure 6.13? Problems such as this, in which we know the measures of three sides of a triangle and we need to find the measurement of a missing angle, cannot be solved by the Law of Sines. To numerically describe which dinosaur in Figure 6.13 made more forward progress with each step, we turn to the Law of Cosines.

The Law of Cosines and Its Derivation

We now look at another relationship that exists among the sides and angles in an oblique triangle. **The Law of Cosines** is used to solve triangles in which two sides and the included angle (SAS) are known, or those in which three sides (SSS) are known.

Discovery

What happens to the Law of Cosines

$$c^2 = a^2 + b^2 - 2ab \cos C$$

if $C = 90°$? What familiar theorem do you obtain?

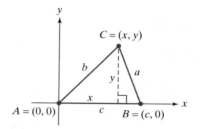

Figure 6.14

The Law of Cosines

If A, B, and C are the measures of the angles of a triangle, and a, b, and c are the lengths of the sides opposite these angles, then

$$a^2 = b^2 + c^2 - 2bc \cos A$$
$$b^2 = a^2 + c^2 - 2ac \cos B$$
$$c^2 = a^2 + b^2 - 2ab \cos C.$$

The square of a side of a triangle equals the sum of the squares of the other two sides minus twice their product times the cosine of their included angle.

To prove the Law of Cosines, we place triangle ABC in a rectangular coordinate system. Figure 6.14 shows a triangle with three acute angles. The vertex A is at the origin and side c lies along the positive x-axis. The coordinates of C are (x, y). Using the right triangle that contains angle A, we apply the definitions of the cosine and the sine.

$$\cos A = \frac{x}{b} \qquad\qquad \sin A = \frac{y}{b}$$

$$x = b \cos A \qquad\qquad y = b \sin A \qquad \text{Multiply both sides of each equation by } b \text{ and solve for } x \text{ and } y, \text{ respectively.}$$

Thus, the coordinates of C are $(x, y) = (b \cos A, b \sin A)$. Although triangle ABC in Figure 6.14 shows angle A as an acute angle, if A is obtuse, the coordinates of C are still $(b \cos A, b \sin A)$. This means that our proof applies to both kinds of oblique triangles.

We now apply the distance formula to the side of the triangle with length a. Notice that a is the distance from (x, y) to $(c, 0)$.

$$a = \sqrt{(x - c)^2 + (y - 0)^2} \qquad \text{Use the distance formula.}$$

$$a^2 = (x - c)^2 + y^2 \qquad \text{Square both sides of the equation.}$$

$$a^2 = (b \cos A - c)^2 + (b \sin A)^2 \qquad x = b \cos A \text{ and } y = b \sin A.$$

$$a^2 = b^2 \cos^2 A - 2bc \cos A + c^2 + b^2 \sin^2 A \qquad \text{Square the two expressions.}$$

$$a^2 = b^2 \sin^2 A + b^2 \cos^2 A + c^2 - 2bc \cos A \qquad \text{Rearrange terms.}$$

$$a^2 = b^2(\sin^2 A + \cos^2 A) + c^2 - 2bc \cos A \qquad \text{Factor } b^2 \text{ from the first two terms.}$$

$$a^2 = b^2 + c^2 - 2bc \cos A \qquad \sin^2 A + \cos^2 A = 1$$

The resulting equation is one of the three formulas for the Law of Cosines. The other two formulas are derived in a similar manner.

① Use the Law of Cosines to solve oblique triangles.

Solving Oblique Triangles

If you are given two sides and an included angle (SAS) of an oblique triangle, none of the three ratios in the Law of Sines is known. This means that we do not begin solving the triangle using the Law of Sines. Instead, we apply the Law of Cosines and the following procedure:

Solving an SAS Triangle

1. Use the Law of Cosines to find the side opposite the given angle.
2. Use the Law of Sines to find the angle opposite the shorter of the two given sides. This angle is always acute.
3. Find the third angle by subtracting the measure of the given angle and the angle found in step 2 from 180°.

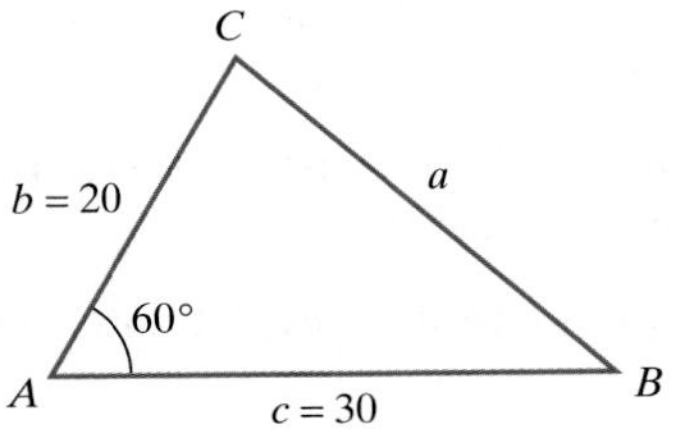

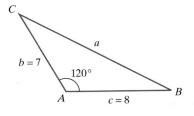

Figure 6.15 Solving an SAS triangle

EXAMPLE 1   Solving an SAS Triangle

Solve the triangle in Figure 6.15 with $A = 60°, b = 20$, and $c = 30$. Round lengths of sides to the nearest tenth and angle measures to the nearest degree.

Solution   We are given two sides and an included angle. Therefore, we apply the three-step procedure for solving an SAS triangle.

Step 1   Use the Law of Cosines to find the side opposite the given angle. Thus, we will find a.

$$a^2 = b^2 + c^2 - 2bc \cos A \qquad \text{Apply the Law of Cosines to find } a.$$

$$a^2 = 20^2 + 30^2 - 2(20)(30) \cos 60° \qquad b = 20, c = 30, \text{ and } A = 60°.$$

$$= 400 + 900 - 1200(0.5) \qquad \text{Perform the indicated operations.}$$

$$= 700$$

$$a = \sqrt{700} \approx 26.5 \qquad \text{Take the square root of both sides and solve for } a.$$

Step 2   Use the Law of Sines to find the angle opposite the shorter of the two given sides. This angle is always acute. The shorter of the two given sides is $b = 20$. Thus, we will find acute angle B.

$$\frac{b}{\sin B} = \frac{a}{\sin A} \qquad \text{Apply the Law of Sines.}$$

$$\frac{20}{\sin B} = \frac{\sqrt{700}}{\sin 60°} \qquad \text{We are given } b = 20 \text{ and } A = 60°. \text{ Use the exact value of } a, \sqrt{700}, \text{ from step 1.}$$

$$\sqrt{700} \sin B = 20 \sin 60° \qquad \text{Cross multiply: If } \frac{a}{b} = \frac{c}{d}, \text{ then } ad = bc.$$

$$\sin B = \frac{20 \sin 60°}{\sqrt{700}} \approx 0.6547 \qquad \text{Divide by } \sqrt{700} \text{ and solve for } \sin B.$$

$$B \approx 41° \qquad \text{Find } \sin^{-1} 0.6547 \text{ using a calculator.}$$

Step 3   Find the third angle. Subtract the measure of the given angle and the angle found in step 2 from 180°.

$$C = 180° - A - B \approx 180° - 60° - 41° = 79°$$

The solution is $a \approx 26.5$, $B \approx 41°$, and $C \approx 79°$.

Check Point 1   Solve the triangle shown in Figure 6.16 with $A = 120°, b = 7$, and $c = 8$. Round as in Example 1.

Figure 6.16

If you are given three sides of a triangle (SSS), solving the triangle involves finding the three angles. We use the following procedure:

Solving an SSS Triangle

1. Use the Law of Cosines to find the angle opposite the longest side.

2. Use the Law of Sines to find either of the two remaining acute angles.

3. Find the third angle by subtracting the measures of the angles found in steps 1 and 2 from 180°.

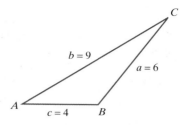

Figure 6.17 Solving an SSS triangle

EXAMPLE 2   Solving an SSS Triangle

Solve triangle ABC if $a = 6, b = 9$, and $c = 4$. Round angle measures to the nearest degree.

Solution   We are given three sides. Therefore, we apply the three-step procedure for solving an SSS triangle. The triangle is shown in Figure 6.17.

Step 1   Use the Law of Cosines to find the angle opposite the longest side. The longest side is $b = 9$. Thus, we will find angle B.

$$b^2 = a^2 + c^2 - 2ac \cos B \qquad \text{Apply the Law of Cosines to find } B.$$
$$2ac \cos B = a^2 + c^2 - b^2 \qquad \text{Solve for } \cos B.$$
$$\cos B = \frac{a^2 + c^2 - b^2}{2ac}$$
$$\cos B = \frac{6^2 + 4^2 - 9^2}{2 \cdot 6 \cdot 4} = -\frac{29}{48} \qquad a = 6, b = 9, \text{ and } c = 4.$$

Using a calculator, $\cos^{-1}\left(\frac{29}{48}\right) \approx 53°$. Because $\cos B$ is negative, B is an obtuse angle. Thus,

$$B \approx 180° - 53° = 127°. \qquad \text{Because the domain of } y = \cos^{-1} x \text{ is } [0, \pi], \text{ you}$$
$$\text{can use a calculator to find } \cos^{-1}\left(-\frac{29}{48}\right) \approx 127°.$$

Step 2   Use the Law of Sines to find either of the two remaining acute angles. We will find angle A.

$$\frac{a}{\sin A} = \frac{b}{\sin B} \qquad \text{Apply the Law of Sines.}$$
$$\frac{6}{\sin A} = \frac{9}{\sin 127°} \qquad \begin{array}{l}\text{We are given } a = 6 \text{ and } b = 9. \text{ We found} \\ \text{that } B \approx 127°.\end{array}$$
$$9 \sin A = 6 \sin 127° \qquad \text{Cross multiply.}$$
$$\sin A = \frac{6 \sin 127°}{9} \approx 0.5324 \qquad \text{Divide by 9 and solve for } \sin A.$$
$$A \approx 32° \qquad \text{Find } \sin^{-1} 0.5324 \text{ using a calculator.}$$

Step 3   Find the third angle. Subtract the measures of the angles found in steps 1 and 2 from 180°.

$$C = 180° - B - A \approx 180° - 127° - 32° = 21°$$

The solution is $B \approx 127°$, $A \approx 32°$, and $C \approx 21°$.

Check Point 2   Solve triangle ABC if $a = 8, b = 10$, and $c = 5$. Round angle measures to the nearest degree.

Applications of the Law of Cosines

Applied problems involving SAS and SSS triangles can be solved using the Law of Cosines.

2 Solve applied problems using the Law of Cosines.

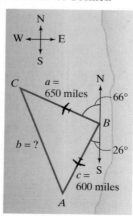

Figure 6.18

EXAMPLE 3   An Application of the Law of Cosines

Two airplanes leave an airport at the same time on different runways. One flies on a bearing of N66°W at 325 miles per hour. The other airplane flies on a bearing of S26°W at 300 miles per hour. How far apart will the airplanes be after two hours?

Solution   After two hours, the plane flying at 325 miles per hour travels $325 \cdot 2$ miles, or 650 miles. Similarly, the plane flying at 300 miles per hour travels 600 miles. The situation is illustrated in Figure 6.18.

Let $b =$ the distance between the planes after two hours. We can use a north-south line to find angle B in triangle ABC. Thus,

$$B = 180° - 66° - 26° = 88°.$$

We now have $a = 650$, $c = 600$, and $B = 88°$. We use the Law of Cosines to find b in this SAS situation.

$$b^2 = a^2 + c^2 - 2ac \cos B \qquad \text{Apply the Law of Cosines.}$$

$$b^2 = 650^2 + 600^2 - 2(650)(600) \cos 88° \qquad \text{Substitute: } a = 650, c = 600, \text{ and } B = 88°.$$

$$\approx 755{,}278 \qquad \text{Use a calculator.}$$

$$b \approx \sqrt{755{,}278} \approx 869 \qquad \text{Take the square root and solve for } b.$$

After two hours, the planes are approximately 869 miles apart.

Check Point 3 Two airplanes leave an airport at the same time on different runways. One flies directly north at 400 miles per hour. The other airplane flies on a bearing of N75°E at 350 miles per hour. How far apart will the airplanes be after two hours?

③ Use Heron's formula to find the area of a triangle.

Heron's Formula

Approximately 2000 years ago, the Greek mathematician Heron of Alexandria derived a formula for the area of a triangle in terms of the lengths of its sides. A more modern derivation uses the Law of Cosines and can be found in the appendix.

> **Heron's Formula for the Area of a Triangle**
>
> The area of a triangle with sides a, b, and c is
>
> $$\text{Area} = \sqrt{s(s - a)(s - b)(s - c)},$$
>
> where s is one-half its perimeter: $s = \frac{1}{2}(a + b + c)$.

EXAMPLE 4   Using Heron's Formula

Find the area of the triangle with $a = 12$ yards, $b = 16$ yards, and $c = 24$ yards. Round to the nearest square yard.

Solution   Begin by calculating one-half the perimeter:

$$s = \frac{1}{2}(a + b + c) = \frac{1}{2}(12 + 16 + 24) = 26.$$

Use Heron's formula to find the area:

$$\text{Area} = \sqrt{s(s - a)(s - b)(s - c)}$$
$$= \sqrt{26(26 - 12)(26 - 16)(26 - 24)}$$
$$= \sqrt{7280} \approx 85.$$

The area of the triangle is approximately 85 square yards.

Check Point 4 Find the area of the triangle with $a = 6$ meters, $b = 16$ meters, and $c = 18$ meters. Round to the nearest square meter.

EXERCISE SET 6.2

Practice Exercises

In Exercises 1–8, solve each triangle. Round lengths of sides to the nearest tenth and angle measures to the nearest degree.

1.

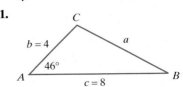

2.

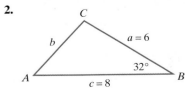

3.

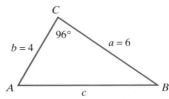

4.

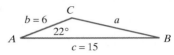

5.

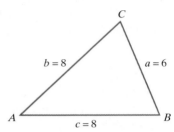

6.

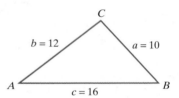

7.

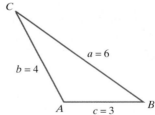

8.

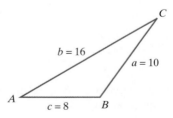

In Exercises 9–24, solve each triangle. Round lengths to the nearest tenth and angle measures to the nearest degree.

9. $a = 5, b = 7, C = 42°$ **10.** $a = 10, b = 3, C = 15°$

11. $b = 5, c = 3, A = 102°$ **12.** $b = 4, c = 1, A = 100°$

13. $a = 6, c = 5, B = 50°$ **14.** $a = 4, c = 7, B = 55°$

15. $a = 5, c = 2, B = 90°$ **16.** $a = 7, c = 3, B = 90°$

17. $a = 5, b = 7, c = 10$ **18.** $a = 4, b = 6, c = 9$

19. $a = 3, b = 9, c = 8$

20. $a = 4, b = 7, c = 6$

21. $a = 3, b = 3, c = 3$

22. $a = 5, b = 5, c = 5$

23. $a = 63, b = 22, c = 50$

24. $a = 66, b = 25, c = 45$

In Exercises 25–30, use Heron's formula to find the area of each triangle. Round to the nearest square unit.

25. $a = 4$ feet, $b = 4$ feet, $c = 2$ feet

26. $a = 5$ feet, $b = 5$ feet, $c = 4$ feet

27. $a = 14$ meters, $b = 12$ meters, $c = 4$ meters

28. $a = 16$ meters, $b = 10$ meters, $c = 8$ meters

29. $a = 11$ yards, $b = 9$ yards, $c = 7$ yards

30. $a = 13$ yards, $b = 9$ yards, $c = 5$ yards

Practice Plus

In Exercises 31–32, solve each triangle. Round lengths of sides to the nearest tenth and angle measures to the nearest degree.

31.

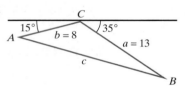

32.

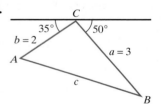

In Exercises 33–34, the three circles are arranged so that they touch each other, as shown in the figure. Use the given radii for the circles with centers A, B, and C, respectively, to solve triangle ABC. Round angle measures to the nearest degree.

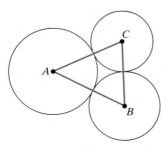

33. 5.0, 4.0, 3.5   **34.** 7.5, 4.3, 3.0

In Exercises 35–36, the three given points are the vertices of a triangle. Solve each triangle, rounding lengths of sides to the nearest tenth and angle measures to the nearest degree.

35. $A(0,0), B(-3,4), C(3,-1)$

36. $A(0,0), B(4,-3), C(1,-5)$

Application Exercises

37. Use Figure 6.13 on page 639 to find the pace angle, to the nearest degree, for the carnivore. Does the angle indicate that this dinosaur was an efficient walker? Describe your answer.

38. Use Figure 6.13 on page 639 to find the pace angle, to the nearest degree, for the herbivore. Does the angle indicate that this dinosaur was an efficient walker? Describe your answer.

39. Two ships leave a harbor at the same time. One ship travels on a bearing of S12°W at 14 miles per hour. The other ship travels on a bearing of N75°E at 10 miles per hour. How far apart will the ships be after three hours? Round to the nearest tenth of a mile.

40. A plane leaves airport A and travels 580 miles to airport B on a bearing of N34°E. The plane later leaves airport B and travels to airport C 400 miles away on a bearing of S74°E. Find the distance from airport A to airport C to the nearest tenth of a mile.

41. Find the distance across the lake from A to C, to the nearest yard, using the measurements shown in the figure.

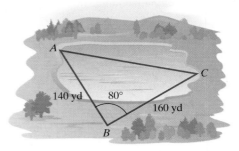

42. To find the distance across a protected cove at a lake, a surveyor makes the measurements shown in the figure. Use these measurements to find the distance from A to B to the nearest yard.

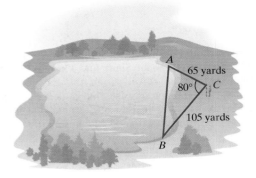

The diagram shows three islands in Florida Bay. You rent a boat and plan to visit each of these remote islands. Use the diagram to solve Exercises 43–44.

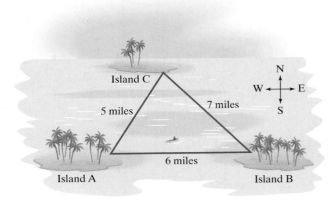

43. If you are on island A, on what bearing should you navigate to go to island C?

44. If you are on island B, on what bearing should you navigate to go to island C?

45. You are on a fishing boat that leaves its pier and heads east. After traveling for 25 miles, there is a report warning of rough seas directly south. The captain turns the boat and follows a bearing of S40°W for 13.5 miles.

   a. At this time, how far are you from the boat's pier? Round to the nearest tenth of a mile.

   b. What bearing could the boat have originally taken to arrive at this spot?

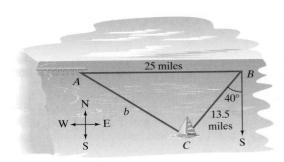

46. You are on a fishing boat that leaves its pier and heads east. After traveling for 30 miles, there is a report warning of rough seas directly south. The captain turns the boat and follows a bearing of S45°W for 12 miles.

   a. At this time, how far are you from the boat's pier? Round to the nearest tenth of a mile.

   b. What bearing could the boat have originally taken to arrive at this spot?

47. The figure shows a 400-foot tower on the side of a hill that forms a 7° angle with the horizontal. Find the length of each of the two guy wires that are anchored 80 feet uphill and downhill from the tower's base and extend to the top of the tower. Round to the nearest tenth of a foot.

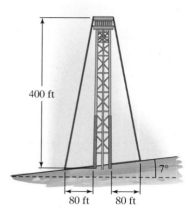

400 ft

7°

80 ft   80 ft

48. The figure shows a 200-foot tower on the side of a hill that forms a 5° angle with the horizontal. Find the length of each of the two guy wires that are anchored 150 feet uphill and downhill from the tower's base and extend to the top of the tower. Round to the nearest tenth of a foot.

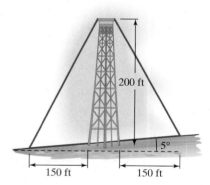

200 ft

5°

150 ft   150 ft

49. A Major League baseball diamond has four bases forming a square whose sides measure 90 feet each. The pitcher's mound is 60.5 feet from home plate on a line joining home plate and second base. Find the distance from the pitcher's mound to first base. Round to the nearest tenth of a foot.

50. A Little League baseball diamond has four bases forming a square whose sides measure 60 feet each. The pitcher's mound is 46 feet from home plate on a line joining home plate and second base. Find the distance from the pitcher's mound to third base. Round to the nearest tenth of a foot.

51. A piece of commercial real estate is priced at $3.50 per square foot. Find the cost, to the nearest dollar, of a triangular lot measuring 240 feet by 300 feet by 420 feet.

52. A piece of commercial real estate is priced at $4.50 per square foot. Find the cost, to the nearest dollar, of a triangular lot measuring 320 feet by 510 feet by 410 feet.

Writing in Mathematics

53. Without using symbols, state the Law of Cosines in your own words.

54. Why can't the Law of Sines be used in the first step to solve an SAS triangle?

55. Describe a strategy for solving an SAS triangle.

56. Describe a strategy for solving an SSS triangle.

57. Under what conditions would you use Heron's formula to find the area of a triangle?

58. Describe an applied problem that can be solved using the Law of Cosines, but not the Law of Sines.

59. The pitcher on a Little League team is studying angles in geometry and has a question. "Coach, suppose I'm on the pitcher's mound facing home plate. I catch a fly ball hit in my direction. If I turn to face first base and throw the ball, through how many degrees should I turn for a direct throw?" Use the information given in Exercise 50 and write an answer to the pitcher's question. Without getting too technical, describe to the pitcher how you obtained this angle.

Critical Thinking Exercises

60. The lengths of the diagonals of a parallelogram are 20 inches and 30 inches. The diagonals intersect at an angle of 35°. Find the lengths of the parallelogram's sides. (*Hint*: Diagonals of a parallelogram bisect one another.)

61. Use the figure to solve triangle ABC. Round lengths of sides to the nearest tenth and angle measures to the nearest degree.

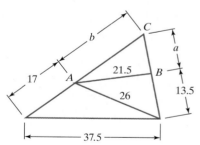

62. The minute hand and the hour hand of a clock have lengths m inches and h inches, respectively. Determine the distance between the tips of the hands at 10:00 in terms of m and h.

Group Exercise

63. The group should design five original problems that can be solved using the Laws of Sines and Cosines. At least two problems should be solved using the Law of Sines, one should be the ambiguous case, and at least two problems should be solved using the Law of Cosines. At least one problem should be an application problem using the Law of Sines and at least one problem should involve an application using the Law of Cosines. The group should turn in both the problems and their solutions.

SECTION 6.3   *Polar Coordinates*

Objectives

❶ Plot points in the polar coordinate system.

❷ Find multiple sets of polar coordinates for a given point.

❸ Convert a point from polar to rectangular coordinates.

❹ Convert a point from rectangular to polar coordinates.

❺ Convert an equation from rectangular to polar coordinates.

❻ Convert an equation from polar to rectangular coordinates.

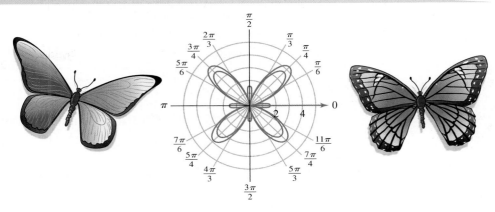

Butterflies are among the most celebrated of all insects. It's hard not to notice their beautiful colors and graceful flight. Their symmetry can be explored with trigonometric functions and a system for plotting points called the *polar coordinate system*. In many cases, polar coordinates are simpler and easier to use than rectangular coordinates.

Plotting Points in the Polar Coordinate System

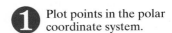

❶ Plot points in the polar coordinate system.

The foundation of the polar coordinate system is a horizontal ray that extends to the right. The ray is called the **polar axis** and is shown in Figure 6.19. The endpoint of the ray is called the **pole**.

A point P in the polar coordinate system is represented by an ordered pair of numbers (r, θ). Figure 6.20 shows $P = (r, \theta)$ in the polar coordinate system.

Figure 6.19

Figure 6.20 Representing a point in the polar coordinate system

- r is a directed distance from the pole to P. (We shall see that r can be positive, negative, or zero.)

- θ is an angle from the polar axis to the line segment from the pole to P. This angle can be measured in degrees or radians. Positive angles are measured counterclockwise from the polar axis. Negative angles are measured clockwise from the polar axis.

We refer to the ordered pair (r, θ) as the **polar coordinates** of P.

Let's look at a specific example. Suppose that the polar coordinates of a point P are $\left(3, \dfrac{\pi}{4}\right)$. Because θ is positive, we locate this point by drawing $\theta = \dfrac{\pi}{4}$ counterclockwise from the polar axis. Then we count out a distance of three units along the terminal side of the angle to reach the point P. Figure 6.21 shows that $(r, \theta) = \left(3, \dfrac{\pi}{4}\right)$ lies three units from the pole on the terminal side of the angle $\theta = \dfrac{\pi}{4}$.

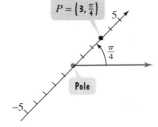

Figure 6.21 Locating a point in polar coordinates

The sign of r is important in locating $P = (r, \theta)$ in polar coordinates.

> ### The Sign of r and a Point's Location in Polar Coordinates
>
> The point $P = (r, \theta)$ is located $|r|$ units from the pole. If $r > 0$, the point lies on the terminal side of θ. If $r < 0$, the point lies along the ray opposite the terminal side of θ. If $r = 0$, the point lies at the pole, regardless of the value of θ.

EXAMPLE 1 Plotting Points in a Polar Coordinate System

Plot the points with the following polar coordinates:

   a. $(2, 135°)$ **b.** $\left(-3, \dfrac{3\pi}{2}\right)$ **c.** $\left(-1, -\dfrac{\pi}{4}\right)$.

Solution

a. To plot the point $(r, \theta) = (2, 135°)$, begin with the $135°$ angle. Because $135°$ is a positive angle, draw $\theta = 135°$ counterclockwise from the polar axis. Now consider $r = 2$. Because $r > 0$, plot the point by going out two units on the terminal side of θ. Figure 6.22(a) shows the point.

b. To plot the point $(r, \theta) = \left(-3, \dfrac{3\pi}{2}\right)$, begin with the $\dfrac{3\pi}{2}$ angle. Because $\dfrac{3\pi}{2}$ is a positive angle, we draw $\theta = \dfrac{3\pi}{2}$ counterclockwise from the polar axis. Now consider $r = -3$. Because $r < 0$, plot the point by going out three units along the ray *opposite* the terminal side of θ. Figure 6.22(b) shows the point.

c. To plot the point $(r, \theta) = \left(-1, -\dfrac{\pi}{4}\right)$, begin with the $-\dfrac{\pi}{4}$ angle. Because $-\dfrac{\pi}{4}$ is a negative angle, draw $\theta = -\dfrac{\pi}{4}$ clockwise from the polar axis. Now consider $r = -1$. Because $r < 0$, plot the point by going out one unit along the ray *opposite* the terminal side of θ. Figure 6.22(c) shows the point.

> ## Study Tip
>
> Wondering where the concentric circles in Figure 6.22 came from and why we've shown them? The circles are drawn to help plot each point at the appropriate distance from the pole.

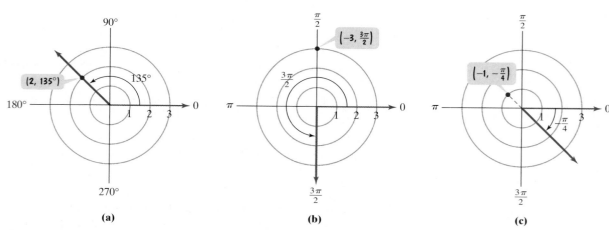

Figure 6.22 Plotting points

(a)   **(b)**   **(c)**

Check Point 1   Plot the points with the following polar coordinates:

   a. $(3, 315°)$ **b.** $(-2, \pi)$ **c.** $\left(-1, -\dfrac{\pi}{2}\right)$.

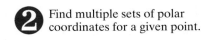

② Find multiple sets of polar coordinates for a given point.

Discovery

Illustrate the statements in the voice balloons by plotting the points with the following polar coordinates:

a. $\left(1, \dfrac{\pi}{2}\right)$ and $\left(1, \dfrac{5\pi}{2}\right)$

b. $\left(3, \dfrac{\pi}{4}\right)$ and $\left(-3, \dfrac{5\pi}{4}\right)$.

Multiple Representations of Points in the Polar Coordinate System

In rectangular coordinates, each point (x, y) has exactly one representation. By contrast, any point in polar coordinates can be represented in infinitely many ways. For example,

$$(r, \theta) = (r, \theta + 2\pi) \qquad \text{and} \qquad (r, \theta) = (-r, \theta + \pi).$$

> Adding 1 revolution, or 2π radians, to the angle does not change the point's location.

> Adding $\frac{1}{2}$ revolution, or π radians, to the angle and replacing r with $-r$ does not change the point's location.

Thus, to find two other representations for the point (r, θ),

- Add 2π to the angle and do not change r.
- Add π to the angle and replace r with $-r$.

Continually adding or subtracting 2π in either of these representations does not change the point's location.

> **Multiple Representations of Points**
>
> If n is any integer, the point (r, θ) can be represented as
> $$(r, \theta) = (r, \theta + 2n\pi) \quad \text{or} \quad (r, \theta) = (-r, \theta + \pi + 2n\pi).$$

EXAMPLE 2   Finding Other Polar Coordinates for a Given Point

The point $\left(2, \dfrac{\pi}{3}\right)$ is plotted in Figure 6.23. Find another representation of this point in which

a. r is positive and $2\pi < \theta < 4\pi$.

b. r is negative and $0 < \theta < 2\pi$.

c. r is positive and $-2\pi < \theta < 0$.

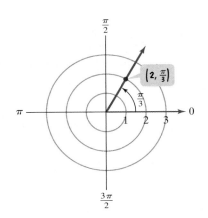

Figure 6.23 Finding other representations of a given point

Solution

a. We want $r > 0$ and $2\pi < \theta < 4\pi$. Using $\left(2, \dfrac{\pi}{3}\right)$, add 2π to the angle and do not change r.

$$\left(2, \frac{\pi}{3}\right) = \left(2, \frac{\pi}{3} + 2\pi\right) = \left(2, \frac{\pi}{3} + \frac{6\pi}{3}\right) = \left(2, \frac{7\pi}{3}\right)$$

b. We want $r < 0$ and $0 < \theta < 2\pi$. Using $\left(2, \dfrac{\pi}{3}\right)$, add π to the angle and replace r with $-r$.

$$\left(2, \frac{\pi}{3}\right) = \left(-2, \frac{\pi}{3} + \pi\right) = \left(-2, \frac{\pi}{3} + \frac{3\pi}{3}\right) = \left(-2, \frac{4\pi}{3}\right)$$

c. We want $r > 0$ and $-2\pi < \theta < 0$. Using $\left(2, \dfrac{\pi}{3}\right)$, subtract 2π from the angle and do not change r.

$$\left(2, \frac{\pi}{3}\right) = \left(2, \frac{\pi}{3} - 2\pi\right) = \left(2, \frac{\pi}{3} - \frac{6\pi}{3}\right) = \left(2, -\frac{5\pi}{3}\right)$$

Check Point 2 Find another representation of $\left(5, \dfrac{\pi}{4}\right)$ in which

a. r is positive and $2\pi < \theta < 4\pi$.

b. r is negative and $0 < \theta < 2\pi$.

c. r is positive and $-2\pi < \theta < 0$.

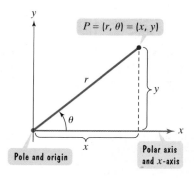

Figure 6.24 Polar and rectangular coordinate systems

Relations between Polar and Rectangular Coordinates

We now consider both polar and rectangular coordinates simultaneously. Figure 6.24 shows the two coordinate systems. The polar axis coincides with the positive x-axis and the pole coincides with the origin. A point P, other than the origin, has rectangular coordinates (x, y) and polar coordinates (r, θ), as indicated in the figure. We wish to find equations relating the two sets of coordinates. From the figure, we see that

$$x^2 + y^2 = r^2$$
$$\sin \theta = \frac{y}{r} \qquad \cos \theta = \frac{x}{r} \qquad \tan \theta = \frac{y}{x}.$$

These relationships hold when P is in any quadrant and when $r > 0$ or $r < 0$.

Relations between Polar and Rectangular Coordinates

$$x = r \cos \theta$$
$$y = r \sin \theta$$
$$x^2 + y^2 = r^2$$
$$\tan \theta = \frac{y}{x}$$

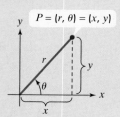

---

3 Convert a point from polar to rectangular coordinates.

Point Conversion from Polar to Rectangular Coordinates

To convert a point from polar coordinates (r, θ) to rectangular coordinates (x, y), use the formulas $x = r \cos \theta$ and $y = r \sin \theta$.

EXAMPLE 3 Polar-to-Rectangular Point Conversion

Find the rectangular coordinates of the points with the following polar coordinates:

a. $\left(2, \dfrac{3\pi}{2}\right)$ b. $\left(-8, \dfrac{\pi}{3}\right)$.

Solution We find (x, y) by substituting the given values for r and θ into $x = r \cos \theta$ and $y = r \sin \theta$.

a. We begin with the rectangular coordinates of the point $(r, \theta) = \left(2, \dfrac{3\pi}{2}\right)$.

$$x = r \cos \theta = 2 \cos \frac{3\pi}{2} = 2 \cdot 0 = 0$$

$$y = r \sin \theta = 2 \sin \frac{3\pi}{2} = 2(-1) = -2$$

The rectangular coordinates of $\left(2, \dfrac{3\pi}{2}\right)$ are $(0, -2)$. See Figure 6.25.

b. We now find the rectangular coordinates of the point $(r, \theta) = \left(-8, \dfrac{\pi}{3}\right)$.

$$x = r \cos \theta = -8 \cos \frac{\pi}{3} = -8\left(\frac{1}{2}\right) = -4$$

$$y = r \sin \theta = -8 \sin \frac{\pi}{3} = -8\left(\frac{\sqrt{3}}{2}\right) = -4\sqrt{3}$$

The rectangular coordinates of $\left(-8, \dfrac{\pi}{3}\right)$ are $\left(-4, -4\sqrt{3}\right)$.

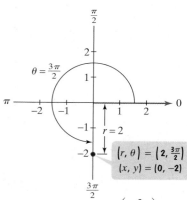

Figure 6.25 Converting $\left(2, \dfrac{3\pi}{2}\right)$ to rectangular coordinates

Technology

Some graphing utilities can convert a point from polar coordinates to rectangular coordinates. Consult your manual. The screen on the right verifies the polar-rectangular conversion in Example 3(a). It shows that the rectangular coordinates of

$(r, \theta) = \left(2, \dfrac{3\pi}{2}\right)$ are $(0, -2)$. Notice that the x- and y-coordinates are displayed separately.

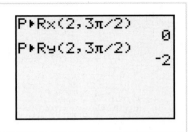

```
P►Rx(2,3π/2)
                    0
P►Ry(2,3π/2)
                   -2
```

Check Point 3 Find the rectangular coordinates of the points with the following polar coordinates:

    a. $(3, \pi)$ **b.** $\left(-10, \dfrac{\pi}{6}\right)$.

④ Convert a point from rectangular to polar coordinates.

Point Conversion from Rectangular to Polar Coordinates

Conversion from rectangular coordinates (x, y) to polar coordinates (r, θ) is a bit more complicated. Keep in mind that there are infinitely many representations for a point in polar coordinates. If the point (x, y) lies in one of the four quadrants, we will use a representation in which

- r is positive, and
- θ is the smallest positive angle with the terminal side passing through (x, y).

These conventions provide the following procedure:

> **Converting a Point from Rectangular to Polar Coordinates**
> $(r > 0$ and $0 \le \theta < 2\pi)$
>
> **1.** Plot the point (x, y).
> **2.** Find r by computing the distance from the origin to (x, y): $r = \sqrt{x^2 + y^2}$.
> **3.** Find θ using $\tan \theta = \dfrac{y}{x}$ with the terminal side θ passing through (x, y).

EXAMPLE 4   Rectangular-to-Polar Point Conversion

Find polar coordinates of the point whose rectangular coordinates are $\left(-1, \sqrt{3}\right)$.

Solution We begin with $(x, y) = \left(-1, \sqrt{3}\right)$ and use our three-step procedure to find a set of polar coordinates (r, θ).

Step 1 Plot the point (x, y). The point $\left(-1, \sqrt{3}\right)$ is plotted in quadrant II in Figure 6.26.

Step 2 Find r by computing the distance from the origin to (x, y).

$$r = \sqrt{x^2 + y^2} = \sqrt{(-1)^2 + \left(\sqrt{3}\right)^2} = \sqrt{1 + 3} = \sqrt{4} = 2$$

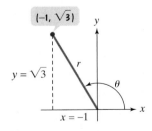

Figure 6.26 Converting $\left(-1, \sqrt{3}\right)$ to polar coordinates

Step 3 Find θ using $\tan \theta = \dfrac{y}{x}$ with the terminal side of θ passing through (x, y).

$$\tan \theta = \frac{y}{x} = \frac{\sqrt{3}}{-1} = -\sqrt{3}$$

We know that $\tan \dfrac{\pi}{3} = \sqrt{3}$. Because θ lies in quadrant II,

$$\theta = \pi - \frac{\pi}{3} = \frac{3\pi}{3} - \frac{\pi}{3} = \frac{2\pi}{3}.$$

One representation of $\left(-1, \sqrt{3}\right)$ in polar coordinates is $(r, \theta) = \left(2, \dfrac{2\pi}{3}\right)$.

Technology

The screen shows the rectangular-polar conversion for $(-1, \sqrt{3})$ on a graphing utility. In Example 4, we showed that $(x, y) = (-1, \sqrt{3})$ can be represented in polar coordinates as $(r, \theta) = \left(2, \dfrac{2\pi}{3}\right)$.

Using $\dfrac{2\pi}{3} \approx 2.09439510239$ verifies that our conversion is correct. Notice that the r- and (approximate) θ-coordinates are displayed separately.

```
R▸Pr(-1,√(3))
              2
R▸Pθ(-1,√(3))
       2.094395102
```

Check Point 4 Find polar coordinates of the point whose rectangular coordinates are $\left(1, -\sqrt{3}\right)$.

If a point (x, y) lies on a positive or negative axis, we use a representation in which

- r is positive, and
- θ is the smallest quadrantal angle that lies on the same positive or negative axis as (x, y).

In these cases, you can find r and θ by plotting (x, y) and inspecting the figure. Let's see how this is done.

EXAMPLE 5   Rectangular-to-Polar Point Conversion

Find polar coordinates of the point whose rectangular coordinates are $(-2, 0)$.

Solution   We begin with $(x, y) = (-2, 0)$ and find a set of polar coordinates (r, θ).

Step 1   Plot the point (x, y). The point $(-2, 0)$ is plotted in Figure 6.27.

Step 2   Find r, the distance from the origin to (x, y). Can you tell by looking at Figure 6.27 that this distance is 2?

$$r = \sqrt{x^2 + y^2} = \sqrt{(-2)^2 + 0^2} = \sqrt{4} = 2$$

Step 3   Find θ with θ lying on the same positive or negative axis as (x, y). The point $(-2, 0)$ is on the negative x-axis. Thus, θ lies on the negative x-axis and $\theta = \pi$. One representation of $(-2, 0)$ in polar coordinates is $(2, \pi)$.

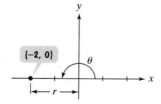

Figure 6.27 Converting $(-2, 0)$ to polar coordinates

Check Point 5 Find polar coordinates of the point whose rectangular coordinates are $(0, -4)$.

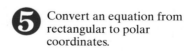

⑤ Convert an equation from rectangular to polar coordinates.

Equation Conversion from Rectangular to Polar Coordinates

A **polar equation** is an equation whose variables are r and θ. Two examples of polar equations are

$$r = \frac{5}{\cos \theta + \sin \theta} \quad \text{and} \quad r = 3 \csc \theta.$$

To convert a rectangular equation in x and y to a polar equation in r and θ, replace x with $r \cos \theta$ and y with $r \sin \theta$.

EXAMPLE 6   Converting Equations from Rectangular to Polar Coordinates

Convert each rectangular equation to a polar equation that expresses r in terms of θ:

a. $x + y = 5$ **b.** $(x - 1)^2 + y^2 = 1$.

Solution   Our goal is to obtain equations in which the variables are r and θ, rather than x and y. We use $x = r \cos \theta$ and $y = r \sin \theta$. We then solve the equations for r, obtaining equivalent equations that give r in terms of θ.

a.
$$x + y = 5$$
This is the given equation in rectangular coordinates. The graph is a line passing through $(5, 0)$ and $(0, 5)$.

$$r \cos \theta + r \sin \theta = 5$$
Replace x with $r \cos \theta$ and y with $r \sin \theta$.

$$r(\cos \theta + \sin \theta) = 5$$
Factor out r.

$$r = \frac{5}{\cos \theta + \sin \theta}$$
Divide both sides of the equation by $\cos \theta + \sin \theta$ and solve for r.

Thus, the polar equation for $x + y = 5$ is $r = \dfrac{5}{\cos \theta + \sin \theta}$.

b.
$$(x - 1)^2 + y^2 = 1$$
This is the given equation in rectangular coordinates. The graph is a circle with radius 1 and center at $(h, k) = (1, 0)$.

> The standard form of a circle's equation is $(x - h)^2 + (y - k)^2 = r^2$, with radius r and center at (h, k).

$$(r \cos \theta - 1)^2 + (r \sin \theta)^2 = 1$$
Replace x with $r \cos \theta$ and y with $r \sin \theta$.

$$r^2 \cos^2 \theta - 2r \cos \theta + 1 + r^2 \sin^2 \theta = 1$$
Use $(A - B)^2 = A^2 - 2AB + B^2$ to square $r \cos \theta - 1$.

$$r^2 \cos^2 \theta + r^2 \sin^2 \theta - 2r \cos \theta = 0$$
Subtract 1 from both sides and rearrange terms.

$$r^2 - 2r \cos \theta = 0$$
Simplify: $r^2 \cos^2 \theta + r^2 \sin^2 \theta = r^2(\cos^2 \theta + \sin^2 \theta) = r^2 \cdot 1 = r^2$.

$$r(r - 2 \cos \theta) = 0$$
Factor out r.

$$r = 0 \quad \text{or} \quad r - 2 \cos \theta = 0$$
Set each factor equal to 0.

$$r = 2 \cos \theta$$
Solve for r.

The graph of $r = 0$ is a single point, the pole. Because the pole also satisfies the equation $r = 2 \cos \theta$ (for $\theta = \frac{\pi}{2}, r = 0$), it is not necessary to include the equation $r = 0$. Thus, the polar equation for $(x - 1)^2 + y^2 = 1$ is $r = 2 \cos \theta$.

Check Point 6 Convert each rectangular equation to a polar equation that expresses r in terms of θ:

a. $3x - y = 6$ **b.** $x^2 + (y + 1)^2 = 1$.

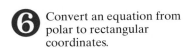

6 Convert an equation from polar to rectangular coordinates.

Equation Conversion from Polar to Rectangular Coordinates

When we convert an equation from polar to rectangular coordinates, our goal is to obtain an equation in which the variables are x and y, rather than r and θ. We use one or more of the following equations:

$$r^2 = x^2 + y^2 \qquad r \cos \theta = x \qquad r \sin \theta = y \qquad \tan \theta = \frac{y}{x}.$$

To use these equations, it is sometimes necessary to do something to the given polar equation. This could include squaring both sides, using an identity, taking the tangent of both sides, or multiplying both sides by r.

EXAMPLE 7   Converting Equations from Polar to Rectangular Form

Convert each polar equation to a rectangular equation in x and y:

a. $r = 5$ **b.** $\theta = \dfrac{\pi}{4}$ **c.** $r = 3 \csc \theta$ **d.** $r = -6 \cos \theta$.

Solution   In each case, let's express the rectangular equation in a form that enables us to recognize its graph.

a. We use $r^2 = x^2 + y^2$ to convert the polar equation $r = 5$ to a rectangular equation.

$$r = 5 \qquad \text{This is the given polar equation.}$$
$$r^2 = 25 \qquad \text{Square both sides.}$$
$$x^2 + y^2 = 25 \qquad \text{Use } r^2 = x^2 + y^2 \text{ on the left side.}$$

The rectangular equation for $r = 5$ is $x^2 + y^2 = 25$. The graph is a circle with center at $(0, 0)$ and radius 5.

b. We use $\tan \theta = \dfrac{y}{x}$ to convert the polar equation $\theta = \dfrac{\pi}{4}$ to a rectangular equation in x and y.

$$\theta = \frac{\pi}{4} \qquad \text{This is the given polar equation.}$$
$$\tan \theta = \tan \frac{\pi}{4} \qquad \text{Take the tangent of both sides.}$$
$$\tan \theta = 1 \qquad \tan \frac{\pi}{4} = 1$$
$$\frac{y}{x} = 1 \qquad \text{Use } \tan \theta = \frac{y}{x} \text{ on the left side.}$$
$$y = x \qquad \text{Multiply both sides by } x.$$

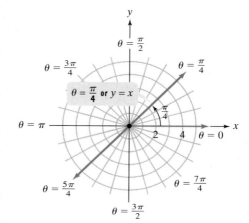

Figure 6.28

The rectangular equation for $\theta = \dfrac{\pi}{4}$ is $y = x$. The graph is a line that bisects quadrants I and III. Figure 6.28 shows the line drawn in a polar coordinate system.

c. We use $r \sin \theta = y$ to convert the polar equation $r = 3 \csc \theta$ to a rectangular equation. To do this, we express the cosecant in terms of the sine.

$$r = 3 \csc \theta \qquad \text{This is the given polar equation.}$$
$$r = \frac{3}{\sin \theta} \qquad \csc \theta = \frac{1}{\sin \theta}$$
$$r \sin \theta = 3 \qquad \text{Multiply both sides by } \sin \theta.$$
$$y = 3 \qquad \text{Use } r \sin \theta = y \text{ on the left side.}$$

The rectangular equation for $r = 3 \csc \theta$ is $y = 3$. The graph is a horizontal line 3 units above the x-axis. Figure 6.29 shows the line drawn in a polar coordinate system.

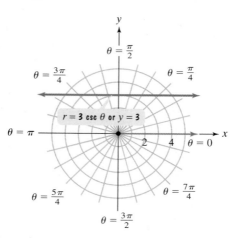

Figure 6.29

d. To convert $r = -6 \cos \theta$ to rectangular coordinates, we multiply both sides by r. Then we use $r^2 = x^2 + y^2$ on the left side and $r \cos \theta = x$ on the right side.

$$r = -6 \cos \theta \qquad \text{This is the given polar equation.}$$
$$r^2 = -6r \cos \theta \qquad \text{Multiply both sides by } r.$$
$$x^2 + y^2 = -6x \qquad \text{Convert to rectangular coordinates:}$$
$$\qquad\qquad\qquad\qquad r^2 = x^2 + y^2 \text{ and } r \cos \theta = x.$$
$$x^2 + 6x + y^2 = 0 \qquad \text{Add 6x to both sides.}$$
$$x^2 + 6x + 9 + y^2 = 9 \qquad \text{Complete the square on } x\text{: } \tfrac{1}{2} \cdot 6 = 3 \text{ and}$$
$$\qquad\qquad\qquad\qquad 3^2 = 9.$$
$$(x + 3)^2 + y^2 = 9 \qquad \text{Factor.}$$

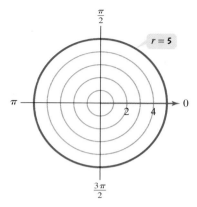

Figure 6.30 The equations $r = 5$ and $x^2 + y^2 = 25$ have the same graph.

The rectangular equation for $r = -6 \cos \theta$ is $(x + 3)^2 + y^2 = 9$.

This last equation is the standard form of the equation of a circle, $(x - h)^2 + (y - k)^2 = r^2$, with radius r and center at (h, k). Thus, the graph of $(x + 3)^2 + y^2 = 9$ is a circle with center at $(-3, 0)$ and radius 3.

Converting a polar equation to a rectangular equation may be a useful way to develop or check a graph. For example, the graph of the polar equation $r = 5$ consists of all points that are five units from the pole. Thus, the graph is a circle centered at the pole with radius 5. The rectangular equation for $r = 5$, namely $x^2 + y^2 = 25$, has precisely the same graph (see Figure 6.30). We will discuss graphs of polar equations in the next section.

Check Point 7 Convert each polar equation to a rectangular equation in x and y:

a. $r = 4$ **b.** $\theta = \dfrac{3\pi}{4}$ **c.** $r = -2 \sec \theta$ **d.** $r = 10 \sin \theta$.

EXERCISE SET 6.3

Practice Exercises

In Exercises 1–10, indicate if the point with the given polar coordinates is represented by A, B, C, or D on the graph.

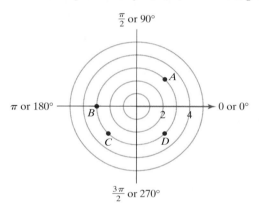

1. $(3, 225°)$ **2.** $(3, 315°)$ **3.** $\left(-3, \dfrac{5\pi}{4}\right)$

4. $\left(-3, \dfrac{\pi}{4}\right)$ **5.** $(3, \pi)$ **6.** $(-3, 0)$

7. $(3, -135°)$ **8.** $(3, -315°)$ **9.** $\left(-3, -\dfrac{3\pi}{4}\right)$

10. $\left(-3, -\dfrac{5\pi}{4}\right)$

In Exercises 11–20, use a polar coordinate system like the one shown for Exercises 1–10 to plot each point with the given polar coordinates.

11. $(2, 45°)$ **12.** $(1, 45°)$ **13.** $(3, 90°)$

14. $(2, 270°)$ **15.** $\left(3, \dfrac{4\pi}{3}\right)$ **16.** $\left(3, \dfrac{7\pi}{6}\right)$

17. $(-1, \pi)$ **18.** $\left(-1, \dfrac{3\pi}{2}\right)$ **19.** $\left(-2, -\dfrac{\pi}{2}\right)$

20. $(-3, -\pi)$

In Exercises 21–26, use a polar coordinate system like the one shown for Exercises 1–10 to plot each point with the given polar coordinates. Then find another representation (r, θ) of this point in which

a. $r > 0$, $2\pi < \theta < 4\pi$.

b. $r < 0$, $0 < \theta < 2\pi$.

c. $r > 0$, $-2\pi < \theta < 0$.

21. $\left(5, \dfrac{\pi}{6}\right)$ **22.** $\left(8, \dfrac{\pi}{6}\right)$ **23.** $\left(10, \dfrac{3\pi}{4}\right)$

24. $\left(12, \dfrac{2\pi}{3}\right)$ **25.** $\left(4, \dfrac{\pi}{2}\right)$ **26.** $\left(6, \dfrac{\pi}{2}\right)$

In Exercises 27–32, select the representations that do not change the location of the given point.

27. $(7, 140°)$
a. $(-7, 320°)$ **b.** $(-7, -40°)$
c. $(-7, 220°)$ **d.** $(7, -220°)$

28. $(4, 120°)$
a. $(-4, 300°)$ **b.** $(-4, -240°)$
c. $(4, -240°)$ **d.** $(4, 480°)$

29. $\left(2, -\dfrac{3\pi}{4}\right)$
a. $\left(2, -\dfrac{7\pi}{4}\right)$ **b.** $\left(2, \dfrac{5\pi}{4}\right)$
c. $\left(-2, -\dfrac{\pi}{4}\right)$ **d.** $\left(-2, -\dfrac{7\pi}{4}\right)$

30. $\left(-2, \dfrac{7\pi}{6}\right)$
a. $\left(-2, -\dfrac{5\pi}{6}\right)$ **b.** $\left(-2, -\dfrac{\pi}{6}\right)$
c. $\left(2, -\dfrac{\pi}{6}\right)$ **d.** $\left(2, \dfrac{\pi}{6}\right)$

31. $\left(-5, -\dfrac{\pi}{4}\right)$

    a. $\left(-5, \dfrac{7\pi}{4}\right)$ **b.** $\left(5, -\dfrac{5\pi}{4}\right)$

    c. $\left(-5, \dfrac{11\pi}{4}\right)$ **d.** $\left(5, \dfrac{\pi}{4}\right)$

32. $(-6, 3\pi)$

    a. $(6, 2\pi)$ **b.** $(6, -\pi)$

    c. $(-6, \pi)$ **d.** $(-6, -2\pi)$

In Exercises 33–40, polar coordinates of a point are given. Find the rectangular coordinates of each point.

33. $(4, 90°)$ **34.** $(6, 180°)$ **35.** $\left(2, \dfrac{\pi}{3}\right)$

36. $\left(2, \dfrac{\pi}{6}\right)$ **37.** $\left(-4, \dfrac{\pi}{2}\right)$ **38.** $\left(-6, \dfrac{3\pi}{2}\right)$

39. $(7.4, 2.5)$ **40.** $(8.3, 4.6)$

In Exercises 41–48, the rectangular coordinates of a point are given. Find polar coordinates of each point.

41. $(-2, 2)$ **42.** $(2, -2)$

43. $\left(2, -2\sqrt{3}\right)$ **44.** $\left(-2\sqrt{3}, 2\right)$

45. $\left(-\sqrt{3}, -1\right)$ **46.** $\left(-1, -\sqrt{3}\right)$

47. $(5, 0)$ **48.** $(0, -6)$

In Exercises 49–58, convert each rectangular equation to a polar equation that expresses r in terms of θ.

49. $3x + y = 7$ **50.** $x + 5y = 8$

51. $x = 7$ **52.** $y = 3$

53. $x^2 + y^2 = 9$ **54.** $x^2 + y^2 = 16$

55. $(x - 2)^2 + y^2 = 4$ **56.** $x^2 + (y + 3)^2 = 9$

57. $y^2 = 6x$ **58.** $x^2 = 6y$

In Exercises 59–74, convert each polar equation to a rectangular equation. Then use a rectangular coordinate system to graph the rectangular equation.

59. $r = 8$ **60.** $r = 10$

61. $\theta = \dfrac{\pi}{2}$ **62.** $\theta = \dfrac{\pi}{3}$

63. $r \sin \theta = 3$ **64.** $r \cos \theta = 7$

65. $r = 4 \csc \theta$ **66.** $r = 6 \sec \theta$

67. $r = \sin \theta$ **68.** $r = \cos \theta$

69. $r = 12 \cos \theta$ **70.** $r = -4 \sin \theta$

71. $r = 6 \cos \theta + 4 \sin \theta$ **72.** $r = 8 \cos \theta + 2 \sin \theta$

73. $r^2 \sin 2\theta = 2$ **74.** $r^2 \sin 2\theta = 4$

Practice Plus

In Exercises 75–78, show that each statement is true by converting the given polar equation to a rectangular equation.

75. Show that the graph of $r = a \sec \theta$ is a vertical line a units to the right of the y-axis if $a > 0$ and $|a|$ units to the left of the y-axis if $a < 0$.

76. Show that the graph of $r = a \csc \theta$ is a horizontal line a units above the x-axis if $a > 0$ and $|a|$ units below the x-axis if $a < 0$.

77. Show that the graph of $r = a \sin \theta$ is a circle with center at $\left(0, \dfrac{a}{2}\right)$ and radius $\dfrac{a}{2}$.

78. Show that the graph of $r = a \cos \theta$ is a circle with center at $\left(\dfrac{a}{2}, 0\right)$ and radius $\dfrac{a}{2}$.

In Exercises 79–80, convert each polar equation to a rectangular equation. Then determine the graph's slope and y-intercept.

79. $r \sin\left(\theta - \dfrac{\pi}{4}\right) = 2$ **80.** $r \cos\left(\theta + \dfrac{\pi}{6}\right) = 8$

In Exercises 81–82, find the rectangular coordinates of each pair of points. Then find the distance, in simplified radical form, between the points.

81. $\left(2, \dfrac{2\pi}{3}\right)$ and $\left(4, \dfrac{\pi}{6}\right)$ **82.** $(6, \pi)$ and $\left(5, \dfrac{7\pi}{4}\right)$

Application Exercises

Use the figure of the merry-go-round to solve Exercises 83–84. There are four circles of horses. Each circle is three feet from the next circle. The radius of the inner circle is 6 feet.

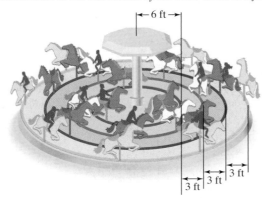

83. If a horse in the outer circle is $\dfrac{2}{3}$ of the way around the merry-go-round, give its polar coordinates.

84. If a horse in the inner circle is $\dfrac{5}{6}$ of the way around the merry-go-round, give its polar coordinates.

The wind is blowing at 10 knots. Sailboat racers look for a sailing angle to the 10-knot wind that produces maximum sailing speed. In this application, (r, θ) describes the sailing speed, r, in knots, at an angle θ to the 10-knot wind. Use this information to solve Exercises 85–87.

85. Interpret the polar coordinates: $(6.3, 50°)$.

86. Interpret the polar coordinates: $(7.4, 85°)$.

87. Four points in this 10-knot-wind situation are $(6.3, 50°)$, $(7.4, 85°)$, $(7.5, 105°)$, and $(7.3, 135°)$. Based on these points, which sailing angle to the 10-knot wind would you recommend to a serious sailboat racer? What sailing speed is achieved at this angle?

Writing in Mathematics

88. Explain how to plot (r, θ) if $r > 0$ and $\theta > 0$.

89. Explain how to plot (r, θ) if $r < 0$ and $\theta > 0$.

90. If you are given polar coordinates of a point, explain how to find two additional sets of polar coordinates for the point.

91. Explain how to convert a point from polar to rectangular coordinates. Provide an example with your explanation.

92. Explain how to convert a point from rectangular to polar coordinates. Provide an example with your explanation.

93. Explain how to convert from a rectangular equation to a polar equation.

94. In converting $r = 5$ from a polar equation to a rectangular equation, describe what should be done to both sides of the equation and why this should be done.

95. In converting $r = \sin \theta$ from a polar equation to a rectangular equation, describe what should be done to both sides of the equation and why this should be done.

96. Suppose that (r, θ) describes the sailing speed, r, in knots, at an angle θ to a wind blowing at 20 knots. You have a list of all ordered pairs (r, θ) for integral angles from $\theta = 0°$ to $\theta = 180°$. Describe a way to present this information so that a serious sailboat racer can visualize sailing speeds at different sailing angles to the wind.

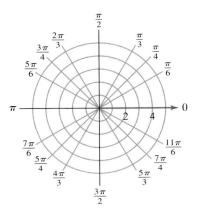

Technology Exercises

In Exercises 97–99, polar coordinates of a point are given. Use a graphing utility to find the rectangular coordinates of each point to three decimal places.

97. $\left(4, \dfrac{2\pi}{3}\right)$ **98.** $(5.2, 1.7)$ **99.** $(-4, 1.088)$

In Exercises 100–102, the rectangular coordinates of a point are given. Use a graphing utility to find polar coordinates of each point to three decimal places.

100. $(-5, 2)$ **101.** $\left(\sqrt{5}, 2\right)$

102. $(-4.308, -7.529)$

Critical Thinking Exercises

103. Prove that the distance, d, between two points with polar coordinates (r_1, θ_1) and (r_2, θ_2) is

$$d = \sqrt{r_1^2 + r_2^2 - 2r_1 r_2 \cos(\theta_2 - \theta_1)}.$$

104. Use the formula in Exercise 103 to find the distance between $\left(2, \dfrac{5\pi}{6}\right)$ and $\left(4, \dfrac{\pi}{6}\right)$. Express the answer in simplified radical form.

SECTION 6.4   *Graphs of Polar Equations*

Objectives

❶ Use point plotting to graph polar equations.

❷ Use symmetry to graph polar equations.

The America's Cup is the supreme event in ocean sailing. Competition is fierce and the costs are huge. Competitors look to mathematics to provide the critical innovation that can make the difference between winning and losing. In this section's exercise set, you will see how graphs of polar equations play a role in sailing faster using mathematics.

Using Polar Grids to Graph Polar Equations

Recall that a **polar equation** is an equation whose variables are r and θ. The **graph of a polar equation** is the set of all points whose polar coordinates satisfy the equation. We use **polar grids** like the one shown in Figure 6.31 to graph polar equations. The grid consists of circles with centers at the pole. This polar grid shows five such circles. A polar grid also shows lines passing through the pole. In this grid, each line represents an angle for which we know the exact values of the trigonometric functions.

Many polar coordinate grids show more circles and more lines through the pole than in Figure 6.31. See if your campus bookstore has paper with polar grids and use the polar graph paper throughout this section.

Figure 6.31 A polar coordinate grid

1 Use point plotting to graph polar equations.

Graphing a Polar Equation by Point Plotting

One method for graphing a polar equation such as $r = 4 \cos \theta$ is the **point-plotting method**. First, we make a table of values that satisfy the equation. Next, we plot these ordered pairs as points in the polar coordinate system. Finally, we connect the points with a smooth curve. This often gives us a picture of all ordered pairs (r, θ) that satisfy the equation.

EXAMPLE 1   Graphing an Equation Using the Point-Plotting Method

Graph the polar equation $r = 4 \cos \theta$ with θ in radians.

Solution   We construct a partial table of coordinates using multiples of $\dfrac{\pi}{6}$. Then we plot the points and join them with a smooth curve, as shown in Figure 6.32.

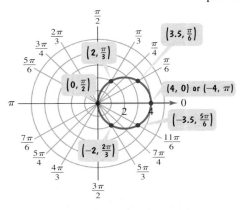

Figure 6.32 The graph of $r = 4 \cos \theta$

θ	$r = 4 \cos \theta$	(r, θ)
0	$4 \cos 0 = 4 \cdot 1 = 4$	$(4, 0)$
$\dfrac{\pi}{6}$	$4 \cos \dfrac{\pi}{6} = 4 \cdot \dfrac{\sqrt{3}}{2} = 2\sqrt{3} \approx 3.5$	$\left(3.5, \dfrac{\pi}{6}\right)$
$\dfrac{\pi}{3}$	$4 \cos \dfrac{\pi}{3} = 4 \cdot \dfrac{1}{2} = 2$	$\left(2, \dfrac{\pi}{3}\right)$
$\dfrac{\pi}{2}$	$4 \cos \dfrac{\pi}{2} = 4 \cdot 0 = 0$	$\left(0, \dfrac{\pi}{2}\right)$
$\dfrac{2\pi}{3}$	$4 \cos \dfrac{2\pi}{3} = 4\left(-\dfrac{1}{2}\right) = -2$	$\left(-2, \dfrac{2\pi}{3}\right)$
$\dfrac{5\pi}{6}$	$4 \cos \dfrac{5\pi}{6} = 4\left(-\dfrac{\sqrt{3}}{2}\right) = -2\sqrt{3} \approx -3.5$	$\left(-3.5, \dfrac{5\pi}{6}\right)$
π	$4 \cos \pi = 4(-1) = -4$	$(-4, \pi)$
Values of r repeat.		

TECHNOLOGY

A graphing utility can be used to obtain the graph of a polar equation. Use the polar mode with angle measure in radians. You must enter the minimum and maximum values for θ and an increment setting for θ, called θ step. θ step determines the number of points that the graphing utility will plot. Make θ step relatively small so that a significant number of points are plotted.

   Shown is the graph of $r = 4 \cos \theta$ in a $[-7.5, 7.5, 1]$ by $[-5, 5, 1]$ viewing rectangle with

$$\theta \min = 0$$
$$\theta \max = 2\pi$$
$$\theta \text{ step} = \dfrac{\pi}{48}.$$

A square setting was used.

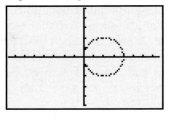

The graph of $r = 4 \cos \theta$ in Figure 6.32 looks like a circle of radius 2 whose center is at the point $(x, y) = (2, 0)$. We can verify this observation by changing the polar equation to a rectangular equation.

$r = 4 \cos \theta$	This is the given polar equation.
$r^2 = 4r \cos \theta$	Multiply both sides by r.
$x^2 + y^2 = 4x$	Convert to rectangular coordinates: $r^2 = x^2 + y^2$ and $r \cos \theta = x$.
$x^2 - 4x + y^2 = 0$	Subtract $4x$ from both sides.
$x^2 - 4x + 4 + y^2 = 4$	Complete the square on x: $\frac{1}{2}(-4) = -2$ and $(-2)^2 = 4$. Add 4 to both sides.
$(x - 2)^2 + y^2 = 2^2$	Factor.

This last equation is the standard form of the equation of a circle, $(x - h)^2 + (y - k)^2 = r^2$, with radius r and center at (h, k). Thus, the radius is 2 and the center is at $(h, k) = (2, 0)$.

   In general, circles have simpler equations in polar form than in rectangular form.

Circles in Polar Coordinates

The graphs of

$$r = a \cos \theta \quad \text{and} \quad r = a \sin \theta$$

are circles.

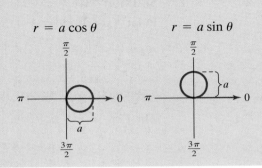

$$r = a \cos \theta \qquad\qquad r = a \sin \theta$$

Check Point 1 Graph the equation $r = 4 \sin \theta$ with θ in radians. Use multiples of $\dfrac{\pi}{6}$ from 0 to π to generate coordinates for points (r, θ).

② Use symmetry to graph polar equations.

Graphing a Polar Equation Using Symmetry

If the graph of a polar equation exhibits symmetry, you may be able to graph it more quickly. Three types of symmetry can be helpful.

Tests for Symmetry in Polar Coordinates

Symmetry with Respect to the Polar Axis (x-Axis)	Symmetry with Respect to the Line $\theta = \dfrac{\pi}{2}$ (y-Axis)	Symmetry with Respect to the Pole (Origin)

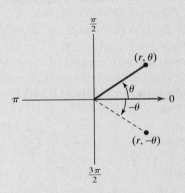 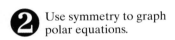 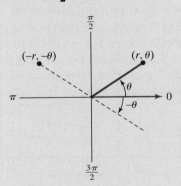 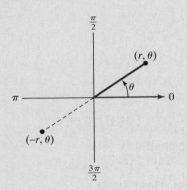

Replace θ with $-\theta$. If an equivalent equation results, the graph is symmetric with respect to the polar axis.

Replace (r, θ) with $(-r, -\theta)$. If an equivalent equation results, the graph is symmetric with respect to $\theta = \dfrac{\pi}{2}$.

Replace r with $-r$. If an equivalent equation results, the graph is symmetric with respect to the pole.

If a polar equation passes a symmetry test, then its graph exhibits that symmetry. By contrast, if a polar equation fails a symmetry test, then its graph *may or may not* have that kind of symmetry. Thus, the graph of a polar equation may have a symmetry even if it fails a test for that particular symmetry. Nevertheless, the symmetry tests are useful. If we detect symmetry, we can obtain a graph of the equation by plotting fewer points.

EXAMPLE 2   Graphing a Polar Equation Using Symmetry

Check for symmetry and then graph the polar equation:

$$r = 1 - \cos \theta.$$

Solution   We apply each of the tests for symmetry.

Polar Axis: Replace θ with $-\theta$ in $r = 1 - \cos \theta$:

$$r = 1 - \cos(-\theta) \qquad \text{Replace } \theta \text{ with } -\theta \text{ in } r = 1 - \cos \theta.$$
$$r = 1 - \cos \theta \qquad \text{The cosine function is even: } \cos(-\theta) = \cos \theta.$$

Because the polar equation does not change when θ is replaced with $-\theta$, the graph is symmetric with respect to the polar axis.

The Line $\theta = \dfrac{\pi}{2}$: Replace (r, θ) with $(-r, -\theta)$ in $r = 1 - \cos \theta$:

$$-r = 1 - \cos(-\theta) \qquad \text{Replace } r \text{ with } -r \text{ and } \theta \text{ with } -\theta \text{ in } r = 1 - \cos \theta.$$
$$-r = 1 - \cos \theta \qquad \cos(-\theta) = \cos \theta.$$
$$r = \cos \theta - 1 \qquad \text{Multiply both sides by } -1.$$

Because the polar equation $r = 1 - \cos \theta$ changes to $r = \cos \theta - 1$ when (r, θ) is replaced with $(-r, -\theta)$, the equation fails this symmetry test. The graph may or may not be symmetric with respect to the line $\theta = \dfrac{\pi}{2}$.

The Pole: Replace r with $-r$ in $r = 1 - \cos \theta$:

$$-r = 1 - \cos \theta \qquad \text{Replace } r \text{ with } -r \text{ in } r = 1 - \cos \theta.$$
$$r = \cos \theta - 1 \qquad \text{Multiply both sides by } -1.$$

Because the polar equation $r = 1 - \cos \theta$ changes to $r = \cos \theta - 1$ when r is replaced with $-r$, the equation fails this symmetry test. The graph may or may not be symmetric with respect to the pole.

Now we are ready to graph $r = 1 - \cos \theta$. Because the period of the cosine function is 2π, we need not consider values of θ beyond 2π. Recall that we discovered the graph of the equation $r = 1 - \cos \theta$ has symmetry with respect to the polar axis. Because the graph has this symmetry, we can obtain a complete graph by plotting fewer points. Let's start by finding the values of r for values of θ from 0 to π.

The values for r and θ are in the table above Figure 6.33(a). These values can be obtained using your calculator or possibly with the TABLE feature on some graphing calculators. The points in the table are plotted in Figure 6.33(a). Examine the graph. Keep in mind that the graph must be symmetric with respect to the polar axis. Thus, if we reflect the graph in Figure 6.33(a) about the polar axis, we will obtain a complete graph of $r = 1 - \cos \theta$. This graph is shown in Figure 6.33(b).

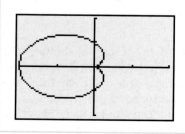
θ	0	$\dfrac{\pi}{6}$	$\dfrac{\pi}{3}$	$\dfrac{\pi}{2}$	$\dfrac{2\pi}{3}$	$\dfrac{5\pi}{6}$	π
r	0	0.13	0.5	1	1.5	1.87	2

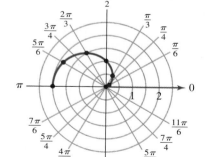

(a) The graph of $r = 1 - \cos \theta$ for $0 \le \theta \le \pi$

(b) A complete graph of $r = 1 - \cos \theta$

Figure 6.33 Graphing $r = 1 - \cos \theta$

Check Point 2 Check for symmetry and then graph the polar equation:
$$r = 1 + \cos \theta.$$

EXAMPLE 3   Graphing a Polar Equation

Graph the polar equation: $r = 1 + 2 \sin \theta$.

Solution   We first check for symmetry.

$$r = 1 + 2 \sin \theta$$

Polar Axis	**The Line $\theta = \dfrac{\pi}{2}$**	**The Pole**
Replace θ with $-\theta$.	Replace (r, θ) with $(-r, -\theta)$.	Replace r with $-r$.

$r = 1 + 2 \sin (-\theta)$	$-r = 1 + 2 \sin (-\theta)$	$-r = 1 + 2 \sin \theta$
$r = 1 + 2 (-\sin \theta)$	$-r = 1 - 2 \sin \theta$	$r = -1 - 2 \sin \theta$
$r = 1 - 2 \sin \theta$	$r = -1 + 2 \sin \theta$	

None of these equations are equivalent to $r = 1 + 2 \sin \theta$. Thus, the graph may or may not have each of these kinds of symmetry.

Now we are ready to graph $r = 1 + 2 \sin \theta$. Because the period of the sine function is 2π, we need not consider values of θ beyond 2π. We identify points on the graph of $r = 1 + 2 \sin \theta$ by assigning values to θ and calculating the corresponding values of r. The values for r and θ are in the tables above Figure 6.34(a), Figure 6.34(b), and Figure 6.34(c). The complete graph of $r = 1 + 2 \sin \theta$ is shown in Figure 6.34(c). The inner loop indicates that the graph passes through the pole twice.

θ	0	$\dfrac{\pi}{6}$	$\dfrac{\pi}{3}$	$\dfrac{\pi}{2}$	$\dfrac{2\pi}{3}$	$\dfrac{5\pi}{6}$	π
r	1	2	2.73	3	2.73	2	1

θ	$\dfrac{7\pi}{6}$	$\dfrac{4\pi}{3}$	$\dfrac{3\pi}{2}$
r	0	-0.73	-1

θ	$\dfrac{5\pi}{3}$	$\dfrac{11\pi}{6}$	2π
r	-0.73	0	1

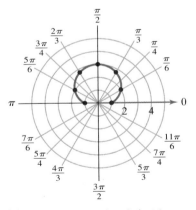

(a) The graph of $r = 1 + 2 \sin \theta$ for $0 \leq \theta \leq \pi$

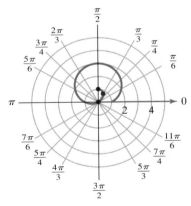

(b) The graph of $r = 1 + 2 \sin \theta$ for $0 \leq \theta \leq \dfrac{3\pi}{2}$

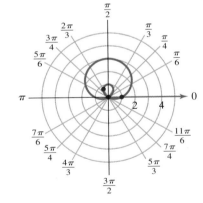

(c) The complete graph of $r = 1 + 2 \sin \theta$ for $0 \leq \theta \leq 2\pi$

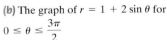

Figure 6.34 Graphing $r = 1 + 2 \sin \theta$

Although the polar equation $r = 1 + 2 \sin \theta$ failed the test for symmetry with respect to the line $\theta = \frac{\pi}{2}$ (the y-axis), its graph in Figure 6.34(c) reveals this kind of symmetry.

We're not quite sure if the polar graph in Figure 6.34(c) looks like a snail. However, the graph is called a *limaçon*, which is a French word for snail. Limaçons come with and without inner loops.

Limaçons

The graphs of

$$r = a + b \sin\theta, \quad r = a - b \sin\theta,$$
$$r = a + b \cos\theta, \quad r = a - b \cos\theta, \quad a > 0, b > 0$$

are called **limaçons**. The ratio $\dfrac{a}{b}$ determines a limaçon's shape.

| Inner loop if $\dfrac{a}{b} < 1$ | Heart-shaped if $\dfrac{a}{b} = 1$ and called cardioids | Dimpled with no inner loop if $1 < \dfrac{a}{b} < 2$ | No dimple and no inner loop if $\dfrac{a}{b} \geq 2$ |

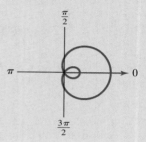 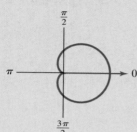 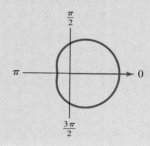 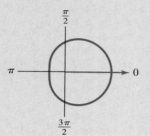

Check Point 3   Graph the polar equation: $r = 1 - 2 \sin\theta$.

EXAMPLE 4   Graphing a Polar Equation

Graph the polar equation: $r = 4 \sin 2\theta$.

Solution   We first check for symmetry.

$$r = 4 \sin 2\theta$$

Polar Axis

Replace θ with $-\theta$.

$$r = 4 \sin 2(-\theta)$$
$$r = 4 \sin(-2\theta)$$
$$r = -4 \sin 2\theta$$

Equation changes and fails this symmetry test.

The Line $\theta = \dfrac{\pi}{2}$

Replace (r, θ) with $(-r, -\theta)$.

$$-r = 4 \sin 2(-\theta)$$
$$-r = 4 \sin(-2\theta)$$
$$-r = -4 \sin 2\theta$$
$$r = 4 \sin 2\theta$$

Equation does not change.

The Pole

Replace r with $-r$.

$$-r = 4 \sin 2\theta$$
$$r = -4 \sin 2\theta$$

Equation changes and fails this symmetry test.

Thus, we can be sure that the graph is symmetric with respect to $\theta = \dfrac{\pi}{2}$. The graph may or may not be symmetric with respect to the polar axis or the pole.

Now we are ready to graph $r = 4 \sin 2\theta$. In Figure 6.35, we plot points on the graph of $r = 4 \sin 2\theta$ using values of θ from 0 to π and the corresponding values of r. These coordinates are shown in the tables at the left of the graph.

θ	0	$\dfrac{\pi}{6}$	$\dfrac{\pi}{4}$	$\dfrac{\pi}{3}$	$\dfrac{\pi}{2}$
r	0	3.46	4	3.46	0

θ	$\dfrac{2\pi}{3}$	$\dfrac{3\pi}{4}$	$\dfrac{5\pi}{6}$	π
r	-3.46	-4	-3.46	0

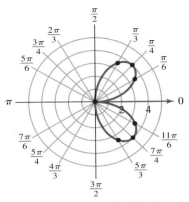

Figure 6.35 The graph of $r = 4 \sin 2\theta$ for $0 \le \theta \le \pi$

Now we can use symmetry with respect to the line $\theta = \dfrac{\pi}{2}$ (the y-axis) to complete the graph. By reflecting the graph in Figure 6.35 about the y-axis, we obtain the complete graph of $r = 4 \sin 2\theta$ from 0 to 2π. The graph is shown in Figure 6.36 .

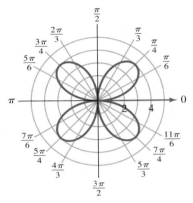

Figure 6.36 The graph of $r = 4 \sin 2\theta$ for $0 \le \theta \le 2\pi$

Although the polar equation $r = 4 \sin 2\theta$ failed the tests for symmetry with respect to the polar axis (the x-axis) and the pole (the origin), its graph in Figure 6.36 reveals all three types of symmetry.

The curve in Figure 6.36 is called a **rose with four petals**. We can use a trigonometric equation to confirm the four angles that give the location of the petal points. The petal points of $r = 4 \sin 2\theta$ are located at values of θ for which $r = 4$ or $r = -4$.

$4 \sin 2\theta = 4$	or $\quad 4 \sin 2\theta = -4$	Use $r = 4 \sin 2\theta$ and set r equal to 4 or -4.
$\sin 2\theta = 1$	$\sin 2\theta = -1$	Divide both sides by 4.
$2\theta = \dfrac{\pi}{2} + 2n\pi$	$2\theta = \dfrac{3\pi}{2} + 2n\pi$	Solve for 2θ, where n is any integer.
$\theta = \dfrac{\pi}{4} + n\pi$	$\theta = \dfrac{3\pi}{4} + n\pi$	Divide both sides by 2 and solve for θ.
If $n = 0$, $\theta = \dfrac{\pi}{4}$. If $n = 1$, $\theta = \dfrac{5\pi}{4}$.	If $n = 0$, $\theta = \dfrac{3\pi}{4}$. If $n = 1$, $\theta = \dfrac{7\pi}{4}$.	

Figure 6.36 confirms that four angles giving the locations of the petal points are $\dfrac{\pi}{4}, \dfrac{3\pi}{4}, \dfrac{5\pi}{4}$, and $\dfrac{7\pi}{4}$.

Technology

The graph of
$$r = 4 \sin 2\theta$$
was obtained using a $[-4, 4, 1]$ by $[-4, 4, 1]$ viewing rectangle and
$$\theta \min = 0, \quad \theta \max = 2\pi,$$
$$\theta \text{ step} = \frac{\pi}{48}.$$

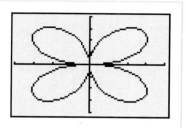

Rose Curves

The graphs of

$$r = a \sin n\theta \quad \text{and} \quad r = a \cos n\theta, \quad a \neq 0,$$

are called **rose curves**. If n is even, the rose has $2n$ petals. If n is odd, the rose has n petals.

$r = a \sin 2\theta$ Rose curve with 4 petals	$r = a \cos 3\theta$ Rose curve with 3 petals	$r = a \cos 4\theta$ Rose curve with 8 petals	$r = a \sin 5\theta$ Rose curve with 5 petals
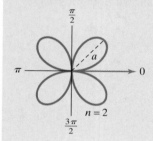	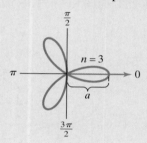	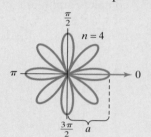	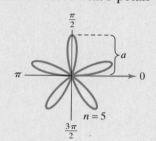

Check Point 4 Graph the polar equation: $r = 3 \cos 2\theta$.

EXAMPLE 5 Graphing a Polar Equation

Graph the polar equation: $r^2 = 4 \sin 2\theta$.

Solution We first check for symmetry.

$$r^2 = 4 \sin 2\theta$$

Polar Axis	**The Line $\theta = \dfrac{\pi}{2}$**	**The Pole**
Replace θ with $-\theta$.	Replace (r, θ) with $(-r, -\theta)$.	Replace r with $-r$.
$r^2 = 4 \sin 2(-\theta)$	$(-r)^2 = 4 \sin 2(-\theta)$	$(-r)^2 = 4 \sin 2\theta$
$r^2 = 4 \sin (-2\theta)$	$r^2 = 4 \sin (-2\theta)$	$r^2 = 4 \sin 2\theta$
$r^2 = -4 \sin 2\theta$	$r^2 = -4 \sin 2\theta$	
Equation changes and fails this symmetry test.	Equation changes and fails this symmetry test.	Equation does not change.

Thus, we can be sure that the graph is symmetric with respect to the pole. The graph may or may not be symmetric with respect to the polar axis or the line $\theta = \dfrac{\pi}{2}$.

Now we are ready to graph $r^2 = 4 \sin 2\theta$. In Figure 6.37(a), we plot points on the graph by using values of θ from 0 to $\frac{\pi}{2}$ and the corresponding values of r. These coordinates are shown in the table above Figure 6.37(a). Notice that the points in Figure 6.37(a) are shown for $r \geq 0$. Because the graph is symmetric with respect to the pole, we can reflect the graph in Figure 6.37(a) about the pole and obtain the graph in Figure 6.37(b).

θ	0	$\frac{\pi}{6}$	$\frac{\pi}{4}$	$\frac{\pi}{3}$	$\frac{\pi}{2}$
r	0	± 1.9	± 2	± 1.9	0

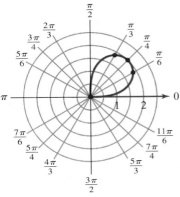

(a) The graph of $r^2 = 4 \sin 2\theta$ for $0 \leq \theta \leq \frac{\pi}{2}$ and $r \geq 0$

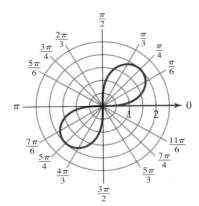

(b) Using symmetry with respect to the pole on the graph of $r^2 = 4 \sin 2\theta$

Figure 6.37 Graphing $r^2 = 4 \sin 2\theta$

Does Figure 6.37(b) show a complete graph of $r^2 = 4 \sin 2\theta$ or do we need to continue graphing for angles greater than $\frac{\pi}{2}$? If θ is in quadrant II, 2θ is in quadrant III or IV, where $\sin 2\theta$ is negative. Thus, $4 \sin 2\theta$ is negative. However, $r^2 = 4 \sin 2\theta$ and r^2 cannot be negative. The same observation applies to quadrant IV. This means that there are no points on the graph in quadrants II or IV. Thus, Figure 6.37(b) shows the complete graph of $r^2 = 4 \sin 2\theta$.

The curve in Figure 6.37(b) is shaped like a propeller and is called a *lemniscate*.

Lemniscates

The graphs of

$$r^2 = a^2 \sin 2\theta \quad \text{and} \quad r^2 = a^2 \cos 2\theta, \quad a \neq 0$$

are called **lemniscates**.

$r^2 = a^2 \sin 2\theta$ is symmetric with respect to the pole.

$r^2 = a^2 \cos 2\theta$ is symmetric with respect to the polar axis, $\theta = \frac{\pi}{2}$, and the pole.

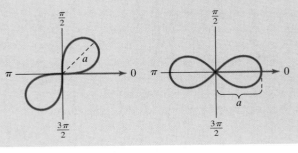

Check Point 5 Graph the polar equation: $r^2 = 4 \cos 2\theta$.

EXERCISE SET 6.4

Practice Exercises

In Exercises 1–6, the graph of a polar equation is given. Select the polar equation for each graph from the following options.

$$r = 2 \sin \theta, \quad r = 2 \cos \theta, \quad r = 1 + \sin \theta,$$
$$r = 1 - \sin \theta, \quad r = 3 \sin 2\theta, \quad r = 3 \sin 3\theta$$

1.

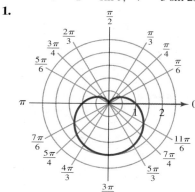

2.

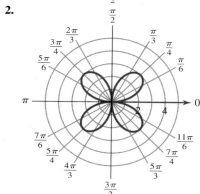

3.

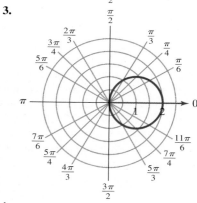

4.

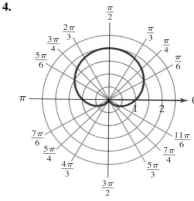

5.

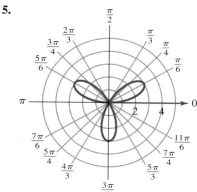

6.

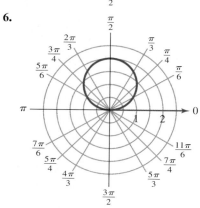

In Exercises 7–12, test for symmetry with respect to

a. *the polar axis.*   **b.** *the line* $\theta = \dfrac{\pi}{2}$.   **c.** *the pole.*

7. $r = \sin \theta$ **8.** $r = \cos \theta$

9. $r = 4 + 3 \cos \theta$ **10.** $r = 2 \cos 2\theta$

11. $r^2 = 16 \cos 2\theta$ **12.** $r^2 = 16 \sin 2\theta$

In Exercises 13–34, test for symmetry and then graph each polar equation.

13. $r = 2 \cos \theta$ **14.** $r = 2 \sin \theta$

15. $r = 1 - \sin \theta$ **16.** $r = 1 + \sin \theta$

17. $r = 2 + 2 \cos \theta$ **18.** $r = 2 - 2 \cos \theta$

19. $r = 2 + \cos \theta$ **20.** $r = 2 - \sin \theta$

21. $r = 1 + 2 \cos \theta$ **22.** $r = 1 - 2 \cos \theta$

23. $r = 2 - 3 \sin \theta$ **24.** $r = 2 + 4 \sin \theta$

25. $r = 2 \cos 2\theta$ **26.** $r = 2 \sin 2\theta$

27. $r = 4 \sin 3\theta$ **28.** $r = 4 \cos 3\theta$

29. $r^2 = 9 \cos 2\theta$ **30.** $r^2 = 9 \sin 2\theta$

31. $r = 1 - 3 \sin \theta$ **32.** $r = 3 + \sin \theta$

33. $r \cos \theta = -3$ **34.** $r \sin \theta = 2$

Practice Plus

In Exercises 35–44, test for symmetry and then graph each polar equation.

35. $r = \cos \dfrac{\theta}{2}$ **36.** $r = \sin \dfrac{\theta}{2}$

37. $r = \sin \theta + \cos \theta$ **38.** $r = 4 \cos \theta + 4 \sin \theta$

39. $r = \dfrac{1}{1 - \cos \theta}$ **40.** $r = \dfrac{2}{1 - \cos \theta}$

41. $r = \sin\theta \cos^2\theta$

42. $r = \dfrac{3\sin 2\theta}{\sin^3\theta + \cos^3\theta}$

43. $r = 2 + 3\sin 2\theta$

44. $r = 2 - 4\cos 2\theta$

Application Exercises

In Exercise Set 6.3, we considered an application in which sailboat racers look for a sailing angle to a 10-knot wind that produces maximum sailing speed. This situation is now represented by the polar graph in the figure shown. Each point (r, θ) on the graph gives the sailing speed, r, in knots, at an angle θ to the 10-knot wind. Use this information to solve Exercises 45–49.

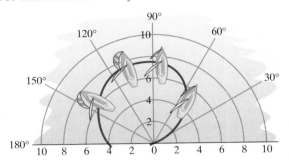

45. What is the speed, to the nearest knot, of a sailboat sailing at a 60° angle to the wind?

46. What is the speed, to the nearest knot, of a sailboat sailing at a 120° angle to the wind?

47. What is the speed, to the nearest knot, of a sailboat sailing at a 90° angle to the wind?

48. What is the speed, to the nearest knot, of a sailboat sailing at a 180° angle to the wind?

49. What angle to the wind produces the maximum sailing speed? What is the speed? Round the angle to the nearest five degrees and the speed to the nearest half knot.

Writing in Mathematics

50. What is a polar equation?

51. What is the graph of a polar equation?

52. Describe how to graph a polar equation.

53. Describe the test for symmetry with respect to the polar axis.

54. Describe the test for symmetry with respect to the line $\theta = \dfrac{\pi}{2}$.

55. Describe the test for symmetry with respect to the pole.

56. If an equation fails the test for symmetry with respect to the polar axis, what can you conclude?

Technology Exercises

Use the polar mode of a graphing utility with angle measure in radians to solve Exercises 57–88. Unless otherwise indicated, use θ min $= 0$, θ max $= 2\pi$, and θ step $= \dfrac{\pi}{48}$.

If you are not pleased with the quality of the graph, experiment with smaller values for θ step. However, if θ step is extremely small, it can take your graphing utility a long period of time to complete the graph.

57. Use a graphing utility to verify any six of your hand-drawn graphs in Exercises 13–34.

In Exercises 58–75, use a graphing utility to graph the polar equation.

58. $r = 4\cos 5\theta$

59. $r = 4\sin 5\theta$

60. $r = 4\cos 6\theta$

61. $r = 4\sin 6\theta$

62. $r = 2 + 2\cos\theta$

63. $r = 2 + 2\sin\theta$

64. $r = 4 + 2\cos\theta$

65. $r = 4 + 2\sin\theta$

66. $r = 2 + 4\cos\theta$

67. $r = 2 + 4\sin\theta$

68. $r = \dfrac{3}{\sin\theta}$

69. $r = \dfrac{3}{\cos\theta}$

70. $r = \cos\dfrac{3}{2}\theta$

71. $r = \cos\dfrac{5}{2}\theta$

72. $r = 3\sin\left(\theta + \dfrac{\pi}{4}\right)$

73. $r = 2\cos\left(\theta - \dfrac{\pi}{4}\right)$

74. $r = \dfrac{1}{1 - \sin\theta}$

75. $r = \dfrac{1}{3 - 2\sin\theta}$

In Exercises 76–78, find the smallest interval for θ starting with θ min $= 0$ so that your graphing utility graphs the given polar equation exactly once without retracing any portion of it.

76. $r = 4\sin\theta$

77. $r = 4\sin 2\theta$

78. $r^2 = 4\sin 2\theta$

In Exercises 79–82, use a graphing utility to graph each butterfly curve. Experiment with the range setting, particularly θ step, to produce a butterfly of the best possible quality.

79. $r = \cos^2 5\theta + \sin 3\theta + 0.3$

80. $r = \sin^4 4\theta + \cos 3\theta$

81. $r = \sin^5\theta + 8\sin\theta \cos^3\theta$

82. $r = 1.5^{\sin\theta} - 2.5\cos 4\theta + \sin^7\dfrac{\theta}{15}$

(Use θ min $= 0$ and θ max $= 20\pi$.)

83. Use a graphing utility to graph $r = \sin n\theta$ for $n = 1, 2, 3, 4, 5$, and 6. Use a separate viewing screen for each of the six graphs. What is the pattern for the number of loops that occur corresponding to each value of n? What is happening to the shape of the graphs as n increases? For each graph, what is the smallest interval for θ so that the graph is traced only once?

84. Repeat Exercise 83 for $r = \cos n\theta$. Are your conclusions the same as they were in Exercise 83?

85. Use a graphing utility to graph $r = 1 + 2\sin n\theta$ for $n = 1, 2, 3$, 4, 5, and 6. Use a separate viewing screen for each of the six graphs. What is the pattern for the number of large and small petals that occur corresponding to each value of n? How are the large and small petals related when n is odd and when n is even?

86. Repeat Exercise 85 for $r = 1 + 2\cos n\theta$. Are your conclusions the same as they were in Exercise 85?

87. Graph the spiral $r = \theta$. Use a $[-30, 30, 1]$ by $[-30, 30, 1]$ viewing rectangle. Let θ min $= 0$ and θ max $= 2\pi$, then θ min $= 0$ and θ max $= 4\pi$, and finally θ min $= 0$ and θ max $= 8\pi$.

88. Graph the spiral $r = \dfrac{1}{\theta}$. Use a $[-1, 1, 1]$ by $[-1, 1, 1]$ viewing rectangle. Let θ min $= 0$ and θ max $= 2\pi$, then θ min $= 0$ and θ max $= 4\pi$, and finally θ min $= 0$ and θ max $= 8\pi$.

Critical Thinking Exercises

In Exercises 89–90, graph r_1 and r_2 in the same polar coordinate system. What is the relationship between the two graphs?

89. $r_1 = 4 \cos 2\theta, r_2 = 4 \cos 2\left(\theta - \dfrac{\pi}{4} \right)$

90. $r_1 = 2 \sin 3\theta, r_2 = 2 \sin 3\left(\theta + \dfrac{\pi}{6} \right)$

91. Describe a test for symmetry with respect to the line $\theta = \dfrac{\pi}{2}$ in which r is not replaced.

CHAPTER 6
MID-CHAPTER CHECK POINT

What You Know: We learned to solve oblique triangles using the Laws of Sines $\left(\dfrac{a}{\sin A} = \dfrac{b}{\sin B} = \dfrac{c}{\sin C} \right)$ and Cosines $(a^2 = b^2 + c^2 - 2bc \cos A)$. We applied the Law of Sines to SAA, ASA, and SSA (the ambiguous case) triangles. We applied the Law of Cosines to SAS and SSS triangles. We found areas of SAS triangles $\left(\text{area} = \frac{1}{2}bc \sin A \right)$ and SSS triangles (Heron's formula: area $= \sqrt{s(s-a)(s-b)(s-c)}$, s is $\frac{1}{2}$ the perimeter). We used the polar coordinate system to plot points and represented them in multiple ways. We used the relations between polar and rectangular coordinates

$$x = r \cos \theta, \; y = r \sin \theta, \; x^2 + y^2 = r^2, \tan \theta = \dfrac{y}{x}$$

to convert points and equations from one coordinate system to the other. Finally, we used point plotting and symmetry to graph polar equations.

In Exercises 1–6, solve each triangle. Round lengths to the nearest tenth and angle measures to the nearest degree. If no triangle exits, state "no triangle." If two triangles exist, solve each triangle.

1. $A = 32°, B = 41°, a = 20$ **2.** $A = 42°, a = 63, b = 57$

3. $A = 65°, a = 6, b = 7$ **4.** $B = 110°, a = 10, c = 16$

5. $C = 42°, a = 16, c = 13$ **6.** $a = 5.0, b = 7.2, c = 10.1$

In Exercises 7–8, find the area of the triangle having the given measurements. Round to the nearest square unit.

7. $C = 36°, a = 5$ feet, $b = 7$ feet

8. $a = 7$ meters, $b = 9$ meters, $c = 12$ meters

9. Two trains leave a station on different tracks that make an angle of 110° with the station as vertex. The first train travels at an average rate of 50 miles per hour and the second train travels at an average rate of 40 miles per hour. How far apart, to the nearest tenth of a mile, are the trains after 2 hours?

10. Two fire-lookout stations are 16 miles apart, with station B directly east of station A. Both stations spot a fire on a mountain to the south. The bearing from station A to the fire is S56°E. The bearing from station B to the fire is S23°W. How far, to the nearest tenth of a mile, is the fire from station A?

11. A tree that is perpendicular to the ground sits on a straight line between two people located 420 feet apart. The angles of elevation from each person to the top of the tree measure 50° and 66°, respectively. How tall, to the nearest tenth of a foot, is the tree?

In Exercises 12–15, convert the given coordinates to the indicated ordered pair.

12. $\left(-3, \dfrac{5\pi}{4} \right)$ to (x, y) **13.** $\left(6, -\dfrac{\pi}{2} \right)$ to (x, y)

14. $\left(2, -2\sqrt{3} \right)$ to (r, θ) **15.** $(-6, 0)$ to (r, θ)

In Exercises 16–17, plot each point in polar coordinates. Then find another representation (r, θ) of this point in which:

   a. $r > 0, \quad 2\pi < \theta < 4\pi$.   **b.** $r < 0, \quad 0 < \theta < 2\pi$.

   c. $r > 0, -2\pi < \theta < 0$.

16. $\left(4, \dfrac{3\pi}{4} \right)$ **17.** $\left(\dfrac{5}{2}, \dfrac{\pi}{2} \right)$

In Exercises 18–20, convert each rectangular equation to a polar equation that expresses r in terms of θ.

18. $5x - y = 7$ **19.** $y = -7$

20. $(x + 1)^2 + y^2 = 1$

In Exercises 21–25, convert each polar equation to a rectangular equation. Then use your knowledge of the rectangular equation to graph the polar equation in a polar coordinate system.

21. $r = 6$ **22.** $\theta = \dfrac{\pi}{3}$

23. $r = -3 \csc \theta$ **24.** $r = -10 \cos \theta$

25. $r = 4 \sin \theta \sec^2 \theta$

In Exercises 26–27, test for symmetry with respect to

   a. *the polar axis.*   **b.** *the line* $\theta = \dfrac{\pi}{2}$.   **c.** *the pole.*

26. $r = 1 - 4 \cos \theta$ **27.** $r^2 = 4 \cos 2\theta$

In Exercises 28–32, graph each polar equation. Be sure to test for symmetry.

28. $r = -4 \sin \theta$ **29.** $r = 2 - 2 \cos \theta$

30. $r = 2 - 4 \cos \theta$ **31.** $r = 2 \sin 3\theta$

32. $r^2 = 16 \sin 2\theta$

SECTION 6.6   Vectors

Objectives

❶ Use magnitude and direction to show vectors are equal.

❷ Visualize scalar multiplication, vector addition, and vector subtraction as geometric vectors.

❸ Represent vectors in the rectangular coordinate system.

❹ Perform operations with vectors in terms of **i** and **j**.

❺ Find the unit vector in the direction of **v**.

❻ Write a vector in terms of its magnitude and direction.

❼ Solve applied problems involving vectors.

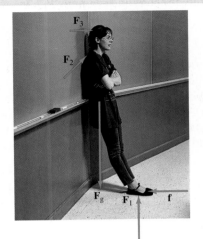
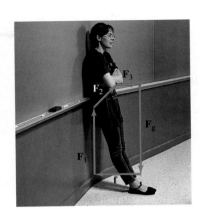

It's been a dynamic lecture, but now that it's over it's obvious that my professor is exhausted. She's slouching motionless against the board and—what's that? The forces acting against her body, including the pull of gravity, are appearing as arrows. I know that mathematics reveals the hidden patterns of the universe, but this is ridiculous. Does the arrangement of the arrows on the right have anything to do with the fact that my wiped-out professor is not sliding down the wall?

This sign shows a distance and direction for each city. Thus, the sign defines a vector for each destination.

Ours is a world of pushes and pulls. For example, suppose you are pulling a cart up a 30° incline, requiring an effort of 100 pounds. This quantity is described by giving its magnitude (a number indicating size, including a unit of measure) and also its direction. The magnitude is 100 pounds and the direction is 30° from the horizontal. Quantities that involve both a magnitude and a direction are called **vector quantities**, or **vectors** for short. Here is another example of a vector:

> You are driving due north at 50 miles per hour. The magnitude is the speed, 50 miles per hour. The direction of motion is due north.

Some quantities can be completely described by giving only their magnitudes. For example, the temperature of the lecture room that you just left is 75°. This temperature has magnitude, 75°, but no direction. Quantities that involve magnitude, but no direction, are called **scalar quantities**, or **scalars** for short. Thus, a scalar has only a numerical value. Another example of a scalar is your professor's height, which you estimate to be 5.5 feet.

In the next two sections, we introduce the world of vectors, which literally surround your every move. Because vectors have nonnegative magnitude as well as direction, we begin our discussion with directed line segments.

Directed Line Segments and Geometric Vectors

A line segment to which a direction has been assigned is called a **directed line segment**. Figure 6.48 shows a directed line segment from P to Q. We call P the **initial point** and Q the **terminal point**. We denote this directed line segment by

$$\overrightarrow{PQ}.$$

The **magnitude** of the directed line segment $\overrightarrow{PQ}$ is its length. We denote this by $\|\overrightarrow{PQ}\|$. Thus, $\|\overrightarrow{PQ}\|$ is the distance from point P to point Q. Because distance is nonnegative, vectors do not have negative magnitudes.

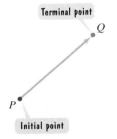

Figure 6.48 A directed line segment from P to Q

Geometrically, a **vector** is a directed line segment. Vectors are often denoted by boldface letters, such as **v**. If a vector **v** has the same magnitude and the same direction as the directed line segment $\overrightarrow{PQ}$, we write

$$\mathbf{v} = \overrightarrow{PQ}.$$

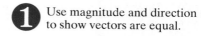

1 Use magnitude and direction to show vectors are equal.

Because it is difficult to write boldface on paper, use an arrow over a single letter, such as $\vec{v}$, to denote **v**, the vector **v**.

Figure 6.49 shows four possible relationships between vectors **v** and **w**. In Figure 6.49(a), the vectors have the same magnitude and the same direction, and are said to be *equal*. In general, vectors **v** and **w** are **equal** if they have the *same magnitude* and the *same direction*. We write this as **v** = **w**.

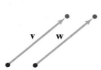 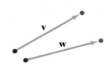 

(a) **v** = **w** because the vectors have the same magnitude and same direction.   **(b)** Vectors **v** and **w** have the same magnitude, but different directions.   **(c)** Vectors **v** and **w** have the same magnitude, but opposite directions.   **(d)** Vectors **v** and **w** have the same direction, but different magnitudes.

Figure 6.49 Relationships between vectors

EXAMPLE 1 Showing That Two Vectors Are Equal

Use Figure 6.50 to show that **u** = **v**.

Solution   Equal vectors have the same magnitude and the same direction. Use the distance formula to show that **u** and **v** have the same magnitude.

Magnitude of **u**
$$\|\mathbf{u}\| = \sqrt{(x_2 - x_1)^2 + (y_2 - y_1)^2} = \sqrt{[0 - (-3)]^2 + [3 - (-3)]^2}$$
$$= \sqrt{3^2 + 6^2} = \sqrt{9 + 36} = \sqrt{45} \quad (\text{or } 3\sqrt{5})$$

Magnitude of **v**
$$\|\mathbf{v}\| = \sqrt{(x_2 - x_1)^2 + (y_2 - y_1)^2} = \sqrt{(3 - 0)^2 + (6 - 0)^2}$$
$$= \sqrt{3^2 + 6^2} = \sqrt{9 + 36} = \sqrt{45} \quad (\text{or } 3\sqrt{5})$$

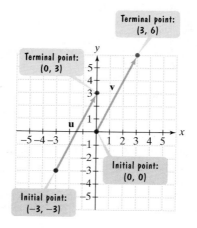

Figure 6.50

Thus, **u** and **v** have the same magnitude: $\|\mathbf{u}\| = \|\mathbf{v}\|$.

One way to show that **u** and **v** have the same direction is to find the slopes of the lines on which they lie.

Line on which **u** lies
$$m = \frac{y_2 - y_1}{x_2 - x_1} = \frac{3 - (-3)}{0 - (-3)} = \frac{6}{3} = 2$$

Line on which **v** lies
$$m = \frac{y_2 - y_1}{x_2 - x_1} = \frac{6 - 0}{3 - 0} = \frac{6}{3} = 2$$

Because **u** and **v** are both directed toward the upper right on lines having the same slope, 2, they have the same direction.

Thus, **u** and **v** have the same magnitude and direction, and **u** = **v**.

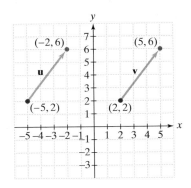

Figure 6.51

 Visualize scalar multiplication, vector addition, and vector subtraction as geometric vectors.

Check Point 1 Use Figure 6.51 to show that **u** = **v**.

A vector can be multiplied by a real number. Figure 6.52 shows three such multiplications: $2\mathbf{v}, \frac{1}{2}\mathbf{v}$, and $-\frac{3}{2}\mathbf{v}$. **Multiplying a vector by any positive real number (except for 1) changes the magnitude of the vector, but not its direction.** This can be seen by the blue and green vectors in Figure 6.52. Compare the black and blue vectors. Can you see that $2\mathbf{v}$ has the same direction as **v** but is twice the magnitude of **v**? Now, compare the black and green vectors: $\frac{1}{2}\mathbf{v}$ has the same direction as **v** but is half the magnitude of **v**.

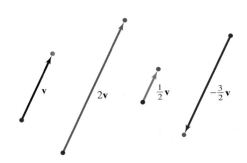

Figure 6.52 Multiplying vector **v** by real numbers

Now compare the black and red vectors in Figure 6.52. **Multiplying a vector by a negative number reverses the direction of the vector.** Notice that $-\frac{3}{2}\mathbf{v}$ has the opposite direction as **v** and is $\frac{3}{2}$ the magnitude of **v**.

The multiplication of a real number k and a vector **v** is called **scalar multiplication**. We write this product as $k\mathbf{v}$.

Scalar Multiplication

If k is a real number and **v** a vector, the vector $k\mathbf{v}$ is called a **scalar multiple** of the vector **v**. The magnitude and direction of $k\mathbf{v}$ are given as follows:

The vector $k\mathbf{v}$ has a *magnitude* of $|k|\|\mathbf{v}\|$. We describe this as the absolute value of k times the magnitude of vector **v**.

The vector $k\mathbf{v}$ has a *direction* that is

- the same as the direction of **v** if $k > 0$, and
- opposite the direction of **v** if $k < 0$.

A geometric method for adding two vectors is shown in Figure 6.53. The sum of **u** and **v**, denoted by **u** + **v** is called the **resultant vector**. Here is how we find this vector:

1. Position **u** and **v** so that the terminal point of **u** coincides with the initial point of **v**.

2. The resultant vector, **u** + **v**, extends from the initial point of **u** to the terminal point of **v**.

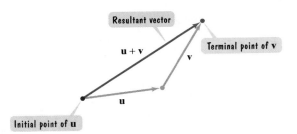

Figure 6.53 Vector addition **u** + **v**; the terminal point of **u** coincides with the initial point of **v**.

Wiped Out, But Not Sliding Down the Wall

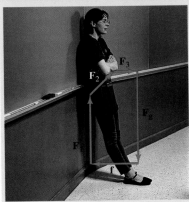

The figure shows the sum of five vectors:

$$\mathbf{F}_1 + \mathbf{F}_2 + \mathbf{F}_3 + \mathbf{F}_g + \mathbf{f}.$$

Notice how the terminal point of each vector coincides with the initial point of the vector that's being added to it. The vector sum, from the initial point of $\mathbf{F}_1$ to the terminal point of **f**, is a single point. The magnitude of a single point is zero. These forces add up to a net force of zero, allowing the professor to be motionless.

The **difference of two vectors**, $\mathbf{v} - \mathbf{u}$, is defined as $\mathbf{v} - \mathbf{u} = \mathbf{v} + (-\mathbf{u})$, where $-\mathbf{u}$ is the scalar multiplication of $\mathbf{u}$ and -1: $-1\mathbf{u}$. The difference $\mathbf{v} - \mathbf{u}$ is shown geometrically in Figure 6.54.

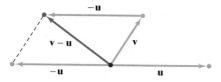

Figure 6.54 Vector subtraction $\mathbf{v} - \mathbf{u}$; the terminal point of $\mathbf{v}$ coincides with the initial point of $-\mathbf{u}$.

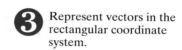

❸ Represent vectors in the rectangular coordinate system.

Vectors in the Rectangular Coordinate System

As you saw in Example 1, vectors can be shown in the rectangular coordinate system. Now let's see how we can use the rectangular coordinate system to represent vectors. We begin with two vectors that both have a magnitude of 1. Such vectors are called **unit vectors**.

The i and j Unit Vectors

Vector **i** is the unit vector whose direction is along the positive x-axis. Vector **j** is the unit vector whose direction is along the positive y-axis.

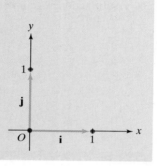

Why are the unit vectors **i** and **j** important? Vectors in the rectangular coordinate system can be represented in terms of **i** and **j**. For example, consider vector **v** with initial point at the origin, $(0, 0)$, and terminal point at $P = (a, b)$. The vector **v** is shown in Figure 6.55. We can represent **v** using **i** and **j** as $\mathbf{v} = a\mathbf{i} + b\mathbf{j}$.

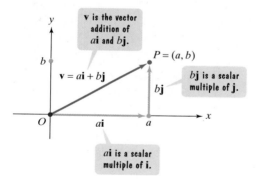

Figure 6.55 Using vector addition, vector **v** is represented as $\mathbf{v} = a\mathbf{i} + b\mathbf{j}$.

Representing Vectors in Rectangular Coordinates

Vector **v**, from $(0, 0)$ to (a, b), is represented as

$$\mathbf{v} = a\mathbf{i} + b\mathbf{j}.$$

The real numbers a and b are called the **scalar components of v**. Note that

- a is the **horizontal component** of **v**, and
- b is the **vertical component** of **v**.

The vector sum $a\mathbf{i} + b\mathbf{j}$ is called a **linear combination** of the vectors **i** and **j**. The magnitude of $\mathbf{v} = a\mathbf{i} + b\mathbf{j}$ is given by

$$\|\mathbf{v}\| = \sqrt{a^2 + b^2}.$$

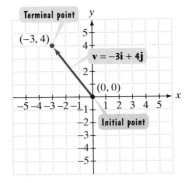

Figure 6.56 Sketching
$\mathbf{v} = -3\mathbf{i} + 4\mathbf{j}$ in the rectangular
coordinate system

EXAMPLE 2   Representing a Vector in Rectangular Coordinates and Finding Its Magnitude

Sketch the vector $\mathbf{v} = -3\mathbf{i} + 4\mathbf{j}$ and find its magnitude.

Solution   For the given vector $\mathbf{v} = -3\mathbf{i} + 4\mathbf{j}$, $a = -3$ and $b = 4$. The vector can be represented with its initial point at the origin, $(0, 0)$, as shown in Figure 6.56. The vector's terminal point is then $(a, b) = (-3, 4)$. We sketch the vector by drawing an arrow from $(0, 0)$ to $(-3, 4)$. We determine the magnitude of the vector by using the distance formula. Thus, the magnitude is

$$\|\mathbf{v}\| = \sqrt{a^2 + b^2} = \sqrt{(-3)^2 + 4^2} = \sqrt{9 + 16} = \sqrt{25} = 5.$$

Check Point 2   Sketch the vector $\mathbf{v} = 3\mathbf{i} - 3\mathbf{j}$ and find its magnitude.

The vector in Example 2 was represented with its initial point at the origin. A vector whose initial point is at the origin is called a **position vector**. Any vector in rectangular coordinates whose initial point is not at the origin can be shown to be equal to a position vector. As shown in the following box, this gives us a way to represent vectors between any two points.

Representing Vectors in Rectangular Coordinates

Vector $\mathbf{v}$ with initial point $P_1 = (x_1, y_1)$ and terminal point $P_2 = (x_2, y_2)$ is equal to the position vector

$$\mathbf{v} = (x_2 - x_1)\mathbf{i} + (y_2 - y_1)\mathbf{j}.$$

We can use congruent triangles, triangles with the same size and shape, to derive this formula. Begin with the right triangle in Figure 6.57(a). This triangle shows vector $\mathbf{v}$ from $P_1 = (x_1, y_1)$ to $P_2 = (x_2, y_2)$. In Figure 6.57(b), we move vector $\mathbf{v}$, without changing its magnitude or its direction, so that its initial point is at the origin. Using this position vector in Figure 6.57(b), we see that

$$\mathbf{v} = a\mathbf{i} + b\mathbf{j},$$

where a and b are the components of $\mathbf{v}$. The equal vectors and the right angles in the right triangles in Figures 6.57(a) and (b) result in congruent triangles. The corresponding sides of these congruent triangles are equal, so that $a = x_2 - x_1$ and $b = y_2 - y_1$. This means that $\mathbf{v}$ may be expressed as

$$\mathbf{v} = a\mathbf{i} + b\mathbf{j} = (x_2 - x_1)\mathbf{i} + (y_2 - y_1)\mathbf{j}.$$

> Horizontal component:
> x-coordinate of terminal point minus x-coordinate of initial point

> Vertical component:
> y-coordinate of terminal point minus y-coordinate of initial point

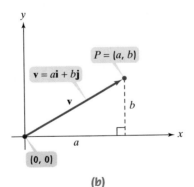

(a)

(b)

Figure 6.57

Thus, any vector between two points in rectangular coordinates can be expressed in terms of $\mathbf{i}$ and $\mathbf{j}$. In rectangular coordinates, the term *vector* refers to the position vector expressed in terms of $\mathbf{i}$ and $\mathbf{j}$ that is equal to it.

EXAMPLE 3   Representing a Vector in Rectangular Coordinates

Let $\mathbf{v}$ be the vector from initial point $P_1 = (3, -1)$ to terminal point $P_2 = (-2, 5)$. Write $\mathbf{v}$ in terms of $\mathbf{i}$ and $\mathbf{j}$.

Solution   We identify the values for the variables in the formula.

$$P_1 = (3, -1) \qquad P_2 = (-2, 5)$$

$x_1 \quad y_1 \qquad\qquad x_2 \quad y_2$

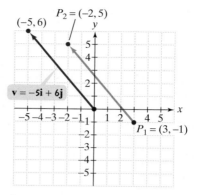

Figure 6.58 Representing the vector from $(3, -1)$ to $(-2, 5)$ as a position vector

Using these values, we write $\mathbf{v}$ in terms of $\mathbf{i}$ and $\mathbf{j}$ as follows:

$$\mathbf{v} = (x_2 - x_1)\mathbf{i} + (y_2 - y_1)\mathbf{j} = (-2 - 3)\mathbf{i} + [5 - (-1)]\mathbf{j} = -5\mathbf{i} + 6\mathbf{j}.$$

Figure 6.58 shows the vector from $P_1 = (3, -1)$ to $P_2 = (-2, 5)$ represented in terms of $\mathbf{i}$ and $\mathbf{j}$ and as a position vector.

Study Tip

When finding the distance from $P_1 = (x_1, y_1)$ to $P_2 = (x_2, y_2)$, the order in which the subtractions are performed makes no difference:

$$d = \sqrt{(x_2 - x_1)^2 + (y_2 - y_1)^2} \quad \text{or} \quad d = \sqrt{(x_1 - x_2)^2 + (y_1 - y_2)^2}.$$

When writing the vector from $P_1 = (x_1, y_1)$ to $P_2 = (x_2, y_2)$, P_2 must be the terminal point and the order in the subtractions is important:

$$\mathbf{v} = (x_2 - x_1)\mathbf{i} + (y_2 - y_1)\mathbf{j}.$$

(x_2, y_2), the terminal point, is used first in each subtraction.

Check Point 3   Let $\mathbf{v}$ be the vector from initial point $P_1 = (-1, 3)$ to terminal point $P_2 = (2, 7)$. Write $\mathbf{v}$ in terms of $\mathbf{i}$ and $\mathbf{j}$.

④ Perform operations with vectors in terms of $\mathbf{i}$ and $\mathbf{j}$.

Operations with Vectors in Terms of i and j

If vectors are expressed in terms of $\mathbf{i}$ and $\mathbf{j}$, we can easily carry out operations such as vector addition, vector subtraction, and scalar multiplication. Recall the geometric definitions of these operations given earlier. Based on these ideas, we can add and subtract vectors using the following procedure:

Adding and Subtracting Vectors in Terms of i and j

If $\mathbf{v} = a_1\mathbf{i} + b_1\mathbf{j}$ and $\mathbf{w} = a_2\mathbf{i} + b_2\mathbf{j}$, then

$$\mathbf{v} + \mathbf{w} = (a_1 + a_2)\mathbf{i} + (b_1 + b_2)\mathbf{j}$$
$$\mathbf{v} - \mathbf{w} = (a_1 - a_2)\mathbf{i} + (b_1 - b_2)\mathbf{j}.$$

EXAMPLE 4   Adding and Subtracting Vectors

If $\mathbf{v} = 5\mathbf{i} + 4\mathbf{j}$ and $\mathbf{w} = 6\mathbf{i} - 9\mathbf{j}$, find each of the following vectors:

a. $\mathbf{v} + \mathbf{w}$ b. $\mathbf{v} - \mathbf{w}$.

Solution

a. $\mathbf{v} + \mathbf{w} = (5\mathbf{i} + 4\mathbf{j}) + (6\mathbf{i} - 9\mathbf{j})$ These are the given vectors.

$\quad\quad\quad = (5 + 6)\mathbf{i} + [4 + (-9)]\mathbf{j}$ Add the horizontal components.
Add the vertical components.

$\quad\quad\quad = 11\mathbf{i} - 5\mathbf{j}$ Simplify.

b. $\mathbf{v} - \mathbf{w} = (5\mathbf{i} + 4\mathbf{j}) - (6\mathbf{i} - 9\mathbf{j})$ These are the given vectors.

$\quad\quad\quad = (5 - 6)\mathbf{i} + [4 - (-9)]\mathbf{j}$ Subtract the horizontal components.
Subtract the vertical components.

$\quad\quad\quad = -\mathbf{i} + 13\mathbf{j}$ Simplify.

Check Point 4   If $\mathbf{v} = 7\mathbf{i} + 3\mathbf{j}$ and $\mathbf{w} = 4\mathbf{i} - 5\mathbf{j}$, find each of the following vectors:

a. $\mathbf{v} + \mathbf{w}$ b. $\mathbf{v} - \mathbf{w}$.

How do we perform scalar multiplication if vectors are expressed in terms of **i** and **j**? We use the following procedure to multiply the vector **v** by the scalar k:

Scalar Multiplication with a Vector in Terms of i and j

If $\mathbf{v} = a\mathbf{i} + b\mathbf{j}$ and k is a real number, then the scalar multiplication of the vector **v** and the scalar k is

$$k\mathbf{v} = (ka)\mathbf{i} + (kb)\mathbf{j}.$$

EXAMPLE 5   Scalar Multiplication

If $\mathbf{v} = 5\mathbf{i} + 4\mathbf{j}$, find each of the following vectors:

  a. 6**v**   **b.** $-3\mathbf{v}$.

Solution

  a. $6\mathbf{v} = 6(5\mathbf{i} + 4\mathbf{j})$ *The scalar multiplication is expressed with the given vector.*

            $= (6 \cdot 5)\mathbf{i} + (6 \cdot 4)\mathbf{j}$ *Multiply each component by 6.*
            $= 30\mathbf{i} + 24\mathbf{j}$ *Simplify.*

  b. $-3\mathbf{v} = -3(5\mathbf{i} + 4\mathbf{j})$ *The scalar multiplication is expressed with the given vector.*

            $= (-3 \cdot 5)\mathbf{i} + (-3 \cdot 4)\mathbf{j}$ *Multiply each component by -3.*
            $= -15\mathbf{i} - 12\mathbf{j}$ *Simplify.*

Check Point 5 If $\mathbf{v} = 7\mathbf{i} + 10\mathbf{j}$, find each of the following vectors:

  a. 8**v**   **b.** $-5\mathbf{v}$.

EXAMPLE 6   Vector Operations

If $\mathbf{v} = 5\mathbf{i} + 4\mathbf{j}$ and $\mathbf{w} = 6\mathbf{i} - 9\mathbf{j}$, find $4\mathbf{v} - 2\mathbf{w}$.

Solution

$4\mathbf{v} - 2\mathbf{w} = 4(5\mathbf{i} + 4\mathbf{j}) - 2(6\mathbf{i} - 9\mathbf{j})$ *Operations are expressed with the given vectors.*
           $= 20\mathbf{i} + 16\mathbf{j} - 12\mathbf{i} + 18\mathbf{j}$ *Perform each scalar multiplication.*
           $= (20 - 12)\mathbf{i} + (16 + 18)\mathbf{j}$ *Add horizontal and vertical components to perform the vector addition.*
           $= 8\mathbf{i} + 34\mathbf{j}$ *Simplify.*

Check Point 6 If $\mathbf{v} = 7\mathbf{i} + 3\mathbf{j}$ and $\mathbf{w} = 4\mathbf{i} - 5\mathbf{j}$, find $6\mathbf{v} - 3\mathbf{w}$.

Properties involving vector operations resemble familiar properties of real numbers. For example, the order in which vectors are added makes no difference:

$$\mathbf{u} + \mathbf{v} = \mathbf{v} + \mathbf{u}.$$

Does this remind you of the commutative property $a + b = b + a$?

Just as 0 plays an important role in the properties of real numbers, the **zero vector 0** plays exactly the same role in the properties of vectors.

The Zero Vector

The vector whose magnitude is 0 is called the **zero vector, 0.** The zero vector is assigned no direction. It can be expressed in terms of **i** and **j** using

$$\mathbf{0} = 0\mathbf{i} + 0\mathbf{j}.$$

Properties of vector addition and scalar multiplication are given as follows:

Properties of Vector Addition and Scalar Multiplication

If **u**, **v**, and **w** are vectors, and c and d are scalars, then the following properties are true.

Vector Addition Properties

1. $\mathbf{u} + \mathbf{v} = \mathbf{v} + \mathbf{u}$ Commutative Property
2. $(\mathbf{u} + \mathbf{v}) + \mathbf{w} = \mathbf{u} + (\mathbf{v} + \mathbf{w})$ Associative Property
3. $\mathbf{u} + \mathbf{0} = \mathbf{0} + \mathbf{u} = \mathbf{u}$ Additive Identity
4. $\mathbf{u} + (-\mathbf{u}) = (-\mathbf{u}) + \mathbf{u} = \mathbf{0}$ Additive Inverse

Scalar Multiplication Properties

1. $(cd)\mathbf{u} = c(d\mathbf{u})$ Associative Property
2. $c(\mathbf{u} + \mathbf{v}) = c\mathbf{u} + c\mathbf{v}$ Distributive Property
3. $(c + d)\mathbf{u} = c\mathbf{u} + d\mathbf{u}$ Distributive Property
4. $1\mathbf{u} = \mathbf{u}$ Multiplicative Identity
5. $0\mathbf{u} = \mathbf{0}$ Multiplication Property of Zero
6. $\|c\mathbf{v}\| = |c|\|\mathbf{v}\|$ Magnitude Property

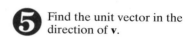 Find the unit vector in the direction of **v**.

Unit Vectors

A **unit vector** is defined to be a vector whose magnitude is one. In many applications of vectors, it is helpful to find the unit vector that has the same direction as a given vector.

Discovery

To find out why the procedure in the box produces a unit vector, work Exercise 105 in Exercise Set 6.6.

Finding the Unit Vector that Has the Same Direction as a Given Nonzero Vector v

For any nonzero vector **v**, the vector

$$\frac{\mathbf{v}}{\|\mathbf{v}\|}$$

is the unit vector that has the same direction as **v**. To find this vector, divide **v** by its magnitude.

EXAMPLE 7   Finding a Unit Vector

Find the unit vector in the same direction as $\mathbf{v} = 5\mathbf{i} - 12\mathbf{j}$. Then verify that the vector has magnitude 1.

Solution   We find the unit vector in the same direction as **v** by dividing **v** by its magnitude. We first find the magnitude of **v**.

$$\|\mathbf{v}\| = \sqrt{a^2 + b^2} = \sqrt{5^2 + (-12)^2} = \sqrt{25 + 144} = \sqrt{169} = 13$$

The unit vector in the same direction as **v** is

$$\frac{\mathbf{v}}{\|\mathbf{v}\|} = \frac{5\mathbf{i} - 12\mathbf{j}}{13} = \frac{5}{13}\mathbf{i} - \frac{12}{13}\mathbf{j}.$$ This is the scalar multiplication of v and $\frac{1}{13}$.

Now we must verify that the magnitude of this vector is 1. Recall that the magnitude of $a\mathbf{i} + b\mathbf{j}$ is $\sqrt{a^2 + b^2}$. Thus, the magnitude of $\frac{5}{13}\mathbf{i} - \frac{12}{13}\mathbf{j}$ is

$$\sqrt{\left(\frac{5}{13}\right)^2 + \left(-\frac{12}{13}\right)^2} = \sqrt{\frac{25}{169} + \frac{144}{169}} = \sqrt{\frac{169}{169}} = \sqrt{1} = 1.$$

Check Point 7   Find the unit vector in the same direction as $\mathbf{v} = 4\mathbf{i} - 3\mathbf{j}$. Then verify that the vector has magnitude 1.

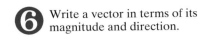

Write a vector in terms of its magnitude and direction.

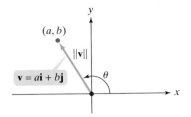

Figure 6.59 Expressing a vector in terms of its magnitude, $\|\mathbf{v}\|$, and its direction angle, θ

Writing a Vector in Terms of Its Magnitude and Direction

Consider the vector $\mathbf{v} = a\mathbf{i} + b\mathbf{j}$. The components a and b can be expressed in terms of the magnitude of $\mathbf{v}$ and the angle θ that $\mathbf{v}$ makes with the positive x-axis. This angle is called the **direction angle** of $\mathbf{v}$ and is shown in Figure 6.59. By the definitions of sine and cosine, we have

$$\cos \theta = \frac{a}{\|\mathbf{v}\|} \quad \text{and} \quad \sin \theta = \frac{b}{\|\mathbf{v}\|}$$

$$a = \|\mathbf{v}\| \cos \theta \qquad\qquad b = \|\mathbf{v}\| \sin \theta.$$

Thus,

$$\mathbf{v} = a\mathbf{i} + b\mathbf{j} = \|\mathbf{v}\| \cos \theta \mathbf{i} + \|\mathbf{v}\| \sin \theta \mathbf{j}.$$

> ### Writing a Vector in Terms of Its Magnitude and Direction
>
> Let $\mathbf{v}$ be a nonzero vector. If θ is the direction angle measured from the positive x-axis to $\mathbf{v}$, then the vector can be expressed in terms of its magnitude and direction angle as
>
> $$\mathbf{v} = \|\mathbf{v}\| \cos \theta \mathbf{i} + \|\mathbf{v}\| \sin \theta \mathbf{j}.$$

A vector that represents the direction and speed of an object in motion is called a **velocity vector**. In Example 8, we express a wind's velocity vector in terms of the wind's magnitude and direction.

EXAMPLE 8   Writing a Vector Whose Magnitude and Direction Are Given

The wind is blowing at 20 miles per hour in the direction N30°W. Express its velocity as a vector $\mathbf{v}$ in terms of $\mathbf{i}$ and $\mathbf{j}$.

Solution   The vector $\mathbf{v}$ is shown in Figure 6.60. The vector's direction angle, from the positive x-axis to $\mathbf{v}$, is

$$\theta = 90° + 30° = 120°.$$

Because the wind is blowing at 20 miles per hour, the magnitude of $\mathbf{v}$ is 20 miles per hour: $\|\mathbf{v}\| = 20$. Thus,

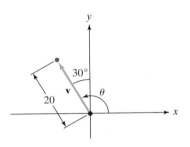

Figure 6.60 Vector $\mathbf{v}$ represents a wind blowing at 20 miles per hour in the direction N30°W.

$$\mathbf{v} = \|\mathbf{v}\| \cos \theta \mathbf{i} + \|\mathbf{v}\| \sin \theta \mathbf{j} \qquad \text{Use the formula for a vector in terms of magnitude and direction.}$$

$$= 20 \cos 120° \mathbf{i} + 20 \sin 120° \mathbf{j} \qquad \|v\| = 20 \text{ and } \theta = 120°.$$

$$= 20\left(-\frac{1}{2}\right)\mathbf{i} + 20\left(\frac{\sqrt{3}}{2}\right)\mathbf{j} \qquad \cos 120° = -\frac{1}{2} \text{ and } \sin 120° = \frac{\sqrt{3}}{2}.$$

$$= -10\mathbf{i} + 10\sqrt{3}\mathbf{j} \qquad \text{Simplify.}$$

The wind's velocity can be expressed in terms of $\mathbf{i}$ and $\mathbf{j}$ as $\mathbf{v} = -10\mathbf{i} + 10\sqrt{3}\mathbf{j}$.

Check Point 8   The jet stream is blowing at 60 miles per hour in the direction N45°E. Express its velocity as a vector $\mathbf{v}$ in terms of $\mathbf{i}$ and $\mathbf{j}$.

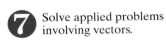

Solve applied problems involving vectors.

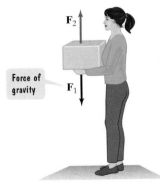

Figure 6.61 Force vectors

Application

Many physical concepts can be represented by vectors. A vector that represents a pull or push of some type is called a **force vector**. If you are holding a 10-pound package, two force vectors are involved. The force of gravity is exerting a force of magnitude 10 pounds directly downward. This force is shown by vector $\mathbf{F}_1$ in Figure 6.61. Assuming there is no upward or downward movement of the package, you are exerting a force of magnitude 10 pounds directly upward. This force is shown by vector $\mathbf{F}_2$ in Figure 6.61. It has the same magnitude as the force exerted on your package by gravity, but it acts in the opposite direction.

If $\mathbf{F}_1$ and $\mathbf{F}_2$ are two forces acting on an object, the net effect is the same as if just the resultant force, $\mathbf{F}_1 + \mathbf{F}_2$, acted on the object. If the object is not moving, as is the case with your 10-pound package, the vector sum of all forces is the zero vector.

EXAMPLE 9 Finding the Resultant Force

Two forces, $\mathbf{F}_1$ and $\mathbf{F}_2$, of magnitude 10 and 30 pounds, respectively, act on an object. The direction of $\mathbf{F}_1$ is N20°E and the direction of $\mathbf{F}_2$ is N65°E. Find the magnitude and the direction of the resultant force. Express the magnitude to the nearest hundredth of a pound and the direction angle to the nearest tenth of a degree.

Solution   The vectors $\mathbf{F}_1$ and $\mathbf{F}_2$ are shown in Figure 6.62. The direction angle for $\mathbf{F}_1$, from the positive x-axis to the vector, is $90° - 20°$, or $70°$. We express $\mathbf{F}_1$ using the formula for a vector in terms of its magnitude and direction.

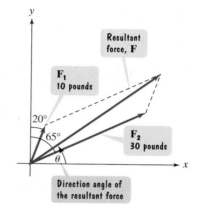

$$\begin{aligned} \mathbf{F}_1 &= \|\mathbf{F}_1\| \cos \theta \mathbf{i} + \|\mathbf{F}_1\| \sin \theta \mathbf{j} \\ &= 10 \cos 70° \mathbf{i} + 10 \sin 70° \mathbf{j} \qquad \text{\small $\|F_1\| = 10$ and $\theta = 70°$.} \\ &\approx 3.42\mathbf{i} + 9.40\mathbf{j} \qquad\qquad \text{\small Use a calculator.} \end{aligned}$$

Figure 6.62

Figure 6.62 illustrates that the direction angle for $\mathbf{F}_2$, from the positive x-axis to the vector, is $90° - 65°$, or $25°$. We express $\mathbf{F}_2$ using the formula for a vector in terms of its magnitude and direction.

$$\begin{aligned} \mathbf{F}_2 &= \|\mathbf{F}_2\| \cos \theta \mathbf{i} + \|\mathbf{F}_2\| \sin \theta \mathbf{j} \\ &= 30 \cos 25° \mathbf{i} + 30 \sin 25° \mathbf{j} \qquad \text{\small $\|F_2\| = 30$ and $\theta = 25°$.} \\ &\approx 27.19\mathbf{i} + 12.68\mathbf{j} \qquad\qquad \text{\small Use a calculator.} \end{aligned}$$

The resultant force, $\mathbf{F}$, is $\mathbf{F}_1 + \mathbf{F}_2$. Thus,

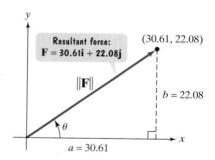

$$\begin{aligned} \mathbf{F} &= \mathbf{F}_1 + \mathbf{F}_2 \\ &\approx (3.42\mathbf{i} + 9.40\mathbf{j}) + (27.19\mathbf{i} + 12.68\mathbf{j}) \qquad \text{\small Use F_1 and F_2, found above.} \\ &= (3.42 + 27.19)\mathbf{i} + (9.40 + 12.68)\mathbf{j} \qquad \text{\small Add the horizontal components. Add the vertical components.} \\ &= 30.61\mathbf{i} + 22.08\mathbf{j}. \qquad\qquad\qquad\qquad \text{\small Simplify.} \end{aligned}$$

Figure 6.63

Figure 6.63 shows the resultant force, $\mathbf{F}$, without showing $\mathbf{F}_1$ and $\mathbf{F}_2$.
Now that we have the resultant force vector, $\mathbf{F}$, we can find its magnitude.

$$\|\mathbf{F}\| = \sqrt{a^2 + b^2} = \sqrt{(30.61)^2 + (22.08)^2} \approx 37.74$$

The magnitude of the resultant force is approximately 37.74 pounds.
To find θ, the direction angle of the resultant force, we can use

$$\cos \theta = \frac{a}{\|\mathbf{F}\|} \quad \text{or} \quad \sin \theta = \frac{b}{\|\mathbf{F}\|}.$$

Study Tip

If $\mathbf{F} = a\mathbf{i} + b\mathbf{j}$, the direction angle, θ, of $\mathbf{F}$ can also be found using

$$\tan \theta = \frac{b}{a}.$$

These ratios are illustrated for the right triangle in Figure 6.63
Using the first formula, we obtain

$$\cos \theta = \frac{a}{\|\mathbf{F}\|} \approx \frac{30.61}{37.74}.$$

Thus,

$$\theta = \cos^{-1}\left(\frac{30.61}{37.74}\right) \approx 35.8°. \qquad \text{\small Use a calculator.}$$

The direction angle of the resultant force is approximately 35.8°.
In summary, the two given forces are equivalent to a single force of approximately 37.74 pounds with a direction angle of approximately 35.8°.

Check Point 9 Two forces, $\mathbf{F}_1$ and $\mathbf{F}_2$, of magnitude 30 and 60 pounds, respectively, act on an object. The direction of $\mathbf{F}_1$ is N10°E and the direction of $\mathbf{F}_2$ is N60°E. Find the magnitude, to the nearest hundredth of a pound, and the direction angle, to the nearest tenth of a degree, of the resultant force.

We have seen that velocity vectors represent the direction and speed of moving objects. Boats moving in currents and airplanes flying in winds are situations in which two velocity vectors act simultaneously. For example, suppose $\mathbf{v}$ represents the velocity of a plane in still air. Further suppose that $\mathbf{w}$ represents the velocity of the wind. The actual speed and direction of the plane is given by the vector $\mathbf{v} + \mathbf{w}$. This resultant vector describes the plane's speed and direction relative to the ground. Problems involving the resultant velocity of a boat or plane are solved using the same method that we used in Example 9 to find a single resultant force equivalent to two given forces.

EXERCISE SET 6.6

Practice Exercises

In Exercises 1–4, $\mathbf{u}$ *and* $\mathbf{v}$ *have the same direction. In each exercise:* **a.** *Find* $\|\mathbf{u}\|$. **b.** *Find* $\|\mathbf{v}\|$. **c.** *Is* $\mathbf{u} = \mathbf{v}$? *Explain.*

1.

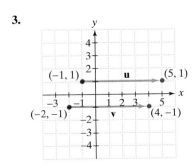

2.

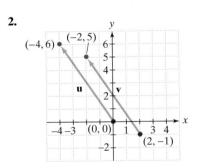

3.

(image)

4.

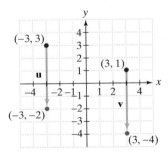

In Exercises 5–12, sketch each vector as a position vector and find its magnitude.

5. $\mathbf{v} = 3\mathbf{i} + \mathbf{j}$ **6.** $\mathbf{v} = 2\mathbf{i} + 3\mathbf{j}$

7. $\mathbf{v} = \mathbf{i} - \mathbf{j}$ **8.** $\mathbf{v} = -\mathbf{i} - \mathbf{j}$

9. $\mathbf{v} = -6\mathbf{i} - 2\mathbf{j}$ **10.** $\mathbf{v} = 5\mathbf{i} - 2\mathbf{j}$

11. $\mathbf{v} = -4\mathbf{i}$ **12.** $\mathbf{v} = -5\mathbf{j}$

In Exercises 13–20, let $\mathbf{v}$ *be the vector from initial point* P_1 *to terminal point* P_2. *Write* $\mathbf{v}$ *in terms of* $\mathbf{i}$ *and* $\mathbf{j}$.

13. $P_1 = (-4, -4), P_2 = (6, 2)$

14. $P_1 = (2, -5), P_2 = (-6, 6)$

15. $P_1 = (-8, 6), P_2 = (-2, 3)$

16. $P_1 = (-7, -4), P_2 = (0, -2)$

17. $P_1 = (-1, 7), P_2 = (-7, -7)$

18. $P_1 = (-1, 6), P_2 = (7, -5)$

19. $P_1 = (-3, 4), P_2 = (6, 4)$

20. $P_1 = (4, -5), P_2 = (4, 3)$

In Exercises 21–38, let

$$\mathbf{u} = 2\mathbf{i} - 5\mathbf{j}, \mathbf{v} = -3\mathbf{i} + 7\mathbf{j}, \text{ and } \mathbf{w} = -\mathbf{i} - 6\mathbf{j}.$$

Find each specified vector or scalar.

21. $\mathbf{u} + \mathbf{v}$ **22.** $\mathbf{v} + \mathbf{w}$

23. $\mathbf{u} - \mathbf{v}$ **24.** $\mathbf{v} - \mathbf{w}$

25. $\mathbf{v} - \mathbf{u}$ **26.** $\mathbf{w} - \mathbf{v}$

27. 5**v**   **28.** 6**v**
29. −4**w**   **30.** −7**w**
31. 3**w** + 2**v**   **32.** 3**u** + 4**v**
33. 3**v** − 4**w**   **34.** 4**w** − 3**v**
35. ‖2**u**‖   **36.** ‖−2**u**‖
37. ‖**w** − **u**‖   **38.** ‖**u** − **w**‖

*In Exercises 39–46, find the unit vector that has the same direction as the vector **v**.*

39. **v** = 6**i**   **40.** **v** = −5**j**
41. **v** = 3**i** − 4**j**   **42.** **v** = 8**i** − 6**j**
43. **v** = 3**i** − 2**j**   **44.** **v** = 4**i** − 2**j**
45. **v** = **i** + **j**   **46.** **v** = **i** − **j**

*In Exercises 47–52, write the vector **v** in terms of **i** and **j** whose magnitude ‖**v**‖ and direction angle θ are given.*

47. ‖**v**‖ = 6, θ = 30°   **48.** ‖**v**‖ = 8, θ = 45°
49. ‖**v**‖ = 12, θ = 225°   **50.** ‖**v**‖ = 10, θ = 330°
51. ‖**v**‖ = $\frac{1}{2}$, θ = 113°   **52.** ‖**v**‖ = $\frac{1}{4}$, θ = 200°

Practice Plus

In Exercises 53–56, let

$$\mathbf{u} = -2\mathbf{i} + 3\mathbf{j}, \mathbf{v} = 6\mathbf{i} - \mathbf{j}, \mathbf{w} = -3\mathbf{i}.$$

Find each specified vector or scalar.

53. 4**u** − (2**v** − **w**)   **54.** 3**u** − (4**v** − **w**)
55. ‖**u** + **v**‖² − ‖**u** − **v**‖²   **56.** ‖**v** + **w**‖² − ‖**v** − **w**‖²

In Exercises 57–60, let

$$\mathbf{u} = a_1\mathbf{i} + b_1\mathbf{j}$$
$$\mathbf{v} = a_2\mathbf{i} + b_2\mathbf{j}$$
$$\mathbf{w} = a_3\mathbf{i} + b_3\mathbf{j}.$$

Prove each property by obtaining the vector on each side of the equation. Have you proved a distributive, associative, or commutative property of vectors?

57. **u** + **v** = **v** + **u**
58. (**u** + **v**) + **w** = **u** + (**v** + **w**)
59. c(**u** + **v**) = c**u** + c**v**
60. (c + d)**u** = c**u** + d**u**

*In Exercises 61–64, find the magnitude ‖**v**‖, to the nearest hundredth, and the direction angle θ, to the nearest tenth of a degree, for each given vector **v**.*

61. **v** = −10**i** + 15**j**   **62.** **v** = 2**i** − 8**j**
63. **v** = (4**i** − 2**j**) − (4**i** − 8**j**)
64. **v** = (7**i** − 3**j**) − (10**i** − 3**j**)

Application Exercises

*In Exercises 65–68, a vector is described. Express the vector in terms of **i** and **j**. If exact values are not possible, round components to the nearest tenth.*

65. A quarterback releases a football with a speed of 44 feet per second at an angle of 30° with the horizontal.

66. A child pulls a sled along level ground by exerting a force of 30 pounds on a handle that makes an angle of 45° with the ground.

67. A plane approaches a runway at 150 miles per hour at an angle of 8° with the runway.

68. A plane with an airspeed of 450 miles per hour is flying in the direction N35°W.

*Vectors are used in computer graphics to determine lengths of shadows over flat surfaces. The length of the shadow for **v** in the figure shown is the absolute value of the vector's horizontal component. In Exercises 69–70, the magnitude and direction angle of **v** are given. Write **v** in terms of **i** and **j**. Then find the length of the shadow to the nearest tenth of an inch.*

69. ‖**v**‖ = 1.5 inches, θ = 25°
70. ‖**v**‖ = 1.8 inches, θ = 40°

71. The magnitude and direction of two forces acting on an object are 70 pounds, S56°E, and 50 pounds, N72°E, respectively. Find the magnitude, to the nearest hundredth of a pound, and the direction angle, to the nearest tenth of a degree, of the resultant force.

72. The magnitude and direction exerted by two tugboats towing a ship are 4200 pounds, N65°E, and 3000 pounds, S58°E, respectively. Find the magnitude, to the nearest pound, and the direction angle, to the nearest tenth of a degree, of the resultant force.

73. The magnitude and direction exerted by two tugboats towing a ship are 1610 kilograms, N35°W, and 1250 kilograms, S55°W, respectively. Find the magnitude, to the nearest kilogram, and the direction angle, to the nearest tenth of a degree, of the resultant force.

74. The magnitude and direction of two forces acting on an object are 64 kilograms, N39°W, and 48 kilograms, S59°W, respectively. Find the magnitude, to the nearest hundredth of a kilogram, and the direction angle, to the nearest tenth of a degree, of the resultant force.

The figure shows a box being pulled up a ramp inclined at 18° from the horizontal.

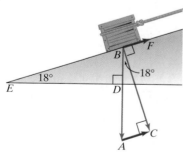

Use the following information to solve Exercises 75–76.

$\overrightarrow{BA}$ = force of gravity

$\|\overrightarrow{BA}\|$ = weight of the box

$\|\overrightarrow{AC}\|$ = magnitude of the force needed to pull the box up the ramp

$|\overrightarrow{BC}|$ = magnitude of the force of the box against the ramp

75. If the box weighs 100 pounds, find the magnitude of the force needed to pull it up the ramp.

76. If a force of 30 pounds is needed to pull the box up the ramp, find the weight of the box.

In Exercises 77–78, round answers to the nearest pound.

77. a. Find the magnitude of the force required to keep a 3500-pound car from sliding down a hill inclined at 5.5° from the horizontal.

b. Find the magnitude of the force of the car against the hill.

78. a. Find the magnitude of the force required to keep a 280-pound barrel from sliding down a ramp inclined at 12.5° from the horizontal.

b. Find the magnitude of the force of the barrel against the ramp.

The forces $\mathbf{F}_1, \mathbf{F}_2, \mathbf{F}_3, \ldots, \mathbf{F}_n$ *acting on an object are in* **equilibrium** *if the resultant force is the zero vector:*

$$\mathbf{F}_1 + \mathbf{F}_2 + \mathbf{F}_3 + \cdots + \mathbf{F}_n = \mathbf{0}.$$

In Exercises 79–82, the given forces are acting on an object.

a. *Find the resultant force.*

b. *What additional force is required for the given forces to be in equilibrium?*

79. $\mathbf{F}_1 = 3\mathbf{i} - 5\mathbf{j}, \quad \mathbf{F}_2 = 6\mathbf{i} + 2\mathbf{j}$

80. $\mathbf{F}_1 = -2\mathbf{i} + 3\mathbf{j}, \quad \mathbf{F}_2 = \mathbf{i} - \mathbf{j}, \quad \mathbf{F}_3 = 5\mathbf{i} - 12\mathbf{j}$

81.

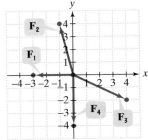

82.

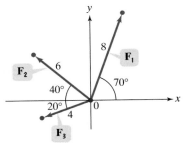

83. The figure shows a small plane flying at a speed of 180 miles per hour on a bearing of N50°E. The wind is blowing from west to east at 40 miles per hour. The figure indicates that **v** represents the velocity of the plane in still air and **w** represents the velocity of the wind.

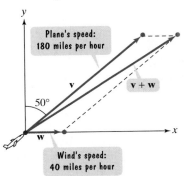

a. Express **v** and **w** in terms of their magnitudes and direction angles.

b. Find the resultant vector, **v** + **w**.

c. The magnitude of **v** + **w**, called the **ground speed** of the plane, gives its speed relative to the ground. Approximate the ground speed to the nearest mile per hour.

d. The direction angle of **v** + **w** gives the plane's true course relative to the ground. Approximate the true course to the nearest tenth of a degree. What is the plane's true bearing?

84. Use the procedure outlined in Exercise 83 to solve this exercise. A plane is flying at a speed of 400 miles per hour on a bearing of N50°W. The wind is blowing at 30 miles per hour on a bearing of N25°E.

a. Approximate the plane's ground speed to the nearest mile per hour.

b. Approximate the plane's true course to the nearest tenth of a degree. What is its true bearing?

85. A plane is flying at a speed of 320 miles per hour on a bearing of N70°E. Its ground speed is 370 miles per hour and its true course is 30°. Find the speed, to the nearest mile per hour, and the direction angle, to the nearest tenth of a degree, of the wind.

86. A plane is flying at a speed of 540 miles per hour on a bearing of S36°E. Its ground speed is 500 miles per hour and its true bearing is S44°E. Find the speed, to the nearest mile per hour, and the direction angle, to the nearest tenth of a degree, of the wind.

Writing in Mathematics

87. What is a directed line segment?

88. What are equal vectors?

89. If vector **v** is represented by an arrow, how is −3**v** represented?

90. If vectors **u** and **v** are represented by arrows, describe how the vector sum **u** + **v** is represented.

91. What is the vector **i**?

92. What is the vector **j**?

93. What is a position vector? How is a position vector represented using **i** and **j**?

94. If **v** is a vector between any two points in the rectangular coordinate system, explain how to write **v** in terms of **i** and **j**.

95. If two vectors are expressed in terms of **i** and **j**, explain how to find their sum.

96. If two vectors are expressed in terms of **i** and **j**, explain how to find their difference.

97. If a vector is expressed in terms of **i** and **j**, explain how to find the scalar multiplication of the vector and a given scalar k.

98. What is the zero vector?

99. Describe one similarity between the zero vector and the number 0.

100. Explain how to find the unit vector in the direction of any given vector **v**.

101. Explain how to write a vector in terms of its magnitude and direction.

102. You are on an airplane. The pilot announces the plane's speed over the intercom. Which speed do you think is being reported: the speed of the plane in still air or the speed after the effect of the wind has been accounted for? Explain your answer.

103. Use vectors to explain why it is difficult to hold a heavy stack of books perfectly still for a long period of time. As you become exhausted, what eventually happens? What does this mean in terms of the forces acting on the books?

 Critical Thinking Exercises

104. Use the figure shown to select a true statement.

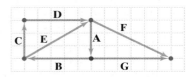

   a. $\mathbf{A} + \mathbf{B} = \mathbf{E}$

   b. $\mathbf{D} + \mathbf{A} + \mathbf{B} + \mathbf{C} = \mathbf{0}$

   c. $\mathbf{B} - \mathbf{E} = \mathbf{G} - \mathbf{F}$

   d. $\|\mathbf{A}\| \neq \|\mathbf{C}\|$

105. Let $\mathbf{v} = a\mathbf{i} + b\mathbf{j}$. Show that $\dfrac{\mathbf{v}}{\|\mathbf{v}\|}$ is a unit vector in the direction of $\mathbf{v}$.

In Exercises 106–107, refer to the navigational compass shown in the figure. The compass is marked clockwise in degrees that start at north 0°.

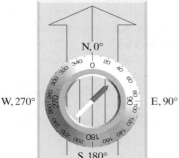

106. An airplane has an air speed of 240 miles per hour and a compass heading of 280°. A steady wind of 30 miles per hour is blowing in the direction of 265°. What is the plane's true speed relative to the ground? What is its compass heading relative to the ground?

107. Two tugboats are pulling on a large ship that has gone aground. One tug pulls with a force of 2500 pounds in a compass direction of 55°. The second tug pulls with a force of 2000 pounds in a compass direction of 95°. Find the magnitude and the compass direction of the resultant force.

108. You want to fly your small plane due north, but there is a 75 kilometer wind blowing from west to east.

   a. Find the direction angle for where you should head the plane if your speed relative to the ground is 310 kilometers per hour.

   b. If you increase your air speed, should the direction angle in part (a) increase or decrease? Explain your answer.

SECTION 6.7 *The Dot Product*

Objectives

❶ Find the dot product of two vectors.

❷ Find the angle between two vectors.

❸ Use the dot product to determine if two vectors are orthogonal.

❹ Find the projection of a vector onto another vector.

❺ Express a vector as the sum of two orthogonal vectors.

❻ Compute work.

Talk about hard work! I can see the weightlifter's muscles quivering from the exertion of holding the barbell in a stationary position above his head. Still, I'm not sure if he's doing as much work as I am, sitting at my desk with my brain quivering from studying trigonometric functions and their applications.

Would it surprise you to know that neither you nor the weightlifter are doing any work at all? The definition of work in physics and mathematics is not the same as what we mean by "work" in everyday use. To understand what is involved in real work, we turn to a new vector operation called the dot product.

① Find the dot product of two vectors.

The Dot Product of Two Vectors

The operations of vector addition and scalar multiplication result in vectors. By contrast, the *dot product* of two vectors results in a scalar (a real number), rather than a vector.

Definition of the Dot Product

If $\mathbf{v} = a_1\mathbf{i} + b_1\mathbf{j}$ and $\mathbf{w} = a_2\mathbf{i} + b_2\mathbf{j}$ are vectors, the **dot product $\mathbf{v} \cdot \mathbf{w}$** is defined as follows:

$$\mathbf{v} \cdot \mathbf{w} = a_1 a_2 + b_1 b_2.$$

The dot product of two vectors is the sum of the products of their horizontal components and their vertical components.

EXAMPLE 1   Finding Dot Products

If $\mathbf{v} = 5\mathbf{i} - 2\mathbf{j}$ and $\mathbf{w} = -3\mathbf{i} + 4\mathbf{j}$, find each of the following dot products:

a. $\mathbf{v} \cdot \mathbf{w}$ **b.** $\mathbf{w} \cdot \mathbf{v}$ **c.** $\mathbf{v} \cdot \mathbf{v}$.

Solution   To find each dot product, multiply the two horizontal components, and then multiply the two vertical components. Finally, add the two products.

a. $\mathbf{v} \cdot \mathbf{w} = 5(-3) + (-2)(4) = -15 - 8 = -23$

> Multiply the horizontal components and multiply the vertical components of $\mathbf{v} = 5\mathbf{i} - 2\mathbf{j}$ and $\mathbf{w} = -3\mathbf{i} + 4\mathbf{j}$.

b. $\mathbf{w} \cdot \mathbf{v} = -3(5) + 4(-2) = -15 - 8 = -23$

> Multiply the horizontal components and multiply the vertical components of $\mathbf{w} = -3\mathbf{i} + 4\mathbf{j}$ and $\mathbf{v} = 5\mathbf{i} - 2\mathbf{j}$.

c. $\mathbf{v} \cdot \mathbf{v} = 5(5) + (-2)(-2) = 25 + 4 = 29$

> Multiply the horizontal components and multiply the vertical components of $\mathbf{v} = 5\mathbf{i} - 2\mathbf{j}$ and $\mathbf{v} = 5\mathbf{i} - 2\mathbf{j}$.

Check Point **1**   If $\mathbf{v} = 7\mathbf{i} - 4\mathbf{j}$ and $\mathbf{w} = 2\mathbf{i} - \mathbf{j}$, find each of the following dot products:

a. $\mathbf{v} \cdot \mathbf{w}$ **b.** $\mathbf{w} \cdot \mathbf{v}$ **c.** $\mathbf{w} \cdot \mathbf{w}$.

In Example 1 and Check Point 1, did you notice that $\mathbf{v} \cdot \mathbf{w}$ and $\mathbf{w} \cdot \mathbf{v}$ produced the same scalar? The fact that $\mathbf{v} \cdot \mathbf{w} = \mathbf{w} \cdot \mathbf{v}$ follows from the definition of the dot product. Properties of the dot product are given in the following box. Proofs for some of these properties are given in the appendix.

Properties of the Dot Product

If **u**, **v**, and **w** are vectors, and c is a scalar, then

  1. $\mathbf{u} \cdot \mathbf{v} = \mathbf{v} \cdot \mathbf{u}$
  2. $\mathbf{u} \cdot (\mathbf{v} + \mathbf{w}) = \mathbf{u} \cdot \mathbf{v} + \mathbf{u} \cdot \mathbf{w}$
  3. $\mathbf{0} \cdot \mathbf{v} = 0$
  4. $\mathbf{v} \cdot \mathbf{v} = \|\mathbf{v}\|^2$
  5. $(c\mathbf{u}) \cdot \mathbf{v} = c(\mathbf{u} \cdot \mathbf{v}) = \mathbf{u} \cdot (c\mathbf{v})$

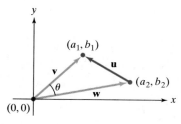

Figure 6.64

The Angle between Two Vectors

The Law of Cosines can be used to derive another formula for the dot product. This formula will give us a way to find the angle between two vectors.

Figure 6.64 shows vectors $\mathbf{v} = a_1\mathbf{i} + b_1\mathbf{j}$ and $\mathbf{w} = a_2\mathbf{i} + b_2\mathbf{j}$. By the definition of the dot product, we know that $\mathbf{v} \cdot \mathbf{w} = a_1 a_2 + b_1 b_2$. Our new formula for the dot product involves the angle between the vectors, shown as θ in the figure. Apply the Law of Cosines to the triangle shown in the figure.

$$\|\mathbf{u}\|^2 = \|\mathbf{v}\|^2 + \|\mathbf{w}\|^2 - 2\|\mathbf{v}\|\,\|\mathbf{w}\|\cos\theta$$
Use the Law of Cosines.

$$\mathbf{u} = (a_1 - a_2)\mathbf{i} + (b_1 - b_2)\mathbf{j} \qquad \mathbf{v} = a_1\mathbf{i} + b_1\mathbf{j} \qquad \mathbf{w} = a_2\mathbf{i} + b_2\mathbf{j}$$
$$\|\mathbf{u}\| = \sqrt{(a_1 - a_2)^2 + (b_1 - b_2)^2} \qquad \|\mathbf{v}\| = \sqrt{a_1^2 + b_1^2} \qquad \|\mathbf{w}\| = \sqrt{a_2^2 + b_2^2}$$

$$(a_1 - a_2)^2 + (b_1 - b_2)^2 = (a_1^2 + b_1^2) + (a_2^2 + b_2^2) - 2\|\mathbf{v}\|\|\mathbf{w}\|\cos\theta$$
Substitute the squares of the magnitudes of vectors u, v, and w into the Law of Cosines.

$$a_1^2 - 2a_1 a_2 + a_2^2 + b_1^2 - 2b_1 b_2 + b_2^2 = a_1^2 + b_1^2 + a_2^2 + b_2^2 - 2\|\mathbf{v}\|\|\mathbf{w}\|\cos\theta$$
Square the binomials using $(A - B)^2 = A^2 - 2AB + B^2$.

$$-2a_1 a_2 - 2b_1 b_2 = -2\|\mathbf{v}\|\|\mathbf{w}\|\cos\theta$$
Subtract a_1^2, a_2^2, b_1^2, and b_2^2 from both sides of the equation.

$$a_1 a_2 + b_1 b_2 = \|\mathbf{v}\|\,\|\mathbf{w}\|\cos\theta$$
Divide both sides by -2.

By definition,
$\mathbf{v} \cdot \mathbf{w} = a_1 a_2 + b_1 b_2$.

$$\mathbf{v} \cdot \mathbf{w} = \|\mathbf{v}\|\|\mathbf{w}\|\cos\theta$$
Substitute v · w for the expression on the left side of the equation.

Alternative Formula for the Dot Product

If **v** and **w** are two nonzero vectors and θ is the smallest nonnegative angle between them, then

$$\mathbf{v} \cdot \mathbf{w} = \|\mathbf{v}\|\|\mathbf{w}\|\cos\theta.$$

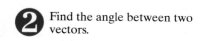 Find the angle between two vectors.

Solving the formula in the box for $\cos\theta$ gives us a formula for finding the angle between two vectors:

Formula for the Angle between Two Vectors

If **v** and **w** are two nonzero vectors and θ is the smallest nonnegative angle between **v** and **w**, then

$$\cos\theta = \frac{\mathbf{v} \cdot \mathbf{w}}{\|\mathbf{v}\|\|\mathbf{w}\|} \quad \text{and} \quad \theta = \cos^{-1}\left(\frac{\mathbf{v} \cdot \mathbf{w}}{\|\mathbf{v}\|\|\mathbf{w}\|}\right).$$

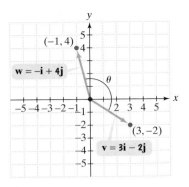

Figure 6.65 Finding the angle between two vectors

EXAMPLE 2   Finding the Angle between Two Vectors

Find the angle θ between the vectors $\mathbf{v} = 3\mathbf{i} - 2\mathbf{j}$ and $\mathbf{w} = -\mathbf{i} + 4\mathbf{j}$, shown in Figure 6.65. Round to the nearest tenth of a degree.

Solution   Use the formula for the angle between two vectors.

$$\cos \theta = \frac{\mathbf{v} \cdot \mathbf{w}}{\|\mathbf{v}\|\|\mathbf{w}\|}$$

Begin with the formula for the cosine of the angle between two vectors.

$$= \frac{(3\mathbf{i} - 2\mathbf{j}) \cdot (-\mathbf{i} + 4\mathbf{j})}{\sqrt{3^2 + (-2)^2}\sqrt{(-1)^2 + 4^2}}$$

Substitute the given vectors in the numerator. Find the magnitude of each vector in the denominator.

$$= \frac{3(-1) + (-2)(4)}{\sqrt{13}\sqrt{17}}$$

Find the dot product in the numerator. Simplify in the denominator.

$$= -\frac{11}{\sqrt{221}}$$

Perform the indicated operations.

The angle θ between the vectors is

$$\theta = \cos^{-1}\left(-\frac{11}{\sqrt{221}}\right) \approx 137.7°.$$

Use a calculator.

 Find the angle between the vectors $\mathbf{v} = 4\mathbf{i} - 3\mathbf{j}$ and $\mathbf{w} = \mathbf{i} + 2\mathbf{j}$. Round to the nearest tenth of a degree.

③ Use the dot product to determine if two vectors are orthogonal.

Parallel and Orthogonal Vectors

Two vectors are **parallel** when the angle θ between the vectors is $0°$ or $180°$. If $\theta = 0°$, the vectors point in the same direction. If $\theta = 180°$, the vectors point in opposite directions. Figure 6.66 shows parallel vectors.

$\theta = 0°$ and $\cos \theta = 1$.
Vectors point in the same direction.

$\theta = 180°$ and $\cos \theta = -1$. Vectors point in opposite directions.

Figure 6.66 Parallel vectors

Two vectors are **orthogonal** when the angle between the vectors is $90°$, shown in Figure 6.67. (The word "orthogonal," rather than "perpendicular," is used to describe vectors that meet at right angles.) We know that $\mathbf{v} \cdot \mathbf{w} = \|\mathbf{v}\|\|\mathbf{w}\| \cos \theta$. If $\mathbf{v}$ and $\mathbf{w}$ are orthogonal, then

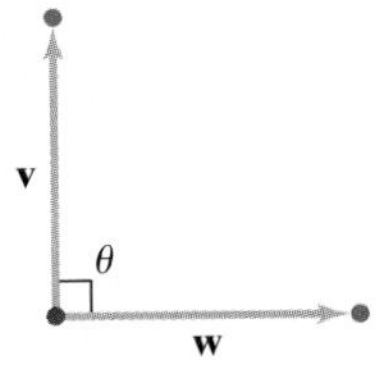

$$\mathbf{v} \cdot \mathbf{w} = \|\mathbf{v}\|\|\mathbf{w}\| \cos 90° = \|\mathbf{v}\|\|\mathbf{w}\|(0) = 0.$$

Conversely, if $\mathbf{v}$ and $\mathbf{w}$ are vectors such that $\mathbf{v} \cdot \mathbf{w} = 0$, then $\|\mathbf{v}\| = 0$ or $\|\mathbf{w}\| = 0$ or $\cos \theta = 0$. If $\cos \theta = 0$, then $\theta = 90°$, so $\mathbf{v}$ and $\mathbf{w}$ are orthogonal.

This discussion is summarized as follows:

Figure 6.67 Orthogonal vectors: $\theta = 90°$ and $\cos \theta = 0$

> ### The Dot Product and Orthogonal Vectors
>
> Two nonzero vectors $\mathbf{v}$ and $\mathbf{w}$ are orthogonal if and only if $\mathbf{v} \cdot \mathbf{w} = 0$.
> Because $\mathbf{0} \cdot \mathbf{v} = 0$, the zero vector is orthogonal to every vector $\mathbf{v}$.

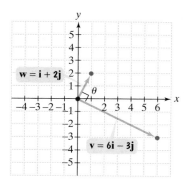

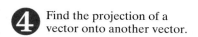

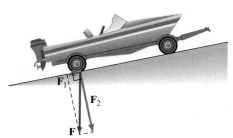

Figure 6.68 Orthogonal vectors

EXAMPLE 3 Determining Whether Vectors Are Orthogonal

Are the vectors $\mathbf{v} = 6\mathbf{i} - 3\mathbf{j}$ and $\mathbf{w} = \mathbf{i} + 2\mathbf{j}$ orthogonal?

Solution The vectors are orthogonal if their dot product is 0. Begin by finding $\mathbf{v} \cdot \mathbf{w}$.

$$\mathbf{v} \cdot \mathbf{w} = (6\mathbf{i} - 3\mathbf{j}) \cdot (\mathbf{i} + 2\mathbf{j}) = 6(1) + (-3)(2) = 6 - 6 = 0$$

The dot product is 0. Thus, the given vectors are orthogonal. They are shown in Figure 6.68.

Check Point 3 Are the vectors $\mathbf{v} = 2\mathbf{i} + 3\mathbf{j}$ and $\mathbf{w} = 6\mathbf{i} - 4\mathbf{j}$ orthogonal?

④ Find the projection of a vector onto another vector.

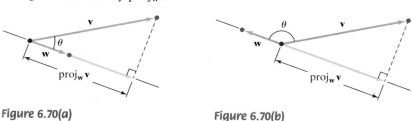

Figure 6.69

Projection of a Vector Onto Another Vector

You know how to add two vectors to obtain a resultant vector. We now reverse this process by expressing a vector as the sum of two orthogonal vectors. By doing this, you can determine how much force is applied in a particular direction. For example, Figure 6.69 shows a boat on a tilted ramp. The force due to gravity, $\mathbf{F}$, is pulling straight down on the boat. Part of this force, $\mathbf{F}_1$, is pushing the boat down the ramp. Another part of this force, $\mathbf{F}_2$, is pressing the boat against the ramp, at a right angle to the incline. These two orthogonal vectors, $\mathbf{F}_1$ and $\mathbf{F}_2$, are called the **vector components** of $\mathbf{F}$. Notice that

$$\mathbf{F} = \mathbf{F}_1 + \mathbf{F}_2.$$

A method for finding $\mathbf{F}_1$ and $\mathbf{F}_2$ involves projecting a vector onto another vector.

Figure 6.70 shows two nonzero vectors, $\mathbf{v}$ and $\mathbf{w}$, with the same initial point. The angle between the vectors, θ, is acute in Figure 6.70(a) and obtuse in Figure 6.70(b). A third vector, called the **vector projection of v onto w**, is also shown in each figure, denoted by $\text{proj}_\mathbf{w}\mathbf{v}$.

Figure 6.70(a)

Figure 6.70(b)

How is the vector projection of $\mathbf{v}$ onto $\mathbf{w}$ formed? Draw the line segment from the terminal point of $\mathbf{v}$ that forms a right angle with a line through $\mathbf{w}$, shown in red. The projection of $\mathbf{v}$ onto $\mathbf{w}$ lies on a line through $\mathbf{w}$, and is parallel to vector $\mathbf{w}$. This vector begins at the common initial point of $\mathbf{v}$ and $\mathbf{w}$. It ends at the point where the dashed red line segment intersects the line through $\mathbf{w}$.

Our goal is to determine an expression for $\text{proj}_\mathbf{w}\mathbf{v}$. We begin with its magnitude. By the definition of the cosine function,

$$\cos \theta = \frac{\|\text{proj}_\mathbf{w}\mathbf{v}\|}{\|\mathbf{v}\|}.$$

> This is the magnitude of the vector projection of $\mathbf{v}$ onto $\mathbf{w}$.

$$\|\mathbf{v}\| \cos \theta = \|\text{proj}_\mathbf{w}\mathbf{v}\| \quad \text{Multiply both sides by } \|\mathbf{v}\|.$$

$$\|\text{proj}_\mathbf{w}\mathbf{v}\| = \|\mathbf{v}\| \cos \theta \quad \text{Reverse the two sides.}$$

We can rewrite the right side of this equation and obtain another expression for the magnitude of the vector projection of $\mathbf{v}$ onto $\mathbf{w}$. To do so, use the alternate formula for the dot product, $\mathbf{v} \cdot \mathbf{w} = \|\mathbf{v}\|\|\mathbf{w}\| \cos \theta$.

Divide both sides of $\mathbf{v} \cdot \mathbf{w} = \|\mathbf{v}\|\|\mathbf{w}\| \cos \theta$ by $\|\mathbf{w}\|$:

$$\frac{\mathbf{v} \cdot \mathbf{w}}{\|\mathbf{w}\|} = \|\mathbf{v}\| \cos \theta.$$

The expression on the right side of this equation, $\|\mathbf{v}\| \cos \theta$, is the same expression that appears in the formula for $\|\text{proj}_{\mathbf{w}}\mathbf{v}\|$. Thus,

$$\|\text{proj}_{\mathbf{w}}\mathbf{v}\| = \|\mathbf{v}\| \cos \theta = \frac{\mathbf{v} \cdot \mathbf{w}}{\|\mathbf{w}\|}.$$

We use the formula for the magnitude of $\text{proj}_{\mathbf{w}}\mathbf{v}$ to find the vector itself. This is done by finding the scalar product of the magnitude and the unit vector in the direction of $\mathbf{w}$.

$$\text{proj}_{\mathbf{w}}\mathbf{v} = \left(\frac{\mathbf{v} \cdot \mathbf{w}}{\|\mathbf{w}\|}\right)\left(\frac{\mathbf{w}}{\|\mathbf{w}\|}\right) = \frac{\mathbf{v} \cdot \mathbf{w}}{\|\mathbf{w}\|^2}\,\mathbf{w}$$

This is the magnitude of the vector projection of v onto w. | This is the unit vector in the direction of w.

The Vector Projection of v Onto w

If $\mathbf{v}$ and $\mathbf{w}$ are two nonzero vectors, the vector projection of $\mathbf{v}$ onto $\mathbf{w}$ is

$$\text{proj}_{\mathbf{w}}\mathbf{v} = \frac{\mathbf{v} \cdot \mathbf{w}}{\|\mathbf{w}\|^2}\,\mathbf{w}.$$

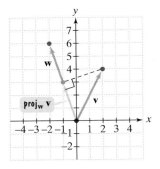

Figure 6.71 The vector projection of $\mathbf{v}$ onto $\mathbf{w}$

EXAMPLE 4   Finding the Vector Projection of One Vector Onto Another

If $\mathbf{v} = 2\mathbf{i} + 4\mathbf{j}$ and $\mathbf{w} = -2\mathbf{i} + 6\mathbf{j}$, find the vector projection of $\mathbf{v}$ onto $\mathbf{w}$.

Solution   The vector projection of $\mathbf{v}$ onto $\mathbf{w}$ is found using the formula for $\text{proj}_{\mathbf{w}}\mathbf{v}$.

$$\text{proj}_{\mathbf{w}}\mathbf{v} = \frac{\mathbf{v} \cdot \mathbf{w}}{\|\mathbf{w}\|^2}\,\mathbf{w} = \frac{(2\mathbf{i} + 4\mathbf{j}) \cdot (-2\mathbf{i} + 6\mathbf{j})}{\left(\sqrt{(-2)^2 + 6^2}\right)^2}\,\mathbf{w}$$

$$= \frac{2(-2) + 4(6)}{\left(\sqrt{40}\right)^2}\,\mathbf{w} = \frac{20}{40}\,\mathbf{w} = \tfrac{1}{2}(-2\mathbf{i} + 6\mathbf{j}) = -\mathbf{i} + 3\mathbf{j}$$

The three vectors, $\mathbf{v}$, $\mathbf{w}$, and $\text{proj}_{\mathbf{w}}\mathbf{v}$, are shown in Figure 6.71.

Check Point 4   If $\mathbf{v} = 2\mathbf{i} - 5\mathbf{j}$ and $\mathbf{w} = \mathbf{i} - \mathbf{j}$, find the vector projection of $\mathbf{v}$ onto $\mathbf{w}$.

⑤ Express a vector as the sum of two orthogonal vectors.

We use the vector projection of $\mathbf{v}$ onto $\mathbf{w}$, $\text{proj}_{\mathbf{w}}\mathbf{v}$, to express $\mathbf{v}$ as the sum of two orthogonal vectors.

The Vector Components of v

Let $\mathbf{v}$ and $\mathbf{w}$ be two nonzero vectors. Vector $\mathbf{v}$ can be expressed as the sum of two orthogonal vectors, $\mathbf{v}_1$ and $\mathbf{v}_2$, where $\mathbf{v}_1$ is parallel to $\mathbf{w}$ and $\mathbf{v}_2$ is orthogonal to $\mathbf{w}$.

$$\mathbf{v}_1 = \text{proj}_{\mathbf{w}}\mathbf{v} = \frac{\mathbf{v} \cdot \mathbf{w}}{\|\mathbf{w}\|^2}\,\mathbf{w}, \quad \mathbf{v}_2 = \mathbf{v} - \mathbf{v}_1$$

Thus, $\mathbf{v} = \mathbf{v}_1 + \mathbf{v}_2$. The vectors $\mathbf{v}_1$ and $\mathbf{v}_2$ are called the **vector components** of $\mathbf{v}$. The process of expressing $\mathbf{v}$ as $\mathbf{v}_1 + \mathbf{v}_2$ is called the **decomposition** of $\mathbf{v}$ into $\mathbf{v}_1$ and $\mathbf{v}_2$.

EXAMPLE 5   Decomposing a Vector into Two Orthogonal Vectors

Let $\mathbf{v} = 2\mathbf{i} + 4\mathbf{j}$ and $\mathbf{w} = -2\mathbf{i} + 6\mathbf{j}$. Decompose $\mathbf{v}$ into two vectors, $\mathbf{v}_1$ and $\mathbf{v}_2$, where $\mathbf{v}_1$ is parallel to $\mathbf{w}$ and $\mathbf{v}_2$ is orthogonal to $\mathbf{w}$.

Solution   These are the vectors we worked with in Example 4. We use the formulas in the preceding box.

$$\mathbf{v}_1 = \text{proj}_{\mathbf{w}}\mathbf{v} = -\mathbf{i} + 3\mathbf{j} \qquad \text{We obtained this vector in Example 4.}$$
$$\mathbf{v}_2 = \mathbf{v} - \mathbf{v}_1 = (2\mathbf{i} + 4\mathbf{j}) - (-\mathbf{i} + 3\mathbf{j}) = 3\mathbf{i} + \mathbf{j}$$

Check Point 5   Let $\mathbf{v} = 2\mathbf{i} - 5\mathbf{j}$ and $\mathbf{w} = \mathbf{i} - \mathbf{j}$. (These are the vectors from Check Point 4.) Decompose $\mathbf{v}$ into two vectors, $\mathbf{v}_1$ and $\mathbf{v}_2$, where $\mathbf{v}_1$ is parallel to $\mathbf{w}$ and $\mathbf{v}_2$ is orthogonal to $\mathbf{w}$.

 **6 Compute work.**

Work: An Application of the Dot Product

The bad news: Your car just died. The good news: It died on a level road just 200 feet from a gas station. Exerting a constant force of 90 pounds, and not necessarily whistling as you work, you manage to push the car to the gas station.

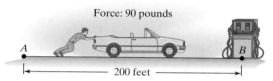

Force: 90 pounds

200 feet

Although you did not whistle, you certainly did work pushing the car 200 feet from point A to point B. How much work did you do? If a constant force $\mathbf{F}$ is applied to an object, moving it from point A to point B in the direction of the force, the work, W, done is

$$W = (\text{magnitude of force})(\text{distance from } A \text{ to } B).$$

You pushed with a force of 90 pounds for a distance of 200 feet. The work done by your force is

$$W = (90 \text{ pounds})(200 \text{ feet})$$

or 18,000 foot-pounds. Work is often measured in foot-pounds or in newton-meters.

 The photo on the left shows an adult pulling a small child in a wagon. Work is being done. However, the situation is not quite the same as pushing your car. Pushing the car, the force you applied was along the line of motion. By contrast, the force of the adult pulling the wagon is not applied along the line of the wagon's motion. In this case, the dot product is used to determine the work done by the force.

Definition of Work

The work, W, done by a force $\mathbf{F}$ moving an object from A to B is

$$W = \mathbf{F} \cdot \overrightarrow{AB}.$$

When computing work, it is often easier to use the alternative formula for the dot product. Thus,

$$W = \mathbf{F} \cdot \overrightarrow{AB} = \|\mathbf{F}\| \, \|\overrightarrow{AB}\| \cos \theta.$$

$\|\mathbf{F}\|$ is the magnitude of the force.

$\|\overrightarrow{AB}\|$ is the distance over which the constant force is applied.

θ is the angle between the force and the direction of motion.

It is correct to refer to W as either the work done or the work done by the force.

EXAMPLE 6   Computing Work

A child pulls a sled along level ground by exerting a force of 30 pounds on a rope that makes an angle of 35° with the horizontal. How much work is done pulling the sled 200 feet?

Solution   The situation is illustrated in Figure 6.72. The work done is

Figure 6.72 Computing work done pulling the sled 200 feet

$$W = \|\mathbf{F}\| \, \|\overrightarrow{AB}\| \cos \theta = (30)(200)\cos 35° \approx 4915.$$

| Magnitude of the force is 30 pounds. | Distance is 200 feet. | The angle between the force and the sled's motion is 35°. |

Thus, the work done is approximately 4915 foot-pounds.

Check Point 6   A child pulls a wagon along level ground by exerting a force of 20 pounds on a handle that makes an angle of 30° with the horizontal. How much work is done pulling the wagon 150 feet?

EXERCISE SET 6.7

Practice Exercises

In Exercises 1–8, use the given vectors to find $\mathbf{v} \cdot \mathbf{w}$ and $\mathbf{v} \cdot \mathbf{v}$.

1. $\mathbf{v} = 3\mathbf{i} + \mathbf{j}, \quad \mathbf{w} = \mathbf{i} + 3\mathbf{j}$
2. $\mathbf{v} = 3\mathbf{i} + 3\mathbf{j}, \quad \mathbf{w} = \mathbf{i} + 4\mathbf{j}$
3. $\mathbf{v} = 5\mathbf{i} - 4\mathbf{j}, \quad \mathbf{w} = -2\mathbf{i} - \mathbf{j}$
4. $\mathbf{v} = 7\mathbf{i} - 2\mathbf{j}, \quad \mathbf{w} = -3\mathbf{i} - \mathbf{j}$
5. $\mathbf{v} = -6\mathbf{i} - 5\mathbf{j}, \quad \mathbf{w} = -10\mathbf{i} - 8\mathbf{j}$
6. $\mathbf{v} = -8\mathbf{i} - 3\mathbf{j}, \quad \mathbf{w} = -10\mathbf{i} - 5\mathbf{j}$
7. $\mathbf{v} = 5\mathbf{i}, \quad \mathbf{w} = \mathbf{j}$ 8. $\mathbf{v} = \mathbf{i}, \quad \mathbf{w} = -5\mathbf{j}$

In Exercises 9–16, let

$$\mathbf{u} = 2\mathbf{i} - \mathbf{j}, \quad \mathbf{v} = 3\mathbf{i} + \mathbf{j}, \quad \text{and} \quad \mathbf{w} = \mathbf{i} + 4\mathbf{j}.$$

Find each specified scalar.

9. $\mathbf{u} \cdot (\mathbf{v} + \mathbf{w})$
10. $\mathbf{v} \cdot (\mathbf{u} + \mathbf{w})$
11. $\mathbf{u} \cdot \mathbf{v} + \mathbf{u} \cdot \mathbf{w}$
12. $\mathbf{v} \cdot \mathbf{u} + \mathbf{v} \cdot \mathbf{w}$
13. $(4\mathbf{u}) \cdot \mathbf{v}$
14. $(5\mathbf{v}) \cdot \mathbf{w}$
15. $4(\mathbf{u} \cdot \mathbf{v})$
16. $5(\mathbf{v} \cdot \mathbf{w})$

In Exercises 17–22, find the angle between **v** and **w**. Round to the nearest tenth of a degree.

17. $\mathbf{v} = 2\mathbf{i} - \mathbf{j}, \quad \mathbf{w} = 3\mathbf{i} + 4\mathbf{j}$
18. $\mathbf{v} = -2\mathbf{i} + 5\mathbf{j}, \quad \mathbf{w} = 3\mathbf{i} + 6\mathbf{j}$
19. $\mathbf{v} = -3\mathbf{i} + 2\mathbf{j}, \quad \mathbf{w} = 4\mathbf{i} - \mathbf{j}$
20. $\mathbf{v} = \mathbf{i} + 2\mathbf{j}, \quad \mathbf{w} = 4\mathbf{i} - 3\mathbf{j}$
21. $\mathbf{v} = 6\mathbf{i}, \quad \mathbf{w} = 5\mathbf{i} + 4\mathbf{j}$
22. $\mathbf{v} = 3\mathbf{j}, \quad \mathbf{w} = 4\mathbf{i} + 5\mathbf{j}$

In Exercises 23–32, use the dot product to determine whether **v** and **w** are orthogonal.

23. $\mathbf{v} = \mathbf{i} + \mathbf{j}, \quad \mathbf{w} = \mathbf{i} - \mathbf{j}$ 24. $\mathbf{v} = \mathbf{i} + \mathbf{j}, \quad \mathbf{w} = -\mathbf{i} + \mathbf{j}$
25. $\mathbf{v} = 2\mathbf{i} + 8\mathbf{j}, \quad \mathbf{w} = 4\mathbf{i} - \mathbf{j}$
26. $\mathbf{v} = 8\mathbf{i} - 4\mathbf{j}, \quad \mathbf{w} = -6\mathbf{i} - 12\mathbf{j}$
27. $\mathbf{v} = 2\mathbf{i} - 2\mathbf{j}, \quad \mathbf{w} = -\mathbf{i} + \mathbf{j}$
28. $\mathbf{v} = 5\mathbf{i} - 5\mathbf{j}, \quad \mathbf{w} = \mathbf{i} - \mathbf{j}$
29. $\mathbf{v} = 3\mathbf{i}, \quad \mathbf{w} = -4\mathbf{i}$ 30. $\mathbf{v} = 5\mathbf{i}, \quad \mathbf{w} = -6\mathbf{i}$
31. $\mathbf{v} = 3\mathbf{i}, \quad \mathbf{w} = -4\mathbf{j}$ 32. $\mathbf{v} = 5\mathbf{i}, \quad \mathbf{w} = -6\mathbf{j}$

In Exercise 33–38, find $\text{proj}_{\mathbf{w}}\mathbf{v}$. Then decompose **v** into two vectors, $\mathbf{v}_1$ and $\mathbf{v}_2$, where $\mathbf{v}_1$ is parallel to **w** and $\mathbf{v}_2$ is orthogonal to **w**.

33. $\mathbf{v} = 3\mathbf{i} - 2\mathbf{j}, \quad \mathbf{w} = \mathbf{i} - \mathbf{j}$
34. $\mathbf{v} = 3\mathbf{i} - 2\mathbf{j}, \quad \mathbf{w} = 2\mathbf{i} + \mathbf{j}$
35. $\mathbf{v} = \mathbf{i} + 3\mathbf{j}, \quad \mathbf{w} = -2\mathbf{i} + 5\mathbf{j}$
36. $\mathbf{v} = 2\mathbf{i} + 4\mathbf{j}, \quad \mathbf{w} = -3\mathbf{i} + 6\mathbf{j}$
37. $\mathbf{v} = \mathbf{i} + 2\mathbf{j}, \quad \mathbf{w} = 3\mathbf{i} + 6\mathbf{j}$
38. $\mathbf{v} = 2\mathbf{i} + \mathbf{j}, \quad \mathbf{w} = 6\mathbf{i} + 3\mathbf{j}$

Practice Plus

In Exercises 39–42, let

$$\mathbf{u} = -\mathbf{i} + \mathbf{j}, \quad \mathbf{v} = 3\mathbf{i} - 2\mathbf{j}, \quad \text{and} \quad \mathbf{w} = -5\mathbf{j}.$$

Find each specified scalar or vector.

39. $5\mathbf{u} \cdot (3\mathbf{v} - 4\mathbf{w})$
40. $4\mathbf{u} \cdot (5\mathbf{v} - 3\mathbf{w})$
41. $\text{proj}_{\mathbf{u}}(\mathbf{v} + \mathbf{w})$
42. $\text{proj}_{\mathbf{u}}(\mathbf{v} - \mathbf{w})$

In Exercises 43–44, find the angle, in degrees, between **v** *and* **w**.

43. $\mathbf{v} = 2\cos\dfrac{4\pi}{3}\mathbf{i} + 2\sin\dfrac{4\pi}{3}\mathbf{j}, \quad \mathbf{w} = 3\cos\dfrac{3\pi}{2}\mathbf{i} + 3\sin\dfrac{3\pi}{2}\mathbf{j}$

44. $\mathbf{v} = 3\cos\dfrac{5\pi}{3}\mathbf{i} + 3\sin\dfrac{5\pi}{3}\mathbf{j}, \quad \mathbf{w} = 2\cos\pi\mathbf{i} + 2\sin\pi\mathbf{j}$

In Exercises 45–50, determine whether **v** *and* **w** *are parallel, orthogonal, or neither.*

45. $\mathbf{v} = 3\mathbf{i} - 5\mathbf{j}, \quad \mathbf{w} = 6\mathbf{i} - 10\mathbf{j}$

46. $\mathbf{v} = -2\mathbf{i} + 3\mathbf{j}, \quad \mathbf{w} = -6\mathbf{i} + 9\mathbf{j}$

47. $\mathbf{v} = 3\mathbf{i} - 5\mathbf{j}, \quad \mathbf{w} = 6\mathbf{i} + 10\mathbf{j}$

48. $\mathbf{v} = -2\mathbf{i} + 3\mathbf{j}, \quad \mathbf{w} = -6\mathbf{i} - 9\mathbf{j}$

49. $\mathbf{v} = 3\mathbf{i} - 5\mathbf{j}, \quad \mathbf{w} = 6\mathbf{i} + \dfrac{18}{5}\mathbf{j}$

50. $\mathbf{v} = -2\mathbf{i} + 3\mathbf{j}, \quad \mathbf{w} = -6\mathbf{i} - 4\mathbf{j}$

Application Exercises

51. The components of $\mathbf{v} = 240\mathbf{i} + 300\mathbf{j}$ represent the respective number of gallons of regular and premium gas sold at a station. The components of $\mathbf{w} = 2.90\mathbf{i} + 3.07\mathbf{j}$ represent the respective prices per gallon for each kind of gas. Find $\mathbf{v} \cdot \mathbf{w}$ and describe what the answer means in practical terms.

52. The components of $\mathbf{v} = 180\mathbf{i} + 450\mathbf{j}$ represent the respective number of one-day and three-day videos rented from a video store. The components of $\mathbf{w} = 3\mathbf{i} + 2\mathbf{j}$ represent the prices to rent the one-day and three-day videos, respectively. Find $\mathbf{v} \cdot \mathbf{w}$ and describe what the answer means in practical terms.

53. Find the work done in pushing a car along a level road from point A to point B, 80 feet from A, while exerting a constant force of 95 pounds. Round to the nearest foot-pound.

54. Find the work done when a crane lifts a 6000-pound boulder through a vertical distance of 12 feet. Round to the nearest foot-pound.

55. A wagon is pulled along level ground by exerting a force of 40 pounds on a handle that makes an angle of 32° with the horizontal. How much work is done pulling the wagon 100 feet? Round to the nearest foot-pound.

56. A wagon is pulled along level ground by exerting a force of 25 pounds on a handle that makes an angle of 38° with the horizontal. How much work is done pulling the wagon 100 feet? Round to the nearest foot-pound.

57. A force of 60 pounds on a rope is used to pull a box up a ramp inclined at 12° from the horizontal. The figure shows that the rope forms an angle of 38° with the horizontal. How much work is done pulling the box 20 feet along the ramp?

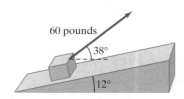

60 pounds
38°
12°

58. A force of 80 pounds on a rope is used to pull a box up a ramp inclined at 10° from the horizontal. The rope forms an angle of 33° with the horizontal. How much work is done pulling the box 25 feet along the ramp?

59. A force is given by the vector $\mathbf{F} = 3\mathbf{i} + 2\mathbf{j}$. The force moves an object along a straight line from the point $(4, 9)$ to the point $(10, 20)$. Find the work done if the distance is measured in feet and the force is measured in pounds.

60. A force is given by the vector $\mathbf{F} = 5\mathbf{i} + 7\mathbf{j}$. The force moves an object along a straight line from the point $(8, 11)$ to the point $(18, 20)$. Find the work done if the distance is measured in meters and the force is measured in newtons.

61. A force of 4 pounds acts in the direction of 50° to the horizontal. The force moves an object along a straight line from the point $(3, 7)$ to the point $(8, 10)$, with distance measured in feet. Find the work done by the force.

62. A force of 6 pounds acts in the direction of 40° to the horizontal. The force moves an object along a straight line from the point $(5, 9)$ to the point $(8, 20)$, with the distance measured in feet. Find the work done by the force.

63. Refer to Figure 6.69 on page 697. Suppose that the boat weighs 700 pounds and is on a ramp inclined at 30°. Represent the force due to gravity, $\mathbf{F}$, using

$$\mathbf{F} = -700\mathbf{j}.$$

a. Write a unit vector along the ramp in the upward direction.

b. Find the vector projection of $\mathbf{F}$ onto the unit vector from part (a).

c. What is the magnitude of the vector projection in part (b)? What does this represent?

64. Refer to Figure 6.69 on page 697. Suppose that the boat weighs 650 pounds and is on a ramp inclined at 30°. Represent the force due to gravity, $\mathbf{F}$, using

$$\mathbf{F} = -650\mathbf{j}.$$

a. Write a unit vector along the ramp in the upward direction.

b. Find the vector projection of $\mathbf{F}$ onto the unit vector from part (a).

c. What is the magnitude of the vector projection in part (b)? What does this represent?

Writing in Mathematics

65. Explain how to find the dot product of two vectors.

66. Using words and no symbols, describe how to find the dot product of two vectors with the alternative formula

$$\mathbf{v} \cdot \mathbf{w} = \|\mathbf{v}\|\|\mathbf{w}\|\cos\theta.$$

67. Describe how to find the angle between two vectors.

68. What are parallel vectors?

69. What are orthogonal vectors?

70. How do you determine if two vectors are orthogonal?

71. Draw two vectors, **v** and **w**, with the same initial point. Show the vector projection of **v** onto **w** in your diagram. Then describe how you identified this vector.

72. How do you determine the work done by a force **F** in moving an object from A to B when the direction of the force is not along the line of motion?

73. A weightlifter is holding a barbell perfectly still above his head, his body shaking from the effort. How much work is the weightlifter doing? Explain your answer.

74. Describe one way in which the everyday use of the word "work" is different from the definition of work given in this section.

Critical Thinking Exercises

In Exercises 75–77, use the vectors

$$\mathbf{u} = a_1\mathbf{i} + b_1\mathbf{j}, \quad \mathbf{v} = a_2\mathbf{i} + b_2\mathbf{j}, \quad \text{and} \quad \mathbf{w} = a_3\mathbf{i} + b_3\mathbf{j},$$

to prove the given property.

75. $\mathbf{u} \cdot \mathbf{v} = \mathbf{v} \cdot \mathbf{u}$

76. $(c\mathbf{u}) \cdot \mathbf{v} = c(\mathbf{u} \cdot \mathbf{v})$

77. $\mathbf{u} \cdot (\mathbf{v} + \mathbf{w}) = \mathbf{u} \cdot \mathbf{v} + \mathbf{u} \cdot \mathbf{w}$

78. If $\mathbf{v} = -2\mathbf{i} + 5\mathbf{j}$, find a vector orthogonal to $\mathbf{v}$.

79. Find a value of b so that $15\mathbf{i} - 3\mathbf{j}$ and $-4\mathbf{i} + b\mathbf{j}$ are orthogonal.

80. Prove that the projection of $\mathbf{v}$ onto $\mathbf{i}$ is $(\mathbf{v} \cdot \mathbf{i})\mathbf{i}$.

81. Find two vectors $\mathbf{v}$ and $\mathbf{w}$ such that the projection of $\mathbf{v}$ onto $\mathbf{w}$ is $\mathbf{v}$.

Group Exercise

82. Group members should research and present a report on unusual and interesting applications of vectors.

Chapter 6
Summary

Summary

DEFINITIONS AND CONCEPTS	EXAMPLES

6.1 and 6.2 The Law of Sines; The Law of Cosines

a. The Law of Sines

$$\frac{a}{\sin A} = \frac{b}{\sin B} = \frac{c}{\sin C}$$

Ex. 1, p. 629;
Ex. 2, p. 630;
Ex. 3, p. 631;
Ex. 4, p. 632;
Ex. 5, p. 632

b. The Law of Sines is used to solve SAA, ASA, and SSA (the ambiguous case) triangles. The ambiguous case may result in no triangle, one triangle, or two triangles; see the box on page 631.

c. The area of a triangle equals one-half the product of the lengths of two sides times the sine of their included angle.

Ex. 6, p. 634

d. The Law of Cosines

$$a^2 = b^2 + c^2 - 2bc \cos A$$
$$b^2 = a^2 + c^2 - 2ac \cos B$$
$$c^2 = a^2 + b^2 - 2ab \cos C$$

e. The Law of Cosines is used to find the side opposite the given angle in an SAS triangle; see the box on page 640. The Law of Cosines is also used to find the angle opposite the longest side in an SSS triangle; see the box on page 641.

Ex. 1, p. 641;
Ex. 2, p. 642

f. Heron's Formula for the Area of a Triangle

The area of a triangle with sides $a, b,$ and c is $\sqrt{s(s-a)(s-b)(s-c)}$, where s is one-half its perimeter: $s = \frac{1}{2}(a + b + c)$.

Ex. 4, p. 643

6.3 and 6.4 Polar Coordinates; Graphs of Polar Equations

a. A point P in the polar coordinate system is represented by (r, θ), where r is the directed distance from the pole to the point and θ is the angle from the polar axis to line segment OP. The elements of the ordered pair (r, θ) are called the polar coordinates of P. See Figure 6.20 on page 647. When r in (r, θ) is negative, a point is located $|r|$ units along the ray opposite the terminal side of θ. Important information about the sign of r and the location of the point (r, θ) is found in the box on page 648.

Ex. 1, p. 648

b. Multiple Representations of Points

If n is any integer, $(r, \theta) = (r, \theta + 2n\pi)$ or $(r, \theta) = (-r, \theta + \pi + 2n\pi)$.

Ex. 2, p. 649

c. Relations between Polar and Rectangular Coordinates

$$x = r \cos \theta, \quad y = r \sin \theta, \quad x^2 + y^2 = r^2, \quad \tan \theta = \frac{y}{x}$$

DEFINITIONS AND CONCEPTS

d. To convert a point from polar coordinates (r, θ) to rectangular coordinates (x, y), use $x = r \cos \theta$ and $y = r \sin \theta$.

Ex. 3, p. 650

e. To convert a point from rectangular coordinates (x, y) to polar coordinates (r, θ), use the procedure in the box on page 651.

Ex. 4, p. 651;
Ex. 5, p. 652

f. To convert a rectangular equation to a polar equation, replace x with $r \cos \theta$ and y with $r \sin \theta$.

Ex. 6, p. 652

g. To convert a polar equation to a rectangular equation, use one or more of

Ex. 7, p. 654

$$r^2 = x^2 + y^2, \quad r \cos \theta = x, \quad r \sin \theta = y, \quad \text{and} \quad \tan \theta = \frac{y}{x}.$$

It is often necessary to do something to the given polar equation before using the preceding expressions.

h. A polar equation is an equation whose variables are r and θ. The graph of a polar equation is the set of all points whose polar coordinates satisfy the equation.

Ex. 1, p. 658

i. Polar equations can be graphed using point plotting and symmetry (see the box on page 659).

Ex. 2, p. 660

j. The graphs of $r = a \cos \theta$ and $r = a \sin \theta$ are circles. See the box on page 659. The graphs of $r = a \pm b \sin \theta$ and $r = a \pm b \cos \theta$ are called limaçons ($a > 0$ and $b > 0$), shown in the box on page 662. The graphs of $r = a \sin n\theta$ and $r = a \cos n\theta$, $a \neq 0$, are rose curves with $2n$ petals if n is even and n petals if n is odd. See the box on page 664. The graphs of $r^2 = a^2 \sin 2\theta$ and $r^2 = a^2 \cos 2\theta$, $a \neq 0$, are called lemniscates and are shown in the box on page 665.

Ex. 3, p. 661;
Ex. 4, p. 662;
Ex. 5, p. 664

6.5 *Complex Numbers in Polar Form; DeMoivre's Theorem*

a. The complex number $z = a + bi$ is represented as a point (a, b) in the complex plane, shown in Figure 6.38 on page 669.

Ex. 1, p. 670

b. The absolute value of $z = a + bi$ is $|z| = |a + bi| = \sqrt{a^2 + b^2}$.

Ex. 2, p. 670

c. The polar form of $z = a + bi$ is $z = r(\cos \theta + i \sin \theta)$, where $a = r \cos \theta$, $b = r \sin \theta$, $r = \sqrt{a^2 + b^2}$, and $\tan \theta = \dfrac{b}{a}$. We call r the modulus and θ the argument of z, with $0 \le \theta < 2\pi$.

Ex. 3, p. 671;
Ex. 4, p. 672

d. Multiplying Complex Numbers in Polar Form: Multiply moduli and add arguments. See the box on page 672.

Ex. 5, p. 673

e. Dividing Complex Numbers in Polar Form: Divide moduli and subtract arguments. See the box on page 673.

Ex. 6, p. 673

f. DeMoivre's Theorem is used to find powers of complex numbers in polar form.

Ex. 7, p. 674;
Ex. 8, p. 675

$$[r(\cos \theta + i \sin \theta)]^n = r^n(\cos n\theta + i \sin n\theta)$$

g. DeMoivre's Theorem can be used to find roots of complex numbers in polar form. The n distinct nth roots of $r(\cos \theta + i \sin \theta)$ are

Ex. 9, p. 676;
Ex. 10, p. 677

$$\sqrt[n]{r}\left[\cos\left(\frac{\theta + 2\pi k}{n}\right) + i \sin\left(\frac{\theta + 2\pi k}{n}\right)\right]$$

or

$$\sqrt[n]{r}\left[\cos\left(\frac{\theta + 360°k}{n}\right) + i \sin\left(\frac{\theta + 360°k}{n}\right)\right],$$

where $k = 0, 1, 2, \ldots, n - 1$.

DEFINITIONS AND CONCEPTS	**EXAMPLES**

6.6 Vectors

a. A vector is a directed line segment.

b. Equal vectors have the same magnitude and the same direction.   Ex. 1, p. 681

c. The vector $k\mathbf{v}$, the scalar multiple of the vector $\mathbf{v}$ and the scalar k, has magnitude $|k|\|\mathbf{v}\|$. The direction of $k\mathbf{v}$ is the same as that of $\mathbf{v}$ if $k > 0$ and opposite $\mathbf{v}$ if $k < 0$.   Figure 6.52, p. 682

d. The sum $\mathbf{u} + \mathbf{v}$, called the resultant vector, can be expressed geometrically. Position $\mathbf{u}$ and $\mathbf{v}$ so that the terminal point of $\mathbf{u}$ coincides with the initial point of $\mathbf{v}$. The vector $\mathbf{u} + \mathbf{v}$ extends from the initial point of $\mathbf{u}$ to the terminal point of $\mathbf{v}$.   Figure 6.53, p. 682

e. The difference of two vectors, $\mathbf{u} - \mathbf{v}$, is defined as $\mathbf{u} + (-\mathbf{v})$.   Figure 6.54, p. 683

f. The vector $\mathbf{i}$ is the unit vector whose direction is along the positive x-axis. The vector $\mathbf{j}$ is the unit vector whose direction is along the positive y-axis.

g. Vector $\mathbf{v}$, from $(0, 0)$ to (a, b), called a position vector, is represented as $\mathbf{v} = a\mathbf{i} + b\mathbf{j}$, where a is the horizontal component and b is the vertical component. The magnitude of $\mathbf{v}$ is given by $\|\mathbf{v}\| = \sqrt{a^2 + b^2}$.   Ex. 2, p. 684

h. Vector $\mathbf{v}$ from (x_1, y_1) to (x_2, y_2) is equal to the position vector $\mathbf{v} = (x_2 - x_1)\mathbf{i} + (y_2 - y_1)\mathbf{j}$. In rectangular coordinates, the term "vector" refers to the position vector in terms of $\mathbf{i}$ and $\mathbf{j}$ that is equal to it.   Ex. 3, p. 684

i. Operations with Vectors in Terms of $\mathbf{i}$ and $\mathbf{j}$ Ex. 4, p. 685; Ex. 5, p. 686; Ex. 6, p. 686

If $\mathbf{v} = a_1\mathbf{i} + b_1\mathbf{j}$ and $\mathbf{w} = a_2\mathbf{i} + b_2\mathbf{j}$, then

- $\mathbf{v} + \mathbf{w} = (a_1 + a_2)\mathbf{i} + (b_1 + b_2)\mathbf{j}$
- $\mathbf{v} - \mathbf{w} = (a_1 - a_2)\mathbf{i} + (b_1 - b_2)\mathbf{j}$
- $k\mathbf{v} = (ka_1)\mathbf{i} + (kb_1)\mathbf{j}$

j. The zero vector $\mathbf{0}$ is the vector whose magnitude is 0 and is assigned no direction. Many properties of vector addition and scalar multiplication involve the zero vector. Some of these properties are listed in the box on page 687.

k. The vector $\dfrac{\mathbf{v}}{\|\mathbf{v}\|}$ is the unit vector that has the same direction as $\mathbf{v}$.   Ex. 7, p. 687

l. A vector with magnitude $\|\mathbf{v}\|$ and direction angle θ, the angle that $\mathbf{v}$ makes with the positive x-axis, can be expressed in terms of its magnitude and direction angle as   Ex. 8, p. 688; Ex. 9, p. 689
$$\mathbf{v} = \|\mathbf{v}\| \cos \theta \mathbf{i} + \|\mathbf{v}\| \sin \theta \mathbf{j}.$$

6.7 The Dot Product

a. Definition of the Dot Product   Ex. 1, p. 694

If $\mathbf{v} = a_1\mathbf{i} + b_1\mathbf{j}$ and $\mathbf{w} = a_2\mathbf{i} + b_2\mathbf{j}$, the dot product of $\mathbf{v}$ and $\mathbf{w}$ is defined by $\mathbf{v} \cdot \mathbf{w} = a_1 a_2 + b_1 b_2$.

b. Alternative Formula for the Dot Product: $\mathbf{v} \cdot \mathbf{w} = \|\mathbf{v}\|\|\mathbf{w}\| \cos \theta$, where θ is the smallest nonnegative angle between $\mathbf{v}$ and $\mathbf{w}$

c. Angle between Two Vectors   Ex. 2, p. 696
$$\cos \theta = \frac{\mathbf{v} \cdot \mathbf{w}}{\|\mathbf{v}\|\|\mathbf{w}\|} \quad \text{and} \quad \theta = \cos^{-1}\left(\frac{\mathbf{v} \cdot \mathbf{w}}{\|\mathbf{v}\|\|\mathbf{w}\|}\right)$$

d. Two vectors are orthogonal when the angle between them is $90°$. To show that two vectors are orthogonal, show that their dot product is zero.   Ex. 3, p. 697

e. The vector projection of $\mathbf{v}$ onto $\mathbf{w}$ is given by   Ex. 4, p. 698
$$\text{proj}_{\mathbf{w}}\mathbf{v} = \frac{\mathbf{v} \cdot \mathbf{w}}{\|\mathbf{w}\|^2}\mathbf{w}.$$

f. Expressing a vector as the sum of two orthogonal vectors, called the vector components, is shown in the box on page 698.   Ex. 5, p. 699

g. The work, W, done by a force $\mathbf{F}$ moving an object from A to B is $W = \mathbf{F} \cdot \overrightarrow{AB}$.   Ex. 6, p. 700

Thus, $W = \|\mathbf{F}\|\|\overrightarrow{AB}\| \cos \theta$, where θ is the angle between the force and the direction of motion.

Vectors

CALCULATE THE TIDAL EFFECTS ON THE COURSE OF A VESSEL

Compiled by Brian Emond

Objectives:

- Express the component form of a vector;
- Determine the magnitude of a vector;
- Calculate the direction of a vector;
- Find the sum of two vectors;
- Use Vector Analysis to determine the speed and direction of a vessel.

Materials:

- Navigation chart of survey area Graphing Calculator

Activities:

- Using NOAA data, have the students choose three points from the listed tow stations, thus forming a triangle, and plot the points on the navigation chart. Connect the three points with vectors. Alphabetically label each resulting vertex, and express each side in Vector Notation. Now, using longitude and latitude, have them label each vertex, and express each vector in Component Form. Using the distance formula, they can now determine the Magnitude of each vector.
- Have the students convert the Magnitude of each vector to lengths in nautical or statute miles.
- In the navigation of a vessel, it is a velocity vector that is used to determine its' course and speed. To accomplish this task, have the students create a vector from two tow stations. Starting with the "lowest" end of the vector as a vertex, draw a second vector parallel to the lines of latitude, terminating directly under the "highest" end of the first vector. Connecting the ends of the two vectors will create a right triangle. The first vector is the hypotenuse. The second vector, parallel to the lines of latitude, is the base. And the third vector becomes the altitude. The tangent of the angle formed by the first two vectors, expressed in degrees, will give the course or direction of the vessel. And the magnitude of the first vector, the hypotenuse, will give the speed.
- Currents and tides can have a significant influence on the speed and direction of a vessel. Have the students suppose that their vessel is traveling north at ten knots (nautical miles per hour). The tide is going out (west to east) at two knots. The vessel's new velocity vector is the sum of the vessel's original velocity vector, and the tide's velocity vector. They can calculate the actual headway speed is the magnitude of the sum of the vectors. By finding the angle formed by the two vectors they can determine the actual course of the vessel.

Resource Guide

NOAA Data Sources
FISHERMAN'S REPORT. NOAA, National Marine Fisheries Service, Northeast Fisheries Science Center, Woods Hole, MA 02543.
(www.nefsc.nmfs.gov/esb/Fishermans%20reports.htm)

SECTION 9.5 *Parametric Equations*

Objectives

❶ Use point plotting to graph plane curves described by parametric equations.

❷ Eliminate the parameter.

❸ Find parametric equations for functions.

❹ Understand the advantages of parametric representations.

What a baseball game! You got to see the great Derek Jeter of the New York Yankees blast a powerful homer. In less than eight seconds, the parabolic path of his home run took the ball a horizontal distance of over 1000 feet. Is there a way to model this path that gives both the ball's location and the time that it is in each of its positions? In this section, we look at ways of describing curves that reveal the where and the when of motion.

Plane Curves and Parametric Equations

You throw a ball from a height of 6 feet, with an initial velocity of 90 feet per second and at an angle of 40° with the horizontal. After t seconds, the location of the ball can be described by

$$x = (90 \cos 40°)t \quad \text{and} \quad y = 6 + (90 \sin 40°)t - 16t^2.$$

> This is the ball's horizontal distance, in feet.

> This is the ball's vertical height, in feet.

Because we can use these equations to calculate the location of the ball at any time t, we can describe the path of the ball. For example, to determine the location when $t = 1$ second, substitute 1 for t in each equation:

$$x = (90 \cos 40°)t = (90 \cos 40°)(1) \approx 68.9 \text{ feet}$$

$$y = 6 + (90 \sin 40°)t - 16t^2 = 6 + (90 \sin 40°)(1) - 16(1)^2 \approx 47.9 \text{ feet}.$$

This tells us that after one second, the ball has traveled a horizontal distance of approximately 68.9 feet, and the height of the ball is approximately 47.9 feet. Figure 9.50 displays this information and the results for calculations corresponding to $t = 2$ seconds and $t = 3$ seconds.

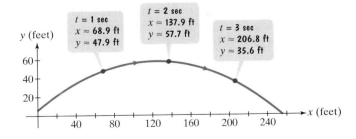

Figure 9.50 The location of a thrown ball after 1, 2, and 3 seconds

The voice balloons in Figure 9.50 tell where the ball is located and when the ball is at a given point (x, y) on its path. The variable t, called a **parameter**, gives the various times for the ball's location. The equations that describe where the ball is located express both x and y as functions of t, and are called **parametric equations**.

$$x = (90 \cos 40°)t \qquad y = 6 + (90 \sin 40°)t - 16t^2$$

This is the parametric equation for x.

This is the parametric equation for y.

The collection of points (x, y) in Figure 9.50 on the previous page is called a **plane curve**.

Plane Curves and Parametric Equations

Suppose that t is a number in an interval I. A **plane curve** is the set of ordered pairs (x, y), where

$$x = f(t), \quad y = g(t) \quad \text{for } t \text{ in interval } I.$$

The variable t is called a **parameter**, and the equations $x = f(t)$ and $y = g(t)$ are called **parametric equations** for the curve.

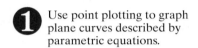

Use point plotting to graph plane curves described by parametric equations.

Graphing Plane Curves

Graphing a plane curve represented by parametric equations involves plotting points in the rectangular coordinate system and connecting them with a smooth curve.

Graphing a Plane Curve Described by Parametric Equations

1. Select some values of t on the given interval.
2. For each value of t, use the given parametric equations to compute x and y.
3. Plot the points (x, y) in the order of increasing t and connect them with a smooth curve.

Turn back a page and take a second look at Figure 9.50. Do you notice arrows along the curve? These arrows show the direction, or **orientation**, along the curve as t increases. After graphing a plane curve described by parametric equations, use arrows between the points to show the orientation of the curve corresponding to increasing values of t.

EXAMPLE 1   Graphing a Curve Defined by Parametric Equations

Graph the plane curve defined by the parametric equations:

$$x = t^2 - 1, \qquad y = 2t, \qquad -2 \le t \le 2.$$

Solution

Step 1   Select some values of t on the given interval. We will select integral values of t on the interval $-2 \le t \le 2$. Let $t = -2, -1, 0, 1,$ and 2.

Step 2   For each value of t, use the given parametric equations to compute x and y. We organize our work in a table. The first column lists the choices for the parameter t. The next two columns show the corresponding values for x and y. The last column lists the ordered pair (x, y).

t	$x = t^2 - 1$	$y = 2t$	(x, y)
-2	$(-2)^2 - 1 = 4 - 1 = 3$	$2(-2) = -4$	$(3, -4)$
-1	$(-1)^2 - 1 = 1 - 1 = 0$	$2(-1) = -2$	$(0, -2)$
0	$0^2 - 1 = -1$	$2(0) = 0$	$(-1, 0)$
1	$1^2 - 1 = 0$	$2(1) = 2$	$(0, 2)$
2	$2^2 - 1 = 4 - 1 = 3$	$2(2) = 4$	$(3, 4)$

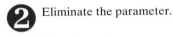

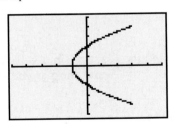

Figure 9.51 The plane curve defined by $x = t^2 - 1$, $y = 2t$, $-2 \le t \le 2$

② Eliminate the parameter.

Technology

A graphing utility can be used to obtain a plane curve represented by parametric equations. Set the mode to parametric and enter the equations. You must enter the minimum and maximum values for t, and an increment setting for t ($t$step). The setting $t$step determines the number of points the graphing utility will plot.

Shown below is the plane curve for

$$x = t^2 - 1$$
$$y = 2t$$

in a $[-5, 5, 1]$ by $[-5, 5, 1]$ viewing rectangle with $t$min $= -2$, $t$max $= 2$, and $t$step $= 0.01$.

Step 3 Plot the points (x, y) in the order of increasing t and connect them with a smooth curve. The plane curve defined by the parametric equations on the given interval is shown in Figure 9.51. The arrows show the direction, or orientation, along the curve as t varies from -2 to 2.

Check Point 1 Graph the plane curve defined by the parametric equations:

$$x = t^2 + 1, \qquad y = 3t, \qquad -2 \le t \le 2.$$

Eliminating the Parameter

The graph in Figure 9.51 shows the plane curve for $x = t^2 - 1$, $y = 2t$, $-2 \le t \le 2$. Even if we examine the parametric equations carefully, we may not be able to tell that the corresponding plane curve is a parabola. By **eliminating the parameter**, we can write one equation in x and y that is equivalent to the two parametric equations. The voice balloons illustrate this process.

> Begin with the parametric equations.

> Solve for t in one of the equations.

> Substitute the expression for t in the other parametric equation.

$$x = t^2 - 1 \qquad \text{Using } y = 2t, \qquad \text{Using } t = \frac{y}{2} \text{ and } x = t^2 - 1,$$
$$y = 2t \qquad\qquad t = \frac{y}{2}. \qquad\qquad x = \left(\frac{y}{2}\right)^2 - 1.$$

The rectangular equation (the equation in x and y), $x = \dfrac{y^2}{4} - 1$, can be written as $y^2 = 4(x + 1)$. This is the standard form of the equation of a parabola with vertex at $(-1, 0)$ and axis of symmetry along the x-axis. Because the parameter t is restricted to the interval $[-2, 2]$, the plane curve in the technology box on the left shows only a part of the parabola.

Our discussion illustrates a second method for graphing a plane curve described by parametric equations. Eliminate the parameter t and graph the resulting rectangular equation in x and y. However, **you may need to change the domain of the rectangular equation to be consistent with the domain for the parametric equation in x.** This situation is illustrated in Example 2.

EXAMPLE 2 Finding and Graphing the Rectangular Equation of a Curve Defined Parametrically

Sketch the plane curve represented by the parametric equations

$$x = \sqrt{t} \quad \text{and} \quad y = \tfrac{1}{2}t + 1$$

by eliminating the parameter.

Solution We eliminate the parameter t and then graph the resulting rectangular equation.

> Begin with the parametric equations.

> Solve for t in one of the equations.

> Substitute the expression for t in the other parametric equation.

$$x = \sqrt{t} \qquad \text{Using } x = \sqrt{t} \text{ and squaring} \qquad \text{Using } t = x^2 \text{ and } y = \frac{1}{2}t + 1,$$
$$y = \frac{1}{2}t + 1 \qquad \text{both sides, } t = x^2. \qquad\qquad y = \frac{1}{2}x^2 + 1.$$

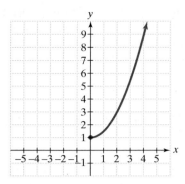

Figure 9.52 The plane curve for $x = \sqrt{t}$ and $y = \frac{1}{2}t + 1$, or $y = \frac{1}{2}x^2 + 1$, $x \geq 0$

Because t is not limited to a closed interval, you might be tempted to graph the entire U-shaped parabola whose equation is $y = \frac{1}{2}x^2 + 1$. However, take a second look at the parametric equation for x:

$$x = \sqrt{t}.$$

This equation is defined only when $t \geq 0$. Thus, x is nonnegative. The plane curve is the parabola given by $y = \frac{1}{2}x^2 + 1$ with the domain restricted to $x \geq 0$. The plane curve is shown in Figure 9.52.

Check Point 2 Sketch the plane curve represented by the parametric equations

$$x = \sqrt{t} \quad \text{and} \quad y = 2t - 1$$

by eliminating the parameter.

Eliminating the parameter is not always a simple matter. In some cases, it may not be possible. When this occurs, you can use point plotting to obtain a plane curve.

Trigonometric identities can be helpful in eliminating the parameter. For example, consider the plane curve defined by the parametric equations

$$x = \sin t, \quad y = \cos t, \quad 0 \leq t < 2\pi.$$

We use the trigonometric identity $\sin^2 t + \cos^2 t = 1$ to eliminate the parameter. Square each side of each parametric equation and then add.

$$
\begin{aligned}
x^2 &= \sin^2 t \\
y^2 &= \cos^2 t \\
\hline
x^2 + y^2 &= \sin^2 t + \cos^2 t
\end{aligned}
$$

> This is the sum of the two equations above the horizontal lines.

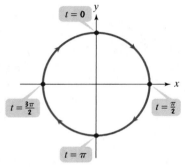

Figure 9.53 The plane curve defined by $x = \sin t$, $y = \cos t$, $0 \leq t < 2\pi$

Using a Pythagorean identity, we write this equation as $x^2 + y^2 = 1$. The plane curve is a circle with center $(0, 0)$ and radius 1. It is shown in Figure 9.53.

EXAMPLE 3   Finding and Graphing the Rectangular Equation of a Curve Defined Parametrically

Sketch the plane curve represented by the parametric equations

$$x = 5 \cos t, \quad y = 2 \sin t, \quad 0 \leq t \leq \pi$$

by eliminating the parameter.

Solution We eliminate the parameter using the identity $\cos^2 t + \sin^2 t = 1$. To apply the identity, divide the parametric equation for x by 5 and the parametric equation for y by 2.

$$\frac{x}{5} = \cos t \quad \text{and} \quad \frac{y}{2} = \sin t$$

Square and add these two equations.

$$
\begin{aligned}
\frac{x^2}{25} &= \cos^2 t \\
\frac{y^2}{4} &= \sin^2 t \\
\hline
\frac{x^2}{25} + \frac{y^2}{4} &= \cos^2 t + \sin^2 t
\end{aligned}
$$

> This is the sum of the two equations above the horizontal lines.

Using a Pythagorean identity, we write this equation as

$$\frac{x^2}{25} + \frac{y^2}{4} = 1.$$

This rectangular equation is the standard form of the equation for an ellipse centered at $(0, 0)$.

$$\frac{x^2}{25} + \frac{y^2}{4} = 1$$

$a^2 = 25$: Endpoints of major axis are 5 units left and right of center.

$b^2 = 4$: Endpoints of minor axis are 2 units above and below center.

The ellipse is shown in Figure 9.54(a). However, this is not the plane curve. Because t is restricted to the interval $[0, \pi]$, the plane curve is only a portion of the ellipse. Use the starting and ending values for t, 0 and π, respectively, and a value of t in the interval $(0, \pi)$ to find which portion to include.

Begin at $t = 0$.

$x = 5 \cos t = 5 \cos 0 = 5 \cdot 1 = 5$

$y = 2 \sin t = 2 \sin 0 = 2 \cdot 0 = 0$

Increase to $t = \frac{\pi}{2}$.

$x = 5 \cos t = 5 \cos \frac{\pi}{2} = 5 \cdot 0 = 0$

$y = 2 \sin t = 2 \sin \frac{\pi}{2} = 2 \cdot 1 = 2$

End at $t = \pi$.

$x = 5 \cos t = 5 \cos \pi = 5(-1) = -5$

$y = 2 \sin t = 2 \sin \pi = 2(0) = 0$

Points on the plane curve include $(5, 0)$, which is the starting point, $(0, 2)$, and $(-5, 0)$, which is the ending point. The plane curve is the top half of the ellipse, shown in Figure 9.54(b).

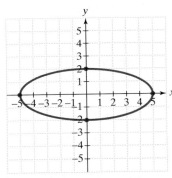

Figure 9.54(a) The graph of $\dfrac{x^2}{25} + \dfrac{y^2}{4} = 1$

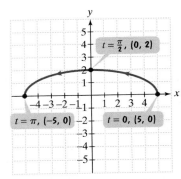

Figure 9.54(b) The plane curve for $x = 5 \cos t, y = 2 \sin t, 0 \le t \le \pi$

Check Point 3 Sketch the plane curve represented by the parametric equations

$$x = 6 \cos t, \quad y = 4 \sin t, \quad \pi \le t \le 2\pi$$

by eliminating the parameter.

③ Find parametric equations for functions.

Finding Parametric Equations

Infinitely many pairs of parametric equations can represent the same plane curve. If the plane curve is defined by the function $y = f(x)$, here is a procedure for finding a set of parametric equations:

> **Parametric Equations for the Function $y = f(x)$**
> One set of parametric equations for the plane curve defined by $y = f(x)$ is
> $$x = t \quad \text{and} \quad y = f(t),$$
> in which t is in the domain of f.

EXAMPLE 4 Finding Parametric Equations

Find a set of parametric equations for the parabola whose equation is $y = 9 - x^2$.

Solution Let $x = t$. Parametric equations for $y = f(x)$ are $x = t$ and $y = f(t)$. Thus, parametric equations for $y = 9 - x^2$ are

$$x = t \quad \text{and} \quad y = 9 - t^2.$$

 Check Point 4 Find a set of parametric equations for the parabola whose equation is $y = x^2 - 25$.

You can write other sets of parametric equations for $y = 9 - x^2$ by starting with a different parametric equation for x. Here are three more sets of parametric equations for

$$y = 9 - x^2:$$

- If $x = t^3$, $y = 9 - (t^3)^2 = 9 - t^6$.

  Parametric equations are $x = t^3$ and $y = 9 - t^6$.

- If $x = t + 1$, $y = 9 - (t + 1)^2 = 9 - (t^2 + 2t + 1) = 8 - t^2 - 2t$.

  Parametric equations are $x = t + 1$ and $y = 8 - t^2 - 2t$.

- If $x = \dfrac{t}{2}$, $y = 9 - \left(\dfrac{t}{2}\right)^2 = 9 - \dfrac{t^2}{4}$.

  Parametric equations are $x = \dfrac{t}{2}$ and $y = 9 - \dfrac{t^2}{4}$.

Can you start with any choice for the parametric equation for x? The answer is no. **The substitution for x must be a function that allows x to take on all the values in the domain of the given rectangular equation.** For example, the domain of the function $y = 9 - x^2$ is the set of all real numbers. If you incorrectly let $x = t^2$, these values of x exclude negative numbers that are included in $y = 9 - x^2$. The parametric equations

$$x = t^2 \quad \text{and} \quad y = 9 - (t^2)^2 = 9 - t^4$$

do not represent $y = 9 - x^2$ because only points for which $x \geq 0$ are obtained.

④ Understand the advantages of parametric representations.

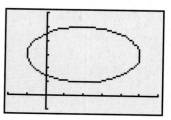
Advantages of Parametric Equations over Rectangular Equations

We opened this section with parametric equations that described the horizontal distance and the vertical height of your thrown baseball after t seconds. Parametric equations are frequently used to represent the path of a moving object. If t represents time, parametric equations give the location of a moving object and tell when the object is located at each of its positions. Rectangular equations tell where the moving object is located but do not reveal when the object is in a particular position.

When using technology to obtain graphs, parametric equations that represent relations that are not functions are often easier to use than their corresponding rectangular equations. It is far easier to enter the equation of an ellipse given by the parametric equations

$$x = 2 + 3 \cos t \quad \text{and} \quad y = 3 + 2 \sin t$$

than to use the rectangular equivalent

$$\frac{(x - 2)^2}{9} + \frac{(y - 3)^2}{4} = 1.$$

The rectangular equation must first be solved for y and then entered as two separate equations before a graphing utility reveals the ellipse.

A curve that is used in physics for much of the theory of light is called a **cycloid**. The path of a fixed point on the circumference of a circle as it rolls along a line is a cycloid. A point on the rim of a bicycle wheel traces out a cycloid curve, shown in Figure 9.55. If the radius of the circle is a, the parametric equations of the cycloid are

$$x = a(t - \sin t) \quad \text{and} \quad y = a(1 - \cos t).$$

It is an extremely complicated task to represent the cycloid in rectangular form.

Cycloids are used to solve problems that involve the "shortest time." For example, Figure 9.56 shows a bead sliding down a wire. The shape of the wire a bead could slide down so that the distance between two points is traveled in the shortest time is an inverted cycloid.

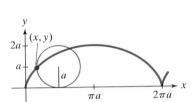

Figure 9.56

Figure 9.55 The curve traced by a fixed point on the circumference of a circle rolling along a straight line is a cycloid.

Rolling

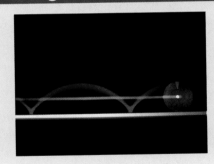

Linear functions and cycloids are used to describe rolling motion. The light at the rolling circle's center shows that it moves linearly. By contrast, the light at the circle's edge has rotational motion and traces out a cycloid. A number of sites on the Internet illustrate rotational motion and show how the cycloid is created.

EXERCISE SET 9.5

Practice Exercises

In Exercises 1–8, parametric equations and a value for the parameter t are given. Find the coordinates of the point on the plane curve described by the parametric equations corresponding to the given value of t.

1. $x = 3 - 5t, y = 4 + 2t; t = 1$

2. $x = 7 - 4t, y = 5 + 6t; t = 1$

3. $x = t^2 + 1, y = 5 - t^3; t = 2$

4. $x = t^2 + 3, y = 6 - t^3; t = 2$

5. $x = 4 + 2 \cos t, y = 3 + 5 \sin t; t = \dfrac{\pi}{2}$

6. $x = 2 + 3 \cos t, y = 4 + 2 \sin t; t = \pi$

7. $x = (60 \cos 30°)t, y = 5 + (60 \sin 30°)t - 16t^2; t = 2$

8. $x = (80 \cos 45°)t, y = 6 + (80 \sin 45°)t - 16t^2; t = 2$

In Exercises 9–20, use point plotting to graph the plane curve described by the given parametric equations. Use arrows to show the orientation of the curve corresponding to increasing values of t.

9. $x = t + 2, y = t^2; -2 \le t \le 2$

10. $x = t - 1, y = t^2; -2 \le t \le 2$

11. $x = t - 2, y = 2t + 1; -2 \le t \le 3$

12. $x = t - 3, y = 2t + 2; -2 \le t \le 3$

13. $x = t + 1, y = \sqrt{t}; t \ge 0$ **14.** $x = \sqrt{t}, y = t - 1; t \ge 0$

15. $x = \cos t, y = \sin t; 0 \le t < 2\pi$

16. $x = -\sin t, y = -\cos t; 0 \le t < 2\pi$

17. $x = t^2, y = t^3; -\infty < t < \infty$

18. $x = t^2 + 1, y = t^3 - 1; -\infty < t < \infty$
19. $x = 2t, y = |t - 1|; -\infty < t < \infty$
20. $x = |t + 1|, y = t - 2; -\infty < t < \infty$

In Exercises 21–40, eliminate the parameter t. Then use the rectangular equation to sketch the plane curve represented by the given parametric equations. Use arrows to show the orientation of the curve corresponding to increasing values of t. (If an interval for t is not specified, assume that $-\infty < t < \infty$.)

21. $x = t, y = 2t$
22. $x = t, y = -2t$
23. $x = 2t - 4, y = 4t^2$
24. $x = t - 2, y = t^2$
25. $x = \sqrt{t}, y = t - 1$
26. $x = \sqrt{t}, y = t + 1$
27. $x = 2 \sin t, y = 2 \cos t; 0 \le t < 2\pi$
28. $x = 3 \sin t, y = 3 \cos t; 0 \le t < 2\pi$
29. $x = 1 + 3 \cos t, y = 2 + 3 \sin t; 0 \le t < 2\pi$
30. $x = -1 + 2 \cos t, y = 1 + 2 \sin t; 0 \le t < 2\pi$
31. $x = 2 \cos t, y = 3 \sin t; 0 \le t < 2\pi$
32. $x = 3 \cos t, y = 5 \sin t; 0 \le t < 2\pi$
33. $x = 1 + 3 \cos t, y = -1 + 2 \sin t; 0 \le t \le \pi$
34. $x = 2 + 4 \cos t, y = -1 + 3 \sin t; 0 \le t \le \pi$
35. $x = \sec t, y = \tan t$
36. $x = 5 \sec t, y = 3 \tan t$
37. $x = t^2 + 2, y = t^2 - 2$
38. $x = \sqrt{t} + 2, y = \sqrt{t} - 2$
39. $x = 2^t, y = 2^{-t}; t \ge 0$
40. $x = e^t, y = e^{-t}; t \ge 0$

In Exercises 41–43, eliminate the parameter. Write the resulting equation in standard form.

41. A circle: $x = h + r \cos t, y = k + r \sin t$
42. An ellipse: $x = h + a \cos t, y = k + b \sin t$
43. A hyperbola: $x = h + a \sec t, y = k + b \tan t$
44. The parametric equations of the line through (x_1, y_1) and (x_2, y_2) are

$$x = x_1 + t(x_2 - x_1) \quad \text{and} \quad y = y_1 + t(y_2 - y_1).$$

Eliminate the parameter and write the resulting equation in point-slope form.

In Exercises 45–52, use your answers from Exercises 41–44 and the parametric equations given in Exercises 41–44 to find a set of parametric equations for the conic section or the line.

45. Circle: Center: $(3, 5)$; Radius: 6
46. Circle: Center: $(4, 6)$; Radius: 9
47. Ellipse: Center: $(-2, 3)$; Vertices: 5 units to the left and right of the center; Endpoints of Minor Axis: 2 units above and below the center
48. Ellipse: Center: $(4, -1)$; Vertices: 5 units above and below the center; Endpoints of Minor Axis: 3 units to the left and right of the center
49. Hyperbola: Vertices: $(4, 0)$ and $(-4, 0)$; Foci: $(6, 0)$ and $(-6, 0)$
50. Hyperbola: Vertices: $(0, 4)$ and $(0, -4)$; Foci: $(0, 5)$ and $(0, -5)$
51. Line: Passes through $(-2, 4)$ and $(1, 7)$
52. Line: Passes through $(3, -1)$ and $(9, 12)$

In Exercises 53–56, find two different sets of parametric equations for each rectangular equation.

53. $y = 4x - 3$
54. $y = 2x - 5$
55. $y = x^2 + 4$
56. $y = x^2 - 3$

In Exercises 57–58, the parametric equations of four plane curves are given. Graph each plane curve and determine how they differ from each other.

57. **a.** $x = t$ and $y = t^2 - 4$
    b. $x = t^2$ and $y = t^4 - 4$
    c. $x = \cos t$ and $y = \cos^2 t - 4$
    d. $x = e^t$ and $y = e^{2t} - 4$

58. **a.** $x = t, y = \sqrt{4 - t^2}; -2 \le t \le 2$
    b. $x = \sqrt{4 - t^2}, y = t; -2 \le t \le 2$
    c. $x = 2 \sin t, y = 2 \cos t; 0 \le t < 2\pi$
    d. $x = 2 \cos t, y = 2 \sin t; 0 \le t < 2\pi$

Practice Plus

In Exercises 59–62, sketch the plane curve represented by the given parametric equations. Then use interval notation to give each relation's domain and range.

59. $x = 4 \cos t + 2, y = 4 \cos t - 1$
60. $x = 2 \sin t - 3, y = 2 \sin t + 1$
61. $x = t^2 + t + 1, y = 2t$
62. $x = t^2 - t + 6, y = 3t$

In Exercises 63–68, sketch the function represented by the given parametric equations. Then use the graph to determine each of the following:

a. *intervals, if any, on which the function is increasing and intervals, if any, on which the function is decreasing.*

b. *the number, if any, at which the function has a maximum and this maximum value, or the number, if any, at which the function has a minimum and this minimum value.*

63. $x = 2^t, y = t$
64. $x = e^t, y = t$
65. $x = \dfrac{t}{2}, y = 2t^2 - 8t + 3$
66. $x = \dfrac{t}{2}, y = -2t^2 + 8t - 1$
67. $x = 2(t - \sin t), y = 2(1 - \cos t); 0 \le t \le 2\pi$
68. $x = 3(t - \sin t), y = 3(1 - \cos t); 0 \le t \le 2\pi$

Application Exercises

The path of a projectile that is launched h feet above the ground with an initial velocity of v_0 feet per second and at an angle θ with the horizontal is given by the parametric equations

$$x = (v_0 \cos \theta)t \quad \text{and} \quad y = h + (v_0 \sin \theta)t - 16t^2,$$

where t is the time, in seconds, after the projectile was launched. The parametric equation for x gives the projectile's horizontal distance, in feet. The parametric equation for y gives the projectile's height, in feet. Use these parametric equations to solve Exercises 69–70.

69. The figure shows the path for a baseball hit by Derek Jeter. The ball was hit with an initial velocity of 180 feet per second at an angle of 40° to the horizontal. The ball was hit at a height 3 feet off the ground.

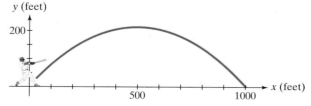

a. Find the parametric equations that describe the position of the ball as a function of time.

b. Describe the ball's position after 1, 2, and 3 seconds. Round to the nearest tenth of a foot. Locate your solutions on the plane curve.

c. How long, to the nearest tenth of a second, is the ball in flight? What is the total horizontal distance that it travels before it lands? Is your answer consistent with the figure shown?

d. You meet Derek Jeter and he asks you to tell him something interesting about the path of the baseball that he hit. Use the graph to respond to his request. Then verify your observation algebraically.

70. The figure shows the path for a baseball that was hit with an initial velocity of 150 feet per second at an angle of $35°$ to the horizontal. The ball was hit at a height of 3 feet off the ground.

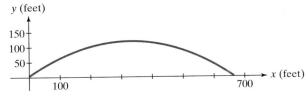

a. Find the parametric equations that describe the position of the ball as a function of time.

b. Describe the ball's position after 1, 2, and 3 seconds. Round to the nearest tenth of a foot. Locate your solutions on the plane curve.

c. How long is the ball in flight? (Round to the nearest tenth of a second.) What is the total horizontal distance that it travels, to the nearest tenth of a foot, before it lands? Is your answer consistent with the figure shown?

d. Use the graph to describe something about the path of the baseball that might be of interest to the player who hit the ball. Then verify your observation algebraically.

Writing in Mathematics

71. What are plane curves and parametric equations?

72. How is point plotting used to graph a plane curve described by parametric equations? Give an example with your description.

73. What is the significance of arrows along a plane curve?

74. What does it mean to eliminate the parameter? What useful information can be obtained by doing this?

75. Explain how the rectangular equation $y = 5x$ can have infinitely many sets of parametric equations.

76. Discuss how the parametric equations for the path of a projectile (see Exercises 69–70) and the ability to obtain plane curves with a graphing utility can be used by a baseball coach to analyze performances of team players.

Technology Exercises

77. Use a graphing utility in a parametric mode to verify any five of your hand-drawn graphs in Exercises 9–40.

In Exercises 78–82, use a graphing utility to obtain the plane curve represented by the given parametric equations.

78. Cycloid: $x = 3(t - \sin t)$,
$y = 3(1 - \cos t); [0, 60, 5] \times [0, 8, 1], 0 \le t < 6\pi$

79. Cycloid: $x = 2(t - \sin t)$,
$y = 2(1 - \cos t); [0, 60, 5] \times [0, 8, 1], 0 \le t < 6\pi$

80. Witch of Agnesi: $x = 2 \cot t, y = 2 \sin^2 t$;
$[-6, 6, 1] \times [-4, 4, 1], 0 \le t < 2\pi$

81. Hypocycloid: $x = 4 \cos^3 t, y = 4 \sin^3 t$;
$[-5, 5, 1] \times [-5, 5, 1], 0 \le t < 2\pi$

82. Lissajous Curve: $x = 2 \cos t, y = \sin 2t$;
$[-3, 3, 1] \times [-2, 2, 1], 0 \le t < 2\pi$

Use the equations for the path of a projectile given prior to Exercises 69–70 to solve Exercises 83–85.

In Exercises 83–84, use a graphing utility to obtain the path of a projectile launched from the ground ($h = 0$) at the specified values of θ and v_0. In each exercise, use the graph to determine the maximum height and the time at which the projectile reaches its maximum height. Also use the graph to determine the range of the projectile and the time it hits the ground. Round all answers to the nearest tenth.

83. $\theta = 55°, v_0 = 200$ feet per second

84. $\theta = 35°, v_0 = 300$ feet per second

85. A baseball player throws a ball with an initial velocity of 140 feet per second at an angle of $22°$ to the horizontal. The ball leaves the player's hand at a height of 5 feet.

a. Write the parametric equations that describe the ball's position as a function of time.

b. Use a graphing utility to obtain the path of the baseball.

c. Find the ball's maximum height and the time at which it reaches this height. Round all answers to the nearest tenth.

d. How long is the ball in the air?

e. How far does the ball travel?

Critical Thinking Exercises

86. Eliminate the parameter: $x = \cos^3 t$ and $y = \sin^3 t$.

87. The plane curve described by the parametric equations $x = 3 \cos t$ and $y = 3 \sin t$, $0 \le t < 2\pi$, has a counterclockwise orientation. Alter one or both parametric equations so that you obtain the same plane curve with the opposite orientation.

88. The figure shows a circle of radius a rolling along a horizontal line. Point P traces out a cycloid. Angle t, in radians, is the angle through which the circle has rolled. C is the center of the circle.

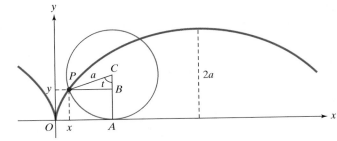

Use the suggestions in parts (a) and (b) to prove that the parametric equations of the cycloid are $x = a(t - \sin t)$ and $y = a(1 - \cos t)$.

a. Derive the parametric equation for x using the figure and

$$x = OA - xA.$$

b. Derive the parametric equation for y using the figure and

$$y = AC - BC.$$

10

Sequences, Induction, and Probability

Taken from:
Precalculus, Third Edition, by Robert Blitzer

Sequences, Induction, and Probability

W E OFTEN SAVE FOR THE FUTURE by investing small amounts at periodic intervals. To understand how our savings accumulate, we need to understand properties of lists of numbers that are related to each other by a rule. Such lists are called sequences. Learning about properties of sequences will show you how to make your financial goals a reality. Your knowledge of sequences will enable you to inform your college roommate of the best of the three appealing offers described below.

SOMETHING INCREDIBLE HAS HAPPENED. Your college roommate, a gifted athlete, has been given a six-year contract with a professional baseball team. He will be playing against the likes of Barry Bonds and Manny Ramirez. Management offers him three options. One is a beginning salary of $1,700,000 with annual increases of $70,000 per year starting in the second year. A second option is $1,700,000 the first year with an annual increase of 2% per year beginning in the second year. The third offer involves less money the first year— $1,500,000—but there is an annual increase of 9% yearly after that. Which option offers the most money over the six-year contract?

This problem appears as Exercise 67 in Exercise Set 10.3 and as the group project on page 958.

SECTION 10.1 *Sequences and Summation Notation*

Objectives

❶ Find particular terms of a sequence from the general term.

❷ Use recursion formulas.

❸ Use factorial notation.

❹ Use summation notation.

Sequences

Many creations in nature involve intricate mathematical designs, including a variety of spirals. For example, the arrangement of the individual florets in the head of a sunflower forms spirals. In some species, there are 21 spirals in the clockwise direction and 34 in the counterclockwise direction. The precise numbers depend on the species of sunflower: 21 and 34, or 34 and 55, or 55 and 89, or even 89 and 144.

This observation becomes even more interesting when we consider a sequence of numbers investigated by Leonardo of Pisa, also known as Fibonacci, an Italian mathematician of the thirteenth century. The **Fibonacci sequence** of numbers is an infinite sequence that begins as follows:

$$1, 1, 2, 3, 5, 8, 13, 21, 34, 55, 89, 144, 233, \ldots .$$

The first two terms are 1. Every term thereafter is the sum of the two preceding terms. For example, the third term, 2, is the sum of the first and second terms: $1 + 1 = 2$. The fourth term, 3, is the sum of the second and third terms: $1 + 2 = 3$, and so on. Did you know that the number of spirals in a daisy or a sunflower, 21 and 34, are two Fibonacci numbers? The number of spirals in a pine cone, 8 and 13, and a pineapple, 8 and 13, are also Fibonacci numbers.

We can think of the Fibonacci sequence as a function. The terms of the sequence

$$1, 1, 2, 3, 5, 8, 13, 21, 34, 55, 89, 144, 233, \ldots$$

are the range values for a function whose domain is the set of positive integers.

Domain:	1,	2,	3,	4,	5,	6,	7,	$\ldots$
	↓	↓	↓	↓	↓	↓	↓	
Range:	1,	1,	2,	3,	5,	8,	13,	$\ldots$

Thus, $f(1) = 1, f(2) = 1, f(3) = 2, f(4) = 3, f(5) = 5, f(6) = 8, f(7) = 13,$ and so on.

The letter a with a subscript is used to represent function values of a sequence, rather than the usual function notation. The subscripts make up the domain of the sequence and they identify the location of a term. Thus, a_1 represents the first term of the sequence, a_2 represents the second term, a_3 the third term, and so on. This notation is shown for the first six terms of the Fibonacci sequence:

$$1, \quad 1, \quad 2, \quad 3, \quad 5, \quad 8.$$

$a_1 = 1$ $a_2 = 1$ $a_3 = 2$ $a_4 = 3$ $a_5 = 5$ $a_6 = 8$

Fibonacci Numbers on the Piano Keyboard

One Octave

Numbers in the Fibonacci sequence can be found in an octave on the piano keyboard. The octave contains 2 black keys in one cluster and 3 black keys in another cluster, for a total of 5 black keys. It also has 8 white keys, for a total of 13 keys. The numbers 2, 3, 5, 8, and 13 are the third through seventh terms of the Fibonacci sequence.

The notation a_n represents the nth term, or **general term**, of a sequence. The entire sequence is represented by $\{a_n\}$.

> **Definition of a Sequence**
>
> An **infinite sequence** $\{a_n\}$ is a function whose domain is the set of positive integers. The function values, or **terms**, of the sequence are represented by
>
> $$a_1, a_2, a_3, a_4, \ldots, a_n, \ldots.$$
>
> Sequences whose domains consist only of the first n positive integers are called **finite sequences**.

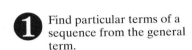 Find particular terms of a sequence from the general term.

EXAMPLE 1   Writing Terms of a Sequence from the General Term

Write the first four terms of the sequence whose nth term, or general term, is given:

a. $a_n = 3n + 4$ **b.** $a_n = \dfrac{(-1)^n}{3^n - 1}.$

Solution

a. We need to find the first four terms of the sequence whose general term is $a_n = 3n + 4$. To do so, we replace n in the formula with 1, 2, 3, and 4.

a_1, 1st term $3 \cdot 1 + 4 = 3 + 4 = 7$ a_2, 2nd term $3 \cdot 2 + 4 = 6 + 4 = 10$

a_3, 3rd term $3 \cdot 3 + 4 = 9 + 4 = 13$ a_4, 4th term $3 \cdot 4 + 4 = 12 + 4 = 16$

The first four terms are 7, 10, 13, and 16. The sequence defined by $a_n = 3n + 4$ can be written as

$$7, 10, 13, 16, \ldots, 3n + 4, \ldots.$$

b. We need to find the first four terms of the sequence whose general term is $a_n = \dfrac{(-1)^n}{3^n - 1}$. To do so, we replace each occurrence of n in the formula with 1, 2, 3, and 4.

a_1, 1st term $\dfrac{(-1)^1}{3^1 - 1} = \dfrac{-1}{3 - 1} = -\dfrac{1}{2}$ a_2, 2nd term $\dfrac{(-1)^2}{3^2 - 1} = \dfrac{1}{9 - 1} = \dfrac{1}{8}$

a_3, 3rd term $\dfrac{(-1)^3}{3^3 - 1} = \dfrac{-1}{27 - 1} = -\dfrac{1}{26}$ a_4, 4th term $\dfrac{(-1)^4}{3^4 - 1} = \dfrac{1}{81 - 1} = \dfrac{1}{80}$

The first four terms are $-\dfrac{1}{2}, \dfrac{1}{8}, -\dfrac{1}{26}$, and $\dfrac{1}{80}$. The sequence defined by $\dfrac{(-1)^n}{3^n - 1}$ can be written as

$$-\dfrac{1}{2}, \dfrac{1}{8}, -\dfrac{1}{26}, \dfrac{1}{80}, \ldots, \dfrac{(-1)^n}{3^n - 1}, \ldots.$$

Check Point 1   Write the first four terms of the sequence whose nth term, or general term, is given:

a. $a_n = 2n + 5$ **b.** $a_n = \dfrac{(-1)^n}{2^n + 1}.$

Although sequences are usually named with the letter a, any lowercase letter can be used. For example, the first four terms of the sequence $\{b_n\} = \left\{\left(\frac{1}{2}\right)^n\right\}$ are $b_1 = \frac{1}{2}, b_2 = \frac{1}{4}, b_3 = \frac{1}{8}$, and $b_4 = \frac{1}{16}$.

Technology

Graphing utilities can write the terms of a sequence and graph them. For example, to find the first six terms of $\{a_n\} = \left\{\dfrac{1}{n}\right\}$, enter

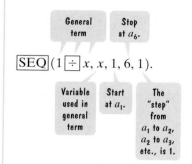

General term   Stop at a_6.

$\boxed{\text{SEQ}}\,(1\,\boxed{\div}\,x,\,x,\,1,\,6,\,1).$

Variable used in general term   Start at a_1.   The "step" from a_1 to a_2, a_2 to a_3, etc., is 1.

The first few terms of the sequence are shown in the viewing rectangle. By pressing the right arrow key to scroll right, you can see the remaining terms.

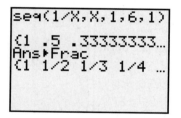

```
seq(1/X,X,1,6,1)
{1 .5 .33333333…
Ans▶Frac
{1 1/2 1/3 1/4 …
```

Because a sequence is a function whose domain is the set of positive integers, the **graph of a sequence** is a set of discrete points. For example, consider the sequence whose general term is $a_n = \dfrac{1}{n}$. How does the graph of this sequence differ from the graph of the function $f(x) = \dfrac{1}{x}$? The graph of $f(x) = \dfrac{1}{x}$ is shown in Figure 10.1(a) for positive values of x. To obtain the graph of the sequence $\{a_n\} = \left\{\dfrac{1}{n}\right\}$, remove all the points from the graph of f except those whose x-coordinates are positive integers. Thus, we remove all points except $\left(1, 1\right)$, $\left(2, \dfrac{1}{2}\right)$, $\left(3, \dfrac{1}{3}\right)$, $\left(4, \dfrac{1}{4}\right)$, and so on. The remaining points are the graph of the sequence $\{a_n\} = \left\{\dfrac{1}{n}\right\}$, shown in Figure 10.1(b). Notice that the horizontal axis is labeled n and the vertical axis is labeled a_n.

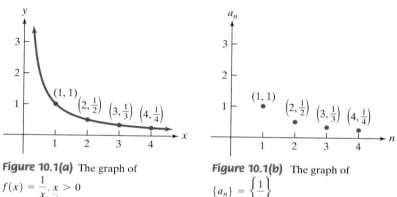

Figure 10.1(a) The graph of
$$f(x) = \frac{1}{x}, x > 0$$

Figure 10.1(b) The graph of
$$\{a_n\} = \left\{\frac{1}{n}\right\}$$

Comparing a continuous graph to the graph of a sequence

Recursion Formulas

In Example 1, the formulas used for the nth term of a sequence expressed the term as a function of n, the number of the term. Sequences can also be defined using **recursion formulas**. A recursion formula defines the nth term of a sequence as a function of the previous term. Our next example illustrates that if the first term of a sequence is known, then the recursion formula can be used to determine the remaining terms.

② Use recursion formulas.

EXAMPLE 2   Using a Recursion Formula

Find the first four terms of the sequence in which $a_1 = 5$ and $a_n = 3a_{n-1} + 2$ for $n \geq 2$.

Solution   Let's be sure we understand what is given.

$$a_1 = 5 \quad \text{and} \quad a_n = 3a_{n-1} + 2$$

The first term is 5.   Each term after the first   is   3 times the previous term   plus 2.

Now let's write the first four terms of this sequence.

$a_1 = 5$ This is the given first term.

$a_2 = 3a_1 + 2$ Use $a_n = 3a_{n-1} + 2$, with $n = 2$.
                 Thus, $a_2 = 3a_{2-1} + 2 = 3a_1 + 2$.

$\quad = 3(5) + 2 = 17$ Substitute 5 for a_1.

$a_3 = 3a_2 + 2$ Again use $a_n = 3a_{n-1} + 2$, with $n = 3$.

$\quad = 3(17) + 2 = 53$ Substitute 17 for a_2.

$a_4 = 3a_3 + 2$ Notice that a_4 is defined in terms of a_3.
                 We used $a_n = 3a_{n-1} + 2$, with $n = 4$.

$\quad = 3(53) + 2 = 161$ Use the value of a_3, the third term, obtained above.

The first four terms are 5, 17, 53, and 161.

Check Point 2 Find the first four terms of the sequence in which $a_1 = 3$ and $a_n = 2a_{n-1} + 5$ for $n \geq 2$.

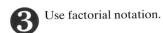 Use factorial notation.

Factorial Notation

Products of consecutive positive integers occur quite often in sequences. These products can be expressed in a special notation, called **factorial notation**.

> ### Factorial Notation
>
> If n is a positive integer, the notation $n!$ (read "n factorial") is the product of all positive integers from n down through 1.
> $$n! = n(n-1)(n-2)\cdots(3)(2)(1)$$
> 0! (zero factorial), by definition, is 1.
> $$0! = 1$$

The values of $n!$ for the first six positive integers are

$$1! = 1$$
$$2! = 2 \cdot 1 = 2$$
$$3! = 3 \cdot 2 \cdot 1 = 6$$
$$4! = 4 \cdot 3 \cdot 2 \cdot 1 = 24$$
$$5! = 5 \cdot 4 \cdot 3 \cdot 2 \cdot 1 = 120$$
$$6! = 6 \cdot 5 \cdot 4 \cdot 3 \cdot 2 \cdot 1 = 720.$$

Factorials affect only the number or variable that they follow unless grouping symbols appear. For example,

$$2 \cdot 3! = 2(3 \cdot 2 \cdot 1) = 2 \cdot 6 = 12$$

whereas

$$(2 \cdot 3)! = 6! = 6 \cdot 5 \cdot 4 \cdot 3 \cdot 2 \cdot 1 = 720.$$

In this sense, factorials are similar to exponents.

EXAMPLE 3   Finding Terms of a Sequence Involving Factorials

Write the first four terms of the sequence whose nth term is

$$a_n = \frac{2^n}{(n-1)!}.$$

Solution   We need to find the first four terms of the sequence. To do so, we replace each n in $\dfrac{2^n}{(n-1)!}$ with 1, 2, 3, and 4.

a_1, 1st term
$$\frac{2^1}{(1-1)!} = \frac{2}{0!} = \frac{2}{1} = 2$$

a_2, 2nd term
$$\frac{2^2}{(2-1)!} = \frac{4}{1!} = \frac{4}{1} = 4$$

a_3, 3rd term
$$\frac{2^3}{(3-1)!} = \frac{8}{2!} = \frac{8}{2 \cdot 1} = 4$$

a_4, 4th term
$$\frac{2^4}{(4-1)!} = \frac{16}{3!} = \frac{16}{3 \cdot 2 \cdot 1} = \frac{16}{6} = \frac{8}{3}$$

The first four terms are $2, 4, 4,$ and $\frac{8}{3}$.

Check Point 3   Write the first four terms of the sequence whose nth term is
$$a_n = \frac{20}{(n+1)!}.$$

Factorials from 0 through 20

0!	1
1!	1
2!	2
3!	6
4!	24
5!	120
6!	720
7!	5040
8!	40,320
9!	362,880
10!	3,628,800
11!	39,916,800
12!	479,001,600
13!	6,227,020,800
14!	87,178,291,200
15!	1,307,674,368,000
16!	20,922,789,888,000
17!	355,687,428,096,000
18!	6,402,373,705,728,000
19!	121,645,100,408,832,000
20!	2,432,902,008,176,640,000

As n increases, $n!$ grows very rapidly. Factorial growth is more explosive than exponential growth discussed in Chapter 3.

Technology

Most calculators have factorial keys. To find 5!, most calculators use one of the following:

Many Scientific Calculators
$$5\,\boxed{x!}$$

Many Graphing Calculators
$$5\,\boxed{!}\ \boxed{\text{ENTER}}.$$

Because $n!$ becomes quite large as n increases, your calculator will display these larger values in scientific notation.

When evaluating fractions with factorials in the numerator and the denominator, try to reduce the fraction before performing the multiplications. For example, consider $\dfrac{26!}{21!}$. Rather than write out 26! as the product of all integers from 26 down to 1, we can express 26! as

$$26! = 26 \cdot 25 \cdot 24 \cdot 23 \cdot 22 \cdot 21!.$$

In this way, we can divide both the numerator and the denominator by the common factor, 21!.

$$\frac{26!}{21!} = \frac{26 \cdot 25 \cdot 24 \cdot 23 \cdot 22 \cdot \cancel{21!}}{\cancel{21!}} = 26 \cdot 25 \cdot 24 \cdot 23 \cdot 22 = 7{,}893{,}600$$

EXAMPLE 4 Evaluating Fractions with Factorials

Evaluate each factorial expression:

a. $\dfrac{10!}{2!8!}$ b. $\dfrac{(n + 1)!}{n!}$.

Solution

a. $\dfrac{10!}{2!8!} = \dfrac{10 \cdot 9 \cdot \cancel{8!}}{2 \cdot 1 \cdot \cancel{8!}} = \dfrac{90}{2} = 45$

b. $\dfrac{(n + 1)!}{n!} = \dfrac{(n + 1) \cdot \cancel{n!}}{\cancel{n!}} = n + 1$

Check Point **4** Evaluate each factorial expression:

a. $\dfrac{14!}{2!12!}$ b. $\dfrac{n!}{(n - 1)!}$.

 Use summation notation.

Summation Notation

It is sometimes useful to find the sum of the first n terms of a sequence. For example, consider the cost of raising a child born in the United States in 2002 to a middle-income ($39,700–$66,900 per year) family, shown in Table 10.1.

Table 10.1   The Cost of Raising a Child Born in the U.S. in 2002 to a Middle-Income Family

Year	2002	2003	2004	2005	2006	2007	2008	2009	2010
Average Cost	$9230	$9530	$9830	$10,420	$10,750	$11,100	$11,440	$11,810	$12,180
	Child is under 1.	Child is 1.	Child is 2.	Child is 3.	Child is 4.	Child is 5.	Child is 6.	Child is 7.	Child is 8.

Year	2011	2012	2013	2014	2015	2016	2017	2018	2019
Average Cost	$12,440	$12,840	$13,250	$14,750	$15,230	$15,710	$16,520	$17,050	$17,600
	Child is 9.	Child is 10.	Child is 11.	Child is 12.	Child is 13.	Child is 14.	Child is 15.	Child is 16.	Child is 17.

Source: U.S. Department of Agriculture

We can let a_n represent the cost of raising a child in year n, where $n = 1$ corresponds to 2002, $n = 2$ to 2003, $n = 3$ to 2004, and so on. The terms of the finite sequence in Table 10.1 are given as follows:

9230,   9530,   9830,   10,420,   10,750,   11,100,   11,440,   11,810,   12,180,

a_1 a_2 a_3 a_4 a_5 a_6 a_7 a_8 a_9

12,440,   12,840,   13,250,   14,750,   15,230,   15,710,   16,520,   17,050,   17,600.

a_{10} a_{11} a_{12} a_{13} a_{14} a_{15} a_{16} a_{17} a_{18}

Why might we want to add the terms of this sequence? We do this to find the total cost of raising a child born in 2002 from birth through age 17. Thus,

$$a_1 + a_2 + a_3 + a_4 + a_5 + a_6 + a_7 + a_8 + a_9 + a_{10} + a_{11} + a_{12} + a_{13} + a_{14} + a_{15} + a_{16} + a_{17} + a_{18}$$
$$= 9230 + 9530 + 9830 + 10,420 + 10,750 + 11,100 + 11,440 + 11,810 + 12,180$$
$$+ 12,440 + 12,840 + 13,250 + 14,750 + 15,230 + 15,710 + 16,520 + 17,050 + 17,600$$
$$= 231,680.$$

We see that the total cost of raising a child born in 2002 from birth through age 17 is $231,680.

There is a compact notation for expressing the sum of the first n terms of a sequence. For example, rather than write

$$a_1 + a_2 + a_3 + a_4 + a_5 + a_6 + a_7 + a_8 + a_9 + a_{10} + a_{11} + a_{12} + a_{13} + a_{14} + a_{15} + a_{16} + a_{17} + a_{18},$$

we can use *summation notation* to express the sum as

$$\sum_{i=1}^{18} a_i.$$

We read this expression as "the sum as i goes from 1 to 18 of a_i." The letter i is called the *index of summation* and is not related to the use of i to represent $\sqrt{-1}$.

You can think of the symbol Σ (the uppercase Greek letter sigma) as an instruction to add up the terms of a sequence.

Summation Notation

The sum of the first n terms of a sequence is represented by the **summation notation**

$$\sum_{i=1}^{n} a_i = a_1 + a_2 + a_3 + a_4 + \cdots + a_n,$$

where i is the **index of summation**, n is the **upper limit of summation**, and 1 is the **lower limit of summation**.

Any letter can be used for the index of summation. The letters $i, j,$ and k are used commonly. Furthermore, the lower limit of summation can be an integer other than 1.

When we write out a sum that is given in summation notation, we are **expanding the summation notation**. Example 5 shows how to do this.

EXAMPLE 5   Using Summation Notation

Expand and evaluate the sum:

a. $\displaystyle\sum_{i=1}^{6} (i^2 + 1)$ **b.** $\displaystyle\sum_{k=4}^{7} [(-2)^k - 5]$ **c.** $\displaystyle\sum_{i=1}^{5} 3.$

Solution

a. To find $\displaystyle\sum_{i=1}^{6} (i^2 + 1)$, we must replace i in the expression $i^2 + 1$ with all consecutive integers from 1 to 6, inclusive. Then we add.

$$\sum_{i=1}^{6} (i^2 + 1) = (1^2 + 1) + (2^2 + 1) + (3^2 + 1) + (4^2 + 1)$$
$$+ (5^2 + 1) + (6^2 + 1)$$
$$= 2 + 5 + 10 + 17 + 26 + 37$$
$$= 97$$

Technology

Graphing utilities can calculate the sum of a sequence. For example, to find the sum of the sequence in Example 5(a), enter

SUM SEQ $(x^2 + 1, x, 1, 6, 1).$

Then press ENTER; 97 should be displayed. Use this capability to verify Example 5(b).

```
sum(seq(X²+1,X,1
,6,1)
              97
```

b. The index of summation in $\sum\limits_{k=4}^{7} [(-2)^k - 5]$ is k. First we evaluate $(-2)^k - 5$ for all consecutive integers from 4 through 7, inclusive. Then we add.

$$\sum_{k=4}^{7} [(-2)^k - 5] = [(-2)^4 - 5] + [(-2)^5 - 5]$$
$$+ [(-2)^6 - 5] + [(-2)^7 - 5]$$
$$= (16 - 5) + (-32 - 5) + (64 - 5) + (-128 - 5)$$
$$= 11 + (-37) + 59 + (-133)$$
$$= -100$$

c. To find $\sum\limits_{i=1}^{5} 3$, we observe that every term of the sum is 3. The notation $i = 1$ through 5 indicates that we must add the first five terms of a sequence in which every term is 3.

$$\sum_{i=1}^{5} 3 = 3 + 3 + 3 + 3 + 3 = 15$$

Check Point 5 Expand and evaluate the sum:

a. $\sum\limits_{i=1}^{6} 2i^2$ **b.** $\sum\limits_{k=3}^{5} (2^k - 3)$ **c.** $\sum\limits_{i=1}^{5} 4.$

For a given sum, we can vary the upper and lower limits of summation, as well as the letter used for the index of summation. By doing so, we can produce different-looking summation notations for the same sum. For example, the sum of the squares of the first four positive integers, $1^2 + 2^2 + 3^2 + 4^2$, can be expressed in a number of equivalent ways:

$$\sum_{i=1}^{4} i^2 = 1^2 + 2^2 + 3^2 + 4^2 = 30$$

$$\sum_{i=0}^{3} (i + 1)^2 = (0 + 1)^2 + (1 + 1)^2 + (2 + 1)^2 + (3 + 1)^2$$
$$= 1^2 + 2^2 + 3^2 + 4^2 = 30$$

$$\sum_{k=2}^{5} (k - 1)^2 = (2 - 1)^2 + (3 - 1)^2 + (4 - 1)^2 + (5 - 1)^2$$
$$= 1^2 + 2^2 + 3^2 + 4^2 = 30.$$

EXAMPLE 6   Writing Sums in Summation Notation

Express each sum using summation notation:

a. $1^3 + 2^3 + 3^3 + \cdots + 7^3$ **b.** $1 + \dfrac{1}{3} + \dfrac{1}{9} + \dfrac{1}{27} + \cdots + \dfrac{1}{3^{n-1}}.$

Solution   In each case, we will use 1 as the lower limit of summation and i for the index of summation.

a. The sum $1^3 + 2^3 + 3^3 + \cdots + 7^3$ has seven terms, each of the form i^3, starting at $i = 1$ and ending at $i = 7$. Thus,

$$1^3 + 2^3 + 3^3 + \cdots + 7^3 = \sum_{i=1}^{7} i^3.$$

b. The sum

$$1 + \frac{1}{3} + \frac{1}{9} + \frac{1}{27} + \cdots + \frac{1}{3^{n-1}}$$

has n terms, each of the form $\dfrac{1}{3^{i-1}}$, starting at $i = 1$ and ending at $i = n$. Thus,

$$1 + \frac{1}{3} + \frac{1}{9} + \frac{1}{27} + \cdots + \frac{1}{3^{n-1}} = \sum_{i=1}^{n} \frac{1}{3^{i-1}}.$$

 Check Point 6 Express each sum using summation notation:

a. $1^2 + 2^2 + 3^2 + \cdots + 9^2$ **b.** $1 + \dfrac{1}{2} + \dfrac{1}{4} + \dfrac{1}{8} + \cdots + \dfrac{1}{2^{n-1}}.$

Table 10.2 contains some important properties of sums expressed in summation notation.

Table 10.2   Properties of Sums

Property	Example
1. $\displaystyle\sum_{i=1}^{n} ca_i = c \sum_{i=1}^{n} a_i$, c any real number	$\displaystyle\sum_{i=1}^{4} 3i^2 = 3 \cdot 1^2 + 3 \cdot 2^2 + 3 \cdot 3^2 + 3 \cdot 4^2$ $3\displaystyle\sum_{i=1}^{4} i^2 = 3(1^2 + 2^2 + 3^2 + 4^2) = 3 \cdot 1^2 + 3 \cdot 2^2 + 3 \cdot 3^2 + 3 \cdot 4^2$ Conclusion: $\displaystyle\sum_{i=1}^{4} 3i^2 = 3 \sum_{i=1}^{4} i^2$
2. $\displaystyle\sum_{i=1}^{n} (a_i + b_i) = \sum_{i=1}^{n} a_i + \sum_{i=1}^{n} b_i$	$\displaystyle\sum_{i=1}^{4} (i + i^2) = (1 + 1^2) + (2 + 2^2) + (3 + 3^2) + (4 + 4^2)$ $\displaystyle\sum_{i=1}^{4} i + \sum_{i=1}^{4} i^2 = (1 + 2 + 3 + 4) + (1^2 + 2^2 + 3^2 + 4^2)$ $\qquad = (1 + 1^2) + (2 + 2^2) + (3 + 3^2) + (4 + 4^2)$ Conclusion: $\displaystyle\sum_{i=1}^{4} (i + i^2) = \sum_{i=1}^{4} i + \sum_{i=1}^{4} i^2$
3. $\displaystyle\sum_{i=1}^{n} (a_i - b_i) = \sum_{i=1}^{n} a_i - \sum_{i=1}^{n} b_i$	$\displaystyle\sum_{i=3}^{5} (i^2 - i^3) = (3^2 - 3^3) + (4^2 - 4^3) + (5^2 - 5^3)$ $\displaystyle\sum_{i=3}^{5} i^2 - \sum_{i=3}^{5} i^3 = (3^2 + 4^2 + 5^2) - (3^3 + 4^3 + 5^3)$ $\qquad = (3^2 - 3^3) + (4^2 - 4^3) + (5^2 - 5^3)$ Conclusion: $\displaystyle\sum_{i=3}^{5} (i^2 - i^3) = \sum_{i=3}^{5} i^2 - \sum_{i=3}^{5} i^3$

EXERCISE SET 10.1

 Practice Exercises

In Exercises 1–12, write the first four terms of each sequence whose general term is given.

1. $a_n = 3n + 2$

2. $a_n = 4n - 1$

3. $a_n = 3^n$

4. $a_n = \left(\dfrac{1}{3}\right)^n$

5. $a_n = (-3)^n$

6. $a_n = \left(-\dfrac{1}{3}\right)^n$

7. $a_n = (-1)^n(n + 3)$

8. $a_n = (-1)^{n+1}(n + 4)$

9. $a_n = \dfrac{2n}{n + 4}$

10. $a_n = \dfrac{3n}{n + 5}$

11. $a_n = \dfrac{(-1)^{n+1}}{2^n - 1}$

12. $a_n = \dfrac{(-1)^{n+1}}{2^n + 1}$

The sequences in Exercises 13–18 are defined using recursion formulas. Write the first four terms of each sequence.

13. $a_1 = 7$ and $a_n = a_{n-1} + 5$ for $n \geq 2$

14. $a_1 = 12$ and $a_n = a_{n-1} + 4$ for $n \geq 2$

15. $a_1 = 3$ and $a_n = 4a_{n-1}$ for $n \geq 2$

16. $a_1 = 2$ and $a_n = 5a_{n-1}$ for $n \geq 2$

17. $a_1 = 4$ and $a_n = 2a_{n-1} + 3$ for $n \geq 2$

18. $a_1 = 5$ and $a_n = 3a_{n-1} - 1$ for $n \geq 2$

In Exercises 19–22, the general term of a sequence is given and involves a factorial. Write the first four terms of each sequence.

19. $a_n = \dfrac{n^2}{n!}$ 　　　　 **20.** $a_n = \dfrac{(n + 1)!}{n^2}$

21. $a_n = 2(n + 1)!$ 　　 **22.** $a_n = -2(n - 1)!$

In Exercises 23–28, evaluate each factorial expression.

23. $\dfrac{17!}{15!}$ 　　 **24.** $\dfrac{18!}{16!}$ 　　 **25.** $\dfrac{16!}{2!14!}$

26. $\dfrac{20!}{2!18!}$ 　　 **27.** $\dfrac{(n + 2)!}{n!}$ 　　 **28.** $\dfrac{(2n + 1)!}{(2n)!}$

In Exercises 29–42, find each indicated sum.

29. $\displaystyle\sum_{i=1}^{6} 5i$ 　　 **30.** $\displaystyle\sum_{i=1}^{6} 7i$ 　　 **31.** $\displaystyle\sum_{i=1}^{4} 2i^2$

32. $\displaystyle\sum_{i=1}^{5} i^3$ 　　 **33.** $\displaystyle\sum_{k=1}^{5} k(k + 4)$ 　　 **34.** $\displaystyle\sum_{k=1}^{4} (k - 3)(k + 2)$

35. $\displaystyle\sum_{i=1}^{4} \left(-\dfrac{1}{2}\right)^i$ 　 **36.** $\displaystyle\sum_{i=2}^{5} \left(-\dfrac{1}{3}\right)^i$ 　 **37.** $\displaystyle\sum_{i=5}^{9} 11$

38. $\displaystyle\sum_{i=3}^{7} 12$ 　　 **39.** $\displaystyle\sum_{i=0}^{4} \dfrac{(-1)^i}{i!}$ 　　 **40.** $\displaystyle\sum_{i=0}^{4} \dfrac{(-1)^{i+1}}{(i + 1)!}$

41. $\displaystyle\sum_{i=1}^{5} \dfrac{i!}{(i - 1)!}$ 　 **42.** $\displaystyle\sum_{i=1}^{5} \dfrac{(i + 2)!}{i!}$

In Exercises 43–54, express each sum using summation notation. Use 1 as the lower limit of summation and i for the index of summation.

43. $1^2 + 2^2 + 3^2 + \cdots + 15^2$

44. $1^4 + 2^4 + 3^4 + \cdots + 12^4$

45. $2 + 2^2 + 2^3 + \cdots + 2^{11}$

46. $5 + 5^2 + 5^3 + \cdots + 5^{12}$

47. $1 + 2 + 3 + \cdots + 30$

48. $1 + 2 + 3 + \cdots + 40$

49. $\dfrac{1}{2} + \dfrac{2}{3} + \dfrac{3}{4} + \cdots + \dfrac{14}{14 + 1}$

50. $\dfrac{1}{3} + \dfrac{2}{4} + \dfrac{3}{5} + \cdots + \dfrac{16}{16 + 2}$

51. $4 + \dfrac{4^2}{2} + \dfrac{4^3}{3} + \cdots + \dfrac{4^n}{n}$

52. $\dfrac{1}{9} + \dfrac{2}{9^2} + \dfrac{3}{9^3} + \cdots + \dfrac{n}{9^n}$

53. $1 + 3 + 5 + \cdots + (2n - 1)$

54. $a + ar + ar^2 + \cdots + ar^{n-1}$

In Exercises 55–60, express each sum using summation notation. Use a lower limit of summation of your choice and k for the index of summation.

55. $5 + 7 + 9 + 11 + \cdots + 31$

56. $6 + 8 + 10 + 12 + \cdots + 32$

57. $a + ar + ar^2 + \cdots + ar^{12}$

58. $a + ar + ar^2 + \cdots + ar^{14}$

59. $a + (a + d) + (a + 2d) + \cdots + (a + nd)$

60. $(a + d) + (a + d^2) + \cdots + (a + d^n)$

Practice Plus

In Exercises 61–68, use the graphs of $\{a_n\}$ and $\{b_n\}$ to find each indicated sum.

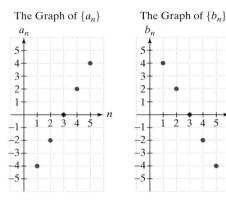

The Graph of $\{a_n\}$ 　　　 The Graph of $\{b_n\}$

61. $\displaystyle\sum_{i=1}^{5} (a_i^2 + 1)$ 　 **62.** $\displaystyle\sum_{i=1}^{5} (b_i^2 - 1)$ 　 **63.** $\displaystyle\sum_{i=1}^{5} (2a_i + b_i)$

64. $\displaystyle\sum_{i=1}^{5} (a_i + 3b_i)$ 　 **65.** $\displaystyle\sum_{i=4}^{5} \left(\dfrac{a_i}{b_i}\right)^2$ 　 **66.** $\displaystyle\sum_{i=4}^{5} \left(\dfrac{a_i}{b_i}\right)^3$

67. $\displaystyle\sum_{i=1}^{5} a_i^2 + \sum_{i=1}^{5} b_i^2$ 　　 **68.** $\displaystyle\sum_{i=1}^{5} a_i^2 - \sum_{i=3}^{5} b_i^2$

Application Exercises

69. The bar graph shows the number of people in the United States who lived below the poverty level from 1995 through 2002. Let a_n represent the number of people, in millions, living below the poverty level in year n, where $n = 1$ corresponds to 1995, $n = 2$ to 1996, and so on.

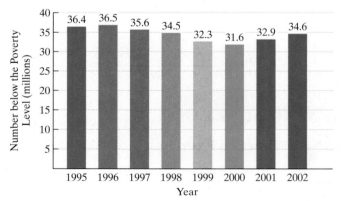

Number of People in the U.S. Living below the Poverty Level

Source: Bureau of the Census

a. Find $\displaystyle\sum_{i=1}^{8} a_i$.

b. Find $\dfrac{\displaystyle\sum_{i=1}^{8} a_i}{8}$. What does this number represent?

70. The bar graph shows the number of flu vaccine doses, in millions, that were available and distributed in the United States from 1999 through 2004. Let a_n represent the available doses, in millions, and let d_n represent the distributed doses, in millions, in year n, where $n = 1$ corresponds to 1999, $n = 2$ to 2000, and so on.

Flu Vaccine Doses in the U.S.

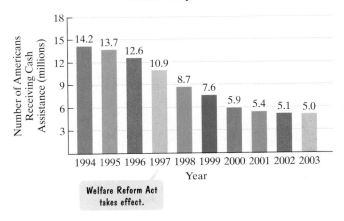

Source: Centers for Disease Control

Find $\sum_{i=1}^{6} (a_i - d_i)$. What does this number represent?

The graph shows the millions of welfare recipients in the United States who received cash assistance from 1994 through 2003. In Exercises 71–72, consider a sequence whose general term, a_n, represents the millions of Americans receiving cash assistance n years after 1993.

Welfare Recipients in the U.S.

Source: Thomas R. Dye, *Politics in America*, Prentice Hall

71. a. Use the numbers given in the graph to find and interpret $\frac{1}{10} \sum_{i=1}^{10} a_i$.

b. The finite sequence whose general term is $a_n = -1.18n + 15.41$, where $n = 1, 2, 3, \ldots, 10$, models the millions of Americans receiving cash assistance, a_n, n years after 1993. Use the model to find $\frac{1}{10} \sum_{i=1}^{10} a_i$. Does this seem reasonable in terms of the actual sum in part (a), or has model breakdown occurred?

72. a. Use the numbers given in the graph to find and interpret $\frac{1}{10} \sum_{i=1}^{10} a_i$.

b. The finite sequence whose general term is $a_n = 0.07n^2 - 1.98n + 17.01$, where $n = 1, 2, 3, \ldots, 10$, models the millions of Americans receiving cash assistance, a_n, n years after 1993. Use the model to find $\frac{1}{10} \sum_{i=1}^{10} a_i$. Does this seem reasonable in terms of the actual sum in part (a), or has model breakdown occurred?

73. A deposit of $6000 is made in an account that earns 6% interest compounded quarterly. The balance in the account after n quarters is given by the sequence
$$a_n = 6000\left(1 + \frac{0.06}{4}\right)^n, \qquad n = 1, 2, 3, \ldots.$$
Find the balance in the account after five years. Round to the nearest cent.

74. A deposit of $10,000 is made in an account that earns 8% interest compounded quarterly. The balance in the account after n quarters is given by the sequence
$$a_n = 10,000\left(1 + \frac{0.08}{4}\right)^n, \qquad n = 1, 2, 3, \ldots.$$
Find the balance in the account after six years. Round to the nearest cent.

Writing in Mathematics

75. What is a sequence? Give an example with your description.

76. Explain how to write terms of a sequence if the formula for the general term is given.

77. What does the graph of a sequence look like? How is it obtained?

78. What is a recursion formula?

79. Explain how to find $n!$ if n is a positive integer.

80. Explain the best way to evaluate $\frac{900!}{899!}$ without a calculator.

81. What is the meaning of the symbol Σ? Give an example with your description.

82. You buy a new car for $24,000. At the end of n years, the value of your car is given by the sequence
$$a_n = 24,000\left(\frac{3}{4}\right)^n, \qquad n = 1, 2, 3, \ldots.$$
Find a_5 and write a sentence explaining what this value represents. Describe the nth term of the sequence in terms of the value of your car at the end of each year.

Technology Exercises

In Exercises 83–87, use a calculator's factorial key to evaluate each expression.

83. $\dfrac{200!}{198!}$ **84.** $\left(\dfrac{300}{20}\right)!$ **85.** $\dfrac{20!}{300}$

86. $\dfrac{20!}{(20-3)!}$ **87.** $\dfrac{54!}{(54-3)!\,3!}$

88. Use the [SEQ] (sequence) capability of a graphing utility to verify the terms of the sequences you obtained for any five sequences from Exercises 1–12 or 19–22.

89. Use the [SUM] [SEQ] (sum of the sequence) capability of a graphing utility to verify any five of the sums you obtained in Exercises 29–42.

90. As n increases, the terms of the sequence

$$a_n = \left(1 + \frac{1}{n}\right)^n$$

get closer and closer to the number e (where $e \approx 2.7183$). Use a calculator to find $a_{10}, a_{100}, a_{1000}, a_{10,000}$, and $a_{100,000}$, comparing these terms to your calculator's decimal approximation for e.

Many graphing utilities have a sequence-graphing mode that plots the terms of a sequence as points on a rectangular coordinate system. Consult your manual; if your graphing utility has this capability, use it to graph each of the sequences in Exercises 91–94. What appears to be happening to the terms of each sequence as n gets larger?

91. $a_n = \dfrac{n}{n+1}$ $n:[0, 10, 1]$ by $a_n:[0, 1, 0.1]$

92. $a_n = \dfrac{100}{n}$ $n:[0, 1000, 100]$ by $a_n:[0, 1, 0.1]$

93. $a_n = \dfrac{2n^2 + 5n - 7}{n^3}$ $n:[0, 10, 1]$ by $a_n:[0, 2, 0.2]$

94. $a_n = \dfrac{3n^4 + n - 1}{5n^4 + 2n^2 + 1}$ $n:[0, 10, 1]$ by $a_n:[0, 1, 0.1]$

Critical Thinking Exercises

95. Which one of the following is true?

  a. $\dfrac{n!}{(n-1)!} = \dfrac{1}{n-1}$

  b. The Fibonacci sequence 1, 1, 2, 3, 5, 8, 13, 21, 34, 55, 89, 144,... can be defined recursively using $a_0 = 1, a_1 = 1$; $a_n = a_{n-2} + a_{n-1}$, where $n \geq 2$.

  c. $\displaystyle\sum_{i=1}^{2} (-1)^i 2^i = 0$

  d. $\displaystyle\sum_{i=1}^{2} a_i b_i = \sum_{i=1}^{2} a_i \sum_{i=1}^{2} b_i$

96. Write the first five terms of the sequence whose first term is 9 and whose general term is

$$a_n = \begin{cases} \dfrac{a_{n-1}}{2} & \text{if } a_{n-1} \text{ is even} \\ 3a_{n-1} + 5 & \text{if } a_{n-1} \text{ is odd} \end{cases}$$

for $n \geq 2$.

Group Exercise

97. Enough curiosities involving the Fibonacci sequence exist to warrant a flourishing Fibonacci Association, which publishes a quarterly journal. Do some research on the Fibonacci sequence by consulting the Internet or the research department of your library, and find one property that interests you. After doing this research, get together with your group to share these intriguing properties.

SECTION 10.2   *Arithmetic Sequences*

Objectives

① Find the common difference for an arithmetic sequence.

② Write terms of an arithmetic sequence.

③ Use the formula for the general term of an arithmetic sequence.

④ Use the formula for the sum of the first n terms of an arithmetic sequence.

Your grandmother and her financial counselor are looking at options in case an adult residential facility is needed in the future. The good news is that your grandmother's total assets are $400,000. The bad news is that yearly adult residential community costs average $58,730, increasing by $1800 each year. In this section, we will see how sequences can be used to describe your grandmother's situation and help her to identify realistic options.

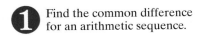

Find the common difference for an arithmetic sequence.

Arithmetic Sequences

The bar graph in Figure 10.2 shows annual salaries, rounded to the nearest thousand dollars, of U.S. senators from 2000 to 2005. The graph illustrates that each year salaries increased by $4 thousand. The sequence of annual salaries

142, 146, 150, 154, 158, 162, . . .

shows that each term after the first, 142, differs from the preceding term by a constant amount, namely 4. This sequence is an example of an *arithmetic sequence*.

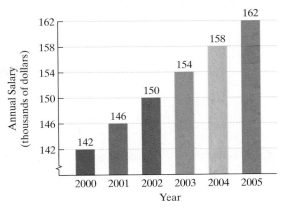

Figure 10.2

Source: U.S. Senate

Definition of an Arithmetic Sequence

An **arithmetic sequence** is a sequence in which each term after the first differs from the preceding term by a constant amount. The difference between consecutive terms is called the **common difference** of the sequence.

The common difference, d, is found by subtracting any term from the term that directly follows it. In the following examples, the common difference is found by subtracting the first term from the second term, $a_2 - a_1$.

Arithmetic Sequence	**Common Difference**
142, 146, 150, 154, 158, . . .	$d = 146 - 142 = 4$
$-5, -2, 1, 4, 7, \ldots$	$d = -2 - (-5) = -2 + 5 = 3$
$8, 3, -2, -7, -12, \ldots$	$d = 3 - 8 = -5$

Figure 10.3 shows the graphs of the last two arithmetic sequences in our list. The common difference for the increasing sequence in Figure 10.3(a) is 3. The common difference for the decreasing sequence in Figure 10.3(b) is -5.

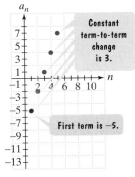

Figure 10.3(a) The graph of $\{a_n\} = -5, -2, 1, 4, 7, \ldots$

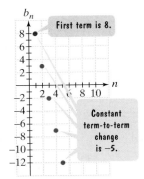

Figure 10.3(b) The graph of $\{b_n\} = 8, 3, -2, -7, -12, \ldots$

The graph of each arithmetic sequence in Figure 10.3 forms a set of discrete points lying on a straight line. This illustrates that **an arithmetic sequence is a linear function whose domain is the set of positive integers**.

If the first term of an arithmetic sequence is a_1, each term after the first is obtained by adding d, the common difference, to the previous term. This can be expressed recursively as follows:

$$a_n = a_{n-1} + d.$$

Add d to the term in any position to get the next term.

To use this recursion formula, we must be given the first term.

② Write terms of an arithmetic sequence.

Men in the U.S. Labor Force

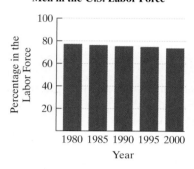

Women in the U.S. Labor Force

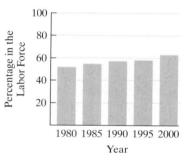

Figure 10.4

Source: U.S. Department of Labor

EXAMPLE 1 Writing the Terms of an Arithmetic Sequence Using the First Term and the Common Difference

Figure 10.4 shows the percentage of men and women in the U.S. labor force for five-year periods starting with 1980. The recursion formula $a_n = a_{n-1} - 0.67$ models the percentage of men working in the U.S. labor force, a_n, for each five-year period starting with 1980. Thus, $n = 1$ corresponds to 1980, $n = 2$ to 1985, $n = 3$ to 1990, and so on. In 1980, 77.4% of U.S. men were working in the labor force. Find the first five terms of this arithmetic sequence in which $a_1 = 77.4$ and $a_n = a_{n-1} - 0.67$.

Solution The recursion formula $a_1 = 77.4$ and $a_n = a_{n-1} - 0.67$ indicates that each term after the first, 77.4, is obtained by adding -0.67 to the previous term. Thus, during each five-year period, the percentage of men in the labor force decreased by 0.67%.

$a_1 = 77.4$	This is given.
$a_2 = a_1 - 0.67 = 77.4 - 0.67 = 76.73$	Use $a_n = a_{n-1} - 0.67$ with $n = 2$.
$a_3 = a_2 - 0.67 = 76.73 - 0.67 = 76.06$	Use $a_n = a_{n-1} - 0.67$ with $n = 3$.
$a_4 = a_3 - 0.67 = 76.06 - 0.67 = 75.39$	Use $a_n = a_{n-1} - 0.67$ with $n = 4$.
$a_5 = a_4 - 0.67 = 75.39 - 0.67 = 74.72$	Use $a_n = a_{n-1} - 0.67$ with $n = 5$.

The first five terms are

$$77.4, 76.73, 76.06, 75.39, \text{ and } 74.72.$$

These numbers represent the percentage of men working in the U.S. labor force in 1980, 1985, 1990, 1995, and 2000, respectively, as given by the model.

Check Point 1 The recursion formula $a_n = a_{n-1} + 2.18$ models the percentage of women working in the U.S. labor force, a_n, for each five-year period starting with 1980. In 1980, 51.5% of U.S. women were working in the labor force. Find the first five terms of the arithmetic sequence in which $a_1 = 51.5$ and $a_n = a_{n-1} + 2.18$.

③ Use the formula for the general term of an arithmetic sequence.

The General Term of an Arithmetic Sequence

Consider an arithmetic sequence whose first term is a_1 and whose common difference is d. We are looking for a formula for the general term, a_n. Let's begin by writing the first six terms. The first term is a_1. The second term is $a_1 + d$. The third term is $a_1 + d + d$, or $a_1 + 2d$. Thus, we start with a_1 and add d to each successive term. The first six terms are

$$a_1, \quad a_1 + d, \quad a_1 + 2d, \quad a_1 + 3d, \quad a_1 + 4d, \quad a_1 + 5d.$$

a_1, first term a_2, second term a_3, third term a_4, fourth term a_5, fifth term a_6, sixth term

Compare the coefficient of d and the subscript of a denoting the term number. Can you see that the coefficient of d is 1 less than the subscript of a denoting the term number?

$$a_3: \text{third term} = a_1 + 2d \qquad a_4: \text{fourth term} = a_1 + 3d$$

| 2 is one less than 3. | 3 is one less than 4. |

Thus, the formula for the nth term is

$$a_n: n\text{th term} = a_1 + (n-1)d.$$

| $n - 1$ is one less than n. |

General Term of an Arithmetic Sequence

The nth term (the general term) of an arithmetic sequence with first term a_1 and common difference d is

$$a_n = a_1 + (n-1)d.$$

EXAMPLE 2   **Using the Formula for the General Term of an Arithmetic Sequence**

Find the eighth term of the arithmetic sequence whose first term is 4 and whose common difference is -7.

Solution   To find the eighth term, a_8, we replace n in the formula with 8, a_1 with 4, and d with -7.

$$a_n = a_1 + (n-1)d$$
$$a_8 = 4 + (8-1)(-7) = 4 + 7(-7) = 4 + (-49) = -45$$

The eighth term is -45. We can check this result by writing the first eight terms of the sequence:

$$4, -3, -10, -17, -24, -31, -38, -45.$$

Check Point 2   Find the ninth term of the arithmetic sequence whose first term is 6 and whose common difference is -5.

EXAMPLE 3   **Using an Arithmetic Sequence to Model Teachers' Earnings**

According to the National Education Association, teachers in the United States earned an average of $30,532 in 1990. This amount has increased by approximately $1472 per year.

    a. Write a formula for the nth term of the arithmetic sequence that describes teachers' average earnings n years after 1989.

    b. How much will U.S. teachers earn, on average, by the year 2010?

Solution

    a. We can express teachers' earnings by the following arithmetic sequence:

$$30{,}532, \qquad 32{,}004, \qquad 33{,}476, \qquad 34{,}948, \ldots.$$

| a_1: earnings in 1990, 1 year after 1989 | a_2: earnings in 1991, 2 years after 1989 | a_3: earnings in 1992, 3 years after 1989 | a_4: earnings in 1993, 4 years after 1989 |

In the sequence $30{,}532, 32{,}004, 33{,}476, \ldots, a_1$, the first term, represents the amount teachers earned in 1990. Each subsequent year this amount increases by \$1472, so $d = 1472$. We use the formula for the general term of an arithmetic sequence to write the nth term of the sequence that describes teachers' earnings n years after 1989.

$$a_n = a_1 + (n - 1)d \qquad \text{This is the formula for the general term of an arithmetic sequence.}$$

$$a_n = 30{,}532 + (n - 1)1472 \qquad a_1 = 30{,}532 \text{ and } d = 1472.$$

$$a_n = 30{,}532 + 1472n - 1472 \qquad \text{Distribute 1472 to each term in parentheses.}$$

$$a_n = 1472n + 29{,}060 \qquad \text{Simplify.}$$

Thus, teachers' earnings n years after 1989 can be described by $a_n = 1472n + 29{,}060$.

b. Now we need to find teachers' earnings in 2010. The year 2010 is 21 years after 1989: That is, $2010 - 1989 = 21$. Thus, $n = 21$. We substitute 21 for n in $a_n = 1472n + 29{,}060$.

$$a_{21} = 1472 \cdot 21 + 29{,}060 = 59{,}972$$

The 21st term of the sequence is 59,972. Therefore, U.S. teachers are predicted to earn an average of \$59,972 by the year 2010.

 Check Point 3 According to the U.S. Census Bureau, new one-family houses sold for an average of \$159,000 in 1995. This average sales price has increased by approximately \$9700 per year.

a. Write a formula for the nth term of the arithmetic sequence that describes the average cost of new one-family houses n years after 1994.

b. How much will new one-family houses cost, on average, by the year 2010?

④ Use the formula for the sum of the first n terms of an arithmetic sequence.

The Sum of the First n Terms of an Arithmetic Sequence

The sum of the first n terms of an arithmetic sequence, denoted by S_n, and called the **nth partial sum**, can be found without having to add up all the terms. Let

$$S_n = a_1 + a_2 + a_3 + \cdots + a_n$$

be the sum of the first n terms of an arithmetic sequence. Because d is the common difference between terms, S_n can be written forward and backward as follows.

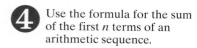

$$
\begin{aligned}
S_n &= a_1 &&+ (a_1 + d) &&+ (a_1 + 2d) &&+ \cdots + a_n \\
S_n &= a_n &&+ (a_n - d) &&+ (a_n - 2d) &&+ \cdots + a_1 \\
\hline
2S_n &= (a_1 + a_n) &&+ (a_1 + a_n) &&+ (a_1 + a_n) &&+ \cdots + (a_1 + a_n)
\end{aligned}
$$

Add the two equations.

Because there are n sums of $(a_1 + a_n)$ on the right side, we can express this side as $n(a_1 + a_n)$. Thus, the last equation can be written as follows:

$$2S_n = n(a_1 + a_n)$$

$$S_n = \frac{n}{2}(a_1 + a_n). \qquad \text{Solve for } S_n, \text{ dividing both sides by 2.}$$

We have proved the following result:

> **The Sum of the First n Terms of an Arithmetic Sequence**
>
> The sum, S_n, of the first n terms of an arithmetic sequence is given by
>
> $$S_n = \frac{n}{2}(a_1 + a_n),$$
>
> in which a_1 is the first term and a_n is the nth term.

To find the sum of the terms of an arithmetic sequence using $S_n = \frac{n}{2}(a_1 + a_n)$, we need to know the first term, a_1, the last term, a_n, and the number of terms, n. The following examples illustrate how to use this formula.

EXAMPLE 4   Finding the Sum of n Terms of an Arithmetic Sequence

Find the sum of the first 100 terms of the arithmetic sequence: $1, 3, 5, 7, \ldots$.

Solution   By finding the sum of the first 100 terms of $1, 3, 5, 7, \ldots$, we are finding the sum of the first 100 odd numbers. To find the sum of the first 100 terms, S_{100}, we replace n in the formula with 100.

$$S_n = \frac{n}{2}(a_1 + a_n)$$

$$S_{100} = \frac{100}{2}(a_1 + a_{100})$$

The first term, a_1, is 1.

We must find a_{100}, the 100th term.

We use the formula for the general term of a sequence to find a_{100}. The common difference, d, of $1, 3, 5, 7, \ldots$, is 2.

$$a_n = a_1 + (n - 1)d$$

This is the formula for the nth term of an arithmetic sequence. Use it to find the 100th term.

$$a_{100} = 1 + (100 - 1) \cdot 2$$

Substitute 100 for n, 2 for d, and 1 (the first term) for a_1.

$$= 1 + 99 \cdot 2$$

$$= 1 + 198 = 199$$

Now we are ready to find the sum of the 100 terms $1, 3, 5, 7, \ldots, 199$.

$$S_n = \frac{n}{2}(a_1 + a_n)$$

Use the formula for the sum of the first n terms of an arithmetic sequence. Let $n = 100$, $a_1 = 1$, and $a_{100} = 199$.

$$S_{100} = \frac{100}{2}(1 + 199) = 50(200) = 10,000$$

The sum of the first 100 odd numbers is 10,000. Equivalently, the 100th partial sum of the sequence $1, 3, 5, 7, \ldots$ is 10,000.

Check Point 4   Find the sum of the first 15 terms of the arithmetic sequence: $3, 6, 9, 12, \ldots$.

EXAMPLE 5   Using S_n to Evaluate a Summation

Find the following sum: $\displaystyle\sum_{i=1}^{25} (5i - 9)$.

Solution

$$\sum_{i=1}^{25} (5i - 9) = (5 \cdot 1 - 9) + (5 \cdot 2 - 9) + (5 \cdot 3 - 9) + \cdots + (5 \cdot 25 - 9)$$

$$= -4 \qquad + 1 \qquad + 6 \qquad + \cdots + 116$$

By evaluating the first three terms and the last term, we see that $a_1 = -4$; d, the common difference, is $1 - (-4)$, or 5; and a_{25}, the last term, is 116.

$$S_n = \frac{n}{2}(a_1 + a_n)$$ Use the formula for the sum of the first n terms of an arithmetic sequence. Let $n = 25$, $a_1 = -4$, and $a_{25} = 116$.

$$S_{25} = \frac{25}{2}(-4 + 116) = \frac{25}{2}(112) = 1400$$

Thus,

$$\sum_{i=1}^{25} (5i - 9) = 1400.$$

Technology

To find:

$$\sum_{i=1}^{25} (5i - 9)$$

on a graphing utility, enter:

$\boxed{\text{SUM}}$ $\boxed{\text{SEQ}}$ $(5x - 9, x, 1, 25, 1)$.

The press $\boxed{\text{ENTER}}$.

```
sum(seq(5X-9,X,1
,25,1))
              1400
```

Check Point 5   Find the following sum: $\displaystyle\sum_{i=1}^{30} (6i - 11)$.

EXAMPLE 6   Modeling Total Residential Community Costs over a Six-Year Period

Your grandmother has assets of $400,000. One option that she is considering involves an adult residential community for a six-year period beginning in 2006. The model

$$a_n = 1800n + 58{,}730$$

describes yearly adult residential community costs n years after 2005. Does your grandmother have enough to pay for the facility?

Solution   We must find the sum of an arithmetic sequence. The first term of the sequence corresponds to the facility's costs in the year 2006. The last term corresponds to costs in the year 2011. Because the model describes costs n years after 2005, $n = 1$ describes the year 2006 and $n = 6$ describes the year 2011.

$$a_n = 1800n + 58{,}730$$ This is the given formula for the general term of the sequence.

$$a_1 = 1800 \cdot 1 + 58{,}730 = 60{,}530$$ Find a_1 by replacing n with 1.

$$a_6 = 1800 \cdot 6 + 58{,}730 = 69{,}530$$ Find a_6 by replacing n with 6.

The first year the facility will cost $60,530. By year six, the facility will cost $69,530. Now we must find the sum of the costs for all six years. We focus on the sum of the first six terms of the arithmetic sequence

$$60{,}530, \ 62{,}330, \ \ldots \ , \ 69{,}530.$$

$$\underset{a_1}{\qquad} \quad \underset{a_2}{\qquad} \qquad \underset{a_6}{\qquad}$$

We find this sum using the formula for the sum of the first n terms of an arithmetic sequence. We are adding 6 terms: $n = 6$. The first term is 60,530: $a_1 = 60{,}530$. The last term—that is, the sixth term—is 69,530: $a_6 = 69{,}530$.

$$S_n = \frac{n}{2}(a_1 + a_n)$$

$$S_6 = \frac{6}{2}(60{,}530 + 69{,}530) = 3(130{,}060) = 390{,}180$$

The total adult residential community costs for your grandmother are predicted to be $390,180. Because your grandmother's assets are $400,000, she has enough to pay for the facility for the six-year period.

Check Point 6 In Example 6, how much would it cost for the adult residential community for a ten-year period beginning in 2006?

EXERCISE SET 10.2

Practice Exercises

In Exercises 1–14, write the first six terms of each arithmetic sequence.

1. $a_1 = 200, d = 20$ **2.** $a_1 = 300, d = 50$

3. $a_1 = -7, d = 4$ **4.** $a_1 = -8, d = 5$

5. $a_1 = 300, d = -90$ **6.** $a_1 = 200, d = -60$

7. $a_1 = \frac{5}{2}, d = -\frac{1}{2}$ **8.** $a_1 = \frac{3}{4}, d = -\frac{1}{4}$

9. $a_n = a_{n-1} + 6, a_1 = -9$ **10.** $a_n = a_{n-1} + 4, a_1 = -7$

11. $a_n = a_{n-1} - 10, a_1 = 30$ **12.** $a_n = a_{n-1} - 20, a_1 = 50$

13. $a_n = a_{n-1} - 0.4, a_1 = 1.6$

14. $a_n = a_{n-1} - 0.3, a_1 = -1.7$

In Exercises 15–22, find the indicated term of the arithmetic sequence with first term, a_1, and common difference, d.

15. Find a_6 when $a_1 = 13, d = 4$.

16. Find a_{16} when $a_1 = 9, d = 2$.

17. Find a_{50} when $a_1 = 7, d = 5$.

18. Find a_{60} when $a_1 = 8, d = 6$.

19. Find a_{200} when $a_1 = -40, d = 5$.

20. Find a_{150} when $a_1 = -60, d = 5$.

21. Find a_{60} when $a_1 = 35, d = -3$.

22. Find a_{70} when $a_1 = -32, d = 4$.

In Exercises 23–34, write a formula for the general term (the nth term) of each arithmetic sequence. Do not use a recursion formula. Then use the formula for a_n to find a_{20}, the 20th term of the sequence.

23. $1, 5, 9, 13, \ldots$ **24.** $2, 7, 12, 17, \ldots$

25. $7, 3, -1, -5, \ldots$ **26.** $6, 1, -4, -9, \ldots$

27. $a_1 = 9, d = 2$ **28.** $a_1 = 6, d = 3$

29. $a_1 = -20, d = -4$ **30.** $a_1 = -70, d = -5$

31. $a_n = a_{n-1} + 3, a_1 = 4$ **32.** $a_n = a_{n-1} + 5, a_1 = 6$

33. $a_n = a_{n-1} - 10, a_1 = 30$ **34.** $a_n = a_{n-1} - 12, a_1 = 24$

35. Find the sum of the first 20 terms of the arithmetic sequence: $4, 10, 16, 22, \ldots$.

36. Find the sum of the first 25 terms of the arithmetic sequence: $7, 19, 31, 43, \ldots$.

37. Find the sum of the first 50 terms of the arithmetic sequence: $-10, -6, -2, 2, \ldots$.

38. Find the sum of the first 50 terms of the arithmetic sequence: $-15, -9, -3, 3, \ldots$.

39. Find $1 + 2 + 3 + 4 + \cdots + 100$, the sum of the first 100 natural numbers.

40. Find $2 + 4 + 6 + 8 + \cdots + 200$, the sum of the first 100 positive even integers.

41. Find the sum of the first 60 positive even integers.

42. Find the sum of the first 80 positive even integers.

43. Find the sum of the even integers between 21 and 45.

44. Find the sum of the odd integers between 30 and 54.

For Exercises 45–50, write out the first three terms and the last term. Then use the formula for the sum of the first n terms of an arithmetic sequence to find the indicated sum.

45. $\sum_{i=1}^{17} (5i + 3)$ **46.** $\sum_{i=1}^{20} (6i - 4)$ **47.** $\sum_{i=1}^{30} (-3i + 5)$

48. $\sum_{i=1}^{40} (-2i + 6)$ **49.** $\sum_{i=1}^{100} 4i$ **50.** $\sum_{i=1}^{50} (-4i)$

Practice Plus

Use the graphs of the arithmetic sequences $\{a_n\}$ and $\{b_n\}$ to solve Exercises 51–58.

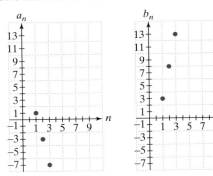

51. Find $a_{14} + b_{12}$. **52.** Find $a_{16} + b_{18}$.

53. If $\{a_n\}$ is a finite sequence whose last term is -83, how many terms does $\{a_n\}$ contain?

54. If $\{b_n\}$ is a finite sequence whose last term is 93, how many terms does $\{b_n\}$ contain?

(Continue using the graphs at the bottom of page 943 to solve Exercises 55–58.)

55. Find the difference between the sum of the first 14 terms of $\{b_n\}$ and the sum of the first 14 terms of $\{a_n\}$.

56. Find the difference between the sum of the first 15 terms of $\{b_n\}$ and the sum of the first 15 terms of $\{a_n\}$.

57. Write a linear function $f(x) = mx + b$, whose domain is the set of positive integers, that represents $\{a_n\}$.

58. Write a linear function $g(x) = mx + b$, whose domain is the set of positive integers, that represents $\{b_n\}$.

Use a system of two equations in two variables, a_1 and d, to solve Exercises 59–60.

59. Write a formula for the general term (the nth term) of the arithmetic sequence whose second term, a_2, is 4 and whose sixth term, a_6, is 16.

60. Write a formula for the general term (the nth term) of the arithmetic sequence whose third term, a_3, is 7 and whose eighth term, a_8, is 17.

Application Exercises

The bar graphs show changes that have taken place in the United States from 1970 to 2002 or 2003. Exercises 61–63 involve developing arithmetic sequences that model the data.

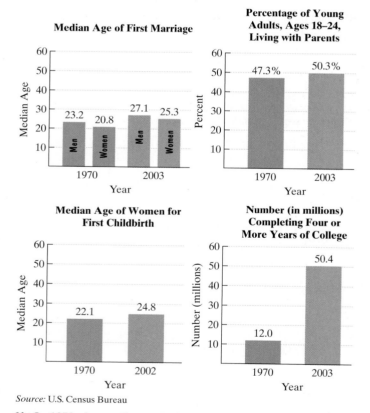

Changing Times in the U.S.

Source: U.S. Census Bureau

61. In 1970, the median age of first marriage for U.S. men was 23.2. On average, this age has increased by approximately 0.12 per year.

a. Write a formula for the nth term of the arithmetic sequence that describes the median age of first marriage for U.S. men n years after 1969.

b. What will be the median age of first marriage for U.S. men in 2009?

62. In 1970, the median age of women for first childbirth was 22.1. On average, this age has increased by approximately 0.08 per year.

a. Write a formula for the nth term of the arithmetic sequence that describes the median age for first childbirth for U.S. women n years after 1969.

b. What will be the median age for first childbirth for U.S. women in 2009?

63. Repeat Exercise 61 or 62 for another one of the changes from 1970 to 2003. Develop a formula for the nth term of the arithmetic sequence that describes the changing phenomenon n years after 1969. Then make a prediction about what might occur in 2009.

The bar graph shows the average cost of tuition, fees, and room and board at public and private colleges in the United States for four academic years. Use this information to solve Exercises 64–66.

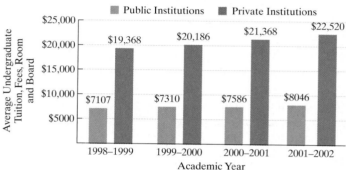

Source: U.S. Department of Education

64. a. Use the numbers shown in the bar graph to find the total cost of higher education at a private college for a four-year period, beginning with the 1998–1999 academic year and ending with the 2001–2002 academic year.

b. The model

$$a_n = 1064n + 18{,}201$$

describes the cost of higher education, a_n, at a private college in academic year n, where $n = 1$ corresponds to 1998–1999, $n = 2$ to 1999–2000, and so on. Use this model and the formula for S_n to find the total cost of a higher education at a private college for a four-year period, beginning with the 1998–1999 academic year and ending with the 2001–2002 academic year. How well does the model describe the actual sum that you obtained in part (a)?

65. a. Use the numbers shown in the bar graph to find the total cost of higher education at a public college for a four-year period, beginning with the 1998–1999 academic year and ending with the 2001–2002 academic year.

b. The model

$$a_n = 309n + 6739$$

describes the cost of higher education, a_n, at a public college in academic year n, where $n = 1$ corresponds to 1998–1999, $n = 2$ to 1999–2000, and so on. Use this model and the formula for S_n to find the total cost of a higher education at a public college for a four-year period, beginning with the 1998–1999 academic year and ending with the 2001–2002 academic year. How well does the model describe the actual sum that you obtained in part (a)?

66. Use one of the models in Exercises 64–65 and the formula for S_n to find the total cost of your undergraduate education. How well does the model describe your anticipated costs?

67. A company offers a starting yearly salary of $33,000 with raises of $2500 per year. Find the total salary over a ten-year period.

68. You are considering two job offers. Company A will start you at $19,000 a year and guarantee a raise of $2600 per year. Company B will start you at a higher salary, $27,000 a year, but will only guarantee a raise of $1200 per year. Find the total salary that each company will pay over a ten-year period. Which company pays the greater total amount?

69. A theater has 30 seats in the first row, 32 seats in the second row, increasing by 2 seats per row for a total of 26 rows. How many seats are there in the theater?

70. A section in a stadium has 20 seats in the first row, 23 seats in the second row, increasing by 3 seats each row for a total of 38 rows. How many seats are in this section of the stadium?

Writing in Mathematics

71. What is an arithmetic sequence? Give an example with your explanation.

72. What is the common difference in an arithmetic sequence?

73. Explain how to find the general term of an arithmetic sequence.

74. Explain how to find the sum of the first n terms of an arithmetic sequence without having to add up all the terms.

Technology Exercises

75. Use the $\boxed{\text{SEQ}}$ (sequence) capability of a graphing utility and the formula you obtained for a_n to verify the value you found for a_{20} in any five exercises from Exercises 23–34.

76. Use the capability of a graphing utility to calculate the sum of a sequence to verify any five of your answers to Exercises 45–50.

Critical Thinking Exercises

77. Give examples of two different arithmetic sequences whose fourth term, a_4, is 10.

78. In the sequence $21,700, 23,172, 24,644, 26,116, \ldots,$ which term is 314,628?

79. A *degree-day* is a unit used to measure the fuel requirements of buildings. By definition, each degree that the average daily temperature is below 65°F is 1 degree-day. For example, a temperature of 42°F constitutes 23 degree-days. If the average temperature on January 1 was 42°F and fell 2°F for each subsequent day up to and including January 10, how many degree-days are included from January 1 to January 10?

80. Show that the sum of the first n positive odd integers,

$$1 + 3 + 5 + \cdots + (2n - 1),$$

is n^2.

SECTION 10.3   *Geometric Sequences and Series*

Objectives

❶ Find the common ratio of a geometric sequence.

❷ Write terms of a geometric sequence.

❸ Use the formula for the general term of a geometric sequence.

❹ Use the formula for the sum of the first n terms of a geometric sequence.

❺ Find the value of an annuity.

❻ Use the formula for the sum of an infinite geometric series.

Here we are at the closing moments of a job interview. You're shaking hands with the manager. You managed to answer all the tough questions without losing your poise, and now you've been offered a job. As a matter of fact, your qualifications are so terrific that you've been offered two jobs—one just the day before, with a rival company in the same field! One company offers $30,000 the first year, with increases of 6% per year for four years after that. The other offers $32,000 the first year, with annual increases of 3% per year after that. Over a five-year period, which is the better offer?

If salary raises amount to a certain percent each year, the yearly salaries over time form a geometric sequence. In this section, we investigate geometric sequences and their properties. After studying the section, you will be in a position to decide which job offer to accept: You will know which company will pay you more over five years.

① Find the common ratio of a geometric sequence.

Geometric Sequences

Figure 10.5 shows a sequence in which the number of squares is increasing. From left to right, the number of squares is $1, 5, 25, 125$, and 625. In this sequence, each term after the first, 1, is obtained by multiplying the preceding term by a constant amount, namely 5. This sequence of increasing numbers of squares is an example of a *geometric sequence*.

Figure 10.5 A geometric sequence of squares

Definition of a Geometric Sequence

A **geometric sequence** is a sequence in which each term after the first is obtained by multiplying the preceding term by a fixed nonzero constant. The amount by which we multiply each time is called the **common ratio** of the sequence.

The common ratio, r, is found by dividing any term after the first term by the term that directly precedes it. In the following examples, the common ratio is found by dividing the second term by the first term, $\dfrac{a_2}{a_1}$.

Geometric sequence	Common ratio
$1, 5, 25, 125, 625, \ldots$	$r = \dfrac{5}{1} = 5$
$4, 8, 16, 32, 64, \ldots$	$r = \dfrac{8}{4} = 2$
$6, -12, 24, -48, 96, \ldots$	$r = \dfrac{-12}{6} = -2$
$9, -3, 1, -\dfrac{1}{3}, \dfrac{1}{9}, \ldots$	$r = \dfrac{-3}{9} = -\dfrac{1}{3}$

Study Tip

When the common ratio of a geometric sequence is negative, the signs of the terms alternate.

Figure 10.6 shows a partial graph of the first geometric sequence in our list. The graph forms a set of discrete points lying on the exponential function $f(x) = 5^{x-1}$. This illustrates that **a geometric sequence with a positive common ratio other than 1 is an exponential function whose domain is the set of positive integers.**

② Write terms of a geometric sequence.

How do we write out the terms of a geometric sequence when the first term and the common ratio are known? We multiply the first term by the common ratio to get the second term, multiply the second term by the common ratio to get the third term, and so on.

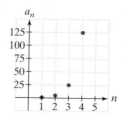

Figure 10.6 The graph of $\{a_n\} = 1, 5, 25, 125, \ldots$

EXAMPLE 1   Writing the Terms of a Geometric Sequence

Write the first six terms of the geometric sequence with first term 6 and common ratio $\frac{1}{3}$.

Solution   The first term is 6. The second term is $6 \cdot \frac{1}{3}$, or 2. The third term is $2 \cdot \frac{1}{3}$, or $\frac{2}{3}$. The fourth term is $\frac{2}{3} \cdot \frac{1}{3}$, or $\frac{2}{9}$, and so on. The first six terms are

$$6, 2, \frac{2}{3}, \frac{2}{9}, \frac{2}{27}, \text{ and } \frac{2}{81}.$$

Check Point 1   Write the first six terms of the geometric sequence with first term 12 and common ratio $\frac{1}{2}$.

③ Use the formula for the general term of a geometric sequence.

The General Term of a Geometric Sequence

Consider a geometric sequence whose first term is a_1 and whose common ratio is r. We are looking for a formula for the general term, a_n. Let's begin by writing the first six terms. The first term is a_1. The second term is $a_1 r$. The third term is $a_1 r \cdot r$, or $a_1 r^2$. The fourth term is $a_1 r^2 \cdot r$, or $a_1 r^3$, and so on. Starting with a_1 and multiplying each successive term by r, the first six terms are

$$a_1, \qquad a_1 r, \qquad a_1 r^2, \qquad a_1 r^3, \qquad a_1 r^4, \qquad a_1 r^5.$$

| a_1, first term | a_2, second term | a_3, third term | a_4, fourth term | a_5, fifth term | a_6, sixth term |

Compare the exponent on r and the subscript of a denoting the term number. Can you see that the exponent on r is 1 less than the subscript of a denoting the term number?

a_3: third term $= a_1 r^2$ a_4: third term $= a_1 r^3$

2 is one less than 3.   **3 is one less than 4.**

Thus, the formula for the nth term is

$$a_n = a_1 r^{n-1}.$$

$n - 1$ is one less than n.

General Term of a Geometric Sequence

The nth term (the general term) of a geometric sequence with first term a_1 and common ratio r is

$$a_n = a_1 r^{n-1}.$$

EXAMPLE 2   Using the Formula for the General Term of a Geometric Sequence

Study Tip

Be careful with the order of operations when evaluating

$$a_1 r^{n-1}.$$

First find r^{n-1}. Then multiply the result by a_1.

Find the eighth term of the geometric sequence whose first term is -4 and whose common ratio is -2.

Solution   To find the eighth term, a_8, we replace n in the formula with 8, a_1 with -4, and r with -2.

$$a_n = a_1 r^{n-1}$$
$$a_8 = -4(-2)^{8-1} = -4(-2)^7 = -4(-128) = 512$$

The eighth term is 512. We can check this result by writing the first eight terms of the sequence:

$$-4, 8, -16, 32, -64, 128, -256, 512.$$

Check Point **2** Find the seventh term of the geometric sequence whose first term is 5 and whose common ratio is -3.

In Chapter 3, we studied exponential functions of the form $f(x) = b^x$ and the explosive exponential growth of world population. In our next example, we consider Florida's geometric population growth. Because a geometric sequence is an exponential function whose domain is the set of positive integers, geometric and exponential growth mean the same thing.

EXAMPLE 3   Geometric Population Growth

The population of Florida from 1990 through 1997 is shown in the following table:

Year	1990	1991	1992	1993	1994	1995	1996	1997
Population in millions	12.94	13.20	13.46	13.73	14.00	14.28	14.57	14.86

a. Show that the population is increasing geometrically.
b. Write the general term for the geometric sequence describing population growth for Florida n years after 1989.
c. Estimate Florida's population, in millions, for the year 2000.

Solution

a. First, we divide the population for each year by the population in the preceding year.

$$\frac{13.20}{12.94} \approx 1.02, \quad \frac{13.46}{13.20} \approx 1.02, \quad \frac{13.73}{13.46} \approx 1.02$$

Continuing in this manner, we will keep getting approximately 1.02. This means that the population is increasing geometrically with $r \approx 1.02$. In this situation, the common ratio is the growth rate, indicating that the population of Florida in any year shown in the table is approximately 1.02 times the population the year before.

b. The sequence of Florida's population growth is

$$12.94, 13.20, 13.46, 13.73, 14.00, 14.28, 14.57, 14.86, \ldots.$$

Because the population is increasing geometrically, we can find the general term of this sequence using

$$a_n = a_1 r^{n-1}.$$

In this sequence, $a_1 = 12.94$ and [from part (a)] $r \approx 1.02$. We substitute these values into the formula for the general term. This gives the general term for the geometric sequence describing Florida's population n years after 1989.

$$a_n = 12.94(1.02)^{n-1}$$

c. We can use the formula for the general term, a_n, in part (b) to estimate Florida's population for the year 2000. The year 2000 is 11 years after 1989—that is, $2000 - 1989 = 11$. Thus, $n = 11$. We substitute 11 for n in $a_n = 12.94(1.02)^{n-1}$.

$$a_{11} = 12.94(1.02)^{11-1} = 12.94(1.02)^{10} \approx 15.77$$

The formula indicates that Florida had a population of approximately 15.77 million in the year 2000. According to the U.S. Census Bureau, Florida's population in 2000 was 15.98 million. Our geometric sequence models the actual population fairly well.

Geometric Population Growth

Economist Thomas Malthus (1766–1834) predicted that population growth would increase as a geometric sequence and food production would increase as an arithmetic sequence. He concluded that eventually population would exceed food production. If two sequences, one geometric and one arithmetic, are increasing, the geometric sequence will eventually overtake the arithmetic sequence, regardless of any head start that the arithmetic sequence might initially have.

Check Point 3 Write the general term for the geometric sequence

$$3, 6, 12, 24, 48, \ldots .$$

Then use the formula for the general term to find the eighth term.

The Sum of the First n Terms of a Geometric Sequence

④ Use the formula for the sum of the first n terms of a geometric sequence.

The sum of the first n terms of a geometric sequence, denoted by S_n, and called the **nth partial sum**, can be found without having to add up all the terms. Recall that the first n terms of a geometric sequence are

$$a_1, a_1 r, a_1 r^2, \ldots, a_1 r^{n-2}, a_1 r^{n-1}.$$

We proceed as follows:

$$S_n = a_1 + a_1 r + a_1 r^2 + \cdots + a_1 r^{n-2} + a_1 r^{n-1} \qquad \text{S_n is the sum of the first n terms of the sequence.}$$

$$r S_n = a_1 r + a_1 r^2 + a_1 r^3 + \cdots + a_1 r^{n-1} + a_1 r^n \qquad \text{Multiply both sides of the equation by r.}$$

$$S_n - r S_n = a_1 - a_1 r^n \qquad \text{Subtract the second equation from the first equation.}$$

$$S_n(1 - r) = a_1(1 - r^n) \qquad \text{Factor out S_n on the left and a_1 on the right.}$$

$$S_n = \frac{a_1(1 - r^n)}{1 - r}. \qquad \text{Solve for S_n by dividing both sides by $1 - r$ (assuming that $r \neq 1$).}$$

We have proved the following result:

Study Tip

If the common ratio is 1, the geometric sequence is

$$a_1, a_1, a_1, a_1, \ldots .$$

The sum of the first n terms of this sequence is na_1:

$$S_n = \underbrace{a_1 + a_1 + a_1 + \cdots + a_1}_{\text{There are n terms.}}$$

$$= na_1.$$

The Sum of the First n Terms of a Geometric Sequence

The sum, S_n, of the first n terms of a geometric sequence is given by

$$S_n = \frac{a_1(1 - r^n)}{1 - r}$$

in which a_1 is the first term and r is the common ratio ($r \neq 1$).

To find the sum of the terms of a geometric sequence, we need to know the first term, a_1, the common ratio, r, and the number of terms, n. The following examples illustrate how to use this formula.

EXAMPLE 4   Finding the Sum of the First n Terms of a Geometric Sequence

Find the sum of the first 18 terms of the geometric sequence: $2, -8, 32, -128, \ldots .$

Solution   To find the sum of the first 18 terms, S_{18}, we replace n in the formula with 18.

$$S_n = \frac{a_1(1 - r^n)}{1 - r}$$

$$S_{18} = \frac{a_1(1 - r^{18})}{1 - r}$$

The first term, a_1, is 2.   We must find r, the common ratio.

We can find the common ratio by dividing the second term of $2, -8, 32, -128, \ldots$ by the first term.

$$r = \frac{a_2}{a_1} = \frac{-8}{2} = -4$$

Now we are ready to find the sum of the first 18 terms of $2, -8, 32, -128, \ldots$.

$$S_n = \frac{a_1(1 - r^n)}{1 - r}$$

Use the formula for the sum of the first n terms of a geometric sequence.

$$S_{18} = \frac{2[1 - (-4)^{18}]}{1 - (-4)}$$

a_1 (the first term) $= 2$, $r = -4$, and $n = 18$ because we want the sum of the first 18 terms.

$$= -27,487,790,694$$

Use a calculator.

The sum of the first 18 terms is $-27,487,790,694$. Equivalently, this number is the 18th partial sum of the sequence $2, -8, 32, -128, \ldots$.

Check Point 4 Find the sum of the first nine terms of the geometric sequence: $2, -6, 18, -54, \ldots$.

EXAMPLE 5 Using S_n to Evaluate a Summation

Find the following sum: $\displaystyle\sum_{i=1}^{10} 6 \cdot 2^i$.

Solution Let's write out a few terms in the sum.

$$\sum_{i=1}^{10} 6 \cdot 2^i = 6 \cdot 2 + 6 \cdot 2^2 + 6 \cdot 2^3 + \cdots + 6 \cdot 2^{10}$$

Do you see that each term after the first is obtained by multiplying the preceding term by 2? To find the sum of the 10 terms ($n = 10$), we need to know the first term, a_1, and the common ratio, r. The first term is $6 \cdot 2$ or 12: $a_1 = 12$. The common ratio is 2.

Technology

To find

$$\sum_{i=1}^{10} 6 \cdot 2^i$$

on a graphing utility, enter

SUM SEQ $(6 \times 2^x, x, 1, 10, 1)$.

Then press ENTER .

```
sum(seq(6*2^X,X,
1,10,1))
            12276
```

$$S_n = \frac{a_1(1 - r^n)}{1 - r}$$

Use the formula for the sum of the first n terms of a geometric sequence.

$$S_{10} = \frac{12(1 - 2^{10})}{1 - 2}$$

a_1 (the first term) $= 12$, $r = 2$, and $n = 10$ because we are adding ten terms.

$$= 12,276$$

Use a calculator.

Thus,

$$\sum_{i=1}^{10} 6 \cdot 2^i = 12,276.$$

Check Point 5 Find the following sum: $\displaystyle\sum_{i=1}^{8} 2 \cdot 3^i$.

Some of the exercises in the previous exercise set involved situations in which salaries increased by a fixed amount each year. A more realistic situation is one in which salary raises increase by a certain percent each year. Example 6 shows how such a situation can be described using a geometric sequence.

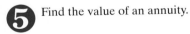

EXAMPLE 6   Computing a Lifetime Salary

A union contract specifies that each worker will receive a 5% pay increase each year for the next 30 years. One worker is paid $20,000 the first year. What is this person's total lifetime salary over a 30-year period?

Solution   The salary for the first year is $20,000. With a 5% raise, the second-year salary is computed as follows:

Salary for year 2 = $20{,}000 + 20{,}000(0.05) = 20{,}000(1 + 0.05) = 20{,}000(1.05)$.

Each year, the salary is 1.05 times what it was in the previous year. Thus, the salary for year 3 is 1.05 times $20{,}000(1.05)$, or $20{,}000(1.05)^2$. The salaries for the first five years are given in the table.

Yearly Salaries					
Year 1	Year 2	Year 3	Year 4	Year 5	. . .
20,000	$20{,}000(1.05)$	$20{,}000(1.05)^2$	$20{,}000(1.05)^3$	$20{,}000(1.05)^4$	. . .

The numbers in the bottom row form a geometric sequence with $a_1 = 20{,}000$ and $r = 1.05$. To find the total salary over 30 years, we use the formula for the sum of the first n terms of a geometric sequence, with $n = 30$.

$$S_n = \frac{a_1(1 - r^n)}{1 - r}$$

$$S_{30} = \frac{20{,}000[1 - (1.05)^{30}]}{1 - 1.05}$$

<small>Total salary over 30 years</small>

$$= \frac{20{,}000[1 - (1.05)^{30}]}{-0.05}$$

$$\approx 1{,}328{,}777 \qquad \text{Use a calculator.}$$

The total salary over the 30-year period is approximately $1,328,777.

Check Point 6   A job pays a salary of $30,000 the first year. During the next 29 years, the salary increases by 6% each year. What is the total lifetime salary over the 30-year period?

⑤ Find the value of an annuity.

Annuities

The compound interest formula

$$A = P(1 + r)^t$$

gives the future value, A, after t years, when a fixed amount of money, P, the principal, is deposited in an account that pays an annual interest rate r (in decimal form) compounded once a year. However, money is often invested in small amounts at periodic intervals. For example, to save for retirement, you might decide to place $1000 into an Individual Retirement Account (IRA) at the end of each year until you retire. An **annuity** is a sequence of equal payments made at equal time periods. An IRA is an example of an annuity.

Suppose P dollars is deposited into an account at the end of each year. The account pays an annual interest rate, r, compounded annually. At the end of the first year, the account contains P dollars. At the end of the second year, P dollars is deposited again. At the time of this deposit, the first deposit has received interest earned during the second year. The **value of the annuity** is the sum of all deposits made plus all interest paid. Thus, the value of the annuity after two years is

$$P + P(1 + r).$$

Deposit of P dollars at end of second year

First-year deposit of P dollars with interest earned for a year

The value of the annuity after three years is

$$P \quad + \quad P(1 + r) \quad + \quad P(1 + r)^2.$$

Deposit of P dollars at end of third year

Second-year deposit of P dollars with interest earned for a year

First-year deposit of P dollars with interest earned over two years

The value of the annuity after t years is

$$P + P(1 + r) + P(1 + r)^2 + P(1 + r)^3 + \cdots + P(1 + r)^{t-1}.$$

Deposit of P dollars at end of year t

First-year deposit of P dollars with interest earned over $t - 1$ years

This is the sum of the terms of a geometric sequence with first term P and common ratio $1 + r$. We use the formula

$$S_n = \frac{a_1(1 - r^n)}{1 - r}$$

to find the sum of the terms:

$$S_t = \frac{P[1 - (1 + r)^t]}{1 - (1 + r)} = \frac{P[1 - (1 + r)^t]}{-r} = \frac{P[(1 + r)^t - 1]}{r}.$$

This formula gives the value of an annuity after t years if interest is compounded once a year. We can adjust the formula to find the value of an annuity if equal payments are made at the end of each of n yearly compounding periods.

Value of an Annuity: Interest Compounded n Times per Year

If P is the deposit made at the end of each compounding period for an annuity at r percent annual interest compounded n times per year, the value, A, of the annuity after t years is

$$A = \frac{P\left[\left(1 + \dfrac{r}{n}\right)^{nt} - 1\right]}{\dfrac{r}{n}}.$$

EXAMPLE 7   Determining the Value of an Annuity

To save for retirement, you decide to deposit $1000 into an IRA at the end of each year for the next 30 years. If the interest rate is 10% per year compounded annually, find the value of the IRA after 30 years.

Solution   The annuity involves 30 year-end deposits of $P = \$1000$. The interest rate is 10%: $r = 0.10$. Because the deposits are made once a year and the interest is compounded once a year, $n = 1$. The number of years is 30: $t = 30$. We replace the variables in the formula for the value of an annuity with these numbers.

$$A = \dfrac{P\left[\left(1 + \dfrac{r}{n}\right)^{nt} - 1\right]}{\dfrac{r}{n}}$$

$$A = \dfrac{1000\left[\left(1 + \dfrac{0.10}{1}\right)^{1 \cdot 30} - 1\right]}{\dfrac{0.10}{1}} \approx 164{,}494$$

The value of the IRA at the end of 30 years is approximately \$164,494.

Check Point 7 If \$3000 is deposited into an IRA at the end of each year for 40 years and the interest rate is 10% per year compounded annually, find the value of the IRA after 40 years.

⑥ Use the formula for the sum of an infinite geometric series.

Geometric Series

An infinite sum of the form

$$a_1 + a_1 r + a_1 r^2 + a_1 r^3 + \cdots + a_1 r^{n-1} + \cdots$$

with first term a_1 and common ratio r is called an **infinite geometric series**. How can we determine which infinite geometric series have sums and which do not? We look at what happens to r^n as n gets larger in the formula for the sum of the first n terms of this series, namely

$$S_n = \dfrac{a_1(1 - r^n)}{1 - r}.$$

If r is any number between -1 and 1, that is, $-1 < r < 1$, the term r^n approaches 0 as n gets larger. For example, consider what happens to r^n for $r = \frac{1}{2}$:

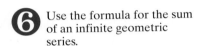

$$\left(\dfrac{1}{2}\right)^1 = \dfrac{1}{2} \quad \left(\dfrac{1}{2}\right)^2 = \dfrac{1}{4} \quad \left(\dfrac{1}{2}\right)^3 = \dfrac{1}{8} \quad \left(\dfrac{1}{2}\right)^4 = \dfrac{1}{16} \quad \left(\dfrac{1}{2}\right)^5 = \dfrac{1}{32} \quad \left(\dfrac{1}{2}\right)^6 = \dfrac{1}{64}.$$

> These numbers are approaching 0 as n gets larger.

Take another look at the formula for the sum of the first n terms of a geometric sequence.

$$S_n = \dfrac{a_1(1 - r^n)}{1 - r}$$

> If $-1 < r < 1$, r^n approaches 0 as n gets larger.

Let us replace r^n with 0 in the formula for S_n. This change gives us a formula for the sum of an infinite geometric series with a common ratio between -1 and 1.

The Sum of an Infinite Geometric Series

If $-1 < r < 1$ (equivalently, $|r| < 1$), then the sum of the infinite geometric series

$$a_1 + a_1 r + a_1 r^2 + a_1 r^3 + \cdots$$

in which a_1 is the first term and r is the common ratio is given by

$$S = \dfrac{a_1}{1 - r}.$$

If $|r| \geq 1$, the infinite series does not have a sum.

To use the formula for the sum of an infinite geometric series, we need to know the first term and the common ratio. For example, consider

First term, a_1, is $\frac{1}{2}$. $\quad\frac{1}{2} + \frac{1}{4} + \frac{1}{8} + \frac{1}{16} + \frac{1}{32} + \cdots$.

Common ratio, r, is $\dfrac{a_2}{a_1}$.

$r = \frac{1}{4} \div \frac{1}{2} = \frac{1}{4} \cdot 2 = \frac{1}{2}$

With $r = \dfrac{1}{2}$, the condition that $|r| < 1$ is met, so the infinite geometric series has a sum given by $S = \dfrac{a_1}{1 - r}$. The sum of the series is found as follows:

$$\frac{1}{2} + \frac{1}{4} + \frac{1}{8} + \frac{1}{16} + \frac{1}{32} + \cdots = \frac{a_1}{1 - r} = \frac{\frac{1}{2}}{1 - \frac{1}{2}} = \frac{\frac{1}{2}}{\frac{1}{2}} = 1.$$

Thus, the sum of the infinite geometric series is 1. Notice how this is illustrated in Figure 10.7. As more terms are included, the sum is approaching the area of one complete circle.

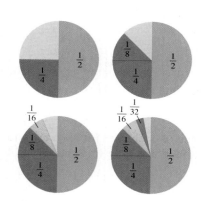

Figure 10.7 The sum $\frac{1}{2} + \frac{1}{4} + \frac{1}{8} + \frac{1}{16} + \frac{1}{32} + \cdots$ is approaching 1.

EXAMPLE 8 Finding the Sum of an Infinite Geometric Series

Find the sum of the infinite geometric series: $\frac{3}{8} - \frac{3}{16} + \frac{3}{32} - \frac{3}{64} + \cdots$.

Solution Before finding the sum, we must find the common ratio.

$$r = \frac{a_2}{a_1} = \frac{-\frac{3}{16}}{\frac{3}{8}} = -\frac{3}{16} \cdot \frac{8}{3} = -\frac{1}{2}$$

Because $r = -\frac{1}{2}$, the condition that $|r| < 1$ is met. Thus, the infinite geometric series has a sum.

$$S = \frac{a_1}{1 - r} \qquad \text{This is the formula for the sum of an infinite geometric series. Let } a_1 = \frac{3}{8} \text{ and } r = -\frac{1}{2}.$$

$$= \frac{\frac{3}{8}}{1 - \left(-\frac{1}{2}\right)} = \frac{\frac{3}{8}}{\frac{3}{2}} = \frac{3}{8} \cdot \frac{2}{3} = \frac{1}{4}$$

Thus, the sum of $\frac{3}{8} - \frac{3}{16} + \frac{3}{32} - \frac{3}{64} + \cdots$ is $\frac{1}{4}$. Put in an informal way, as we continue to add more and more terms, the sum is approximately $\frac{1}{4}$.

Check Point 8 Find the sum of the infinite geometric series: $3 + 2 + \frac{4}{3} + \frac{8}{9} + \cdots$.

We can use the formula for the sum of an infinite geometric series to express a repeating decimal as a fraction in lowest terms.

EXAMPLE 9 Writing a Repeating Decimal as a Fraction

Express $0.\overline{7}$ as a fraction in lowest terms.

Solution

$$0.\overline{7} = 0.7777\ldots = \frac{7}{10} + \frac{7}{100} + \frac{7}{1000} + \frac{7}{10{,}000} + \cdots$$

Observe that $0.\overline{7}$ is an infinite geometric series with first term $\frac{7}{10}$ and common ratio $\frac{1}{10}$. Because $r = \frac{1}{10}$, the condition that $|r| < 1$ is met. Thus, we can use our formula to find the sum. Therefore,

$$0.\overline{7} = \frac{a_1}{1-r} = \frac{\frac{7}{10}}{1-\frac{1}{10}} = \frac{\frac{7}{10}}{\frac{9}{10}} = \frac{7}{10} \cdot \frac{10}{9} = \frac{7}{9}.$$

An equivalent fraction for $0.\overline{7}$ is $\frac{7}{9}$.

Check Point 9 Express $0.\overline{9}$ as a fraction in lowest terms.

Infinite geometric series have many applications, as illustrated in Example 10.

EXAMPLE 10   Tax Rebates and the Multiplier Effect

A tax rebate that returns a certain amount of money to taxpayers can have a total effect on the economy that is many times this amount. In economics, this phenomenon is called the **multiplier effect**. Suppose, for example, that the government reduces taxes so that each consumer has $2000 more income. The government assumes that each person will spend 70% of this (= $1400). The individuals and businesses receiving this $1400 in turn spend 70% of it (= $980), creating extra income for other people to spend, and so on. Determine the total amount spent on consumer goods from the initial $2000 tax rebate.

Solution   The total amount spent is given by the infinite geometric series

$$1400 + 980 + 686 + \cdots.$$

$1400

70% is spent.

$980

70% is spent.

$686

70% of 1400   70% of 980

The first term is 1400: $a_1 = 1400$. The common ratio is 70%, or 0.7: $r = 0.7$. Because $r = 0.7$, the condition that $|r| < 1$ is met. Thus, we can use our formula to find the sum. Therefore,

$$1400 + 980 + 686 + \cdots = \frac{a_1}{1-r} = \frac{1400}{1-0.7} \approx 4667.$$

This means that the total amount spent on consumer goods from the initial $2000 rebate is approximately $4667.

Check Point 10 Rework Example 10 and determine the total amount spent on consumer goods with a $1000 tax rebate and 80% spending down the line.

EXERCISE SET 10.3

Practice Exercises

In Exercises 1–8, write the first five terms of each geometric sequence.

1. $a_1 = 5, \quad r = 3$

2. $a_1 = 4, \quad r = 3$

3. $a_1 = 20, \quad r = \frac{1}{2}$

4. $a_1 = 24, \quad r = \frac{1}{3}$

5. $a_n = -4a_{n-1}, \quad a_1 = 10$

6. $a_n = -3a_{n-1}, \quad a_1 = 10$

7. $a_n = -5a_{n-1}, \quad a_1 = -6$

8. $a_n = -6a_{n-1}, \quad a_1 = -2$

In Exercises 9–16, use the formula for the general term (the nth term) of a geometric sequence to find the indicated term of each sequence with the given first term, a_1, and common ratio, r.

9. Find a_8 when $a_1 = 6, r = 2$.

10. Find a_8 when $a_1 = 5, r = 3$.

11. Find a_{12} when $a_1 = 5, r = -2$.

12. Find a_{12} when $a_1 = 4, r = -2$.

13. Find a_{40} when $a_1 = 1000$, $r = -\frac{1}{2}$.

14. Find a_{30} when $a_1 = 8000$, $r = -\frac{1}{2}$.

15. Find a_8 when $a_1 = 1,000,000$, $r = 0.1$.

16. Find a_8 when $a_1 = 40,000$, $r = 0.1$.

In Exercises 17–24, write a formula for the general term (the nth term) of each geometric sequence. Then use the formula for a_n to find a_7, the seventh term of the sequence.

17. $3, 12, 48, 192, \ldots$

18. $3, 15, 75, 375, \ldots$

19. $18, 6, 2, \frac{2}{3}, \ldots$

20. $12, 6, 3, \frac{3}{2}, \ldots$

21. $1.5, -3, 6, -12, \ldots$

22. $5, -1, \frac{1}{5}, -\frac{1}{25}, \ldots$

23. $0.0004, -0.004, 0.04, -0.4, \ldots$

24. $0.0007, -0.007, 0.07, -0.7, \ldots$

Use the formula for the sum of the first n terms of a geometric sequence to solve Exercises 25–30.

25. Find the sum of the first 12 terms of the geometric sequence: $2, 6, 18, 54, \ldots$.

26. Find the sum of the first 12 terms of the geometric sequence: $3, 6, 12, 24, \ldots$.

27. Find the sum of the first 11 terms of the geometric sequence: $3, -6, 12, -24, \ldots$.

28. Find the sum of the first 11 terms of the geometric sequence: $4, -12, 36, -108, \ldots$.

29. Find the sum of the first 14 terms of the geometric sequence: $-\frac{3}{2}, 3, -6, 12, \ldots$.

30. Find the sum of the first 14 terms of the geometric sequence: $-\frac{1}{24}, \frac{1}{12}, -\frac{1}{6}, \frac{1}{3}, \ldots$.

In Exercises 31–36, find the indicated sum. Use the formula for the sum of the first n terms of a geometric sequence.

31. $\sum_{i=1}^{8} 3^i$

32. $\sum_{i=1}^{6} 4^i$

33. $\sum_{i=1}^{10} 5 \cdot 2^i$

34. $\sum_{i=1}^{7} 4(-3)^i$

35. $\sum_{i=1}^{6} \left(\frac{1}{2}\right)^{i+1}$

36. $\sum_{i=1}^{6} \left(\frac{1}{3}\right)^{i+1}$

In Exercises 37–44, find the sum of each infinite geometric series.

37. $1 + \frac{1}{3} + \frac{1}{9} + \frac{1}{27} + \cdots$

38. $1 + \frac{1}{4} + \frac{1}{16} + \frac{1}{64} + \cdots$

39. $3 + \frac{3}{4} + \frac{3}{4^2} + \frac{3}{4^3} + \cdots$

40. $5 + \frac{5}{6} + \frac{5}{6^2} + \frac{5}{6^3} + \cdots$

41. $1 - \frac{1}{2} + \frac{1}{4} - \frac{1}{8} + \cdots$

42. $3 - 1 + \frac{1}{3} - \frac{1}{9} + \cdots$

43. $\sum_{i=1}^{\infty} 8(-0.3)^{i-1}$

44. $\sum_{i=1}^{\infty} 12(-0.7)^{i-1}$

In Exercises 45–50, express each repeating decimal as a fraction in lowest terms.

45. $0.\overline{5} = \frac{5}{10} + \frac{5}{100} + \frac{5}{1000} + \frac{5}{10,000} + \cdots$

46. $0.\overline{1} = \frac{1}{10} + \frac{1}{100} + \frac{1}{1000} + \frac{1}{10,000} + \cdots$

47. $0.\overline{47} = \frac{47}{100} + \frac{47}{10,000} + \frac{47}{1,000,000} + \cdots$

48. $0.\overline{83} = \frac{83}{100} + \frac{83}{10,000} + \frac{83}{1,000,000} + \cdots$

49. $0.\overline{257}$

50. $0.\overline{529}$

In Exercises 51–56, the general term of a sequence is given. Determine whether the sequence is arithmetic, geometric, or neither. If the sequence is arithmetic, find the common difference; if it is geometric, find the common ratio.

51. $a_n = n + 5$

52. $a_n = n - 3$

53. $a_n = 2^n$

54. $a_n = \left(\frac{1}{2}\right)^n$

55. $a_n = n^2 + 5$

56. $a_n = n^2 - 3$

Practice Plus

In Exercises 57–62, let

$$\{a_n\} = -5, 10, -20, 40, \ldots,$$
$$\{b_n\} = 10, -5, -20, -35, \ldots,$$

and

$$\{c_n\} = -2, 1, -\frac{1}{2}, \frac{1}{4}, \ldots.$$

57. Find $a_{10} + b_{10}$.

58. Find $a_{11} + b_{11}$.

59. Find the difference between the sum of the first 10 terms of $\{a_n\}$ and the sum of the first 10 terms of $\{b_n\}$.

60. Find the difference between the sum of the first 11 terms of $\{a_n\}$ and the sum of the first 11 terms of $\{b_n\}$.

61. Find the product of the sum of the first 6 terms of $\{a_n\}$ and the sum of the infinite series containing all the terms of $\{c_n\}$.

62. Find the product of the sum of the first 9 terms of $\{a_n\}$ and the sum of the infinite series containing all the terms of $\{c_n\}$.

In Exercises 63–64, find a_2 and a_3 for each geometric sequence.

63. $8, a_2, a_3, 27$

64. $2, a_2, a_3, -54$

Application Exercises

Use the formula for the general term (the nth term) of a geometric sequence to solve Exercises 65–68.

In Exercises 65–66, suppose you save $1 the first day of a month, $2 the second day, $4 the third day, and so on. That is, each day you save twice as much as you did the day before.

65. What will you put aside for savings on the fifteenth day of the month?

66. What will you put aside for savings on the thirtieth day of the month?

67. A professional baseball player signs a contract with a beginning salary of $3,000,000 for the first year and an annual increase of 4% per year beginning in the second year. That is, beginning in year 2, the athlete's salary will be 1.04 times what it was in the previous year. What is the athlete's salary for year 7 of the contract? Round to the nearest dollar.

68. You are offered a job that pays $30,000 for the first year with an annual increase of 5% per year beginning in the second year. That is, beginning in year 2, your salary will be 1.05 times what it was in the previous year. What can you expect to earn in your sixth year on the job?

69. The population of California from 1990 through 1997 is shown in the following table.

Year	1990	1991	1992	1993
Population in millions	29.76	30.15	30.54	30.94

Year	1994	1995	1996	1997
Population in millions	31.34	31.75	32.16	32.58

a. Divide the population for each year by the population in the preceding year. Round to three decimal places and show that the population of California is increasing geometrically.

b. Write the general term of the geometric sequence describing population growth for California n years after 1989.

c. Use your model from part (b) to estimate California's population, in millions, for the year 2000. According to the U.S. Census Bureau, California's population in 2000 was 33.87 million. How well does your geometric sequence model the actual population?

70. The population of Texas from 1990 through 1997 is shown in the following table.

Year	1990	1991	1992	1993
Population in millions	16.99	17.35	17.71	18.08

Year	1994	1995	1996	1997
Population in millions	18.46	18.85	19.25	19.65

a. Divide the population for each year by the population in the preceding year. Round to three decimal places and show that the population of Texas is increasing geometrically.

b. Write the general term of the geometric sequence describing population growth for Texas n years after 1989.

c. Use your model from part (b) to estimate Texas's population in millions for the year 2000. According to the U.S. Census Bureau, Texas's population in 2000 was 20.85 million. How well does your geometric sequence model the actual population?

Use the formula for the sum of the first n terms of a geometric sequence to solve Exercises 71–76.

In Exercises 71–72, you save $1 the first day of a month, $2 the second day, $4 the third day, continuing to double your savings each day.

71. What will your total savings be for the first 15 days?

72. What will your total savings be for the first 30 days?

73. A job pays a salary of $24,000 the first year. During the next 19 years, the salary increases by 5% each year. What is the total lifetime salary over the 20-year period? Round to the nearest dollar.

74. You are investigating two employment opportunities. Company A offers $30,000 the first year. During the next four years, the salary is guaranteed to increase by 6% per year. Company B offers $32,000 the first year, with guaranteed annual increases of 3% per year after that. Which company offers the better total salary for a five-year contract? By how much? Round to the nearest dollar.

75. A pendulum swings through an arc of 20 inches. On each successive swing, the length of the arc is 90% of the previous length.

$$20, \quad 0.9(20), \quad 0.9^2(20), \quad 0.9^3(20), \ldots$$

1st swing   2nd swing   3rd swing   4th swing

After 10 swings, what is the total length of the distance the pendulum has swung?

76. A pendulum swings through an arc of 16 inches. On each successive swing, the length of the arc is 96% of the previous length.

$$16, \quad 0.96(16), \quad (0.96)^2(16), \quad (0.96)^3(16), \ldots$$

1st swing   2nd swing   3rd swing   4th swing

After 10 swings, what is the total length of the distance the pendulum has swung?

Use the formula for the value of an annuity to solve Exercises 77–80. Round answers to the nearest dollar.

77. To save for retirement, you decide to deposit $2500 into an IRA at the end of each year for the next 40 years. If the interest rate is 9% per year compounded annually, find the value of the IRA after 40 years.

78. You decide to deposit $100 at the end of each month into an account paying 8% interest compounded monthly to save for your child's education. How much will you save over 16 years?

79. You contribute $600 at the end of each quarter to a Tax Sheltered Annuity (TSA) paying 8% annual interest compounded quarterly. Find the value of the TSA after 18 years.

80. To save for a new home, you invest $500 per month in a mutual fund with an annual rate of return of 10% compounded monthly. How much will you have saved after four years?

Use the formula for the sum of an infinite geometric series to solve Exercises 81–83.

81. A new factory in a small town has an annual payroll of $6 million. It is expected that 60% of this money will be spent in the town by factory personnel. The people in the town who receive this money are expected to spend 60% of what they receive in the town, and so on. What is the total of all this spending, called the *total economic impact* of the factory, on the town each year?

82. How much additional spending will be generated by a $10 billion tax rebate if 60% of all income is spent?

83. If the shading process shown in the figure is continued indefinitely, what fractional part of the largest square will eventually be shaded?

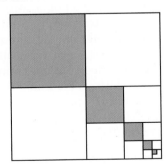

Writing in Mathematics

84. What is a geometric sequence? Give an example with your explanation.

85. What is the common ratio in a geometric sequence?

86. Explain how to find the general term of a geometric sequence.

87. Explain how to find the sum of the first n terms of a geometric sequence without having to add up all the terms.

88. What is an annuity?

89. What is the difference between a geometric sequence and an infinite geometric series?

90. How do you determine if an infinite geometric series has a sum? Explain how to find the sum of such an infinite geometric series.

91. Would you rather have $10,000,000 and a brand new BMW, or 1¢ today, 2¢ tomorrow, 4¢ on day 3, 8¢ on day 4, 16¢ on day 5, and so on, for 30 days? Explain.

92. For the first 30 days of a flu outbreak, the number of students on your campus who become ill is increasing. Which is worse: The number of students with the flu is increasing arithmetically or is increasing geometrically? Explain your answer.

Technology Exercises

93. Use the $\boxed{\text{SEQ}}$ (sequence) capability of a graphing utility and the formula you obtained for a_n to verify the value you found for a_7 in any three exercises from Exercises 17–24.

94. Use the capability of a graphing utility to calculate the sum of a sequence to verify any three of your answers to Exercises 31–36.

In Exercises 95–96, use a graphing utility to graph the function. Determine the horizontal asymptote for the graph of f and discuss its relationship to the sum of the given series.

95. Function   **Series**

$$f(x) = \frac{2\left[1 - \left(\frac{1}{3}\right)^x\right]}{1 - \frac{1}{3}} \qquad 2 + 2\left(\frac{1}{3}\right) + 2\left(\frac{1}{3}\right)^2 + 2\left(\frac{1}{3}\right)^3 + \cdots$$

96. Function   **Series**

$$f(x) = \frac{4[1 - (0.6)^x]}{1 - 0.6} \qquad 4 + 4(0.6) + 4(0.6)^2 + 4(0.6)^3 + \cdots$$

Critical Thinking Exercises

97. Which one of the following is true?
   a. The sequence $2, 6, 24, 120, \ldots$ is an example of a geometric sequence.
   b. The sum of the geometric series $\frac{1}{2} + \frac{1}{4} + \frac{1}{8} + \cdots + \frac{1}{512}$ can only be estimated without knowing precisely which terms occur between $\frac{1}{8}$ and $\frac{1}{512}$.
   c. $10 - 5 + \frac{5}{2} - \frac{5}{4} + \cdots = \dfrac{10}{1 - \frac{1}{2}}$
   d. If the nth term of a geometric sequence is $a_n = 3(0.5)^{n-1}$, the common ratio is $\frac{1}{2}$.

98. In a pest-eradication program, sterilized male flies are released into the general population each day. Ninety percent of those flies will survive a given day. How many flies should be released each day if the long-range goal of the program is to keep 20,000 sterilized flies in the population?

99. You are now 25 years old and would like to retire at age 55 with a retirement fund of $1,000,000. How much should you deposit at the end of each month for the next 30 years in an IRA paying 10% annual interest compounded monthly to achieve your goal? Round to the nearest dollar.

Group Exercise

100. Group members serve as a financial team analyzing the three options given to the professional baseball player described in the chapter opener on page 925. As a group, determine which option provides the most amount of money over the six-year contract and which provides the least. Describe one advantage and one disadvantage to each option.

CHAPTER 10
MID-CHAPTER CHECK POINT

What You Know: We learned that a sequence is a function whose domain is the set of positive integers. In an arithmetic sequence, each term after the first differs from the preceding term by a constant, the common difference, d. In a geometric sequence, each term after the first is obtained by multiplying the preceding term by a nonzero constant, the common ratio, r. We found the general term of arithmetic sequences $[a_n = a_1 + (n-1)d]$ and geometric sequences $[a_n = a_1 r^{n-1}]$ and used these formulas to find particular terms. We determined the sum of the first n terms of arithmetic sequences $\left[S_n = \frac{n}{2}(a_1 + a_n)\right]$ and geometric sequences $\left[S_n = \frac{a_1(1 - r^n)}{1 - r}\right]$. Finally, we determined the sum of an infinite geometric series,

$$a_1 + a_1 r + a_1 r^2 + a_1 r^3 + \cdots, \text{ if } -1 < r < 1 \left(S = \frac{a_1}{1 - r}\right).$$

In Exercises 1–4, write the first five terms of each sequence. Assume that d represents the common difference of an arithmetic sequence and r represents the common ratio of a geometric sequence.

1. $a_n = (-1)^{n+1}\dfrac{n}{(n-1)!}$ **2.** $a_1 = 5, d = -3$

3. $a_1 = 5, r = -3$ **4.** $a_1 = 3, a_n = -a_{n-1} + 4$

In Exercises 5–7, write a formula for the general term (the nth term) of each sequence. Then use the formula to find the indicated term.

5. $2, 6, 10, 14, \ldots; a_{20}$ **6.** $3, 6, 12, 24, \ldots; a_{10}$

7. $\dfrac{3}{2}, 1, \dfrac{1}{2}, 0, \ldots; a_{30}$

8. Find the sum of the first ten terms of the sequence:
$$5, 10, 20, 40, \ldots.$$

9. Find the sum of the first 50 terms of the sequence:
$$-2, 0, 2, 4, \ldots.$$

10. Find the sum of the first ten terms of the sequence:

$$-20, 40, -80, 160, \ldots.$$

11. Find the sum of the first 100 terms of the sequence:

$$4, -2, -8, -14, \ldots.$$

In Exercises 12–15, find each indicated sum.

12. $\sum_{i=1}^{4} (i + 4)(i - 1)$ **13.** $\sum_{i=1}^{50} (3i - 2)$

14. $\sum_{i=1}^{6} \left(\frac{3}{2}\right)^i$ **15.** $\sum_{i=1}^{\infty} \left(-\frac{2}{5}\right)^{i-1}$

16. Express $0.\overline{45}$ as a fraction in lowest terms.

17. Express the sum using summation notation. Use i for the index of summation.

$$\frac{1}{3} + \frac{2}{4} + \frac{3}{5} + \cdots + \frac{18}{20}$$

18. A skydiver falls 16 feet during the first second of a dive, 48 feet during the second second, 80 feet during the third second, 112 feet during the fourth second, and so on. Find the distance that the skydiver falls during the 15th second and the total distance the skydiver falls in 15 seconds.

19. If the average value of a house increases 10% per year, how much will a house costing $120,000 be worth in 10 years? Round to the nearest dollar.

SECTION 10.4 *Mathematical Induction*

Objectives

❶ Understand the principle of mathematical induction.

❷ Prove statements using mathematical induction.

After ten years of work, Princeton University's Andrew Wiles proved Fermat's Last Theorem.

Pierre de Fermat (1601–1665) was a lawyer who enjoyed studying mathematics. In a margin of one of his books, he claimed that no positive integers satisfy

$$x^n + y^n = z^n$$

if n is an integer greater than or equal to 3.

If $n = 2$, we can find positive integers satisfying $x^n + y^n = z^n$, or $x^2 + y^2 = z^2$:

$$3^2 + 4^2 = 5^2.$$

However, Fermat claimed that no positive integers satisfy

$$x^3 + y^3 = z^3, \quad x^4 + y^4 = z^4, \quad x^5 + y^5 = z^5,$$

and so on. Fermat claimed to have a proof of his conjecture, but added, "The margin of my book is too narrow to write it down." Some believe that he never had a proof and intended to frustrate his colleagues.

In 1994, 40-year-old Princeton math professor Andrew Wiles proved Fermat's Last Theorem using a principle called *mathematical induction*. In this section, you will learn how to use this powerful method to prove statements about the positive integers.

❶ Understand the principle of mathematical induction.

The Principle of Mathematical Induction

How do we prove statements using mathematical induction? Let's consider an example. We will prove a statement that appears to give a correct formula for the sum of the first n positive integers:

$$S_n: 1 + 2 + 3 + \cdots + n = \frac{n(n + 1)}{2}.$$

We can verify $S_n: 1 + 2 + 3 + \cdots + n = \dfrac{n(n+1)}{2}$ for, say, the first four positive integers. If $n = 1$, the statement S_1 is

| Take the first term on the left. | $1 \overset{?}{=} \dfrac{1(1+1)}{2}$ | Substitute 1 for n on the right. |

$$1 \overset{?}{=} \dfrac{1 \cdot 2}{2}$$

$$1 = 1 \checkmark. \qquad \text{This true statement shows that } S_1 \text{ is true.}$$

If $n = 2$, the statement S_2 is

| Add the first two terms on the left. | $1 + 2 \overset{?}{=} \dfrac{2(2+1)}{2}$ | Substitute 2 for n on the right. |

$$3 \overset{?}{=} \dfrac{2 \cdot 3}{2}$$

$$3 = 3 \checkmark. \qquad \text{This true statement shows that } S_2 \text{ is true.}$$

If $n = 3$, the statement S_3 is

| Add the first three terms on the left. | $1 + 2 + 3 \overset{?}{=} \dfrac{3(3+1)}{2}$ | Substitute 3 for n on the right. |

$$6 \overset{?}{=} \dfrac{3 \cdot 4}{2}$$

$$6 = 6 \checkmark. \qquad \text{This true statement shows that } S_3 \text{ is true.}$$

Finally, if $n = 4$, the statement S_4 is

| Add the first four terms on the left. | $1 + 2 + 3 + 4 \overset{?}{=} \dfrac{4(4+1)}{2}$ | Substitute 4 for n on the right. |

$$10 \overset{?}{=} \dfrac{4 \cdot 5}{2}$$

$$10 = 10 \checkmark. \qquad \text{This true statement shows that } S_4 \text{ is true.}$$

This approach does *not* prove that the given statement S_n is true for every positive integer n. The fact that the formula produces true statements for $n = 1, 2, 3,$ and 4 does not guarantee that it is valid for all positive integers n. Thus, we need to be able to verify the truth of S_n without verifying the statement for each and every one of the positive integers.

A legitimate proof of the given statement S_n involves a technique called **mathematical induction**.

The Principle of Mathematical Induction

Let S_n be a statement involving the positive integer n. If

1. S_1 is true, and
2. the truth of the statement S_k implies the truth of the statement S_{k+1}, for every positive integer k,

then the statement S_n is true for all positive integers n.

The principle of mathematical induction can be illustrated using an unending line of dominoes, as shown in Figure 10.8. If the first domino is pushed over, it knocks down the next, which knocks down the next, and so on, in a chain reaction. To topple all the dominoes in the infinite sequence, two conditions must be satisfied:

1. The first domino must be knocked down.
2. If the domino in position k is knocked down, then the domino in position $k + 1$ must be knocked down.

Figure 10.8 Falling dominoes illustrate the principle of mathematical induction.

If the second condition is not satisfied, it does not follow that all the dominoes will topple. For example, suppose the dominoes are spaced far enough apart so that a falling domino does not push over the next domino in the line.

The domino analogy provides the two steps that are required in a proof by mathematical induction.

The Steps in a Proof by Mathematical Induction

Let S_n be a statement involving the positive integer n. To prove that S_n is true for all positive integers n requires two steps.

Step 1   Show that S_1 is true.

Step 2   Show that if S_k is assumed to be true, then S_{k+1} is also true, for every positive integer k.

Notice that to prove S_n, we work only with the statements S_1, S_k, and S_{k+1}. Our first example provides practice in writing these statements.

EXAMPLE 1   Writing S_1, S_k, and S_{k+1}

For the given statement S_n, write the three statements S_1, S_k, and S_{k+1}.

a. $S_n: 1 + 2 + 3 + \cdots + n = \dfrac{n(n + 1)}{2}$

b. $S_n: 1^2 + 2^2 + 3^2 + \cdots + n^2 = \dfrac{n(n + 1)(2n + 1)}{6}$

Solution

a. We begin with

$$S_n: 1 + 2 + 3 + \cdots + n = \frac{n(n + 1)}{2}.$$

Write S_1 by taking the first term on the left and replacing n with 1 on the right.

$$S_1: 1 = \frac{1(1 + 1)}{2}$$

Write S_k by taking the sum of the first k terms on the left and replacing n with k on the right.

$$S_k: 1 + 2 + 3 + \cdots + k = \frac{k(k + 1)}{2}$$

Write S_{k+1} by taking the sum of the first $k + 1$ terms on the left and replacing n with $k + 1$ on the right.

$$S_{k+1}: 1 + 2 + 3 + \cdots + (k + 1) = \frac{(k + 1)[(k + 1) + 1]}{2}$$

$$S_{k+1}: 1 + 2 + 3 + \cdots + (k + 1) = \frac{(k + 1)(k + 2)}{2} \qquad \text{Simplify on the right.}$$

b. We begin with

$$S_n: 1^2 + 2^2 + 3^2 + \cdots + n^2 = \frac{n(n + 1)(2n + 1)}{6}.$$

Write S_1 by taking the first term on the left and replacing n with 1 on the right.

$$S_1: 1^2 = \frac{1(1 + 1)(2 \cdot 1 + 1)}{6}$$

Using S_n: $1^2 + 2^2 + 3^2 + \cdots + n^2 = \dfrac{n(n+1)(2n+1)}{6}$, we write S_k by taking the sum of the first k terms on the left and replacing n with k on the right.

$$S_k: 1^2 + 2^2 + 3^2 + \cdots + k^2 = \dfrac{k(k+1)(2k+1)}{6}$$

Write S_{k+1} by taking the sum of the first $k+1$ terms on the left and replacing n with $k+1$ on the right.

$$S_{k+1}: 1^2 + 2^2 + 3^2 + \cdots + (k+1)^2 = \dfrac{(k+1)[(k+1)+1][2(k+1)+1]}{6}$$

$$S_{k+1}: 1^2 + 2^2 + 3^2 + \cdots + (k+1)^2 = \dfrac{(k+1)(k+2)(2k+3)}{6} \qquad \text{Simplify on the right.}$$

Check Point 1 For the given statement S_n, write the three statements S_1, S_k, and S_{k+1}.

a. $2 + 4 + 6 + \cdots + 2n = n(n+1)$

b. $1^3 + 2^3 + 3^3 + \cdots + n^3 = \dfrac{n^2(n+1)^2}{4}$

Always simplify S_{k+1} before trying to use mathematical induction to prove that S_n is true. For example, consider

$$S_n: 1^2 + 3^2 + 5^2 + \cdots + (2n-1)^2 = \dfrac{n(2n-1)(2n+1)}{3}.$$

Begin by writing S_{k+1} as follows:

$$S_{k+1}: 1^2 + 3^2 + 5^2 + \cdots + [2(k+1)-1]^2$$

The sum of the first $k+1$ terms

$$= \dfrac{(k+1)[2(k+1)-1][2(k+1)+1]}{3}.$$

Replace n with $k+1$ on the right side of S_n.

Now simplify both sides of the equation.

$$S_{k+1}: 1^2 + 3^2 + 5^2 + \cdots + (2k+2-1)^2 = \dfrac{(k+1)(2k+2-1)(2k+2+1)}{3}$$

$$S_{k+1}: 1^2 + 3^2 + 5^2 + \cdots + (2k+1)^2 = \dfrac{(k+1)(2k+1)(2k+3)}{3}$$

② Prove statements using mathematical induction.

Proving Statements about Positive Integers Using Mathematical Induction

Now that we know how to find S_1, S_k, and S_{k+1}, let's see how we can use these statements to carry out the two steps in a proof by mathematical induction. In Examples 2 and 3, we will use the statements S_1, S_k, and S_{k+1} to prove each of the statements S_n that we worked with in Example 1.

EXAMPLE 2   Proving a Formula by Mathematical Induction

Use mathematical induction to prove that

$$1 + 2 + 3 + \cdots + n = \dfrac{n(n+1)}{2}$$

for all positive integers n.

Visualizing Summation Formulas

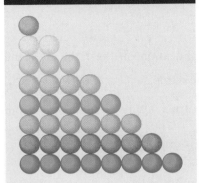

Finding the sum of consecutive positive integers leads to **triangular numbers** of the form $\dfrac{n(n + 1)}{2}$.

$\dfrac{n(n + 1)}{2}$

$n = 1$:
1

$\dfrac{n(n + 1)}{2}$

$n = 2$:
3

$\dfrac{n(n + 1)}{2}$

$n = 3$:
6

$\dfrac{n(n + 1)}{2}$

$n = 4$:
10

Solution

Step 1   Show that S_1 is true. Statement S_1 is

$$1 = \frac{1(1 + 1)}{2}.$$

Simplifying on the right, we obtain $1 = 1$. This true statement shows that S_1 is true.

Step 2   Show that if S_k is true, then S_{k+1} is true. Using S_k and S_{k+1} from Example 1(a), show that the truth of S_k,

$$1 + 2 + 3 + \cdots + k = \frac{k(k + 1)}{2}$$

implies the truth of S_{k+1},

$$1 + 2 + 3 + \cdots + (k + 1) = \frac{(k + 1)(k + 2)}{2}.$$

We will work with S_k. Because we assume that S_k is true, we add the next consecutive integer after k—namely, $k + 1$—to both sides.

$$1 + 2 + 3 + \cdots + k = \frac{k(k + 1)}{2}$$

This is S_k, which we assume is true.

$$1 + 2 + 3 + \cdots + k + (k + 1) = \frac{k(k + 1)}{2} + (k + 1)$$

Add $k + 1$ to both sides of the equation.

> We do not have to write this k because k is understood to be the integer that precedes $k + 1$.

$$1 + 2 + 3 + \cdots + (k + 1) = \frac{k(k + 1)}{2} + \frac{2(k + 1)}{2}$$

Write the right side with a common denominator of 2.

$$1 + 2 + 3 + \cdots + (k + 1) = \frac{(k + 1)}{2}(k + 2)$$

Factor out the common factor $\dfrac{k + 1}{2}$ on the right.

$$1 + 2 + 3 + \cdots + (k + 1) = \frac{(k + 1)(k + 2)}{2}$$

This final result is the statement S_{k+1}.

We have shown that if we assume that S_k is true and we add $k + 1$ to both sides of S_k, then S_{k+1} is also true. By the principle of mathematical induction, the statement S_n, namely,

$$1 + 2 + 3 + \cdots + n = \frac{n(n + 1)}{2}$$

is true for every positive integer n.

Check Point 2 Use mathematical induction to prove that
$$2 + 4 + 6 + \cdots + 2n = n(n + 1)$$
for all positive integers n.

EXAMPLE 3   Proving a Formula by Mathematical Induction

Use mathematical induction to prove that

$$1^2 + 2^2 + 3^2 + \cdots + n^2 = \frac{n(n + 1)(2n + 1)}{6}$$

for all positive integers n.

$S_n: 1^2 + 2^2 + 3^2 + \cdots + n^2$

$$= \frac{n(n+1)(2n+1)}{6}$$

The given statement (repeated)

Solution

Step 1   Show that S_1 is true. Statement S_1 is

$$1^2 = \frac{1(1+1)(2 \cdot 1 + 1)}{6}.$$

Simplifying, we obtain $1 = \dfrac{1 \cdot 2 \cdot 3}{6}$. Further simplification on the right gives the statement $1 = 1$. This true statement shows that S_1 is true.

Step 2   Show that if S_k is true, then S_{k+1} is true. Using S_k and S_{k+1} from Example 1(b), show that the truth of

$$S_k: 1^2 + 2^2 + 3^2 + \cdots + k^2 = \frac{k(k+1)(2k+1)}{6}$$

implies the truth of

$$S_{k+1}: 1^2 + 2^2 + 3^2 + \cdots + (k+1)^2 = \frac{(k+1)(k+2)(2k+3)}{6}.$$

We will work with S_k. Because we assume that S_k is true, we add the square of the next consecutive integer after k—namely, $(k+1)^2$—to both sides of the equation.

$1^2 + 2^2 + 3^2 + \cdots + k^2 = \dfrac{k(k+1)(2k+1)}{6}$ This is S_k, assumed to be true. We must work with this and show S_{k+1} is true.

$1^2 + 2^2 + 3^2 + \cdots + k^2 + (k+1)^2 = \dfrac{k(k+1)(2k+1)}{6} + (k+1)^2$ Add $(k+1)^2$ to both sides.

$1^2 + 2^2 + 3^2 + \cdots + (k+1)^2 = \dfrac{k(k+1)(2k+1)}{6} + \dfrac{6(k+1)^2}{6}$ It is not necessary to write k^2 on the left. Express the right side with the least common denominator, 6.

$= \dfrac{(k+1)}{6}[k(2k+1) + 6(k+1)]$ Factor out the common factor $\dfrac{k+1}{6}$.

$= \dfrac{(k+1)}{6}(2k^2 + 7k + 6)$ Multiply and combine like terms.

$= \dfrac{(k+1)}{6}(k+2)(2k+3)$ Factor $2k^2 + 7k + 6$.

$= \dfrac{(k+1)(k+2)(2k+3)}{6}$ This final statement is S_{k+1}.

We have shown that if we assume that S_k is true, and we add $(k+1)^2$ to both sides of S_k, then S_{k+1} is also true. By the principle of mathematical induction, the statement S_n, namely,

$$1^2 + 2^2 + 3^2 + \cdots + n^2 = \frac{n(n+1)(2n+1)}{6}$$

is true for every positive integer n.

Check Point 3   Use mathematical induction to prove that

$$1^3 + 2^3 + 3^3 + \cdots + n^3 = \frac{n^2(n+1)^2}{4}$$

for all positive integers n.

Example 4 illustrates how mathematical induction can be used to prove statements about positive integers that do not involve sums.

EXAMPLE 4   Using the Principle of Mathematical Induction

Prove that 2 is a factor of $n^2 + 5n$ for all positive integers n.

Solution

Step 1   Show that S_1 is true. Statement S_1 reads

$$\text{2 is a factor of } 1^2 + 5 \cdot 1.$$

Simplifying the arithmetic, the statement reads

$$\text{2 is a factor of 6.}$$

This statement is true: that is, $6 = 2 \cdot 3$. This shows that S_1 is true.

Step 2   Show that if S_k is true, then S_{k+1} is true. Let's write S_k and S_{k+1}:

$$S_k: \quad \text{2 is a factor of } k^2 + 5k.$$
$$S_{k+1}: \quad \text{2 is a factor of } (k+1)^2 + 5(k+1).$$

We can rewrite statement S_{k+1} by simplifying the algebraic expression in the statement as follows:

$$(k+1)^2 + 5(k+1) = k^2 + 2k + 1 + 5k + 5 = k^2 + 7k + 6.$$

Use the formula $(A + B)^2 = A^2 + 2AB + B^2$.

Statement S_{k+1} now reads

$$\text{2 is a factor of } k^2 + 7k + 6.$$

We need to use statement S_k—that is, 2 is a factor of $k^2 + 5k$—to prove statement S_{k+1}. We do this as follows:

$$k^2 + 7k + 6 = (k^2 + 5k) + (2k + 6) = (k^2 + 5k) + 2(k+3).$$

We assume that 2 is a factor of $k^2 + 5k$ because we assume S_k is true.

Factoring the last two terms shows that 2 is a factor of $2k + 6$.

The voice balloons show that 2 is a factor of $k^2 + 5k$ and of $2(k+3)$. Thus, if S_k is true, 2 is a factor of the sum $(k^2 + 5k) + 2(k+3)$, or of $k^2 + 7k + 6$. This is precisely statement S_{k+1}. We have shown that if we assume that S_k is true, then S_{k+1} is also true. By the principle of mathematical induction, the statement S_n, namely 2 is a factor of $n^2 + 5n$, is true for every positive integer n.

Check Point 4   Prove that 2 is a factor of $n^2 + n$ for all positive integers n.

EXERCISE SET 10.4

Practice Exercises

In Exercises 1–4, a statement S_n about the positive integers is given. Write statements S_1, S_2, and S_3, and show that each of these statements is true.

1. $S_n: 1 + 3 + 5 + \cdots + (2n - 1) = n^2$

2. $S_n: 3 + 4 + 5 + \cdots + (n + 2) = \dfrac{n(n + 5)}{2}$

3. $S_n:$ 2 is a factor of $n^2 - n$.

4. $S_n:$ 3 is a factor of $n^3 - n$.

In Exercises 5–10, a statement S_n about the positive integers is given. Write statements S_k and S_{k+1}, simplifying statement S_{k+1} completely.

5. $S_n: 4 + 8 + 12 + \cdots + 4n = 2n(n + 1)$

6. $S_n: 3 + 4 + 5 + \cdots + (n + 2) = \dfrac{n(n + 5)}{2}$

7. $S_n: 3 + 7 + 11 + \cdots + (4n - 1) = n(2n + 1)$

8. $S_n: 2 + 7 + 12 + \cdots + (5n - 3) = \dfrac{n(5n - 1)}{2}$

9. $S_n:$ 2 is a factor of $n^2 - n + 2$.

10. $S_n:$ 2 is a factor of $n^2 - n$.

In Exercises 11–24, use mathematical induction to prove that each statement is true for every positive integer n.

11. $4 + 8 + 12 + \cdots + 4n = 2n(n + 1)$

12. $3 + 4 + 5 + \cdots + (n + 2) = \dfrac{n(n + 5)}{2}$

13. $1 + 3 + 5 + \cdots + (2n - 1) = n^2$

14. $3 + 6 + 9 + \cdots + 3n = \dfrac{3n(n + 1)}{2}$

15. $3 + 7 + 11 + \cdots + (4n - 1) = n(2n + 1)$

16. $2 + 7 + 12 + \cdots + (5n - 3) = \dfrac{n(5n - 1)}{2}$

17. $1 + 2 + 2^2 + \cdots + 2^{n-1} = 2^n - 1$

18. $1 + 3 + 3^2 + \cdots + 3^{n-1} = \dfrac{3^n - 1}{2}$

19. $2 + 4 + 8 + \cdots + 2^n = 2^{n+1} - 2$

20. $\dfrac{1}{2} + \dfrac{1}{4} + \dfrac{1}{8} + \cdots + \dfrac{1}{2^n} = 1 - \dfrac{1}{2^n}$

21. $1 \cdot 2 + 2 \cdot 3 + 3 \cdot 4 + \cdots + n(n + 1) = \dfrac{n(n + 1)(n + 2)}{3}$

22. $1 \cdot 3 + 2 \cdot 4 + 3 \cdot 5 + \cdots + n(n + 2) = \dfrac{n(n + 1)(2n + 7)}{6}$

23. $\dfrac{1}{1 \cdot 2} + \dfrac{1}{2 \cdot 3} + \dfrac{1}{3 \cdot 4} + \cdots + \dfrac{1}{n(n + 1)} = \dfrac{n}{n + 1}$

24. $\dfrac{1}{2 \cdot 3} + \dfrac{1}{3 \cdot 4} + \dfrac{1}{4 \cdot 5} + \cdots + \dfrac{1}{(n + 1)(n + 2)} = \dfrac{n}{2n + 4}$

Practice Plus

In Exercises 25–34, use mathematical induction to prove that each statement is true for every positive integer n.

25. 2 is a factor of $n^2 - n$.

26. 2 is a factor of $n^2 + 3n$.

27. 6 is a factor of $n(n + 1)(n + 2)$.

28. 3 is a factor of $n(n + 1)(n - 1)$.

29. $\displaystyle\sum_{i=1}^{n} 5 \cdot 6^i = 6(6^n - 1)$

30. $\displaystyle\sum_{i=1}^{n} 7 \cdot 8^i = 8(8^n - 1)$

31. $n + 2 > n$

32. If $0 < x < 1$, then $0 < x^n < 1$.

33. $(ab)^n = a^n b^n$

34. $\left(\dfrac{a}{b}\right)^n = \dfrac{a^n}{b^n}$

Writing in Mathematics

35. Explain how to use mathematical induction to prove that a statement is true for every positive integer n.

36. Consider the statement S_n given by

$$n^2 - n + 41 \text{ is prime.}$$

Although $S_1, S_2, \ldots, S_{40}$ are true, S_{41} is false. Verify that S_{41} is false. Then describe how this is illustrated by the dominoes in the figure. What does this tell you about a pattern, or formula, that seems to work for several values of n?

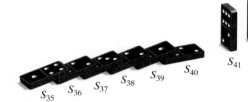

S_{35} S_{36} S_{37} S_{38} S_{39} S_{40} S_{41} S_{42}

Critical Thinking Exercises

Some statements are false for the first few positive integers, but true for some positive integer on. In these instances, you can prove S_n for $n \geq k$ by showing that S_k is true and that S_k implies S_{k+1}. Use this extended principle of mathematical induction to prove that each statement in Exercises 37–38 is true.

37. Prove that $n^2 > 2n + 1$ for $n \geq 3$. Show that the formula is true for $n = 3$ and then use step 2 of mathematical induction.

38. Prove that $2^n > n^2$ for $n \geq 5$. Show that the formula is true for $n = 5$ and then use step 2 of mathematical induction.

In Exercises 39–40, find S_1 through S_5 and then use the pattern to make a conjecture about S_n. Prove the conjectured formula for S_n by mathematical induction.

39. $S_n: \dfrac{1}{4} + \dfrac{1}{12} + \dfrac{1}{24} + \cdots + \dfrac{1}{2n(n + 1)} = ?$

40. $S_n: \left(1 - \dfrac{1}{2}\right)\left(1 - \dfrac{1}{3}\right)\left(1 - \dfrac{1}{4}\right)\cdots\left(1 - \dfrac{1}{n + 1}\right) = ?$

Group Exercise

41. Fermat's most notorious theorem, described in the section opener on page 959, baffled the greatest minds for more than three centuries. In 1994, after ten years of work, Princeton University's Andrew Wiles proved Fermat's Last Theorem. *People* magazine put him on its list of "the 25 most intriguing people of the year," the Gap asked him to model jeans, and Barbara Walters chased him for an interview. "Who's Barbara Walters?" asked the bookish Wiles, who had somehow gone through life without a television.

    Using the 1993 PBS documentary "Solving Fermat: Andrew Wiles" or information about Andrew Wiles on the Internet, research and present a group seminar on what Wiles did to prove Fermat's Last Theorem, problems along the way, and the role of mathematical induction in the proof.

Appendix

Taken from:
Precalculus, Third Edition, by Robert Blitzer
and Brian Emond

Appendix A

NOAA Data Sources

1. FISHERMAN'S REPORT, NOAA, National Marine Fisheries Service, Northeast Fisheries Science Center, Woods Hole, MA 02543. (www.nefsc.nmfs.gov/esb/fishermans%20reports.htm)

2. Observer Data Set from the U.S. Pelagic Longline Fishery, Statistics and Monitoring section of the *International Comission for the Conservation of Atlantic Tuna's* website. (www.iccat.es/)

3. Alaskan Observer data, Alaska Fisheries Science Center. (www.afsc.noaa.gov/)

Appendix B

The charts you will need for the East Coast Fisheries Reports are listed below and can nbe found at: (www.noaa.gov/)

1. Gulf of Maine
2. George's Banks
3. Nantucket Lightship
4. Hudson Canyon/Cape Hatteras

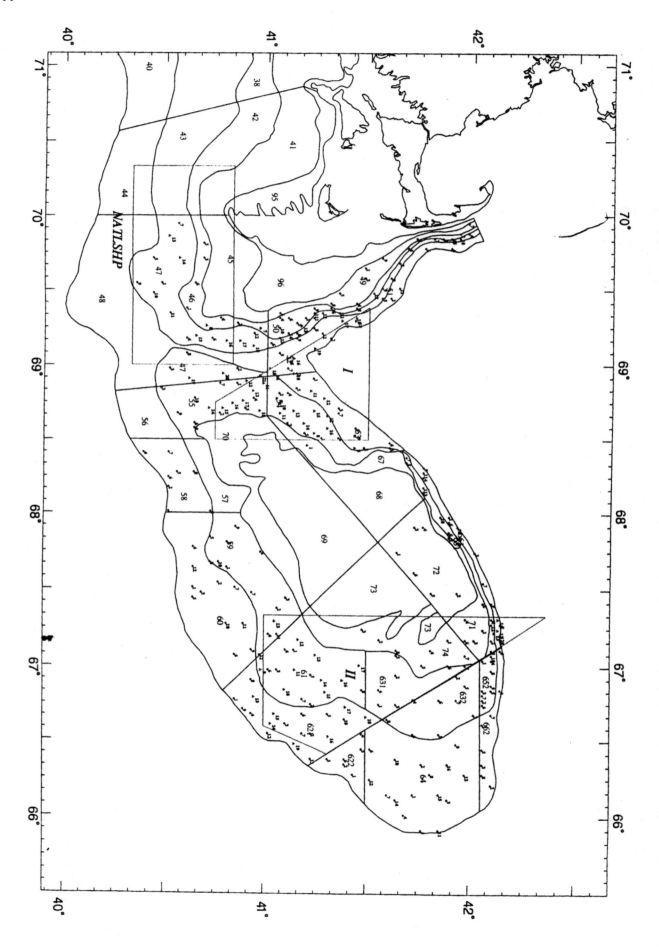

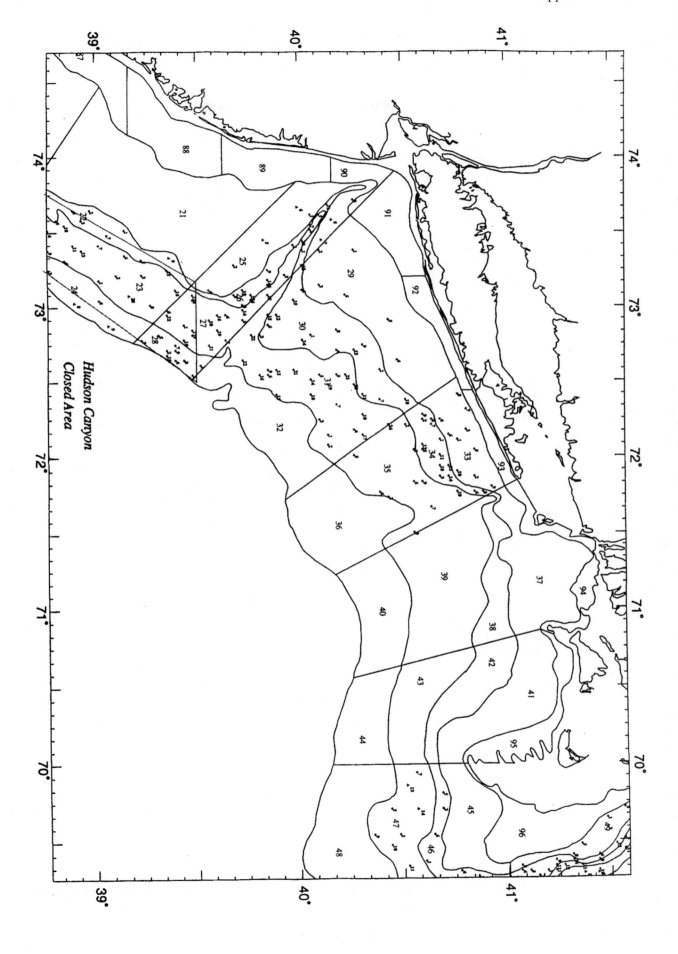

Hudson Canyon
Closed Area

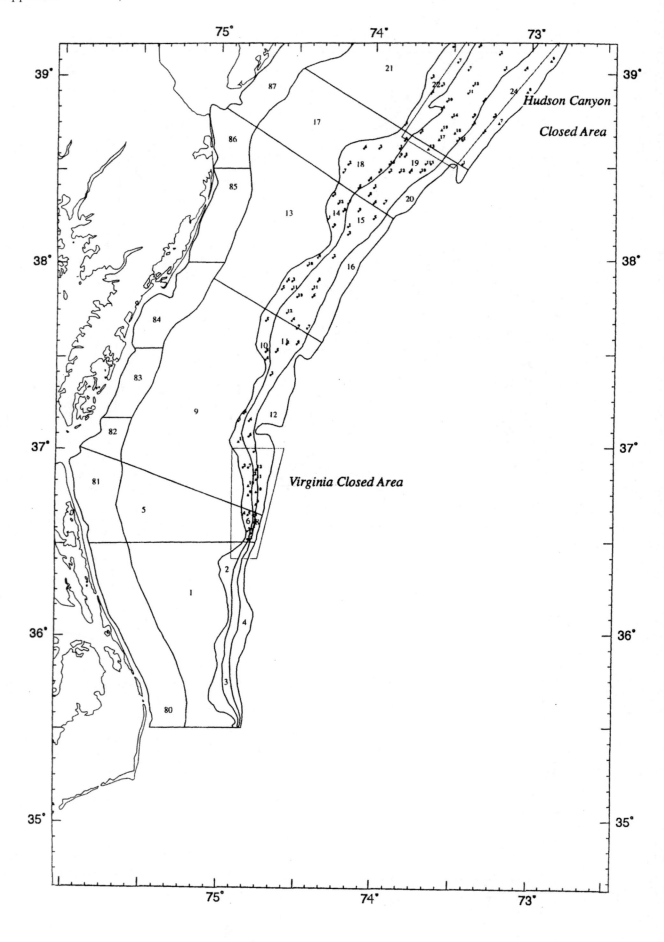

Appendix
Where Did That Come From? Selected Proofs

Properties of Logarithms

The Product Rule

Let b, M, and N be positive real numbers with $b \neq 1$.

$$\log_b(MN) = \log_b M + \log_b N$$

Proof

We begin by letting $\log_b M = R$ and $\log_b N = S$.
Now we write each logarithm in exponential form.

$$\log_b M = R \quad \text{means} \quad b^R = M.$$
$$\log_b N = S \quad \text{means} \quad b^S = N.$$

By substituting and using a property of exponents, we see that

$$MN = b^R b^S = b^{R+S}.$$

Now we change $MN = b^{R+S}$ to logarithmic form.

$$MN = b^{R+S} \quad \text{means} \quad \log_b(MN) = R + S.$$

Finally, substituting $\log_b M$ for R and $\log_b N$ for S gives us

$$\log_b(MN) = \log_b M + \log_b N,$$

the property that we wanted to prove.

The quotient and power rules for logarithms are proved using similar procedures.

The Change-of-Base Property

For any logarithmic bases a and b, and any positive number M,

$$\log_b M = \frac{\log_a M}{\log_a b}.$$

Proof

To prove the change-of-base property, we let x equal the logarithm on the left side:

$$\log_b M = x.$$

Now we rewrite this logarithm in exponential form.

$$\log_b M = x \quad \text{means} \quad b^x = M.$$

915

Because b^x and M are equal, the logarithms with base a for each of these expressions must be equal. This means that

$$\log_a b^x = \log_a M$$

$$x \log_a b = \log_a M \qquad \text{Apply the power rule for logarithms on the left side.}$$

$$x = \frac{\log_a M}{\log_a b} \qquad \text{Solve for x by dividing both sides by } \log_a b.$$

In our first step we let x equal $\log_b M$. Replacing x on the left side by $\log_b M$ gives us

$$\log_b M = \frac{\log_a M}{\log_a b},$$

which is the change-of-base property.

SECTION 6.2   *The Law of Cosines*

Heron's Formula for the Area of a Triangle

The area of a triangle with sides a, b, and c is

$$\text{Area} = \sqrt{s(s-a)(s-b)(s-c)},$$

where s is one-half its perimeter: $s = \frac{1}{2}(a+b+c)$.

Proof

The proof of Heron's formula begins with a half-angle formula and the Law of Cosines.

$$\cos \frac{C}{2} = \sqrt{\frac{1 + \cos C}{2}} = \sqrt{\frac{1 + \dfrac{a^2 + b^2 - c^2}{2ab}}{2}} \qquad \begin{array}{l} \text{This is the Law of Cosines} \\ c^2 = a^2 + b^2 - 2ab \cos C \\ \text{solved for cos } C. \end{array}$$

$$= \sqrt{\frac{a^2 + 2ab + b^2 - c^2}{4ab}} = \sqrt{\frac{(a+b)^2 - c^2}{4ab}} = \sqrt{\frac{(a+b+c)(a+b-c)}{4ab}}$$

Multiply the numerator and denominator of the radicand by 2ab.   *Factor $a^2 + 2ab + b^2$.*   *Factor the numerator as the difference of two squares.*

We now introduce the expression for one-half the perimeter: $s = \frac{1}{2}(a+b+c)$. We replace $a + b + c$ in the numerator by $2s$. We also find an expression for $a + b - c$ as follows:

$$a + b - c = a + b + c - 2c = 2s - 2c = 2(s-c).$$

Thus,

$$\cos \frac{C}{2} = \sqrt{\frac{(a+b+c)(a+b-c)}{4ab}} = \sqrt{\frac{2s \cdot 2(s-c)}{4ab}} = \sqrt{\frac{s(s-c)}{ab}}.$$

In a similar manner, we obtain

$$\sin \frac{C}{2} = \sqrt{\frac{1 - \cos C}{2}} = \sqrt{\frac{(s-a)(s-b)}{ab}}.$$

From our work in Section 6.1, we know that the area of a triangle is one-half the product of the length of two sides times the sine of their included angle.

$$\text{Area} = \frac{1}{2}ab \sin C$$

$$= \frac{1}{2}ab \cdot 2 \sin \frac{C}{2} \cos \frac{C}{2} \qquad\qquad \sin C = \sin 2\frac{C}{2} = 2 \sin \frac{C}{2} \cos \frac{C}{2}$$

$$= ab\sqrt{\frac{(s-a)(s-b)}{ab}}\sqrt{\frac{s(s-c)}{ab}} \qquad \text{Use the expressions for } \sin \frac{C}{2} \text{ and } \cos \frac{C}{2} \text{ on page A2.}$$

$$= ab\frac{\sqrt{s(s-a)(s-b)(s-c)}}{\sqrt{a^2b^2}} \qquad\qquad \text{Multiply the radicands.}$$

$$= \sqrt{s(s-a)(s-b)(s-c)} \qquad\qquad \text{Simplify: } \frac{ab}{\sqrt{a^2b^2}} = \frac{ab}{ab} = 1.$$

SECTION 6.5 Complex Numbers in Polar Form; DeMoivre's Theorem

The Quotient of Two Complex Numbers in Polar Form

Let $z_1 = r_1(\cos \theta_1 + i \sin \theta_1)$ and $z_2 = r_2(\cos \theta_2 + i \sin \theta_2)$ be two complex numbers in polar form. Their quotient, $\dfrac{z_1}{z_2}$, is

$$\frac{z_1}{z_2} = \frac{r_1}{r_2}[\cos(\theta_1 - \theta_2) + i \sin(\theta_1 - \theta_2)].$$

Proof

We begin by multiplying the numerator and denominator of the quotient, $\dfrac{z_1}{z_2}$, by the conjugate of the denominator. Then we simplify the quotient using the difference formulas for sine and cosine.

$$\frac{z_1}{z_2} = \frac{r_1(\cos \theta_1 + i \sin \theta_1)}{r_2(\cos \theta_2 + i \sin \theta_2)} \qquad\qquad \text{This is the given quotient.}$$

$$= \frac{r_1(\cos \theta_1 + i \sin \theta_1)(\cos \theta_2 - i \sin \theta_2)}{r_2(\cos \theta_2 + i \sin \theta_2)(\cos \theta_2 - i \sin \theta_2)} \qquad \begin{array}{l}\text{Multiply the numerator and denominator by the}\\ \text{conjugate of the denominator. Recall that the}\\ \text{conjugate of } a + bi \text{ is } a - bi.\end{array}$$

$$= \frac{r_1(\cos \theta_1 + i \sin \theta_1)(\cos \theta_2 - i \sin \theta_2)}{r_2(\cos^2 \theta_2 + \sin^2 \theta_2)} \qquad \text{Multiply the conjugates in the denominator.}$$

$$= \frac{r_1(\cos \theta_1 + i \sin \theta_1)(\cos \theta_2 - i \sin \theta_2)}{r_2} \qquad \begin{array}{l}\text{Use a Pythagorean identity:}\\ \cos^2 \theta_2 + \sin^2 \theta_2 = 1.\end{array}$$

$$= \frac{r_1}{r_2}(\cos \theta_1 \cos \theta_2 - i \cos \theta_1 \sin \theta_2 + i \sin \theta_1 \cos \theta_2 - i^2 \sin \theta_1 \sin \theta_2) \qquad \text{Use the FOIL method.}$$

$$= \frac{r_1}{r_2}[\cos \theta_1 \cos \theta_2 + i(\sin \theta_1 \cos \theta_2 - \cos \theta_1 \sin \theta_2) - i^2 \sin \theta_1 \sin \theta_2] \qquad \text{Factor } i \text{ from the second and third terms.}$$

$$= \frac{r_1}{r_2}[\cos \theta_1 \cos \theta_2 + i(\sin \theta_1 \cos \theta_2 - \cos \theta_1 \sin \theta_2) - (-1) \sin \theta_1 \sin \theta_2] \qquad i^2 = -1.$$

$$= \frac{r_1}{r_2}\Big[\underbrace{\cos \theta_1 \cos \theta_2 + \sin \theta_1 \sin \theta_2}_{\text{This is } \cos(\theta_1 - \theta_2).} + i(\underbrace{\sin \theta_1 \cos \theta_2 - \cos \theta_1 \sin \theta_2}_{\text{This is } \sin(\theta_1 - \theta_2).})\Big] \qquad \text{Rearrange terms.}$$

$$= \frac{r_1}{r_2}[\cos(\theta_1 - \theta_2) + i \sin(\theta_1 - \theta_2)]$$

SECTION 6.7 *The Dot Product*

Properties of the Dot Product

If **u**, **v**, and **w** are vectors, and c is a scalar, then

1. $\mathbf{u} \cdot \mathbf{v} = \mathbf{v} \cdot \mathbf{u}$
2. $\mathbf{u} \cdot (\mathbf{v} + \mathbf{w}) = \mathbf{u} \cdot \mathbf{v} + \mathbf{u} \cdot \mathbf{w}$
3. $\mathbf{0} \cdot \mathbf{v} = 0$
4. $\mathbf{v} \cdot \mathbf{v} = \|\mathbf{v}\|^2$
5. $(c\mathbf{u}) \cdot \mathbf{v} = c(\mathbf{u} \cdot \mathbf{v}) = \mathbf{u} \cdot (c\mathbf{v})$

Proof

To prove the second property, let

$$\mathbf{u} = u_1\mathbf{i} + u_2\mathbf{j}, \quad \mathbf{v} = v_1\mathbf{i} + v_2\mathbf{j}, \quad \text{and} \quad \mathbf{w} = w_1\mathbf{i} + w_2\mathbf{j}.$$

Then,

$$
\begin{aligned}
\mathbf{u} \cdot (\mathbf{v} + \mathbf{w}) &= (u_1\mathbf{i} + u_2\mathbf{j}) \cdot [(v_1\mathbf{i} + v_2\mathbf{j}) + (w_1\mathbf{i} + w_2\mathbf{j})] && \text{These are the given vectors.} \\
&= (u_1\mathbf{i} + u_2\mathbf{j}) \cdot [(v_1 + w_1)\mathbf{i} + (v_2 + w_2)\mathbf{j}] && \text{Add horizontal components and add vertical components.} \\
&= u_1(v_1 + w_1) + u_2(v_2 + w_2) && \text{Multiply horizontal components and multiply vertical components.} \\
&= u_1 v_1 + u_1 w_1 + u_2 v_2 + u_2 w_2 && \text{Use the distributive property.} \\
&= u_1 v_1 + u_2 v_2 + u_1 w_1 + u_2 w_2 && \text{Rearrange terms.}
\end{aligned}
$$

> This is the dot product of **u** and **v**.

> This is the dot product of **u** and **w**.

$$= \mathbf{u} \cdot \mathbf{v} + \mathbf{u} \cdot \mathbf{w}.$$

To prove the third property, let

$$\mathbf{0} = 0\mathbf{i} + 0\mathbf{j} \quad \text{and} \quad \mathbf{v} = v_1\mathbf{i} + v_2\mathbf{j}.$$

Then,

$$
\begin{aligned}
\mathbf{0} \cdot \mathbf{v} &= (0\mathbf{i} + 0\mathbf{j}) \cdot (v_1\mathbf{i} + v_2\mathbf{j}) && \text{These are the given vectors.} \\
&= 0 \cdot v_1 + 0 \cdot v_2 && \text{Multiply horizontal components and multiply vertical components.} \\
&= 0 + 0 \\
&= 0.
\end{aligned}
$$

To prove the first part of the fifth property, let

$$\mathbf{u} = u_1\mathbf{i} + u_2\mathbf{j} \quad \text{and} \quad \mathbf{v} = v_1\mathbf{i} + v_2\mathbf{j}.$$

Then,

$$
\begin{aligned}
(c\mathbf{u}) \cdot \mathbf{v} &= [c(u_1\mathbf{i} + u_2\mathbf{j})] \cdot (v_1\mathbf{i} + v_2\mathbf{j}) && \text{These are the given vectors.} \\
&= (cu_1\mathbf{i} + cu_2\mathbf{j}) \cdot (v_1\mathbf{i} + v_2\mathbf{j}) && \text{Multiply each component of } u_1\mathbf{i} + u_2\mathbf{j} \text{ by } c. \\
&= cu_1 v_1 + cu_2 v_2 && \text{Multiply horizontal components and multiply vertical components.} \\
&= c(u_1 v_1 + u_2 v_2) && \text{Factor out } c \text{ from both terms.}
\end{aligned}
$$

> This is the dot product of **u** and **v**.

$$= c(\mathbf{u} \cdot \mathbf{v})$$

Answers

Taken from:
Intermediate Algebra, Third Edition, by Elayn Martin-Gay
and
Precalculus, Third Edition, by Robert Blitzer

ANSWERS TO SELECTED EXERCISES

CHAPTER 1   Real Numbers and Algebraic Expressions

Exercise Set 1.2   1. $\{1, 2, 3, 4, 5\}$ **3.** $\{11, 12, 13, 14, 15, 16\}$ **5.** $\{0\}$ **7.** $\{0, 2, 4, 6, 8\}$ **9.** $\{3, 0, \sqrt{36}\}$ **11.** $\{3, \sqrt{36}\}$ **13.** $\{\sqrt{7}\}$
15. $\in$ **17.** $\notin$ **19.** $\notin$ **21.** true   **23.** true   **25.** false   **27.** true   **29.** true   **31.** false   **33.** true   **35.** true   **37.** false
39. $2x$ **41.** $x - 10$ **43.** $x + 2$ **45.** $\frac{x}{11}$ or $x \div 11$ **47.** $x - 4$ **49.** $x + 2.3$ or $x + 2\frac{3}{10}$ **51.** $1\frac{1}{3} - x$ **53.** $9x$ **55.** $x + 9$
57. $2x + 5$ **59.** $12 - 3x$ **61.** $1 + 2x$ **63.** $5x - 10$ **65.** $\frac{5}{4 - x}$ **67.** $2(x + 3)$ **69.** answers may vary   **71.** answers may vary
73. 0 **75.** $5.4; 2.1; 1.7; 2.6; 1.4; 0.7$ **77.** answers may vary

Exercise Set 1.3   1. $10 + x = -12$ **3.** $2x + 5 = -14$ **5.** $\frac{n}{5} = 4n$ **7.** $z - \frac{1}{2} = \frac{1}{2}z$ **9.** $>$ **11.** $>$ **13.** $<$
15. $=$ **17.** $>$ **19.** $<$ **21.** $<$ **23.** $<$ **25.** true   **27.** true   **29.** false   **31.** true   **33.** -9 **35.** 6.2
37. $-\frac{4}{7}$ **39.** $\frac{5}{11}$ **41.** 0 **43.** $\frac{1}{5}$ **45.** $-\frac{1}{8}$ **47.** -4 **49.** undefined   **51.** $\frac{8}{7}$ **53.** $-25; \frac{1}{25}$ **55.** $-10; -\frac{1}{10}$ **57.** $\frac{1}{7}; -7$
59. 0; undefined   **61.** $\frac{16}{19}; -\frac{16}{19}$ **63.** $y + 7x$ **65.** $w \cdot z$ **67.** $\frac{x}{5} \cdot \frac{1}{3}$ **69.** $(5 \cdot 7)x$ **71.** $x + (1.2 + y)$ **73.** $14(z \cdot y)$ **75.** $3x + 15$
77. $4z - 24$ **79.** $16a + 8b$ **81.** $6xy - 24x$ **83.** $0.8x + 2y$ **85.** $2x - \frac{9}{2}y$ **87.** $12x + 10y + 4z$ **89.** $6 + 3x$ **91.** 0 **93.** 7
95. $(10 \cdot 2)y$ **97.** $3x + 12$ **99.** $8y + 4$ **101.** zero; answers may vary   **103.** no; answers may vary   **105.** answers may vary

Exercise Set 1.4   1. 2 **3.** 4 **5.** 0 **7.** -3 **9.** $-\frac{2}{9}$ **11.** 5 **13.** -24 **15.** -11 **17.** -4 **19.** $\frac{4}{3}$ **21.** -2 **23.** -21
25. $-\frac{1}{2}$ **27.** -6 **29.** -60 **31.** 80 **33.** 0 **35.** 0 **37.** -3 **39.** 3 **41.** $-\frac{1}{6}$ **43.** 0.56 **45.** -7 **47.** -8 **49.** -49
51. 36 **53.** -8 **55.** $-\frac{1}{27}$ **57.** 7 **59.** 8 **61.** $\frac{1}{3}$ **63.** 4 **65.** $\frac{2}{5}$ **67.** 3 **69.** -12 **71.** -18 **73.** -72 **75.** 121
77. -8 **79.** -3 **81.** $\frac{1}{21}$ **83.** 7.2 **85.** 15 **87.** -12.2 **89.** 0 **91.** undefined   **93.** $\frac{1}{4}$ **95.** $-\frac{3}{7}$ **97.** 4 **99.** 5
101. 3 **103.** 2 **105.** $-\frac{5}{27}$ **107.** -1 **109.** $-\frac{3}{2}$ **111.** -1 **113.** -22 **115.** 35 **117.** 0 **119.** -256 **121.** answers may vary
123. true   **125.** $\frac{13}{35}$ **127.** 4205 m   **129.** b   **131.** d   **133.** yes; two players have 6 points each (the third player has 0 points);
or two players have 5 points each (the third player has 2 points)   **135.** 16.5227 **137.** 4.4272 **139.** 17% **141.** 40%

Integrated Review   1. $\{1, 2, 3\}$ **2.** $\{1, 3, 5\}$ **3.** $\{8, 10, 12, \ldots\}$ **4.** $\{11, 12, 13, 14\}$ **5.** $2(x - 3)$ **6.** $\frac{6}{x + 10}$ **7.** $>$ **8.** $=$
9. $<$ **10.** $<$ **11.** $5x = 20$ **12.** $a + 12 = 14$ **13.** $\frac{y}{10} = y \cdot 10$ **14.** $x + 1 = x - 1$ **15.** 3 **16.** 9 **17.** -28 **18.** -220
19. 5 **20.** -28 **21.** 5 **22.** -3 **23.** -25 **24.** 25 **25.** 13 **26.** -5 **27.** 0 **28.** undefined   **29.** -24 **30.** 30
31. $-\frac{3}{7}$ **32.** $-\frac{1}{10}$ **33.** $-\frac{1}{2}$ **34.** $-\frac{11}{12}$ **35.** -8 **36.** -0.3 **37.** 8 **38.** 4.4 **39.** $-\frac{3}{8}$ **40.** $-\frac{4}{7}$ **41.** 7 **42.** 3 **43.** -4
44. -8 **45.** $\frac{1}{9}$ **46.** $\frac{1}{10}$ **47.** $6; -\frac{1}{6}$ **48.** $-4; \frac{1}{4}$ **49.** $\frac{5}{7}; -\frac{5}{7}$ **50.** $-\frac{7}{30}; -\frac{30}{7}$ **51.** $9m + 45$ **52.** $77 + 11r$ **53.** $6y - 9x$
54. $32m - 56n$ **55.** $0.6a + 1.4$ **56.** $1.2n + 3$ **57.** $2x - \frac{19}{5}y + 4$ **58.** $5x - \frac{19}{2}y + 10$

Exercise Set 1.5   1. 48 **3.** -1 **5.** -9 **7.** 14.4 **9.** 17 **11.** -4 **13.** 40 **15.** -2 **17.** 11 **19.** $-\frac{3}{4}$ **21.** 7 **23.** 3
25. -11 **27.** -2.1 **29.** $-\frac{1}{3}$ **31.** $-\frac{79}{15}$ **33.** $-\frac{4}{5}$ **35.** -81 **37.** $-\frac{20}{33}$ **39.** -235.5 **41.** 12.25 **43.** 93 **45.** -12
47. $-\frac{23}{18}$ **49.** 5 **51.** $-\frac{3}{19}$ **53. a.** $18; 22; 28; 208$ **b.** increase; answers may vary   **55. a.** $600; 150; 105$ **b.** decrease; answers may vary
57. $\$3690.88$ **59.** $8x$ **61.** $18y$ **63.** $-x - 8$ **65.** $-6x + 9$ **67.** $4a - 13b$ **69.** $2x - 2y$ **71.** $0.8x - 3.6$ **73.** $\frac{11}{12}b - \frac{7}{6}$
75. $-3ab - 12.8$ **77.** $6x + 14$ **79.** $2k + 10$ **81.** $-3x + 5$ **83.** $4x + 9$ **85.** $4n - 8$ **87.** -24 **89.** $-2x + \frac{6}{5}y - 1$
91. $2x + 10$ **93.** $3a + \frac{3}{35}$ **95.** $-0.6a + 3.5$ **97.** $-8t + 12$ **99.** $1.91x + 4.32$ **101.** $15.4z + 31.11$ **103.** $(2 + 7) \cdot (1 + 3)$
105. answers may vary   **107.** $(3x + 2) - (5x + 7) = 3x + 2 - 5x - 7 = -2x - 5$ **109.** 20 million   **111.** 70 million
113. increasing; answers may vary   **115.** -0.5876

Calculator Explorations   1. 6×10^{43} **3.** 3.796×10^{28}

Mental Math   1. $\frac{5}{xy^2}$ **3.** $\frac{a^2}{bc^5}$ **5.** $\frac{x^4}{y^2}$

Exercise Set 1.6 **1.** 4^5 **3.** x^8 **5.** m^{14} **7.** $-20x^2y$ **9.** $-16x^6y^3p^2$ **11.** -1 **13.** 1 **15.** -1 **17.** 9 **19.** a^3 **21.** $-13z^4$

23. x **25.** $\frac{4}{3}x^3y^2$ **27.** $-6a^4b^4c^6$ **29.** $\frac{1}{16}$ **31.** $-\frac{1}{27}$ **33.** $\frac{1}{x^8}$ **35.** $\frac{5}{a^4}$ **37.** $\frac{y^2}{x^7}$ **39.** $\frac{1}{x^7}$ **41.** $4r^8$ **43.** 1 **45.** $\frac{b^7}{9a^7}$

47. $\frac{6x^{16}}{5}$ **49.** $-140x^{12}$ **51.** x^{16} **53.** $10x^{10}$ **55.** 6 **57.** $\frac{1}{z^3}$ **59.** -2 **61.** y^4 **63.** $\frac{13}{36}$ **65.** $\frac{3}{x}$ **67.** r^8 **69.** $\frac{1}{x^9y^4}$

71. $24x^7y^6$ **73.** $\frac{x}{16}$ **75.** 625 **77.** $\frac{1}{8}$ **79.** $\frac{a^5}{81}$ **81.** $\frac{7}{x^3z^5}$ **83.** x^{7a+5} **85.** x^{2t-1} **87.** x^{4a+7} **89.** z^{6x-7} **91.** x^{6t-1}

93. 3.125×10^7 **95.** 1.6×10^{-2} **97.** 6.7413×10^4 **99.** 1.25×10^{-2} **101.** 5.3×10^{-5} **103.** 7.783×10^8 **105.** 6.404×10^9

107. 1.24×10^{11} **109.** 1.0×10^{-3} **111.** 0.0000000036 **113.** $93,000,000$ **115.** $1,278,000$ **117.** $7,350,000,000,000$ **119.** 0.000000403

121. $300,000,000$ **123.** $4,900,000,000$ **125.** answers may vary **127.** answers may vary

Mental Math **1.** x^{20} **3.** x^9 **5.** y^{42} **7.** z^{36} **9.** z^{18}

Exercise Set 1.7 **1.** $\frac{1}{9}$ **3.** $\frac{1}{x^{36}}$ **5.** $9x^4y^6$ **7.** $16x^{20}y^{12}$ **9.** $\frac{c^{18}}{64a^{12}b^6}$ **11.** $\frac{343}{512}$ **13.** $-64y^3$ **15.** $\frac{1}{a^2}$ **17.** $\frac{36}{p^{12}}$ **19.** $-\frac{a^6}{512x^3y^9}$

21. $\frac{64}{27}$ **23.** $4a^8b^4$ **25.** $\frac{x^{14}y^{14}}{a^{21}}$ **27.** $\frac{1}{y^{10}}$ **29.** $\frac{1}{125}$ **31.** $\frac{1}{x^{63}}$ **33.** $\frac{y^{15}}{x^{35}z^{20}}$ **35.** $16x^4$ **37.** $4^8x^2y^6$ **39.** $\frac{x^9}{8y^3}$ **41.** $\frac{x^4}{4z^2}$

43. $\frac{x^4}{16}$ **45.** $\frac{1}{y^{15}}$ **47.** $\frac{16a^2b^9}{9}$ **49.** $\frac{3}{8x^8y^7}$ **51.** $\frac{1}{x^{30}b^6c^6}$ **53.** $\frac{25}{8x^5y^4}$ **55.** $\frac{2}{x^4y^{10}}$ **57.** x^{9a+18} **59.** x^{16a-1} **61.** b^{10x-4} **63.** y^{15a+3}

65. $16x^{4t+4}$ **67.** $5x^{a+2b}y^{a-2b}$ **69.** 1.45×10^9 **71.** 8×10^{15} **73.** 4×10^{-7} **75.** 3×10^{-1} **77.** 2×10^1 **79.** 1×10^1

81. 8×10^{-5} **83.** 1.1×10^7 **85.** 3.5×10^{22} **87.** 2×10^{-3} sec **89.** 6.232×10^{-11} cu m **91.** $\frac{15y^3}{x^8}$ sq ft **93.** 1.331928×10^{13} tons

95. no **97.** 83 people per sq mi **99.** 3.9

Vocabulary Check **1.** algebraic expression **2.** opposite **3.** distributive **4.** absolute value **5.** exponent **6.** variable
7. inequality **8.** reciprocals **9.** commutative **10.** associative **11.** whole **12.** real

Chapter 1 Review **1.** $\frac{x}{7}$ **2.** $7x$ **3.** $4(x+10)$ **4.** $3x-9$ **5.** $\{-1, 1, 3\}$ **6.** $\{-2, 0, 2, 4, 6\}$ **7.** $\{\ \}$ **8.** $\{\ \}$
9. $\{6, 7, 8, \dots\}$ **10.** $\{\dots, -1, 0, 1, 2\}$ **11.** true **12.** false **13.** true **14.** true **15.** false **16.** true **17.** false **18.** true

19. $\left\{5, \frac{8}{2}, \sqrt{9}\right\}$ **20.** $\left\{5, \frac{8}{2}, \sqrt{9}\right\}$ **21.** $\left\{5, -\frac{2}{3}, \frac{8}{2}, \sqrt{9}, 0.3, 1\frac{5}{8}, -1\right\}$ **22.** $\{\sqrt{7}, \pi\}$ **23.** $\left\{5, -\frac{2}{3}, \frac{8}{2}, \sqrt{9}, 0.3, \sqrt{7}, 1\frac{5}{8}, -1, \pi\right\}$

24. $\left\{5, \frac{8}{2}, \sqrt{9}, -1\right\}$ **25.** $12 = -4x$ **26.** $n + 2n = -15$ **27.** $4(y+3) = -1$ **28.** $6(t-5) = 4$ **29.** $z - 7 = 6$

30. $9x - 10 = 5$ **31.** $x - 5 = 12$ **32.** $-4 = 7y$ **33.** $\frac{2}{3} = 2\left(n + \frac{1}{4}\right)$ **34.** $t + 6 = -12$ **35.** $\frac{3}{4}$ **36.** -0.6 **37.** 0 **38.** 1

39. $-\frac{4}{3}$ **40.** 5 **41.** undefined **42.** -1 **43.** associative property of addition **44.** distributive property
45. additive inverse property **46.** commutative property of addition **47.** associative property of multiplication
48. multiplicative inverse property **49.** multiplicative identity property **50.** commutative property of addition
51. additive identity property **52.** multiplicative identity property **53.** $5x - 15z$ **54.** $(3+x) + (7+y)$ **55.** $2 + (-2)$, for example
56. $2 \cdot \frac{1}{2}$, for example **57.** $(3.4)[(0.7)5]$ **58.** $7 + 0$ **59.** $>$ **60.** $>$ **61.** $<$ **62.** $=$ **63.** $<$ **64.** $>$

65. $-6x + 21y$ **66.** $-90a - 36b$ **67.** $9m - 4n + \frac{1}{2}$ **68.** $4x - 11y + \frac{2}{3}$ **69.** -4 **70.** -35 **71.** -2 **72.** 0.31 **73.** 8

74. 13.3 **75.** -4 **76.** -22 **77.** undefined **78.** 0 **79.** 4 **80.** -5 **81.** $-\frac{2}{15}$ **82.** 4 **83.** $\frac{5}{12}$

84. 29,852 ft below sea level **85.** 9 **86.** 13 **87.** 3 **88.** 54 **89.** $-\frac{32}{135}$ **90.** $-\frac{15}{56}$ **91.** $-\frac{5}{4}$ **92.** $-\frac{5}{2}$ **93.** $\frac{5}{8}$ **94.** $-6\frac{1}{2}$

95. -1 **96.** 24 **97.** 1 **98.** 18 **99.** -4 **100.** $\frac{7}{3}$ **101.** $\frac{5}{7}$ **102.** $-\frac{8}{25}$ **103.** $\frac{1}{5}$ **104.** 1 **105.** $6.28; 62.8; 628$

106. increase **107.** $3x - 13$ **108.** $80y - 1$ **109.** $a + 7y - 6$ **110.** $-23b + 13x - 10$ **111.** $n + 5$ **112.** $y - 4$ **113.** 4

114. 81 **115.** -4 **116.** -81 **117.** 1 **118.** -1 **119.** $-\frac{1}{16}$ **120.** $\frac{1}{16}$ **121.** $-x^2y^7z$ **122.** $12x^2y^3b$ **123.** $\frac{1}{a^9}$ **124.** $\frac{1}{a}$

125. $\frac{1}{x^{11}}$ **126.** $\frac{1}{2a^{17}}$ **127.** $\frac{1}{y^5}$ **128.** $9x^{4a+2b}y^{-6b}$ or $\frac{9x^{4a+2b}}{y^{6b}}$ **129.** 3.689×10^7 **130.** 3.62×10^{-4} **131.** 0.000001678

132. $410,000$ **133.** 8^{15} **134.** $\frac{a^2}{16}$ **135.** $27x^3$ **136.** $\frac{1}{16x^2}$ **137.** $\frac{36x^2}{25}$ **138.** $\frac{1}{8^{18}}$ **139.** $\frac{9}{16}$ **140.** $-\frac{1}{8x^9}$ **141.** $\frac{1}{4p^4}$

142. $-\frac{27y^6}{x^6}$ **143.** $x^{25}y^{15}z^{15}$ **144.** $\frac{xz}{4}$ **145.** $\frac{x^2}{625y^4z^4}$ **146.** $\frac{2}{27z^3}$ **147.** $27x^{19a}$ **148.** $2y^{x-7}$

149. $\dfrac{3}{4}$; $-\dfrac{4}{3}$ **150.** 5; $\dfrac{1}{5}$ **151.** $-10x + 6.1$ **152.** 9 **153.** $-\dfrac{6}{11}$ **154.** 15 **155.** $-\dfrac{4}{15}$ **156.** $\dfrac{1}{11}$ **157.** $-x + 3y + 1$

158. $-\dfrac{1}{25}$ **159.** $\dfrac{8}{x^{30}}$ **160.** $\dfrac{9b^2c^4}{25a^2}$

Chapter 1 Test **1.** true   **2.** false   **3.** false   **4.** $\{0, 1\}$ **5.** true   **6.** false   **7.** -3 **8.** -225 **9.** -2 **10.** 1 **11.** $-\dfrac{3}{2}$

12. 12 **13.** 1 **14. a.** 5.75; 17.25; 57.50; 115.00 **b.** increase   **15.** $3\left(\dfrac{n}{5}\right) = -n$ **16.** $20 = 2x - 6$ **17.** $-2 = \dfrac{x}{x+5}$

18. distributive property   **19.** associative property of addition   **20.** additive inverse property   **21.** reciprocal: $-\dfrac{11}{7}$; opposite: $\dfrac{7}{11}$

22. $6x + 12y + 13.8$ **23.** $-x - 11y$ **24.** $\dfrac{1}{81x^2}$ **25.** $\dfrac{3a^7}{2b^5}$ **26.** $-\dfrac{y^{40}}{z^5}$ **27.** $\dfrac{a^{12}}{4b^{14}}$ **28.** x^{10w} **29.** 6.3×10^8 **30.** 1.2×10^{-2}

31. 0.000005 **32.** 5.76×10^4 **33.** 9×10^{-4} **34.** 8.486×10^8

CHAPTER 2 Equations, Inequalities, and Problem Solving

Mental Math **1.** $\{6\}$ **3.** $\{17\}$ **5.** $\{8\}$ **7.** $\{10\}$

Exercise Set 2.1 **1.** yes   **3.** no   **5.** yes   **7.** no   **9.** no   **11.** yes   **13.** $\{6\}$ **15.** $\{-22\}$ **17.** $\{4.7\}$ **19.** $\{10\}$ **21.** $\{-1.1\}$
23. $\{-5\}$ **25.** $\{-2\}$ **27.** $\{0\}$ **29.** $\{2\}$ **31.** $\{-9\}$ **33.** $\left\{-\dfrac{10}{7}\right\}$ **35.** $\left\{\dfrac{9}{10}\right\}$ **37.** $\{4\}$ **39.** $\{1\}$ **41.** $\{5\}$ **43.** $\left\{\dfrac{40}{3}\right\}$
45. $\{17\}$ **47.** $\{n \mid n \text{ is a real number}\}$ **49.** $\varnothing$ **51.** $\{x \mid x \text{ is a real number}\}$ **53.** $\varnothing$ **55.** $\left\{\dfrac{1}{8}\right\}$ **57.** $\{0\}$ **59.** $\{x \mid x \text{ is a real number}\}$
61. $\{4\}$ **63.** $\left\{\dfrac{4}{5}\right\}$ **65.** $\{8\}$ **67.** $\varnothing$ **69.** $\{-8\}$ **71.** $\left\{-\dfrac{5}{4}\right\}$ **73.** $\{-2\}$ **75.** $\{23\}$ **77.** $\left\{-\dfrac{2}{9}\right\}$ **79.** $\dfrac{8}{x}$ **81.** $8x$
83. $2x - 5$ **85.** add 19 instead of subtracting; -3 **87.** $0.4 - 1.6 = -1.2$, not 1.2; -0.24 **89. a.** $4x + 5$ **b.** $\{-3\}$ **c.** answers may vary
91. answers may vary   **93.** $K = -11$ **95.** $K = -23$ **97.** answers may vary   **99.** $\{5.217\}$ **101.** $\{1\}$

Exercise Set 2.2 **1.** $4y$ **3.** $3z + 3$ **5.** $(65x + 30)$ cents   **7.** $10x + 3$ **9.** $2x + 14$ **11.** -5 **13.** $45, 145, 225$
15. approximately 1612.41 million acres   **17.** 3145 earthquakes   **19.** 1275 shoppers   **21.** 23% **23.** 417 employees
25. INVESCO Field: $76{,}125$ seats; Heinz Field: $64{,}450$ seats   **27.** 40.5 ft; 202.5 ft; 240 ft   **29.** Tokyo: 35.0 million; New York:
18.3 million; Mexico City: 18.7 million   **31.** $29°, 35°, 116°$ **33.** 28 m, 36 m, 38 m   **35.** 18 in., 18 in., 27 in., 36 in.
37. 317 thousand; 279 thousand; 184 thousand   **39.** medical assistant: 215 thousand; postsecondary teacher jobs: 603 thousand; registered nurses:
623 thousand   **41.** B767-300ER: 207 seats; B737-200: 119 seats; F-100: 87 seats   **43.** $\$430.00$ **45.** $\$100.34$ **47.** $75, 76, 77$
49. $64°, 32°, 84°$ **51.** square: 18 cm; triangle: 24 cm   **53.** $41{,}741{,}000$ **55.** Fallon's zip code is 89406; Fernley's zip code is 89408; Gardnerville
Ranchos' zip code is 89410 **57.** $40°, 140°$ **59.** incandescent: 1500 bulb hours; fluorescent: $100{,}000$ bulb hours; halogen: 4000 bulb hours
61. Jeter: 23; Mulder: 25; Jenkins: 27 **63.** 208 **65.** -55 **67.** 3195 **69.** yes; answers may vary   **71.** answers may vary
73. a. 2029 **b.** 1387.5 **c.** 4; no: this is the average daily number of cigarettes for all American adults—smokers and nonsmokers
75. no such odd integers exist   **77.** 500 boards; $\$30{,}000$ **79.** company makes a profit

Mental Math **1.** $y = 5 - 2x$ **3.** $a = 5b + 8$ **5.** $k = h - 5j + 6$

Exercise Set 2.3 **1.** $t = \dfrac{d}{r}$ **3.** $r = \dfrac{I}{Pt}$ **5.** $c = P - a - b$ **7.** $y = \dfrac{9x - 16}{4}$ or $y = \dfrac{9}{4}x - 4$ **9.** $l = \dfrac{P - 2w}{2}$ or $l = \dfrac{P}{2} - w$
11. $r = \dfrac{E}{I} - R$ **13.** $y = \dfrac{20 - 5x}{4}$ or $y = 5 - \dfrac{5}{4}x$ **15.** $H = \dfrac{S - 2LW}{2L + 2W}$ **17.** $r = \dfrac{C}{2\pi}$ **19.** $F = \dfrac{9}{5}C + 32$

21.

n	1	2	4	12	365
A	\$4703.71	\$4713.99	\$4719.22	\$4722.74	\$4724.45

23. a. $\$7313.97$ **b.** $\$7321.14$ **c.** $\$7325.98$ **25.** $40°C$ **27.** 3 hr, 36 min   **29.** 171 packages   **31.** 9 ft   **33.** 2 gal
35. a. 1174.86 cu m   **b.** 310.34 cu m   **c.** 1485.20 cu m   **37.** $164{,}921$ mi   **39.** 0.42 ft   **41.** 41.125π ft; 129.1325 ft
43. $f = \dfrac{C - 4h - 4p}{9}$ **45.** 178 cal   **47.** 1.5 g   **49.** $\{-3, -2, -1\}$ **51.** $\{-3, -2, -1, 0, 1\}$ **53.** answers may vary
55. $0.388; 0.723; 1.00; 1.523; 5.202; 9.538; 19.193; 30.065; 39.505$ **57.** $\$6.80$ per person   **59.** answers may vary
61. $n_e = \dfrac{N}{R^* \times f_p \times f_l \times f_i \times f_c \times L}$

Mental Math **1.** $\{x \mid x < 6\}$ **3.** $\{x \mid x \geq 10\}$ **5.** $\{x \mid x > 4\}$ **7.** $\{x \mid x \leq 2\}$

Exercise Set 2.4 **1.** $(-\infty, -3)$ **3.** $[0.3, \infty)$ **5.** $[-7, \infty)$
7. $(-2, 5)$ **9.** $(-1, 5]$ **11.** $[-2, \infty)$ **13.** $(-\infty, 1)$
15. $(-\infty, 2]$ **17.** $[8, \infty)$ **19.** $(-\infty, -4.7)$ **21.** $(-\infty, -3]$

23. $(-\infty, -1]$ **25.** $(-\infty, 11]$ **27.** $(0, \infty)$ **29.** $(-13, \infty)$ **31.** $\left[-\dfrac{79}{3}, \infty\right)$ **33.** $\left(-\infty, -\dfrac{35}{6}\right)$ **35.** $(-\infty, -6)$ **37.** $(4, \infty)$

39. $[-0.5, \infty)$ **41.** $(-\infty, 7]$ **43.** $[0, \infty)$ **45.** $(-\infty, -29]$ **47.** $[3, \infty)$ **49.** $(-\infty, -1]$ **51.** $[-31, \infty)$ **53.** $(-\infty, -2]$

55. $(-\infty, 9)$ **57.** $\left(-\infty, -\dfrac{11}{2}\right]$ **59. a.** $\{x \mid x \geq 81\}$ **b.** A final exam grade of 81 or higher will result in an average of 77 or higher.

61. a. $\{x \mid x \leq 1040\}$ **b.** The luggage and cargo must weight 1040 pounds or less.   **63. a.** $\{x \mid x \leq 20\}$ **b.** She can move at most 20 whole boxes at one time.   **65. a.** $\{x \mid x > 200\}$ **b.** If you make more than 200 calls, plan 1 is more economical.   **67.** $\{F \mid F \geq 932°\}$

69. a. 2000   **b.** answers may vary   **71.** decreasing; answers may vary   **73.** 43.5 lb   **75.** during 2006   **77.** answers may vary

79. a. $\{t \mid t > 32.\overline{54}\}$ **b.** 2029   **81.** $\{0, 1, 2, 3, 4, 5, 6, 7\}$ **83.** $\{\ldots, -9, -8, -7, -6\}$ **85.** $\{5\}$ **87.** $\{0\}$

89. yes   **91.** yes   **93.** $\{4\}$ **95.** $(4, \infty)$ **97.** $(-\infty, \infty)$ **99.** $\varnothing$ **101.** answers may vary   **103.** answers may vary

Integrated Review   **1.** $\{-5\}$ **2.** $(-5, \infty)$ **3.** $\left[\dfrac{8}{3}, \infty\right)$ **4.** $[-1, \infty)$ **5.** $\{0\}$ **6.** $\left[-\dfrac{1}{10}, \infty\right)$ **7.** $\left(-\infty, -\dfrac{1}{6}\right]$ **8.** $\{0\}$ **9.** $\varnothing$

10. $\left[-\dfrac{3}{5}, \infty\right)$ **11.** $\{4.2\}$ **12.** $\{6\}$ **13.** $\{-8\}$ **14.** $(-\infty, -16)$ **15.** $\left\{\dfrac{20}{11}\right\}$ **16.** $\{1\}$ **17.** $(38, \infty)$ **18.** $\{-5.5\}$ **19.** $\left\{\dfrac{3}{5}\right\}$

20. $(-\infty, \infty)$ **21.** $\{29\}$ **22.** $\{x \mid x \text{ is a real number}\}$ **23.** $(-\infty, 5)$ **24.** $\left\{\dfrac{9}{13}\right\}$ **25.** $(23, \infty)$ **26.** $(-\infty, 6]$ **27.** $\left(-\infty, \dfrac{3}{5}\right]$

28. $\left(-\infty, -\dfrac{19}{32}\right)$

Exercise Set 2.5   **1.** $\{2, 3, 4, 5, 6, 7\}$ **3.** $\{4, 6\}$ **5.** $\{\ldots, -2, -1, 0, 1, \ldots\}$ **7.** $\{5, 7\}$ **9.** $\{x \mid x \text{ is an odd integer or } x = 2 \text{ or } x = 4\}$

11. $\{2, 4\}$ **13.** (number line: -3 to 1)   **15.** (number line)   **17.** (number line)   **19.** $[6, \infty)$ **21.** $(-\infty, -3]$ **23.** $(4, 10)$

25. $(11, 17)$ **27.** $[1, 4]$ **29.** $\left[-3, \dfrac{3}{2}\right]$ **31.** $\left[-\dfrac{7}{3}, 7\right]$ **33.** (number line: 5)   **35.** (number line: -4, 1)   **37.** (number line)

39. $[2, \infty)$ **41.** $(-\infty, -4) \cup (-2, \infty)$ **43.** $(-\infty, \infty)$ **45.** $\left(-\dfrac{1}{2}, \dfrac{2}{3}\right)$ **47.** $(-\infty, \infty)$ **49.** $\left[\dfrac{3}{2}, 6\right]$ **51.** $\left(\dfrac{5}{4}, \dfrac{11}{4}\right)$ **53.** $\varnothing$

55. $\left(-\infty, -\dfrac{56}{5}\right) \cup \left(\dfrac{5}{3}, \infty\right)$ **57.** $\left(-5, \dfrac{5}{2}\right)$ **59.** $\left(0, \dfrac{14}{3}\right]$ **61.** $(-\infty, -3]$ **63.** $(-\infty, 1] \cup \left(\dfrac{29}{7}, \infty\right)$ **65.** $\varnothing$ **67.** $\left[-\dfrac{1}{2}, \dfrac{3}{2}\right)$

69. $\left(-\dfrac{4}{3}, \dfrac{7}{3}\right)$ **71.** $(6, 12)$ **73.** -12 **75.** -4 **77.** $\{-7, 7\}$ **79.** $\{0\}$ **81.** 1993, 1994, 1995, 1998, 1999, and 2002

83. answers may vary   **85.** $(-3, 5)$ **87.** $(2, \infty)$ **89.** $-20.2° \leq F \leq 95°$ **91.** $67 \leq$ final score ≤ 94

Mental Math   **1.** d   **3.** c   **5.** a

Exercise Set 2.6   **1.** $\{7, -7\}$ **3.** $\varnothing$ **5.** $\{4.2, -4.2\}$ **7.** $\{-4, 4\}$ **9.** $\{-9, 9\}$ **11.** $\{-5, 23\}$ **13.** $\{7, -2\}$ **15.** $\{8, 4\}$

17. $\{5, -5\}$ **19.** $\{3, -3\}$ **21.** $\{-3, 6\}$ **23.** $\{0\}$ **25.** $\varnothing$ **27.** $\left\{-\dfrac{1}{3}, \dfrac{7}{3}\right\}$ **29.** $\left\{-\dfrac{1}{2}, 9\right\}$ **31.** $\left\{-\dfrac{5}{2}\right\}$ **33.** $\{3, 2\}$

35. $\{-4, 16\}$ **37.** $\{4\}$ **39.** $\left\{\dfrac{3}{2}\right\}$ **41.** $\left\{\dfrac{32}{21}, \dfrac{38}{9}\right\}$ **43.** $\left\{-8, \dfrac{2}{3}\right\}$ **45.** (number line: -4, 4) $[-4, 4]$

47. (number line: -3, 3) $(-\infty, -3) \cup (3, \infty)$ **49.** (number line: -5, -1) $(-5, -1)$ **51.** (number line: -1, 13) $(-\infty, -1] \cup [13, \infty)$

53. (number line: -5, 1) $(-5, 1)$ **55.** (number line: -5, 5) $[-5, 5]$ **57.** (number line: $-\dfrac{3}{2}$) $\left\{-\dfrac{3}{2}\right\}$ **59.** (number line: -4, 4) $(-\infty, -4) \cup (4, \infty)$

61. (number line: -10, 3) $[-10, 3]$ **63.** (number line: 1, $\dfrac{13}{3}$) $\left(1, \dfrac{13}{3}\right)$ **65.** (number line: -24, 4) $(-\infty, -24] \cup [4, \infty)$ **67.** (number line: -2, 9) $[-2, 9]$

69. (number line) $(-\infty, \infty)$ **71.** (number line: $-\dfrac{1}{2}$, 1) $\left[-\dfrac{1}{2}, 1\right]$ **73.** (number line: $\dfrac{2}{3}$, 2) $\left(-\infty, \dfrac{2}{3}\right) \cup (2, \infty)$ **75.** (number line) $\varnothing$

77. (number line: -12, 0) $(-\infty, -12) \cup (0, \infty)$ **79.** $\{-13, 13\}$ **81.** $(-13, 13)$ **83.** $\varnothing$ **85.** $[-10, 10]$ **87.** $\{5, -2\}$

89. $(-\infty, -7] \cup [17, \infty)$ **91.** $\left\{-\dfrac{9}{4}\right\}$ **93.** $(-2, 1)$ **95.** $(-\infty, -18) \cup (12, \infty)$ **97.** $\left\{2, \dfrac{4}{3}\right\}$ **99.** $\varnothing$ **101.** $\left\{-\dfrac{17}{2}, \dfrac{19}{2}\right\}$

103. $\left(-\infty, -\dfrac{25}{3}\right) \cup \left(\dfrac{35}{3}, \infty\right)$ **105.** $\left\{4, -\dfrac{1}{5}\right\}$ **107.** $\left\{-\dfrac{17}{3}, 5\right\}$ **109.** 32%   **111.** 28.8°   **113.** $\varnothing$ **115.** $\{x \mid x \text{ is a real number}\}$

117. $|x| = 5$ **119.** $|x| < 7$ **121.** $|x| \leq 5$, answers may vary   **123.** $3.45 < x < 3.55$

CHAPTER 3   Graphs and Functions

Calculator Explorations   1. 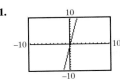   **3.** 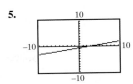   **5.**

Mental Math   1. $(5, 2)$ **3.** $(3, -1)$ **5.** $(-5, -2)$ **7.** $(-1, 0)$

Exercise Set 3.1   1. 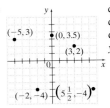   quadrant I;
quadrant II;
quadrant IV;
y-axis; quadrant III   **3.** quadrant IV   **5.** x-axis   **7.** quadrant III   **9.**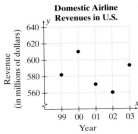

Domestic Airline
Revenues in U.S.

11. no; yes   **13.** yes; yes   **15.** yes; no   **17.** 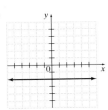   **19.** 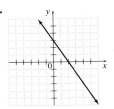   **21.**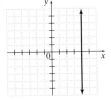

23. 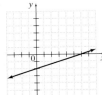   **25.** 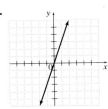   **27.** 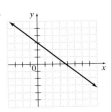   **29.** 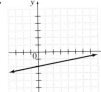   **31.**

33. 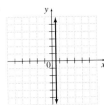   **35.** 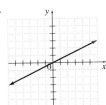   **37.** 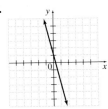   **39.** 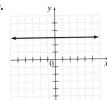   **41.**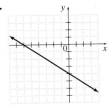

43. 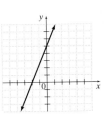   **45.** $\dfrac{3}{2}$ **47.** 6   **49.** $-\dfrac{6}{5}$ **51.** b   **53.** B   **55.** C   **57.** 1991   **59.** answers may vary

61. a. 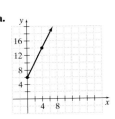   **b.** 14 in.   **63.** $7000   **65.** $500   **67.** depreciation is the same from year to year

69. a. $(0, 500)$; 0 tables and 500 chairs are produced   **b.** $(750, 0)$; 750 tables and 0 chairs are produced   **c.** 466 chairs   **71.** answers may vary

73. vertical line $x = 0$ has y-intercepts. **75.** 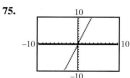 **77.**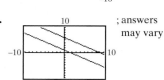

Calculator Explorations 1. 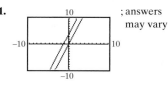 ; answers may vary **3.** 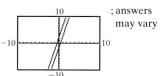 ; answers may vary **5.** 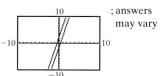 ; answers may vary

Mental Math 1. upward **3.** horizontally

Exercise Set 3.2 1. $\frac{9}{5}$ **3.** $-\frac{7}{2}$ **5.** $-\frac{5}{6}$ **7.** $\frac{1}{3}$ **9.** $-\frac{4}{3}$ **11.** 0 **13.** $m = 2$ **15.** $m = -\frac{4}{5}$ **17.** $\frac{2}{3}$ **19.** $\frac{3}{20}$

21. $m = -1; (0, 5)$ **23.** $m = 5; (0, -2)$ **25.** $m = -2; (0, 7)$ **27.** $m = \frac{2}{3}; \left(0, -\frac{10}{3}\right)$ **29.** m undefined; no y-intercept

31. $m = 0; (0, -2)$ **33.** $m = \frac{1}{2}; (0, 0)$ **35.** $m = \frac{1}{3}; \left(0, -\frac{8}{3}\right)$ **37.** $m = \frac{6}{5}; (0, 6)$ **39.** $m = 7; (0, 0)$ **41.** m undefined; no y-intercept

43. A **45.** B **47.** l_2 **49.** l_2 **51.** l_2 **53.** neither **55.** neither **57.** perpendicular **59.** parallel **61.** parallel

63. perpendicular **65.** perpendicular **67.** neither **69.** $\{9, -3\}$ **71.** $(-\infty, -4) \cup (-1, \infty)$ **73.** $\left[\frac{2}{3}, 2\right]$

75. incorrect; $m = \frac{-14 - 6}{7 - (-2)} = -\frac{20}{9}$ **77.** correct **79.** $-\frac{7}{2}$ **81.** $\frac{2}{7}$ **83.** $\frac{5}{2}$ **85.** $-\frac{2}{5}$ **87.** $(10, 13)$ **89.** $\frac{3}{2}$ yd per sec

91. answers may vary **93. a.** $l_1: -2; l_2: -1; l_3: -\frac{2}{3}$ **b.** lesser

Calculator Explorations 1. $y = \frac{1}{3.5}x$ 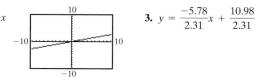 **3.** $y = \frac{-5.78}{2.31}x + \frac{10.98}{2.31}$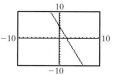

5. $y = x + 3.78$ 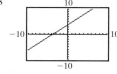 **7.** $y = 13.3x + 1.5$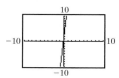

Mental Math 1. $m = -4; (0, 12)$ **3.** $m = 5; (0, 0)$ **5.** $m = \frac{1}{2}; (0, 6)$

Exercise Set 3.3 1. 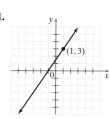 **3.** 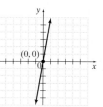 **5.** 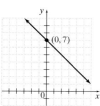 **7.**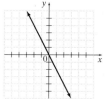

9. 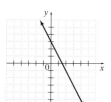 **11.** 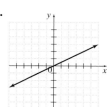 **13.** 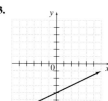 **15.** 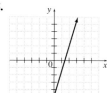 **17.**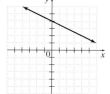

19. C **21.** D **23.** $y = -x + 1$ **25.** $y = 2x + \frac{3}{4}$ **27.** $y = \frac{2}{7}x$ **29. a.** $\$44,955$ **b.** $m = 1983$; annual income increases $\$1983$ each year **c.** $(0, 42,972)$ at year $= 0$, or 1999, annual average income was $\$42,972$ **31. a.** $m = 10.6; (0, 186)$ **b.** number of people employed as network systems and data communications analysts increases 10.6 thousand for every 1 year **c.** 930 thousand network systems and data communications analysts employed in 2002 **33. a.** 168.8 million **b.** in 2006 **c.** answers may vary **35.** $y = 5x + 32$ **37.** $y = 2x - 1$ **39.** incorrect; $y = 3x + 1.7$ **41.** correct **43.** $y = 42,000x + 2,900,000$, where y is revenue and x is number of years since 1995

Calculator Explorations   1. 18.4   **3.** -1.5 **5.** 8.7; 7.6

Mental Math   1. $m = -2; (1, 4)$ **3.** $m = \dfrac{1}{4}; (2, 0)$ **5.** $m = 5; (3, -2)$

Exercise Set 3.4   1. $y = 3x - 1$ **3.** $y = -2x - 1$ **5.** $y = \dfrac{1}{2}x + 5$ **7.** $y = -\dfrac{9}{10}x - \dfrac{27}{10}$ **9.** $3x - y = 6$ **11.** $2x + y = 1$

13. $x + 2y = -10$ **15.** $x - 3y = 21$ **17.** $3x + 8y = 5$ **19.** $x = 2$ **21.** $y = 1$ **23.** $x = 0$ **25.** $y = 4x - 4$ **27.** $y = -3x + 1$

29. $y = 4$ **31.** $y = -\dfrac{3}{2}x - 6$ **33.** $y = -5$ **35.** $y = -4x + 1$ **37.** $2x - y = -7$ **39.** $y = -x + 7$ **41.** $y = -\dfrac{1}{2}x + \dfrac{3}{8}$

43. $2x + 7y = -42$ **45.** $4x + 3y = -20$ **47.** $x = -2$ **49.** $x + 2y = 2$ **51.** $y = 12$ **53.** $8x - y = 47$ **55.** $x = 5$

57. $y = -\dfrac{3}{8}x - \dfrac{29}{4}$ **59. a.** $y = 32x$ **b.** 128 ft per sec   **61. a.** $y = 12,000x + 18,000$ **b.** \$102,000   **c.** 9 yr   **63. a.** $y = 9266.7x + 142,200$

b. \$216,334   **65. a.** $y = 0.1x + 70.0$ **b.** 70.7 million subscribers   **67.** 31.   **69.** -8.4 **71.** 4   **73.** $2x + y = 3$ **75.** $2x - 3y = -7$

77. true   **79.** answers may vary   **81.**

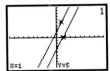

Integrated Review   1.

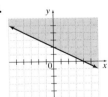

2.

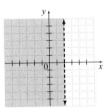

3.

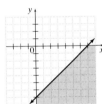

4.

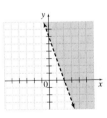

5. 0

6. $-\dfrac{3}{5}$ **7.** $m = 3; (0, -5)$ **8.** $m = \dfrac{5}{2}; \left(0, -\dfrac{7}{2}\right)$ **9.** parallel   **10.** perpendicular   **11.** $y = -x + 7$ **12.** $x = -2$ **13.** $y = 0$

14. $y = -\dfrac{3}{8}x - \dfrac{29}{4}$ **15.** $y = -5x - 6$ **16.** $y = -4x + \dfrac{1}{3}$ **17.** $y = \dfrac{1}{2}x - 1$ **18.** $y = 3x - \dfrac{3}{2}$ **19.** $y = 3x - 2$

20. $y = -\dfrac{5}{4}x + 4$ **21.** $y = \dfrac{1}{4}x - \dfrac{7}{2}$ **22.** $y = -\dfrac{5}{2}x - \dfrac{5}{2}$ **23.** $x = -1$ **24.** $y = 3$

Exercise Set 3.5   1.

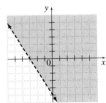

3.

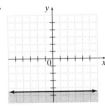

5.

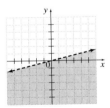

7.

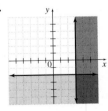

9.

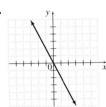

11.

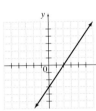

13.

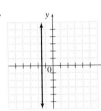

15.

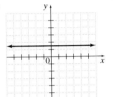

17.

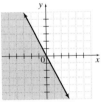

19.

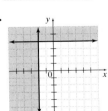

21.

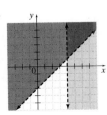

23.

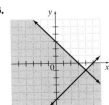

25.

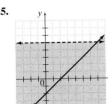

27.

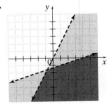

29. D   **31.** A   **33.** yes   **35.** no   **37.** with $<$ or $>$ **39.**

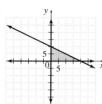

Exercise Set 3.6   **1.** domain; $\{-1, 0, -2, 5\}$; range: $\{7, 6, 2\}$; function   **3.** domain; $\{-2, 6, -7\}$; range: $\{4, -3, -8\}$; not a function

5. domain: $\{1\}$; range: $\{1, 2, 3, 4\}$; not a function   **7.** domain: $\left\{\dfrac{3}{2}, 0\right\}$; range: $\left\{\dfrac{1}{2}, -7, \dfrac{4}{5}\right\}$; not a function   **9.** domain: $\{-3, 0, 3\}$;

range: $\{-3, 0, 3\}$; function   **11.** domain: $\{-1, 1, 2, 3\}$; range: $\{2, 1\}$; function

13. domain; $\{$Colorado, Alaska, Massachusetts, Delaware, Illinois, Pennsylvania$\}$; range: $\{1, 7, 10, 19\}$; function

15. domain: $\{32°, 104°, 212°, 50°\}$; range: $\{0°, 40°, 10°, 100°\}$; function   **17.** domain: $\{2, -1, 5, 100\}$; range: $\{0\}$; function

19. function   **21.** yes   **23.** no   **25.** yes   **27.** function   **29.** not a function   **31.** function   **33.** not a function

35. not a function   **37.** not a function   **39.** not a function   **41.** not a function   **43.** function   **45.** 15   **47.** 38

49. 7   **51.** 3   **53. a.** 0   **b.** 1   **c.** -1 **55. a.** -5 **b.** -5 **c.** -5 **57.** 25π sq cm   **59.** 2744 cu in.   **61.** 166.38 cm   **63.** 163.2 mg

65. a. 99.42; per capita consumption of poultry was 99.42 lb in 2003.   **b.** 108.54 lb

67.

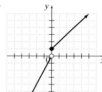

69.

71.

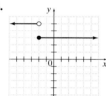

73. $(-\infty, 14]$ **75.** $\left[\dfrac{7}{2}, \infty\right)$ **77.** $\left(-\infty, -\dfrac{1}{4}\right)$

79. no; answers may vary   **81.** yes; answers may vary   **83.** true   **85.** true   **87.** answers may vary   **89.** $f(x) = x + 7$

91. answers may vary   **93. a.** $f(12) = 132$ **b.** $f(a) = a^2 - 12$ **c.** $f(-x) = x^2 - 12$ **d.** $f(x + h) = x^2 + 2xh + h^2 - 12$

Exercise Set 3.7   **1.** domain; $[0, \infty)$; range: $(-\infty, \infty)$ **3.** domain: $(-\infty, \infty)$; range: $[0, \infty)$ **5.** domain: $(-\infty, \infty)$; range: $(-\infty, -3] \cup [3, \infty)$

7. domain: $[1, 7]$; range: $[1, 7]$ **9.** domain: $\{-2\}$; range: $(-\infty, \infty)$ **11.** domain: $(-\infty, \infty)$; range: $(-\infty, 3]$ **13.** domain: $(-\infty, \infty)$;

range: $(-\infty, 3]$ **15.** domain: $[2, \infty)$; range: $[3, \infty)$

17.

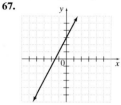

19.

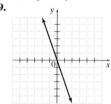

21.

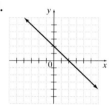

23.

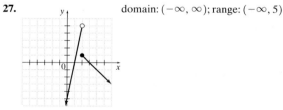

25.

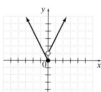

domain: $(-\infty, \infty)$; range: $[0, \infty)$ **27.**

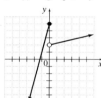

domain: $(-\infty, \infty)$; range: $(-\infty, 5)$

29.

domain: $(-\infty, \infty)$; range: $(-\infty, 6]$ **31.**

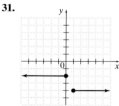

domain: $(-\infty, 0] \cup [1, \infty)$; range: $\{-4, -2\}$

33. A   **35.** D   **37.** answers may vary   **39.**

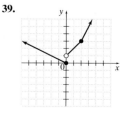

Mental Math **1.** c   **3.** d

Exercise Set 3.8 **1.** 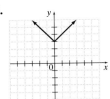 **3.** 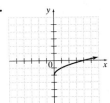 **5.** 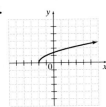 **7.**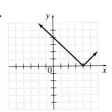

9. 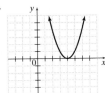 **11.** 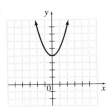 **13.** 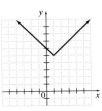 **15.** 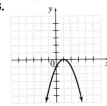 **17.**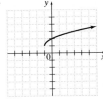

19. 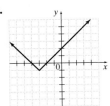 **21.** 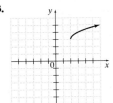 **23.** 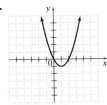 **25.** 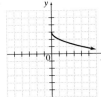 **27.**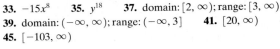

29. 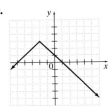 **31.**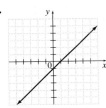

33. $-15x^8$ **35.** y^{18} **37.** domain: $[2, \infty)$; range: $[3, \infty)$
39. domain: $(-\infty, \infty)$; range: $(-\infty, 3]$ **41.** $[20, \infty)$ **43.** $(-\infty, \infty)$
45. $[-103, \infty)$

47. 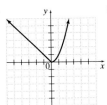 domain: $(-\infty, \infty)$; range: $[0, \infty)$ **49.** 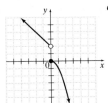 domain: $(-\infty, \infty)$; range: $(-\infty, 0] \cup (2, \infty)$

Chapter 3 Vocabulary Check   **1.** relation   **2.** line   **3.** linear inequality   **4.** standard   **5.** range   **6.** parallel   **7.** slope-intercept
8. function   **9.** slope   **10.** perpendicular   **11.** y **12.** domain   **13.** linear function   **14.** x **15.** point-slope

Chapter 3 Review **1.** 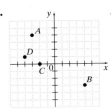 A, quadrant IV; B, quadrant II; C, y-axis; D, quadrant III

2. 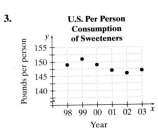 A and D, quadrant II; C, x-axis; B, quadrant IV   **3.**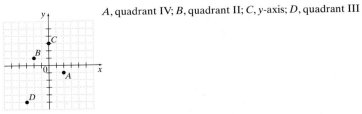

CHAPTER 4   Systems of Equations and Inequalities

Calculator Explorations   **1.** $(2.11, 0.17)$ **3.** $(-8.20, -6.30)$

Mental math   **1.** B   **3.** A

Exercise Set 4.1   **1.** yes   **3.** no   **5.** yes   **7.** no   **9.** 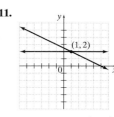   **11.** 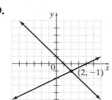   **13.** $\varnothing$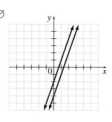

15.

17. $(2, 8)$ **19.** $(0, -9)$ **21.** $(1, -1)$ **23.** $\{x \mid x = -3y + 4\}$ **25.** $\left(\dfrac{5}{2}, \dfrac{5}{4}\right)$ **27.** $(1, -2)$

29. $(9, 9)$ **31.** $(7, 2)$ **33.** $\varnothing$ **35.** $\{(x, y) \mid 3x + y = 1\}$ **37.** $\left(\dfrac{3}{2}, 1\right)$ **39.** $(2, -1)$ **41.** $(-5, 3)$

43. $\varnothing$ **45.** $\left(\dfrac{1}{2}, \dfrac{1}{5}\right)$ **47.** $(8, 2)$ **49.** $\{(x, y) \mid x = 3y + 2\}$ **51.** $(-5, 3)$ **53.** $(3, 2)$ **55.** $(7, -3)$

57. $\varnothing$ **59.** $(3, 4)$ **61.** $\left(-\dfrac{1}{4}, \dfrac{1}{2}\right)$ **63.** $(-2, 1)$ **65.** $(1.2, -3.6)$ **67.** true   **69.** false

71. $6y - 4z = 25$ **73.** $x + 10y = 2$ **75.** no solution   **77.** infinite number of solutions   **79.** no   **81.** 5000 DVDs; $21

83. supply greater than demand   **85.** $(1875, 4687.5)$ **87.** makes money   **89.** for x-values greater than 1875

91. answers may vary; one possibility: $\begin{cases} -2x + y = 1 \\ x - 2y = -8 \end{cases}$ **93. a.** Consumption of red meat is decreasing while consumption of poultry is increasing.

b. $(31, 97)$ **c.** In the year 2028, red meat and poultry consumption will both be about 97 pounds per person.   **95.** $\left(\dfrac{1}{4}, 8\right)$ **97.** $\left(\dfrac{1}{3}, \dfrac{1}{2}\right)$

99. $\left(\dfrac{1}{4}, -\dfrac{1}{3}\right)$ **101.** $\varnothing$

Exercise Set 4.2   **1.** a, b, d   **3.** yes; answers may vary   **5.** $(-1, 5, 2)$ **7.** $(-2, 5, 1)$ **9.** $(-2, 3, -1)$ **11.** $\{(x, y, z) \mid x - 2y + z = -5\}$
13. $\varnothing$ **15.** $(0, 0, 0)$ **17.** $(-3, -35, -7)$ **19.** $(6, 22, -20)$ **21.** $\varnothing$ **23.** $(3, 2, 2)$ **25.** $\{(x, y, z) \mid x + 2y - 3z = 4\}$

27. $(-3, -4, -5)$ **29.** $\left(0, \dfrac{1}{2}, -4\right)$ **31.** $(12, 6, 4)$ **33.** $\{5\}$ **35.** $\left\{-\dfrac{5}{3}\right\}$ **37.** 15 and 30   **39.** answers may vary

41. answers may vary   **43.** $(1, 1, -1)$ **45.** $(1, 1, 0, 2)$ **47.** $(1, -1, 2, 3)$ **49.** answers may vary

Exercise Set 4.3   **1.** 10 and 8   **3. a.** Enterprise class: 1101 ft; Nimitz class: 1092 ft   **b.** 3.67 football fields   **5.** plane: 520 mph; wind: 40 mph

7. 20 qt of 4%; 40 qt of 1%   **9.** United Kingdom: 31,706 students; Italy: 18,936 students   **11.** 9 large frames; 13 small frames

13. -10 and -8 **15.** 2008   **17.** tablets: $0.80; pens: $0.20   **19.** speed of plane: 630 mph; speed of wind: 90 mph

21. a. answers may vary   **b.** 1984   **23.** 28 cm; 28 cm; 37 cm   **25.** 600 mi   **27.** $x = 75; y = 105$ **29.** 625 units   **31.** 3000 units

33. 1280 units   **35. a.** $R(x) = 450x$ **b.** $C(x) = 200x + 6000$ **c.** 24 desks   **37.** 2 units of Mix A; 3 units of Mix B; 1 unit of Mix C

39. 5 in.; 7 in.; 10 in.   **41.** 18, 13, and 9   **43.** free throws: 142; two-point field goals: 220; three-point field goals: 52   **45.** $x = 60; y = 55; z = 65$

47. $5x + 5z = 10$ **49.** $-5y + 2z = 2$ **51.** 1993: 897,231; 2003: 1,661,996   **53.** $a = 3, b = 4, c = -1$

55. $a = -\dfrac{7}{60}; b = 32\dfrac{23}{60}; c = 828\dfrac{9}{10}$; or $a = -0.11; b = 32.38; c = 828.9; 2009 - 1317$ thousand students

Integrated Review   **1.** C   **2.** D   **3.** A   **4.** B   **5.** $(1, 3)$ **6.** $\left(\dfrac{4}{3}, \dfrac{16}{3}\right)$ **7.** $(2, -1)$ **8.** $(5, 2)$ **9.** $\left(\dfrac{3}{2}, 1\right)$ **10.** $\left(-2, \dfrac{3}{4}\right)$

11. $\varnothing$ **12.** $\{(x, y) \mid 2x - 5y = 3\}$ **13.** $\left(1, \dfrac{1}{3}\right)$ **14.** $\left(3, \dfrac{3}{4}\right)$ **15.** $(-1, 3, 2)$ **16.** $(1, -3, 0)$ **17.** $\varnothing$

18. $\{(x, y, z) \mid x - y + 3z = 2\}$ **19.** $\left(2, 5, \dfrac{1}{2}\right)$ **20.** $\left(1, 1, \dfrac{1}{3}\right)$ **21.** 19 and 27   **22.** 70°; 70°; 100°; 120°

Exercise Set 4.4   **1.** $(2, -1)$ **3.** $(-4, 2)$ **5.** $\varnothing$ **7.** $\{(x, y) \mid 3x - 3y = 9\}$ **9.** $(-2, 5, -2)$ **11.** $(1, -2, 3)$ **13.** $(4, -3)$

15. $(2, 1, -1)$ **17.** $(9, 9)$ **19.** $\varnothing$ **21.** $\varnothing$ **23.** $(1, -4, 3)$ **25.** function   **27.** not a function   **29.** c   **31. a.** end of 1984
b. black-and-white sets; microwave ovens; the percent of households owning black-and-white television sets is decreasing and the percent of households owning microwave ovens is increasing; answers may vary   **c.** in 2002   **d.** answers may vary   **33.** answers may vary

Exercise Set 4.5   1. 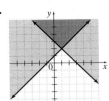   **3.** 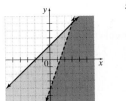   **5.** 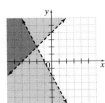   **7.**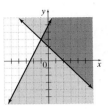

9. 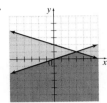   **11.** 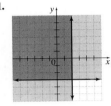   **13.** 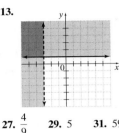   **15.** 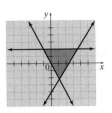   **17.**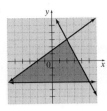

19. 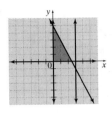   **21.** C   **23.** D   **25.** 9   **27.** $\frac{4}{9}$ **29.** 5   **31.** 59   **33.** the line $y = 3$ **35.** answers may vary

Vocabulary Check   1. system of equations   **2.** solution   **3.** consistent   **4.** square   **5.** inconsistent   **6.** matrix

Chapter 4 Review

1. $(-3, 1)$ **2.** $\left(0, \frac{2}{3}\right)$ **3.** $\varnothing$ **4.** $\{(x, y) \mid 3x - 6y = 12\}$ **5.** $\left(3, \frac{8}{3}\right)$ **6.** 1500 backpacks   **7.** $(2, 0, 2)$ **8.** $(2, 0, -3)$

9. $\left(-\frac{1}{2}, \frac{3}{4}, 1\right)$ **10.** $(-1, 2, 0)$ **11.** $\varnothing$ **12.** $(5, 3, 0)$ **13.** $(1, 1, -2)$ **14.** $(3, 1, 1)$ **15.** 10, 40, and 48   **16.** 63 and 21

17. 58 mph; 65 mph   **18.** width: 37 ft; length: 111 ft   **19.** 20 L of 10% solution; 30 L of 60% solution   **20.** 30 lb of creme-filled; 5 lb of chocolate-covered nuts; 10 lb of chocolate-covered raisins   **21.** 17 pennies; 20 nickels; 16 dimes   **22.** larger investment: 9.5%; smaller investment: 7.5%   **23.** two sides: 22 cm each; third side: 29 cm   **24.** 120, 115, and 60   **25.** $(-3, 1)$ **26.** $\{(x, y) \mid x - 2y = 4\}$

27. $\left(-\frac{2}{3}, 3\right)$ **28.** $\left(\frac{1}{3}, \frac{7}{6}\right)$ **29.** $\left(\frac{5}{4}, \frac{5}{8}\right)$ **30.** $(-7, -15)$ **31.** $(1, 3)$ **32.** $(2, 1)$ **33.** $(1, 2, 3)$ **34.** $(2, 0, -3)$ **35.** $(3, -2, 5)$

36. $(-1, 2, 0)$ **37.** $(1, 1, -2)$ **38.** $\varnothing$ **39.** 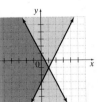   **40.** 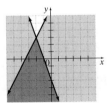   **41.**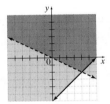

42. 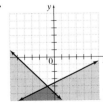   **43.** 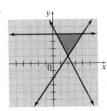   **44.** 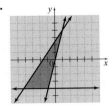   **45.** 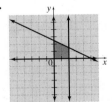   **46.**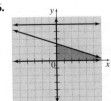

47. $\left(\frac{7}{3}, -\frac{8}{3}\right)$ **48.** $(10, -4)$ **49.** $\{(x, y) \mid 5x - 2y = 10\}$ **50.** $\varnothing$ **51.** $(-1, 3, 5)$ **52.** 33 and 94   **53.** 28 units, 42 units, 56 units

54. 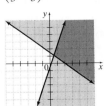   **55.** 2000

Chapter 4 Test   **1.** $(1, 3)$ **2.** $\varnothing$ **3.** $(2, -3)$ **4.** $\{(x, y) \,|\, 10x + 4y = 10\}$ **5.** $(-1, -2, 4)$ **6.** $\varnothing$ **7.** $\left(\dfrac{7}{2}, -10\right)$

8. $\{(x, y) \,|\, x - y = -2\}$ **9.** $(5, -3)$ **10.** $(-1, -1, 0)$ **11.** 53 double rooms; 27 single rooms   **12.** 5 gal of 10%; 15 gal of 20%
13. 800 packages   **14.** $23°, 45°, 112°$ **15.**

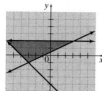

Cumulative Review   **1.** true; Sec. 1.2, Ex. 4   **2.** false; Sec. 1.2   **3.** false; Sec. 1.2, Ex. 7   **4.** true; Sec. 1.2   **5.** $<$; Sec. 1.3, Ex. 4

6. $>$; Sec. 1.3   **7.** $<$; Sec. 1.3, Ex. 7   **8.** $=$; Sec. 1.3   **9.** $<$; Sec. 1.3, Ex. 11   **10.** $<$; Sec. 1.3   **11.** $\dfrac{1}{7}$; Sec. 1.4, Ex. 3   **12.** 7.8; Sec. 1.4

13. -8; Sec. 1.4, Ex. 5   **14.** $-\dfrac{3}{8}$; Sec. 1.4   **15.** -1; Sec. 1.5, Ex. 3   **16. a.** -5 **b.** -24; Sec. 1.4   **17.** $\dfrac{1}{3x}$; Sec. 1.6, Ex. 16   **18.** $\dfrac{1}{81}$; Sec. 1.6

19. $\dfrac{11}{18}$; Sec. 1.6, Ex. 17   **20.** x^{16}; Sec. 1.6   **21.** solution; Sec. 2.1, Ex. 1   **22.** $\{0\}$; Sec. 2.1   **23.** \$2350; Sec. 2.2, Ex. 4

24. $100°, 100°, 110°, 50°$; Sec. 2.2   **25.** $b = \dfrac{2A - Bh}{h}$; Sec. 2.3, Ex. 3   **26.** $\{m \,|\, m \text{ is a real number}\}$; Sec. 2.1   **27.** $(-2, \infty)$; Sec. 2.4, Ex. 5

28. $(0, \infty)$; Sec. 2.4   **29.** $\{4, 6\}$; Sec. 2.5, Ex. 1   **30.** $\{2, 3, 4, 5, 6, 8\}$; Sec. 2.5   **31.** $\{0\}$; Sec. 2.5, Ex. 3   **32.** $\{1, 9\}$; Sec. 2.6

33.

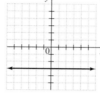

; Sec. 3.1, Ex. 8   **34.** $(-\infty, -3) \cup (2, \infty)$; Sec. 2.6   **35.** slope: $\dfrac{3}{4}$; y-intercept: $(0, -1)$; Sec. 3.2, Ex. 4

36. a. quadrant III   **b.** quadrant IV   **c.** y-axis; Sec. 3.1   **37.** $y = -3x - 2$; Sec. 3.4, Ex. 1   **38. a.** 75   **b.** 12; Sec. 3.6

39. function; Sec. 3.6, Ex. 7   **40.** $m = \dfrac{3}{2}$; Sec. 3.2   **41.**

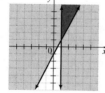

; Sec. 3.5, Ex. 3   **42.** $y = -2x + 2$; Sec. 3.3

43. $(0, -5)$; Sec. 4.1, Ex. 10   **44.** $(-1, 3)$; Sec. 4.1   **45.** $\varnothing$; Sec. 4.2, Ex. 2   **46.** $(-1, 2, 5)$; Sec. 4.2   **47.** 7 and 11; Sec. 4.3, Ex. 2
48. $\varnothing$; Sec. 4.1

CHAPTER 5   Polynomials and Polynomial Functions

Calculator Explorations   **1.** $x^3 - 4x^2 + 7x - 8$ **3.** $-2.1x^2 - 3.2x - 1.7$ **5.** $7.69x^2 - 1.26x + 5.3$

Mental Math   **1.** $10x$ **3.** $5y$ **5.** $-9z$

Exercise Set 5.1   **1.** 0   **3.** 2   **5.** 3   **7.** 3   **9.** 9   **11.** binomial of degree 1   **13.** trinomial of degree 2   **15.** monomial of degree 3

17. degree 4; none of these   **19.** $6y - 7y^2$ **21.** $-3x^4 + 11x$ **23.** $x^2y - 5x - \dfrac{1}{2}$ **25.** $18y^2 - 17$ **27.** $3x^2 - 3xy + 6y^2$
29. $x^2 - 4x + 8$ **31.** $12x^3y + 8x + 8$ **33.** $4.5x^3 + 0.2x^2 - 3.8x + 9.1$ **35.** $y^2 + 3$ **37.** $-2x^2 + 5x$ **39.** $7y^2 - 12y - 3$
41. $7x^3 + 4x^2 + 8x - 10$ **43.** $-20y^2 + 3yx$ **45.** $-3x^2 + 3$ **47.** $2y^4 - 5y^2 + x^2 + 1$ **49.** $5x^2 - 9x - 3$ **51.** $3x^2 + x + 18$
53. $4x - 13$ **55.** $-x^3 + 8a - 12$ **57.** $14ab + 10a^2b - 18a^2 + 12b^2$ **59.** $5x^2 + 22x + 16$ **61.** 0   **63.** $8xy^2 + 2x^3 + 3x^2 - 3$

65. $3x^2 - 9x + 15$ **67.** $15x^2 + 8x - 6$ **69.** $\dfrac{1}{3}x^2 - x + 1$ **71.** 57   **73.** 499   **75.** 1   **77.** 202 sq in.   **79. a.** 284 ft   **b.** 536 ft
c. 756 ft   **d.** 944 ft   **e.** answers may vary   **f.** 19 sec   **81.** \$80,000   **83.** \$40,000   **85.** $-14z + 42y$ **87.** $-15y^2 - 10y + 35$ **89.** a and c
91. $(12x - 1.7) - (15x + 6.2) = 12x - 1.7 - 15x - 6.2 = -3x - 7.9$ **93.** answers may vary   **95.** answers may vary
97. a. 0.6 million   **b.** 3.1 million   **c.** 9.7 million   **d.** answers may vary   **99.** $4x^2 - 3x + 6$ **101.** $2a - 3; -2x - 3; 2x + 2h - 3$
103. $12z^{5x} + 13z^{2x} - 2z$ **105.** $(2x^2 + 7xy + 10y^2)$ units

Calculator Explorations   **1.** $x^2 - 16$ **3.** $9x^2 - 42x + 49$ **5.** $5x^3 - 14x^2 - 13x - 2$

Exercise Set 5.2   **1.** $-12x^5$ **3.** $86a^5b^8c^3$ **5.** $12x^2 + 21x$ **7.** $-24x^2y - 6xy^2$ **9.** $-4a^3bx - 4a^3by + 12ab$ **11.** $2x^2 - 2x - 12$

13. $2x^4 + 3x^3 - 2x^2 + x + 6$ **15.** $15x^2 - 7x - 2$ **17.** $15m^3 + 16m^2 - m - 2$ **19.** $-30a^4b^4 + 36a^3b^2 + 36a^2b^3$ **21.** $x^2 + x - 12$
23. $10x^2 - 21xy - 8y^2$ **25.** $16x^2 - \dfrac{2}{3}x - \dfrac{1}{6}$ **27.** $5x^4 - 17x^2y^2 + 6y^4$ **29.** $x^2 + 8x + 16$ **31.** $36y^2 - 1$ **33.** $9x^2 - 6xy + y^2$

CHAPTER 11

Section 11.1

Check Point Exercises

1. 36   **2.** 0   **3. a.** 5   **b.** 3   **4.** ; 4   **5. a.** 2   **b.** 1   **c.** does not exist   **d.** 1

Exercise Set 11.1

1. 4   **3.** 3   **5.** 20   **7.** 1   **9.** 0   **11.** 12   **13.** 1   **15.** 1   **17.** 1   **19. a.** -1 **b.** -1 **21. a.** 2   **b.** 1   **23.** -3 **25.** -1
27. a. 4   **b.** 2   **c.** does not exist   **d.** 4   **29. a.** 2   **b.** 2   **c.** 2   **d.** 2   **e.** 4   **f.** 3   **g.** does not exist   **h.** does not exist
i. 2   **j.** 2   **k.** 2   **l.** 1   **31. a.** 1   **b.** 2   **c.** does not exist   **d.** 2   **e.** 2   **f.** 2   **g.** 2   **h.** 2   **33.** 7   **35.** -5 **37.** 0
39. -1 **41.** 2   **43.** 1   **45.** 0   **47.** 3   **49.** does not exist   **51.** 2   **53.** does not exist   **55.** -3 **57.** 2   **59.** 3   **61.** 0
63. 2
65. 0   **67. a.** 8; As your nose approaches the fan, the speed of the breeze that your nose feels approaches 8 miles per hour.   **b.** Answers may vary.
69. $\lim\limits_{x \to 67} f(x) = 45$ **71. a.** 30; The cost to rent the car one day and drive it 100 miles is \$30.   **b.** \$40   **c.** \$60   **85.** 0.69315; 0.693147
87. 1.5000; 1.50000   **91.** 31.544281

Section 11.2

Check Point Exercises

1. a. 11   **b.** -9 **2. a.** 19   **b.** $-\sqrt{2}$ **3.** 13   **4.** 5   **5.** -70 **6. a.** -22 **b.** 72   **7.** -56 **8.** 61   **9.** 343   **10.** $\sqrt{2}$
11. -3 **12. a.** -1 **b.** 1   **c.** does not exist   **13.** 4   **14.** $\dfrac{1}{6}$

Exercise Set 11.2

1. 8   **3.** 2   **5.** 14   **7.** 28   **9.** 6   **11.** 8   **13.** 16   **15.** 5   **17.** $\dfrac{5}{6}$ **19.** 3   **21.** 2   **23.** 2   **25.** 2   **27.** $\dfrac{8}{9}$ **29.** $\dfrac{1}{2}$
31. 1125   **33.** $\dfrac{1}{4}$ **35.** $-\dfrac{1}{4}$ **37.** -7 **39.** $-\dfrac{1}{9}$ **41.** $\dfrac{1}{3}$ **43. a.** 6   **b.** 8   **c.** does not exist   **45. a.** 9   **b.** 9   **c.** 9
47. a. 6   **b.** 6   **c.** 6   **49. a.** 0   **b.** 0   **c.** 0   **51.** 13; 2   **53.** 0; 3   **55.** 2   **57.** $\dfrac{5}{2}$ **59. a.** 0   **b.** The length of the starship
appears to approach 0.   **c.** It is not possible to exceed the speed of light.   **75.** $-\dfrac{1}{16}$ **77.** $\dfrac{1}{2}$ **79.** $\dfrac{2}{3}$

Section 11.3

Check Point Exercises

1. a. continuous   **b.** discontinuous   **2.** discontinuous at 0

Exercise Set 11.3

1. continuous   **3.** continuous   **5.** continuous   **7.** discontinuous   **9.** continuous   **11.** discontinuous   **13.** discontinuous
15. continuous   **17.** continuous   **19.** continuous for every number x **21.** -1 and 4   **23.** 0   **25.** continuous for every number x
27. 1
29. continuous for every number x **31.** 2   **33.** 4   **35.** discontinuous at π **37.** discontinuous at each integer   **39.** continuous for
every
number x **41.** discontinuous at $\dfrac{\pi}{2}$ **43. a.** 20; 20   **b.** yes   **c.** 40; 10   **d.** no   **e.** does not exist; 70   **f.** no   **g.** 100
h. As the end of the course approached, the percentage of material learned by the student approached 100%.   **45. a.** \$1.06   **b.** \$1.29
c. $\lim\limits_{x \to 4} f(x)$ does not exist. The graph shows a discontinuity at $x = 4$ ounces.   **d.** The graph jumps at its discontinuities due to per-ounce charges.

53. 2.7183; 2.71828   **55.** No. In Exercise 54, $\lim\limits_{x \to 9} f(x)$ exists. In this exercise, however, $\lim\limits_{x \to 9} \dfrac{1}{x - 9}$ does not exist.

Mid-Chapter 11 Check Point

1. 2   **2.** 1   **3.** does not exist   **4.** -2 **5.** -1 **6.** -3 **7.** 3   **8.** discontinuous at -1 and 0   **9.** -1 **10.** 1   **11.** 4
12. -1 **13.** 2   **14.** $\dfrac{49}{4}$ **15.** 13   **16.** $\dfrac{1}{6}$ **17.** does not exist   **18. a.** 1   **b.** 0   **c.** does not exist   **19. a.** 32   **b.** 32   **c.** 32
20. yes   **21.** yes   **22.** discontinuous at 5

Section 11.4

Check Point Exercises

1. 7   **2.** $y = \frac{1}{2}x + \frac{1}{2}$ **3. a.** $2x - 5$ **b.** $-7; 1$ **4. a.** 49.21 cubic inches per inch; 48.1201 cubic inches per inch
b. 48 cubic inches per inch   **5. a.** -32 ft/sec   **b.** -96 ft/sec

Exercise Set 11.4

1. a. 2   **b.** $y = 2x + 3$ **3. a.** -2 **b.** $y = -2x + 3$ **5. a.** -20 **b.** $y = -20x - 20$ **7. a.** 7   **b.** $y = 7x - 8$ **9. a.** 1
b. $y = x - 3$ **11. a.** $\frac{1}{6}$ **b.** $y = \frac{1}{6}x + \frac{3}{2}$ **13. a.** -1 **b.** $y = -x + 2$ **15. a.** -3 **b.** $-3; -3$ **17. a.** $2x$ **b.** $-2; 6$
19. a. $2x - 3$ **b.** $0; 1$ **21. a.** $3x^2$ **b.** $3; 3$ **23. a.** $\frac{1}{2\sqrt{x}}$ **b.** $\frac{1}{2}; \frac{1}{4}$ **25. a.** $-\frac{4}{x^2}$ **b.** $-1; -4$ **27. a.** $6.4x + 2.1$ **b.** $2.1; 27.7$

29. a. & c.   **b.** $y = 2x - 5$ **31. a. & c.**   **b.** $y = \frac{1}{2}x - 1$ **33. a. & c.**   **b.** $y = 3x + 4$ **35. a. & c.**   **b.** $y = x + 1$

37. a. 12.1 square inches per inch; 12.01 square inches per inch   **b.** 12 square inches per inch   **39. a.** 4.1π square inches per inch; 4.01π square inches per inch   **b.** 4π square inches per inch   **41.** 48π square inches per inch   **43. a.** 32 feet per second; -32 feet per second   **b.** -64 feet per second   **45. a.** 32 feet per second; -32 feet per second   **b.** 3 sec; 148 ft   **47. a.** Very well   **b.** 0.1   **c.** 0.1 million audits per year
65. -0.33 **67.** 3.64   **69.** e   **71.** d   **73.** b

75. $A'(r) = \lim\limits_{h \to 0} \dfrac{A(r + h) - A(r)}{h}$

$= \lim\limits_{h \to 0} \dfrac{\pi(r + h)^2 - \pi r^2}{h}$

$= \lim\limits_{h \to 0} \dfrac{\pi(r^2 + 2rh + h^2) - \pi r^2}{h}$

$= \lim\limits_{h \to 0} \dfrac{\pi r^2 + 2\pi rh + \pi h^2 - \pi r^2}{h}$

$= \lim\limits_{h \to 0} \dfrac{h(2\pi r + \pi h)}{h}$

$= \lim\limits_{h \to 0}(2\pi r + \pi h) = 2\pi r + 0 = 2\pi r$

Chapter 11 Review Exercises

1. 3   **2.** $\frac{1}{2}$ **3.** 2   **4.** 0   **5.** 1   **6.** 3   **7.** 2   **8.** 3   **9.** 3   **10.** 5   **11.** -3 **12.** does not exist   **13.** 1   **14.** 3   **15.** -3
16. does not exist   **17.** 3   **18.** does not exist   **19.** 5   **20.** 5   **21.** 5   **22.** 0   **23.** 0   **24.** 6   **25.** -1 **26.** 1   **27.** 15
28. 8   **29.** 1000   **30.** 5   **31.** 2   **32.** -8 **33.** 5   **34.** $\frac{1}{20}$ **35.** 2   **36.** $\frac{1}{20}$ **37.** $-\frac{1}{25}$ **38. a.** 5   **b.** 7   **c.** does not exist
39. a. 2   **b.** 4   **c.** does not exist   **40. a.** -10 **b.** -10 **c.** -10 **41.** continuous   **42.** discontinuous   **43.** discontinuous
44. continuous   **45.** discontinuous   **46.** continuous for every number x **47.** 1 and -3 **48.** 0   **49.** continuous for every number x
50. -2 **51.** 11   **52. a.** 9   **b.** $y = 9x - 2$ **53. a.** -9 **b.** $y = -9x - 5$ **54. a.** $6x + 12$ **b.** $0; 18$ **55. a.** $6x^2 - 1$
b. $5; 5$ **56. a.** $-\frac{1}{x^2}$ **b.** $-\frac{1}{4}; -\frac{1}{4}$ **57. a.** $\frac{1}{2\sqrt{x}}$ **b.** $\frac{1}{12}; \frac{1}{18}$ **58. a.** 20.5 cubic inches per inch; 20.05 cubic inches per inch
b. 20 cubic inches per inch   **59.** 100π cubic inches per inch   **60. a.** 16 feet per second; -48 feet per second   **b.** 2.5 sec; 105 ft

Chapter 11 Test

1. 6   **2.** -3 **3.** -5 **4.** 4   **5.** 6   **6.** does not exist   **7.** 4   **8.** 81   **9.** -3 **10.** $\frac{1}{6}$ **11.** discontinuous   **12.** continuous
13. $2x - 5$ **14.** $-\frac{10}{x^2}$ **15.** $y = -6x - 9$ **16.** -24 feet per second

Integrated Review   1. $2y^2 + 2y - 11$ **2.** $-2z^4 - 6z^2 + 3z$ **3.** $x^2 - 7x + 7$ **4.** $7x^2 - 4x - 5$ **5.** $25x^2 - 30x + 9$ **6.** $x - 3$
7. $2x^3 - 4x^2 + 5x - 5 + \dfrac{8}{x+2}$ **8.** $4x^3 - 13x^2 - 5x + 2$ **9.** $(x - 4 + y)(x - 4 - y)$ **10.** $2(3x + 2)(2x - 5)$
11. $x(x - 1)(x^2 + x + 1)$ **12.** $2x(2x - 1)$ **13.** $2xy(7x - 1)$ **14.** $6ab(4b - 1)$ **15.** $4(x + 2)(x - 2)$ **16.** $9(x + 3)(x - 3)$
17. $(3x - 11)(x + 1)$ **18.** $(5x + 3)(x - 1)$ **19.** $4(x + 3)(x - 1)$ **20.** $6(x + 1)(x - 2)$ **21.** $(2x + 9)^2$ **22.** $(5x + 4)^2$
23. $(2x + 5y)(4x^2 - 10xy + 25y^2)$ **24.** $(3x - 4y)(9x^2 + 12xy + 16y^2)$ **25.** $8x^2(2y - 1)(4y^2 + 2y + 1)$
26. $27x^2y(xy - 2)(x^2y^2 + 2xy + 4)$ **27.** $(x + 5 + y)(x^2 + 10x + 25 - xy - 5y + y^2)$
28. $(y - 1 + 3x)(y^2 - 2y + 1 - 3xy + 3x + 9x^2)$ **29.** $(5a - 6)^2$ **30.** $(4r + 5)^2$ **31.** $7x(x - 9)$ **32.** $(4x + 3)(5x + 2)$
33. $(a + 7)(b - 6)$ **34.** $20(x - 6)(x - 5)$ **35.** $(x^2 + 1)(x + 1)(x - 1)$ **36.** $5x(3x - 4)$ **37.** $(5x - 11)(2x + 3)$
38. $9m^2n^2(5mn - 3)$ **39.** $5a^3b(b^2 - 10)$ **40.** $x(x + 1)(x^2 - x + 1)$ **41.** prime   **42.** $20(x + y)(x^2 - xy + y^2)$
43. $10x(x - 10)(x - 11)$ **44.** $(3y - 7)^2$ **45.** $a^3b(4b - 3)(16b^2 + 12b + 9)$ **46.** $(y^2 + 4)(y + 2)(y - 2)$ **47.** $2(x - 3)(x^2 + 3x + 9)$
48. $(2s - 1)(r + 5)$ **49.** $(y^4 + 2)(3y - 5)$ **50.** prime   **51.** $100(z + 1)(z^2 - z + 1)$ **52.** $2x(5x - 2)(25x^2 + 10x + 4)$
53. $(2b - 9)^2$ **54.** $(a^4 + 3)(2a - 1)$ **55.** $(y - 4)(y - 5)$ **56.** $(c - 3)(c + 1)$ **57.** $A = 9 - 4x^2 = (3 + 2x)(3 - 2x)$

Calculator Explorations   1. $-3.562, 0.562$ **3.** $-0.874, 2.787$ **5.** $-0.465, 1.910$

Mental Math   1. $\{3, -5\}$ **3.** $\{3, -7\}$ **5.** $\{0, 9\}$

Exercise Set 5.7   1. $\left\{-3, \dfrac{4}{3}\right\}$ **3.** $\left\{-\dfrac{3}{4}, \dfrac{5}{2}\right\}$ **5.** $\{-3, -8\}$ **7.** $\left\{\dfrac{1}{4}, -\dfrac{2}{3}\right\}$ **9.** $\{1, 9\}$ **11.** $\left\{\dfrac{3}{5}, -1\right\}$ **13.** $\{0\}$ **15.** $\{6, -3\}$
17. $\left\{\dfrac{2}{5}, -\dfrac{1}{2}\right\}$ **19.** $\left\{\dfrac{3}{4}, -\dfrac{1}{2}\right\}$ **21.** $\left\{-2, 7, \dfrac{8}{3}\right\}$ **23.** $\{0, 3, -3\}$ **25.** $\{-1, 1, 2\}$ **27.** $\left\{-\dfrac{7}{2}, 10\right\}$ **29.** $\{0, 5\}$ **31.** $\{-3, 5\}$
33. $\left\{-\dfrac{1}{2}, \dfrac{1}{3}\right\}$ **35.** $\{-4, 9\}$ **37.** $\left\{\dfrac{4}{5}\right\}$ **39.** $\{-5, 0, 2\}$ **41.** $\left\{-3, 0, \dfrac{4}{5}\right\}$ **43.** $\varnothing$ **45.** $\{-7, 4\}$ **47.** $\{4, 6\}$
49. $\left\{-\dfrac{1}{2}\right\}$ **51.** $\{-4, -3, 3\}$ **53.** $\{-5, 0, 5\}$ **55.** $\{-6, 5\}$ **57.** $\left\{-\dfrac{1}{3}, 0, 1\right\}$ **59.** $\left\{-\dfrac{1}{3}, 0\right\}$ **61.** $\left\{-\dfrac{7}{8}\right\}$ **63.** $\left\{\dfrac{31}{4}\right\}$ **65.** $\{1\}$

67. -11 and -6, or 6 and 11 **69.** 75 ft   **71.** 105 units   **73.** 12 cm and 9 cm   **75.** 2 in.   **77.** 10 sec   **79.** Width: $7\dfrac{1}{2}$ ft; length: 12 ft
81. 10-in. square tier   **83.** E   **85.** F   **87.** B   **89.** $(-3, 0), (0, 2)$ **91.** $(-4, 0), (4, 0), (0, 2), (0, -2)$

93. $x - 5 = 0$ or $x + 2 = 0$ **95.** $y(y - 5) = -6$ **97.** $\left\{-3, -\dfrac{1}{3}, 2, 5\right\}$ **99.** answers may vary   **101.** no; answers may vary
 $x = 5$ or $x = -2$ $y^2 - 5y + 6 = 0$
 $ (y - 2)(y - 3) = 0$ **103.** answers may vary
 $ y - 2 = 0$ or $y - 3 = 0$
 $ y = 2$ or $y = 3$

The Bigger Picture   1. $\left\{-\dfrac{1}{2}, 6\right\}$ **2.** $(-7, 3)$ **3.** $\left\{-\dfrac{5}{3}\right\}$ **4.** $\left\{-\dfrac{3}{2}, 6\right\}$ **5.** $(-\infty, \infty)$ **6.** $\{-8, 3\}$ **7.** $\{-3, 10\}$ **8.** $(-\infty, 0]$

Vocabulary Check   1. polynomial   **2.** factoring   **3.** degree of a term   **4.** monomial   **5.** trinomial   **6.** quadratic equation
7. degree of a polynomial   **8.** binomial   **9.** 0   **10.** FOIL   **11.** synthetic division

Chapter 5 Review   1. 5   **2.** 1   **3.** $12x - 6x^2 - 6x^2y$ **4.** $-4xy^3 - 3x^3y$ **5.** $4x^2 + 8y + 6$ **6.** $-4x^2 + 10y^2$ **7.** $8x^2 + 2b - 22$
8. $-4x^3 + 4x^2 + 16xy - 9x + 18$ **9.** $12x^2y - 7xy + 3$ **10.** $x^2 - 6x + 3$ **11.** $x^3 + x - 2xy^2 - y - 7$ **12.** 290   **13.** 58
14. 110   **15.** $x^2 + 4x - 6$ **16.** $-x^2 + 2x + 3$ **17.** $(6x^2y - 12x + 12)$ cm   **18.** $-24x^3 + 36x^2 - 6x$ **19.** $-12a^2b^5 - 28a^2b^3 - 4ab^2$

20. $2x^2 + x - 36$ **21.** $9x^2a^2 - 24xab + 16b^2$ **22.** $36x^3 - 11x^2 - 8x - 3$ **23.** $15x^2 + 18xy - 81y^2$ **24.** $x^2 + \dfrac{1}{3}x - \dfrac{2}{9}$
25. $x^4 + 18x^3 + 83x^2 + 18x + 1$ **26.** $2x^3 + 3x^2 - 12x + 5$ **27.** $9x^2 - 6xy + y^2$ **28.** $16x^2 + 72x + 81$ **29.** $x^2 - 9y^2$
30. $16 - 9a^2 + 6ab - b^2$ **31.** $(9y^2 - 49z^2)$ sq units   **32.** $1 + \dfrac{x}{2y} - \dfrac{9}{4xy}$ **33.** $\dfrac{3}{b} + 4b$ **34.** $3x^3 + 9x^2 + 2x + 6 - \dfrac{2}{x - 3}$
35. $2x^3 + 6x^2 + 17x + 56 + \dfrac{156}{x - 3}$ **36.** $2x^3 + 2x - 2$ **37.** $x^2 + \dfrac{7}{2}x - \dfrac{1}{4} + \dfrac{15}{8\left(x - \dfrac{1}{2}\right)}$ **38.** $3x^2 + 2x - 1$ **39.** $3x^2 + 6$
40. $3x^2 + 6x + 24 + \dfrac{44}{x - 2}$ **41.** $4x^2 - 4x + 2 - \dfrac{5}{x + \dfrac{3}{2}}$ **42.** $x^4 - x^3 + x^2 - x + 1 - \dfrac{2}{x + 1}$ **43.** $x^2 + 3x + 9 - \dfrac{54}{x - 3}$
44. $3x^3 + 13x^2 + 51x + 204 + \dfrac{814}{x - 4}$ **45.** $3x^3 - 6x^2 + 10x - 20 + \dfrac{50}{x + 2}$ **46.** $8x^2(2x - 3)$ **47.** $12y(3 - 2y)$
48. $2ab(3 + 4 - 2ab)$ **49.** $7ab(2ab - 3b + 1)$ **50.** $(a + 3b)(6a - 5)$ **51.** $(x - 2y)(4x - 5)$ **52.** $(x - 6)(y + 3)$
53. $(a - 8)(b + 4)$ **54.** $(p - 5)(q - 3)$ **55.** $(x^2 - 2)(x - 1)$ **56.** $x(2y - x)$ **57.** $(x - 18)(x + 4)$ **58.** $(x - 4)(x + 20)$
59. $2(x - 2)(x - 7)$ **60.** $3(x + 2)(x + 9)$ **61.** $x(2x - 9)(x + 1)$ **62.** $(3x + 8)(x - 2)$ **63.** $(6x + 5)(x + 2)$
64. $(15x - 1)(x - 6)$ **65.** $2(2x - 3)(x + 2)$ **66.** $3(x - 2)(3x + 2)$ **67.** $(x + 6)^2(y - 3)(y + 1)$ **68.** $(x + 7)(x + 9)$
69. $(x^2 - 8)(x^2 + 2)$ **70.** $(x^2 - 2)(x^2 + 10)$ **71.** $(x + 10)(x - 10)$ **72.** $(x + 9)(x - 9)$ **73.** $2(x + 4)(x - 4)$
74. $6(x + 3)(x - 3)$ **75.** $(9 + x^2)(3 + x)(3 - x)$ **76.** $(4 + y^2)(2 + y)(2 - y)$ **77.** $(y + 7)(y - 3)$ **78.** $(x - 7)(x + 1)$
79. $(x + 6)(x^2 - 6x + 36)$ **80.** $(y + 8)(y^2 - 8y + 64)$ **81.** $(2 - 3y)(4 + 6y + 9y^2)$ **82.** $(1 - 4y)(1 + 4y + 16y^2)$
83. $6xy(x + 2)(x^2 - 2x + 4)$ **84.** $2x^2(x + 2y)(x^2 - 2xy + 4y^2)$ **85.** $(x - 1 + y)(x - 1 - y)$ **86.** $(x - 3 + 2y)(x - 3 - 2y)$
87. $(2x + 3)^2$ **88.** $(4a - 5b)^2$ **89.** $\pi h(R + r)(R - r)$ cu units   **90.** $\left\{\dfrac{1}{3}, -7\right\}$ **91.** $\left\{-5, \dfrac{3}{8}\right\}$ **92.** $\left\{0, 4, \dfrac{9}{2}\right\}$ **93.** $\left\{-3, -\dfrac{1}{5}, 4\right\}$

94. $\{0, 6\}$ **95.** $\{-3, 0, 3\}$ **96.** $\left\{-\dfrac{1}{3}, 2\right\}$ **97.** $\{2, 10\}$ **98.** $\{-4, 1\}$ **99.** $\left\{\dfrac{7}{2}, -5\right\}$ **100.** $\{0, 6, -3\}$ **101.** $\{-21, 0, 2\}$ **102.** $\{0, -2, 1\}$

103. $\left\{-\dfrac{3}{2}, 0, \dfrac{1}{4}\right\}$ **104.** $-\dfrac{15}{2}$ or 7   **105.** width: 2 m; length: 8 m   **106.** 5 sec   **107.** $3x^3 + 13x^2 - 9x + 5$ **108.** $-2x^2 + 5x - 6.9$

109. $8x^2 + 3x + 4.5$ **110.** $49a^2b^2 - 7ab + \dfrac{1}{4}$ **111.** -24 **112.** -10 **113.** $6y^4(2y - 1)$ **114.** $(x^2 - 3)(y + 4)$

115. $2(3x + 1)(x - 6)$ **116.** $(4x + 3)^2(y - 20)(y + 1)$ **117.** $z^5(2z + 7)(2z - 7)$ **118.** $(x + 1)(x - 1)(5x^2 + 9)$ **119.** $\{0, 3\}$
120. $\{-2, 13\}$

Chapter 5 Test   **1.** $-5x^3 - 11x - 9$ **2.** $-12x^2y - 3xy^2$ **3.** $12x^2 - 5x - 28$ **4.** $25a^2 - 4b^2$ **5.** $36m^2 + 12mn + n^2$

6. $2x^3 - 13x^2 + 14x - 4$ **7.** $\dfrac{4xy}{3z} + \dfrac{3}{z} + \dfrac{1}{3x}$ **8.** $2x^4 + 2x - 2 + \dfrac{1}{2x - 1}$ **9.** $4x^3 - 15x^2 + 47x - 142 + \dfrac{425}{x + 3}$ **10.** $4x^2y(4x - 3y^3)$

11. $(x - 15)(x + 2)$ **12.** $(2y + 5)^2$ **13.** $3(2x + 1)(x - 3)$ **14.** $(2x + 5)(2x - 5)$ **15.** $(x + 4)(x^2 - 4x + 16)$

16. $3y(x + 3y)(x - 3y)$ **17.** $2(2y - 1)(4y^2 + 2y + 1)$ **18.** $(x + 3)(x - 3)(y + 3)$ **19.** $\left\{4, -\dfrac{8}{7}\right\}$ **20.** $\{-3, 8\}$ **21.** $\left\{-\dfrac{5}{2}, -2, 2\right\}$

22. $(x + 2y)(x - 2y)$ **23. a.** 960 ft   **b.** 953.44 ft   **c.** $-16(t - 11)(t + 5)$ **d.** 11 sec

Cumulative Review   **1.** $-2x + 1$; Sec. 1.5, Ex. 13   **2.** $-2x - \dfrac{7}{8}$; Sec. 1.5   **3.** $2x + 23$; Sec. 1.5, Ex. 14   **4.** $16.3x - 0.8$; Sec. 1.5

5. 6×10^{-5}; Sec. 1.7, Ex. 20   **6. a.** $\dfrac{a^3}{64}$ **b.** $\dfrac{1}{a^4}$ **c.** $\dfrac{27}{8}$ **d.** $\dfrac{b^{17}}{9a^6}$; Sec. 1.7   **7.** $\{0\}$; Sec. 2.1, Ex. 6   **8.** $\{8\}$; Sec. 2.1

9. $y = \dfrac{7 + 2x}{3}$ or $y = \dfrac{7}{3} + \dfrac{2}{3}x$; Sec. 2.3, Ex. 2   **10.** 3 gal; Sec. 2.3   **11.** $\left[\dfrac{5}{2}, \infty\right)$; Sec. 2.4, Ex. 9   **12.** $(-\infty, -5)$; Sec. 2.4

13. $\left[-9, -\dfrac{9}{2}\right)$; Sec. 2.5, Ex. 5   **14.** $\left(-1, \dfrac{1}{3}\right]$; Sec. 2.5   **15.** $\left\{\dfrac{3}{4}, 5\right\}$; Sec. 2.6, Ex. 7   **16.** $(-\infty, \infty)$; Sec. 2.6   **17.** undefined; Sec. 3.2, Ex. 5

18. -2; Sec. 3.2   **19.** 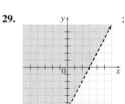 ; Sec. 3.3, Ex. 1   **20.** 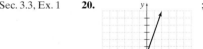 ; Sec. 3.3   **21.** $y = \dfrac{5}{3}x + \dfrac{13}{3}$; Sec. 3.4, Ex. 6

22. $x = -3$; Sec. 3.4
23. domain: $\{2, 0, 3\}$; range: $\{3, 4, -1\}$; Sec. 3.6, Ex. 1
24. $y = 3$; Sec. 3.4   **25.** -2; Sec. 3.6, Ex. 15
26. 24; Sec. 3.6   **27.** 5; Sec. 3.6, Ex. 16
28. a. $14.1y^8$ **b.** $-6a^5b^3c^4$; Sec. 1.7

29. 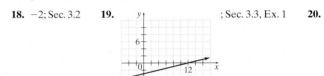 ; Sec. 3.5, Ex. 1   **30.** 37.5 oz. of 20% solution; 12.5 oz. of 60% solution; Sec. 4.3   **31.** $\left(-4, \dfrac{1}{2}\right)$; Sec. 4.1, Ex. 6

32. $(5, 2)$; Sec. 4.1   **33.** $(-4, 2, -1)$; Sec. 4.2, Ex. 1   **34.** $(-3, -2, 5)$; Sec. 4.2   **35.** $(-1, 2)$; Sec. 4.4, Ex. 1
36. $(-3, -4, -5)$; Sec. 4.2   **37.** 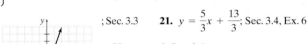 ; Sec. 4.5, Ex. 2   **38. a.** 8.25×10^6 **b.** 3.46×10^{-5}; Sec. 1.6
39. 4; Sec. 5.1, Ex. 9   **40.** $-2x^2 - 5x$; Sec. 5.1
41. $10x^2 - 8x$; Sec. 5.2, Ex. 3
42. $10x^3 - 17x^2 + 10x - 2$; Sec. 5.2
43. $-7x^3y^2 - 3x^2y^2 + 11xy$; Sec. 5.2, Ex. 5
44. $49x^2 - 7x + \dfrac{1}{4}$; Sec. 5.2   **45.** $2x^2 - x + 4$; Sec. 5.3, Ex. 1

46. $3xy(2x + y)(2x - y)$; Sec. 5.6   **47.** $(x + 2)(x + 8)$; Sec. 5.5, Ex. 1   **48.** $(5a - 1)(a + 3)$; Sec. 5.5   **49.** $\left\{-5, \dfrac{1}{2}\right\}$; Sec. 5.7, Ex. 2
50. $\left\{4, -\dfrac{2}{3}\right\}$; Sec. 5.7

CHAPTER 6   Rational Expressions

Calculator Explorations   **1.** $\{x \mid x \text{ is a real number and } x \neq 6\}$ **3.** $\{x \mid x \text{ is a real number and } x \neq -2, x \neq 2\}$

5. $\left\{x \mid x \text{ is a real number and } x \neq -4, x \neq \dfrac{1}{2}\right\}$ **7.** $\{x \mid x \text{ is a real number}\}$

Mental Math   **1.** $\dfrac{xy}{10}$ **3.** $\dfrac{2y}{3x}$ **5.** $\dfrac{m^2}{36}$

Exercise Set 6.1   **1.** $\{x \mid x \text{ is a real number}\}$ **3.** $\{t \mid t \text{ is a real number and } t \neq 0\}$ **5.** $\{x \mid x \text{ is a real number and } x \neq 7\}$

7. $\left\{x \mid x \text{ is a real number and } x \neq \dfrac{1}{3}\right\}$ **9.** $\{x \mid x \text{ is a real number and } x \neq -2, x \neq 0, x \neq 1\}$ **11.** $\{x \mid x \text{ is a real number and } x \neq 2, x \neq -2\}$

13. $1 - 2x$ **15.** $3 - x$ **17.** $\dfrac{9}{7}$ **19.** $x - 4$ **21.** -1 **23.** $-(x + 7)$ **25.** $\dfrac{2x + 1}{x - 1}$ **27.** $\dfrac{x^2 + 5x + 25}{2}$ **29.** $\dfrac{x - 2}{2x^2 + 1}$

31. $\dfrac{1}{3x + 5}$ **33.** $-\dfrac{4}{5}$ **35.** $-\dfrac{6a}{2a + 1}$ **37.** $\dfrac{3}{2(x - 1)}$ **39.** $\dfrac{x + 2}{x + 3}$ **41.** $\dfrac{3a}{5(a - b)}$ **43.** $\dfrac{1}{6}$ **45.** $\dfrac{x}{3}$ **47.** $\dfrac{4a^2}{a - b}$ **49.** $\dfrac{4}{(x + 2)(x + 3)}$

51. $\dfrac{1}{2}$ **53.** -1 **55.** $\dfrac{8(a-2)}{3(a+2)}$ **57.** $\dfrac{(x+2)(x+3)}{4}$ **59.** $\dfrac{2(x+3)(x-3)}{5(x^2-8x-15)}$ **61.** r^2-rs+s^2 **63.** $\dfrac{8}{x^2y}$ **65.** $\dfrac{(y+5)(2x-1)}{(y+2)(5x+1)}$

67. $\dfrac{10}{3},-8,-\dfrac{7}{3}$ **69.** $-\dfrac{17}{48},\dfrac{2}{7},-\dfrac{3}{8}$ **71. a.** \$200 million   **b.** \$500 million   **c.** \$300 million   **d.** $\{x|x \text{ is a real number}\}$ **73.** $\dfrac{7}{5}$ **75.** $\dfrac{1}{12}$

77. $\dfrac{11}{16}$ **79.** b and d   **81.** no; answers may vary   **83.** $\dfrac{5}{x-2}$ sq m   **85.** $\dfrac{(x+2)(x-1)^2}{x^5}$ ft   **87.** answers may vary   **89. a.** 1   **b.** -1

c. neither   **d.** -1 **e.** -1 **f.** 1   **91.** $(x-5)(2x+7)$ **93.** -1 **95.** $\dfrac{1}{x^n-4}$

Exercise Set 6.2   **1.** $-\dfrac{3}{xz^2}$ **3.** $\dfrac{x+2}{x-2}$ **5.** $x-2$ **7.** $\dfrac{-1}{x-2}$ or $\dfrac{1}{2-x}$ **9.** $-\dfrac{5}{x}$ **11.** $35x$ **13.** $x(x+1)$ **15.** $(x+7)(x-7)$

17. $6(x+2)(x-2)$ **19.** $(a+b)(a-b)^2$ **21.** $-4x(x+3)(x-3)$ **23.** $\dfrac{17}{6x}$ **25.** $\dfrac{35-4y}{14y^2}$ **27.** $\dfrac{-13x+4}{(x+4)(x-4)}$ **29.** $\dfrac{3}{x+4}$

31. 0   **33.** $-\dfrac{x}{x-1}$ **35.** $\dfrac{-x+1}{x-2}$ **37.** $\dfrac{y^2+2y+10}{(y+4)(y-4)(y-2)}$ **39.** $\dfrac{5(x^2+x-4)}{(3x+2)(x+3)(2x-5)}$ **41.** $\dfrac{x^2+5x-21}{(x-2)(x+1)(x+3)}$

43. $\dfrac{5(x^2+x-4)}{(3x+2)(x+3)(2x-5)}$ **45.** $\dfrac{5a+1}{(a+1)^2(a-1)}$ **47.** $\dfrac{3}{x^2y^3}$ **49.** $-\dfrac{5}{x}$ **51.** $\dfrac{25}{6(x+5)}$ **53.** $\dfrac{-2x-1}{x^2(x-3)}$ **55.** $\dfrac{b(2a-b)}{(a+b)(a-b)}$

57. $\dfrac{2(x+8)}{(x+2)^2(x-2)}$ **59.** $\dfrac{3x^2+23x-7}{(2x-1)(x-5)(x+3)}$ **61.** $\dfrac{5-2x}{2(x+1)}$ **63.** $\dfrac{2(x^2+x-21)}{(x+3)^2(x-3)}$ **65.** $\dfrac{6x}{(x+3)(x-3)^2}$ **67.** $\dfrac{4}{3}$ **69.** 10

71. $4+x^2$ **73.** $\dfrac{2x-3}{x^2+1}-\dfrac{x-6}{x^2+1}=\dfrac{2x-3-x+6}{x^2+1}=\dfrac{x+3}{x^2+1}$ **75.** $\dfrac{4x}{x+5}$ ft; $\dfrac{x^2}{(x+5)^2}$ sq ft   **77.** answers may vary

79. answers may vary   **81.** answers may vary   **83.** $\dfrac{(x+6)(2x-3)}{6x^2}$ or $\dfrac{2x^2+9x-18}{6x^2}$ **85.** $\dfrac{4a^2}{9(a-1)}$ **87.** 4   **89.** $-\dfrac{4}{x-1}$

91. $\dfrac{32}{x(x+2)(x-2)}$ **93.** $\dfrac{3}{2x}$ **95.** $\dfrac{4-3x}{x^2}$ **97.**

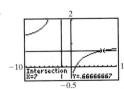

Exercise Set 6.3   **1.** $\dfrac{7}{13}$ **3.** $\dfrac{4}{x}$ **5.** $\dfrac{9(x-2)}{9x^2+4}$ **7.** 4   **9.** $2x+y$ **11.** $\dfrac{2(x+1)}{2x-1}$ **13.** $\dfrac{2x+3}{4-9x}$ **15.** $\dfrac{1}{x^2-2x+4}$ **17.** $\dfrac{x}{5x-10}$

19. $\dfrac{x-2}{2x-1}$ **21.** $\dfrac{x}{2-3x}$ **23.** $-\dfrac{y}{x+y}$ **25.** $-\dfrac{2x^2}{y(x-y)}$ **27.** $\dfrac{2x+1}{y+x^2}$ **29.** $\dfrac{x-3}{9}$ **31.** $\dfrac{1}{x+2}$ **33.** 2   **35.** $\dfrac{xy^2}{x^2+y^2}$

37. $\dfrac{2b^2+3a}{b(b-a)}$ **39.** $\dfrac{x}{(x+1)(x-1)}$ **41.** $\dfrac{1+a}{1-a}$ **43.** $\dfrac{x(x+6y)}{2y}$ **45.** $\dfrac{5a}{2(a+2)}$ **47.** $5xy^2+2x^2y$ **49.** $\dfrac{xy}{5y+2x}$ **51.** $\left\{-\dfrac{5}{6}\right\}$

53. $\{2\}$ **55.** $\{54\}$ **57.** a and c   **59.** $\dfrac{770a}{770-s}$ **61.** a and b   **63.** $\dfrac{x-3y}{x+3y}$ **65.** $\dfrac{1+x}{2+x}$ **67.** $x(x+1)$ **69. a.** $\dfrac{1}{a+h}$ **b.** $\dfrac{1}{a}$

c. $\dfrac{\dfrac{1}{a+h}-\dfrac{1}{a}}{h}$ **d.** $\dfrac{-1}{a(a+h)}$ **71. a.** $\dfrac{3}{a+h+1}$ **b.** $\dfrac{3}{a+1}$ **c.** $\dfrac{\dfrac{3}{a+h+1}-\dfrac{3}{a+1}}{h}$ **d.** $\dfrac{-3}{(a+h+1)(a+1)}$

Mental Math   **1.** equation   **3.** expression   **5.** equation

Exercise Set 6.4   **1.** $\{72\}$ **3.** $\{2\}$ **5.** $\{6\}$ **7.** $\{2,-2\}$ **9.** $\varnothing$ **11.** $\left\{-\dfrac{28}{3}\right\}$ **13.** $\{3\}$ **15.** $\{-8\}$ **17.** $\{3\}$ **19.** $\varnothing$

21. $\{1\}$ **23.** $\{3\}$ **25.** $\{-1\}$ **27.** $\{6\}$ **29.** $\left\{\dfrac{1}{3}\right\}$ **31.** $\{-5,5\}$ **33.** $\{3\}$ **35.** $\{7\}$ **37.** $\varnothing$ **39.** $\left\{\dfrac{4}{3}\right\}$ **41.** $\{-12\}$

43. $\left\{1,\dfrac{11}{4}\right\}$ **45.** $\{-5,-1\}$ **47.** $\left\{-\dfrac{7}{5}\right\}$ **49.** 5   **51.** length: 15 in.; width: 10 in.   **53.** 13.5%   **55.** 25–29   **57.** 6370 inmates

59. answers may vary   **61.** 3000 game disks   **63.** $\left\{\dfrac{1}{16},\dfrac{1}{3}\right\}$ **65.** $\left\{-\dfrac{1}{5},1\right\}$ **67.** $\{-0.17\}$ **69.** $\{0.42\}$ **71.** $\{-1,0\}$

73. $\{-2\}$ **75.**

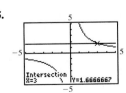

77.

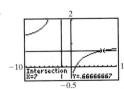

The Bigger Picture   **1.** $\left(-2,\dfrac{16}{7}\right)$ **2.** $\left\{-2,\dfrac{16}{7}\right\}$ **3.** $\{\pm 11\}$ **4.** $\{5\}$ **5.** $\left\{-\dfrac{8}{5}\right\}$ **6.** $(-\infty,2]$ **7.** $(-\infty,-5]$

8. $(7,10]$ **9.** $(-\infty,-17)\cup(18,\infty)$ **10.** $\left\{0,-\dfrac{1}{3},\dfrac{7}{5}\right\}$

Cumulative Review   **1.** true; Sec. 1.2, Ex. 3   **2. a.** $x - \dfrac{1}{3}$ **b.** $5x - 6$ **c.** $8x + 3$ **d.** $\dfrac{7}{2-x}$; Sec. 1.2   **3.** -1; Sec. 1.6, Ex. 7   **4.** x^2y^2; Sec. 1.6

5. 1; Sec. 1.6, Ex. 8   **6.** $\dfrac{8a^7}{9b^{11}}$; Sec. 1.7   **7.** $\varnothing$; Sec. 2.5, Ex. 3   **8.** $\varnothing$; Sec. 2.6   **9.** $\{4, -10\}$; Sec. 2.6, Ex. 4   **10.** $\left(-\infty, -\dfrac{5}{3}\right] \cup \left[\dfrac{11}{3}, \infty\right)$; Sec. 2.6

11. $(0, -12)$, solution; $(1, 9)$, not a solution; $(2, -6)$, solution; Sec. 3.1, Ex. 3   **12. a.** -2 **b.** -20 **c.** $-\dfrac{10}{9}$; Sec. 3.6   **13.** parallel; Sec. 3.2, Ex. 8

14. 7; Sec. 2.1   **15.** $-5x + 8y = -20$ or $5x - 8y = 20$; Sec. 3.4, Ex. 2   **16.** $f(x) = \dfrac{1}{2}x + \dfrac{7}{2}$; Sec. 3.6

17. domain: $(-\infty, \infty)$; range: $[0, \infty)$; Sec. 3.7, Ex. 2   **18.** domain: $(-\infty, \infty)$; range: $(-\infty, \infty)$; Sec. 3.7

19. domain: $[-4, 4]$; range: $[-2, 2]$; Sec. 3.7, Ex. 3   **20.** domain: $(-\infty, \infty)$; range: $(-\infty, -1]$; Sec. 3.7   **21.** $\left(-\dfrac{21}{10}, \dfrac{3}{10}\right)$; Sec. 4.1, Ex. 7

22. $(3, 4)$; Sec. 4.1   **23.** $\left(\dfrac{1}{2}, 0, \dfrac{3}{4}\right)$; Sec. 4.2, Ex. 3   **24.** $(2, 1, 1)$; Sec. 4.2   **25.** 52 mph; 47 mph; Sec. 4.3, Ex. 3

26. Paper, \$3.80; folders, \$5.25; Sec. 4.3   **27.** $(1, -1, 3)$; Sec. 4.4, Ex. 3   **28.** $(0, 5, 4)$; Sec. 4.4   **29.** $\dfrac{z^2}{9x^4y^{20}}$; Sec. 1.7, Ex. 14

30. a. $\dfrac{7}{12}$ **b.** -6 **c.** $\dfrac{1}{x^3}$; Sec. 1.7   **31.** 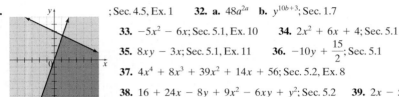 ; Sec. 4.5, Ex. 1   **32. a.** $48a^{2a}$ **b.** y^{10b+3}; Sec. 1.7

33. $-5x^2 - 6x$; Sec. 5.1, Ex. 10   **34.** $2x^2 + 6x + 4$; Sec. 5.1

35. $8xy - 3x$; Sec. 5.1, Ex. 11   **36.** $-10y + \dfrac{15}{2}$; Sec. 5.1

37. $4x^4 + 8x^3 + 39x^2 + 14x + 56$; Sec. 5.2, Ex. 8

38. $16 + 24x - 8y + 9x^2 - 6xy + y^2$; Sec. 5.2   **39.** $2x - 5$; Sec. 5.3, Ex. 3

40. $(y + 2)(x - 5)$; Sec. 5.4   **41.** $xy(-3x^2 + 2x - 5)$ or $-xy(3x^2 - 2x + 5)$; Sec. 5.4, Ex. 5   **42.** $(2x - 5)(3x + 7)$; Sec. 5.5

43. $(x + 2)(x + 8)$; Sec. 5.5, Ex. 1   **44.** $(2x - 1 + 3y)(2x - 1 - 3y)$; Sec. 5.6   **45.** $(p^2 + 4)(p + 2)(p - 2)$; Sec. 5.6, Ex. 9

46. a. domain: $(-\infty, \infty)$; range: $[-4, \infty)$ **b.** x-intercepts: $(-2, 0), (2, 0)$; y-intercept: $(0, -4)$ **c.** There is no such point.   **d.** $(0, -4)$ **e.** $-2, 2$

f. between $x = -2$ and $x = 2$ **g.** $\{-2, 2\}$; Sec. 3.6   **47.** $\{-2, 6\}$; Sec. 5.7, Ex. 1   **48.** $\left\{0, -\dfrac{1}{3}, 3\right\}$; Sec. 5.7   **49.** $\dfrac{x(x + 5)}{2(x - 5)}$; Sec. 6.3, Ex. 1

50. $\{-4\}$; Sec. 6.4

CHAPTER 7   Rational Exponents, Radicals, and Complex Numbers

Exercise Set 7.1   **1.** $2, -2$ **3.** no real number square roots   **5.** $10, -10$ **7.** 10 **9.** $\dfrac{1}{2}$ **11.** 0.01 **13.** -6 **15.** x^5 **17.** $4y^3$

19. 2.646 **21.** 6.164 **23.** 14.142 **25.** 4 **27.** $\dfrac{1}{2}$ **29.** -1 **31.** x^4 **33.** $-3x^3$ **35.** -2 **37.** not a real number   **39.** -2

41. x^4 **43.** $2x^2$ **45.** $9x^2$ **47.** $4x^2$ **49.** 8 **51.** -8 **53.** $2|x|$ **55.** x **57.** $|x - 2|$ **59.** $|x + 2|$ **61.** -11 **63.** $2x$

65. y^6 **67.** $5ab^{10}$ **69.** $-3x^4y^3$ **71.** a^4b **73.** $-2x^2y$ **75.** $\dfrac{5}{7}$ **77.** $\dfrac{x}{2y}$ **79.** $-\dfrac{z^7}{3x}$ **81.** $\dfrac{x}{2}$ **83.** $\sqrt{3}$ **85.** -1 **87.** -3

89. $\sqrt{7}$ **91.** $(-\infty, \infty)$;   **93.** $(-\infty, \infty)$;   **95.** $-32x^{15}y^{10}$ **97.** $-60x^7y^{10}z^5$ **99.** $\dfrac{x^9y^5}{2}$

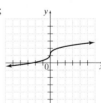   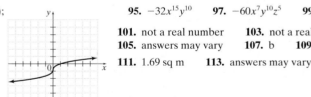

101. not a real number   **103.** not a real number
105. answers may vary   **107.** b   **109.** b
111. 1.69 sq m   **113.** answers may vary

Exercise Set 7.2   **1.** 7 **3.** 3 **5.** $\dfrac{1}{2}$ **7.** 13 **9.** $2\sqrt[3]{m}$ **11.** $3x^2$ **13.** -3 **15.** -2 **17.** 8 **19.** 16 **21.** not a real number

23. $\sqrt[5]{(2x)^3}$ **25.** $\sqrt[3]{(7x + 2)^2}$ or $\left(\sqrt[3]{7x + 2}\right)^2$ **27.** $\dfrac{64}{27}$ **29.** $\dfrac{1}{16}$ **31.** $\dfrac{1}{16}$ **33.** not a real number   **35.** $\dfrac{1}{x^{1/4}}$ **37.** $a^{2/3}$

39. $\dfrac{5x^{3/4}}{7}$ **41.** $a^{7/3}$ **43.** x **45.** $3^{5/8}$ **47.** $y^{1/6}$ **49.** $8u^3$ **51.** $-b$ **53.** $\dfrac{1}{x^2}$ **55.** $27x^{2/3}$ **57.** $\dfrac{y}{z^{1/6}}$ **59.** $\dfrac{1}{x^{7/4}}$ **61.** $\sqrt{x}$

63. $\sqrt[3]{2}$ **65.** $2\sqrt{x}$ **67.** $\sqrt{x + 3}$ **69.** $\sqrt{xy}$ **71.** $\sqrt[3]{a^2b}$ **73.** $\sqrt[15]{y^{11}}$ **75.** $\sqrt[12]{b^5}$ **77.** $\sqrt[24]{x^{23}}$ **79.** $\sqrt{a}$ **81.** $\sqrt[6]{432}$

83. $\sqrt[15]{343y^5}$ **85.** $\sqrt[6]{125r^3s^2}$ **87.** $25 \cdot 3$ **89.** $16 \cdot 3$ or $4 \cdot 12$ **91.** $8 \cdot 2$ **93.** $27 \cdot 2$ **95.** 1509 calories   **97.** 176.1 million

99. answers may vary   **101.** $a^{1/3}$ **103.** $x^{1/5}$ **105.** 1.6818   **107.** $\dfrac{t^{1/2}}{u^{1/2}}$

Exercise Set 7.3   **1.** $\sqrt{14}$ **3.** 2 **5.** $\sqrt[3]{36}$ **7.** $\sqrt{6x}$ **9.** $\sqrt{\dfrac{14}{xy}}$ **11.** $\sqrt[4]{20x^3}$ **13.** $\dfrac{\sqrt{6}}{7}$ **15.** $\dfrac{\sqrt{2}}{7}$ **17.** $\dfrac{\sqrt[4]{x^3}}{2}$ **19.** $\dfrac{\sqrt[3]{4}}{3}$

21. $\dfrac{\sqrt[4]{8}}{x^2}$ **23.** $\dfrac{\sqrt[3]{2x}}{3y^4\sqrt[3]{3}}$ **25.** $\dfrac{x\sqrt{y}}{10}$ **27.** $\dfrac{x\sqrt{5}}{13y}$ **29.** $-\dfrac{z^2\sqrt[3]{z}}{5x}$ **31.** $4\sqrt{2}$ **33.** $4\sqrt[3]{3}$ **35.** $25\sqrt{3}$ **37.** $2\sqrt{6}$ **39.** $10x^2\sqrt{x}$

41. $2y^2\sqrt[3]{2y}$ **43.** $a^2b\sqrt[4]{b^3}$ **45.** $y^2\sqrt{y}$ **47.** $5ab\sqrt{b}$ **49.** $-2x^2\sqrt[5]{y}$ **51.** $x^4\sqrt[3]{50x^2}$ **53.** $-4a^4b^3\sqrt{2b}$ **55.** $3x^3y^4\sqrt{xy}$

57. $5r^3s^4$ **59.** $\sqrt{2}$ **61.** 2   **63.** 10   **65.** x^2y **67.** $24m^2$ **69.** $\dfrac{15x\sqrt{2x}}{2}$ or $\dfrac{15x}{2}\sqrt{2x}$ **71.** $2a^2\sqrt[4]{2}$ **73.** 5 units

75. $\sqrt{41}$ units ≈ 6.403 **77.** $\sqrt{5}$ units ≈ 2.236 **79.** $\sqrt{192.58}$ units ≈ 13.877 **81.** $(4, -2)$ **83.** $\left(-5, \dfrac{5}{2}\right)$ **85.** $\left(-\dfrac{1}{2}, \dfrac{1}{2}\right)$

87. $\left(\sqrt{2}, \dfrac{\sqrt{5}}{2}\right)$ **89.** $14x$ **91.** $2x^2 - 7x - 15$ **93.** y^2 **95.** $x^2 - 8x + 16$ **97.** $\dfrac{\sqrt[3]{64}}{\sqrt{64}} = \dfrac{4}{8} = \dfrac{1}{2}$ **99.** $r = 1.6$ meters

101. a. 3.8 times   **b.** 2.9 times   **c.** answers may vary

Mental Math   1. $6\sqrt{3}$ **3.** $3\sqrt{x}$ **5.** $12\sqrt[3]{x}$ **7.** 3

Exercise Set 7.4   1. $-2\sqrt{2}$ **3.** $10x\sqrt{2x}$ **5.** $17\sqrt{2} - 15\sqrt{5}$ **7.** $-\sqrt[3]{2x}$ **9.** $5b\sqrt{b}$ **11.** $\dfrac{31\sqrt{2}}{15}$ **13.** $\dfrac{\sqrt[3]{11}}{3}$ **15.** $\dfrac{5\sqrt{5x}}{9}$

17. $14 + \sqrt{3}$ **19.** $7 - 3y$ **21.** $6\sqrt{3} - 6\sqrt{2}$ **23.** $-23\sqrt[3]{5}$ **25.** $2b\sqrt{b}$ **27.** $20y\sqrt{2y}$ **29.** $2y\sqrt[3]{2x}$ **31.** $6\sqrt[3]{11} - 4\sqrt{11}$

33. $4x\sqrt[4]{x^3}$ **35.** $\dfrac{2\sqrt{3}}{3}$ **37.** $\dfrac{5x\sqrt[3]{x}}{7}$ **39.** $\dfrac{5\sqrt{7}}{2x}$ **41.** $\dfrac{\sqrt[3]{2}}{6}$ **43.** $\dfrac{14x\sqrt[3]{2x}}{9}$ **45.** $15\sqrt{3}$ in.   **47.** $\sqrt{35} + \sqrt{21}$ **49.** $7 - 2\sqrt{10}$

51. $3\sqrt{x} - x\sqrt{3}$ **53.** $6x - 13\sqrt{x} - 5$ **55.** $\sqrt[3]{a^2} + \sqrt[3]{a} - 20$ **57.** $6\sqrt{2} - 12$ **59.** $2 + 2x\sqrt{3}$ **61.** $-16 - \sqrt{35}$ **63.** $x - y^2$

65. $3 + 2x\sqrt{3} + x^2$ **67.** $5x - 3\sqrt{15x} - 3\sqrt{10x} + 9\sqrt{6}$ **69.** $-\sqrt[3]{4} + 2\sqrt[3]{2}$ **71.** $\sqrt[3]{x^2} - 4\sqrt[6]{x^5} + 8\sqrt[3]{x} - 4\sqrt{x} + 7$

73. $x + 24 + 10\sqrt{x - 1}$ **75.** $2x + 6 - 2\sqrt{2x + 5}$ **77.** $x - 7$ **79.** $\dfrac{7}{x + y}$ **81.** $2a - 3$ **83.** $\dfrac{-2 + \sqrt{3}}{3}$ **85.** $22\sqrt{5}$ ft; 150 sq ft
87. a. $2\sqrt{3}$ **b.** 3   **c.** answers may vary

Mental Math   1. $\sqrt{2} - x$ **3.** $5 + \sqrt{a}$ **5.** $7\sqrt{4} - 8\sqrt{x}$

Exercise Set 7.5   1. $\dfrac{\sqrt{14}}{7}$ **3.** $\dfrac{\sqrt{5}}{5}$ **5.** $\dfrac{4\sqrt[3]{9}}{3}$ **7.** $\dfrac{3\sqrt{2x}}{4x}$ **9.** $\dfrac{3\sqrt[3]{2x}}{2x}$ **11.** $\dfrac{3\sqrt{3a}}{a}$ **13.** $\dfrac{3\sqrt[3]{4}}{2}$ **15.** $\dfrac{2\sqrt{21}}{7}$ **17.** $\dfrac{\sqrt{10xy}}{5y}$

19. $\dfrac{\sqrt[3]{75}}{5}$ **21.** $\dfrac{\sqrt{6x}}{10}$ **23.** $\dfrac{\sqrt{3z}}{6z}$ **25.** $\dfrac{\sqrt[3]{6xy^2}}{3x}$ **27.** $\dfrac{2\sqrt[4]{9x}}{3x^2}$ **29.** $\dfrac{5\sqrt[5]{4ab^4}}{2ab^3}$ **31.** $-2(2 + \sqrt{7})$ **33.** $\dfrac{7(\sqrt{x} + 3)}{9 - x}$

35. $-5 + 2\sqrt{6}$ **37.** $\dfrac{2a + \sqrt{ab} + 2\sqrt{a} + \sqrt{b}}{4a - b}$ **39.** $-\dfrac{8(1 - \sqrt{10})}{9}$ **41.** $\dfrac{x - \sqrt{xy}}{x - y}$ **43.** $\dfrac{5 + 3\sqrt{2}}{7}$ **45.** $\dfrac{5}{\sqrt{15}}$ **47.** $\dfrac{6}{\sqrt{10}}$

49. $\dfrac{2x}{7\sqrt{x}}$ **51.** $\dfrac{5y}{\sqrt[3]{100xy}}$ **53.** $\dfrac{2}{\sqrt{10}}$ **55.** $\dfrac{2x}{11\sqrt{2x}}$ **57.** $\dfrac{7}{2\sqrt[3]{49}}$ **59.** $\dfrac{3x^2}{10\sqrt[3]{9x}}$ **61.** $\dfrac{6x^2y^3}{\sqrt{6z}}$ **63.** answers may vary

65. $\dfrac{-7}{12 + 6\sqrt{11}}$ **67.** $\dfrac{3}{10 + 5\sqrt{7}}$ **69.** $\dfrac{x - 9}{x - 3\sqrt{x}}$ **71.** $\dfrac{x - 1}{x - 2\sqrt{x} + 1}$ **73.** $\{5\}$ **75.** $\left\{-\dfrac{1}{2}, 6\right\}$ **77.** $\{2, 6\}$ **79.** $r = \dfrac{\sqrt{A\pi}}{2\pi}$

81. answers may vary   **83.** $\sqrt[3]{25}$

Integrated Review   1. 9   **2.** -2 **3.** $\dfrac{1}{2}$ **4.** x^3 **5.** y^3 **6.** $2y^5$ **7.** $-2y$ **8.** $3b^3$ **9.** 6   **10.** $\sqrt[4]{3y}$ **11.** $\dfrac{1}{16}$ **12.** $\sqrt[5]{(x + 1)^3}$

13. y **14.** $16x^{1/2}$ **15.** $x^{5/4}$ **16.** $4^{11/15}$ **17.** $2x^2$ **18.** $\sqrt[4]{a^3b^2}$ **19.** $\sqrt[4]{x^3}$ **20.** $\sqrt[6]{500}$ **21.** $2\sqrt{10}$ **22.** $2xy^2\sqrt[4]{x^3y^2}$

23. $3x\sqrt[3]{2x}$ **24.** $-2b^2\sqrt[5]{2}$ **25.** $\sqrt{5x}$ **26.** $4x$ **27.** $7y^2\sqrt{y}$ **28.** $2a^2\sqrt[3]{3}$ **29.** $2\sqrt{5} - 5\sqrt{3} + 5\sqrt{7}$ **30.** $y\sqrt[3]{2y}$

31. $\sqrt{15} - \sqrt{6}$ **32.** $10 + 2\sqrt{21}$ **33.** $4x^2 - 5$ **34.** $x + 2 - 2\sqrt{x + 1}$ **35.** $\dfrac{\sqrt{21}}{3}$ **36.** $\dfrac{5\sqrt[3]{4x}}{2x}$ **37.** $\dfrac{13 - 3\sqrt{21}}{5}$ **38.** $\dfrac{7}{\sqrt{21}}$

39. $\dfrac{3y}{\sqrt[3]{33y^2}}$ **40.** $\dfrac{x - 4}{x + 2\sqrt{x}}$

Graphing Calculator Explorations   1. $\{3.19\}$ **3.** $\varnothing$ **5.** $\{3.23\}$

Exercise Set 7.6   1. $\{8\}$ **3.** $\{7\}$ **5.** $\varnothing$ **7.** $\{7\}$ **9.** $\{6\}$ **11.** $\left\{-\dfrac{9}{2}\right\}$ **13.** $\{29\}$ **15.** $\{4\}$ **17.** $\{-4\}$ **19.** $\varnothing$

21. $\{7\}$ **23.** $\{9\}$ **25.** $\{50\}$ **27.** $\varnothing$ **29.** $\left\{\dfrac{15}{4}\right\}$ **31.** $\{7\}$ **33.** $\{5\}$ **35.** $\{-12\}$ **37.** $\{9\}$ **39.** $\{-3\}$ **41.** $\{1\}$

43. $\{1\}$ **45.** $\left\{\dfrac{1}{2}\right\}$ **47.** $\{0, 4\}$ **49.** $\left\{\dfrac{37}{4}\right\}$ **51.** $3\sqrt{5}$ ft   **53.** $2\sqrt{10}$ m   **55.** $2\sqrt{131}$ m ≈ 22.9 m   **57.** $\sqrt{100.84}$ mm ≈ 10.0 mm

59. 17 ft   **61.** 13 ft   **63.** 14,657,415 sq mi   **65.** 100 ft   **67.** 100   **69.** $\dfrac{\pi}{2}$ sec ≈ 1.57 sec   **71.** 12.97 ft   **73.** answers may vary

75. $15\sqrt{3}$ sq mi ≈ 25.98 sq mi   **77.** answers may vary   **79.** 0.51 km   **81.** $\dfrac{x}{4x + 3}$ **83.** $-\dfrac{4z + 2}{3z}$ **85.** $\{1\}$

87. $\sqrt{5x - 1} + 4 = 7$ **89.** 2743 deliveries
$$\sqrt{5x - 1} = 3$$
$$\left(\sqrt{5x - 1}\right)^2 = 3^2$$
$$5x - 1 = 9$$
$$5x = 10$$
$$x = 2$$

The Bigger Picture **1.** $\{-19\}$ **2.** $\left\{-\dfrac{5}{3}, 5\right\}$ **3.** $\left\{-\dfrac{9}{2}, 5\right\}$ **4.** $\left[-\dfrac{11}{5}, 1\right]$ **5.** $\left(-\dfrac{7}{5}, \infty\right)$ **6.** $\{25\}$ **7.** $(-5, \infty)$ **8.** $\varnothing$
9. $(-\infty, -13) \cup (17, \infty)$ **10.** $\left\{\dfrac{17}{25}\right\}$

Mental Math **1.** $9i$ **3.** $i\sqrt{7}$ **5.** -4 **7.** $8i$

Exercise Set 7.7 **1.** $2i\sqrt{6}$ **3.** $-6i$ **5.** $24i\sqrt{7}$ **7.** $-3\sqrt{6}$ **9.** $-\sqrt{14}$ **11.** $-5\sqrt{2}$ **13.** $4i$ **15.** $i\sqrt{3}$ **17.** $2\sqrt{2}$ **19.** $6 - 4i$
21. $-2 + 6i$ **23.** $-2 - 4i$ **25.** $2 - i$ **27.** $5 - 10i$ **29.** $8 - i$ **31.** -12 **33.** 63 **35.** -40 **37.** $18 + 12i$ **39.** $27 + 3i$
41. $18 + 13i$ **43.** 7 **45.** $12 - 16i$ **47.** 20 **49.** 2 **51.** $17 + 144i$ **53.** $-2i$ **55.** $-4i$ **57.** $\dfrac{28}{25} - \dfrac{21}{25}i$ **59.** $-\dfrac{12}{5} + \dfrac{6}{5}i$
61. $4 + i$ **63.** $-\dfrac{5}{2} - 2i$ **65.** $-5 + \dfrac{16}{3}i$ **67.** $\dfrac{3}{5} - \dfrac{1}{5}i$ **69.** $\dfrac{1}{5} - \dfrac{8}{5}i$ **71.** 1 **73.** i **75.** $-i$ **77.** -1 **79.** -64 **81.** $-243i$
83. 5 people **85.** 14 people **87.** 16.7% **89.** $1 - i$ **91.** 0 **93.** $2 + 3i$ **95.** $2 + i\sqrt{2}$ **97.** $\dfrac{1}{2} - \dfrac{\sqrt{3}}{2}i$ **99.** answers may vary
101. $6 - 6i$ **103.** yes

Chapter 7 Vocabulary Check **1.** conjugate **2.** principal square root **3.** rationalizing **4.** imaginary unit **5.** cube root
6. index, radicand **7.** like radicals **8.** complex number **9.** distance **10.** midpoint

Chapter 7 Review **1.** 9 **2.** 3 **3.** -2 **4.** not a real number **5.** $-\dfrac{1}{7}$ **6.** x^{32} **7.** -6 **8.** 4 **9.** $-a^2 b^3$ **10.** $4a^2 b^6$ **11.** $2ab^2$
12. $-2x^3 y^4$ **13.** $\dfrac{x^6}{6y}$ **14.** $\dfrac{3y}{z^4}$ **15.** $|x|$ **16.** $|x^2 - 4|$ **17.** -27 **18.** -5 **19.** $-x$ **20.** $2|2y + z|$ **21.** $5|x - y|$ **22.** y
23. $|x|$ **24.** $3, 6$ **25.** $2, \sqrt[3]{17}$ **26.** $\dfrac{1}{3}$ **27.** $-\dfrac{1}{3}$ **28.** $-\dfrac{1}{3}$ **29.** $-\dfrac{1}{4}$ **30.** -27 **31.** $\dfrac{1}{4}$ **32.** not a real number **33.** $\dfrac{343}{125}$
34. $\dfrac{9}{4}$ **35.** not a real number **36.** $x^{2/3}$ **37.** $5^{1/5} x^{2/5} y^{3/5}$ **38.** $\sqrt[5]{y^4}$ **39.** $5\sqrt[3]{xy^2 z^5}$ **40.** $\dfrac{1}{\sqrt{x + 2y}}$ **41.** $a^{13/6}$ **42.** $\dfrac{1}{b}$ **43.** $\dfrac{1}{a^{9/2}}$
44. $\dfrac{y^2}{x}$ **45.** $a^4 b^6$ **46.** $\dfrac{1}{x^{11/12}}$ **47.** $\dfrac{b^{5/6}}{49a^{1/4} c^{5/3}}$ **48.** $a - a^2$ **49.** 4.472 **50.** -3.391 **51.** 5.191 **52.** 3.826 **53.** -26.246
54. 0.045 **55.** $\sqrt[6]{1372}$ **56.** $\sqrt[12]{81x^3}$ **57.** $2\sqrt{6}$ **58.** $\sqrt[3]{7x^2 yz}$ **59.** $2x$ **60.** ab^3 **61.** $2\sqrt{15}$ **62.** $-5\sqrt{3}$ **63.** $3\sqrt[3]{6}$
64. $-2\sqrt[3]{4}$ **65.** $6x^3 \sqrt{x}$ **66.** $2ab^2 \sqrt[3]{3a^2 b}$ **67.** $\dfrac{p^8 \sqrt{p}}{11}$ **68.** $\dfrac{y\sqrt[3]{y^2}}{3x^2}$ **69.** $\dfrac{y\sqrt[4]{xy^2}}{3}$ **70.** $\dfrac{x\sqrt{2x}}{7y^2}$
71. a. $\dfrac{5}{\sqrt{\pi}}$ m or $\dfrac{5\sqrt{\pi}}{\pi}$ m **b.** 5.75 in. **72.** $\sqrt{197}$ units ≈ 14.036 **73.** $\sqrt{130}$ units ≈ 11.402 **74.** $\sqrt{73}$ units ≈ 8.544
75. $7\sqrt{2}$ units ≈ 9.899 **76.** $2\sqrt{11}$ units ≈ 6.633 **77.** $\sqrt{275.6}$ units ≈ 16.601 **78.** $(-5, 5)$ **79.** $\left(-\dfrac{15}{2}, 1\right)$ **80.** $\left(-\dfrac{11}{2}, -2\right)$
81. $\left(\dfrac{1}{20}, -\dfrac{3}{16}\right)$ **82.** $\left(\dfrac{1}{4}, -\dfrac{2}{7}\right)$ **83.** $(\sqrt{3}, -3\sqrt{6})$ **84.** $-2\sqrt{5}$ **85.** $2x\sqrt{3x}$ **86.** $9\sqrt[3]{2}$ **87.** $3a\sqrt[4]{2a}$ **88.** $\dfrac{15 + 2\sqrt{3}}{6}$
89. $\dfrac{3\sqrt{2}}{4x}$ **90.** $17\sqrt{2} - 15\sqrt{5}$ **91.** $-4ab\sqrt[4]{2b}$ **92.** 6 **93.** $x - 6\sqrt{x} + 9$ **94.** $-8\sqrt{5}$ **95.** $4x - 9y$ **96.** $a - 9$
97. $\sqrt[3]{a^2} + 4\sqrt[3]{a} + 4$ **98.** $\sqrt[3]{25x^2} - 81$ **99.** $a + 64$ **100.** $\dfrac{3\sqrt{7}}{7}$ **101.** $\dfrac{\sqrt{3x}}{6}$ **102.** $\dfrac{5\sqrt[3]{2}}{2}$ **103.** $\dfrac{2x^2 \sqrt{2x}}{y}$ **104.** $\dfrac{x^2 y^2 \sqrt[3]{15yz}}{z}$
105. $\dfrac{3\sqrt[4]{2x^2}}{2x^3}$ **106.** $\dfrac{3\sqrt{y} + 6}{y - 4}$ **107.** $-5 + 2\sqrt{6}$ **108.** $\dfrac{11}{3\sqrt{11}}$ **109.** $\dfrac{6}{\sqrt{2y}}$ **110.** $\dfrac{3}{7\sqrt[3]{3}}$ **111.** $\dfrac{4x^3}{y\sqrt{2x}}$ **112.** $\dfrac{xy}{\sqrt[3]{10x^2 yz}}$
113. $\dfrac{x - 25}{-3\sqrt{x} + 15}$ **114.** $\{32\}$ **115.** $\varnothing$ **116.** $\{35\}$ **117.** $\varnothing$ **118.** $\{9\}$ **119.** $\{16\}$ **120.** $3\sqrt{2}$ cm **121.** $\sqrt{241}$ ft
122. 51.2 ft **123.** 4.24 ft **124.** $2i\sqrt{2}$ **125.** $-i\sqrt{6}$ **126.** $6i$ **127.** $-\sqrt{10}$ **128.** $15 - 4i$ **129.** $-13 - 3i$ **130.** -64
131. $-12 - 18i$ **132.** $1 + 5i$ **133.** $-5 - 12i$ **134.** 87 **135.** $\dfrac{3}{2} - i$ **136.** $-\dfrac{1}{3} + \dfrac{1}{3}i$ **137.** x **138.** $|x + 2|$ **139.** -10
140. $-x^4 y$ **141.** $\dfrac{y^5}{2x^3}$ **142.** 3 **143.** $\dfrac{1}{8}$ **144.** $\dfrac{16}{9}$ **145.** $\dfrac{1}{x^{13/2}}$ **146.** $10x^4 \sqrt{2x}$ **147.** $\dfrac{n\sqrt{3n}}{11m^5}$ **148.** $6\sqrt{5} - 11x\sqrt[3]{5}$
149. $4x - 20\sqrt{x} + 25$ **150.** $\sqrt{41}$ units **151.** $(4, 16)$ **152.** $\dfrac{7\sqrt{13}}{13}$ **153.** $\dfrac{2\sqrt{x} - 6}{x - 9}$ **154.** $\{4\}$

Chapter 7 Test **1.** $6\sqrt{6}$ **2.** $-x^{16}$ **3.** $\dfrac{1}{5}$ **4.** 5 **5.** $\dfrac{4x^2}{9}$ **6.** $-a^6 b^3$ **7.** $\dfrac{8a^{1/3} c^{2/3}}{b^{5/12}}$ **8.** $a^{7/12} - a^{7/3}$ **9.** $|4xy|$ or $4|xy|$ **10.** -27
11. $\dfrac{3\sqrt{y}}{y}$ **12.** $\dfrac{8 - 6\sqrt{x} + x}{8 - 2x}$ **13.** $\dfrac{2\sqrt[3]{3x^2}}{3x}$ **14.** $\dfrac{6 - x^2}{8(\sqrt{6} - x)}$ **15.** $-x\sqrt{5x}$ **16.** $4\sqrt{3} - \sqrt{6}$ **17.** $x + 2\sqrt{x} + 1$
18. $\sqrt{6} + \sqrt{2} - 4\sqrt{3} - 4$ **19.** -20 **20.** 23.685 **21.** 0.019 **22.** $\{2, 3\}$ **23.** $\varnothing$ **24.** $\{6\}$ **25.** $i\sqrt{2}$ **26.** $-2i\sqrt{2}$
27. $-3i$ **28.** 40 **29.** $7 + 24i$ **30.** $-\dfrac{3}{2} + \dfrac{5}{2}i$ **31.** $x = \dfrac{5\sqrt{2}}{2}$ in. **32.** $\sqrt{2}, 5$ **33.** $2\sqrt{26}$ units **34.** $\sqrt{95}$ units **35.** $\left(-4, \dfrac{7}{2}\right)$
36. $\left(-\dfrac{1}{2}, \dfrac{3}{10}\right)$ **37.** 27 mph **38.** 360 ft

Cumulative Review **1.** $4x^b$; Sec. 1.7, Ex. 16 **2.** $\frac{2}{15}x^{2a}$; Sec. 1.7 **3.** y^{5a+6}; Sec. 1.7, Ex. 17 **4.** $-1.4y^{9a}$; Sec. 1.7 **5.** $\{-7, 5\}$; Sec. 2.6, Ex. 12

6. $\left\{\frac{2}{3}\right\}$; Sec. 2.6 **7.** $y = -2x + 12$; Sec. 3.4, Ex. 5 **8.** $\frac{13}{14}$; Sec. 2.1 **9.** $(-2, 2)$; Sec. 4.1, Ex. 8 **10.** 0; Sec. 3.2

11. $\{(x, y, z)| x - 5y - 2z = 6\}$; Sec. 4.2, Ex. 4 **12.** $(6, 0)$; Sec. 4.1 **13.** $\varnothing$; Sec. 4.4, Ex. 2 **14. a.** $7x - 3$ **b.** $-3x + 11$

c. $6x - 14$; Sec. 1.5 **15.** $13x^3y - xy^3 + 7$; Sec. 5.1, Ex. 14 **16.** 5×10^{-2}; Sec. 1.7 **17.** -4; Sec. 5.1, Ex. 18 **18.** -5; Sec. 5.1

19. 35; Sec. 5.1, Ex. 19 **20.** $-\frac{85}{16}$; Sec. 5.1 **21.** $x^2 + 10x + 25$; Sec. 5.2, Ex. 12 **22.** $3y^2 - 2y - 8$; Sec. 5.2

23. $16m^4 - 24m^2n + 9n^2$; Sec. 5.2, Ex. 15 **24.** $6y^3 + 7y^2 - 6y + 1$; Sec. 5.2 **25.** $2x^2 + 5x + 2 + \frac{7}{x-3}$; Sec. 5.3, Ex. 8

26. $4y^2 - 1 + \frac{9}{y-3}$; Sec. 5.3 **27.** $(b - 6)(a + 2)$; Sec. 5.4, Ex. 8 **28.** $(x - 1)(x^2 + 4)$; Sec. 5.4 **29.** $2(n^2 - 19n + 40)$; Sec. 5.5, Ex. 4

30. $2(x - 2)(x^2 + 2x + 4)$; Sec. 5.6 **31.** $(4x + 3y)^2$; Sec. 5.5, Ex. 8 **32.** $(x + 1 + y)(x + 1 - y)$; Sec. 5.6

33. $2(5 + 2y)(5 - 2y)$; Sec. 5.6, Ex. 7 **34.** $(x^2 + 1)(x + 1)(x - 1)$; Sec. 5.6 **35.** $\left\{-\frac{1}{2}, 4\right\}$; Sec. 5.7, Ex. 3 **36.** $x^2 + 3$; Sec. 5.3

37. $\{-2, 0, 2\}$; Sec. 5.7, Ex. 6 **38. a.** $\frac{3(y-2)}{4(2y+3)}$ **b.** $\frac{x+4}{16}$; Sec. 6.3 **39.** 1; Sec. 6.1, Ex. 4 **40.** $-a^2 - 2a - 4$; Sec. 6.1

41. $\frac{1}{5x-1}$; Sec. 6.1, Ex. 2 **42.** $\frac{3}{a+5}$; Sec. 6.1 **43.** $\frac{5+x}{7z^2}$; Sec. 6.2, Ex. 1 **44. a.** $\frac{9x-2y}{3x^2y^2}$ **b.** $\frac{3x(x-7)}{(x+3)(x-3)}$ **c.** $\frac{x+5}{x-2}$; Sec. 6.2

45. $\{-2\}$; Sec. 6.4, Ex. 2 **46.** $\{-1, -5\}$; Sec. 6.4 **47.** $\frac{1}{8}$; Sec. 7.2, Ex. 12 **48.** $\frac{1}{27}$; Sec. 7.2 **49.** $\frac{1}{9}$; Sec. 7.2, Ex. 13 **50.** $\frac{1}{25}$; Sec. 7.2

CHAPTER 8 Quadratic Equations and Functions

Exercise Set 8.1 **1.** $\{-4, 4\}$ **3.** $\{-\sqrt{7}, \sqrt{7}\}$ **5.** $\{-3\sqrt{2}, 3\sqrt{2}\}$ **7.** $\{-\sqrt{10}, \sqrt{10}\}$ **9.** $\{-8, -2\}$ **11.** $\{6 - 3\sqrt{2}, 6 + 3\sqrt{2}\}$

13. $\left\{\frac{3 - 2\sqrt{2}}{2}, \frac{3 + 2\sqrt{2}}{2}\right\}$ **15.** $\{-3i, 3i\}$ **17.** $\{-\sqrt{6}, \sqrt{6}\}$ **19.** $\{-2i\sqrt{2}, 2i\sqrt{2}\}$ **21.** $\left\{\frac{1 - 4i}{3}, \frac{1 + 4i}{3}\right\}$

23. $\{-7 - \sqrt{5}, -7 + \sqrt{5}\}$ **25.** $\{-3 - 2i\sqrt{2}, -3 + 2i\sqrt{2}\}$ **27.** $x^2 + 16x + 64 = (x + 8)^2$ **29.** $z^2 - 12z + 36 = (z - 6)^2$

31. $p^2 + 9p + \frac{81}{4} = \left(p + \frac{9}{2}\right)^2$ **33.** $r^2 - r + \frac{1}{4} = \left(r - \frac{1}{2}\right)^2$ **35.** $\{-5, -3\}$ **37.** $\{-3 - \sqrt{7}, -3 + \sqrt{7}\}$

39. $\left\{\frac{-1 - \sqrt{5}}{2}, \frac{-1 + \sqrt{5}}{2}\right\}$ **41.** $\{-1 - \sqrt{6}, -1 + \sqrt{6}\}$ **43.** $\left\{\frac{-1 - \sqrt{29}}{2}, \frac{-1 + \sqrt{29}}{2}\right\}$ **45.** $\{-4 - \sqrt{15}, -4 + \sqrt{15}\}$

47. $\left\{\frac{6 - \sqrt{30}}{3}, \frac{6 + \sqrt{30}}{3}\right\}$ **49.** $\left\{-4, \frac{1}{2}\right\}$ **51.** $\left\{\frac{-3 - \sqrt{21}}{3}, \frac{-3 + \sqrt{21}}{3}\right\}$ **53.** $\{-1 - i, -1 + i\}$ **55.** $\{-2 - i\sqrt{2}, -2 + i\sqrt{2}\}$

57. $\left\{\frac{1 - i\sqrt{47}}{4}, \frac{1 + i\sqrt{47}}{4}\right\}$ **59.** $\{-5 - i\sqrt{3}, -5 + i\sqrt{3}\}$ **61.** $\{-4, 1\}$ **63.** $\left\{\frac{2 - i\sqrt{2}}{2}, \frac{2 + i\sqrt{2}}{2}\right\}$ **65.** $\left\{\frac{-3 - \sqrt{69}}{6}, \frac{-3 + \sqrt{69}}{6}\right\}$

67. 20% **69.** 11% **71.** 9.63 sec **73.** 8.29 sec **75.** 15 ft by 15 ft **77.** $10\sqrt{2}$ cm **79.** $5 - 10\sqrt{3}$ **81.** $\frac{3 - 2\sqrt{7}}{4}$ **83.** $2\sqrt{7}$

85. $\sqrt{13}$ **87.** complex, but not real numbers **89.** real solutions **91.** complex, but not real numbers **93.** compound; answers may vary
95. $-8x, 8x$ **97.** 6 thousand scissors

Calculator Explorations **1.** $\{-1.27, 6.27\}$ **3.** $\{-1.10, 0.90\}$ **5.** $\varnothing$

Mental Math **1.** $a = 1, b = 3, c = 1$ **3.** $a = 7, b = 0, c = -4$ **5.** $a = 6, b = -1, c = 0$

Exercise Set 8.2 **1.** $\{-6, 1\}$ **3.** $\left\{-\frac{3}{5}, 1\right\}$ **5.** $\{3\}$ **7.** $\left\{\frac{-7 - \sqrt{33}}{2}, \frac{-7 + \sqrt{33}}{2}\right\}$ **9.** $\left\{\frac{1 - \sqrt{57}}{8}, \frac{1 + \sqrt{57}}{8}\right\}$

11. $\left\{\frac{7 - \sqrt{85}}{6}, \frac{7 + \sqrt{85}}{6}\right\}$ **13.** $\{1 - \sqrt{3}, 1 + \sqrt{3}\}$ **15.** $\left\{-\frac{3}{2}, 1\right\}$ **17.** $\left\{\frac{3 - \sqrt{11}}{2}, \frac{3 + \sqrt{11}}{2}\right\}$ **19.** $\left\{\frac{-5 - \sqrt{17}}{2}, \frac{-5 + \sqrt{17}}{2}\right\}$

21. $\left\{\frac{5}{2}, 1\right\}$ **23.** $\{-3 - 2i, -3 + 2i\}$ **25.** $\{-2 - \sqrt{11}, -2 + \sqrt{11}\}$ **27.** $\left\{\frac{3 - i\sqrt{87}}{8}, \frac{3 + i\sqrt{87}}{8}\right\}$ **29.** $\left\{\frac{3 - \sqrt{29}}{2}, \frac{3 + \sqrt{29}}{2}\right\}$

31. $\left\{\frac{-5 - i\sqrt{5}}{10}, \frac{-5 + i\sqrt{5}}{10}\right\}$ **33.** $\left\{\frac{-1 - \sqrt{19}}{6}, \frac{-1 + \sqrt{19}}{6}\right\}$ **35.** $\left\{\frac{-1 - i\sqrt{23}}{4}, \frac{-1 + i\sqrt{23}}{4}\right\}$ **37.** $\{1\}$ **39.** $\{3 + \sqrt{5}, 3 - \sqrt{5}\}$
41. two real solutions **43.** one real solutions **45.** two real solutions **47.** two complex but not real solutions **49.** two real solutions

51. 14 ft **53.** $(2 + 2\sqrt{2})$ cm, $(2 + 2\sqrt{2})$ cm, $(4 + 2\sqrt{2})$ cm **55.** width: $(-5 + 5\sqrt{17})$ ft; length: $(5 + 5\sqrt{17})$ ft

57. a. $50\sqrt{2}$ m **b.** 5000 sq m **59.** 37.4 ft by 38.5 ft **61.** base: $(2 + 2\sqrt{43})$ cm; height: $(-1 + \sqrt{43})$ cm **63.** 8.9 sec **65.** 2.8 sec

67. $\left\{\frac{11}{5}\right\}$ **69.** $\{15\}$ **71.** $(x^2 + 5)(x + 2)(x - 2)$ **73.** $(z + 3)(z - 3)(z + 2)(z - 2)$ **75.** b **77.** answers may vary

79. $\{0.6, 2.4\}$ **81.** Sunday to Monday **83.** Wednesday **85.** $f(4) = 33$; answers may vary **87. a.** $6406.8 million **b.** 2006
89. a. 8684 thousand barrels per day **b.** 2006 or 2011 **91.** $\{0.6, 2.4\}$

Exercise Set 8.3 **1.** $\{2\}$ **3.** $\{16\}$ **5.** $\{1, 4\}$ **7.** $\{3 - \sqrt{7}, 3 + \sqrt{7}\}$ **9.** $\left\{\dfrac{3 - \sqrt{57}}{4}, \dfrac{3 + \sqrt{57}}{4}\right\}$ **11.** $\left\{\dfrac{1 - \sqrt{29}}{2}, \dfrac{1 + \sqrt{29}}{2}\right\}$

13. $\{-2, 2, -2i, 2i\}$ **15.** $\{-3, 3, -2, 2\}$ **17.** $\left\{-\dfrac{1}{2}, \dfrac{1}{2}, -i\sqrt{3}, i\sqrt{3}\right\}$ **19.** $\{125, -8\}$ **21.** $\left\{-\dfrac{4}{5}, 0\right\}$ **23.** $\left\{-\dfrac{1}{8}, 27\right\}$ **25.** $\left\{-\dfrac{2}{3}, \dfrac{4}{3}\right\}$

27. $\left\{-\dfrac{1}{125}, \dfrac{1}{8}\right\}$ **29.** $\{-\sqrt{2}, \sqrt{2}, -\sqrt{3}, \sqrt{3}\}$ **31.** $\left\{\dfrac{-9 - \sqrt{201}}{6}, \dfrac{-9 + \sqrt{201}}{6}\right\}$ **33.** $\{2, 3\}$ **35.** $\{3\}$ **37.** $\{27, 125\}$ **39.** $\{5\}$

41. $\left\{\dfrac{1}{8}, -8\right\}$ **43.** $\{-5, 1\}$ **45.** $\{4\}$ **47.** $\{-3\}$ **49.** $\{-\sqrt{5}, \sqrt{5}, -2i, 2i\}$ **51.** $\{6, 12\}$ **53.** $\left\{-\dfrac{1}{3}, \dfrac{1}{3}, -\dfrac{i\sqrt{6}}{3}, \dfrac{i\sqrt{6}}{3}\right\}$

55. 5 mph, then 4 mph **57.** inlet pipe: 15.5 hr; hose: 16.5 hr **59.** 55 mph; 66 mph **61.** 8.5 hr **63.** 12 or -8
65. a. $(x - 6)$ in. **b.** $300 = (x - 6) \cdot (x - 6) \cdot 3$ **c.** 16 in. by 16 in. **67.** 22 feet **69.** $(-\infty, 3]$ **71.** $(-5, \infty)$ **73.** $\{1, -3i, 3i\}$

75. $\left\{-\dfrac{1}{2}, \dfrac{1}{3}\right\}$ **77.** $\left\{-3, \dfrac{3 - 3i\sqrt{3}}{2}, \dfrac{3 + 3i\sqrt{3}}{2}\right\}$ **79.** answers may vary **81. a.** 189.265 feet/sec **b.** 189.149 feet/sec **c.** 128.965 mph

Integrated Review **1.** $\{-\sqrt{10}, \sqrt{10}\}$ **2.** $\{-2i\sqrt{2}, 2i\sqrt{2}\}$ **3.** $\{1 - 2\sqrt{2}, 1 + 2\sqrt{2}\}$ **4.** $\left\{\dfrac{-5 - 2\sqrt{3}}{2}, \dfrac{-5 + 2\sqrt{3}}{2}\right\}$

5. $\{-1 - \sqrt{13}, -1 + \sqrt{13}\}$ **6.** $\{1, 11\}$ **7.** $\left\{\dfrac{-3 - \sqrt{17}}{2}, \dfrac{-3 + \sqrt{17}}{2}\right\}$ **8.** $\left\{\dfrac{-2 - \sqrt{5}}{4}, \dfrac{-2 + \sqrt{5}}{4}\right\}$ **9.** $\left\{\dfrac{2 - \sqrt{2}}{2}, \dfrac{2 + \sqrt{2}}{2}\right\}$

10. $\{-3 - \sqrt{5}, -3 + \sqrt{5}\}$ **11.** $\{-2 + i\sqrt{3}, -2 - i\sqrt{3}\}$ **12.** $\left\{\dfrac{-3 - i\sqrt{6}}{5}, \dfrac{-3 + i\sqrt{6}}{5}\right\}$ **13.** $\left\{\dfrac{-3 + i\sqrt{15}}{2}, \dfrac{-3 - i\sqrt{15}}{2}\right\}$

14. $\{3i, -3i\}$ **15.** $\{0, -17\}$ **16.** $\left\{\dfrac{1 + \sqrt{13}}{4}, \dfrac{1 - \sqrt{13}}{4}\right\}$ **17.** $\{2 + 3\sqrt{3}, 2 - 3\sqrt{3}\}$ **18.** $\{2 + \sqrt{3}, 2 - \sqrt{3}\}$ **19.** $\left\{-2, \dfrac{4}{3}\right\}$

20. $\left\{\dfrac{-5 + \sqrt{17}}{4}, \dfrac{-5 - \sqrt{17}}{4}\right\}$ **21.** $\{1 - \sqrt{6}, 1 + \sqrt{6}\}$ **22.** $\{-\sqrt{31}, \sqrt{31}\}$ **23.** $\{-2\sqrt{3}, 2\sqrt{3}\}$ **24.** $\{-i\sqrt{11}, i\sqrt{11}\}$

25. $\{-11, 6\}$ **26.** $\left\{\dfrac{-3 + \sqrt{19}}{5}, \dfrac{-3 - \sqrt{19}}{5}\right\}$ **27.** $\left\{\dfrac{-3 + \sqrt{17}}{4}, \dfrac{-3 - \sqrt{17}}{4}\right\}$ **28.** $\{4\}$ **29.** $\left\{\dfrac{-1 + \sqrt{17}}{8}, \dfrac{-1 - \sqrt{17}}{8}\right\}$

30. $10\sqrt{2}$ ft ≈ 14.1 ft **31.** Diane: 9.1 hr; Lucy: 7.1 hr **32.** 5 mph during the first part, then 6 mph

Exercise Set 8.4 **1.** $(-\infty, -5) \cup (-1, \infty)$ **3.** $[-4, 3]$ **5.** $(-\infty, -5] \cup [-3, \infty)$ **7.** $\left(-5, -\dfrac{1}{3}\right)$ **9.** $(2, 4) \cup (6, \infty)$

11. $(-\infty, -4] \cup [0, 1]$ **13.** $(-\infty, -3) \cup (-2, 2) \cup (3, \infty)$ **15.** $(-7, 2)$ **17.** $(-1, \infty)$ **19.** $(-\infty, -1] \cup (4, \infty)$

21. $(-\infty, 2) \cup \left(\dfrac{11}{4}, \infty\right)$ **23.** $(0, 2] \cup [3, \infty)$ **25.** $(-\infty, 3)$ **27.** $\left[-\dfrac{5}{4}, \dfrac{3}{2}\right]$ **29.** $(-\infty, 0) \cup (1, \infty)$ **31.** $(0, 10)$

33. $(-\infty, -4] \cup [4, 6]$ **35.** $\left(-\infty, -\dfrac{2}{3}\right] \cup \left[\dfrac{3}{2}, \infty\right)$ **37.** $(-\infty, -4) \cup [5, \infty)$ **39.** $(-\infty, 1) \cup (2, \infty)$ **41.** $\left(-4, -\dfrac{3}{2}\right) \cup \left(\dfrac{3}{2}, \infty\right)$

43. $(-\infty, -5] \cup [-1, 1] \cup [5, \infty)$ **45.** $(-\infty, -6] \cup (-1, 0] \cup (7, \infty)$ **47.** $(-\infty, -8] \cup (-4, \infty)$ **49.** $\left(-\infty, -\dfrac{5}{3}\right) \cup \left(\dfrac{7}{2}, \infty\right)$

51. $(-\infty, 0] \cup \left(5, \dfrac{11}{2}\right]$ **53.** $(0, \infty)$ **55.** $0; 1; 1; 4; 4$ **57.** $0; -1; -1; -4; -4$ **59.** answers may vary
61. $(-\infty, -1) \cup (0, 1)$ **63.** when x is between 2 and 11 **65.** $(-\infty, -7) \cup (8, \infty)$

The Bigger Picture **1.** $\left\{-9, \dfrac{7}{3}\right\}$ **2.** $(4, 7)$ **3.** $\{4, 5\}$ **4.** $\left\{\dfrac{-1 - \sqrt{13}}{6}, \dfrac{-1 + \sqrt{13}}{6}\right\}$ **5.** $[-2, 7)$ **6.** $\left\{\dfrac{5}{4}\right\}$ **7.** $\left\{\dfrac{1}{5}, 7\right\}$

8. $\left(-\infty, -\dfrac{1}{2}\right] \cup [4, \infty)$ **9.** $(-\infty, -8) \cup (22, \infty)$ **10.** $(7, \infty)$

Calculator Explorations **1.**  **3.** 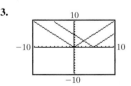 **5.**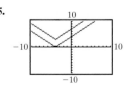

Mental Math **1.** $(0, 0)$ **3.** $(2, 0)$ **5.** $(0, 3)$ **7.** $(-1, 5)$

Exercise Set 8.5 **1.** 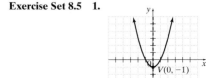 **3.** 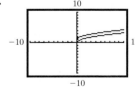 **5.** 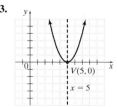 **7.**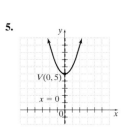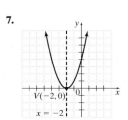

9. 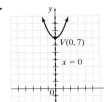 $V(0,7)$ $x = 0$

11. 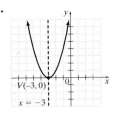 $V(-3,0)$ $x = -3$

13. 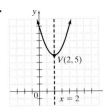 $V(2,5)$ $x = 2$

15. 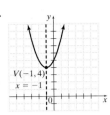 $V(-1,4)$ $x = -1$

17. 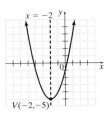 $x = -2$ $V(-2,-5)$

19. 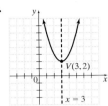 $V(3,2)$ $x = 3$

21. 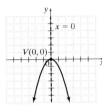 $x = 0$ $V(0,0)$

23. 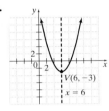 $V(0,0)$ $x = 0$

25. 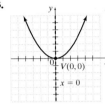 $V(0,0)$ $x = 0$

27. 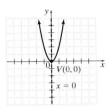 $x = 0$ $V(0,0)$

29. 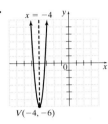 $x = -4$ $V(-4,-6)$

31. 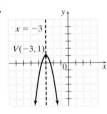 $x = -3$ $V(-3,1)$

33. 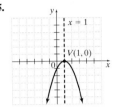 $V(6,-3)$ $x = 6$

35. 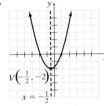 $x = 1$ $V(1,0)$

37. 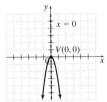 $V\left(-\frac{1}{2}, -2\right)$ $x = -\frac{1}{2}$

39. 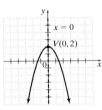 $x = 0$ $V(0,2)$

41. $x^2 + 8x + 16$ **43.** $z^2 - 16z + 64$ **45.** $y^2 + y + \dfrac{1}{4}$

47. $g(x) = 5(x - 2)^2 + 3$ **49.** $g(x) = 5(x + 3)^2 + 6$

51.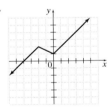

53.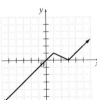

55.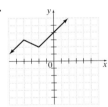

57. c

Exercise Set 8.6   **1.** $(-4, -9)$ **3.** $(5, 30)$ **5.** $(1, -2)$ **7.** $\left(\dfrac{1}{2}, \dfrac{5}{4}\right)$ **9.** D   **11.** B

13.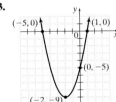
$(-5,0)$ $(1,0)$ $(0,-5)$ $(-2,-9)$

vertex: $(-2, -9)$; opens upward;
x-intercepts: $(-5, 0)$, $(1, 0)$;
y-intercept: $(0, -5)$

15.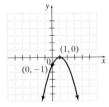
$(1,0)$ $(0,-1)$

vertex: $(1, 0)$; opens downward;
x-intercept: $(1, 0)$;
y-intercept: $(0, -1)$

17.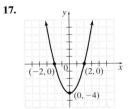
$(-2,0)$ $(2,0)$ $(0,-4)$

vertex: $(0, -4)$; opens upward;
x-intercepts: $(-2, 0)$, $(2, 0)$;
y-intercept: $(0, -4)$

19.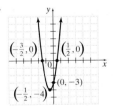
$\left(-\frac{3}{2},0\right)$ $\left(\frac{1}{2},0\right)$ $(0,-3)$ $\left(-\frac{1}{2},-4\right)$

vertex: $\left(-\dfrac{1}{2}, -4\right)$; opens upward;

x-intercepts: $\left(-\dfrac{3}{2}, 0\right)$, $\left(\dfrac{1}{2}, 0\right)$;

y-intercept: $(0, -3)$

21.

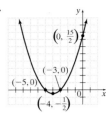

23.

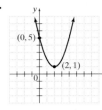

25.

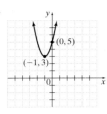

27.

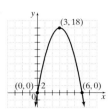

vertex: $\left(-4, -\dfrac{1}{2}\right)$; opens upward;

x-intercepts: $(-5, 0), (-3, 0)$;

y-intercept: $\left(0, \dfrac{15}{2}\right)$

vertex: $(2, 1)$; opens upward;
y-intercept: $(0, 5)$

vertex: $(-1, 3)$; opens upward;
y-intercept: $(0, 5)$

vertex: $(3, 18)$; opens downward;
x-intercepts: $(0, 0), (6, 0)$;
y-intercept: $(0, 0)$

29. 144 ft **31. a.** 200 bicycles **b.** \$12,000 **33.** 30, 30 **35.** 5, -5 **37.** length: 20 units; width: 20 units **39.** $(0, 2)$
41. $(-2, 0)$ **43.** $(-5, 2)$ **45.** $(4, 1)$ **47.** minimum value **49.** maximum value
51. vertex: $(-5, -10)$; opens upward; y-intercept: $(0, 15)$; x-intercepts: $(-1.8, 0), (-8.2, 0)$ **55.** -0.84
57. a. maximum, answers may vary **b.** 2003 **c.** 2,220,000 or 2220 thousand

Chapter 8 Vocabulary Check **1.** discriminant **2.** $\pm\sqrt{b}$ **3.** $\dfrac{-b}{2a}$ **4.** quadratic inequality **5.** completing the square **6.** $(0, k)$
7. $(h, 0)$ **8.** (h, k) **9.** quadratic formula **10.** quadratic

Chapter 8 Review **1.** $\{14, 1\}$ **2.** $\left\{-\dfrac{6}{7}, 5\right\}$ **3.** $\{-7, 7\}$ **4.** $\left\{\dfrac{2 - \sqrt{2}}{5}, \dfrac{2 + \sqrt{2}}{5}\right\}$ **5.** $\left\{\dfrac{-3 - \sqrt{5}}{2}, \dfrac{-3 + \sqrt{5}}{2}\right\}$
6. $\left\{\dfrac{-3 - i\sqrt{7}}{8}, \dfrac{-3 + i\sqrt{7}}{8}\right\}$ **7.** 4.25% **8.** $75\sqrt{2}$ mi; 106.1 mi **9.** two complex but not real solutions **10.** two real solutions
11. two real solutions **12.** one real solution **13.** $\{8\}$ **14.** $\{-5, 0\}$ **15.** $\left\{-\dfrac{5}{2}, 1\right\}$ **16.** $\left\{\dfrac{5 - i\sqrt{143}}{12}, \dfrac{5 + i\sqrt{143}}{12}\right\}$
17. $\left\{\dfrac{1 - i\sqrt{35}}{9}, \dfrac{1 + i\sqrt{35}}{9}\right\}$ **18.** $\left\{1, \dfrac{9}{4}\right\}$ **19. a.** 20 ft **b.** $\dfrac{15 + \sqrt{321}}{16}$ sec; 2.1 sec **20.** $(6 + 6\sqrt{2})$ cm
21. $\left\{3, \dfrac{-3 + 3i\sqrt{3}}{2}, \dfrac{-3 - 3i\sqrt{3}}{2}\right\}$ **22.** $\{-4, 2 - 2i\sqrt{3}, 2 + 2i\sqrt{3}\}$ **23.** $\left\{\dfrac{2}{3}, 5\right\}$ **24.** $\{-5, 5, -2i, 2i\}$ **25.** $\left\{-\dfrac{16}{5}, 1\right\}$
26. $\{1, 125\}$ **27.** $\{-1, 1, -i, i\}$ **28.** $\left\{-\dfrac{1}{5}, \dfrac{1}{4}\right\}$ **29.** Jerome: 10.5 hr; Tim: 9.5 hr **30.** -5 **31.** $[-5, 5]$ **32.** $\left(-\dfrac{1}{2}, \dfrac{1}{2}\right)$
33. $(-\infty, -4) \cup (-1, 1) \cup (4, \infty)$ **34.** $(5, 6)$ **35.** $(-\infty, -6) \cup \left(-\dfrac{3}{4}, 0\right) \cup (5, \infty)$ **36.** $(-\infty, -5] \cup [-2, 6]$
37. $(-5, -3) \cup (5, \infty)$ **38.** $(-\infty, 0)$ **39.** $\left(-\dfrac{6}{5}, 0\right) \cup \left(\dfrac{5}{6}, 3\right)$

40.

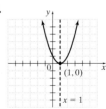

41.

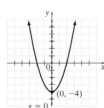

42.

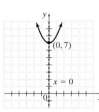

43.

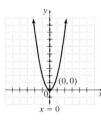

44.

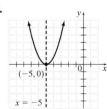

45.

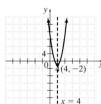

46.

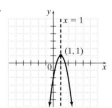

47.

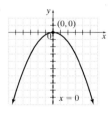

37. $S = krh$; Sec. 6.6, Ex. 5　**38.** 192; $y = \dfrac{192}{x}$; Sec. 6.6　**39.** -4; Sec. 7.1, Ex. 14　**40.** $2a^2b^3\sqrt[3]{3a}$; Sec. 7.1　**41.** $\dfrac{2}{5}$; Sec. 7.1, Ex. 15

42. $\dfrac{8\sqrt{x}}{3x}$; Sec. 7.5　**43.** 2; Sec. 7.3, Ex. 3　**44.** $5 - 2x\sqrt{5} + x^2$; Sec. 7.4　**45.** $\sqrt{\dfrac{2b}{3a}}$; Sec. 7.3, Ex. 5　**46.** $a - b^2$; Sec. 7.4

47. $-6\sqrt[3]{2}$; Sec. 7.4, Ex. 5　**48.** {2, 6}; Sec. 7.6　**49.** $\dfrac{5\sqrt[3]{7x}}{2}$; Sec. 7.4, Ex. 10　**50.** $2x^2\sqrt[4]{3x}$; Sec. 7.3

51. $\left\{-1 + \sqrt{5}, -1 - \sqrt{5}\right\}$; Sec. 8.1, Ex. 7　**52.** $\left\{1 + 2\sqrt{6}, 1 - 2\sqrt{6}\right\}$; Sec. 8.1　**53.** $\left\{\dfrac{2 + \sqrt{10}}{2}, \dfrac{2 - \sqrt{10}}{2}\right\}$; Sec. 8.2, Ex. 2

54. $\left\{2 - 2\sqrt{3}, 2 + 2\sqrt{3}\right\}$; Sec. 8.2　**55.** 3.9 sec; Sec. 8.2, Ex. 9　**56.** 15 hours; Sec. 6.5

CHAPTER 9　Exponential and Logarithmic Functions

Exercise Set 9.1　**1. a.** $3x - 6$　**b.** $-x - 8$　**c.** $2x^2 - 13x - 7$　**d.** $\dfrac{x - 7}{2x + 1}$ where $x \neq -\dfrac{1}{2}$　**3. a.** $x^2 + 5x + 1$　**b.** $x^2 - 5x + 1$　**c.** $5x^3 + 5x$

d. $\dfrac{x^2 + 1}{5x}$ where $x \neq 0$　**5. a.** $\sqrt{x} + x + 5$　**b.** $\sqrt{x} - x - 5$　**c.** $x\sqrt{x} + 5\sqrt{x}$　**d.** $\dfrac{\sqrt{x}}{x + 5}$ where $x \neq -5$　**7. a.** $5x^2 - 3x$　**b.** $-5x^2 - 3x$

c. $-15x^3$　**d.** $-\dfrac{3}{5x}$ where $x \neq 0$　**9.** 42　**11.** -18　**13.** 0　**15.** $(f \circ g)(x) = 25x^2 + 1$; $(g \circ f)(x) = 5x^2 + 5$

17. $(f \circ g)(x) = 2x + 11$; $(g \circ f)(x) = 2x + 4$　**19.** $(f \circ g)(x) = -8x^3 - 2x - 2$; $(g \circ f)(x) = -2x^3 - 2x + 4$

21. $(f \circ g)(x) = |10x - 3|$; $(g \circ f)(x) = 10|x| - 3$　**23.** $(f \circ g)(x) = \sqrt{-5x + 2}$; $(g \circ f)(x) = -5\sqrt{x} + 2$　**25.** $H(x) = (g \circ h)(x)$

27. $F(x) = (h \circ f)(x)$　**29.** $G(x) = (f \circ g)(x)$　**31.** answers may vary　**33.** answers may vary　**35.** answers may vary

37. $y = x - 2$　**39.** $y = \dfrac{x}{3}$　**41.** $y = -\dfrac{x + 7}{2}$　**43.** $P(x) = R(x) - C(x)$　**45.** answers may vary

Exercise Set 9.2　**1.** not one-to-one　**3.** one-to-one; $h^{-1} = \{(10 , 10)\}$　**5.** one-to-one; $f^{-1} = \{(12, 11), (3, 4), (4, 3), (6, 6)\}$

7. not one-to-one　**9.** one-to-one;

Rank in Population (Input)	1	47	14	24	36
State (Output)	California	Alaska	Indiana	Louisiana	New Mexico

11. a. 3　**b.** 1　**13. a.** 1　**b.** -1　**15.** one-to-one　**17.** not one-to-one　**19.** one-to-one　**21.** not one-to-one

23. 　**25.**　**27.**　**29.**　**31.** $f^{-1}(x) = 5x + 2$

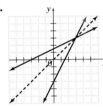 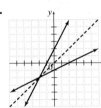 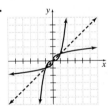

33. $f^{-1}(x) = x^3$　**35.** $f^{-1}(x) = \dfrac{\dfrac{5}{x} - 1}{3}$　**37.** $f^{-1}(x) = \sqrt[3]{x} - 2$　**39.**　**41.**　**43.** 5　**45.** 8

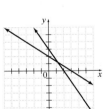 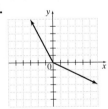

47. $\dfrac{1}{27}$　**49.** 9　**51.** $3^{1/2} \approx 1.73$　**53. a.** $(2, 9)$　**b.** $(9, 2)$　**55. a.** $\left(-2, \dfrac{1}{4}\right), \left(-1, \dfrac{1}{2}\right), (0 , 1), (1 , 2), (2 , 5)$

b. $\left(\dfrac{1}{4}, -2\right), \left(\dfrac{1}{2}, -1\right), (1 , 0), (2 , 1)(5 , 2)$　**c.**　**d.**　**57.** answers may vary

 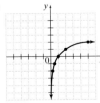

59. 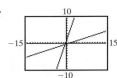 ; $f^{-1}(x) = \dfrac{x-1}{3}$ **61.** 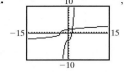 ; $f^{-1}(x) = x^3 - 3$

Calculator Explorations **1.** 81.98% **3.** 22.54%

Exercise Set 9.3 **1.** 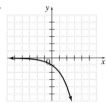 **3.** 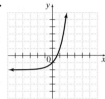 **5.** 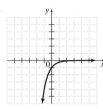 **7.**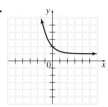

9. 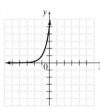 **11.** 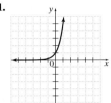 **13.** 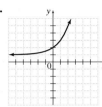 **15.** 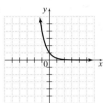 **17.**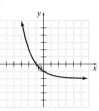

19. 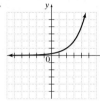 **21.** $\{3\}$ **23.** $\left\{\dfrac{3}{4}\right\}$ **25.** $\left\{\dfrac{8}{5}\right\}$ **27.** $\left\{-\dfrac{2}{3}\right\}$ **29.** $\left\{\dfrac{3}{2}\right\}$ **31.** $\left\{-\dfrac{1}{3}\right\}$ **33.** $\{-2\}$ **35.** $\{4\}$

37. 24.6 lb **39. a.** 568.7 millibars **b.** 9.1 millibars **c.** answers may vary **41. a.** \$56.8 billion **b.** \$261.6 billion
43. 537.6 million cellular phone users **45.** \$7621.42 **47.** $\{4\}$ **49.** $\varnothing$ **51.** no **53.** no **55.** C **57.** D **59.** answers may vary
61. 24.6 lb **63.** 18.62 lb

Exercise Set 9.4 **1.** $6^2 = 36$ **3.** $3^{-3} = \dfrac{1}{27}$ **5.** $10^3 = 1000$ **7.** $e^4 = x$ **9.** $e^{-2} = \dfrac{1}{e^2}$ **11.** $7^{1/2} = \sqrt{7}$ **13.** $0.7^3 = 0.343$

15. $3^{-4} = \dfrac{1}{81}$ **17.** $\log_2 16 = 4$ **19.** $\log_{10}100 = 2$ **21.** $\log_e x = 3$ **23.** $\log_{10} \dfrac{1}{10} = -1$ **25.** $\log_4 \dfrac{1}{16} = -2$ **27.** $\log_5 \sqrt{5} = \dfrac{1}{2}$

29. 3 **31.** -2 **33.** $\dfrac{1}{2}$ **35.** -1 **37.** 0 **39.** 2 **41.** 4 **43.** -3 **45.** $\{2\}$ **47.** $\{81\}$ **49.** $\{7\}$ **51.** $\{-3\}$

53. $\{-3\}$ **55.** $\{2\}$ **57.** $\{2\}$ **59.** $\left\{\dfrac{27}{64}\right\}$ **61.** $\{10\}$ **63.** $\{4\}$ **65.** $\{5\}$ **67.** $\left\{\dfrac{1}{49}\right\}$ **69.** 3 **71.** 3 **73.** 1

75. 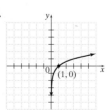 **77.** 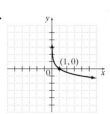 **79.** **81.** 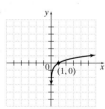 **83.** 1 **85.** $\dfrac{x-4}{2}$

87. a. $g(2) = 25$ **b.** $(25, 2)$ **c.** $f(25) = 2$ **89.** answers may vary **91.** 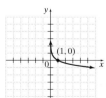 **93.**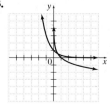

95. answers may vary **97.** 0.0827

Exercise Set 9.5   **1.** $\log_5 14$ **3.** $\log_4 9x$ **5.** $\log_6(x^2 + x)$ **7.** $\log_{10}(10x^2 + 20)$ **9.** $\log_5 3$ **11.** $\log_3 4$ **13.** $\log_2 \dfrac{x}{y}$ **15.** $\log_2 \dfrac{x^2 + 6}{x^2 + 1}$

17. $2\log_3 x$ **19.** $-1\log_4 5 = -\log_4 5$ **21.** $\dfrac{1}{2}\log_5 y$ **23.** $\log_2 5x^3$ **25.** $\log_4 48$ **27.** $\log_5 x^3 z^6$ **29.** $\log_4 4$, or 1   **31.** $\log_7 \dfrac{9}{2}$

33. $\log_{10} \dfrac{x^3 - 2x}{x + 1}$ **35.** $\log_2 \dfrac{x^{7/2}}{(x + 1)^2}$ **37.** $\log_8 x^{16/3}$ **39.** $\log_3 4 + \log_3 y - \log_3 5$ **41.** $\log_4 2 - \log_4 9 - \log_4 z$ **43.** $3\log_2 x - \log_2 y$

45. $\dfrac{1}{2}\log_b 7 + \dfrac{1}{2}\log_b x$ **47.** $4\log_6 x + 5\log_6 y$ **49.** $3\log_5 x + \log_5(x + 1)$ **51.** $2\log_6 x - \log_6(x + 3)$ **53.** 0.2   **55.** 1.2   **57.** 0.35

59. 1.29   **61.** -0.68 **63.** -0.125 **65.**   **67.** -1 **69.** $\dfrac{1}{2}$ **71.** a and d   **73.** false   **75.** true   **77.** false

Integrated Review   **1.** $x^2 + x - 5$ **2.** $-x^2 + x - 7$ **3.** $x^3 - 6x^2 + x - 6$ **4.** $\dfrac{x - 6}{x^2 + 1}$ **5.** $\sqrt{3x - 1}$ **6.** $3\sqrt{x} - 1$

7. one-to-one; $\{(6, -2), (8, 4), (-6, 2), (3, 3)\}$,   **8.** not one-to-one   **9.** not one-to-one   **10.** one-to-one   **11.** not one-to-one

12. $f^{-1}(x) = \dfrac{x}{3}$ **13.** $f^{-1}(x) = x - 4$ **14.** $f^{-1}(x) = \dfrac{x + 1}{5}$ **15.** $f^{-1}(x) = \dfrac{x - 2}{3}$ **16.**

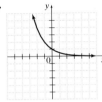

17.

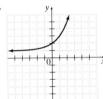

18.

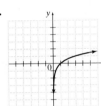

19.

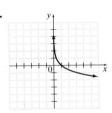

20. $\{3\}$ **21.** $\{7\}$ **22.** $\{-8\}$ **23.** $\{3\}$

24. $\{2\}$ **25.** $\left\{\dfrac{1}{2}\right\}$ **26.** $\{32\}$ **27.** $\{4\}$ **28.** $\{5\}$ **29.** $\left\{\dfrac{1}{9}\right\}$ **30.** $\log_2 14x$ **31.** $\log_2 5^x \cdot 8$ **32.** $\log_5 \dfrac{x^3}{y^5}$ **33.** $\log_5 x^9 y^3$

34. $\log_2 \dfrac{x^2 - 3x}{x^2 + 4}$ **35.** $\log_3 \dfrac{y^4 + 11y}{y + 2}$ **36.** $\log_7 9 + 2\log_7 x - \log_7 y$ **37.** $\log_6 5 + \log_6 y - 2\log_6 z$

Exercise Set 9.6   **1.** 0.9031   **3.** 0.3636   **5.** 0.6931   **7.** -2.6367 **9.** 1.1004   **11.** 1.6094   **13.** 1.6180   **15.** 2   **17.** -3 **19.** 2

21. $\dfrac{1}{4}$ **23.** 3   **25.** 3.1   **27.** -4 **29.** $\dfrac{1}{2}$ **31.** $\{10^{1.3}\}$; $\{19.9526\}$ **33.** $\{e^{1.4}\}$; $\{4.0552\}$ **35.** $\{10^{2.3}\}$; $\{199.5262\}$

37. $\{e^{-2.3}\}$; $\{0.1003\}$ **39.** $\left\{\dfrac{10^{1.1}}{2}\right\}$; $\{6.2946\}$ **41.** $\left\{\dfrac{e^{0.18}}{4}\right\}$; $\{0.2993\}$ **43.** $\left\{\dfrac{4 + e^{2.3}}{3}\right\}$; $\{4.6581\}$ **45.** $\left\{\dfrac{10^{-0.5} - 1}{2}\right\}$; $\{-0.3419\}$

47. \$3656.38   **49.** \$2542.50   **51.** 1.5850   **53.** 0.8617   **55.** 1.5850   **57.** -1.6309 **59.** -2.3219 **61.** $\left\{\dfrac{4}{7}\right\}$ **63.** $x = \dfrac{3y}{4}$

65. $\{-6, -1\}$ **67.** answers may vary   **69.**   **71.**   **73.** answers may vary   **75.** 4.2   **77.** 5.3

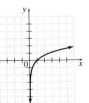

Calculator Explorations   **1.** 3.67 yr, or 3 yr and 8 mo   **3.** 23.16 yr, or 23 yr and 2 mo

Exercise Set 9.7   **1.** $\left\{\dfrac{\log 6}{\log 3}\right\}$; $\{1.6309\}$ **3.** $\left\{\dfrac{\log 5}{\log 9}\right\}$; $\{0.7325\}$ **5.** $\left\{\dfrac{\log 3.8}{2\log 3}\right\}$; $\{0.6076\}$ **7.** $\left\{\dfrac{\ln 5}{6}\right\}$; $\{0.2682\}$ **9.** $\left\{3 + \dfrac{\log 5}{\log 2}\right\}$; $\{5.3219\}$

11. $\left\{\dfrac{\log 3}{\log 4} - 7\right\}$; $\{-6.2075\}$ **13.** $\left\{\dfrac{1}{3}\left(4 + \dfrac{\log 11}{\log 7}\right)\right\}$; $\{1.7441\}$ **15.** $\{11\}$ **17.** $\left\{\dfrac{1}{2}\right\}$ **19.** $\left\{\dfrac{3}{4}\right\}$ **21.** $\{-2, 1\}$ **23.** $\{2\}$ **25.** $\left\{\dfrac{1}{8}\right\}$

27. $\{4, -1\}$ **29.** $\left\{\dfrac{2}{3}\right\}$ **31.** 103 wolves **33.** 7,192,916 people **35.** 27.1 years **37.** 9.9 yr **39.** 1.7 yr **41.** 8.8 yr **43.** 55.7 in.

45. 11.9 lb per sq in. **47.** 3.2 mi **49.** 12 weeks **51.** 18 weeks **53.** $-\dfrac{5}{3}$ **55.** $\dfrac{17}{4}$ **57.** 4.5% **59.** answers may vary

61.

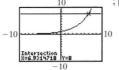 ; $\{6.93\}$

The Bigger Picture **1.** $\left\{-\dfrac{3}{2}\right\}$ **2.** $\left\{\dfrac{\log 5}{\log 11} \approx 0.6712\right\}$ **3.** $[-5, \infty)$ **4.** $\left[-\dfrac{13}{3}, -2\right]$ **5.** $\left(-\dfrac{6}{5}, 0\right)$ **6.** $\left\{6, -\dfrac{1}{5}\right\}$

7. $\left\{\dfrac{21}{8}\right\}$ **8.** $\left\{-\dfrac{7}{3}, 3\right\}$ **9.** $(-\infty, \infty)$ **10.** $\{-2, 2\}$ **11.** $\{-5 + \sqrt{3}, -5 - \sqrt{3}\}$ **12.** $\left\{-\dfrac{1}{4}, 7\right\}$

Chapter 9 Vocabulary Check **1.** inverse **2.** composition **3.** exponential **4.** symmetric **5.** natural **6.** common **7.** vertical; horizontal **8.** logarithmic

Chapter 9 Review **1.** $3x - 4$ **2.** $-x - 6$ **3.** $2x^2 - 9x - 5$ **4.** $\dfrac{2x + 1}{x - 5}$ where $x \neq 5$ **5.** $x^2 + 2x - 1$ **6.** $x^2 - 1$ **7.** 18

8. $x^4 - 4x^2 + 2$ **9.** -2 **10.** 48 **11.** one-to-one; $h^{-1} = \{(14, -9), (8, 6), (12, -11), (15, 15)\}$ **12.** not one-to-one

13. one-to-one;

Rank in Automobile Thefts (Input)	2	4	1	3
U.S. Region (Output)	West	Midwest	South	Northeast

14. not one-to-one **15.** not one-to-one **16.** not one-to-one **17.** not one-to-one **18.** one-to-one **19.** $f^{-1}(x) = \dfrac{x - 11}{6}$

20. $f^{-1}(x) = \dfrac{x}{12}$ **21.** $f^{-1}(x) = \dfrac{x + 5}{3}$ **22.** $f^{-1}(x) = \dfrac{x - 1}{2}$ **23.** **24.**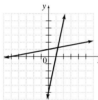

25. $\{3\}$ **26.** $\left\{-\dfrac{4}{3}\right\}$ **27.** $\left\{\dfrac{3}{2}\right\}$ **28.** 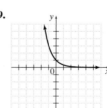 **29.** 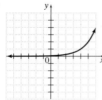 **30.**

31.

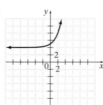

32. $2963.11 **33.** $1131.82 **34.** $\log_7 49 = 2$ **35.** $\log_2 \dfrac{1}{16} = -4$ **36.** $\left(\dfrac{1}{2}\right)^{-4} = 16$

37. $0.4^3 = 0.064$ **38.** $\left\{\dfrac{1}{64}\right\}$ **39.** $\{9\}$ **40.** $\{0\}$ **41.** $\{8\}$ **42.** $\{5\}$ **43.** $\{-2\}$ **44.** $\{4\}$ **45.** $\{9\}$ **46.** $\{2\}$ **47.** $\{-8, 1\}$

48. 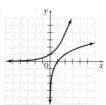 **49.** **50.** $\log_3 32$ **51.** $\log_2 18$ **52.** $\log_7 \dfrac{3}{4}$ **53.** $\log_e \dfrac{3}{2}$ **54.** $\log_{11} 4$ **55.** $\log_5 2$

56. $\log_5 \dfrac{x^3}{(x + 1)^2}$ **57.** $\log_3 (x^4 + 2x^3)$ **58.** $3\log_3 x - \log_3 (x + 2)$ **59.** $\log_4 (x + 5) - 2\log_4 x$ **60.** $\log_2 3 + 2\log_2 x + \log_2 y - \log_2 z$

CHAPTER 10 Conic Sections

Calculator Explorations   1. 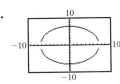   **3.**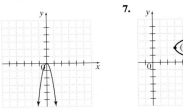

Mental Math   1. upward   **3.** to the left   **5.** downward

Exercise Set 10.1   1. 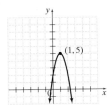   **3.** 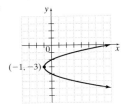   **5.** 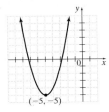   **7.**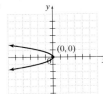

9. 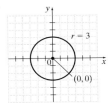   **11.** 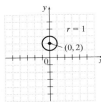   **13.** 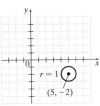   **15.**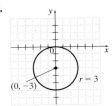

17. 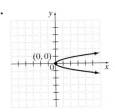   **19.** 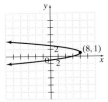   **21.**   **23.**

25. 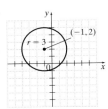   **27.** 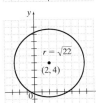   **29.** 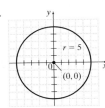   **31.**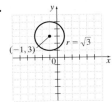

33. $(x - 2)^2 + (y - 3)^2 = 36$ **35.** $x^2 + y^2 = 3$ **37.** $(x + 5)^2 + (y - 4)^2 = 45$

43. $\dfrac{\sqrt{3}}{3}$ **45.** $\dfrac{2\sqrt{42}}{3}$

39. 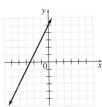   **41.**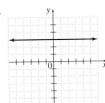

47. a. 16.5 meters **b.** 103.67 meters **c.** 3.5 meters apart **d.** $(0, 16.5)$ **e.** $x^2 + (y - 16.5)^2 = (16.5)^2$

49. a. 125 ft **b.** 14 ft **c.** 139 ft **d.** $(0, 139)$ **e.** $x^2 + (y - 139)^2 = 125^2$ **51.** answers may vary   **53.** 20 m   **55.** $y = -\dfrac{2}{125}x^2 + 40$

Calculator Explorations   1. 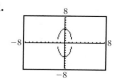 **3.**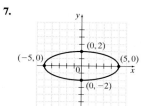

Mental Math   1. ellipse   **3.** hyperbola   **5.** hyperbola

Exercise Set 10.2   1. 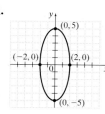   **3.** 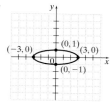   **5.** 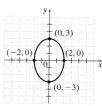   **7.**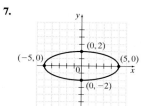

9. 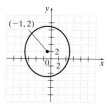   **11.** 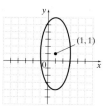   **13.** 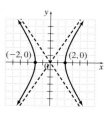   **15.** 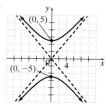   **17.**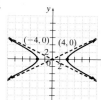

19. 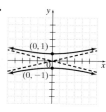   **21.** 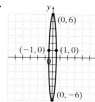   **23.** 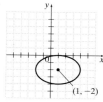   **25.** 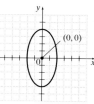   **27.**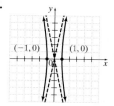

29. $-8x^5$ **31.** $-4x^2$ **33.** y-intercepts; 2 units   **35.** y-intercepts; 4 units   **37.** $\dfrac{x^2}{25} + \dfrac{y^2}{25} = 1$; ellipse; when $a = b$

39. A: 36, 13; B: 4, 4; C: 25, 16; D: 39, 25; E: 17, 81; F: 36, 36; G: 16, 65; H: 144, 140   **41.** A: 6; B: 2; C: 5; D: 5; E: 9; F: 6; G: 4; H: 12

43. greater than 0 and less than 1   **45.** greater than 1

47.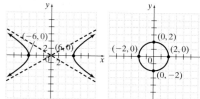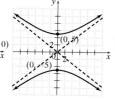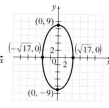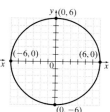

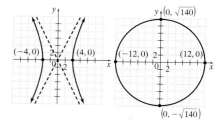

Integrated Review   1. circle 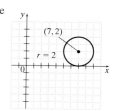   **2.** parabola 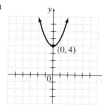   **3.** parabola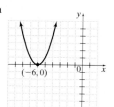

4. ellipse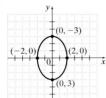

5. hyperbola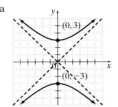

6. hyperbola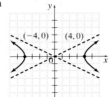

7. ellipse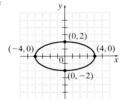

8. circle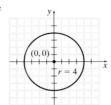

9. parabola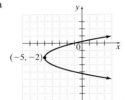

10. parabola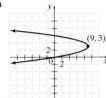

11. hyperbola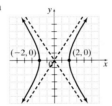

12. ellipse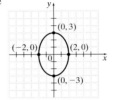

13. ellipse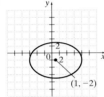

14. hyperbola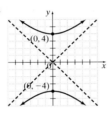

15. circle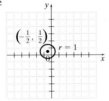

Exercise Set 10.3   **1.** $\{(3,-4),(-3,4)\}$ **3.** $\{(\sqrt{2},\sqrt{2}),(-\sqrt{2},-\sqrt{2})\}$ **5.** $\{(4,0),(0,-2)\}$

7. $\{(-\sqrt{5},-2),(-\sqrt{5},2),(\sqrt{5},-2),(\sqrt{5},2)\}$ **9.** $\varnothing$ **11.** $\{(1,-2),(3,6)\}$ **13.** $\{(2,4),(-5,25)\}$ **15.** $\varnothing$ **17.** $\{(1,-3)\}$

19. $\{(-1,-2),(-1,2),(1,-2),(1,2)\}$ **21.** $\{(0,-1)\}$ **23.** $\{(-1,3),(1,3)\}$ **25.** $\{(\sqrt{3},0),(-\sqrt{3},0)\}$ **27.** $\varnothing$

29. $\{(-6,0),(6,0),(0,-6)\}$ **31.** $\{(3\sqrt{3})\}$ **33.** 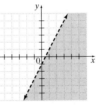   **35.** 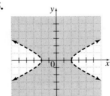   **37.** answers may vary

39. 0, 1, 2, 3, or 4   **41.** -9 and 7; 9 and -7; 9 and 7; -9 and -7 **43.** 15 cm by 19 cm   **45.** 15 thousand compact discs; price: \$3.75

Exercise Set 10.4   **1.** 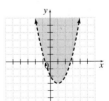   **3.** 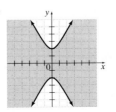   **5.** 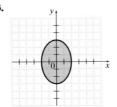   **7.**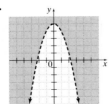

9. 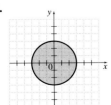   **11.** 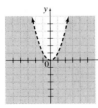   **13.** 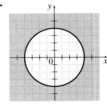   **15.**

2. a. $\left(5, \dfrac{9\pi}{4}\right)$ **b.** $\left(-5, \dfrac{5\pi}{4}\right)$ **c.** $\left(5, -\dfrac{7\pi}{4}\right)$ **3. a.** $(-3, 0)$ **b.** $(-5\sqrt{3}, -5)$ **4.** $\left(2, \dfrac{5\pi}{3}\right)$ **5.** $\left(4, \dfrac{3\pi}{2}\right)$

6. a. $r = \dfrac{6}{3\cos\theta - \sin\theta}$ **b.** $r = -2\sin\theta$ **7. a.** $x^2 + y^2 = 16$ **b.** $y = -x$ **c.** $x = -2$ **d.** $x^2 + (y - 5)^2 = 25$

Exercise Set 6.3

1. C **3.** A **5.** B **7.** C **9.** A

11.

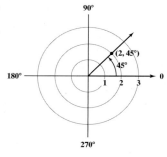

13.

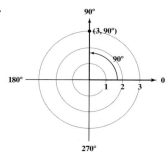

15.

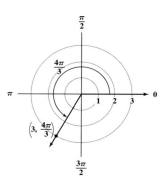

17.

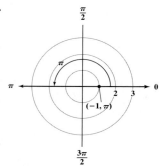

19.

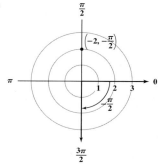

21.

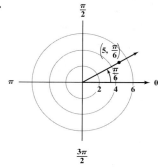

a. $\left(5, \dfrac{13\pi}{6}\right)$ **b.** $\left(-5, \dfrac{7\pi}{6}\right)$

c. $\left(5, -\dfrac{11\pi}{6}\right)$

23.

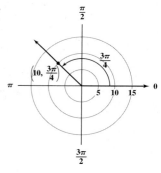

25.

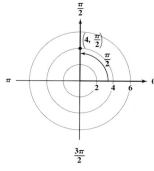

a. $\left(10, \dfrac{11\pi}{4}\right)$ **b.** $\left(-10, \dfrac{7\pi}{4}\right)$ **a.** $\left(4, \dfrac{5\pi}{2}\right)$ **b.** $\left(-4, \dfrac{3\pi}{2}\right)$

c. $\left(10, -\dfrac{5\pi}{4}\right)$ **c.** $\left(4, -\dfrac{3\pi}{2}\right)$

27. a, b, d   **29.** b, d   **31.** a, b   **33.** $(0, 4)$ **35.** $(1, \sqrt{3})$ **37.** $(0, -4)$ **39.** approximately $(-5.9, 4.4)$ **41.** $\left(\sqrt{8}, \dfrac{3\pi}{4}\right)$ **43.** $\left(4, \dfrac{5\pi}{3}\right)$

45. $\left(2, \dfrac{7\pi}{6}\right)$ **47.** $(5, 0)$ **49.** $r = \dfrac{7}{3\cos\theta + \sin\theta}$ **51.** $r = \dfrac{7}{\cos\theta}$ **53.** $r = 3$ **55.** $r = 4\cos\theta$ **57.** $r = \dfrac{6\cos\theta}{\sin^2\theta}$

59. $x^2 + y^2 = 64$

$x^2 + y^2 = 64$

61. $x = 0$

$x = 0$

63. $y = 3$

$y = 3$

65. $y = 4$

$y = 4$

67. $x^2 + y^2 = y$

$x^2 + y^2 = y$

69. $(x - 6)^2 + y^2 = 36$

$(x - 6)^2 + y^2 = 36$

71. $x^2 + y^2 = 6x + 4y$

$x^2 + y^2 = 6x + 4y$

73. $y = \dfrac{1}{x}$

$y = \dfrac{1}{x}$

75. $r = a \sec \theta$; $r \cos \theta = a$; $x = a$; $x = a$ is a vertical line a units to the right of the y-axis when $a > 0$ and $|a|$ to the left of the y-axis when $a < 0$.

77. $r = a \sin \theta$; $r^2 = ar \sin \theta$; $x^2 + y^2 = ay$; $x^2 + y^2 - ay = 0$; $x^2 + \left(y - \dfrac{a}{2}\right)^2 = \left(\dfrac{a}{2}\right)^2$ **79.** $y = x + 2\sqrt{2}$; slope: 1; y-intercept: $2\sqrt{2}$

81. $(-1, \sqrt{3}), (2\sqrt{3}, 2); 2\sqrt{5}$ **83.** $\left(15, \dfrac{4\pi}{3}\right)$ **85.** 6.3 knots at an angle of 50° to the wind   **87.** Answers may vary.

97. $(-2, 3.464)$ **99.** $(-1.857, -3.543)$ **101.** $(3, 0.730)$

Section 6.4

Check Point Exercises

1.

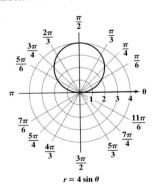

$r = 4 \sin \theta$

2.

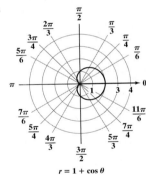

$r = 1 + \cos \theta$

3.

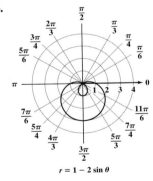

$r = 1 - 2 \sin \theta$

4.

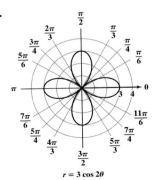

$r = 3 \cos 2\theta$

5.

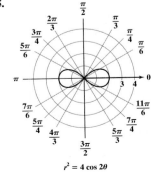

$r^2 = 4 \cos 2\theta$

Exercise Set 6.4

1. $r = 1 - \sin\theta$ **3.** $r = 2\cos\theta$ **5.** $r = 3\sin 3\theta$ **7. a.** May or may not have symmetry with respect to polar axis.
b. Has symmetry with respect to the line $\theta = \dfrac{\pi}{2}$. **c.** May or may not have symmetry about the pole.
9. a. Has symmetry with respect to polar axis. **b.** May or may not have symmetry with respect to the line $\theta = \dfrac{\pi}{2}$.
c. May or may not have symmetry about pole. **11. a.** Has symmetry with respect to polar axis.
b. Has symmetry with respect to the line $\theta = \dfrac{\pi}{2}$. **c.** Has symmetry about the pole.

13.

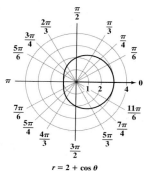

$r = 2\cos\theta$

15.

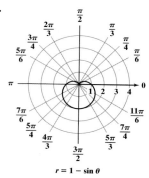

$r = 1 - \sin\theta$

17.

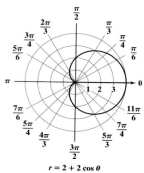

$r = 2 + 2\cos\theta$

19.

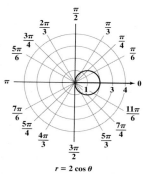

$r = 2 + \cos\theta$

21.

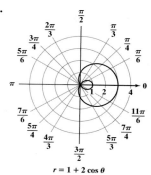

$r = 1 + 2\cos\theta$

23.

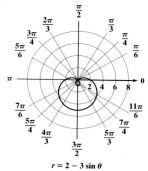

$r = 2 - 3\sin\theta$

25.

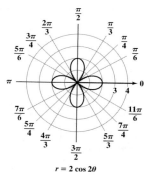

$r = 2\cos 2\theta$

27.

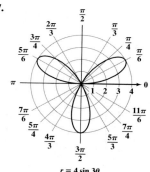

$r = 4\sin 3\theta$

29.

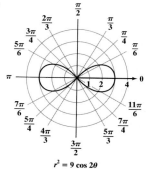

$r^2 = 9\cos 2\theta$

31.

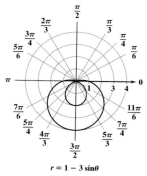

$r = 1 - 3\sin\theta$

33.

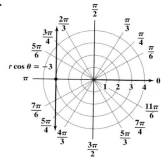

$r\cos\theta = -3$

35.

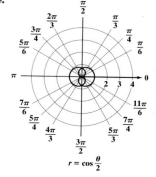

$r = \cos\dfrac{\theta}{2}$

37.

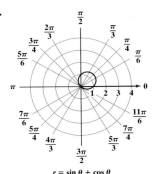

$$r = \sin \theta + \cos \theta$$

39.

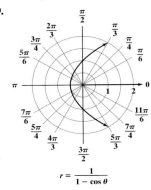

$$r = \frac{1}{1 - \cos \theta}$$

41.

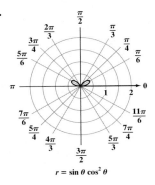

$$r = \sin \theta \cos^2 \theta$$

43.

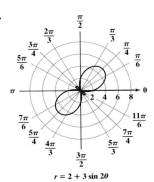

$$r = 2 + 3 \sin 2\theta$$

45. 6 knots

47. 8 knots

49. 90°; about $7\frac{1}{2}$ knots

59.

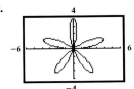

61.

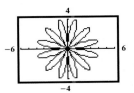

63.

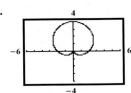

65.

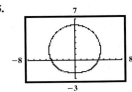

67.

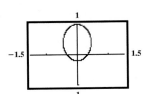

69.

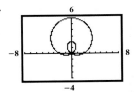

71.

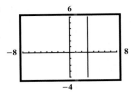

73.

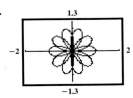

75.

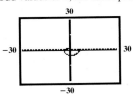

77. 2π

79.

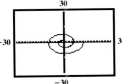

81.

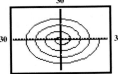

83. If n is odd, there are n loops and $\theta\max = \pi$ traces the graph once; while if n is even, there are $2n$ loops and $\theta\max = 2\pi$ traces the graph once. In each separate case, as n increases, $\sin n\theta$ increases its number of loops. **85.** There are n small petals and n large petals for each value of n. For odd values of n, the small petals are inside the large petals. For even n, they are between the large petals.

87.

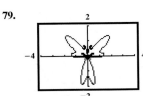

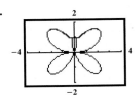

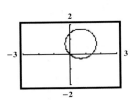

89.

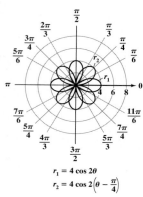

$r_1 = 4 \cos 2\theta$

$r_2 = 4 \cos 2\left(\theta - \frac{\pi}{4}\right)$

The graph of r_2 is the

graph of r_1 rotated $\dfrac{\pi}{4}$ or 45°.

Mid-Chapter 6 Check Point

1. $C = 107°, b \approx 24.8, c \approx 36.1$ **2.** $B \approx 37°, C \approx 101°, c \approx 92.4$ **3.** no triangle **4.** $A \approx 26°, C \approx 44°, b \approx 21.6$ **5.** Two triangles:
$A_1 \approx 55°, B_1 \approx 83°, b_1 \approx 19.3; A_2 \approx 125°, B_2 \approx 13°, b_2 \approx 4.4$ **6.** $A \approx 28°, B \approx 42°, C \approx 110°$ **7.** 10 ft² **8.** $14\sqrt{5} \approx 31$ m² **9.** 148 miles

10. 15.0 miles **11.** 327 ft **12.** $\left(\dfrac{3\sqrt{2}}{2}, \dfrac{3\sqrt{2}}{2}\right)$ **13.** $(0, -6)$ **14.** $\left(4, -\dfrac{\pi}{3}\right)$ **15.** $(6, \pi)$

16.

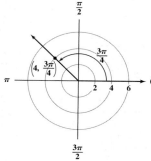

17.

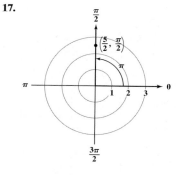

18. $r = \dfrac{7}{5\cos\theta - \sin\theta}$ **19.** $r = -7\csc\theta$

20. $r = -2\cos\theta$

a. $\left(4, \dfrac{11\pi}{4}\right)$ **b.** $\left(-4, \dfrac{7\pi}{4}\right)$

c. $\left(4, -\dfrac{5\pi}{4}\right)$

a. $\left(\dfrac{5}{2}, \dfrac{5\pi}{2}\right)$ **b.** $\left(-\dfrac{5}{2}, \dfrac{3\pi}{2}\right)$

c. $\left(\dfrac{5}{2}, -\dfrac{3\pi}{2}\right)$

21. $x^2 + y^2 = 36$ **22.** $y = \sqrt{3}x$ **23.** $y = -3$

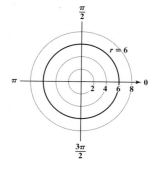

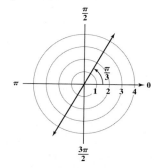

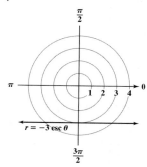

24. $(x + 5)^2 + y^2 = 25$

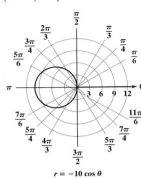

$r = -10 \cos \theta$

25. $y = \dfrac{1}{4}x^2$

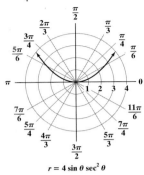

$r = 4 \sin \theta \sec^2 \theta$

26. a. Has symmetry with respect to the polar axis.   **b.** May or may not have symmetry with respect to the line $\theta = \dfrac{\pi}{2}$.   **c.** May or may not have symmetry with respect to the pole.   **27. a.** Has symmetry with respect to the polar axis.   **b.** Has symmetry with respect to the line $\theta = \dfrac{\pi}{2}$.   **c.** Has symmetry with respect to the pole.

28.

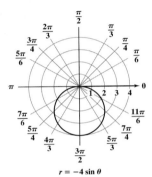

$r = -4 \sin \theta$

29.

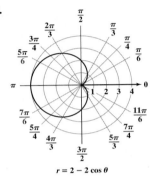

$r = 2 - 2 \cos \theta$

30.

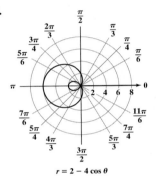

$r = 2 - 4 \cos \theta$

31.

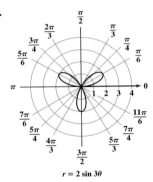

$r = 2 \sin 3\theta$

32.

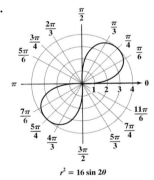

$r^2 = 16 \sin 2\theta$

Section 6.5

Check Point Exercises

1. a.

$z = 2 + 3i$

b.

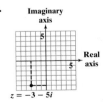

$z = -3 - 5i$

c.

$z = -4$

d.

$z = -i$

2. a. 13   **b.** $\sqrt{13}$

3.

$z = -1 - \sqrt{3}i$

$; 2\left(\cos \dfrac{4\pi}{3} + i \sin \dfrac{4\pi}{3}\right)$

4. $z = 2\sqrt{3} + 2i$ **5.** $30(\cos 60° + i \sin 60°)$ **6.** $10(\cos \pi + i \sin \pi)$ **7.** $-16\sqrt{3} + 16i$ **8.** -4

9. $2(\cos 15° + i \sin 15°)$; $2(\cos 105° + i \sin 105°)$; $2(\cos 195° + i \sin 195°)$; $2(\cos 285° + i \sin 285°)$ **10.** $3; -\dfrac{3}{2} + \dfrac{3\sqrt{3}}{2}i; -\dfrac{3}{2} - \dfrac{3\sqrt{3}}{2}i$

Exercise Set 6.5

1. 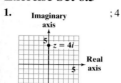 ; 4

3. 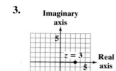 ; 3

5. 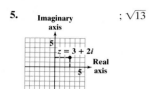 ; $\sqrt{13}$

7. 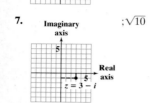 ; $\sqrt{10}$

9. 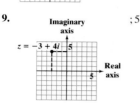 ; 5

11.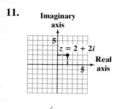

$2\sqrt{2}\left(\cos\dfrac{\pi}{4} + i \sin\dfrac{\pi}{4}\right)$
or $2\sqrt{2}(\cos 45° + i \sin 45°)$

13.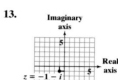

$\sqrt{2}\left(\cos\dfrac{5\pi}{4} + i \sin\dfrac{5\pi}{4}\right)$ or $\sqrt{2}(\cos 225° + i \sin 225°)$

15.

$4\left(\cos\dfrac{3\pi}{2} + i \sin\dfrac{3\pi}{2}\right)$ or $4(\cos 270° + i \sin 270°)$

17.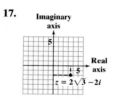

$4\left(\cos\dfrac{11\pi}{6} + i \sin\dfrac{11\pi}{6}\right)$ or $4(\cos 330° + i \sin 330°)$

19.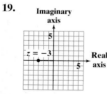

$3(\cos\pi + i \sin \pi)$ or $3(\cos 180° + i \sin 180°)$

21.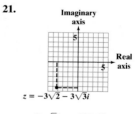

$\approx 3\sqrt{5}(\cos 230.8° + i \sin 230.8°)$

23.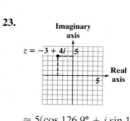

$\approx 5(\cos 126.9° + i \sin 126.9°)$

25.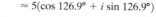

$\approx \sqrt{7}(\cos 319.1° + i \sin 319.1°)$

27. $3\sqrt{3} + 3i$ **29.** $-2 - 2\sqrt{3}i$ **31.** $4\sqrt{2} - 4\sqrt{2}i$ **33.** $5i$ **35.** $z \approx -18.1 - 8.5i$ **37.** $30(\cos 70° + i \sin 70°)$

39. $12\left(\cos\dfrac{3\pi}{10} + i \sin\dfrac{3\pi}{10}\right)$ **41.** $\cos\dfrac{7\pi}{12} + i \sin\dfrac{7\pi}{12}$ **43.** $2(\cos \pi + i \sin \pi)$ **45.** $5(\cos 50° + i \sin 50°)$ **47.** $\dfrac{3}{4}\left(\cos\dfrac{\pi}{10} + i \sin\dfrac{\pi}{10}\right)$

49. $\cos 240° + i \sin 240°$ **51.** $2(\cos 0° + i \sin 0°)$ **53.** $32\sqrt{2} + 32\sqrt{2}i$ **55.** $-4 - 4\sqrt{3}i$ **57.** $\dfrac{1}{64}i$ **59.** $-2 - 2\sqrt{3}i$

61. $-4 - 4i$ **63.** -64 **65.** $3(\cos 15° + i \sin 15°)$; $3(\cos 195° + i \sin 195°)$

67. $2(\cos 70° + i \sin 70°)$; $2(\cos 190° + i \sin 190°)$; $2(\cos 310° + i \sin 310°)$ **69.** $\dfrac{3}{2} + \dfrac{3\sqrt{3}}{2}i; -\dfrac{3\sqrt{3}}{2} + \dfrac{3}{2}i; -\dfrac{3}{2} - \dfrac{3\sqrt{3}}{2}i; \dfrac{3\sqrt{3}}{2} - \dfrac{3}{2}i$

71. $2; \approx 0.6 + 1.9i; \approx -1.6 + 1.2i; \approx -1.6 - 1.2i; \approx 0.6 - 1.9i$ **73.** $1; -\dfrac{1}{2} + \dfrac{\sqrt{3}}{2}i; -\dfrac{1}{2} - \dfrac{\sqrt{3}}{2}i$

75. $\approx 1.1 + 0.2i; \approx -0.2 + 1.1i; \approx -1.1 - 0.2i; \approx 0.2 - 1.1i$

77. $[1(\cos 90° + i \sin 90°)][2\sqrt{2}(\cos 45° + i \sin 45°)][2(\cos 150° + i \sin 150°)]; 4\sqrt{2}(\cos 285° + i \sin 285°); \approx 1.4641 - 5.4641i$

79. $\dfrac{[2(\cos 60° + i \sin 60°)][\sqrt{2}(\cos(-45°) + i \sin(-45°))]}{8(\cos(-30°) + i \sin(-30°))}; \dfrac{\sqrt{2}}{2}(\cos 45° + i \sin 45°); \dfrac{1}{2} + \dfrac{1}{2}i$

81. $\cos 0° + i \sin 0°, \cos 60° + i \sin 60°, \cos 120° + i \sin 120°, \cos 180° + i \sin 180°, \cos 240° + i \sin 240°, \cos 300° + i \sin 300°;$

$1, \dfrac{1}{2} + \dfrac{\sqrt{3}}{2}i, -\dfrac{1}{2} + \dfrac{\sqrt{3}}{2}i, -1, -\dfrac{1}{2} - \dfrac{\sqrt{3}}{2}i, \dfrac{1}{2} - \dfrac{\sqrt{3}}{2}i$

83. $2(\cos 67.5° + i \sin 67.5°), 2(\cos 157.5° + i \sin 157.5°), 2(\cos 247.5° + i \sin 247.5°), 2(\cos 337.5° + i \sin 337.5°);$

$0.7654 + 1.8478i, -1.8478 + 0.7654i, -0.7654 - 1.8478i, 1.8478 - 0.7654i$

85. $\sqrt[3]{2}(\cos 20° + i \sin 20°), \sqrt[3]{2}(\cos 140° + i \sin 140°), \sqrt[3]{2}(\cos 260° + i \sin 260°); 1.1839 + 0.4309i, -0.9652 + 0.8099i, -0.2188 - 1.2408i$

87.
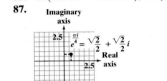

89.

91. a. $i; -1 + i; -i; -1 + i; -i; -1 + i$ **b.** Complex numbers may vary.   **107.**

Section 6.6

Check Point Exercises

1. $\|\mathbf{u}\| = 5 = \|\mathbf{v}\|$ and $m_u = \dfrac{4}{3} = m_v$ **2.** $; \|\mathbf{v}\| = 3\sqrt{2}$ **3.** $\mathbf{v} = 3\mathbf{i} + 4\mathbf{j}$ **4. a.** $11\mathbf{i} - 2\mathbf{j}$ **b.** $3\mathbf{i} + 8\mathbf{j}$

5. a. $56\mathbf{i} + 80\mathbf{j}$ **b.** $-35\mathbf{i} - 50\mathbf{j}$ **6.** $30\mathbf{i} + 33\mathbf{j}$ **7.** $\dfrac{4}{5}\mathbf{i} - \dfrac{3}{5}\mathbf{j}; \sqrt{\left(\dfrac{4}{5}\right)^2 + \left(-\dfrac{3}{5}\right)^2} = \sqrt{\dfrac{16}{25} + \dfrac{9}{25}} = \sqrt{\dfrac{25}{25}} = 1$ **8.** $30\sqrt{2}\mathbf{i} + 30\sqrt{2}\mathbf{j}$

9. 82.55 lb; 46.2°

Exercise Set 6.6

1. a. $\sqrt{41}$ **b.** $\sqrt{41}$ **c.** $\mathbf{u} = \mathbf{v}$ **3. a.** 6   **b.** 6   **c.** $\mathbf{u} = \mathbf{v}$

5.

$\sqrt{10}$

7.

$\sqrt{2}$

9.

$2\sqrt{10}$

11.
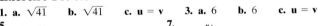

4

13. $10\mathbf{i} + 6\mathbf{j}$ **15.** $6\mathbf{i} - 3\mathbf{j}$ **17.** $-6\mathbf{i} - 14\mathbf{j}$ **19.** $9\mathbf{i}$ **21.** $-\mathbf{i} + 2\mathbf{j}$ **23.** $5\mathbf{i} - 12\mathbf{j}$ **25.** $-5\mathbf{i} + 12\mathbf{j}$ **27.** $-15\mathbf{i} + 35\mathbf{j}$ **29.** $4\mathbf{i} + 24\mathbf{j}$

31. $-9\mathbf{i} - 4\mathbf{j}$ **33.** $-5\mathbf{i} + 45\mathbf{j}$ **35.** $2\sqrt{29}$ **37.** $\sqrt{10}$ **39.** $\mathbf{i}$ **41.** $\dfrac{3}{5}\mathbf{i} - \dfrac{4}{5}\mathbf{j}$ **43.** $\dfrac{3\sqrt{13}}{13}\mathbf{i} - \dfrac{2\sqrt{13}}{3}\mathbf{j}$ **45.** $\dfrac{\sqrt{2}}{2}\mathbf{i} + \dfrac{\sqrt{2}}{2}\mathbf{j}$

47. $3\sqrt{3}\mathbf{i} + 3\mathbf{j}$ **49.** $-6\sqrt{2}\mathbf{i} - 6\sqrt{2}\mathbf{j}$ **51.** $\approx -0.20\mathbf{i} + 0.46\mathbf{j}$ **53.** $-23\mathbf{i} + 14\mathbf{j}$ **55.** -60 **57.** commutative property

59. distributive property   **61.** 18.03; 123.7°   **63.** 6; 90°   **65.** $22\sqrt{3}\mathbf{i} + 22\mathbf{j}$ **67.** $148.5\mathbf{i} + 20.9\mathbf{j}$ **69.** $\approx 1.4\mathbf{i} + 0.6\mathbf{j}$; 1.4 in.

71. ≈ 108.21 lbs; S 77.4° E   **73.** 2038.28 lb; 162.8°   **75.** ≈ 30.9 lbs   **77. a.** 335 lb   **b.** 3484 lb   **79. a.** $\mathbf{F} = 9\mathbf{i} - 3\mathbf{j}$ **b.** $\mathbf{F}_3 = -9\mathbf{i} + 3\mathbf{j}$

81. a. $\mathbf{F} = -2\mathbf{j}$ **b.** $\mathbf{F}_5 = 2\mathbf{j}$ **83. a.** $\mathbf{v} = 180 \cos 40°\mathbf{i} + 180 \sin 40°\mathbf{j} \approx 137.89\mathbf{i} + 115.70\mathbf{j}$ $\mathbf{w} = 40 \cos 0°\mathbf{i} + 40 \sin 0°\mathbf{j} = 40\mathbf{i}$

b. $\mathbf{v} + \mathbf{w} \approx 177.89\mathbf{i} + 115.70\mathbf{j}$ **c.** 212 mph   **d.** 33.0°; N 57°E   **85.** 78 mph, 75.4°   **107.** $\approx 4232.1; \approx 72.7°$

Section 6.7

Check Point Exercises

1. a. 18   **b.** 18   **c.** 5   **2.** 100.3°   **3.** orthogonal   **4.** $\dfrac{7}{2}\mathbf{i} - \dfrac{7}{2}\mathbf{j}$ **5.** $\mathbf{v}_1 = \dfrac{7}{2}\mathbf{i} - \dfrac{7}{2}\mathbf{j}; \mathbf{v}_2 = -\dfrac{3}{2}\mathbf{i} - \dfrac{3}{2}\mathbf{j}$ **6.** approximately 2598 ft-lb

Exercise Set 6.7

1. 6; 10   **3.** -6; 41   **5.** 100; 61   **7.** 0; 25   **9.** 3   **11.** 3   **13.** 20   **15.** 20   **17.** 79.7°   **19.** 160.3°   **21.** 38.7°

23. orthogonal   **25.** orthogonal   **27.** not orthogonal   **29.** not orthogonal   **31.** orthogonal   **33.** $\mathbf{v}_1 = \text{proj}_{\mathbf{w}}\mathbf{v} = \dfrac{5}{2}\mathbf{i} - \dfrac{5}{2}\mathbf{j}; \mathbf{v}_2 = \dfrac{1}{2}\mathbf{i} + \dfrac{1}{2}\mathbf{j}$

35. $\mathbf{v}_1 = \text{proj}_{\mathbf{w}}\mathbf{v} = -\dfrac{26}{29}\mathbf{i} + \dfrac{65}{29}\mathbf{j}; \mathbf{v}_2 = \dfrac{55}{29}\mathbf{i} + \dfrac{22}{29}\mathbf{j}$ **37.** $\mathbf{v}_1 = \text{proj}_{\mathbf{w}}\mathbf{v} = \mathbf{i} + 2\mathbf{j}; \mathbf{v}_2 = 0$ **39.** 25   **41.** $5\mathbf{i} - 5\mathbf{j}$ **43.** 30°   **45.** parallel

47. neither   **49.** orthogonal   **51.** 1617; $\mathbf{v} \cdot \mathbf{w} = 1617$ means that \$1617 in revenue is generated when 240 gallons of regular gasoline are sold at \$2.90 per gallon and 300 gallons of premium gasoline are sold at \$3.09 per gallon.   **53.** 7600 foot-pounds   **55.** 3392 foot-pounds
57. 1079 foot-pounds   **59.** 40 foot-pounds   **61.** 22.05 foot-pounds
63. a. $\dfrac{\sqrt{3}}{2}\mathbf{i} + \dfrac{1}{2}\mathbf{j}$ **b.** $-175\sqrt{3}\mathbf{i} - 175\mathbf{j}$ **c.** 350; A force of 350 pounds is required to keep the boat from rolling down the ramp.

75. $\mathbf{u} \cdot \mathbf{w} = (a_1\mathbf{i} + b_1\mathbf{j}) \cdot (a_2\mathbf{i} + b_2\mathbf{j})$

$\qquad = a_1a_2 + b_1b_2$

$\qquad = a_2a_1 + b_2b_1$

$\qquad = (a_2\mathbf{i} + b_2\mathbf{j}) \cdot (a_1\mathbf{i} + b_1\mathbf{j})$

$\qquad = \mathbf{v} \cdot \mathbf{u}$

77. $\mathbf{u} \cdot (\mathbf{v} + \mathbf{w}) = (a_1\mathbf{i} + b_1\mathbf{j}) \cdot [(a_2\mathbf{i} + b_2\mathbf{j}) + (a_3\mathbf{i} + b_3\mathbf{j})]$

$\qquad = (a_1\mathbf{i} + b_1\mathbf{j}) \cdot [(a_2 + a_3)\mathbf{i} + (b_2 + b_3)\mathbf{j}]$

$\qquad = a_1(a_2 + a_3) + b_1(b_2 + b_3)$

$\qquad = a_1a_2 + a_1a_3 + b_1b_2 + b_1b_3$

$\qquad = a_1a_2 + b_1b_2 + a_1a_3 + b_1b_3$

$\qquad = (a_1\mathbf{i} + b_1\mathbf{j}) \cdot (a_2\mathbf{i} + b_2\mathbf{j}) + (a_1\mathbf{i} + b_1\mathbf{j}) \cdot (a_3\mathbf{i} + b_3\mathbf{j})$

$\qquad = \mathbf{u} \cdot \mathbf{v} + \mathbf{u} \cdot \mathbf{w}$

79. $b = -20$ **81.** any two vectors, $\mathbf{v}$ and $\mathbf{w}$, having the same direction

Chapter 6 Review Exercises

1. $C = 55°$, $b \approx 10.5$, and $c \approx 10.5$ **2.** $A = 43°$, $a \approx 171.9$, and $b \approx 241.0$ **3.** $b \approx 16.3$, $A \approx 72°$, and $C \approx 42°$
4. $C \approx 98°$, $A \approx 55°$, and $B \approx 27°$ **5.** $C = 120°$, $a \approx 45.0$, and $b \approx 33.2$ **6.** two triangles; $B_1 \approx 55°$, $C_1 \approx 86°$, and $c_1 \approx 31.7$;
$B_2 \approx 125°$, $C_2 \approx 16°$, and $c_2 \approx 8.8$ **7.** no triangle   **8.** $a \approx 59.0$, $B \approx 3°$, and $C \approx 15°$ **9.** $B \approx 78°$, $A \approx 39°$, and $C \approx 63°$
10. $B \approx 25°$, $C \approx 115°$, and $c \approx 8.5$ **11.** two triangles; $A_1 \approx 59°$, $C_1 \approx 84°$, $c_1 \approx 14.4$; $A_2 \approx 121°$, $C_2 \approx 22°$, $c_2 \approx 5.4$
12. $B \approx 9°$, $C \approx 148°$, and $c \approx 73.6$ **13.** 8 sq ft   **14.** 4 sq ft   **15.** 4 sq m   **16.** 2 sq m   **17.** 35 ft   **18.** 35.6 mi
19. 861 mi   **20.** 404 ft; 551 ft   **21.** \$214,194

22.

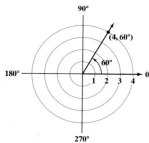

$(2, 2\sqrt{3})$

23.

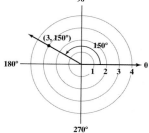

$\left(-\dfrac{3\sqrt{3}}{2}, \dfrac{3}{2}\right)$

24.

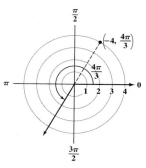

$(2, 2\sqrt{3})$

25.

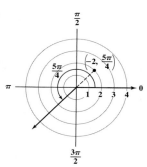

$(\sqrt{2}, \sqrt{2})$

26.

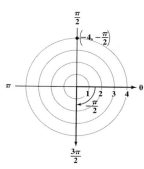

$(0, 4)$

27.

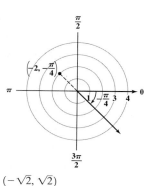

$(-\sqrt{2}, \sqrt{2})$

28.

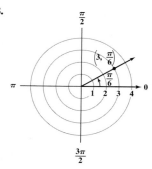

a. $\left(3, \dfrac{13\pi}{6}\right)$ **b.** $\left(-3, \dfrac{7\pi}{6}\right)$

c. $\left(3, -\dfrac{11\pi}{6}\right)$

29.

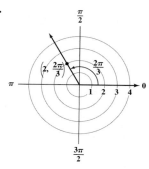

a. $\left(2, \dfrac{8\pi}{3}\right)$ **b.** $\left(-2, \dfrac{5\pi}{3}\right)$

c. $\left(2, -\dfrac{4\pi}{3}\right)$

30.

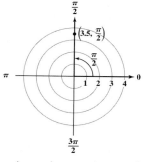

a. $\left(3.5, \dfrac{5\pi}{2}\right)$ **b.** $\left(-3.5, \dfrac{3\pi}{2}\right)$

c. $\left(3.5, -\dfrac{3\pi}{2}\right)$

31. $\left(4\sqrt{2}, \frac{3\pi}{4}\right)$ **32.** $\left(3\sqrt{2}, \frac{7\pi}{4}\right)$ **33.** approximately $(13, 67°)$ **34.** approximately $(5, 127°)$ **35.** $\left(5, \frac{3\pi}{2}\right)$ **36.** $(1, 0)$

37. $r = \dfrac{8}{2\cos\theta + 3\sin\theta}$ **38.** $r = 10$ **39.** $r = 12\cos\theta$

40. $x^2 + y^2 = 9$

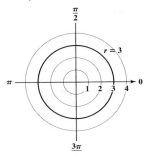

41. $y = -x$

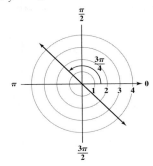

42. $x = -1$

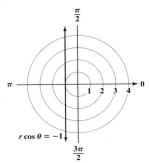

43. $y = 5$

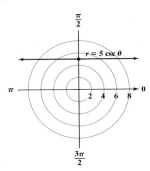

44. $\left(x - \dfrac{3}{2}\right)^2 + y^2 = \dfrac{9}{4}$

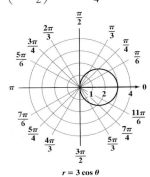

$r = 3\cos\theta$

45. $y = -4x + 8$

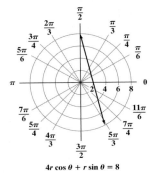

$4r\cos\theta + r\sin\theta = 8$

46. $y = -\dfrac{1}{x}$

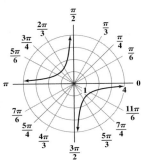

$r^2 \sin 2\theta = -2$

47. a. has symmetry   **b.** may or may not have symmetry   **c.** may or may not have symmetry   **48. a.** may or may not have symmetry
b. has symmetry   **c.** may or may not have symmetry   **49. a.** has symmetry   **b.** has symmetry   **c.** has symmetry

50.

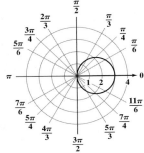

$r = 3\cos\theta$

51.

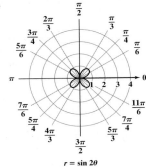

$r = 2 + 2\sin\theta$

52.

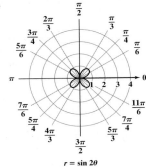

$r = \sin 2\theta$

53.

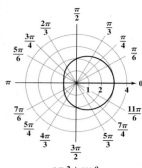

$r = 2 + \cos\theta$

54.

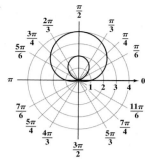

$r = 1 + 3\sin\theta$

55.

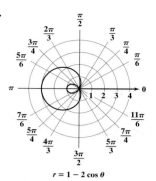

$r = 1 - 2\cos\theta$

56.

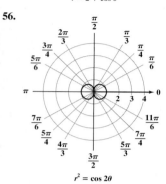

$r^2 = \cos 2\theta$

57.

$$\sqrt{2}\left(\cos\frac{7\pi}{4} + i\sin\frac{7\pi}{4}\right) \text{ or}$$

$$\sqrt{2}(\cos 315° + i\sin 315°)$$

58.

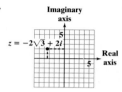

$$4(\cos 150° + i\sin 150°) \text{ or}$$

$$4\left(\cos\frac{5\pi}{6} + i\sin\frac{5\pi}{6}\right)$$

59.

$z = -3 - 4i \approx 5(\cos 233° + i\sin 233°)$

60.

$$5\left(\cos\frac{3\pi}{2} + i\sin\frac{3\pi}{2}\right) \text{ or}$$

$$5(\cos 270° + i\sin 270°)$$

61. $z = 4 + 4\sqrt{3}i$
62. $z = -2\sqrt{3} - 2i$
63. $z = -3 + 3\sqrt{3}i$
64. $z \approx -0.1 + 0.6i$
65. $15(\cos 110° + i\sin 110°)$
66. $\cos 265° + i\sin 265°$
67. $40(\cos\pi + i\sin\pi)$
68. $2(\cos 5° + i\sin 5°)$

69. $\frac{1}{2}(\cos\pi + i\sin\pi)$ **70.** $2\left(\cos\frac{7\pi}{6} + i\sin\frac{7\pi}{6}\right)$ **71.** $4 + 4\sqrt{3}i$ **72.** $-32\sqrt{3} + 32i$ **73.** $\frac{1}{128}i$ **74.** $64 - 64\sqrt{3}i$ **75.** $128 + 128i$

76. $7(\cos 25° + i\sin 25°)$; $7(\cos 205° + i\sin 205°)$ **77.** $5(\cos 55° + i\sin 55°)$; $5(\cos 175° + i\sin 175°)$; $5(\cos 295° + i\sin 295°)$

78. $\sqrt{3} + i$; $-1 + \sqrt{3}i$; $-\sqrt{3} - i$; $1 - \sqrt{3}i$ **79.** $\sqrt{3} + i$; $-\sqrt{3} + i$; $-2i$ **80.** $\frac{1}{2} + \frac{\sqrt{3}}{2}i$; -1; $\frac{1}{2} - \frac{\sqrt{3}}{2}i$

81. $\frac{\sqrt[5]{8}}{2} + \frac{\sqrt[5]{8}}{2}i$; $\approx -0.49 + 0.95i$; $\approx -1.06 - 0.17i$; $\approx -0.17 - 1.06i$; $\approx 0.95 - 0.49i$

82.

; 5

83.

; $\sqrt{29}$

84.

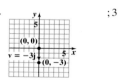

; 3

85. $3i - 2j$ **86.** $i - 2j$ **87.** $-i + 2j$ **88.** $-3i + 12j$ **89.** $12i - 51j$ **90.** $2\sqrt{26}$ **91.** $\frac{4}{5}i - \frac{3}{5}j$ **92.** $-\frac{1}{\sqrt{5}}i + \frac{2}{\sqrt{5}}j$

93. $6i + 6\sqrt{3}j$ **94.** 270 lb; 27.7° **95. a.** $13.59i + 6.34j$ **b.** 14.0 mph **c.** 13.9° **96.** 4 **97.** 2; 86.1° **98.** -32; 124.8°

99. 1; 71.6° **100.** orthogonal **101.** not orthogonal **102.** $v_1 = \text{proj}_w v = \frac{50}{41}i + \frac{40}{41}j$; $v_2 = -\frac{132}{41}i + \frac{165}{41}j$

103. $v_1 = \text{proj}_w v = -\frac{3}{2}i + \frac{1}{2}j$; $v_2 = \frac{1}{2}i + \frac{3}{2}j$ **104.** 1115 ft-lb **105.** Answers may vary.

Chapter 6 Test

1. 8.0 **2.** 6.2 **3.** 206 sq in.

4.

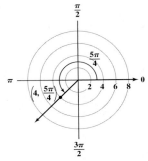

; Ordered pairs may vary.   **5.** $\left(\sqrt{2}, \dfrac{7\pi}{4}\right)$ **6.** $r = -16 \sin\theta$ **7.** $x = -4$

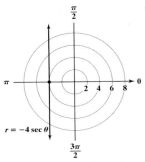

$r = -4 \sec\theta$

8.

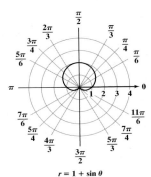

$r = 1 + \sin\theta$

9.

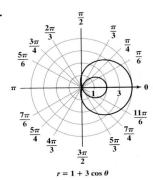

$r = 1 + 3\cos\theta$

10. $2(\cos 150° + i \sin 150°)$ or $2\left(\cos\dfrac{5\pi}{6} + i \sin\dfrac{5\pi}{6}\right)$

11. $50(\cos 20° + i \sin 20°)$

12. $\dfrac{1}{2}\left(\cos\dfrac{\pi}{6} + i \sin\dfrac{\pi}{6}\right)$

13. $32(\cos 50° + i \sin 50°)$

14. $3; -\dfrac{3}{2} + \dfrac{\sqrt{3}}{2}i; -\dfrac{3}{2} - \dfrac{\sqrt{3}}{2}i$

15. a. $i + 2j$ **b.** $\sqrt{5}$

16. $-23i + 22j$

17. -18

18. $138°$ **19.** $-\dfrac{9}{5}i + \dfrac{18}{5}j$

20. 1.0 mi   **21.** 323 pounds; 3.4°   **22.** 1966 ft-lb

Cumulative Review Exercises (Chapter P–6)

1. $\{-1, 2, i, -i\}$ **2.** $\dfrac{\pi}{6}, \dfrac{5\pi}{6}, \dfrac{\pi}{2}$ **3.** $\{x \mid x < -4 \text{ or } x > 2\}$ **4.** $\dfrac{3\pi}{4}, \dfrac{7\pi}{4}$

5.

6.

7. $\sin\theta \csc\theta - \cos^2\theta = \sin\theta\left(\dfrac{1}{\sin\theta}\right) - \cos^2\theta$
$= 1 - \cos^2\theta = \sin^2\theta$

8. $\cos\left(\theta + \dfrac{3\pi}{2}\right) = \cos\theta \cos\dfrac{3\pi}{2} - \sin\theta \sin\dfrac{3\pi}{2}$
$= \cos\theta(0) - \sin\theta(-1) = \sin\theta$

9. slope is $-\dfrac{1}{2}$; y-intercept is 2.   **10.** 0   **11.** $\dfrac{\sqrt{5}}{5}$ **12.** $\{x \mid x \le 5\}$ **13.** $\{x \mid x \ne 3, x \ne -3\}$ **14.** 1.5 sec; 44 ft

15. a. 4 m   **b.** $\dfrac{5}{2\pi}$ **c.** $\dfrac{2\pi}{5}$ sec   **16.** $\dfrac{\sqrt{\sqrt{2}+2}}{2}$ **17. a.** $5i + 23j$ **b.** -12 **18.** $\log_b \dfrac{\sqrt{x}}{x^2 + 1}$ **19.** $y = -\dfrac{1}{2}x + 1$

20. a. 0.014   **b.** 73 words   **c.** about 144 min

CHAPTER 7

Section 7.1

Check Point Exercises

1. a. solution   **b.** not a solution   **2.** $\{(-2, 5)\}$ **3.** $\{(2, -1)\}$ **4.** $\left\{\left(\dfrac{60}{17}, -\dfrac{11}{17}\right)\right\}$ **5.** no solution or $\varnothing$

6. $\{(x, y) \mid x = 4y - 8\}$ or $\{(x, y) \mid 5x - 20y = -40\}$ **7.** 4 l of 18% solution; 8 l of 45% solution   **8.** boat: 35 mph; current: 7 mph

9. a. $C(x) = 300,000 + 30x$ **b.** $R(x) = 80x$ **c.** $(6000, 480,000)$; The company will break even if it produces and sells 6000 pairs of shoes.

Exercise Set 7.1

1. solution   **3.** not a solution   **5.** $\{(1, 3)\}$ **7.** $\{(5, 1)\}$ **9.** $\{(-22, -5)\}$ **11.** $\{(0, 0)\}$ **13.** $\{(3, -2)\}$ **15.** $\{(5, 4)\}$ **17.** $\{(7, 3)\}$

19. $\{(2, -1)\}$ **21.** $\{(3, 0)\}$ **23.** $\{(-4, 3)\}$ **25.** $\{(3, 1)\}$ **27.** $\{(1, -2)\}$ **29.** $\left\{\left(\dfrac{7}{25}, -\dfrac{1}{25}\right)\right\}$ **31.** $\varnothing$ **33.** $\{(x, y) \mid y = 3x - 5\}$

35. $\{(1, 4)\}$ **37.** $\{(x, y) \mid x + 3y = 2\}$ **39.** $\{(-5, -1)\}$ **41.** $\left\{\left(\dfrac{29}{22}, -\dfrac{5}{11}\right)\right\}$ **43.** $x + y = 7; x - y = -1;$ 3 and 4

45. $3x - y = 1; x + 2y = 12;$ 2 and 5   **47.** $(6, -1)$ **49.** $\left\{\left(\dfrac{1}{a}, 3\right)\right\}$ **51.** $m = -4, b = 3$ **53.** $y = x - 4; y = -\dfrac{1}{3}x + 4$

55. California: 100 gal; French: 100 gal   **57.** 18-karat gold: 96 g; 12-karat gold: 204 g   **59.** cheaper candy: 30 lb; more expensive candy: 45 lb

51.

$(x - 1)^2 + (y + 1)^2 < 25$
$(x - 1) + (y + 1)^2 \geq 16$

53.

$x^2 + y^2 \leq 1$
$y - x^2 > 0$

55.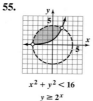

$x^2 + y^2 < 16$
$y \geq 2^x$

57. $x - y \leq 2$
$x > -2$
$y \leq 3$ 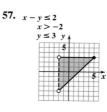

59. $x \geq 0$
$y \geq 0$
$2x + 5y < 10$
$3x + 4y \leq 12$ 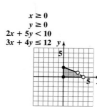

61. $3x + y \leq 6$
$2x - y \leq -1$
$x > -2$
$y < 4$ 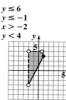

63. $y \geq -2x + 4$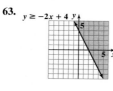

65. $x + y \leq 4$
$3x + y \leq 6$

67.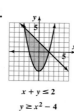

$x + y \leq 2$
$y \geq x^2 - 4$

69. $-2 \leq x \leq 2$
$-3 \leq y \leq 3$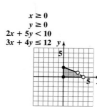

71. $y > \frac{3}{2}x - 2$ or $y < 4$

73. no solution
75. infinitely many solutions
77. a. $A = (20, 150)$; A 20-year-old with a heart rate of 150 beats per minute is within the target range.
    b. $10 \leq 20 \leq 70$, true; $150 \geq 0.7(220 - 20)$, true; $150 \leq 0.8(220 - 20)$, true
79. $10 \leq a \leq 70$; $H \geq 0.6(220 - a)$; $H \leq 0.7(220 - a)$

81. a. $50x + 150y > 2000$
  b.

$50x + 150y > 2000$

  c. Answers may vary. Example:
    (20, 20): 20 children and 20 adults
    will cause the elevator to be overloaded.

83. a. $y \geq 0$; $x + y \geq 5$; $x \geq 1$; $200x + 100y \leq 700$
  b. $y \geq 0$
    $x + y \geq 5$
    $x \geq 1$
    $200x + 100y \leq 700$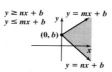
  c. 2 nights

85. a. 27.1   **b.** overweight

97.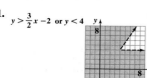

99.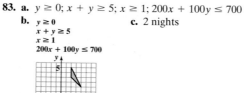

101.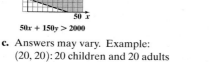

107. $y > x - 3$; $y \leq x$ **109.** $x + 2y \leq 6$ or $2x + y \leq 6$ **111.** $y \geq nx + b$ $y = mx + b$
$y \leq mx + b$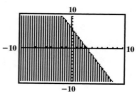
$(0, b)$
$y = nx + b$

Section 7.6

Check Point Exercises

1. $z = 25x + 55y$ **2.** $x + y \leq 80$ **3.** $30 \leq x \leq 80$; $10 \leq y \leq 30$; objective function: $z = 25x + 55y$; constraints:
$x + y \leq 80$; $30 \leq x \leq 80$; $10 \leq y \leq 30$ **4.** 50 bookshelves and 30 desks; $2900   **5.** 30

Exercise Set 7.6

1. $(1, 2)$: 17; $(2, 10)$: 70; $(7, 5)$: 65; $(8, 3)$: 58; maximum: $z = 70$; minimum: $z = 17$
3. $(0, 0)$: 0; $(0, 8)$: 400; $(4, 9)$: 610; $(8, 0)$: 320; maximum: $z = 610$; minimum: $z = 0$

5. a.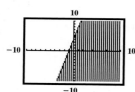

7. a.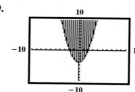

9. a.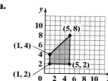

b. $(0, 8)$: 16; $(0, 4)$: 8; $(4, 0)$: 12
c. maximum value: 16 at $x = 0$
  and $y = 8$

b. $(0, 4)$: 4; $(0, 3)$: 3; $(3, 0)$: 12; $(6, 0)$: 24
c. maximum value: 24 at $x = 6$ and
  $y = 0$

b. $(1, 2)$: -1; $(1, 4)$: -5; $(5, 8)$: -1; $(5, 2)$: 11
c. maximum value: 11 at $x = 5$ and $y = 2$

11. a.
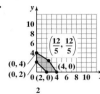

13. a.
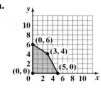

b. $(0, 4)$: 8; $(0, 2)$: 4; $(2, 0)$: 8; $(4, 0)$: 16;
$\left(\dfrac{12}{5}, \dfrac{12}{5}\right)$: $\dfrac{72}{5}$

c. maximum value: 16 at $x = 4$ and $y = 0$

b. $(0, 6)$: 72, $(0, 0)$: 0; $(5, 0)$: 50; $(3, 4)$: 78

c. maximum value: 78 at $x = 3$ and $y = 4$

15. a. $z = 125x + 200y$ **b.** $x \le 450$; $y \le 200$; $600x + 900y \le 360{,}000$

c.

d. $(0, 0)$: 0; $(0, 200)$: 40,000;
$(300, 200)$: 77,500; $(450, 100)$: 76,250;
$(450, 0)$: 56,250

e. 300; 200; $77,500

17. 40 model A bicycles and no model B bicycles   **19.** 300 cartons of food and 200 cartons of clothing   **21.** 50 students and 100 parents
23. 10 Boeing 727s and 42 Falcon 20s   **29.** $5000 in stocks and $5000 in bonds

Chapter 7 Review Exercises

1. $\{(1, 5)\}$ **2.** $\{(2, 3)\}$ **3.** $\{(2, -3)\}$ **4.** $\varnothing$ **5.** $\{(x, y)|3x - 6y = 12\}$ **6. a.** $C(x) = 60{,}000 + 200x$ **b.** $R(x) = 450x$
c. $(240, 108{,}000)$; This means the company will break even if it produces and sells 240 desks.   **7.** Japan: 73.6 yr; Switzerland: 72.8 yr
8. $80 per day for the room, $60 per day for the car   **9.** 10 ml of 34%; 90 ml of 4%   **10.** plane: 630 mph; wind: 90 mph
11. $\{(0, 1, 2)\}$ **12.** $\{(2, 1, -1)\}$ **13.** $y = 3x^2 - 4x + 5$ **14. a.** $(0, 3.5), (15, 5.0), (33, 3.8)$
b. $c = 3.5$; $225a + 15b + c = 5.0$; $1089a + 33b + c = 3.8$ **15.** Labrador retrievers: 147; Golden retrievers: 53; German shepherds: 46
16. $\dfrac{3}{5(x - 3)} + \dfrac{2}{5(x + 2)}$ **17.** $\dfrac{6}{x - 4} + \dfrac{5}{x + 3}$ **18.** $\dfrac{2}{x} + \dfrac{3}{x + 2} - \dfrac{1}{x - 1}$ **19.** $\dfrac{2}{x - 2} + \dfrac{5}{(x - 2)^2}$ **20.** $-\dfrac{4}{x - 1} + \dfrac{4}{x - 2} - \dfrac{2}{(x - 2)^2}$
21. $\dfrac{6}{5(x - 2)} + \dfrac{-6x + 3}{5(x^2 + 1)}$ **22.** $\dfrac{5}{x - 3} + \dfrac{2x - 1}{x^2 + 4}$ **23.** $\dfrac{x}{x^2 + 4} - \dfrac{4x}{(x^2 + 4)^2}$ **24.** $\dfrac{4x + 1}{x^2 + x + 1} + \dfrac{2x - 2}{(x^2 + x + 1)^2}$ **25.** $\{(4, 3), (1, 0)\}$
26. $\{(0, 1), (-3, 4)\}$ **27.** $\{(1, -1), (-1, 1)\}$ **28.** $\{(3, \sqrt{6}), (3, -\sqrt{6}), (-3, \sqrt{6}), (-3, -\sqrt{6})\}$ **29.** $\{(2, 2), (-2, -2)\}$ **30.** $\{(9, 6), (1, 2)\}$
31. $\{(-3, -1), (1, 3)\}$ **32.** $\left\{\left(\dfrac{1}{2}, 2\right), (-1, -1)\right\}$ **33.** $\left\{\left(\dfrac{5}{2}, -\dfrac{7}{2}\right), (0, -1)\right\}$ **34.** $\{(2, -3), (-2, -3), (3, 2), (-3, 2)\}$
35. $\{(3, 1), (3, -1), (-3, 1), (-3, -1)\}$ **36.** 8 m and 5 m   **37.** $(1, 6), (3, 2)$ **38.** $x = 46$ and $y = 28$ or $x = 50$ and $y = 20$

39.

$3x - 4y > 12$

40.

$y \le -\dfrac{1}{2}x + 2$

41.

$x < -2$

42.

$y \ge 3$

43.

$x^2 + y^2 > 4$

44.

$y \le x^2 - 1$

45.

$y \le 2^x$

46.

$3x + 2y \ge 6$
$2x + y \ge 6$

47.

$2x - y \ge 4$
$x + 2y < 2$

48.

$y < x$
$y \le 2$

49.

$x + y \le 6$
$y \ge 2x - 3$

50.

$0 \le x \le 3$
$y > 2$

51. no solution

52.
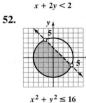

$x^2 + y^2 \le 16$
$x + y < 2$

53.

$x^2 + y^2 \le 9$
$y < -3x + 1$

54.

$y > x^2$
$x + y < 6$
$y < x + 6$

55.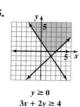

$y \geq 0$
$3x + 2y \geq 4$
$x - y \leq 3$

56. $(2, 2)$: 10; $(4, 0)$: 8; $\left(\frac{1}{2}, \frac{1}{2}\right)$: $\frac{5}{2}$; $(1, 0)$: 2; maximum value: 10; minimum value: 2

57.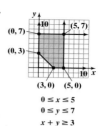

$x \geq 0, \ y \geq 0$
$x + y \leq 8$
$3x + 2y \geq 6$

Maximum is 24 at $x = 0, \ y = 8$.

58.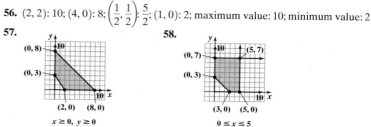

$0 \leq x \leq 5$
$0 \leq y \leq 7$
$x + y \geq 3$

Maximum is 33 at $x = 5, \ y = 7$.

59.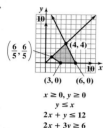

$x \geq 0, \ y \geq 0$
$y \leq x$
$2x + y \leq 12$
$2x + 3y \geq 6$

Maximum is 44 at $x = y = 4$.

60. a. $z = 500x + 350y$
b. $x + y \leq 200; \ x \geq 10; \ y \geq 80$
c.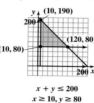

$x + y \leq 200$
$x \geq 10, \ y \geq 80$

d. $(10, 80)$: 33,000; $(10, 190)$: 71,500; $(120, 80)$: 88,000
e. 120; 80; 88,000

61. 480 of model A and 240 of model B

Chapter 7 Test

1. $\{(1, -3)\}$ **2.** $\{(4, -2)\}$ **3.** $\{(1, 3, 2)\}$ **4.** $\{(4, -3), (-3, 4)\}$ **5.** $\{(3, 2), (3, -2), (-3, 2), (-3, -2)\}$ **6.** $\dfrac{-1}{10(x + 1)} + \dfrac{x + 9}{10(x^2 + 9)}$

7.

$x - 2y < 8$

8.

$x \geq 0, \ y \geq 0$
$3x + y \leq 9$
$2x + 3y \geq 6$

9.

$x^2 + y^2 > 1$
$x^2 + y^2 < 4$

10.

$y \leq 1 - x^2$
$x^2 + y^2 \leq 9$

11. 26 **12.** Shrimp: 42 mg; scallops: 15mg **13. a.** $C(x) = 360,000 + 850x$ **b.** $R(x) = 1150x$ **c.** $(1200, 1,380,000)$; The company will break even if it produces and sells 1200 computers. **14.** 40 oz of 20%; 20 oz of 50% **15.** plane: 725 km/hr; wind: 75 km/hr **16.** $y = x^2 - 3$ **17.** $x = 7.5$ ft and $y = 24$ ft or $x = 12$ ft and $y = 15$ ft **18.** 50 regular and 100 deluxe jet skis; $35,000

Cumulative Review Exercises (Chapters P–7)

1. Domain: $(-2, 2)$; Range: $(-\infty, 3]$ **2.** -1 and 1, each of multiplicity 1 **3.** maximum of 3 at $x = 0$ **4.** $(0, 2)$
5. positive **6.** 3 **7.** $x \to -2^+; x \to 2^-$ **8.** even

9.

$g(x) = f(x + 2) - 1$

10.

$h(x) = \frac{1}{2} f\left(\frac{1}{2} x\right)$

11. $\{3, 4\}$ **12.** $\left\{\dfrac{2 + i\sqrt{3}}{2}, \dfrac{2 - i\sqrt{3}}{2}\right\}$ **13.** $\{(-18, 6)\}$

14. $\{(1, 7)\}$ **15.** $\left\{-3, \dfrac{1}{2}, 2\right\}$ **16.** $\{-2\}$ **17.** $\{2\}$

18. $\{-2 + \log_3 11\}$ **19.** $\{625\}$ **20.** $\left\{\left(-\dfrac{1}{2}, \dfrac{1}{2}\right), (2, 8)\right\}$

21. $\{(8, -2, -2)\}$

22.

$f(x) = (x + 2)^2 - 4$

23.

$2x - 3y \leq 6$

24.

$y = 3^{x-2}$

25.

$f(x) = \dfrac{x^2 - x - 6}{x + 1}$

26.

$f(x) = 2x - 4$
$f^{-1}(x) = \dfrac{x + 4}{2}$

27.

$(x - 2)^2 + (y - 4)^2 > 9$

28.

$f(x) = |x|$
$g(x) = -|x - 2|$

29. $(f \circ g)(x) = 2x^2 - 3x$;
$(g \circ f)(x) = -2x^2 + x + 2$
30. $4x + 2h - 1$
31. $y = -3x + 10$
32. $y = 3x + 3$
33. $2600 at 12%; $1400 at 14%
34. 4 m by 9 m
35. 10.99%

36. $\sec\theta - \cos\theta = \dfrac{1}{\cos\theta} - \cos\theta = \dfrac{1-\cos^2\theta}{\cos\theta} = \dfrac{\sin^2\theta}{\cos\theta} = \dfrac{\sin\theta}{\cos\theta}\sin\theta = \tan\theta\sin\theta\theta$

37. $\tan x + \tan y = \dfrac{\sin x}{\cos x} + \dfrac{\sin y}{\cos y} = \dfrac{\sin x\cos y + \sin y\cos x}{\cos x\cos y} = \dfrac{\sin(x+y)}{\cos x\cos y}$ **38.** $\{0, \pi\}$ **39.** $\left\{0, \dfrac{\pi}{3}, \dfrac{5\pi}{3}\right\}$ **40.** 92.9

CHAPTER 8

Section 8.1

Check Point Exercises

1. $\{(4, -3, 1)\}$ **2. a.** $\begin{bmatrix} 1 & 6 & -3 & | & 7 \\ 4 & 12 & -20 & | & 8 \\ -3 & -2 & 1 & | & -9 \end{bmatrix}$ **b.** $\begin{bmatrix} 1 & 3 & -5 & | & 2 \\ 1 & 6 & -3 & | & 7 \\ -3 & -2 & 1 & | & -9 \end{bmatrix}$ **c.** $\begin{bmatrix} 4 & 12 & -20 & | & 8 \\ 1 & 6 & -3 & | & 7 \\ 0 & 16 & -8 & | & 12 \end{bmatrix}$ **3.** $\{(5, 2, 3)\}$

4. $\{(1, -1, 2, -3)\}$ **5.** $\{(5, 2, 3)\}$

Exercise Set 8.1

1. $\begin{bmatrix} 2 & 1 & 2 & | & 2 \\ 3 & -5 & -1 & | & 4 \\ 1 & -2 & -3 & | & -6 \end{bmatrix}$ **3.** $\begin{bmatrix} 1 & -1 & 1 & | & 8 \\ 0 & 1 & -12 & | & -15 \\ 0 & 0 & 1 & | & 1 \end{bmatrix}$ **5.** $\begin{bmatrix} 5 & -2 & -3 & | & 0 \\ 1 & 1 & 0 & | & 5 \\ 2 & 0 & -3 & | & 4 \end{bmatrix}$ **7.** $\begin{bmatrix} 2 & 5 & -3 & 1 & | & 2 \\ 0 & 3 & 1 & 0 & | & 4 \\ 1 & -1 & 5 & 0 & | & 9 \\ 5 & -5 & -2 & 0 & | & 1 \end{bmatrix}$ **9.** $\begin{aligned} 5x + 3z &= -11 \\ y - 4z &= 12 \\ 7x + 2y &= 3 \end{aligned}$

11. $\begin{aligned} w + x + 4y + z &= 3 \\ -w + x - y &= 7 \\ 2w + 5z &= 11 \\ 12y + 4z &= 5 \end{aligned}$ **13.** $\begin{aligned} x - 4z &= 5 \\ y - 12z &= 13 \\ z &= -\dfrac{1}{2} \end{aligned}$; $\left\{\left(3, 7, -\dfrac{1}{2}\right)\right\}$ **15.** $\begin{aligned} x + \dfrac{1}{2}y + z &= \dfrac{11}{2} \\ y + \dfrac{3}{2}z &= 7 \\ z &= 4 \end{aligned}$; $\{(1, 1, 4)\}$ **17.** $\begin{aligned} w - x + y + z &= 3 \\ x - 2y - z &= 0 \\ y + 6z &= 17 \\ z &= 3 \end{aligned}$; $\{(2, 1, -1, 3)\}$

19. $\begin{bmatrix} 1 & -3 & 2 & | & 5 \\ 1 & 5 & -5 & | & 0 \\ 3 & 0 & 4 & | & 7 \end{bmatrix}$ **21.** $\begin{bmatrix} 1 & -3 & 2 & | & 0 \\ 0 & 10 & -7 & | & 7 \\ 2 & -2 & 1 & | & 3 \end{bmatrix}$ **23.** $\begin{bmatrix} 1 & -1 & 1 & 1 & | & 3 \\ 0 & 1 & -2 & -1 & | & 0 \\ 0 & 2 & 1 & 2 & | & 5 \\ 0 & 6 & -3 & -1 & | & -9 \end{bmatrix}$ **25.** $R_2: -3, -18;\ R_3: -12, -15;\ R_2: -\dfrac{3}{5}, -\dfrac{18}{5};\ R_3: -12, -15$

27. $\{(1, -1, 2)\}$ **29.** $\{(3, -1, -1)\}$ **31.** $\{2, -1, 1\}$ **33.** $\{(2, 1, 1)\}$ **35.** $\{(2, -1, 1)\}$ **37.** $\{(-1, 2, -2)\}$ **39.** $\{(1, 2, -1)\}$

41. $\{(1, 2, 3, -2)\}$ **43.** $\{(0, -3, 0, -3)\}$ **45.** $f(x) = -x^2 + x + 2$ **47.** $f(x) = x^3 - 2x^2 + 3$ **49.** $\{(e^{-1}, e, e^{-3}, e^{-2})\}$

51. a. $a = -32,\ v_0 = 56,\ s_0 = 0$ **b.** 0; The ball hits the ground 3.5 seconds after it it thrown.   **c.** 1.75 sec; 49 ft

53. $\begin{aligned} x + y + z &= 100 \\ x + z &= y - 22 \\ 2x &= y + 7 \end{aligned}$; yes: 34%; no: 61%; not sure: 5%   **55.** $\begin{aligned} 40x + 200y + 400z &= 660 \\ 5x + 2y + 4z &= 25 \\ 30x + 10y + 300z &= 425 \end{aligned}$; 4 oz of Food A; $\dfrac{1}{2}$ oz of Food B; 1 oz of Food C **65.** d

Section 8.2

Check Point Exercises

1. $\varnothing$ **2.** $\{(11t + 13, 5t + 4, t)\}$ **3.** $\{(t + 50, -2t + 10, t)\}$

4. a. $\begin{aligned} w + z &= 15 \\ w + x &= 30 \\ x + y &= 45 \\ y + z &= 30 \end{aligned}$ **b.** $\{(-t + 15, t + 15, -t + 30, t)\}$ **c.** $w = 5;\ x = 25;\ y = 20$

Exercise Set 8.2

1. $\varnothing$ **3.** $\left\{\left(-2t + 2, 2t + \dfrac{1}{2}, t\right)\right\}$ **5.** $\{(-3, 4, -2)\}$ **7.** $\{(5 - 2t, -2 + t, t)\}$ **9.** $\{(-1, 2, 1, 1)\}$ **11.** $\{(1, 3, 2, 1)\}$

13. $\{(1, -2, 1, 1)\}$ **15.** $\left\{\left(1 + \dfrac{1}{3}t, \dfrac{1}{3}t, t\right)\right\}$ **17.** $\{(-13t + 5, 5t, t)\}$ **19.** $\left\{\left(2t - \dfrac{5}{4}, \dfrac{13}{4}, t\right)\right\}$ **21.** $\{(1, -t - 1, 2, t)\}$

23. $\left\{\left(-\dfrac{2}{11}t + \dfrac{81}{11}, \dfrac{1}{22}t + \dfrac{10}{11}, \dfrac{4}{11}t - \dfrac{8}{11}, t\right)\right\}$ **25. a.** $4w - 2x + 2y - 3z = 0;\ 7w - x - y - 3z = 0;\ w + x + y - z = 0$ **b.** $\{(0.5t, 0, 0.5t, t)\}$

27. a. $w + 2x + 5y + 5z = -3;\ w + x + 3y + 4z = -1;\ w - x - y + 2z = 3$ **b.** $\{(1 - 3s - t, -2 - s - 2t, t, s)\}$

29. $z + 12 = x + 6$ **31.** $\{(t + 6, t + 2, t)\}$ **33. a.** $\begin{aligned} w + z &= 380 \\ w + x &= 600 \\ x - y &= 170 \\ y - z &= 50 \end{aligned}$ **b.** $\{(380 - t, 220 + t, 50 + t, t)\}$ **c.** $w = 330,\ x = 270,\ y = 100$

35. a. The system has no solution, so there is no way to satisfy these dietary requirements with no Food 1 available.   **b.** 4 oz of Food 1, 0 oz of Food 2, 10 oz of Food 3; 2 oz of Food 1, 5 oz of Food 2, 9 oz of Food 3 (other answers are possible).   **41.** $a = 1$ or $a = 3$

Section 8.3

Check Point Exercises

1. a. 3×2 **b.** $a_{12} = -2;\ a_{31} = 1$ **2. a.** $\begin{bmatrix} 2 & 0 \\ 9 & -10 \end{bmatrix}$ **b.** $\begin{bmatrix} 9 & -4 \\ -9 & 7 \\ 5 & -2 \end{bmatrix}$ **3. a.** $\begin{bmatrix} 6 & 12 \\ -48 & -30 \end{bmatrix}$ **b.** $\begin{bmatrix} -14 & -1 \\ 25 & 10 \end{bmatrix}$ **4.** $\begin{bmatrix} -4 & 3 \\ -3 & \dfrac{13}{3} \end{bmatrix}$

5. $\begin{bmatrix} 7 & 6 \\ 13 & 12 \end{bmatrix}$ **6.** $[30]; \begin{bmatrix} 2 & 0 & 4 \\ 6 & 0 & 12 \\ 14 & 0 & 28 \end{bmatrix}$ **7. a.** $\begin{bmatrix} 2 & 18 & 11 & 9 \\ 0 & 10 & 8 & 2 \end{bmatrix}$ **b.** The product is undefined.

8. $\begin{bmatrix} 2 & 1 & 1 \\ 2 & 1 & 1 \\ 2 & 2 & 1 \end{bmatrix} + \begin{bmatrix} -1 & 2 & 2 \\ -1 & 2 & 2 \\ -1 & -1 & 2 \end{bmatrix} = \begin{bmatrix} 1 & 3 & 3 \\ 1 & 3 & 3 \\ 1 & 1 & 3 \end{bmatrix}$

9. a. $\begin{bmatrix} 0 & 3 & 4 \\ 0 & 5 & 2 \end{bmatrix} + \begin{bmatrix} -3 & -3 & -3 \\ -1 & -1 & -1 \end{bmatrix} = \begin{bmatrix} -3 & 0 & 1 \\ -1 & 4 & 1 \end{bmatrix};$ **b.** $2\begin{bmatrix} 0 & 3 & 4 \\ 0 & 5 & 2 \end{bmatrix} = \begin{bmatrix} 0 & 6 & 8 \\ 0 & 10 & 4 \end{bmatrix};$

c. $\begin{bmatrix} 0 & 3 & 4 \\ 0 & -5 & -2 \end{bmatrix};$ Multiplying by B reflects the triangle over the x-axis.

Exercise Set 8.3

1. a. 2×3 **b.** a_{32} does not exist; $a_{23} = -1$ **3. a.** 3×4 **b.** $a_{32} = \frac{1}{2}; a_{23} = -6$ **5.** $x = 6; y = 4$ **7.** $x = 4; y = 6; z = 3$

9. a. $\begin{bmatrix} 9 & 10 \\ 3 & 9 \end{bmatrix}$ **b.** $\begin{bmatrix} -1 & -8 \\ 3 & -5 \end{bmatrix}$ **c.** $\begin{bmatrix} -16 & -4 \\ -12 & -8 \end{bmatrix}$ **d.** $\begin{bmatrix} 22 & 21 \\ 9 & 20 \end{bmatrix}$ **11. a.** $\begin{bmatrix} 3 & 2 \\ 6 & 2 \\ 5 & 7 \end{bmatrix}$ **b.** $\begin{bmatrix} -1 & 4 \\ 0 & 6 \\ 5 & 5 \end{bmatrix}$ **c.** $\begin{bmatrix} -4 & -12 \\ -12 & -16 \\ -20 & -24 \end{bmatrix}$ **d.** $\begin{bmatrix} 7 & 7 \\ 15 & 8 \\ 15 & 20 \end{bmatrix}$

13. a. $\begin{bmatrix} -3 \\ -1 \\ 0 \end{bmatrix}$ **b.** $\begin{bmatrix} 7 \\ -7 \\ 2 \end{bmatrix}$ **c.** $\begin{bmatrix} -8 \\ 16 \\ -4 \end{bmatrix}$ **d.** $\begin{bmatrix} -4 \\ -6 \\ 1 \end{bmatrix}$ **15. a.** $\begin{bmatrix} 8 & 0 & -4 \\ 14 & 0 & 6 \\ -1 & 0 & 0 \end{bmatrix}$ **b.** $\begin{bmatrix} -4 & -20 & 0 \\ 14 & 24 & 14 \\ 9 & -4 & 4 \end{bmatrix}$ **c.** $\begin{bmatrix} -8 & 40 & 8 \\ -56 & -48 & -40 \\ -16 & 8 & -8 \end{bmatrix}$ **d.** $\begin{bmatrix} 18 & -10 & -10 \\ 42 & 12 & 22 \\ 2 & -2 & 2 \end{bmatrix}$

17. $\begin{bmatrix} -8 & -8 \\ 2 & -9 \\ 8 & -4 \end{bmatrix}$ **19.** $\begin{bmatrix} -1 & 3 \\ -1 & \frac{9}{2} \\ -1 & -2 \end{bmatrix}$ **21.** $\begin{bmatrix} \frac{1}{3} & \frac{13}{3} \\ -\frac{4}{3} & 6 \\ -\frac{7}{3} & -\frac{4}{3} \end{bmatrix}$ **23.** $\begin{bmatrix} 7 & 27 \\ -8 & 36 \\ -17 & -4 \end{bmatrix}$ **25.** $\begin{bmatrix} \frac{27}{2} & \frac{31}{2} \\ -4 & 18 \\ -\frac{29}{2} & 6 \end{bmatrix}$ **27. a.** $\begin{bmatrix} 0 & 16 \\ 12 & 8 \end{bmatrix}$ **b.** $\begin{bmatrix} -7 & 3 \\ 29 & 15 \end{bmatrix}$

29. a. $[30]$ **b.** $\begin{bmatrix} 1 & 2 & 3 & 4 \\ 2 & 4 & 6 & 8 \\ 3 & 6 & 9 & 12 \\ 4 & 8 & 12 & 16 \end{bmatrix}$ **31. a.** $\begin{bmatrix} 4 & -5 & 8 \\ 6 & -1 & 5 \\ 0 & 4 & -6 \end{bmatrix}$ **b.** $\begin{bmatrix} 5 & -2 & 7 \\ 17 & -3 & 2 \\ 3 & 0 & -5 \end{bmatrix}$ **33. a.** $\begin{bmatrix} 6 & 8 & 16 \\ 11 & 16 & 24 \\ 1 & -1 & 12 \end{bmatrix}$ **b.** $\begin{bmatrix} 38 & 27 \\ -16 & -4 \end{bmatrix}$

35. a. $\begin{bmatrix} 0 & 0 \\ 0 & 0 \end{bmatrix}$ **b.** $\begin{bmatrix} 4 & -1 & -3 & 1 \\ -1 & 4 & -3 & 2 \\ 14 & -11 & -3 & -1 \\ 25 & -25 & 0 & -5 \end{bmatrix}$ **37.** $\begin{bmatrix} 17 & 7 \\ -5 & -11 \end{bmatrix}$ **39.** $\begin{bmatrix} 11 & -1 \\ -7 & -3 \end{bmatrix}$ **41.** $A - C$ is not defined because A is 3×2 and C is 2×2.

43. $\begin{bmatrix} 16 & -16 \\ -12 & 12 \\ 0 & 0 \end{bmatrix}$ **45.** $\begin{bmatrix} 0 & 0 \\ 0 & 0 \end{bmatrix}$ **47.** Answers will vary.; Example:

$$A(B + C) = \begin{bmatrix} 1 & 0 \\ 0 & 1 \end{bmatrix}\left(\begin{bmatrix} 1 & 0 \\ 0 & -1 \end{bmatrix} + \begin{bmatrix} -1 & 0 \\ 0 & 1 \end{bmatrix}\right) = \begin{bmatrix} 1 & 0 \\ 0 & 1 \end{bmatrix}\begin{bmatrix} 0 & 0 \\ 0 & 0 \end{bmatrix} = \begin{bmatrix} 0 & 0 \\ 0 & 0 \end{bmatrix}$$

$$AB + AC = \begin{bmatrix} 1 & 0 \\ 0 & 1 \end{bmatrix}\begin{bmatrix} 1 & 0 \\ 0 & -1 \end{bmatrix} + \begin{bmatrix} 1 & 0 \\ 0 & 1 \end{bmatrix}\begin{bmatrix} -1 & 0 \\ 0 & 1 \end{bmatrix} = \begin{bmatrix} 1 & 0 \\ 0 & -1 \end{bmatrix} + \begin{bmatrix} -1 & 0 \\ 0 & 1 \end{bmatrix} = \begin{bmatrix} 0 & 0 \\ 0 & 0 \end{bmatrix}$$

So, $A(B + C) = AB + AC$.

49. $\begin{bmatrix} x \\ -y \end{bmatrix};$ It changes the sign of the y-coordinate.

51. a. $\begin{bmatrix} 1 & 3 & 1 \\ 3 & 3 & 3 \\ 1 & 3 & 1 \end{bmatrix}$ **b.** $\begin{bmatrix} 1 & 3 & 1 \\ 3 & 3 & 3 \\ 1 & 3 & 1 \end{bmatrix} + \begin{bmatrix} -1 & -1 & -1 \\ -1 & -1 & -1 \\ -1 & -1 & -1 \end{bmatrix} = \begin{bmatrix} 0 & 2 & 0 \\ 2 & 2 & 2 \\ 0 & 2 & 0 \end{bmatrix}$ **c.** $\begin{bmatrix} 1 & 3 & 1 \\ 3 & 3 & 3 \\ 1 & 3 & 1 \end{bmatrix} + \begin{bmatrix} 1 & -2 & 1 \\ -2 & -2 & -2 \\ 1 & -2 & 1 \end{bmatrix} = \begin{bmatrix} 2 & 1 & 2 \\ 1 & 1 & 1 \\ 2 & 1 & 2 \end{bmatrix}$

53. $\begin{bmatrix} -2 & 1 & 1 & -1 & -1 & -2 \\ -3 & -3 & -2 & -2 & 2 & 2 \end{bmatrix}$ **55.** $\begin{bmatrix} 0 & \frac{3}{2} & \frac{3}{2} & \frac{1}{2} & \frac{1}{2} & 0 \\ 1 & 1 & \frac{3}{2} & \frac{3}{2} & \frac{7}{2} & \frac{7}{2} \end{bmatrix}$ **57. a.** $\begin{bmatrix} 0 & 3 & 3 & 1 & 1 & 0 \\ 0 & 0 & -1 & -1 & -5 & -5 \end{bmatrix}$

b. The effect is a reflection across the x-axis.

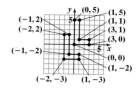 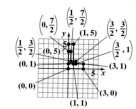 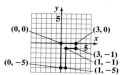

59. a. $\begin{bmatrix} 0 & 0 & -1 & -1 & -5 & -5 \\ 0 & 3 & 3 & 1 & 1 & 0 \end{bmatrix}$

61. a. $A = \begin{bmatrix} 61 & 24 \\ 33 & 47 \\ 6 & 29 \end{bmatrix}$ **b.** $B = \begin{bmatrix} 67 & 23 \\ 28 & 44 \\ 5 & 33 \end{bmatrix}$

b.
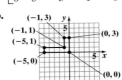

The effect is a 90° counterclockwise rotation about the origin.

c. $B - A = \begin{bmatrix} 6 & -1 \\ -5 & -3 \\ -1 & 4 \end{bmatrix}$

The change in the percentage who identified themselves as belonging to each category.

63. a. System 1: The midterm and final both count for 50% of the course grade. System 2: The midterm counts for 30% of the course grade and the final counts for 70%.

b. $\begin{bmatrix} 84 & 87.2 \\ 79 & 81 \\ 90 & 88.4 \\ 73 & 68.6 \\ 69 & 73.4 \end{bmatrix}$ System 1 grades are listed first (if different). Student 1: B; Student 2: C or B; Student 3: A or B; Student 4: C or D; Student 5: D or C

79. $AB = -BA$ so they are anticommutative.

Mid-Chapter 8 Check Point

1. $\{(1, -1, 2)\}$ **2.** $\varnothing$ **3.** $\left\{\left(-\dfrac{4}{7} - \dfrac{4}{7}t, \dfrac{5}{7} + \dfrac{5}{7}t, t\right)\right\}$ **4.** $\{(3, 6, -4, 1)\}$ **5.** $\varnothing$ **6.** $\begin{bmatrix} -4 & -\dfrac{1}{2} \\ 3 & 3 \end{bmatrix}$ **7.** $\begin{bmatrix} -12 & -2 \\ -21 & -4 \\ 3 & 1 \end{bmatrix}$ **8.** $\begin{bmatrix} 12 & -4 \\ 22 & -7 \\ -4 & 1 \end{bmatrix}$

9. $A + C$ does not exist because A is 3×2 and C is 2×2. **10.** $\begin{bmatrix} \dfrac{1}{2} & \dfrac{1}{2} \\ -3 & \dfrac{1}{2} \end{bmatrix}$

Section 8.4

Check Point Exercises

1. $AB = I_2$; $BA = I_2$ **2.** $\begin{bmatrix} 3 & -7 \\ -2 & 5 \end{bmatrix}$ **3.** $\begin{bmatrix} 1 & 2 \\ 1 & 3 \end{bmatrix}$ **4.** $\begin{bmatrix} 3 & -2 & -4 \\ 3 & -2 & -5 \\ -1 & 1 & 2 \end{bmatrix}$ **5.** $\{(4, -2, 1)\}$ **6.** The encoded message is $-7, 10, -53, 77$.

7. The decoded message is $2, 1, 19, 5$ or BASE.

Exercise Set 8.4

1. $AB = I_2$; $BA = I_2$; $B = A^{-1}$ **3.** $AB = \begin{bmatrix} 8 & -16 \\ -2 & 7 \end{bmatrix}$; $BA = \begin{bmatrix} 12 & 12 \\ 1 & 3 \end{bmatrix}$; $B \neq A^{-1}$ **5.** $AB = I_2$; $BA = I_2$; $B = A^{-1}$

7. $AB = I_3$; $BA = I_3$; $B = A^{-1}$ **9.** $AB = I_3$; $BA = I_3$; $B = A^{-1}$ **11.** $AB = I_4$; $BA = I_4$; $B = A^{-1}$ **13.** $\begin{bmatrix} \dfrac{2}{7} & -\dfrac{3}{7} \\ \dfrac{1}{7} & \dfrac{2}{7} \end{bmatrix}$

15. $\begin{bmatrix} 1 & \dfrac{1}{2} \\ 2 & \dfrac{3}{2} \end{bmatrix}$ **17.** A does not have an inverse. **19.** $\begin{bmatrix} \dfrac{1}{2} & 0 & 0 \\ 0 & \dfrac{1}{4} & 0 \\ 0 & 0 & \dfrac{1}{6} \end{bmatrix}$ **21.** $\begin{bmatrix} 1 & 1 & 2 \\ 1 & 1 & 1 \\ 2 & 3 & 4 \end{bmatrix}$ **23.** $\begin{bmatrix} 1 & 0 & 1 \\ 1 & 1 & 2 \\ 3 & 2 & 6 \end{bmatrix}$ **25.** $\begin{bmatrix} -3 & 2 & -4 \\ -1 & 1 & -1 \\ 8 & -5 & 10 \end{bmatrix}$

27. $\begin{bmatrix} 1 & 0 & 0 & 0 \\ 0 & -1 & 0 & 0 \\ 0 & 0 & \dfrac{1}{3} & 0 \\ -1 & 0 & 0 & 1 \end{bmatrix}$ **29.** $\begin{bmatrix} 6 & 5 \\ 5 & 4 \end{bmatrix}\begin{bmatrix} x \\ y \end{bmatrix} = \begin{bmatrix} 13 \\ 10 \end{bmatrix}$ **31.** $\begin{bmatrix} 1 & 3 & 4 \\ 1 & 2 & 3 \\ 1 & 4 & 3 \end{bmatrix}\begin{bmatrix} x \\ y \\ z \end{bmatrix} = \begin{bmatrix} -3 \\ -2 \\ -6 \end{bmatrix}$ **33.** $\begin{array}{l} 4x - 7y = -3 \\ 2x - 3y = 1 \end{array}$ **35.** $\begin{array}{l} 2x - z = 6 \\ 3y = 9 \\ x + y = 5 \end{array}$

37. a. $\begin{bmatrix} 2 & 6 & 6 \\ 2 & 7 & 6 \\ 2 & 7 & 7 \end{bmatrix}\begin{bmatrix} x \\ y \\ z \end{bmatrix} = \begin{bmatrix} 8 \\ 10 \\ 9 \end{bmatrix}$ **b.** $\{(1, 2, -1)\}$ **39. a.** $\begin{bmatrix} 1 & -1 & 1 \\ 0 & 2 & -1 \\ 2 & 3 & 0 \end{bmatrix}\begin{bmatrix} x \\ y \\ z \end{bmatrix} = \begin{bmatrix} 8 \\ -7 \\ 1 \end{bmatrix}$ **b.** $\{(2, -1, 5)\}$

41. a. $\begin{bmatrix} 1 & -1 & 2 & 0 \\ 0 & 1 & -1 & 1 \\ -1 & 1 & -1 & 2 \\ 0 & -1 & 1 & -2 \end{bmatrix}\begin{bmatrix} w \\ x \\ y \\ z \end{bmatrix} = \begin{bmatrix} -3 \\ 4 \\ 2 \\ -4 \end{bmatrix}$ **b.** $\{(2, 3, -1, 0)\}$ **43.** $\begin{bmatrix} \dfrac{1}{2}e^{-x} & -\dfrac{1}{2}e^{-3x} \\ \dfrac{1}{2}e^{-3x} & \dfrac{1}{2}e^{-5x} \end{bmatrix}$ **45.** $\begin{bmatrix} \dfrac{1}{8} & \dfrac{5}{8} \\ \dfrac{3}{8} & \dfrac{7}{8} \end{bmatrix}$

47. $(AB)^{-1} = \begin{bmatrix} -23 & 16 \\ 13 & -9 \end{bmatrix}$; $A^{-1}B^{-1} = \begin{bmatrix} -3 & 11 \\ 8 & -29 \end{bmatrix}$; $B^{-1}A^{-1} = \begin{bmatrix} -23 & 16 \\ 13 & -9 \end{bmatrix}$; $(AB)^{-1} = B^{-1}A^{-1}$ **49.** $AA^{-1} = I_3$ and $A^{-1}A = I_3$

51. The encoded message is $27, -19, 32, -20$.; The decoded message is $8, 5, 12, 16$ or HELP.

53. The encoded message is 14, 85, −33, 4, 18, −7, −18, 19, −9.   **65.** $\begin{bmatrix} 1 & 1 \\ 2 & 3 \end{bmatrix}$ **67.** $\begin{bmatrix} 1 & 0 & 1 \\ 2 & 1 & 3 \\ -1 & 1 & 1 \end{bmatrix}$ **69.** $\begin{bmatrix} 0 & -1 & 0 & 1 \\ -1 & -5 & 0 & 3 \\ -2 & -4 & 1 & -2 \\ -1 & -4 & 0 & 1 \end{bmatrix}$

71. $\{(2, 3, -5)\}$ **73.** $\{(1, 2, -1)\}$ **75.** $\{(2, 1, 3, -2, 4)\}$ **79.** c   **83.** $a = 3$ or $a = -2$

Section 8.5

Check Point Exercises

1. a. −4   **b.** −17   **2.** $\{(4, -2)\}$ **3.** 80   **4.** −24   **5.** $\{(2, -3, 4)\}$ **6.** −250

Exercise Set 8.5

1. 1   **3.** −29   **5.** 0   **7.** 33   **9.** $-\dfrac{7}{16}$ **11.** $\{(5, 2)\}$ **13.** $\{(2, -3)\}$ **15.** $\{(3, -1)\}$ **17.** The system is dependent.   **19.** $\{(4, 2)\}$
21. $\{(7, 4)\}$ **23.** The system is inconsistent.   **25.** The system is dependent.   **27.** 72   **29.** −75   **31.** 0   **33.** $\{(-5, -2, 7)\}$
35. $\{(2, -3, 4)\}$ **37.** $\{(3, -1, 2)\}$ **39.** $\{(2, 3, 1)\}$ **41.** −200   **43.** 195   **45.** −42   **47.** $2x - 4y = 8; 3x + 5y = -10$ **49.** −11
51. 4   **53.** 28 sq units   **55.** yes   **57.** The equation of the line is $y = -\dfrac{11}{5}x + \dfrac{8}{5}$.   **69.** 13,200   **71. a.** a^2 **b.** a^3 **c.** a^4
d. Each determinant has zeros below the main diagonal and a's everywhere else.   **e.** Each determinant equals a raised to the power equal to the order of the determinant.   **73.** The sign of the value is changed when 2 columns are interchanged in a 2nd order determinant.
75. $\begin{vmatrix} x & y & 1 \\ x_1 & y_1 & 1 \\ x_2 & y_2 & 1 \end{vmatrix} = x(y_1 - y_2) - y(x_1 - x_2) + (x_1 y_2 - x_2 y_1) = 0$; solving for y, $y = \dfrac{y_1 - y_2}{x_1 - x_2}x + \dfrac{x_1 y_2 - x_2 y_1}{x_1 - x_2}$, and $m = \dfrac{y_1 - y_2}{x_1 - x_2}$ and $b = \dfrac{x_1 y_2 - x_2 y_1}{x_1 - x_2}$.

Chapter 8 Review Exercises

1. $\begin{aligned} x + y + 3z &= 12; \{(1, 2, 3)\} \\ y - 2z &= -4 \\ z &= 3 \end{aligned}$ **2.** $\begin{aligned} w - 2y + 2z &= 1 \\ x + y - z &= 0 \\ y - \tfrac{7}{3}z &= -\tfrac{1}{3} \\ z &= 1 \end{aligned}$;$\{(3, -1, 2, 1)\}$ **3.** $\begin{bmatrix} 1 & 2 & 2 & | & 2 \\ 0 & 1 & -1 & | & 2 \\ 0 & 0 & 9 & | & -9 \end{bmatrix}$ **4.** $\begin{bmatrix} 1 & -1 & \tfrac{1}{2} & | & -\tfrac{1}{2} \\ 1 & 2 & -1 & | & 2 \\ 6 & 4 & 3 & | & 5 \end{bmatrix}$

5. $\{(1, 3, -4)\}$ **6.** $\{(-2, -1, 0)\}$ **7.** $\{(2, -2, 3, 4)\}$ **8. a.** $a = -2; b = 32; c = 42$ **b.** 2:00 p.m.; 170 parts per million   **9.** $\varnothing$
10. $\{(2t + 4, t + 1, t)\}$ **11.** $\{(-37t + 2, 16t, -7t + 1, t)\}$ **12.** $\{(7t + 18, -3t - 7, t)\}$

13. a. $\begin{aligned} x + z &= 750 \\ y - z &= -250 \\ x + y &= 500 \end{aligned}$ **b.** $\{(-t + 750, t - 250, t)\}$ **c.** $x = 350; y = 150$ **14.** $x = -5; y = 6; z = 6$ **15.** $\begin{bmatrix} 0 & 2 & 3 \\ 8 & 1 & 3 \end{bmatrix}$ **16.** $\begin{bmatrix} 0 & -4 \\ 6 & 4 \\ 2 & -10 \end{bmatrix}$

17. $\begin{bmatrix} -4 & 4 & -1 \\ -2 & -5 & 5 \end{bmatrix}$ **18.** Not possible since B is 3×2 and C is 3×3.   **19.** $\begin{bmatrix} 2 & 3 & 8 \\ 21 & 5 & 5 \end{bmatrix}$ **20.** $\begin{bmatrix} -12 & 14 & 0 \\ 2 & -14 & 18 \end{bmatrix}$ **21.** $\begin{bmatrix} 0 & -10 & -15 \\ -40 & -5 & -15 \end{bmatrix}$

22. $\begin{bmatrix} -1 & -16 \\ 8 & 1 \end{bmatrix}$ **23.** $\begin{bmatrix} -10 & -6 & 2 \\ 16 & 3 & 4 \\ -23 & -16 & 7 \end{bmatrix}$ **24.** $\begin{bmatrix} -6 & 4 & -8 \\ 0 & 5 & 11 \\ -17 & 13 & -19 \end{bmatrix}$ **25.** $\begin{bmatrix} 10 & 5 \\ -2 & -30 \end{bmatrix}$ **26.** Not possible since AB is 2×2 and BA is 3×3.

27. $\begin{bmatrix} 7 & 6 & 5 \\ 2 & -1 & 11 \end{bmatrix}$ **28.** $\begin{bmatrix} -6 & -22 & -40 \\ 9 & 43 & 58 \\ -14 & -48 & -94 \end{bmatrix}$ **29.** $\begin{bmatrix} -2 & -6 \\ 3 & \tfrac{1}{3} \end{bmatrix}$ **30.** $\begin{bmatrix} 2 & 2 & 2 \\ 1 & 2 & 1 \\ 1 & 2 & 1 \end{bmatrix}$ **31.** $\begin{bmatrix} 1 & 1 & 1 \\ -1 & 1 & -1 \\ -1 & 1 & -1 \end{bmatrix}$

32. $\begin{bmatrix} -2 & 0 & 0 \\ 1 & 1 & -3 \end{bmatrix}$ **33.** $\begin{bmatrix} 0 & 1 & 1 \\ -2 & -2 & -4 \end{bmatrix}$ **34.** $\begin{bmatrix} 0 & 2 & 2 \\ 0 & 0 & 4 \end{bmatrix}$

The effect is a reflection over the x-axis

35. $\begin{bmatrix} 0 & -2 & -2 \\ 0 & 0 & -4 \end{bmatrix}$ **36.** $\begin{bmatrix} 0 & 0 & 4 \\ 0 & 2 & 2 \end{bmatrix}$ **37.** $\begin{bmatrix} 0 & 4 & 4 \\ 0 & 0 & -4 \end{bmatrix}$

The effect is a reflection over the y-axis

The effect is a 90° counterclockwise rotation about the origin

The effect is a horizontal stretch by a factor of 2.

38. $AB = \begin{bmatrix} 1 & 7 \\ 0 & 5 \end{bmatrix}; BA = \begin{bmatrix} 1 & 0 \\ 1 & 5 \end{bmatrix}; B \neq A^{-1}$ **39.** $AB = I_3; BA = I_3; B = A^{-1}$ **40.** $\begin{bmatrix} 3 & 1 \\ 2 & 1 \end{bmatrix}$ **41.** $\begin{bmatrix} -\dfrac{3}{5} & \dfrac{1}{5} \\ 1 & 0 \end{bmatrix}$ **42.** $\begin{bmatrix} 3 & 0 & -2 \\ -6 & 1 & 4 \\ 1 & 0 & -1 \end{bmatrix}$

43. $\begin{bmatrix} 8 & -8 & 5 \\ -3 & 2 & -1 \\ -1 & -1 & 1 \end{bmatrix}$ **44. a.** $\begin{bmatrix} 1 & 1 & 2 \\ 0 & 1 & 3 \\ 3 & 0 & -2 \end{bmatrix}\begin{bmatrix} x \\ y \\ z \end{bmatrix} = \begin{bmatrix} 7 \\ -2 \\ 0 \end{bmatrix}$ **b.** $\{(-18, 79, -27)\}$ **45. a.** $\begin{bmatrix} 1 & -1 & 2 \\ 0 & 1 & -1 \\ 1 & 0 & 2 \end{bmatrix}\begin{bmatrix} x \\ y \\ z \end{bmatrix} = \begin{bmatrix} 12 \\ -5 \\ 10 \end{bmatrix}$

b. $\{(4, -2, 3)\}$ **46.** The encoded message is $96, 135, 46, 63$; The decoded message is $18, 21, 12, 5$ or RULE. **47.** 17 **48.** 4

49. -86 **50.** -236 **51.** 4 **52.** 16 **53.** $\left\{\left(\dfrac{7}{4}, -\dfrac{25}{8}\right)\right\}$ **54.** $\{(2, -7)\}$ **55.** $\{(23, -12, 3)\}$ **56.** $\{(-3, 2, 1)\}$

57. $a = \dfrac{5}{8}; b = -50; c = 1150$; 30- and 50-year-olds are involved in an average of 212.5 automobile accidents per day.

Chapter 8 Test

1. $\left\{\left(-3, \dfrac{1}{2}, 1\right)\right\}$ **2.** $\{(t, t - 1, t)\}$ **3.** $\begin{bmatrix} 5 & 4 \\ 1 & 11 \end{bmatrix}$ **4.** $\begin{bmatrix} 5 & -2 \\ 1 & -1 \\ 4 & -1 \end{bmatrix}$ **5.** $\begin{bmatrix} \dfrac{3}{5} & -\dfrac{2}{5} \\ \dfrac{1}{5} & \dfrac{1}{5} \end{bmatrix}$ **6.** $\begin{bmatrix} -1 & 2 \\ -5 & 4 \end{bmatrix}$ **7.** $AB = I_3; BA = I_3$

8. a. $\begin{bmatrix} 3 & 5 \\ 2 & -3 \end{bmatrix}\begin{bmatrix} x \\ y \end{bmatrix} = \begin{bmatrix} 9 \\ -13 \end{bmatrix}$ **b.** $\begin{bmatrix} \dfrac{3}{19} & \dfrac{5}{19} \\ \dfrac{2}{19} & -\dfrac{3}{19} \end{bmatrix}$ **c.** $\{(-2, 3)\}$ **9.** 18 **10.** $x = 2$

Cumulative Review Exercises (Chapters P–8)

1. $\left\{\dfrac{-1 + \sqrt{33}}{4}, \dfrac{-1 - \sqrt{33}}{4}\right\}$ **2.** $\left[\dfrac{1}{2}, \infty\right)$ **3.** $[-2, -1]\cup[2, \infty)$ **4.** $\left\{-4, \dfrac{1}{3}, 1\right\}$ **5.** $\{\ln 5, \ln 9\}$ **6.** $\{1\}$ **7.** $\{(7, -4, 6)\}$

8. $y = -1$ **9.** $f^{-1}(x) = \dfrac{x^2 + 7}{4}(x \geq 0)$

10.
$f(x) = \dfrac{x}{x^2 - 16}$

11. $f(x) = (x + 2)(x - 3)(2x + 1)(2x - 1)$ **13. a.** $A = 900e^{-0.017t}$ **b.** 759.30 g

12.
$y = \log_2(x + 1)$
$x = -1$
$y = \log_2 x$

14. $\begin{bmatrix} 2 & -1 \\ 13 & 1 \end{bmatrix}$ **15.** $\dfrac{8}{x - 3} + \dfrac{-2}{x - 2} + \dfrac{-3}{x + 2}$

16.
$y = -\dfrac{2}{3}x - 1$

17.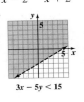
$3x - 5y < 15$

18.
$f(x) = x^2 - 2x - 3$

19.
$(x - 1)^2 + (y + 1)^2 = 9$

20. $x^2 + 2x - 2$

21.
$y = 2 \sin 2\pi x$

22. $\dfrac{3}{5}$ **23.** $\dfrac{\cos 2x}{\cos x - \sin x} = \dfrac{\cos^2 x - \sin^2 x}{\cos x - \sin x} = \dfrac{(\cos x + \sin x)(\cos x - \sin x)}{\cos x - \sin x} = \cos x + \sin x$

24. $\dfrac{3\pi}{2}$ **25.** $2\mathbf{i} - 13\mathbf{j}$

CHAPTER 9

Section 9.1

Check Point Exercises

1. foci at $(-3\sqrt{3}, 0)$ and $(3\sqrt{3}, 0)$ **2.** foci at $(0, -\sqrt{7})$ and $(0, \sqrt{7})$ **3.** $\dfrac{x^2}{9} + \dfrac{y^2}{5} = 1$ **4.** foci at $(-1 - \sqrt{5}, 2)$ and $(-1 + \sqrt{5}, 2)$ **5.** Yes

1.
$\dfrac{x^2}{36} + \dfrac{y^2}{9} = 1$

2.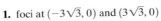
$16x^2 + 9y^2 = 144$

4.
$\dfrac{(x + 1)^2}{9} + \dfrac{(y - 2)^2}{4} = 1$

Exercise Set 9.1

1. foci at $(-2\sqrt{3}, 0)$ and $(2\sqrt{3}, 0)$

$$\frac{x^2}{16} + \frac{y^2}{4} = 1$$

3. foci at $(0, -3\sqrt{3})$ and $(0, 3\sqrt{3})$

$$\frac{x^2}{9} + \frac{y^2}{36} = 1$$

5. foci at $(0, -\sqrt{39})$ and $(0, \sqrt{39})$

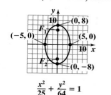

$$\frac{x^2}{25} + \frac{y^2}{64} = 1$$

7. foci at $(0, -4\sqrt{2})$ and $(0, 4\sqrt{2})$

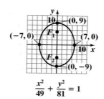

$$\frac{x^2}{49} + \frac{y^2}{81} = 1$$

9. foci at $(0, -2)$ and $(0, 2)$

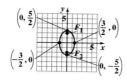

11. foci at $\left(-\frac{\sqrt{3}}{2}, 0\right)$ and $\left(\frac{\sqrt{3}}{2}, 0\right)$

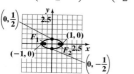

13. foci at $(0, -\sqrt{21})$ and $(0, \sqrt{21})$

15. foci at $(-2\sqrt{3}, 0)$ and $(2\sqrt{3}, 0)$

17. foci at $(0, -\sqrt{2})$ and $(0, \sqrt{2})$

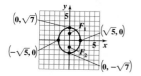

19. $\frac{x^2}{4} + \frac{y^2}{1} = 1$; foci at $(-\sqrt{3}, 0)$ and $(\sqrt{3}, 0)$ **21.** $\frac{x^2}{1} + \frac{y^2}{4} = 1$; foci at $(0, \sqrt{3})$ and $(0, -\sqrt{3})$

23. $\frac{(x+1)^2}{4} + \frac{(y-1)^2}{1} = 1$; foci at $(-1-\sqrt{3}, 1)$ and $(-1+\sqrt{3}, 1)$ **25.** $\frac{x^2}{64} + \frac{y^2}{39} = 1$ **27.** $\frac{x^2}{33} + \frac{y^2}{49} = 1$

29. $\frac{x^2}{13} + \frac{y^2}{9} = 1$ **31.** $\frac{x^2}{16} + \frac{y^2}{4} = 1$ **33.** $\frac{(x+2)^2}{4} + \frac{(y-3)^2}{25} = 1$ **35.** $\frac{(x-7)^2}{4} + \frac{(y-6)^2}{9} = 1$

37. foci at $(2-\sqrt{5}, 1)$ and $(2+\sqrt{5}, 1)$

$$\frac{(x-2)^2}{9} + \frac{(y-1)^2}{4} = 1$$

39. foci at $(-3-2\sqrt{3}, 2)$ and $(-3+2\sqrt{3}, 2)$

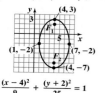

$$(x+3)^2 + 4(y-2)^2 = 16$$

41. foci at $(4, 2)$ and $(4, -6)$

$$\frac{(x-4)^2}{9} + \frac{(y+2)^2}{25} = 1$$

43. foci at $(0, 2+\sqrt{11}), (0, 2-\sqrt{11})$

$$\frac{x^2}{25} + \frac{(y-2)^2}{36} = 1$$

45. foci at $(-3-2\sqrt{2}, 2)$ and $(-3+2\sqrt{2}, 2)$

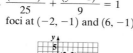

$$\frac{(x+3)^2}{9} + (y-2)^2 = 1$$

47. foci at $(1, -3+\sqrt{3})$ and $(1, -3-\sqrt{3})$

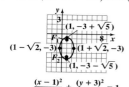

$$\frac{(x-1)^2}{2} + \frac{(y+3)^2}{5} = 1$$

49. foci at $(1, -3+\sqrt{5})$ and $(1, -3-\sqrt{5})$

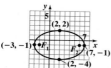

$$9(x-1)^2 + 4(y+3)^2 = 36$$

51. $\frac{(x-2)^2}{25} + \frac{(y+1)^2}{9} = 1$
foci at $(-2, -1)$ and $(6, -1)$

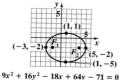

$$9x^2 + 25y^2 - 36x + 50y - 164 = 0$$

53. $\frac{(x-1)^2}{16} + \frac{(y+2)^2}{9} = 1$
foci at $(1-\sqrt{7}, -2)$ and $(1+\sqrt{7}, -2)$

$$9x^2 + 16y^2 - 18x + 64y - 71 = 0$$

55. $\dfrac{(x+2)^2}{16} + \dfrac{(y-3)^2}{64} = 1$ **57.** $\{(0,-1),(0,1)\}$
foci at $(-2, 3+4\sqrt{3})$ and $(-2, 3-4\sqrt{3})$ **59.** $\{(0,3)\}$
61. $\{(0,-2),(1,0)\}$
63.

$4x^2 + y^2 + 16x - 6y - 39 = 0$

$y = -\sqrt{16-4x^2}$

65. Yes   **67. a.** $\dfrac{x^2}{2304} + \dfrac{y^2}{529} = 1$ **b.** about 42 feet   **79.** $\dfrac{x^2}{\frac{36}{5}} + \dfrac{y^2}{36} = 1$ **81.** large circle: $x^2 + y^2 = 25$; small circle: $x^2 + y^2 = 9$

Section 9.2

Check Point Exercises

1. a. vertices at $(5,0)$ and $(-5,0)$; foci at $(\sqrt{41},0)$ and $(-\sqrt{41},0)$ **b.** vertices at $(0,5)$ and $(0,-5)$; foci at $(0,\sqrt{41})$ and $(0,-\sqrt{41})$ **2.** $\dfrac{y^2}{9} - \dfrac{x^2}{16} = 1$

3. foci at $(-3\sqrt{5},0)$ and $(3\sqrt{5},0)$;   **4.** foci at $(0,\sqrt{5})$ and $(0,-\sqrt{5})$;   **5.** foci at $(3-\sqrt{5},1)$ and $(3+\sqrt{5},1)$;
asymptotes: $y = \pm\dfrac{1}{2}x$ asymptotes: $y = \pm 2x$ asymptotes: $(y-1) = \pm\dfrac{1}{2}(x-3)$

$\dfrac{x^2}{36} - \dfrac{y^2}{9} = 1$

$y^2 - 4x^2 = 4$

$\dfrac{(x-3)^2}{4} - \dfrac{(y-1)^2}{1} = 1$

6. foci at $(3, -5+\sqrt{13})$ and $(3, -5-\sqrt{13})$;   **7.** $\dfrac{x^2}{2{,}722{,}500} - \dfrac{y^2}{25{,}155{,}900} = 1$
asymptotes: $(y+5) = \pm\dfrac{2}{3}(x-3)$;

$4x^2 - 24x - 9y^2 - 90y - 153 = 0$

Exercise Set 9.2

1. vertices at $(2,0)$ and $(-2,0)$; foci at $(\sqrt{5},0)$ and $(-\sqrt{5},0)$; graph (b)   **3.** vertices at $(0,2)$ and $(0,-2)$; foci at $(0,\sqrt{5})$ and $(0,-\sqrt{5})$; graph (a)

5. $y^2 - \dfrac{x^2}{8} = 1$ **7.** $\dfrac{x^2}{9} - \dfrac{y^2}{7} = 1$ **9.** $\dfrac{y^2}{36} - \dfrac{x^2}{9} = 1$ **11.** $\dfrac{(x-4)^2}{4} - \dfrac{(y+2)^2}{5} = 1$

13. foci: $(\pm\sqrt{34},0)$;   **15.** foci: $(\pm 2\sqrt{41},0)$;   **17.** foci: $(0,\pm 2\sqrt{13})$;   **19.** foci: $\left(0, \pm\dfrac{\sqrt{5}}{2}\right)$;
asymptotes: $y = \pm\dfrac{5}{3}x$ asymptotes: $y = \pm\dfrac{4}{5}x$ asymptotes: $y = \pm\dfrac{2}{3}x$ asymptotes: $y = \pm\dfrac{1}{2}x$

$\dfrac{x^2}{9} - \dfrac{y^2}{25} = 1$

$\dfrac{x^2}{100} - \dfrac{y^2}{64} = 1$

$\dfrac{y^2}{16} - \dfrac{x^2}{36} = 1$

$4y^2 - x^2 = 1$

21. foci: $(\pm\sqrt{13},0)$;   **23.** foci: $(0,\pm\sqrt{34})$;   **25.** foci: $(\pm 2,0)$;   **27.** $\dfrac{x^2}{9} - \dfrac{y^2}{25} = 1$
asymptotes: $y = \pm\dfrac{3}{2}x$ asymptotes: $y = \pm\dfrac{5}{3}x$ asymptotes: $y = \pm x$

29. $\dfrac{y^2}{4} - \dfrac{x^2}{9} = 1$

31. $\dfrac{(x-2)^2}{4} - \dfrac{(y+3)^2}{9} = 1$

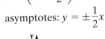

$9x^2 - 4y^2 = 36$

$9y^2 - 25x^2 = 225$

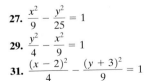

$y = \pm\sqrt{x^2-2}$

33. foci: $(-9, -3), (1, -3)$;

asymptotes: $(y + 3) = \pm\frac{4}{3}(x + 4)$

$$\frac{(x + 4)^2}{9} - \frac{(y + 3)^2}{16} = 1$$

35. foci: $(-3 \pm \sqrt{41}, 0)$;

asymptotes: $y = \pm\frac{4}{5}(x + 3)$

$$\frac{(x + 3)^2}{25} - \frac{y^2}{16} = 1$$

37. foci: $(1, -2 \pm 2\sqrt{5})$;

asymptotes: $(y + 2) = \pm\frac{1}{2}(x - 1)$

$$\frac{(y + 2)^2}{4} - \frac{(x - 1)^2}{16} = 1$$

39. foci: $(3 \pm \sqrt{5}, -3)$;

asymptotes: $(y + 3) = \pm\frac{1}{2}(x - 3)$

$$(x - 3)^2 - 4(y + 3)^2 = 4$$

41. foci: $(1 \pm \sqrt{6}, 2)$;

asymptotes: $(y - 2) = \pm(x - 1)$

$$(x - 1)^2 - (y - 2)^2 = 3$$

43. $(x - 1)^2 - (y + 2)^2 = 1$;

foci: $(1 \pm \sqrt{2}, -2)$;

asymptotes: $(y + 2) = \pm(x - 1)$

$$x^2 - y^2 - 2x - 4y - 4 = 0$$

45. $\frac{(y + 1)^2}{4} - \frac{(x + 2)^2}{0.25} = 1$;

foci: $(-2, -1 \pm \sqrt{4.25})$;

asymptotes: $(y + 1) = \pm 4(x + 2)$

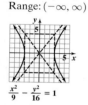

$$16x^2 - y^2 + 64x - 2y + 67 = 0$$

47. $\frac{(x - 2)^2}{9} - \frac{(y - 3)^2}{4} = 1$;

foci: $(2 \pm \sqrt{13}, 3)$

asymptotes: $(y - 3) = \pm\frac{2}{3}(x - 2)$

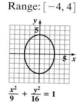

$$4x^2 - 9y^2 - 16x + 5y - 101 = 0$$

49. $\frac{y^2}{4} - \frac{(x - 4)^2}{25} = 1$

foci: $(4, \pm\sqrt{29})$;

asymptotes: $y = \pm\frac{2}{5}(x - 4)$

$$4x^2 - 25y^2 - 32x + 164 = 0$$

51. Domain: $(-\infty, -3] \cup [3, \infty)$;
Range: $(-\infty, \infty)$

$$\frac{x^2}{9} - \frac{y^2}{16} = 1$$

53. Domain: $[-3, 3]$;
Range: $[-4, 4]$

$$\frac{x^2}{9} + \frac{y^2}{16} = 1$$

55. Domain: $(-\infty, \infty)$;
Range: $(-\infty, -4] \cup [4, \infty)$

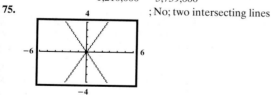

$$\frac{y^2}{16} - \frac{x^2}{9} = 1$$

57. $\{(-2, 0), (2, 0)\}$

59. $\{(0, -3), (0, 3)\}$

61. If M_1 is located 2640 feet to the right of the origin on the x-axis, the explosion is located on the right branch of the hyperbola given

by the equation $\frac{x^2}{1,210,000} - \frac{y^2}{5,759,600} = 1$.   **63.** 40 yd

75.

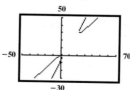

; No; two intersecting lines

77. $2y^2 + (10 - 6x)y + (4x^2 - 3x - 6) = 0$

$y = \frac{3x - 5 \pm \sqrt{x^2 - 24x + 37}}{2}$

The xy-term rotates the hyperbola.

79. c   **81.** $\frac{y^2}{36} - \frac{(x - 5)^2}{20} = 1$

Section 9.3

Check Point Exercises

1. focus: $(2, 0)$
directrix: $x = -2$

$y^2 = 8x$

2. focus: $(0, -3)$
directrix: $y = 3$

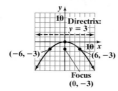

$(-6, -3)$ $(6, -3)$

Focus
$(0, -3)$

3. $y^2 = 32x$
4. vertex: $(2, -1)$; focus: $(2, 0)$;
directrix: $y = -2$

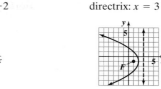

$(x - 2)^2 = 4(y + 1)$

5. vertex: $(2, -1)$; focus: $(1, -1)$;
directrix: $x = 3$

$y^2 + 2y + 4x - 7 = 0$

6. $x^2 = \dfrac{9}{4}y$; The light should be placed at $\left(0, \dfrac{9}{16}\right)$, or $\dfrac{9}{16}$ inch above the vertex.

Exercise Set 9.3

1. focus: $(1, 0)$; directrix: $x = -1$; graph (c)   **3.** focus: $(0, -1)$, directrix: $y = 1$; graph (b)
5. focus: $(4, 0)$; directrix: $x = -4$ **7.** focus: $(-2, 0)$; directrix: $x = 2$ **9.** focus: $(0, 3)$; directrix: $y = -3$

$y^2 = 16x$ $y^2 = -8x$ $x^2 = 12y$

11. focus: $(0, -4)$; directrix: $y = 4$

$x^2 = -16y$

13. focus: $\left(\dfrac{3}{2}, 0\right)$; directrix: $x = -\dfrac{3}{2}$

$y^2 - 6x = 0$

15. focus: $\left(0, -\dfrac{1}{8}\right)$; directrix: $y = \dfrac{1}{8}$

$8x^2 + 4y = 0$

17. $y^2 = 28x$ **19.** $y^2 = -20x$ **21.** $x^2 = 60y$ **23.** $x^2 = -100y$ **25.** $(x - 2)^2 = -8(y + 3)$ **27.** $(y - 2)^2 = 8(x - 1)$
29. $(x + 3)^2 = 4(y - 3)$ **31.** vertex: $(1, 1)$; focus: $(2, 1)$; directrix: $x = 0$; graph (c)   **33.** vertex: $(-1, -1)$; focus: $(-1, -2)$; directrix: $y = 0$; graph (d)
35. vertex: $(2, 1)$; focus: $(2, 3)$;
directrix: $y = -1$

$(x - 2)^2 = 8(y - 1)$

37. vertex: $(-1, -1)$; focus: $(-1, -3)$;
directrix: $y = 1$

$(x + 1)^2 = -8(y + 1)$

39. vertex: $(-1, -3)$; focus: $(2, -3)$;
directrix: $x = -4$

$(y + 3)^2 = 12(x + 1)$

41. vertex: $(0, -1)$; focus: $(-2, -1)$;
directrix: $x = 2$

$(y + 1)^2 = -8x$

43. $(x - 1)^2 = 4(y - 2)$; vertex: $(1, 2)$;
focus: $(1, 3)$; directrix: $y = 1$

$x^2 - 2x - 4y + 9 = 0$

45. $(y - 1)^2 = -12(x - 3)$;
vertex: $(3, 1)$; focus: $(0, 1)$;
directrix: $x = 6$

$y^2 - 2y + 12x - 35 = 0$

47. $(x + 3)^2 = 4(y + 2)$;
vertex: $(-3, -2)$; focus: $(-3, -1)$;
directrix: $y = -3$

$x^2 + 6x - 4y + 1 = 0$

49. Domain: $[-4, \infty)$;
Range: $(-\infty, \infty)$; not a function
51. Domain: $(-\infty, \infty)$;
Range: $(-\infty, 1]$; function
53. Domain: $(-\infty, 3]$;
Range: $(-\infty, \infty)$; not a function

55. $\{(-4, 2), (0, 0)\}$

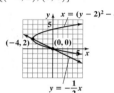

57. $\{(-2, 1)\}$

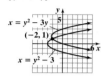

59. $\varnothing$

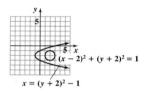

61. 1 inch above the vertex   **63.** 4.5 feet from the base of the dish   **65.** 76 m   **67.** yes

77. $y = -1 \pm \sqrt{6x - 12}$

79. $9y^2 + (-24x - 80)y + 16x^2 - 60x + 100 = 0$
$$y = \frac{12x + 40 \pm 10\sqrt{15x + 7}}{9}$$

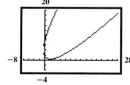

81. b   **83.** $(x + 1)^2 = -8(y - 2)$

Mid-Chapter 9 Check Point

1. foci: $(\pm\sqrt{21}, 0)$

$$\frac{x^2}{25} + \frac{y^2}{4} = 1$$

2. foci: $(0, \pm\sqrt{5})$

$9x^2 + 4y^2 = 36$

3. foci: $(2, 2), (2, -4)$

$$\frac{(x - 2)^2}{16} + \frac{(y + 1)^2}{25} = 1$$

4. foci: $(-5, 1), (1, 1)$

$$\frac{(x + 2)^2}{25} + \frac{(y - 1)^2}{16} = 1$$

5. foci: $(2 \pm 4\sqrt{2}, -3)$

$x^2 + 9y^2 - 4x + 54y + 49 = 0$

6. foci: $(\pm\sqrt{10}, 0)$;
asymptotes: $y = \pm\frac{1}{3}x$

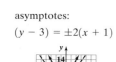

$$\frac{x^2}{9} - y^2 = 1$$

7. foci: $(0, \pm\sqrt{10})$;
asymptotes: $y = \pm 3x$

$$\frac{y^2}{9} - x^2 = 1$$

8. foci: $(0, \pm 2\sqrt{5})$;
asymptotes: $y = \pm 2x$

$y^2 - 4x^2 = 16$

9. foci: $(\pm\sqrt{53}, 0)$;
asymptotes: $y = \pm\frac{2}{7}x$

$4x^2 - 49y^2 = 196$

10. foci: $(-3, -2), (7, -2)$;
asymptotes: $(y + 2) = \pm\frac{4}{3}(x - 2)$

$$\frac{(x-2)^2}{9} - \frac{(y+2)^2}{16} = 1$$

11. foci: $(-1, 3 \pm 2\sqrt{5})$;
asymptotes:
$(y - 3) = \pm 2(x + 1)$

$4x^2 - y^2 + 8x + 6y + 11 = 0$

12. focus: $(2, -4)$;
directrix: $y = 2$;

$(x - 2)^2 = -12(y + 1)$

13. focus: $\left(-\frac{5}{2}, 1\right)$;
directrix: $x = -\frac{7}{2}$;

14.

$x^2 + y^2 = 4$

15.

$x + y = 4$

16.

$x^2 - y^2 = 4$

17.

$x^2 + 4y^2 = 4$

18.

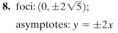

$(x + 1)^2 + (y - 1)^2 = 4$

19.

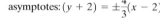
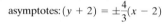

$x^2 + 4(y - 1)^2 = 4$

20.

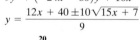

$(x-1)^2 - (y-1)^2 = 4$

21.

22. $\dfrac{x^2}{25} + \dfrac{y^2}{9} = 1$ **23.** $\dfrac{(x - 1)^2}{81} + \dfrac{(y - 2)^2}{56} = 1$ **24.** $\dfrac{y^2}{4} - \dfrac{x^2}{5} = 1$ **25.** $\dfrac{(x + 1)^2}{4} - \dfrac{(y - 5)^2}{5} = 1$

26. $(x - 4)^2 = 12(y - 2)$ **27.** $(y - 6)^2 = -20(x - 3)$ **28.** No   **29.** $20\sqrt{3}$ cm

30. a. $\dfrac{x^2}{1.1025} - \dfrac{y^2}{7.8975} = 1$ **b.**

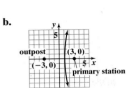

31. 1.4 m

Section 9.4

Check Point Exercises

1. a. ellipse   **b.** circle   **c.** parabola   **d.** hyperbola

2. $\dfrac{x'^2}{4} - \dfrac{y'^2}{4} = 1$

3. $\dfrac{x'^2}{\frac{4}{5}} + \dfrac{y'^2}{4} = 1$

4.

5. parabola

Exercise Set 9.4

1. parabola   **3.** hyperbola   **5.** circle   **7.** hyperbola   **9.** $\dfrac{y'^2}{2} - \dfrac{x'^2}{2} = 1$ **11.** $\dfrac{y'^2}{1} - \dfrac{x'^2}{3} = 1$ **13.** $\dfrac{x'^2}{4} - \dfrac{y'^2}{9} = 1$

15. $x = \dfrac{\sqrt{2}}{2}(x' - y'); y = \dfrac{\sqrt{2}}{2}(x' + y')$ **17.** $x = \dfrac{\sqrt{2}}{2}(x' - y'); y = \dfrac{\sqrt{2}}{2}(x' + y')$ **19.** $x = \dfrac{\sqrt{3}x' - y'}{2}; y = \dfrac{x' + \sqrt{3}y'}{2}$

21. $x = \dfrac{3x' - 4y'}{5}; y = \dfrac{4x' + 3y'}{5}$ **23.** $x = \sqrt{5}\left(\dfrac{2x' - y'}{5}\right); y = \sqrt{5}\left(\dfrac{x' + 2y'}{5}\right)$ **25.** $x = \dfrac{4x' - 3y'}{5}; y = \dfrac{3x' + 4y'}{5}$

27. a. $3x'^2 + y'^2 = 20$
b. $\dfrac{x'^2}{\frac{20}{3}} + \dfrac{y'^2}{20} = 1$
c.

29. a. $-4x'^2 + 16y'^2 = 64$
b. $\dfrac{y'^2}{4} - \dfrac{x'^2}{16} = 1$
c.

31. a. $64x'^2 - 16y'^2 = 16$
b. $\dfrac{x'^2}{\frac{1}{4}} - \dfrac{y'^2}{1} = 1$
c.

33. a. $650x'^2 + 25y'^2 = 225$
b. $\dfrac{x'^2}{\frac{9}{26}} + \dfrac{y'^2}{9} = 1$
c.

35. a. $50x'^2 - 75y'^2 = 25$
b. $\dfrac{x'^2}{\frac{1}{2}} - \dfrac{y'^2}{\frac{1}{3}} = 1$
c.

37. a. $625x'^2 + 1250y'^2 = 625$
b. $\dfrac{x'^2}{1} + \dfrac{y'^2}{\frac{1}{2}} = 1$
c.

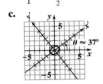

39. ellipse or circle   **41.** parabola   **43.** hyperbola   **45.** ellipse; $(0, 1), (0, -1)$ **47.** parabola; $(3, -1)$

55.

57.

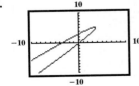

59.

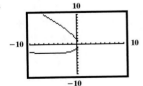

61. There are no solutions to this equation just as there is no such sound.

63.
$$A' = A \cos^2 \theta + B \sin \theta \cos \theta + C \sin^2 \theta$$
$$C' = A \sin^2 \theta - B \sin \theta \cos \theta + C \cos^2 \theta$$
$$A' + C' = A \cos^2 \theta + B \sin \theta \cos \theta + C \sin^2 \theta + A \sin^2 \theta - B \sin \theta \cos \theta + C \cos^2 \theta$$
$$= A(\cos^2 \theta + \sin^2 \theta) + B(\sin \theta \cos \theta - \sin \theta \cos \theta) + C(\sin^2 \theta + \cos^2 \theta)$$
$$= A(1) + B(0) + C(1)$$
$$= A + C$$

Section 9.5

Check Point Exercises

1.   **2.**   **3.**   **4.** $x = t$ and $y = t^2 - 25$

Exercise Set 9.5

1. $(-2, 6)$ **3.** $(5, -3)$ **5.** $(4, 8)$ **7.** $(60\sqrt{3}, 1)$

9.   **11.**   **13.**   **15.** 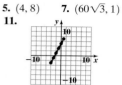   **17.**

19.   **21.** $y = 2x$ **23.** $y = (x + 4)^2$ **25.** $y = x^2 - 1, x \geq 0$ **27.** $\dfrac{x^2}{4} + \dfrac{y^2}{4} = 1$

29. $\dfrac{(x - 1)^2}{9} + \dfrac{(y - 2)^2}{9} = 1$ **31.** $\dfrac{x^2}{4} + \dfrac{y^2}{9} = 1$ **33.** $\dfrac{(x - 1)^2}{9} + \dfrac{(y + 1)^2}{4} = 1, -2 \leq x \leq 4, -1 \leq y \leq 1$

35. $x^2 - y^2 = 1$ **37.** $y = x - 4, x \geq 2, y \geq -2$ **39.** $y = \dfrac{1}{x}, x \geq 1, y \geq 0$

41. $(x - h)^2 + (y - k)^2 = r^2$ **43.** $\dfrac{(x - h)^2}{a^2} - \dfrac{(y - k)^2}{b^2} = 1$ **45.** $x = 3 + 6\cos t; y = 5 + 6\sin t$ **47.** $x = -2 + 5\cos t; y = 3 + 2\sin t$

49. $x = 4\sec t; y = \sqrt{20}\tan t$ **51.** $x = -2 + 3t; y = 4 + 3t$ **53.** Answers may vary. Sample answer: $x = t$ and $y = 4t - 3; x = t + 1$ and $y = 4t + 1$ **55.** Answers may vary. Sample answer: $x = t$ and $y = t^2 + 4; x = t + 1$ and $y = t^2 + 2t + 5$

57. a.   **b.**   **c.**   **d.**

59.   **61.**   **63.**    **65.**

domain: $[-2, 6]$;   range: $[-5, 3]$

domain: $\left[\dfrac{3}{4}, \infty\right)$;   range: $(-\infty, \infty)$

a. increasing: $(-\infty, \infty)$ **b.** no maximum or minimum

a. decreasing: $(-\infty, 1)$; increasing: $(1, \infty)$ **b.** minimum of -5 at $x = 1$

67.

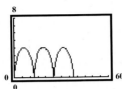

a. increasing: $(0, 2\pi)$; decreasing: $(2\pi, 4\pi)$
b. maximum of 4 at $x = 2\pi$;
   minimum of 0 at $x = 0$ and $x = 4\pi$
69. a. $x = (180 \cos 40°)t$; $y = 3 + (180 \sin 40°)t - 16t^2$
   b. After 1 second: 137.9 feet in distance, 102.7 feet in height;
      After 2 seconds: 275.8 feet in distance, 170.4 feet in height;
      After 3 seconds: 413.7 feet in distance, 206.1 feet in height
   c. $t = 7.3$ sec; total horizontal distance: 1006.6 ft; yes

79. 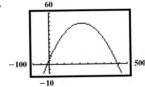   **81.** 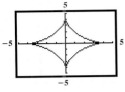   **83.**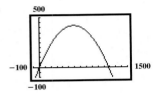

85. a. $x = (140 \cos 22°)t$; $y = 5 + (140 \sin 22°)t - 16t^2$ **87.** $x = 3 \sin t$; $y = 3 \cos t$
   b.

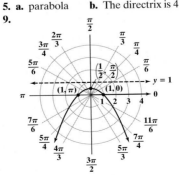

   Window: $[-100, 500] \times [-10, 60]$
   c. The maximum height is 48.0 feet. It occurs at 1.6 seconds.   **d.** 3.4 sec   **e.** 437.5 ft

Section 9.6

Check Point Exercises

1. 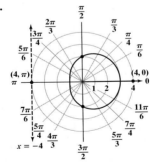   **2.** 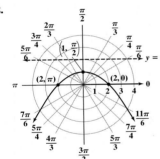   **3.**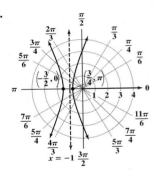

Exercise Set 9.6

1. a. parabola   **b.** The directrix is 3 units above the pole, at $y = 3$.   **3. a.** ellipse   **b.** The directrix is 3 units to the left of the pole, at $x = -3$.
5. a. parabola   **b.** The directrix is 4 units above the pole, at $y = 4$.   **7. a.** hyperbola   **b.** The directrix is 3 units to the left of the pole, at $x = -3$.

9. 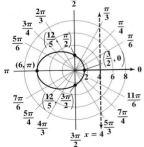   **11.**   **13.**

36. a. $x'^2 - 9y'^2 = -36$
    b. $\dfrac{y'^2}{4} - \dfrac{x'^2}{36} = 1$
    c.
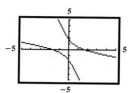

37. a. $625x'^2 + 1250y'^2 = 625$
    b. $\dfrac{x'^2}{1} + \dfrac{y'^2}{\frac{1}{2}} = 1$
    c.
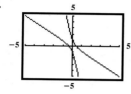

38. a. $500x'^2 + 1500y'^2 = 4500$
    b. $\dfrac{x'^2}{9} + \dfrac{y'^2}{3} = 1$
    c.
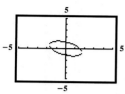

39. ellipse or circle   **40.** ellipse or circle   **41.** parabola   **42.** parabola   **43.** hyperbola   **44.** hyperbola   **45.** ellipse; $(0, 1), (0, -1)$

46. ellipse: $(0, \sqrt{6}), (0, -\sqrt{6})$ **47.** parabola; $(3, -1)$ **48.** hyperbola: $y = \pm\dfrac{\sqrt{6}}{3}x$

54.

55.
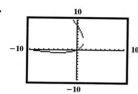

56.
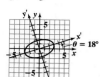

57.
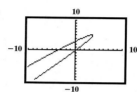

58.
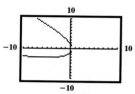

59.
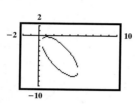

60.

61. There are no solutions to this equation just as there is no such sound.
62. In a rotated $x'y'$-system, x and y are replaced with x' and y', respectively.

63.
$$A' = A\cos^2\theta + B\sin\theta\cos\theta + C\sin^2\theta$$
$$C' = A\sin^2\theta - B\sin\theta\cos\theta + C\cos^2\theta$$
$$A' + C' = A\cos^2\theta + B\sin\theta\cos\theta + C\sin^2\theta + A\sin^2\theta - B\sin\theta\cos\theta + C\cos^2\theta$$
$$= A(\cos^2\theta + \sin^2\theta) + B(\sin\theta\cos\theta - \sin\theta\cos\theta) + C(\sin^2\theta + \cos^2\theta)$$
$$= A(1) + B(0) + C(1)$$
$$= A + C$$

64. $B'^2 - 4A'C'$
$$= [B(\cos^2\theta - \sin^2\theta) + 2(C - A)(\sin\theta\cos\theta)]^2 - 4[A\cos^2\theta + B\sin\theta\cos\theta + C\sin^2\theta][A\sin^2\theta - B\sin\theta\cos\theta + C\cos^2\theta]$$
$$= 4A^2[(\sin\theta\cos\theta)^2 - (\sin\theta\cos\theta)^2] + B^2[\cos^4\theta + 2\cos^2\theta\sin^2\theta + \sin^4\theta] + 4C^2[(\sin\theta\cos\theta)^2 - (\sin\theta\cos\theta)^2]$$
$$\quad + 4AB[\cos^2\theta(\sin\theta\cos\theta) - \sin^2\theta(\sin\theta\cos\theta) - (\sin\theta\cos\theta)(\cos^2\theta - \sin^2\theta)]$$
$$\quad - 4AC[\cos^4\theta + 2(\sin\theta\cos\theta)^2 + \sin^4\theta] + 4BC[(\sin\theta\cos\theta)(\cos^2\theta - \sin^2\theta) - (\sin\theta\cos\theta)(\cos^2\theta - \sin^2\theta)]$$
$$= 4A^2[0] + B^2[(\cos^2\theta + \sin^2\theta)^2] + 4C^2[0] + 4AB[\sin\theta\cos\theta(\cos^2\theta - \sin^2\theta - \cos^2\theta + \sin^2\theta)]$$
$$\quad - 4AC[(\cos^2\theta + \sin^2\theta)^2] + 4BC[\sin\theta\cos\theta(\cos^2\theta - \sin^2\theta - \cos^2\theta + \sin^2\theta)]$$
$$= B^2[(1)^2] + 4AB[0] - 4AC[(1)^2] + 4BC[0] = B^2 - 4AC$$

Section 9.5

Check Point Exercises

1.

2.

3.

4. $x = t$ and $y = t^2 - 25$

Exercise Set 9.5

1. $(-2, 6)$ **2.** $(3, 11)$ **3.** $(5, -3)$ **4.** $(7, -2)$ **5.** $(4, 8)$ **6.** $(-1, 4)$ **7.** $(60\sqrt{3}, 1)$ **8.** $(80\sqrt{2}, -58 + 80\sqrt{2})$

9.

10.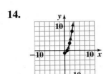

11.

12.

13.

14.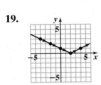

15.

16.

17.

18.

19.

20.

21. $y = 2x$

22. $y = -2x$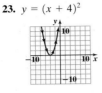

23. $y = (x + 4)^2$

24. $y = (x + 2)^2$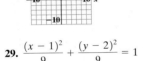

25. $y = x^2 - 1, x \geq 0$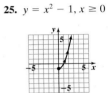

26. $y = x^2 + 1, x \geq 0$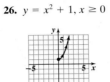

27. $\dfrac{x^2}{4} + \dfrac{y^2}{4} = 1$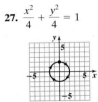

28. $\dfrac{x^2}{9} + \dfrac{y^2}{9} = 1$

29. $\dfrac{(x - 1)^2}{9} + \dfrac{(y - 2)^2}{9} = 1$

30. $\dfrac{(x + 1)^2}{4} + \dfrac{(y - 1)^2}{4} = 1$

31. $\dfrac{x^2}{4} + \dfrac{y^2}{9} = 1$

32. $\dfrac{x^2}{9} + \dfrac{y^2}{25} = 1$

33. $\dfrac{(x - 1)^2}{9} + \dfrac{(y + 1)^2}{4} = 1, -2 \leq x \leq 4, -1 \leq y \leq 1$

34. $\dfrac{(x - 2)^2}{16} + \dfrac{(y + 1)^2}{9} = 1, -2 \leq x \leq 6, -1 \leq y \leq 2$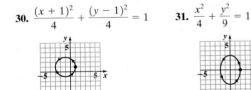

35. $x^2 - y^2 = 1$

36. $\dfrac{x^2}{25} - \dfrac{y^2}{9} = 1$

37. $y = x - 4, x \geq 2, y \geq -2$

38. $y = x - 4, x \geq 2, y \geq -2$

39. $y = \dfrac{1}{x}, x \geq 1, y \geq 0$

40. $y = \dfrac{1}{x}, x \geq 1, y \geq 0$

41. $(x - h)^2 + (y - k)^2 = r^2$ **42.** $\dfrac{(x - h)^2}{a^2} + \dfrac{(y - k)^2}{b^2} = 1$ **43.** $\dfrac{(x - h)^2}{a^2} - \dfrac{(y - k)^2}{b^2} = 1$ **44.** $y - y_1 = \dfrac{y_2 - y_1}{x_2 - x_1}(x - x_1)$

45. $x = 3 + 6 \cos t; y = 5 + 6 \sin t$ **46.** $x = 4 + 9 \cos t, y = 6 + 9 \sin t$ **47.** $x = -2 + 5 \cos t; y = 3 + 2 \sin t$

48. $x = 4 + 3 \cos t, y = -1 + 5 \sin t$ **49.** $x = 4 \sec t; y = \sqrt{20} \tan t$ **50.** $x = 3 \tan t, y = 4 \sec t$ **51.** $x = -2 + 3t; y = 4 + 3t$

52. $x = 3 + 6t, y = -1 + 13t$ **53.** Answers may vary. Sample answer: $x = t$ and $y = 4t - 3$; $x = t + 1$ and $y = 4t + 1$

54. Answers may vary. Sample answer: $x = t$ and $y = 2t - 5$; $x = t + 1$ and $y = 2t - 3$

55. Answers may vary. Sample answer: $x = t$ and $y = t^2 + 4$; $x = t + 1$ and $y = t^2 + 2t + 5$

56. Answers may vary. Sample answer: $x = t$ and $y = t^2 - 3$; $x = t + 1$ and $y = t^2 + 2t - 2$

57. **a.**   **b.**   **c.**   **d.**

58. **a.**   **b.**   **c.**   **d.**

59.   **60.**   **61.**   **62.**

domain: $[-2, 6]$;   domain: $[-5, -1]$;   domain: $\left[\dfrac{3}{4}, \infty\right)$;   domain: $\left[\dfrac{23}{4}, \infty\right)$;

range: $[-5, 3]$ range: $[-1, 3]$ range: $(-\infty, \infty)$ range: $(-\infty, \infty)$

63.   **64.**   **65.**

a. increasing: $(-\infty, \infty)$ **a.** increasing: $(-\infty, \infty)$ **a.** decreasing: $(-\infty, 1)$; increasing: $(1, \infty)$
b. no maximum or minimum   **b.** no maximum or minimum   **b.** minimum of -5 at $x = 1$

66.   **67.**   **68.**

a. increasing: $(-\infty, 1)$; decreasing: $(1, \infty)$ **a.** increasing: $(0, 2\pi)$; decreasing: $(2\pi, 4\pi)$ **a.** increasing: $(0, 3\pi)$; decreasing: $(3\pi, 6\pi)$
b. maximum of 7 at $x = 1$ **b.** maximum of 4 at $x = 2\pi$;   **b.** maximum of 6 at $x = 3\pi$;
   minimum of 0 at $x = 0$ and $x = 4\pi$ minimum of 0 at $x = 0$ and $x = 6\pi$

69. **a.** $x = (180 \cos 40°)t$; $y = 3 + (180 \sin 40°)t - 16t^2$
b. After 1 second: 137.9 feet in distance, 102.7 feet in height;
After 2 seconds: 275.8 feet in distance, 170.4 feet in height;
After 3 seconds: 413.7 feet in distance, 206.1 feet in height
c. $t = 7.3$ sec; total horizontal distance: 1006.6 ft; yes

70. **a.** $x = (150 \cos 35°)t$; $y = 3 + (150 \sin 35°)t - 16t^2$
b. After 1 second; 122.9 feet in distance, 73.0 feet in height;
After 2 seconds; 245.7 feet in distance, 111.1 feet in height;
After 3 seconds; 368.6 feet in distance, 117.1 feet in height
c. $t = 5.4$ sec; total horizontal distance: 663.5 ft; yes

78. 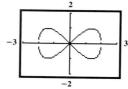   **79.** 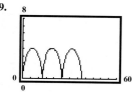   **80.** 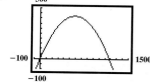   **81.**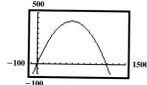

82. 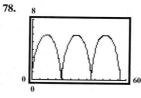   **83.** 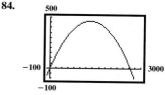   **84.**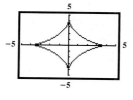

Window: $[-100, 1500] \times [-100, 500]$;
The maximum height is 419.4 feet at a time of 5.1 seconds.
The range of the projectile is 1174.6 feet horizontally.
It hits the ground at 10.2 seconds.

Window: $[-100, 3000] \times [-100, 500]$;
The maximum height is 462.6 feet at a time of 5.4 seconds.
The range of the projectile is 2642.9 feet horizontally.
It hits the ground at 10.8 seconds.

85. a. $x = (140 \cos 22°)t$; $y = 5 + (140 \sin 22°)t - 16t^2$ **86.** $\sqrt[3]{x^2} + \sqrt[3]{y^2} = 1$ **87.** $x = 3 \sin t$; $y = 3 \cos t$

b.

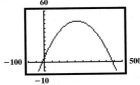

Window: $[-100, 500] \times [-10, 60]$

c. The maximum height is 48.0 feet. It occurs at 1.6 seconds.   **d.** 3.4 sec   **e.** 437.5 ft

88. a. $\sin t = \dfrac{PB}{a} \Rightarrow \sin t = \dfrac{XA}{a} \Rightarrow a \sin t = XA$

OA is the same as the length of arc PA. Since the radius is a, and the central angle is t, the length of the arc is at.
So $OA = at$. Therefore,

$x = OA - XA$
$x = at - a \sin t$
$x = a(t - \sin t)$

b. $\cos t = \dfrac{BC}{a} \Rightarrow a \sin t = BC$ and $AC = a$, since a is the radius of the circle. So,

$y = AC - BC$
$y = a - a \cos t$
$y = a(1 - \cos t)$

Section 9.6

Check Point Exercises

1.

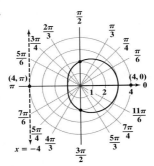

2.

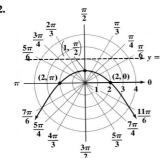

3.

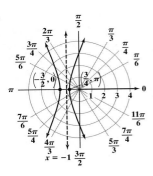

Exercise Set 9.6

1. a. parabola   **b.** The directrix is 3 units above the pole, at $y = 3$.   **2. a.** parabola   **b.** The directrix is 3 units to the right of the pole, at $x = 3$.
3. a. ellipse   **b.** The directrix is 3 units to the left of the pole, at $x = -3$.   **4. a.** ellipse   **b.** The directrix is 3 units to the right of the pole, at $x = 3$.
5. a. parabola   **b.** The directrix is 4 units above the pole, at $y = 4$.   **6. a.** parabola   **b.** The directrix is 4 units below the pole, at $y = -4$.
7. a. hyperbola   **b.** The directrix is 3 units to the left of the pole, at $x = -3$.   **8. a.** hyperbola   **b.** The directrix is 3 units to the right of the
pole, at $x = 3$.

9.

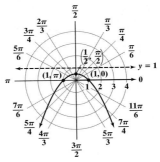

10.

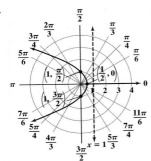

11.

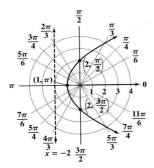

17. ellipse

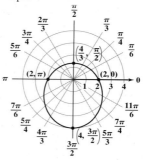

Cumulative Review Exercises (Chapters P–9)

1. $\{2\}$ **2.** $\{x \mid x < 2\}$ or $(-\infty, 2)$ **3.** $\{9\}$ **4.** $\{2 + 2\sqrt{5}, 2 - 2\sqrt{5}\}$ **5.** $\{x \mid x \geq 4 \text{ or } x \leq -3\}$ or $(-\infty, -3] \cup [4, \infty)$ **6.** $\left\{ \dfrac{2}{3}, -1 \pm \sqrt{2} \right\}$
7. $\{3\}$ **8.** $\{(2, -1)\}$ **9.** $\{(2, -4), (-14, -20)\}$ **10.** $\{(7, -4, 6)\}$
11.   **12.**   **13.**

$f(x) = (x - 1)^2 - 4$ $\dfrac{x^2}{9} + \dfrac{y^2}{4} = 1$

14. a. $\pm 1, \pm 3, \pm\dfrac{1}{2}, \pm\dfrac{3}{2}, \pm\dfrac{1}{4}, \pm\dfrac{3}{4}, \pm\dfrac{1}{8}, \pm\dfrac{3}{8}, \pm\dfrac{1}{16}, \pm\dfrac{3}{16}, \pm\dfrac{1}{32}, \pm\dfrac{3}{32}$ **b.** $\left\{ -\dfrac{1}{8}, \dfrac{3}{4}, 1 \right\}$

15. a. Domain: $(-2, 2)$; Range: $[-3, \infty)$ **b.** minimum of -3 at $x = 0$ **c.** $(0, 2)$ **d.** 3 **e.** -3 **f.** $x \to -2^+; x \to 2^-$

g.   **h.**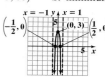

$g(x) = f(x - 2) + 1$ $h(x) = -f(2x)$

16. $(g \circ f)(x) = x^2 - 2$ **17.** $3 \log_5 x + \dfrac{1}{2}\log_5 y - 3$ **18.** $y = -2x - 2$ **19.** The costs will be the same when the number of miles driven is 175 miles. The cost will be \$67.   **20.** \$25 for basic cable service and \$10 for each movie channel

21. $\dfrac{\csc\theta - \sin\theta}{\sin\theta} = \dfrac{\csc\theta}{\sin\theta} - \dfrac{\sin\theta}{\sin\theta} = \dfrac{\frac{1}{\sin\theta}}{\sin\theta} - 1 = \dfrac{1}{\sin^2\theta} - 1 = \dfrac{1 - \sin^2\theta}{\sin^2\theta} = \dfrac{\cos^2\theta}{\sin^2\theta} = \cot^2\theta$

22.   **23.** $-3\mathbf{i} - 3\mathbf{j}$ **24.** $\theta = 0, \theta = \pi, \theta = \dfrac{\pi}{3}, \text{ or } \theta = \dfrac{5\pi}{3}$ **25.** $b \approx 14.4, C = 44°, c \approx 10.5$

CHAPTER 10

Section 10.1

Check Point Exercises

1. a. $7, 9, 11, 13$ **b.** $-\dfrac{1}{3}, \dfrac{1}{5}, -\dfrac{1}{9}, \dfrac{1}{17}$ **2.** $3, 11, 27, 59$ **3.** $10, \dfrac{10}{3}, \dfrac{5}{6}, \dfrac{1}{6}$ **4. a.** 91 **b.** n **5. a.** 182 **b.** 47 **c.** 20

6. a. $\displaystyle\sum_{i=1}^{9} i^2$ **b.** $\displaystyle\sum_{i=1}^{n} \dfrac{1}{2^{i-1}}$

Exercise Set 10.1

1. $5, 8, 11, 14$ **2.** $3, 7, 11, 15$ **3.** $3, 9, 27, 81$ **4.** $\dfrac{1}{3}, \dfrac{1}{9}, \dfrac{1}{27}, \dfrac{1}{81}$ **5.** $-3, 9, -27, 81$ **6.** $-\dfrac{1}{3}, \dfrac{1}{9}, -\dfrac{1}{27}, \dfrac{1}{81}$ **7.** $-4, 5, -6, 7$ **8.** $5, -6, 7, -8$

9. $\dfrac{2}{5}, \dfrac{2}{3}, \dfrac{6}{7}, 1$ **10.** $\dfrac{1}{2}, \dfrac{6}{7}, \dfrac{9}{8}, \dfrac{4}{3}$ **11.** $1, -\dfrac{1}{3}, \dfrac{1}{7}, -\dfrac{1}{15}$ **12.** $\dfrac{1}{3}, -\dfrac{1}{5}, \dfrac{1}{9}, -\dfrac{1}{17}$ **13.** $7, 12, 17, 22$ **14.** $12, 16, 20, 24$ **15.** $3, 12, 48, 192$

16. $2, 10, 50, 250$ **17.** $4, 11, 25, 53$ **18.** $5, 14, 41, 122$ **19.** $1, 2, \dfrac{3}{2}, \dfrac{2}{3}$ **20.** $2, \dfrac{3}{2}, \dfrac{8}{3}, \dfrac{15}{2}$ **21.** $4, 12, 48, 240$ **22.** $-2, -2, -4, -12$

23. 272 **24.** 306 **25.** 120 **26.** 190 **27.** $(n + 2)(n + 1)$ **28.** $2n + 1$ **29.** 105 **30.** 147 **31.** 60 **32.** 225 **33.** 115

34. -4 **35.** $-\dfrac{5}{16}$ **36.** $\dfrac{7}{81}$ **37.** 55 **38.** 60 **39.** $\dfrac{3}{8}$ **40.** $-\dfrac{19}{30}$ **41.** 15 **42.** 110 **43.** $\displaystyle\sum_{i=1}^{15} i^2$ **44.** $\displaystyle\sum_{i=1}^{12} i^4$ **45.** $\displaystyle\sum_{i=1}^{11} 2^i$

46. $\sum_{i=1}^{12} 5^i$ **47.** $\sum_{i=1}^{30} i$ **48.** $\sum_{i=1}^{40} i$ **49.** $\sum_{i=1}^{14} \dfrac{i}{i+1}$ **50.** $\sum_{i=1}^{16} \dfrac{i}{i+2}$ **51.** $\sum_{i=1}^{n} \dfrac{4^i}{i}$ **52.** $\sum_{i=1}^{n} \dfrac{i}{9^i}$ **53.** $\sum_{i=1}^{n} (2i-1)$ **54.** $\sum_{i=1}^{n} (ar^{i-1})$

55. $\sum_{k=1}^{14} (2k+3)$ **56.** $\sum_{k=3}^{16} 2k$ **57.** $\sum_{k=0}^{12} ar^k$ **58.** $\sum_{k=0}^{14} ar^k$ **59.** $\sum_{k=0}^{n} (a+kd)$ **60.** $\sum_{k=1}^{n} (a+d^k)$

61. 45   **62.** 35   **63.** 0   **64.** 0   **65.** 2   **66.** −2   **67.** 80   **68.** 20   **69. a.** 274.4   **b.** 34.3; From 1995 through 2002, the average number of people living below the poverty level each year was 34.3 million.   **70.** 38.2; From 1999 through 2004, there were a total of 38.2 million more doses available than were distributed.   **71. a.** 8.91; From 1994 through 2003, the average number of welfare recipients each year was 8.91 million.   **b.** 8.92; This is a fairly reasonable model.   **72. a.** 8.91; From 1994 through 2003, the average number of welfare recipients each year was 8.91 million.   **b.** 8.815; This is a reasonable model.

73. $8081.13   **74.** $16,084.37   **83.** 39,800   **84.** 1,307,674,368,000   **85.** 8.109673361 E15   **86.** 6840   **87.** 24,804

90. $a_{10} = 2.5937$; $a_{100} = 2.7048$; $a_{1000} = 2.7169$; $a_{10,000} = 2.7181$; $a_{100,000} = 2.7183$; As n gets larger, a_n gets closer to $e \approx 2.7183$.

91.

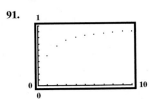

As n gets larger, a_n approaches 1.

92.

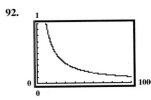

As n gets larger, a_n approaches 0.

93.

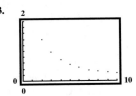

As n gets larger, a_n approaches 0.

94.

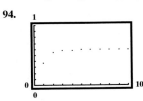

As n gets larger, a_n approaches $\dfrac{3}{5}$.

95. b

96. 9, 32, 16, 8, 4

Section 10.2

Check Point Exercises

1. 51.5, 53.68, 55.86, 58.04, 60.22   **2.** −34   **3. a.** $a_n = 9700n + 149{,}300$ **b.** $304,500   **4.** 360   **5.** 2460   **6.** $686,300

Exercise Set 10.2

1. 200, 220, 240, 260, 280, 300   **2.** 300, 350, 400, 450, 500, 550   **3.** −7, −3, 1, 5, 9, 13   **4.** −8, −3, 2, 7, 12, 17

5. 300, 210, 120, 30, −60, −150   **6.** 200, 140, 80, 20, −40, −100   **7.** $\dfrac{5}{2}, 2, \dfrac{3}{2}, 1, \dfrac{1}{2}, 0$ **8.** $\dfrac{3}{4}, \dfrac{1}{2}, \dfrac{1}{4}, 0, -\dfrac{1}{4}, -\dfrac{1}{2}$ **9.** −9, −3, 3, 9, 15, 21

10. −7, −3, 1, 5, 9, 13   **11.** 30, 20, 10, 0, −10, −20   **12.** 50, 30, 10, −10, −30, −50   **13.** 1.6, 1.2, 0.8, 0.4, 0, −0.4

14. −1.7, −2, −2.3, −2.6, −2.9, −3.2   **15.** 33   **16.** 39   **17.** 252   **18.** 362   **19.** 955   **20.** 685   **21.** −142   **22.** 244

23. $a_n = 4n - 3$; $a_{20} = 77$ **24.** $a_n = 5n - 3$; $a_{20} = 97$ **25.** $a_n = 11 - 4n$; $a_{20} = -69$ **26.** $a_n = 11 - 5n$; $a_{20} = -89$

27. $a_n = 7 + 2n$; $a_{20} = 47$ **28.** $a_n = 3n + 3$; $a_{20} = 63$ **29.** $a_n = -16 - 4n$; $a_{20} = -96$ **30.** $a_n = -65 - 5n$; $a_{20} = -165$

31. $a_n = 1 + 3n$; $a_{20} = 61$ **32.** $a_n = 5n + 1$; $a_{20} = 101$ **33.** $a_n = 40 - 10n$; $a_{20} = -160$ **34.** $a_n = 36 - 12n$; $a_{20} = -204$

35. 1220   **36.** 3775   **37.** 4400   **38.** 6600   **39.** 5050   **40.** 10,100   **41.** 3660   **42.** 6480   **43.** 396   **44.** 504

45. $8 + 13 + 18 + \cdots + 88$; 816   **46.** $2 + 8 + 14 + \cdots + 116$; 1180   **47.** $2 - 1 - 4 - \cdots - 85$; −1245

48. $4 + 2 + 0 - \cdots - 74$; −1400   **49.** $4 + 8 + 12 + \cdots + 400$; 20,200   **50.** $-4 - 8 - 12 - \cdots - 200$; −5100   **51.** 7

52. 29   **53.** 22   **54.** 19   **55.** 847   **56.** 975   **57.** $f(x) = -4x + 5$ **58.** $g(x) = 5x - 2$ **59.** $a_n = 3n - 2$

60. $a_n = 2n + 1$ **61. a.** $a_n = 23.08 + 0.12n$ **b.** 27.88 years old   **62. a.** $a_n = 22.02 + 0.08n$ **b.** 25.22 years old

63. median age of first marriage for women: $a_n = 20.66 + 0.14n$; 26.26 years old

young adults living with parents: $a_n = 47.21 + 0.09n$; 50.81%

number completing four or more years of college: $a_n = 10.84 + 1.16n$; 57.24 million

64. a. $83,442   **b.** $83,444; very well   **65. a.** $30,049   **b.** $30,046; very well   **67.** $442,500   **68.** Company A: $307,000; Company B: $324,000; Company B pays the greater total amount.   **69.** 1430 seats   **70.** 2869 seats   **77.** Answers will vary;

Possible answers are $a_n = 3n - 2$ and $a_n = 2n + 2$.   **78.** the 200th term   **79.** 320 degree-days   **80.** $S_n = \dfrac{n}{2}(1 + 2n - 1) = \dfrac{n}{2}(2n) = n^2$

Section 10.3

Check Point Exercises

1. $12, 6, 3, \dfrac{3}{2}, \dfrac{3}{4}, \dfrac{3}{8}$ **2.** 3645   **3.** $a_n = 3(2)^{n-1}$; 384   **4.** 9842   **5.** 19,680   **6.** $2,371,746   **7.** $1,327,778   **8.** 9   **9.** 1   **10.** $4000

Exercise Set 10.3

1. 5, 15, 45, 135, 405   **2.** 4, 12, 36, 108, 324   **3.** $20, 10, 5, \dfrac{5}{2}, \dfrac{5}{4}$ **4.** $24, 8, \dfrac{8}{3}, \dfrac{8}{9}, \dfrac{8}{27}$ **5.** 10, −40, 160, −640, 2560   **6.** 10, −30, 90, −270, 810

7. −6, 30, −150, 750, −3750   **8.** −2, 12, −72, 432, −2592   **9.** $a_8 = 768$ **10.** $a_8 = 10{,}935$ **11.** $a_{12} = -10{,}240$ **12.** $a_{12} = -8192$

13. $a_{40} \approx -0.000000002$ **14.** $a_{30} \approx -0.000014901$ **15.** $a_8 = 0.1$ **16.** $a_8 = 0.004$ **17.** $a_n = 3(4)^{n-1}$; $a_7 = 12,288$

18. $a_n = 3(5)^{n-1}$; $a_7 = 46,875$ **19.** $a_n = 18\left(\frac{1}{3}\right)^{n-1}$; $a_7 = \frac{2}{81}$ **20.** $a_n = 12\left(\frac{1}{2}\right)^{n-1}$; $a_7 = \frac{3}{16}$ **21.** $a_n = 1.5(-2)^{n-1}$; $a_7 = 96$

22. $a_n = 5\left(-\frac{1}{5}\right)^{n-1}$; $a_7 = \frac{1}{3125}$ **23.** $a_n = 0.0004(-10)^{n-1}$; $a_7 = 400$ **24.** $a_n = 0.0007(-10)^{n-1}$; $a_7 = 700$ **25.** 531,440   **26.** 12,285

27. 2049   **28.** 177,148   **29.** $\frac{16,383}{2}$ **30.** $\frac{5461}{24}$ **31.** 9840   **32.** 5460   **33.** 10,230   **34.** -6564 **35.** $\frac{63}{128}$ **36.** $\frac{364}{2187}$

37. $\frac{3}{2}$ **38.** $\frac{4}{3}$ **39.** 4   **40.** 6   **41.** $\frac{2}{3}$ **42.** $\frac{9}{4}$ **43.** $\frac{80}{13} \approx 6.15385$ **44.** $\frac{120}{17} \approx 7.05882$ **45.** $\frac{5}{9}$ **46.** $\frac{1}{9}$ **47.** $\frac{47}{99}$ **48.** $\frac{83}{99}$

49. $\frac{257}{999}$ **50.** $\frac{529}{999}$ **51.** arithmetic, $d = 1$ **52.** arithmetic, $d = 1$ **53.** geometric, $r = 2$ **54.** geometric, $r = \frac{1}{2}$ **55.** neither

56. neither   **57.** 2435   **58.** -5260 **59.** 2280   **60.** -2700 **61.** -140 **62.** 1140   **63.** $a_2 = 12$, $a_3 = 18$

64. $a_2 = -6$, $a_3 = 18$ **65.** $16,384   **66.** $536,870,912   **67.** $3,795,957   **68.** $38,288.45   **69. a.** 1.013, 1.013, 1.013, 1.013, 1.013, 1.013,

1.013; The population is increasing geometrically with $r \approx 1.013$.   **b.** $a_n = 29.76(1.013)^{n-1}$ **c.** ≈ 33.86; very well   **70. a.** 1.021; 1.021; 1.021;

1.021; 1.021; 1.021; 1.021; The population is increasing geometrically with $r \approx 1.021$.   **b.** $a_n = 16.99(1.021)^{n-1}$ **c.** ≈ 20.91; very well

71. $32,767   **72.** $1,073,741,823   **73.** $793,583   **74.** Company B; $780   **75.** 130.26 in.   **76.** 134.07 in.   **77.** $844,706

78. $38,721   **79.** $94,834   **80.** $29,361   **81.** $9 million   **82.** $15 billion   **83.** $\frac{1}{3}$

95.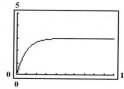

horizontal asymptote: $y = 3$; sum of series: 3

96.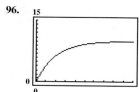

horizontal asymptote: $y = 10$; sum of series: 10

97. d
98. Release 2000 flies each day.
99. $442

Mid-Chapter 10 Check Point

1. $1, -2, \frac{3}{2}, -\frac{2}{3}, \frac{5}{24}$ **2.** $5, 2, -1, -4, -7$ **3.** $5, -15, 45, -135, 405$ **4.** $3, 1, 3, 1, 3$ **5.** $a_n = 4n - 2$; $a_{20} = 78$

6. $a_n = 3(2)^{n-1}$; $a_{10} = 1536$ **7.** $a_n = -\frac{1}{2}n + 2$; $a_{30} = -13$ **8.** 5115   **9.** 2350   **10.** 6820   **11.** $-29,300$ **12.** 44   **13.** 3725

14. $\frac{1995}{64}$ **15.** $\frac{5}{7}$ **16.** $\frac{5}{11}$ **17.** Answers will vary. An example is $\sum_{i=1}^{18} \frac{i}{i + 2}$.   **18.** 464 ft; 3600 ft   **19.** $311,249

Section 10.4

Check Point Exercises

1. a. S_1: $2 = 1(1 + 1)$; S_k: $2 + 4 + 6 + \cdots + 2k = k(k + 1)$; S_{k+1}: $2 + 4 + 6 + \cdots + 2(k + 1) = (k + 1)(k + 2)$

   b. S_1: $1^3 = \frac{1^2(1 + 1)^2}{4}$; S_k: $1^3 + 2^3 + 3^3 + \cdots + k^3 = \frac{k^2(k + 1)^2}{4}$; S_{k+1}: $1^3 + 2^3 + 3^3 + \cdots + (k + 1)^3 = \frac{(k + 1)^2(k + 2)^2}{4}$

2. S_1: $2 = 1(1 + 1)$; S_k: $2 + 4 + 6 + \cdots + 2k = k(k + 1)$; S_{k+1}: $2 + 4 + 6 + \cdots + 2k + 2(k + 1) = (k + 1)(k + 2)$; S_{k+1} can be obtained by

   adding $2k + 2$ to both sides of S_k.

3. S_1: $1^3 = \frac{1^2(1 + 1)^2}{4}$; S_k: $1^3 + 2^3 + 3^3 + \cdots + k^3 = \frac{k^2(k + 1)^2}{4}$; S_{k+1}: $1^3 + 2^3 + 3^3 + \cdots + k^3 + (k + 1)^3 = \frac{(k + 1)^2(k + 2)^2}{4}$; S_{k+1} can

   be obtained by adding $k^3 + 3k^2 + 3k + 1$ to both sides of S_k.

4. S_1: 2 is a factor of $1^2 + 1$; S_k: 2 is a factor of $k^2 + k$; S_{k+1}: 2 is a factor of $(k + 1)^2 + (k + 1) = k^2 + 3k + 2$; S_{k+1} can be obtained from S_k by

   writing $k^2 + 3k + 2$ as $(k^2 + k) + 2(k + 1)$.

Exercise Set 10.4

1. S_1: $1 = 1^2$; S_2: $1 + 3 = 2^2$; S_3: $1 + 3 + 5 = 3^2$ **2.** S_1: $3 = \frac{1(6)}{2}$; S_2: $3 + 4 = \frac{2(7)}{2}$; S_3: $3 + 4 + 5 = \frac{3(8)}{2}$

3. S_1: 2 is a factor of $1 - 1 = 0$; S_2: 2 is a factor of $2^2 - 2 = 2$; S_3: 2 is a factor of $3^2 - 3 = 6$.

4. S_1: 3 is a factor of $1^3 - 1 = 0$; S_2: 3 is a factor of $2^3 - 2 = 6$; S_3: 3 is a factor of $3^3 - 3 = 24$.

5. S_k: $4 + 8 + 12 + \cdots + 4k = 2k(k + 1)$; S_{k+1}: $4 + 8 + 12 + \cdots + (4k + 4) = 2(k + 1)(k + 2)$

6. S_k: $3 + 4 + 5 + \cdots + (k + 2) = \frac{k(k + 5)}{2}$; S_{k+1}: $3 + 4 + 5 + \cdots + (k + 3) = \frac{(k + 1)(k + 6)}{2}$

7. S_k: $3 + 7 + 11 + \cdots + (4k - 1) = k(2k + 1)$; S_{k+1}: $3 + 7 + 11 + \cdots + (4k + 3) = (k + 1)(2k + 3)$

8. S_k: $2 + 7 + 12 + \cdots + (5k - 3) = \frac{k(5k - 1)}{2}$; S_{k+1}: $2 + 7 + 12 + \cdots + (5k + 2) = \frac{(k + 1)(5k + 4)}{2}$

9. S_k: 2 is a factor of $k^2 - k + 2$; S_{k+1}: 2 is a factor of $k^2 + k + 2$.   **10.** S_k: 2 is a factor of $k^2 - k$; S_{k+1}: 2 is a factor of $k^2 + k$.

11. S_1: $4 = 2(1)(1 + 1)$; S_k: $4 + 8 + 12 + \cdots + 4k = 2k(k + 1)$; S_{k+1}: $4 + 8 + 12 + \cdots + 4(k + 1) = 2(k + 1)(k + 2)$; S_{k+1} can be obtained by

   adding $4k + 4$ to both sides of S_k.

12. S_1: $3 = \frac{1(1 + 5)}{2}$; S_k: $3 + 4 + 5 + \cdots + (k + 2) = \frac{k(k + 5)}{2}$; S_{k+1}: $3 + 4 + 5 + \cdots + (k + 3) = \frac{(k + 1)(k + 6)}{2}$; S_{k+1} can be obtained by

   adding $k + 3$ to both sides of S_k.

13. S_1: $1 = 1^2$; S_k: $1 + 3 + 5 + \cdots + (2k - 1) = k^2$; S_{k+1}: $1 + 3 + 5 + \cdots + (2k + 1) = (k + 1)^2$; S_{k+1} can be obtained by adding $2k + 1$

to both sides of S_k.

14. S_1: $3 = \dfrac{3(1)(1+1)}{2}$; S_k: $3 + 6 + 9 + \cdots + 3k = \dfrac{3k(k+1)}{2}$; S_{k+1}: $3 + 6 + 9 + \cdots + 3(k+1) = \dfrac{3(k+1)(k+2)}{2}$; S_{k+1} can be obtained by adding $3k + 3$ to both sides of S_k.

15. S_1: $3 = 1[2(1) + 1]$; S_k: $3 + 7 + 11 + \cdots + (4k - 1) = k(2k + 1)$; S_{k+1}: $3 + 7 + 11 + \cdots + (4k + 3) = (k + 1)(2k + 3)$; S_{k+1} can be obtained by adding $4k + 3$ to both sides of S_k.

16. S_1: $2 = \dfrac{1[5(1) - 1]}{2}$; S_k: $2 + 7 + 12 + \cdots + (5k - 3) = \dfrac{k(5k - 1)}{2}$; S_{k+1}: $2 + 7 + 12 + \cdots + (5k + 2) = \dfrac{(k + 1)(5k + 4)}{2}$; S_{k+1} can be obtained by adding $5k + 2$ to both sides of S_k.

17. S_1: $1 = 2^1 - 1$; S_k: $1 + 2 + 2^2 + \cdots + 2^{k-1} = 2^k - 1$; S_{k+1}: $1 + 2 + 2^2 + \cdots + 2^k = 2^{k+1} - 1$; S_{k+1} can be obtained by adding 2^k to both sides of S_k.

18. S_1: $1 = \dfrac{3^1 - 1}{2}$; S_k: $1 + 3 + 3^2 + \cdots + 3^{k-1} = \dfrac{3^k - 1}{2}$; S_{k+1}: $1 + 3 + 3^2 + \cdots + 3^k = \dfrac{3^{k+1} - 1}{2}$; S_{k+1} can be obtained by adding 3^k to both sides of S_k.

19. S_1: $2 = 2^{1+1} - 2$; S_k: $2 + 4 + 8 + \cdots + 2^k = 2^{k+1} - 2$; S_{k+1}: $2 + 4 + 8 + \cdots + 2^{k+1} = 2^{k+2} - 2$; S_{k+1} can be obtained by adding 2^{k+1} to both sides of S_k.

20. S_1: $\dfrac{1}{2} = 1 - \dfrac{1}{2^1}$; S_k: $\dfrac{1}{2} + \dfrac{1}{4} + \dfrac{1}{8} + \cdots + \dfrac{1}{2^k} = 1 - \dfrac{1}{2^k}$; S_{k+1}: $\dfrac{1}{2} + \dfrac{1}{4} + \dfrac{1}{8} + \cdots + \dfrac{1}{2^{k+1}} = 1 - \dfrac{1}{2^{k+1}}$; S_{k+1} can be obtained by adding $\dfrac{1}{2^{k+1}}$ to both sides of S_k.

21. S_1: $1 \cdot 2 = \dfrac{1(1 + 1)(1 + 2)}{3}$; S_k: $1 \cdot 2 + 2 \cdot 3 + 3 \cdot 4 + \cdots + k(k + 1) = \dfrac{k(k + 1)(k + 2)}{3}$;

S_{k+1}: $1 \cdot 2 + 2 \cdot 3 + 3 \cdot 4 + \cdots + (k + 1)(k + 2) = \dfrac{(k + 1)(k + 2)(k + 3)}{3}$; S_{k+1} can be obtained by adding $(k + 1)(k + 2)$ to both sides of S_k.

22. S_1: $1 \cdot 3 = \dfrac{1(1 + 1)[2(1) + 7]}{6}$; S_k: $1 \cdot 3 + 2 \cdot 4 + 3 \cdot 5 + \cdots + k(k + 2) = \dfrac{k(k + 1)(2k + 7)}{6}$;

S_{k+1}: $1 \cdot 3 + 2 \cdot 4 + 3 \cdot 5 + \cdots + (k + 1)(k + 3) = \dfrac{(k + 1)(k + 2)(2k + 9)}{6}$; S_{k+1} can be obtained by adding $(k + 1)(k + 3)$ to both sides of S_k.

23. S_1: $\dfrac{1}{1 \cdot 2} = \dfrac{1}{1 + 1}$; S_k: $\dfrac{1}{1 \cdot 2} + \dfrac{1}{2 \cdot 3} + \dfrac{1}{3 \cdot 4} + \cdots + \dfrac{1}{k(k + 1)} = \dfrac{k}{k + 1}$; S_{k+1}: $\dfrac{1}{1 \cdot 2} + \dfrac{1}{2 \cdot 3} + \dfrac{1}{3 \cdot 4} + \cdots + \dfrac{1}{(k + 1)(k + 2)} = \dfrac{k + 1}{k + 2}$; S_{k+1} can be obtained by adding $\dfrac{1}{(k + 1)(k + 2)}$ to both sides of S_k.

24. S_1: $\dfrac{1}{2 \cdot 3} = \dfrac{1}{2(1) + 4}$; S_k: $\dfrac{1}{2 \cdot 3} + \dfrac{1}{3 \cdot 4} + \dfrac{1}{4 \cdot 5} + \cdots + \dfrac{1}{(k + 1)(k + 2)} = \dfrac{k}{2k + 4}$; S_{k+1}:

$\dfrac{1}{2 \cdot 3} + \dfrac{1}{3 \cdot 4} + \dfrac{1}{4 \cdot 5} + \cdots + \dfrac{1}{(k + 2)(k + 3)} = \dfrac{k + 1}{2k + 6}$; S_{k+1} can be obtained by adding $\dfrac{1}{(k + 2)(k + 3)}$ to both sides of S_k.

25. S_1: 2 is a factor of 0; S_k: 2 is a factor of $k^2 - k$; S_{k+1}: 2 is a factor of $k^2 + k$; S_{k+1} can be obtained from S_k by rewriting $k^2 + k$ as $(k^2 - k) + 2k$.

26. S_1: 2 is a factor of 4; S_k: 2 is a factor of $k^2 + 3k$; S_{k+1}: 2 is a factor of $k^2 + 5k + 4$; S_{k+1} can be obtained from S_k by rewriting $k^2 + 5k + 4$ as $(k^2 + 3k) + 2(k + 2)$.

27. S_1: 6 is a factor of 6; S_k: 6 is a factor of $k(k + 1)(k + 2)$; S_{k+1}: 6 is a factor of $(k + 1)(k + 2)(k + 3)$; S_{k+1} can be obtained from S_k by rewriting $(k + 1)(k + 2)(k + 3)$ as $k(k + 1)(k + 2) + 3(k + 1)(k + 2)$ and noting that either $k + 1$ or $k + 2$ is even, so 6 is a factor of $3(k + 1)(k + 2)$.

28. S_1: 3 is a factor of 0; S_k: 3 is a factor of $k(k + 1)(k - 1)$ or $k^3 - k$; S_{k+1}: 3 is a factor of $(k + 1)(k + 2)k$ or $k^3 + 3k^2 + 2k$; S_{k+1} can be obtained from S_k by rewriting $k^3 + 3k^2 + 2k$ as $(k^3 - k) + 3(k^2 + k)$.

29. S_1: $5 \cdot 6^1 = 6(6^1 - 1)$; S_k: $\displaystyle\sum_{i=1}^{k} 5 \cdot 6^i = 6(6^k - 1)$; S_{k+1}: $\displaystyle\sum_{i=1}^{k+1} 5 \cdot 6^i = 6(6^{k+1} - 1)$; S_{k+1} can be obtained by adding $5 \cdot 6^{k+1}$ to both sides of S_k.

30. S_1: $7 \cdot 8^1 = 8(8^1 - 1)$; S_k: $\displaystyle\sum_{i=1}^{k} 7 \cdot 8^i = 8(8^k - 1)$; S_{k+1}: $\displaystyle\sum_{i=1}^{k+1} 7 \cdot 8^i = 8(8^{k+1} - 1)$; S_{k+1} can be obtained by adding $7 \cdot 8^{k+1}$ to both sides of S_k.

31. S_1: $1 + 2 > 1$; S_k: $k + 2 > k$; S_{k+1}: $k + 3 > k + 1$; S_{k+1} can be obtained by adding 1 to both sides of S_k.

32. S_1: If $0 < x < 1$, then $0 < x^1 < 1$; S_k: If $0 < x < 1$, then $0 < x^k < 1$; S_{k+1}: If $0 < x < 1$, then $0 < x^{k+1} < 1$; S_{k+1} can be obtained by multiplying the respective parts of $0 < x < 1$ and $0 < x^k < 1$.

33. S_1: $(ab)^1 = a^1b^1$; S_k: $(ab)^k = a^k b^k$; S_{k+1}: $(ab)^{k+1} = a^{k+1} b^{k+1}$; S_{k+1} can be obtained by multiplying both sides of S_k by (ab).

34. S_1: $\left(\dfrac{a}{b}\right)^1 = \dfrac{a^1}{b^1}$; S_k: $\left(\dfrac{a}{b}\right)^k = \dfrac{a^k}{b^k}$; S_{k+1}: $\left(\dfrac{a}{b}\right)^{k+1} = \dfrac{a^{k+1}}{b^{k+1}}$; S_{k+1} can be obtained by multiplying both sides of S_k by $\left(\dfrac{a}{b}\right)$.

37. S_3: $3^2 > 2(3) + 1$; S_k: $k^2 > 2k + 1$ for $k \geq 3$; S_{k+1}: $(k + 1)^2 > 2(k + 1) + 1$ or $k^2 + 2k + 1 > 2k + 3$; S_{k+1} can be obtained from S_k by noting that S_{k+1} is the same as $k^2 > 2$ which is true for $k \geq 3$.

38. S_5: $2^5 > 5^2$; S_k: $2^k > k^2$ for $k \geq 5$; S_{k+1}: $2^{k+1} > (k + 1)^2$ or $2(2^k) > k^2 + 2k + 1$; S_{k+1} can be obtained from S_k by multiplying both sides of S_k by 2 and noting that $k^2 > 2k + 1$ for $k \geq 5$.

39. S_1: $\dfrac{1}{4}$; S_2: $\dfrac{1}{3}$; S_3: $\dfrac{3}{8}$; S_4: $\dfrac{2}{5}$; S_5: $\dfrac{5}{12}$; S_n: $\dfrac{n}{2n + 2}$; Use S_k to obtain the conjectured formula.

40. S_1: $\dfrac{1}{2}$; S_2: $\dfrac{1}{3}$; S_3: $\dfrac{1}{4}$; S_4: $\dfrac{1}{5}$; S_5: $\dfrac{1}{6}$; S_n: $\dfrac{1}{n + 1}$; Use S_k to obtain the conjectured formula.

Photo Credits

Photo Credits